Instructor's Resource Manual
to accompany

Introductory Circuit Analysis

Eleventh Edition

Robert L. Boylestad

Upper Saddle River, New Jersey
Columbus, Ohio

10 9 8 7 6 5 4 3 2

ISBN 0-13-219616-6

Contents

Chapter 1

1. –

2. –

3. –

4. $$\upsilon = \frac{d}{t} = \frac{20{,}000\ \text{ft}}{10\ \text{s}}\left[\frac{1\ \text{mi}}{5{,}280\ \text{ft}}\right]\left[\frac{60\ \text{s}}{1\ \text{min}}\right]\left[\frac{60\ \text{min}}{1\ \text{h}}\right] = \mathbf{1363.64\ mph}$$

5. $$4\ \text{min}\left[\frac{1\ \text{h}}{60\ \text{min}}\right] = \mathbf{0.067\ h}$$
$$\upsilon = \frac{d}{t} = \frac{31\ \text{mi}}{1.067\ \text{h}} = \mathbf{29.05\ mph}$$

6. a. $$\frac{95\ \text{mi}}{\text{h}}\left[\frac{5{,}280\ \text{ft}}{\text{mi}}\right]\left[\frac{1\ \text{h}}{60\ \text{min}}\right]\left[\frac{1\ \text{min}}{60\ \text{s}}\right] = \mathbf{139.33\ ft/s}$$
b. $$t = \frac{d}{\upsilon} = \frac{60\ \text{ft}}{139.33\ \text{ft/s}} = \mathbf{0.431\ s}$$
c. $$\upsilon = \frac{d}{t} = \frac{60\ \text{ft}}{1\ \text{s}}\left[\frac{60\ \text{s}}{1\ \text{min}}\right]\left[\frac{60\ \text{min}}{1\ \text{h}}\right]\left[\frac{1\ \text{mi}}{5{,}280\ \text{ft}}\right] = \mathbf{40.91\ mph}$$

7. –

8. –

9. –

10. MKS, CGS, $°\text{C} = \frac{5}{9}(°\text{F} - 32) = \frac{5}{9}(68 - 32) = \frac{5}{9}(36) = \mathbf{20°}$
SI: $\text{K} = 273.15 + °\text{C} = 273.15 + 20 = \mathbf{293.15}$

11. $$1000\ \text{J}\left[\frac{0.7378\ \text{ft-lb}}{1\ \text{J}}\right] = \mathbf{737.8\ ft\text{-}lbs}$$

12. $$0.5\ \text{yd}\left[\frac{3\ \text{ft}}{1\ \text{yd}}\right]\left[\frac{12\ \text{in.}}{1\ \text{ft}}\right]\left[\frac{2.54\ \text{cm}}{1\ \text{in.}}\right] = \mathbf{45.72\ cm}$$

13. a. $\mathbf{10^{4}}$ b. $\mathbf{10^{6}}$ c. $\mathbf{10^{3}}$ d. $\mathbf{10^{-3}}$ e. $\mathbf{10^{0}}$ f. $\mathbf{10^{-1}}$

14. a. $\mathbf{15 \times 10^{3}}$ b. $\mathbf{30 \times 10^{-3}}$ c. $\mathbf{2.4 \times 10^{6}}$ d. $\mathbf{150 \times 10^{3}}$
e. $\mathbf{4.02 \times 10^{-4}}$ f. $\mathbf{2 \times 10^{-10}}$

15. a. $4.2 \times 10^3 + 48.0 \times 10^3 = 52.2 \times 10^3 = \mathbf{5.22 \times 10^4}$
b. $90 \times 10^3 + 360 \times 10^3 = 450 \times 10^3 = \mathbf{4.50 \times 10^5}$
c. $50 \times 10^{-5} - 6 \times 10^{-5} = 44 \times 10^{-5} = \mathbf{4.4 \times 10^{-4}}$
d. $1.2 \times 10^3 + 0.05 \times 10^3 - 0.6 \times 10^3 = 0.65 \times 10^3 = \mathbf{6.5 \times 10^2}$

16. a. $(10^2)(10^3) = 10^5 = \mathbf{100 \times 10^3}$
b. $(10^{-2})(10^3) = 10^1 = \mathbf{10}$
c. $(10^3)(10^6) = \mathbf{1 \times 10^9}$
d. $(10^2)(10^{-5}) = \mathbf{1 \times 10^{-3}}$
e. $(10^{-6})(10 \times 10^6) = \mathbf{10}$
f. $(10^4)(10^{-8})(10^{28}) = \mathbf{1 \times 10^{24}}$

17. a. $(50 \times 10^3)(3 \times 10^{-4}) = 150 \times 10^{-1} = \mathbf{1.5 \times 10^1}$
b. $(2.2 \times 10^3)(2 \times 10^{-3}) = 4.4 \times 10^0 = \mathbf{4.4}$
c. $(82 \times 10^6)(2.8 \times 10^{-6}) = 229.6 = \mathbf{2.296 \times 10^2}$
d. $(30 \times 10^{-4})(4 \times 10^{-3})(7 \times 10^8) = 840 \times 10^1 = \mathbf{8.40 \times 10^3}$

18. a. $10^2/10^4 = 10^{-2} = \mathbf{10 \times 10^{-3}}$
b. $10^{-2}/10^3 = 10^{-5} = \mathbf{10 \times 10^{-6}}$
c. $10^4/10^{-3} = 10^7 = \mathbf{10 \times 10^6}$
d. $10^{-7}/10^2 = \mathbf{1.0 \times 10^{-9}}$
e. $10^{38}/10^{-4} = \mathbf{1.0 \times 10^{42}}$
f. $\sqrt{100}/10^{-2} = 10^1/10^{-2} = \mathbf{1 \times 10^3}$

19. a. $(2 \times 10^3)/(8 \times 10^{-5}) = 0.25 \times 10^8 = \mathbf{2.50 \times 10^7}$
b. $(4 \times 10^{-3})/(60 \times 10^4) = 4/60 \times 10^{-7} = 0.667 \times 10^{-7} = \mathbf{6.67 \times 10^{-8}}$
c. $(22 \times 10^{-5})/(5 \times 10^{-5}) = 22/5 \times 10^0 = \mathbf{4.4}$
d. $(78 \times 10^{18})/(4 \times 10^{-6}) = \mathbf{1.95 \times 10^{25}}$

20. a. $(10^2)^3 = \mathbf{1.0 \times 10^6}$
b. $(10^{-4})^{1/2} = \mathbf{10.0 \times 10^{-3}}$
c. $(10^4)^8 = \mathbf{100.0 \times 10^{30}}$
d. $(10^{-7})^9 = \mathbf{1.0 \times 10^{-63}}$

21. a. $(4 \times 10^2)^2 = 16 \times 10^4 = \mathbf{1.6 \times 10^5}$
b. $(6 \times 10^{-3})^3 = 216 \times 10^{-9} = \mathbf{2.16 \times 10^{-7}}$
c. $(4 \times 10^{-3})(6 \times 10^2)^2 = (4 \times 10^{-3})(36 \times 10^4) = 144 \times 10^1 = \mathbf{1.44 \times 10^3}$
d. $((2 \times 10^{-3})(0.8 \times 10^4)(0.003 \times 10^5))^3 = (4.8 \times 10^3)^3 = (4.8)^3 \times (10^3)^3$
$= 110.6 \times 10^9 = \mathbf{1.11 \times 10^{11}}$

22. a. $(-10^{-3})^2 = \mathbf{1.0 \times 10^{-6}}$
b. $\dfrac{(10^2)(10^{-4})}{10^3} = 10^{-2}/10^3 = \mathbf{1.0 \times 10^{-5}}$
c. $\dfrac{(10^{-3})^2(10^2)}{10^4} = \dfrac{(10^{-6})(10^2)}{10^4} = \dfrac{10^{-4}}{10^4} = \mathbf{1.0 \times 10^{-8}}$
d. $\dfrac{(10^3)(10^4)}{10^{-4}} = 10^7/10^{-4} = \mathbf{1.0 \times 10^{11}}$

e. $(1 \times 10^{-4})^3(10^2)/10^6 = (10^{-12})(10^2)/10^6 = 10^{-10}/10^6 = \mathbf{1.0 \times 10^{-16}}$

f. $$\frac{\left[(10^2)(10^{-2})\right]^{-3}}{\left[(10^2)^2\right]\left[10^{-3}\right]} = \frac{1}{(10^4)(10^{-3})} = \frac{1}{10} = \mathbf{1.0 \times 10^{-1}}$$

23. a. $$\frac{(3\times10^2)^2(10^2)}{3\times10^4} = (9 \times 10^4)(10^2)/(3 \times 10^4) = (9 \times 10^6)/(3 \times 10^4) = 3 \times 10^2 = \mathbf{300}$$

b. $$\frac{(4\times10^4)^2}{(20)^3} = \frac{16\times10^8}{8\times10^3} = 2 \times 10^5 = \mathbf{200.0 \times 10^3}$$

c. $$\frac{(6\times10^4)^2}{(2\times10^{-2})^2} = \frac{36\times10^8}{4\times10^{-4}} = \mathbf{9.0 \times 10^{12}}$$

d. $$\frac{(27\times10^{-6})^{1/3}}{2\times10^5} = \frac{3\times10^{-2}}{2\times10^5} = 1.5 \times 10^{-7} = \mathbf{150.0 \times 10^{-9}}$$

e. $$\frac{(4\times10^3)^2(3\times10^2)}{2\times10^{-4}} = \frac{(16\times10^6)(3\times10^2)}{2\times10^{-4}} = \frac{48\times10^8}{2\times10^{-4}} = \mathbf{24.0 \times 10^{12}}$$

f. $(16 \times 10^{-6})^{1/2}(10^5)^5(2 \times 10^{-2}) = (4 \times 10^{-3})(10^{25})(2 \times 10^{-2}) = 8 \times 10^{20}$
$= \mathbf{800.0 \times 10^{18}}$

g. $$\frac{\left[(3\times10^{-3})^3\right]\left[1.60\times10^2\right]^2\left[(2\times10^2)(8\times10^{-4})\right]^{1/2}}{(7\times10^{-5})^2}$$

$$= \frac{(27\times10^{-9})(2.56\times10^4)(16\times10^{-2})^{1/2}}{49\times10^{-10}}$$

$$= \frac{(69.12\times10^{-5})(4\times10^{-1})}{49\times10^{-10}} = \frac{276.48\times10^{-6}}{49\times10^{-10}}$$

$= 5.64 \times 10^4 = \mathbf{56.4 \times 10^3}$

24. a.

+3

$6 \times 10^3 = \underline{0.006} \times 10^{+6}$

−3

b.

−3

$4 \times 10^{-3} = \underline{4000} \times 10^{-6}$

+3

c.

−2 +3 +3

$50 \times 10^5 = \underline{5000} \times 10^3 = \underline{5} \times 10^6 = \underline{0.005} \times 10^9$

+2 −3 −3

d. $30 \times 10^{-8} = \underline{0.0003} \times 10^{-3} = \underline{0.3} \times 10^{-6} = \underline{300} \times 10^{-9}$

(arrows above: +5, −3, −3; arrows below: −5, +3, +3)

25. a. $0.05 \times 10^{0}\ \text{s} = \underline{50} \times 10^{-3}\ \text{s} = \mathbf{50\ ms}$

(arrow above: −3; arrow below: +3)

b. $2000 \times 10^{-6}\ \text{s} = \underline{2} \times 10^{-3}\ \text{s} = \mathbf{2\ ms}$

(arrow above: +3; arrow below: −3)

c. $0.04 \times 10^{-3}\ \text{s} = \underline{40} \times 10^{-6}\ \text{s} = \mathbf{40\ \mu s}$

(arrow above: −3; arrow below: +3)

d. $8400 \times 10^{-12}\ \text{s} \Rightarrow \underline{0.0084} \times 10^{-6}\ \text{s} = \mathbf{0.0084\ \mu s}$

(arrow above: +6; arrow below: −6)

e. $4 \times 10^{-3} \times 10^{3}\ \text{m} = 4 \times 10^{0}\ \text{m} = \underline{4000} \times 10^{-3}\ \text{m} = \mathbf{4000\ mm}$

(arrow above: −3; arrow below: +3)

f. $\underbrace{}_{}260 \times \overbrace{10^{3} \times 10^{-3}}^{10^{0}}\ \text{m} = \underline{0.26} \times 10^{3}\ \text{m} = \mathbf{0.26\ km}$

(increase by 3; arrow below: −3)

26. a. $1.5\ \cancel{\text{min}} \left[\dfrac{60\ \text{s}}{1\ \cancel{\text{min}}}\right] = \mathbf{90\ s}$

b. $0.04\ \cancel{\text{h}} \left[\dfrac{60\ \cancel{\text{min}}}{1\ \cancel{\text{h}}}\right]\left[\dfrac{60\ \text{s}}{1\ \cancel{\text{min}}}\right] = \mathbf{144\ s}$

c. $0.05\ \cancel{\text{s}} \left[\dfrac{1\ \mu\text{s}}{10^{-6}\ \cancel{\text{s}}}\right] = \mathbf{0.05 \times 10^{6}\ \mu s = 50 \times 10^{3}\ \mu s}$

d. $0.16\ \cancel{\text{m}} \left[\dfrac{1\ \text{mm}}{10^{-3}\ \cancel{\text{m}}}\right] = 0.16 \times 10^{3}\ \text{mm} = \mathbf{160\ mm}$

e. $1.2 \times 10^{-7}\,\text{s}\left[\frac{1\text{ ns}}{10^{-9}\text{ s}}\right] = 1.2 \times 10^{2}\text{ ns} = \mathbf{120\ ns}$

f. $3.62 \times 10^{6}\,\text{s}\left[\frac{1\text{ min}}{60\text{ s}}\right]\left[\frac{1\text{ h}}{60\text{ min}}\right]\left[\frac{1\text{ day}}{24\text{ h}}\right] = \mathbf{41.90\ days}$

27. a. $0.1\,\mu\text{F}\left[\frac{10^{-6}\text{ F}}{1\,\mu\text{F}}\right]\left[\frac{1\text{ pF}}{10^{-12}\text{ F}}\right] = 0.1 \times 10^{-6} \times 10^{12}\text{ pF} = \mathbf{10^{5}\ pF}$

b. $80 \times 10^{-3}\text{ m}\left[\frac{100\text{ cm}}{1\text{ m}}\right] = 8000 \times 10^{-3}\text{ cm} = \mathbf{8\ cm}$

c. $60\text{ cm}\left[\frac{1\text{ m}}{100\text{ cm}}\right]\left[\frac{1\text{ km}}{1000\text{ m}}\right] = \mathbf{60 \times 10^{-5}\ km}$

d. $3.2\text{ h}\left[\frac{60\text{ min}}{1\text{ h}}\right]\left[\frac{60\text{ s}}{1\text{ min}}\right]\left[\frac{1\text{ ms}}{10^{-3}\text{ s}}\right] = \mathbf{11.52 \times 10^{6}\ ms}$

e. $0.016\text{ mm}\left[\frac{10^{-3}\text{ m}}{1\text{ mm}}\right]\left[\frac{1\,\mu\text{m}}{10^{-6}\text{ m}}\right] = 0.016 \times 10^{3}\,\mu\text{m} = \mathbf{16\ \mu m}$

f. $60\text{ cm}^2\left[\frac{1\text{ m}}{100\text{ cm}}\right]\left[\frac{1\text{ m}}{100\text{ cm}}\right] = \mathbf{60 \times 10^{-4}\ m^2}$

28. a. $100\text{ in.}\left[\frac{1\text{ m}}{39.37\text{ in.}}\right] = \mathbf{2.54\ m}$

b. $4\text{ ft}\left[\frac{12\text{ in.}}{1\text{ ft}}\right]\left[\frac{1\text{ m}}{39.37\text{ in.}}\right] = \mathbf{1.22\ m}$

c. $6\text{ lb}\left[\frac{4.45\text{ N}}{1\text{ lb}}\right] = \mathbf{26.7\ N}$

d. $60 \times 10^{3}\text{ dynes}\left[\frac{1\text{ N}}{10^{5}\text{ dynes}}\right]\left[\frac{1\text{ lb}}{4.45\text{ N}}\right] = \mathbf{0.13\ lb}$

e. $150{,}000\text{ cm}\left[\frac{1\text{ in.}}{2.54\text{ cm}}\right]\left[\frac{1\text{ ft}}{12\text{ in.}}\right] = \mathbf{4921.26\ ft}$

f. $0.002\text{ mi}\left[\frac{5280\text{ ft}}{1\text{ mi}}\right]\left[\frac{12\text{ in.}}{1\text{ ft}}\right]\left[\frac{1\text{ m}}{39.37\text{ in.}}\right] = \mathbf{3.22\ m}$

29. **5280 ft**, $5280\,\cancel{ft}\left[\frac{1\text{ yd}}{3\,\cancel{ft}}\right] = \mathbf{1760\ yds}$

$$5280\,\cancel{ft}\left[\frac{12\,\cancel{in.}}{1\,\cancel{ft}}\right]\left[\frac{1\text{ m}}{39.37\,\cancel{in.}}\right] = \mathbf{1609.35\ m,\ 1.61\ km}$$

30. $$299{,}792{,}458\ \frac{\cancel{m}}{\cancel{s}}\left[\frac{39.37\,\cancel{in.}}{1\,\cancel{m}}\right]\left[\frac{1\,\cancel{ft}}{12\,\cancel{in.}}\right]\left[\frac{1\text{ mi}}{5280\,\cancel{ft}}\right]\left[\frac{60\,\cancel{s}}{1\,\cancel{min}}\right]\left[\frac{60\,\cancel{min}}{1\text{ h}}\right]$$
$$= 670{,}615{,}288.1\text{ mph} \cong \mathbf{670.62 \times 10^6\ mph}$$

31. $$100\ \cancel{yds}\left[\frac{3\,\cancel{ft}}{1\,\cancel{yd}}\right]\left[\frac{1\text{ mi}}{5{,}280\,\cancel{ft}}\right] = 0.0568\text{ mi}$$

$$\frac{60\text{ mi}}{\cancel{h}}\left[\frac{1\,\cancel{h}}{60\,\cancel{min}}\right]\left[\frac{1\,\cancel{min}}{60\text{ s}}\right] = 0.0167\text{ mi/s}$$

$$t = \frac{d}{\upsilon} = \frac{0.0568\text{ mi}}{0.0167\text{ mi/s}} = \mathbf{3.40\ s}$$

32. $$\frac{30\,\cancel{mi}}{\cancel{h}}\left[\frac{5280\,\cancel{ft}}{1\,\cancel{mi}}\right]\left[\frac{12\,\cancel{in.}}{1\,\cancel{ft}}\right]\left[\frac{1\text{ m}}{39.37\,\cancel{in.}}\right]\left[\frac{1\,\cancel{h}}{60\,\cancel{min}}\right]\left[\frac{1\,\cancel{min}}{60\text{ s}}\right] = \mathbf{13.41\ m/s}$$

33. $$\frac{50\,\cancel{yd}}{\cancel{min}}\left[\frac{60\,\cancel{min}}{1\text{ h}}\right]\left[\frac{3\,\cancel{ft}}{1\,\cancel{yd}}\right]\left[\frac{1\text{ mi}}{5{,}280\,\cancel{ft}}\right] = 1.705\text{ mi/h}$$

$$t = \frac{d}{\upsilon} = \frac{3000\text{ mi}}{1.705\text{ mi/h}} = 1760\,\cancel{h}\left[\frac{1\text{ day}}{24\,\cancel{h}}\right] = \mathbf{73.33\ days}$$

34. $$10\,\cancel{km}\left[\frac{1000\,\cancel{m}}{1\,\cancel{km}}\right]\left[\frac{39.37\,\cancel{in.}}{1\,\cancel{m}}\right]\left[\frac{1\,\cancel{ft}}{12\,\cancel{in.}}\right]\left[\frac{1\text{ mi}}{5280\,\cancel{ft}}\right] = 6.214\text{ mi}$$

$$\upsilon = \frac{1\text{ mi}}{6.5\text{ min}},\ t = \frac{d}{\upsilon} = \frac{6.214\,\cancel{mi}}{\dfrac{1\,\cancel{mi}}{6.5\text{ min}}} = \mathbf{40.39\ min}$$

35. $$100\,\cancel{yds}\left[\frac{3\,\cancel{ft}}{1\,\cancel{yd}}\right]\left[\frac{12\text{ in.}}{1\,\cancel{ft}}\right] = 3600\text{ in} \Rightarrow \mathbf{3600\ quarters}$$

36. 60 mph: $t = \frac{d}{\upsilon} = \frac{100\text{ mi}}{60\text{ mi/h}} = 1.67\text{ h} = \mathbf{1\ h{:}40.2\ min}$

75 mph: $t = \frac{d}{\upsilon} = \frac{100\text{ mi}}{75\text{ mi/h}} = 1.33\text{ h} = \mathbf{1h{:}19.98\ min}$

difference = **20.22 minutes**

37. $d = vt = \left[600\frac{\text{cm}}{\text{s}}\right][0.016\text{h}]\left[\frac{60\text{ min}}{1\text{h}}\right]\left[\frac{60\text{s}}{1\text{ min}}\right]\left[\frac{1\text{ m}}{100\text{ cm}}\right]$ = **345.6 m**

38. $d = 86\text{ stories}\left[\frac{14\text{ ft}}{\text{story}}\right]\left[\frac{1\text{ step}}{\frac{9}{12}\text{ ft}}\right] = 1605\text{ steps}$

$v = \frac{d}{t} \Rightarrow t = \frac{d}{v} = \frac{1605\text{ steps}}{\frac{2\text{ steps}}{\text{second}}} = 802.5\text{ seconds}\left[\frac{1\text{ minute}}{60\text{ seconds}}\right]$ = **13.38 minutes**

39. $d = (86\text{ stories})\left[\frac{14\text{ ft}}{\text{story}}\right] = 1204\text{ ft}\left[\frac{1\text{ mile}}{5{,}280\text{ ft}}\right] = 0.228\text{ miles}$

$\frac{\text{min}}{\text{mile}} = \frac{10.7833\text{ min}}{0.228\text{ miles}}$ = **47.30 min/mile**

40. $\frac{5\text{ min}}{\text{mile}} \Rightarrow \frac{1\text{ mile}}{5\text{ min}}\left[\frac{5{,}280\text{ ft}}{1\text{ mile}}\right] = \frac{1056\text{ ft}}{\text{minute}}$, distance $= 86\text{ stories}\left[\frac{14\text{ ft}}{\text{story}}\right] = 1204\text{ ft}$

$v = \frac{d}{t} \Rightarrow t = \frac{d}{v} = \frac{1204\text{ ft}}{1056\frac{\text{ft}}{\text{min}}}$ = **1.14 minutes**

41. a. $5\text{ J}\left[\frac{1\text{ Btu}}{1054.35\text{ J}}\right]$ = **4.74×10^{-3} Btu**

b. $24\text{ ounces}\left[\frac{1\text{ gallon}}{128\text{ ounces}}\right]\left[\frac{1\text{ m}^3}{264.172\text{ gallons}}\right]$ = **$7.1 \times 10^{-4}\text{m}^3$**

c. $1.4\text{ days}\left[\frac{86{,}400\text{ s}}{1\text{ day}}\right]$ = **1.21×10^5 s**

d. $1\text{ m}^3\left[\frac{264.172\text{ gallons}}{1\text{ m}^3}\right]\left[\frac{8\text{ pints}}{1\text{ gallon}}\right]$ = **2113.38 pints**

42. 6(4 + 8) = **72**

43. (20 + 32)/4 = **13**

44. $\sqrt{(8^2 + 12^2)}$ = **14.42**

45. MODE = DEGREES: cos 50° = **0.64**

46. MODE = DEGREES: $\tan^{-1}(3/4)$ = **36.87°**

47. $\sqrt{\left(400/(6^2+10)\right)}$ = **2.95**

48. $\mathbf{205 \times 10^{-6}}$

49. $\mathbf{1.20 \times 10^{12}}$

50. $6.667 \times 10^6 + 0.5 \times 10^6 = \mathbf{7.17 \times 10^6}$

Chapter 2

1. –

2. a. $F = k\dfrac{Q_1Q_2}{r^2} = \dfrac{(9\times10^9)(1\text{ C})(2\text{ C})}{(1\text{ m})^2}$ = **18 × 10⁹ N**

b. $F = k\dfrac{Q_1Q_2}{r^2} = \dfrac{(9\times10^9)(1\text{ C})(2\text{ C})}{(3\text{ m})^2}$ = **2 × 10⁹ N**

c. $F = k\dfrac{Q_1Q_2}{r^2} = \dfrac{(9\times10^9)(1\text{ C})(2\text{ C})}{(10\text{ m})^2}$ = **0.18 × 10⁹ N**

d. Exponentially, $\dfrac{r_3}{r_1} = \dfrac{10\text{ m}}{1\text{ m}} = 10$ while $\dfrac{F_1}{F_2} = \dfrac{18\times10^9\text{ N}}{0.18\times10^9\text{ N}}$ = **100**

3. a. $r = 1$ mi:

$$1\,\text{mi}\left[\frac{5280\text{ ft}}{1\text{ mi}}\right]\left[\frac{12\text{ in.}}{1\text{ ft}}\right]\left[\frac{1\text{ m}}{39.37\text{ in.}}\right] = 1609.35\text{ m}$$

$$F = \frac{kQ_1Q_2}{r^2} = \frac{(9\times10^9)(8\times10^{-6}\text{ C})(40\times10^{-6}\text{ C})}{(1609.35\text{ m})^2} = \frac{2880\times10^{-3}}{2.59\times10^6}$$

$= \mathbf{1.11\ \mu N}$

b. $r = 10$ ft:

$$10\,\text{ft}\left[\frac{12\text{ in.}}{1\text{ ft}}\right]\left[\frac{1\text{ m}}{39.37\text{ in.}}\right] = 3.05\text{ m}$$

$$F = \frac{kQ_1Q_2}{r^2} = \frac{2880\times10^{-3}}{(3.05\text{ m})^2} = \frac{2880\times10^{-3}}{9.30} = \mathbf{0.31\ N}$$

c. $$\frac{1\text{ in.}}{16}\left[\frac{1\text{ m}}{39.37\text{ in.}}\right] = 1.59\text{ mm}$$

$$F = \frac{kQ_1Q_2}{r^2} = \frac{2880\times10^{-3}}{(1.59\times10^{-3}\text{ m})^2} = \frac{2880\times10^{-3}}{2.53\times10^{-6}} = 1138.34\times10^3\text{ N}$$

$= \mathbf{1138.34\ kN}$

4. –

5. $$F = \frac{kQ_1Q_2}{r^2} \Rightarrow r = \sqrt{\frac{kQ_1Q_2}{F}} = \sqrt{\frac{(9\times10^9)(20\times10^{-6})^2}{3.6\times10^4}} = \mathbf{10\ mm}$$

6. $F = \frac{kQ_1Q_2}{r^2} \Rightarrow 1.8 = \frac{kQ_1Q_2}{(2\text{ m})^2} \Rightarrow kQ_1Q_2 = 4(1.8) = 7.2$

a. $F = \frac{kQ_1Q_2}{r^2} = \frac{7.2}{(10)^2} = \mathbf{72\ mN}$

b. $Q_1/Q_2 = 1/2 \Rightarrow Q_2 = 2Q_1$

$7.2 = kQ_1Q_2 = (9 \times 10^9)(Q_1)(2Q_1) = 9 \times 10^9\left(2Q_1^2\right)$

$\frac{7.2}{18 \times 10^9} = Q_1^2 \Rightarrow Q_1 = \sqrt{\frac{7.2}{18 \times 10^9}} = \mathbf{20\ \mu C}$

$Q_2 = 2Q_1 = 2(2 \times 10^{-5}\text{ C}) = \mathbf{40\ \mu C}$

7. $V = \frac{W}{Q} = \frac{1.2\text{ J}}{0.4\text{ mC}} = \mathbf{3\ kV}$

8. $W = VQ = (60\text{ V})(8\text{ mC}) = \mathbf{0.48\ J}$

9. $Q = \frac{W}{V} = \frac{96\text{ J}}{16\text{ V}} = \mathbf{6\ C}$

10. $Q = \frac{W}{V} = \frac{72\text{ J}}{9\text{ V}} = \mathbf{8\ C}$

11. $I = \frac{Q}{t} = \frac{12\text{ mC}}{2.8\text{ s}} = \mathbf{4.29\ mA}$

12. $I = \frac{Q}{t} = \frac{312\text{ C}}{(2)(60\text{ s})} = \mathbf{2.60\ A}$

13. $Q = It = (40\text{ mA})(0.8)(60\text{ s}) = \mathbf{1.92\ C}$

14. $Q = It = (250\text{ mA})(1.2)(60\text{ s}) = \mathbf{18.0\ C}$

15. $t = \frac{Q}{I} = \frac{6\text{ mC}}{2\text{ mA}} = \mathbf{3\ s}$

16. $21.847 \times 10^{18}\ \cancel{\text{electrons}}\left[\frac{1\text{C}}{6.242 \times 10^{18}\ \cancel{\text{electrons}}}\right] = 3.5\text{ C}$

$I = \frac{Q}{t} = \frac{3.5\text{C}}{12\text{s}} = 0.29\text{ A}$

17. $Q = It = (4\text{ mA})(90\text{ s}) = 360\text{ mC}$

$360\text{ m}\cancel{\text{C}}\left[\frac{6.242 \times 10^{18}\text{ electrons}}{1\cancel{\text{C}}}\right] = \mathbf{2.25 \times 10^{18}\ electrons}$

18. $I = \frac{Q}{t} = \frac{86\text{ C}}{(1.2)(60\text{ s})} = 1.194\text{ A} > 1\text{ A}$ **(yes)**

19. $0.84 \times 10^{16}\ \cancel{\text{electrons}}\left[\frac{1\text{ C}}{6.242\times10^{18}\ \cancel{\text{electrons}}}\right] = 1.346\text{ mC}$

$I = \frac{Q}{t} = \frac{1.346\text{ mC}}{60\text{ ms}} = \mathbf{22.43\ mA}$

20. a. $Q = It = (2\text{ mA})(0.01\ \mu\text{s}) = 2 \times 10^{-11}\text{ C}$

$2 \times 10^{-11}\ \cancel{\text{C}}\left[\frac{6.242\times10^{18}\ \cancel{\text{electrons}}}{1\cancel{\text{C}}}\right]\left[\frac{1\ ¢}{\cancel{\text{electron}}}\right]$

$= 1.25 \times 10^{8}\ ¢ = \$1.25 \times 10^{6} = \mathbf{1.25\ million}$

b. $Q = It = (100\ \mu\text{A})(1.5\text{ ns}) = 1.5 \times 10^{-13}\text{ C}$

$1.5 \times 10^{-13}\ \cancel{\text{C}}\left[\frac{6.242\times10^{18}\ \cancel{\text{electrons}}}{1\cancel{\text{C}}}\right]\left[\frac{\$1}{\cancel{\text{electron}}}\right] = \mathbf{0.94\ million}$

(a) > (b)

21. $Q = It = (200 \times 10^{-3}\text{ A})(30\text{ s}) = 6\text{ C}$

$V = \frac{W}{Q} = \frac{40\text{ J}}{6\text{ C}} = \mathbf{6.67\ V}$

22. $Q = It = \left[\frac{420\text{ C}}{\cancel{\text{min}}}\right](0.5\ \cancel{\text{min}}) = 210\text{ C}$

$V = \frac{W}{Q} = \frac{742\text{ J}}{210\text{ C}} = \mathbf{3.53\ V}$

23. $Q = \frac{W}{V} = \frac{0.4\text{ J}}{24\text{ V}} = 0.0167\text{ C}$

$I = \frac{Q}{t} = \frac{0.0167\text{ C}}{5\times10^{-3}\text{ s}} = \mathbf{3.34\ A}$

24. $I = \frac{\text{Ah rating}}{t\text{(hours)}} = \frac{200\text{ Ah}}{40\text{ h}} = \mathbf{5\ A}$

25. $\text{Ah} = (0.8\text{ A})(75\text{ h}) = \mathbf{60.0\ Ah}$

26. $t\text{(hours)} = \frac{\text{Ah rating}}{I} = \frac{32\text{ Ah}}{1.28\text{ A}} = \mathbf{25\ h}$

27. 40 Ah(for 1 h): $W_1 = VQ = V \cdot I \cdot t = (12\text{ V})(40\text{ A})(1\text{ h})\left[\frac{60\text{ min}}{1\text{ h}}\right]\left[\frac{60\text{ s}}{1\text{ min}}\right] = 1.728 \times 10^6\text{ J}$

60 Ah(for 1 h): $W_2 = (12\text{ V})(60\text{ A})(1\text{ h})\left[\frac{60\text{ min}}{1\text{ h}}\right]\left[\frac{60\text{ s}}{1\text{ min}}\right] = 2.592 \times 10^6\text{ J}$

Ratio $W_2/W_1 = 1.5$ or 50% more energy available with 60 Ah rating.

For 60 s discharge: $40\text{ Ah} = It = I[60\text{ s}]\left[\frac{1\text{ min}}{60\text{ s}}\right]\left[\frac{1\text{ h}}{60\text{ min}}\right] = I(16.67 \times 10^{-3}\text{ h})$

$$\text{and } I = \frac{40\text{ Ah}}{16.67 \times 10^{-3}\text{ h}} = \mathbf{2400\text{ A}}$$

$$60\text{ Ah} = It = I[60\text{ s}]\left[\frac{1\text{ min}}{60\text{ s}}\right]\left[\frac{1\text{ h}}{60\text{ min}}\right] = I(16.67 \times 10^{-3}\text{ h})$$

$$\text{and } I = \frac{60\text{ Ah}}{16.67 \times 10^{-3}\text{ h}} = \mathbf{3600\text{ A}}$$

$I_2/I_1 = 1.5$ or 50 % more starting current available at 60 Ah

28. $I = \frac{3\text{ Ah}}{6.0\text{ h}} = 500\text{ mA}$

$Q = It = (500\text{ mA})(6\text{ h})\left[\frac{60\text{ min}}{1\text{ h}}\right]\left[\frac{60\text{ s}}{1\text{ min}}\right] = 10.80\text{ kC}$

$W = QV = (10.8\text{ kC})(12\text{ V}) \cong$ $\mathbf{129.6\text{ kJ}}$

29. –

30. –

31. –

32. –

33. –

34. –

35. $4\text{ min}\left[\frac{60\text{ s}}{1\text{ min}}\right] = 240\text{ s}$

$Q = It = (2.5\text{ A})(240\text{ s}) = \mathbf{600\text{ C}}$

36. $Q = It = (10 \times 10^{-3}\text{ A})(20\text{ s}) = \mathbf{200\text{ mC}}$

$W = VQ = (12.5\text{ V})(200 \times 10^{-3}\text{ C}) = \mathbf{2.5\text{ J}}$

Chapter 3

1. a. $0.5 \text{ in.} = \mathbf{500 \text{ mils}}$

   b. $0.02 \text{ in.}\left[\frac{1000 \text{ mils}}{1 \text{ in.}}\right] = \mathbf{20 \text{ mils}}$

   c. $\frac{1}{4} \text{ in.} = 0.25 \text{ in.}\left[\frac{1000 \text{ mils}}{1 \text{ in.}}\right] = \mathbf{250 \text{ mils}}$

   d. $1 \text{ in.} = \mathbf{1000 \text{ mils}}$

   e. $0.02 \text{ ft}\left[\frac{12 \text{ in.}}{1 \text{ ft}}\right]\left[\frac{10^3 \text{ mils}}{1 \text{ in.}}\right] = \mathbf{240 \text{ mils}}$

   f. $0.1 \text{ cm}\left[\frac{1 \text{ in.}}{2.54 \text{ cm}}\right]\left[\frac{1000 \text{ mils}}{1 \text{ in.}}\right] = \mathbf{39.37 \text{ mils}}$

2. a. $A_{CM} = (30 \text{ mils})^2 = \mathbf{900 \text{ CM}}$

   b. $0.016 \text{ in.} = 16 \text{ mils}, A_{CM} = (16 \text{ mils})^2 = \mathbf{256 \text{ CM}}$

   c. $\frac{1}{8}'' = 0.125'' = 125 \text{ mils}, A_{CM} = (125 \text{ mils})^2 = \mathbf{15.63 \times 10^3 \text{ CM}}$

   d. $1 \text{ cm}\left[\frac{1 \text{ in.}}{2.54 \text{ cm}}\right]\left[\frac{1000 \text{ mils}}{1 \text{ in.}}\right] = 393.7 \text{ mils}, A_{CM} = (393.7 \text{ mils})^2 = \mathbf{155 \times 10^3 \text{ CM}}$

   e. $0.02 \text{ ft}\left[\frac{12 \text{ in.}}{1 \text{ ft}}\right]\left[\frac{1000 \text{ mils}}{1 \text{ in.}}\right] = 240 \text{ mils}, A_{CM} = (240 \text{ mils})^2 = \mathbf{57.60 \times 10^3 \text{ CM}}$

   f. $0.0042 \text{ m}\left[\frac{39.37 \text{ in.}}{1 \text{ m}}\right] = 0.1654 \text{ in.} = 165.4 \text{ mils}, A_{CM} = (165.4 \text{ mils})^2 = \mathbf{27.36 \times 10^3 \text{ CM}}$

3. $A_{CM} = (d_{mils})^2 \rightarrow d_{mils} = \sqrt{A_{CM}}$

   a. $d = \sqrt{1600 \text{ CM}} = 40 \text{ mils} = \mathbf{0.04 \text{ in.}}$

   b. $d = \sqrt{820 \text{ CM}} = 28.64 \text{ mils} = \mathbf{0.029 \text{ in.}}$

   c. $d = \sqrt{40{,}000 \text{ CM}} = 200 \text{ mils} = \mathbf{0.2 \text{ in.}}$

d. $d = \sqrt{625\text{ CM}} = 25\text{ mils} = \mathbf{0.025\text{ in.}}$

e. $d = \sqrt{6.25\text{ CM}} = 2.5\text{ mils} = \mathbf{0.0025\text{ in.}}$

f. $d = \sqrt{100\text{ CM}} = 10\text{ mils} = \mathbf{0.01\text{ in.}}$

4. $0.01\text{ in.} = 10\text{ mils}, A_{CM} = (10\text{ mils})^2 = 100\text{ CM}$

$$R = \rho\frac{l}{A} = (10.37)\frac{(200')}{100\text{ CM}} = \mathbf{20.74\ \Omega}$$

5. $A_{CM} = (4\text{ mils})^2 = 16\text{ CM}, R = \rho\frac{l}{A} = (9.9)\frac{(150\text{ ft})}{16\text{ CM}} = \mathbf{92.81\ \Omega}$

6. a. $A = \rho\frac{l}{R} = 17\left(\frac{80'}{2.5\ \Omega}\right) = \mathbf{544\text{ CM}}$

b. $d = \sqrt{A_{CM}} = \sqrt{544\text{ CM}} = 23.32\text{ mils} = \mathbf{23.3 \times 10^{-3}\text{ in.}}$

7. $\frac{1}{32}'' = 0.03125'' = 31.25\text{ mils}, A_{CM} = (31.25\text{ mils})^2 = 976.56\text{ CM}$

$$R = \rho\frac{l}{R} \Rightarrow l = \frac{RA}{\rho} = \frac{(2.2\ \Omega)(976.56\text{ CM})}{600} = \mathbf{3.58\text{ ft}}$$

8. a. $A_{CM} = \rho\frac{l}{A} = \frac{(10.37)(300')}{3.3\ \Omega} = \mathbf{942.73\text{ CM}}$

$d = \sqrt{942.73\text{ CM}} = 30.70\text{ mils} = \mathbf{30.7 \times 10^{-3}\text{ in.}}$

b. larger

c. smaller

9. a. $R_{\text{silver}} > R_{\text{copper}} > R_{\text{aluminum}}$

b. Silver: $R = \rho\frac{l}{A} = \frac{(9.9)(10\text{ ft})}{1\text{ CM}} = \mathbf{99\ \Omega}$ { $A_{CM} = (1\text{ mil})^2 = 1\text{ CM}$

Copper: $R = \rho\frac{l}{A} = \frac{(10.37)(50\text{ ft})}{100\text{ CM}} = \mathbf{5.19\ \Omega}$ { $A_{CM} = (10\text{ mils})^2 = 100\text{ CM}$

Aluminum: $R = \rho\frac{l}{A} = \frac{(17)(200\text{ ft})}{2500\text{ CM}} = \mathbf{1.36\ \Omega}$ { $A_{CM} = (50\text{ mils})^2 = 2500\text{ CM}$

10. $\rho = \frac{RA}{l} = \frac{(500\ \Omega)(94\text{ CM})}{1000'} = 47 \Rightarrow$ **nickel**

11. a. 3" = 3000 mils, 1/2" = 0.5 in. = 500 mils

Area = $(3 \times 10^3 \text{ mils})(5 \times 10^2 \text{ mils}) = 15 \times 10^5$ sq. mils

$$15 \times 10^5 \text{ sq mils} \left[\frac{4/\pi \text{ CM}}{1 \text{ sq mil}}\right] = 19.108 \times 10^5 \text{ CM}$$

$$R = \rho\frac{l}{A} = \frac{(10.37)(4')}{19.108 \times 10^5 \text{ CM}} = \mathbf{21.71\ \mu\Omega}$$

b. $$R = \rho\frac{l}{A} = \frac{(17)(4')}{19.108 \times 10^5 \text{ CM}} = \mathbf{35.59\ \mu\Omega}$$

Aluminum bus-bar has almost 64% higher resistance.

c. increases

d. decreases

12. $l_2 = 2l_1$, $A_2 = A_1/4$, $\rho_2 = \rho_1$

$$\frac{R_2}{R_1} = \frac{\frac{\rho_2 l_2}{A_2}}{\frac{\rho_1 l_1}{A_1}} = \frac{\rho_2 l_2 A_1}{\rho_1 l_1 A_2} = \frac{2l_1 A_1}{l_1 A_1/4} = 8$$

and $R_2 = 8R_1 = 8(0.2\ \Omega) = 1.6\ \Omega$

$\Delta R = 1.6\ \Omega - 0.2\ \Omega = \mathbf{1.4\ \Omega}$

13. $$A = \frac{\pi d^2}{4} \Rightarrow d = \sqrt{\frac{4A}{\pi}} = \sqrt{\frac{4(0.04 \text{ in.}^2)}{\pi}} = 0.2257 \text{ in.}$$

$d_{\text{mils}} = 225.7$ mils

$A_{\text{CM}} = (225.7 \text{ mils})^2 = 50{,}940.49$ CM

$$\frac{R_1}{R_2} = \frac{\rho_1\frac{l_1}{A_1}}{\rho_2\frac{l_2}{A_2}} = \frac{\rho_1 l_1 A_2}{\rho_2 l_2 A_1} = \frac{l_1 A_2}{l_2 A_1} \qquad (\rho_1 = \rho_2)$$

and $$R_2 = \frac{R_1 l_2 A_1}{l_1 A_2} = \frac{(800\text{ m}\Omega)(300\text{ ft})(40{,}000\text{ CM})}{(200\text{ ft})(50{,}940.49\text{ CM})} = \mathbf{942.28\ m\Omega}$$

14. a. #11: $$450 \text{ ft}\left[\frac{1.260\ \Omega}{1000 \text{ ft}}\right] = \mathbf{0.567\ \Omega}$$

#14: $$450 \text{ ft}\left[\frac{2.525\ \Omega}{1000 \text{ ft}}\right] = \mathbf{1.136\ \Omega}$$

b. Resistance: #14:#11 = 1.136 Ω:0.567 Ω ≅ **2:1**

c. Area: #14:#11 = 4106.8 CM:8234.0 CM ≅ **1:2**

15. a. #8: $R = 1800\not{ft}\left[\dfrac{0.6282\ \Omega}{1000\not{ft}}\right] = \mathbf{1.13\ \Omega}$

#18: $R = 1800\not{ft}\left[\dfrac{6.385\ \Omega}{1000\not{ft}}\right] = \mathbf{11.49\ \Omega}$

b. #18:#8 = 11.49 Ω:1.13 Ω = 10.17:1 ≅ **10:1**

c. #18:#8 = 1624.3 CM:16,509 CM = 1:10.16 ≅ **1:10**

16. a. $A = \rho\dfrac{l}{R} = \dfrac{(10.37)(30')}{6\ \text{m}\Omega} = \dfrac{311.1\text{CM}}{6\times10^{-3}} = 51{,}850\ \text{CM} \Rightarrow \#3$

but 110 A ⇒ **#2**

b. $A = \rho\dfrac{l}{R} = \dfrac{(10.37)(30')}{3\ \text{m}\Omega} = \dfrac{311.1\text{CM}}{3\times10^{-3}} = 103{,}700\ \text{CM} \Rightarrow \mathbf{\#0}$

17. a. A/CM = 230 A/211,600 CM = **1.09 mA/CM**

b. $\dfrac{1.09\ \text{mA}}{\not{CM}}\left[\dfrac{1\ \not{CM}}{\frac{\pi}{4}\text{sq mils}}\right]\left[\dfrac{1000\ \not{mils}}{1\ \text{in.}}\right]\left[\dfrac{1000\ \not{mils}}{1\ \text{in.}}\right] = \mathbf{1.39\ kA/in.^2}$

c. $5\ \not{kA}\left[\dfrac{1\ \text{in.}^2}{1.39\ \not{kA}}\right] = \mathbf{3.6\ in.^2}$

18. $\dfrac{1}{12}\ \text{in.} = 0.083\ \not{in.}\left(\dfrac{2.54\ \text{cm}}{1\ \not{in.}}\right) = 0.21\ \text{cm}$

$A = \dfrac{\pi d^2}{4} = \dfrac{(3.14)(0.21\ \text{cm})^2}{4} = 0.035\ \text{cm}^2$

$l = \dfrac{RA}{\rho} = \dfrac{(2\ \Omega)(0.035\ \text{cm}^2)}{1.724\times10^{-6}} = 40{,}603\ \text{cm} = \mathbf{406.03\ m}$

19. a. $\dfrac{1''}{2}\left[\dfrac{2.54\ \text{cm}}{1''}\right] = 1.27\ \text{cm},\ 3\ \not{in.}\left[\dfrac{2.54\ \text{cm}}{1\ \not{in.}}\right] = 7.62\ \text{cm}$

$4\not{ft}\left[\dfrac{12\ \not{in.}}{1\not{ft}}\right]\left[\dfrac{2.54\ \text{cm}}{1\ \not{in.}}\right] = 121.92\ \text{cm}$

$R = \rho\dfrac{l}{A}\ \dfrac{(1.724\ \text{x}\ 10^{-6})(121.92\ \text{cm})}{(1.27\ \text{cm})(7.62\ \text{cm})} = \mathbf{21.71\ \mu\Omega}$

b. $R = \rho\dfrac{\ell}{A} = \dfrac{(2.825\times10^{-6})(121.92\ \text{cm})}{(1.27\ \text{cm})(7.62\ \text{cm})} = \mathbf{35.59\ \mu\Omega}$

c. increases

d. decreases

20. $R_s = \dfrac{\rho}{d} = 100 \Rightarrow d = \dfrac{\rho}{100} = \dfrac{250 \times 10^{-6}}{100} = \mathbf{2.5\ \mu cm}$

21. $R = R_s \dfrac{l}{w} \Rightarrow w = \dfrac{R_s l}{R} = \dfrac{(150\ \Omega)(1/2\text{ in.})}{500\ \Omega} = \mathbf{0.15\ in.}$

22. a. $d = 1$ in. = 1000 mils

$A_{CM} = (10^3\text{ mils})^2 = 10^6$ CM

$\rho_1 = \dfrac{RA}{l} = \dfrac{(1\text{ m}\Omega)(10^6\text{ CM})}{10^3\text{ ft}} = \mathbf{1\ CM\text{-}\Omega/ft}$

b. 1 in. = 2.54 cm

$A = \dfrac{\pi d^2}{4} = \dfrac{\pi(2.54\text{ cm})^2}{4} = 5.067\text{ cm}^2$

$l = 1000\text{ ft}\left[\dfrac{12\text{ in.}}{1\text{ ft}}\right]\left[\dfrac{2.54\text{ cm}}{1\text{ in.}}\right] = 30{,}480\text{ cm}$

$\rho_2 = \dfrac{RA}{l} = \dfrac{(1\text{ m}\Omega)(5.067\text{ cm}^2)}{30{,}480\text{ cm}} = \mathbf{1.66 \times 10^{-7}\ \Omega\text{-cm}}$

c. $k = \dfrac{\rho_2}{\rho_1} = \dfrac{1.66 \times 10^{-7}\ \Omega\text{-cm}}{1\text{ CM-}\Omega/\text{ft}} = \mathbf{1.66 \times 10^{-7}}$

23. $\dfrac{234.5 + 10}{2\ \Omega} = \dfrac{234.5 + 80}{R_2}, \quad R_2 = \dfrac{(314.5)(2\ \Omega)}{244.5} = \mathbf{2.57\ \Omega}$

24. $\dfrac{236 + 0}{0.02\ \Omega} = \dfrac{236 + 100}{R_2}$

$R_2 = \dfrac{(0.02\ \Omega)(336)}{236} = \mathbf{0.028\ \Omega}$

25. $\text{C} = \dfrac{5}{9}(°\text{F} - 32) = \dfrac{5}{9}(32 - 32) = 0°\ (=32°\text{F})$

$\text{C} = \dfrac{5}{9}(70 - 32) = 21.11°\quad (=70°\text{F})$

$\dfrac{234.5° + 21.11°}{4\ \Omega} = \dfrac{234.5° + 0°}{R_2}$

$R_2 = \dfrac{(234.5)(4\ \Omega)}{255.61} = \mathbf{3.67\ \Omega}$

26. $$\frac{234.5+30}{0.76\ \Omega}=\frac{234.5-40}{R_2}$$

$$R_2=\frac{(194.5)(0.76\ \Omega)}{264.5}=\mathbf{0.56\ \Omega}$$

27. $$\frac{243+(-30)}{0.04\ \Omega}=\frac{243+0}{R_2}$$

$$R_2=\frac{(243)(40\ \text{m}\Omega)}{213}=\mathbf{46\ m\Omega}$$

28. a. 68°F = 20°C, 32°F = 0°C

$$\frac{234.5+20}{0.002}=\frac{234.5+0}{R_2}$$

$$R_2=\frac{(234.5)(2\ \text{m}\Omega)}{254.5}=\mathbf{1.84\ m\Omega}$$

212°F = 100 °C

$$\frac{234.5+20}{2\ \text{m}\Omega}=\frac{234.5+100}{R_2}$$

$$R_2=\frac{(334.5)(2\ \text{m}\Omega)}{254.5}=\mathbf{2.63\ m\Omega}$$

b. $$\frac{\Delta R}{\Delta T}=\frac{2.63\ \text{m}\Omega-2\ \text{m}\Omega}{100°\text{C}-20°\text{C}}=\frac{0.63\ \text{m}\Omega}{80°\text{C}}=7.88\ \mu\Omega/°\text{C}\ \text{or}\ \mathbf{7.88\times10^{-5}\ \Omega/10°C}$$

29. a. $$\frac{234.5+4}{1\ \Omega}=\frac{234.5+t_2}{1.1\ \Omega},\quad t_2=\mathbf{27.85°C}$$

b. $$\frac{234.5+4}{1\ \Omega}=\frac{234.5+t_2}{0.1\ \Omega},\quad t_2=\mathbf{-210.65°C}$$

30. a. K = 273.15 + °C

50 = 273.15 + °C

°C = –223.15°

$$\frac{234.5+20}{10\ \Omega}=\frac{234.5-223.15}{R_2}$$

$$R_2=\frac{11.35}{254.5}(10\ \Omega)=\mathbf{0.446\ \Omega}$$

b. K = 273.15 + °C

38.65 = 273.15 + °C

°C = –234.5°

$$\frac{234.5+20}{10\ \Omega}=\frac{234.5-234.5}{R_2}$$

$$R_2=\frac{(0)10\ \Omega}{254.5}=\mathbf{0\ \Omega}$$

Recall: –234.5° = Inferred absolute zero

$R=\mathbf{0\ \Omega}$

c. $$F=\frac{9}{5}°\text{C}+32=\frac{9}{5}(-273.15°)+32=\mathbf{-459.67°}$$

31. a. $\alpha_{20} = \dfrac{1}{|T_i| + 20°\text{C}} = \dfrac{1}{234.5 + 20} = \dfrac{1}{254.5} = 0.003929 \cong \mathbf{0.00393}$

b. $R = R_{20}[1 + \alpha_{20}(t - 20°\text{C})]$

$1\ \Omega = 0.8\ \Omega[1 + 0.00393(t - 20°)]$

$1.25 = 1 + 0.00393t - 0.0786$

$1.25 - 0.9214 = 0.00393t$

$0.3286 = 0.00393t$

$$t = \frac{0.3286}{0.00393} = \mathbf{83.61°C}$$

32. $R = R_{20}[1 + \alpha_{20}(t - 20°\text{C})]$

$= 0.4\ \Omega[1 + 0.00393(16 - 20)] = 0.4\ \Omega[1 - 0.01572] = \mathbf{0.39\ \Omega}$

33. Table: 1000′ of #12 copper wire = 1.588 Ω @ 20°C

$$\text{C}° = \frac{5}{9}(\text{F}° - 32) = \frac{5}{9}(115 - 32) = 46.11°\text{C}$$

$R = R_{20}[1 + \alpha_{20}(t - 20°\text{C})]$

$= 1.588\ \Omega[1 + 0.00393(46.11 - 20)]$

$= \mathbf{1.75\ \Omega}$

34. $\Delta R = \dfrac{R_{\text{nominal}}}{10^6}(\text{PPM})(\Delta\text{T}) = \dfrac{22\ \Omega}{10^6}(200)(65° - 20°) = 0.198\ \Omega$

$R = R_{\text{nominal}} + \Delta R = \mathbf{22.198\ \Omega}$

35. $\Delta R = \dfrac{R_{\text{nominal}}}{10^6}(\text{PPM})(\Delta\text{T}) = \dfrac{100\ \Omega}{10^6}(100)(50° - 20°) = 0.30\ \Omega$

$R = R_{\text{nominal}} + \Delta R = 100\ \Omega + 0.30\ \Omega = \mathbf{100.30\ \Omega}$

36. –

37. –

38. #12: Area = 6529 CM

$$d = \sqrt{6529\ \text{CM}} = 80.8\ \text{mils} = 0.0808\ \cancel{\text{in.}}\left[\frac{2.54\ \text{cm}}{1\ \cancel{\text{in.}}}\right] = 0.205\ \text{cm}$$

$$A = \frac{\pi d^2}{4} = \frac{\pi(0.205\ \text{cm})^2}{4} = 0.033\ \text{cm}^2$$

$$I = \frac{1\ \text{MA}}{\cancel{\text{cm}^2}}[0.033\ \cancel{\text{cm}^2}] = \mathbf{33\ kA} >> 20\ \text{A}$$

39. –

40. a. 2 times larger b. 4 times larger

41. 10 kΩ – 3.5 kΩ = **6.5 kΩ**

42. **6.25 kΩ** and **18.75 kΩ**

43. –

44.
a. 560 kΩ ± 5%, 560 kΩ ± 28 kΩ, **532 kΩ ↔ 588 kΩ**
b. 220 Ω ± 10%, 220 Ω ± 22 Ω, **198 Ω ↔ 242 Ω**
c. 100 Ω ± 20%, 100 Ω ± 20 Ω, **80 Ω ↔ 120 Ω**

45.
a. 120 Ω = Brown, Red, Brown, Silver
b. 8.2 Ω = Gray, Red, Gold, Silver
c. 6.8 kΩ = Blue, Gray, Red, Silver
d. 3.3 MΩ = Orange, Orange, Green, Silver

46.
$$\left.\begin{array}{l} 10\,\Omega \pm 20\% \Rightarrow 8\,\Omega - 12\,\Omega \\ 15\,\Omega \pm 20\% \Rightarrow 12\,\Omega - 18\,\Omega \end{array}\right\}\text{ no overlap, continuance}$$

47.
$$\left.\begin{array}{l} 10\,\Omega \pm 10\% \Rightarrow 10\,\Omega \pm 1\,\Omega = 9\,\Omega - 11\,\Omega \\ 15\,\Omega \pm 10\% \Rightarrow 15\,\Omega \pm 1.5\,\Omega = 13.5\,\Omega - 16.5\,\Omega \end{array}\right\}\text{ No overlap}$$

48.
a. $621 = 62 \times 10^1\ \Omega = 620\ \Omega =$ **0.62 kΩ**
b. $333 = 33 \times 10^3\ \Omega =$ **33 kΩ**
c. $Q2 = 3.9 \times 10^2\ \Omega =$ **390 Ω**
d. $C6 = 1.2 \times 10^6\ \Omega =$ **1.2 MΩ**

49.
a. $G = \dfrac{1}{R} = \dfrac{1}{120\,\Omega} = \mathbf{8.33\ mS}$

b. $G = \dfrac{1}{4\,\text{k}\Omega} = \mathbf{0.25\ mS}$

c. $G = \dfrac{1}{2.2\,\text{M}\Omega} = \mathbf{0.46\ \mu S}$

$G_a > G_b > G_c$ vs. $R_c > R_b > R_a$

50.
a. Table 3.2, Ω/1000′ = 1.588 Ω

$G = \dfrac{1}{R} = \dfrac{1}{1.588\,\Omega} = \mathbf{629.72\ mS}$

or $G = \dfrac{A}{\rho l} = \dfrac{6529.9\text{ CM (Table 3.2)}}{(10.37)(1000')} = \mathbf{629.69\ mS}$ (Cu)

b. $G = \dfrac{6529.9\text{ CM}}{(17)(1000')} = \mathbf{384.11\ mS}$ (Al)

c. $G = \dfrac{6529.9\text{ CM}}{(74)(1000')} = \mathbf{88.24\ mS}$ (Fe)

51. $A_2 = 1\frac{2}{3}A_1 = \frac{5}{3}A_1,\ l_2 = \left(1-\frac{2}{3}\right)l_1 = \frac{l_1}{3},\ \rho_2 = \rho_1$

$$\frac{G_1}{G_2} = \frac{\rho_1\dfrac{A_1}{l_1}}{\rho_2\dfrac{A_2}{l_2}} = \frac{\rho_2 l_2 A_1}{\rho_1 l_1 A_2} = \frac{\left(\dfrac{l_1}{3}\right)A_1}{l_1\left(\dfrac{5}{3}A_1\right)} = \frac{1}{5}$$

$G_2 = 5G_1 = 5(100\text{ S}) = \mathbf{500\ S}$

52. –

53. –

54. –

55. a. –50°C specific resistance ≅ 10^5 Ω-cm
50°C specific resistance ≅ 500 Ω-cm
200°C specific resistance ≅ 7 Ω-cm

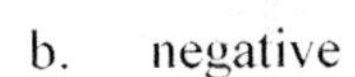

b. negative

c. No

d. $\rho = \dfrac{\Delta\Omega - \text{cm}}{\Delta T} = \dfrac{300-30}{125-50} = \dfrac{270\ \Omega-\ \text{cm}}{75°\text{ C}} \cong$ **3.6 Ω-cm/°C**

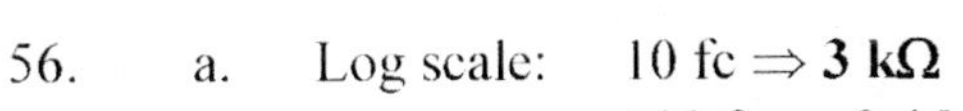

56. a. Log scale: 10 fc ⇒ **3 kΩ**
100 fc ⇒ **0.4 kΩ**

b. negative

c. no—log scales imply linearity

d. 1 kΩ ⇒ ≅ 30 fc
10 kΩ ⇒ ≅ 2 fc

$$\left|\frac{\Delta R}{\Delta fc}\right| = \frac{10\text{ k}\Omega - 1\text{ k}\Omega}{30\text{ fc} - 2\text{ fc}} = 321.43\ \Omega/\text{fc}$$

and $\dfrac{\Delta R}{\Delta \text{fc}} = \mathbf{-321.43\ \Omega/fc}$

57. a. @ 0.5 mA, $V \cong$ **195 V**
@ 1 mA, $V \cong$ **200 V**
@ 5 mA, $V \cong$ **215 V**

b. $\Delta V_{\text{total}} = 215\text{ V} - 195\text{ V} =$ **20 V**

c. 5 mA:0.5 mA = **10:1**
compared to
215 V: 200 V = **1.08:1**

Chapter 4

1. $V = IR = (2.5\text{ A})(47\ \Omega) = \mathbf{117.5\ V}$

2. $I = \dfrac{V}{R} = \dfrac{12\text{ V}}{6.8\ \Omega} = \mathbf{1.76\ A}$

3. $R = \dfrac{V}{I} = \dfrac{6\text{ V}}{1.5\text{ mA}} = \mathbf{4\ k\Omega}$

4. $I = \dfrac{V}{R} = \dfrac{12\text{ V}}{40\times10^{-3}\ \Omega} = \mathbf{300\ A}$

5. $V = IR = (3.6\ \mu\text{A})(0.02\text{ M}\Omega) = 0.072\text{ V} = \mathbf{72\ mV}$

6. $I = \dfrac{V}{R} = \dfrac{62\text{ V}}{15\text{ k}\Omega} = \mathbf{4.13\ mA}$

7. $R = \dfrac{V}{I} = \dfrac{120\text{ V}}{2.2\text{ A}} = \mathbf{54.55\ \Omega}$

8. $I = \dfrac{V}{R} = \dfrac{120\text{ V}}{7.5\text{ k}\Omega} = \mathbf{16\ mA}$

9. $R = \dfrac{V}{I} = \dfrac{120\text{ V}}{4.2\text{ A}} = \mathbf{28.57\ \Omega}$

10. $R = \dfrac{V}{I} = \dfrac{4.5\text{ V}}{125\text{ mA}} = \mathbf{36\ \Omega}$

11. $R = \dfrac{V}{I} = \dfrac{24\text{ mV}}{20\ \mu\text{A}} = \mathbf{1.2\ k\Omega}$

12. $V = IR = (15\text{ A})(0.5\ \Omega) = \mathbf{7.5\ V}$

13. a. $R = \dfrac{V}{I} = \dfrac{120\text{ V}}{9.5\text{ A}} = \mathbf{12.63\ \Omega}$

    b. $t = 1\cancel{\text{h}}\left[\dfrac{60\ \cancel{\text{min}}}{1\ \cancel{\text{h}}}\right]\left[\dfrac{60\text{ s}}{1\ \cancel{\text{min}}}\right] = 3600\text{ s}$

    $W = Pt = VIt$
    $= (120\text{ V})(9.5\text{ A})(3600\text{ s})$
    $= \mathbf{4.1 \times 10^6\ J}$

14. $V = IR = (2.4\ \mu\text{A})(3.3\text{ M}\Omega) = \mathbf{7.92\ V}$

15. –

16. b. (0.13 mA)(500 h) = **65 mAh**

17. –

18. –

19. –

20. $P = \frac{W}{t} = \frac{420\text{ J}}{4\ \cancel{\text{min}}\left[\frac{60\text{ s}}{1\ \cancel{\text{min}}}\right]} = \frac{420\text{ J}}{240\text{ s}} = \mathbf{1.75\ W}$

21. $t = \frac{W}{P} = \frac{640\text{ J}}{40\text{ J/s}} = \mathbf{16\ s}$

22. a. $8\ \cancel{\text{h}}\left[\frac{60\ \cancel{\text{min}}}{1\ \cancel{\text{h}}}\right]\left[\frac{60\text{ s}}{1\ \cancel{\text{min}}}\right] = 28{,}800\text{ s}$

$W = Pt = (2\text{ W})(28{,}000\text{ s}) = \mathbf{57.6\ kJ}$

b. $\text{kWh} = \frac{(2\text{ W})(8\text{ h})}{1000} = \mathbf{16 \times 10^{-3}\ kWh}$

23. $I = \frac{Q}{t} = \frac{300\text{ C}}{1\ \cancel{\text{min}}}\left[\frac{1\ \cancel{\text{min}}}{60\text{ s}}\right] = 5\text{ C/s} = 5\text{ A}$

$P = I^2R = (5\text{ A})^2\ 10\ \Omega = \mathbf{250\ W}$

24. $P = VI = (3\text{ V})(1.4\text{ A}) = 4.20\text{ W}$

$t = \frac{W}{P} = \frac{12\text{ J}}{4.2\text{ W}} = \mathbf{2.86\ s}$

25. $I = \frac{48\text{ C}}{\cancel{\text{min}}}\left[\frac{1\ \cancel{\text{min}}}{60\text{ s}}\right] = 0.8\text{ A}$

$P = EI = (6\text{ V})(0.8\text{ A}) = \mathbf{4.8\ W}$

26. $P = I^2R = (7.2\text{ mA})^2\ 4\text{ k}\Omega = \mathbf{207.36\ mW}$

27. $P = I^2R \Rightarrow I = \sqrt{\frac{P}{R}} = \sqrt{\frac{240\text{ mW}}{2.2\text{ k}\Omega}} = \mathbf{10.44\ mA}$

28. $I = \sqrt{\frac{P}{R}} = \sqrt{\frac{2\text{ W}}{120\ \Omega}} = \mathbf{129.10\ mA}$

$V = IR = (129.10\text{ mA})(120\ \Omega) = \mathbf{15.49\ V}$

29. $I = \frac{E}{R} = \frac{12\text{ V}}{5.6\text{ k}\Omega} = \mathbf{2.14\text{ mA}}$

$P = I^2R = (2.14\text{ mA})^2\ 5.6\text{ k}\Omega = \mathbf{25.65\text{ mW}}$

$W = P \cdot t = (25.65\text{ mW})\left(1\cancel{\text{h}}\left[\frac{60\ \cancel{\text{min}}}{1\ \cancel{\text{h}}}\right]\left[\frac{60\text{ s}}{1\ \cancel{\text{min}}}\right]\right) = \mathbf{92.34\text{ J}}$

30. $E = \frac{P}{I} = \frac{324\text{ W}}{2.7\text{ A}} = \mathbf{120\text{ V}}$

31. $I = \sqrt{\frac{P}{R}} = \sqrt{\frac{1\text{ W}}{4.7\text{ M}\Omega}} = \mathbf{461.27\ \mu A}$

no

32. $V = \sqrt{PR} = \sqrt{(42\text{ mW})(2.2\text{ k}\Omega)} = \sqrt{92.40} = \mathbf{9.61\text{ V}}$

33. $P = EI = (9\text{ V})(45\text{ mA}) = \mathbf{405\text{ mW}}$

34. $P = VI,\ I = \frac{P}{V} = \frac{100\text{ W}}{120\text{ V}} = 0.833\text{ A}$

$R = \frac{V}{I} = \frac{120\text{ V}}{0.833\text{ A}} = \mathbf{144.06\ \Omega}$

35. $V = \frac{P}{I} = \frac{450\text{ W}}{3.75\text{ A}} = \mathbf{120\text{ V}}$

$R = \frac{V}{I} = \frac{120\text{ V}}{3.75\text{ A}} = \mathbf{32\ \Omega}$

36. a. $P = EI$ and $I = \frac{P}{E} = \frac{0.4 \times 10^{-3}\text{ W}}{3\text{ V}} = \mathbf{0.13\text{ mA}}$

b. Ah rating = (0.13 mA)(500 h) = **66.5 mAh**

37. $I = \sqrt{\frac{P}{R}} = \sqrt{\frac{100\text{ W}}{20\text{ k}\Omega}} = \sqrt{5 \times 10^{-3}} = \mathbf{70.71\text{ mA}}$

$V = \sqrt{PR} = \sqrt{(100\text{ W})(20\text{ k}\Omega)} = \mathbf{1.42\text{ kV}}$

38. a. $W = Pt = \left(\frac{V^2}{R}\right)t = \left(\frac{12\text{ V}}{10\ \Omega}\right)^2 60\text{ s} = \mathbf{864\text{ J}}$

b. Energy doubles, power the same

39. $\dfrac{12\text{ h}}{\cancel{\text{week}}}\left[\dfrac{4\frac{1}{3}\cancel{\text{weeks}}}{1\cancel{\text{month}}}\right][5\text{ months}] = 260\text{ h}$

$$\text{kWh} = \frac{(230\text{ W})(260\text{ h})}{1000} = \mathbf{59.80\ kWh}$$

40. $\text{kWh} = \dfrac{Pt}{1000} \Rightarrow t = \dfrac{(1000)(\text{kWh})}{P} = \dfrac{(1000)(12\text{ kWh})}{1500\text{ W}} = \mathbf{8\ h}$

41. $\text{kWh} = \dfrac{(24\text{ W})(3\text{ h})}{1000} = 72 \times 10^{-3}\text{ kWh}$

$(72 \times 10^{-3}\text{ kWh})(9¢/\text{kWh}) = \mathbf{0.65¢}$

42. a. $\text{kWh} = \dfrac{Pt}{1000} \Rightarrow P = \dfrac{(1000)(\text{kWh})}{P} = \dfrac{(1000)(1200\text{ kWh})}{10\text{ h}} = \mathbf{120\ kW}$

b. $I = \dfrac{P}{E} = \dfrac{120 \times 10^3\text{ W}}{208\text{ V}} = \mathbf{576.92\ A}$

c. $P_{\text{lost}} = P_i - P_o = P_i - \eta P_i = P_i(1 - \eta) = 120\text{ kW}(1 - 0.82) = 21.6\text{ kW}$

$\text{kWh}_{\text{lost}} = \dfrac{Pt}{1000} = \dfrac{(21.6\text{ kW})(10\text{ h})}{1000} = \mathbf{216\ kWh}$

43. $\#\text{kWh} = \dfrac{\$1.00}{9¢} = 11.11$

$\text{kWh} = \dfrac{Pt}{1000} \Rightarrow t = \dfrac{(\text{kWh})(1000)}{P} = \dfrac{(11.11)(1000)}{.250} = \mathbf{44.44\ h}$

$t = \dfrac{(\text{kWh})(1000)}{P} = \dfrac{(11.11)(1000)}{4800} = \mathbf{2.32\ h}$

44. a. $W = Pt = (60\text{ W})(1\text{ h}) = \mathbf{60\ Wh}$

b. $W = Pt = (60\text{ W})\left(1\cancel{\text{h}}\left[\dfrac{60\cancel{\text{min}}}{1\cancel{\text{h}}}\right]\left[\dfrac{60\text{ s}}{1\cancel{\text{min}}}\right]\right) = \mathbf{216\ kWs}$

c. $1\text{ kJ} = 1\text{ Ws}, \therefore \mathbf{216\ kJ}$

d. $W = \dfrac{Pt}{1000} = \dfrac{(60\text{ W})(1\text{ h})}{1000} = \mathbf{60 \times 10^{-3}\ kWh}$

45. a. $P = EI = (9\text{ V})(0.455\text{ A}) = \mathbf{4.1\text{ W}}$

b. $R = \dfrac{E}{I} = \dfrac{9\text{ V}}{0.455\text{ A}} = \mathbf{19.78\ \Omega}$

c. $W = Pt = (4.1\text{ W})(21{,}600\text{ s}) = \mathbf{88.56\text{ kJ}}$

$$6\not{\text{h}}\left[\frac{60\not{\text{min}}}{1\not{\text{h}}}\right]\left[\frac{60\text{ s}}{1\not{\text{min}}}\right] = 21{,}600\text{ s}$$

46. a. $P = EI = (120\text{ V})(100\text{ A}) = \mathbf{12\text{ kW}}$

b. $$P_T = 5\not{\text{hp}}\left[\frac{746\text{ W}}{\not{\text{hp}}}\right] + 3000\text{ W} + 2400\text{ W} + 1000\text{ W}$$

$$= 10{,}130 < 12{,}000\text{ W}\ \ \textbf{(Yes)}$$

c. $W = Pt = (10.13\text{ kW})(2\text{ h}) = \mathbf{20.26\text{ kWh}}$

47. $$\text{kWh} = \frac{(860\text{ W})(6\text{ h}) + (4800\text{ W})(1/2\text{ h}) + (900\text{ W})\left(20\not{\text{min}}\left(\dfrac{1\text{ h}}{60\not{\text{min}}}\right)\right) + (110\text{ W})(3.5\text{ h})}{1000}$$

$$= \frac{5160\text{ Wh} + 2400\text{ Wh} + 300\text{ Wh} + 385\text{ Wh}}{1000} = 8.245\text{ kWh}$$

$(8.245\text{ kWh})(9¢/\text{kWh}) = \mathbf{74.21¢}$

48. $$\text{kWh} = \frac{(200\text{ W})(4\text{ h}) + (1200\text{ W})\left(20\not{\text{min}}\left(\dfrac{1\text{ h}}{60\not{\text{min}}}\right)\right) + (70\text{ W})(1.5\text{ h}) + (150\text{ W})\left(130\not{\text{min}}\left(\dfrac{1\text{ h}}{60\not{\text{min}}}\right)\right)}{1000}$$

$$= \frac{800\text{ Wh} + 400\text{ Wh} + 105\text{ Wh} + 325\text{ Wh}}{1000} = \mathbf{1.63\text{ kWh}}$$

$(1.63\text{ kWh})(9¢/\text{kWh}) = \mathbf{14.67¢}$

49. $$\eta = \frac{P_o}{P_i} \times 100\% = \frac{(0.5\not{\text{hp}})\left[\dfrac{746\text{ W}}{\not{\text{hp}}}\right]}{395\text{ W}} \times 100\% = \frac{373}{395} \times 100\% = 94.43\%$$

50. $$\eta = \frac{P_o}{P_i},\ P_i = \frac{P_o}{\eta} = \frac{(1.8\not{\text{hp}})(746\text{ W}/\not{\text{hp}})}{0.685} = 1960.29\text{ W}$$

$$P_i = EI,\ I = \frac{P_i}{E} = \frac{1960.29\text{ W}}{120\text{ V}} = \mathbf{16.34\text{ A}}$$

51. $$\eta = \frac{P_o}{P_i} \times 100\% = \frac{746\text{ W}}{(4\text{ A})(220\text{ V})} \times 100\% = \frac{746}{880} \times 100\% = \mathbf{84.77\%}$$

52. a. $P_i = EI = (120 \text{ V})(2.4 \text{ A}) = 288 \text{ W}$

$P_i = P_o + P_{\text{lost}},\ P_{\text{lost}} = P_i - P_o = 288 \text{ W} - 50 \text{ W} = \mathbf{238\ W}$

b. $$\eta\% = \frac{P_o}{P_i} \times 100\% = \frac{50 \text{ W}}{288 \text{ W}} \times 100\% = \mathbf{17.36\%}$$

53. $$P_i = EI = \frac{P_o}{\eta} \Rightarrow I = \frac{P_o}{\eta E} = \frac{(3.6 \not{\text{hp}})(746 \text{ W}/\not{\text{hp}})}{(0.76)(220 \text{ V})} = \mathbf{16.06\ A}$$

54. a. $$P_i = \frac{P_o}{\eta} = \frac{(2 \not{\text{hp}})(746 \text{ W}/\not{\text{hp}})}{0.9} = \mathbf{1657.78\ W}$$

b. $P_i = EI = 1657.78 \text{ W}$

$(110 \text{ V})I = 1657.78 \text{ W}$

$$I = \frac{1657.78 \text{ W}}{110 \text{ V}} = \mathbf{15.07\ A}$$

c. $$P_i = \frac{P_o}{\eta} = \frac{(2 \not{\text{hp}})(746 \text{ W}/\not{\text{hp}})}{0.7} = 2131.43 \text{ W}$$

$P_i = EI = 2131.43 \text{ W}$

$(110 \text{ V})I = 2131.43 \text{ W}$

$$I = \frac{2131.43 \text{ W}}{110 \text{ V}} = \mathbf{19.38\ A}$$

55. $$P_i = \frac{P_o}{\eta} = \frac{(15 \not{\text{hp}})(746 \text{ W}/\not{\text{hp}})}{0.9} = 12{,}433.33 \text{ W}$$

$$I = \frac{P_i}{E} = \frac{12{,}433.33 \text{ W}}{220 \text{ V}} = \mathbf{56.52\ A}$$

56. $\eta_T = \eta_1 \cdot \eta_2$

$0.75 = 0.85 \times \eta_2$

$\eta_2 = \mathbf{0.88}$

57. $\eta_T = \eta_1 \cdot \eta_2 = (0.87)(0.75) = 0.6525 \Rightarrow \mathbf{65.25\%}$

58. $\eta_1 = \eta_2 = .08$

$\eta_T = (\eta_1)(\eta_2) = (0.8)(0.8) = 0.64$

$$\eta_T = \frac{W_o}{W_i} \Rightarrow W_o = \eta_T W_i = (0.64)(60 \text{ J}) = \mathbf{38.4\ J}$$

59. $\eta_T = \eta_1 \cdot \eta_2 = 0.72 = 0.9\eta_2$

$$\eta_2 = \frac{0.72}{0.9} = 0.8 \Rightarrow \mathbf{80\%}$$

60. a. $\eta_T = \eta_1 \cdot \eta_2 \cdot \eta_3 = (0.98)(0.87)(0.21) = 0.1790 \Rightarrow$ **17.9%**

b. $\eta_T = \eta_1 \cdot \eta_2 \cdot \eta_3 = (0.98)(0.87)(0.90) = 0.7673 \Rightarrow$ **76.73%**

$$\frac{76.73\% - 17.9\%}{17.9\%} \times 100\% = \mathbf{328.66\%}$$

61. $\eta_T = \frac{P_o}{P_i} = \eta_1 \cdot \eta_2 = \eta_1 \cdot 2\eta_1 = 2\eta_1^2$

$$\eta_1^2 = \frac{P_o}{2P_i} \Rightarrow \eta_1 = \sqrt{\frac{P_o}{2P_i}} = \sqrt{\frac{128\text{ W}}{2(400\text{ W})}} = 0.4$$

$\eta_2 = 2\eta_1 = 2(0.4) = 0.8$

$\therefore\ \eta_2 =$ **40%**, $\eta_2 =$ **80%**

Chapter 5

1.
   a. E and R_1
   b. R_1 and R_2
   c. E and R_1
   d. E and R_1, R_3 and R_4

2.
   a. $R_T = 0.1\ k\Omega + 0.39\ k\Omega + 1.2\ k\Omega = \mathbf{1.69\ k\Omega}$
   b. $R_T = 1.2\ \Omega + 2.7\ \Omega + 8.2\ \Omega = \mathbf{12.1\ \Omega}$
   c. $R_T = 8.2\ k\Omega + 10\ k\Omega + 9.1\ k\Omega + 1.8\ k\Omega + 2.7\ k\Omega = \mathbf{31.8\ k\Omega}$
   d. $R_T = 47\ \Omega + 820\ \Omega + 91\ \Omega + 1.2\ k\Omega = \mathbf{2158.0\ \Omega}$

3.
   a. $R_T = 1.2\ k\Omega + 1\ k\Omega + 2.2\ k\Omega + 3.3\ k\Omega = \mathbf{7.7\ k\Omega}$
   b. $R_T = 1\ k\Omega + 2\ k\Omega + 3\ k\Omega + 4.7\ k\Omega + 6.8\ k\Omega = \mathbf{17.5\ k\Omega}$

4.
   a. **1 MΩ**
   b. **100 Ω, 1 kΩ**
   c. $R_T = 100\ \Omega + 1\ k\Omega + 1\ M\Omega + 200\ k\Omega = \mathbf{1.2011\ M\Omega}$ vs. **1.2 MΩ** for part b.

5.
   a. $R_T = 105\ \Omega = 10\ \Omega + 33\ \Omega + R$, $\quad R = \mathbf{62\ \Omega}$
   b. $R_T = 10\ k\Omega = 2.2\ k\Omega + R + 2.7\ k\Omega + 3.3\ k\Omega$, $\quad R = \mathbf{1.8\ k\Omega}$
   c. $R_T = 138\ k\Omega = R + 56\ k\Omega + 22\ k\Omega + 33\ k\Omega$, $\quad R = \mathbf{27\ k\Omega}$
   d. $R_T = 91\ k\Omega = 24\ k\Omega + R_1 + 43\ k\Omega + 2R_1 = 67\ k\Omega + 3R_1$, $\quad R_1 = \mathbf{8\ k\Omega}$
      $R_2 = \mathbf{16\ k\Omega}$

6.
   a. **1.2 kΩ**
   b. 3.3 kΩ + 4.3 kΩ = **7.6 kΩ**
   c. **0 Ω**
   d. **∞ Ω**

7.
   a. $R_T = 10\ \Omega + 12\ \Omega + 18\ \Omega = \mathbf{40\ \Omega}$
   b. $I_s = \dfrac{E}{R_T} = \dfrac{120\ \text{V}}{40\ \Omega} = \mathbf{3\ A}$
   c. $V_1 = I_1R_1 = (3\ \text{A})(10\ \Omega) = \mathbf{30\ V}$, $V_2 = I_2R_2 = (3\ \text{A})(12\ \Omega) = \mathbf{36\ V}$,
      $V_3 = I_3R_3 = (3\ \text{A})(18\ \Omega) = \mathbf{54\ V}$

8.
   a. the most: R_3, the least: R_1
   b. R_3, $R_T = 1.2\ k\Omega + 6.8\ k\Omega + 82\ k\Omega = \mathbf{90\ k\Omega}$
      $I_s = \dfrac{E}{R_T} = \dfrac{45\ \text{V}}{90\ k\Omega} = \mathbf{0.5\ mA}$
   c. $V_1 = I_1R_1 = (0.5\ \text{mA})(1.2\ k\Omega) = \mathbf{0.6\ V}$, $V_2 = I_2R_2 = (0.5\ \text{mA})(6.8\ k\Omega) = \mathbf{3.4\ V}$,
      $V_3 = I_3R_3 = (0.5\ \text{mA})(82\ k\Omega) = \mathbf{41\ V}$, results agree with part (a)

9.
   a. $R_T = 12\ k\Omega + 4\ k\Omega + 6\ k\Omega = 22\ k\Omega$
      $E = IR_T = (4\ \text{mA})(22\ k\Omega) = \mathbf{88\ V}$
   b. $R_T = 18\ \Omega + 14\ \Omega + 8\ \Omega + 40\ \Omega = 80\ \Omega$
      $E = IR_T = (250\ \text{mA})(80\ \Omega) = \mathbf{20\ V}$

10. a. a. $I = \dfrac{V}{R} = \dfrac{5.2\text{ V}}{1.3\,\Omega} = \mathbf{4\text{ A}}$

b. $E = IR_T = (4\text{ A})(9\,\Omega) = \mathbf{36\text{ V}}$

c. $R_T = 9\,\Omega = 4.7\,\Omega + 1.3\,\Omega + R, \quad R = \mathbf{3\,\Omega}$

d. $V_{4.7\,\Omega} = (4\text{ A})(4.7\,\Omega) = \mathbf{18.8\text{ V}}$

$V_{1.3\,\Omega} = (4\text{ A})(1.3\,\Omega) = \mathbf{5.2\text{ V}}$

$V_{3\,\Omega} = (4\text{ A})(3\,\Omega) = \mathbf{12\text{ V}}$

b. a. $I = \dfrac{V}{R} = \dfrac{6.6\text{ V}}{2.2\text{ k}\Omega} = \mathbf{3\text{ mA}}$

b. $V_{3.3\text{ k}\Omega} = (3\text{ mA})(3.3\text{ k}\Omega) = 9.9\text{ V}$

$E = 6.6\text{ V} + 9\text{ V} + 9.9\text{ V} = \mathbf{25.5\text{ V}}$

c. $R = \dfrac{V}{I} = \dfrac{9\text{ V}}{3\text{ mA}} = \mathbf{3\text{ k}\Omega}$

d. $V_{2.2\text{ k}\Omega} = \mathbf{6.6\text{ V}}, V_{3\text{ k}\Omega} = \mathbf{9\text{ V}}, V_{3.3\text{ k}\Omega} = \mathbf{9.9\text{ V}}$

11. a. $I = \dfrac{E}{R_T} = \dfrac{36\text{ V}}{4.4\text{ k}\Omega} = \mathbf{8.18\text{ mA}}, V = \dfrac{1}{2}E = \dfrac{1}{2}(36\text{ V}) = \mathbf{18\text{ V}}$

b. $R_T = 1\text{ k}\Omega + 2.4\text{ k}\Omega + 5.6\text{ k}\Omega = 9\text{ k}\Omega$

$I = \dfrac{E}{R_T} = \dfrac{22.5\text{ V}}{9\text{ k}\Omega} = \mathbf{2.5\text{ mA}}, V = 2.5\text{ mA}(2.4\text{ k}\Omega + 5.6\text{ k}\Omega) = \mathbf{20\text{ V}}$

c. $R_T = 10\text{ k}\Omega + 22\text{ k}\Omega + 33\text{ k}\Omega + 10\text{ M}\Omega = 10.065\text{ M}\Omega$

$I = \dfrac{E}{R_T} = \dfrac{100\text{ V}}{10.065\text{ M}\Omega} = \mathbf{9.94\,\mu A}$

$V = (9.935\,\mu\text{A})(10\text{ M}\Omega) = \mathbf{99.35\text{ V}}$

12. a. $R_T = 3\text{ k}\Omega + 1\text{ k}\Omega + 2\text{ k}\Omega = \mathbf{6\text{ k}\Omega}$

$I_s = \dfrac{E}{R_T} = \dfrac{120\text{ V}}{6\text{ k}\Omega} = \mathbf{20\text{ mA}}$

$V_{R_1} = (20\text{ mA})(3\text{ k}\Omega) = \mathbf{60\text{ V}}$

$V_{R_2} = (20\text{ mA})(1\text{ k}\Omega) = \mathbf{20\text{ V}}$

$V_{R_3} = (20\text{ mA})(2\text{ k}\Omega) = \mathbf{40\text{ V}}$

b. $P_{R_1} = I_1^2 R_1 = (20\text{ mA})^2 \cdot 3\text{ k}\Omega = \mathbf{1.2\text{ W}}$

$P_{R_2} = I_2^2 R_2 = (20\text{ mA})^2 \cdot 1\text{ k}\Omega = \mathbf{0.4\text{ W}}$

$P_{R_3} = I_3^2 R_3 = (20\text{ mA})^2 \cdot 2\text{ k}\Omega = \mathbf{0.8\text{ W}}$

c. $P_T = P_{R_1} + P_{R_2} + P_{R_3} = 1.2\text{ W} + 0.4\text{ W} + 0.8\text{ W} = \mathbf{2.4\text{ W}}$

d. $P_T = EI_s = (120\text{ V})(20\text{ mA}) = \mathbf{2.4\text{ W}}$

e. the same

f. R_1 – the largest

g. dissipated

h. R_1: 2 W, R_2 : 1/2 W, R_3: 1 W

13. a. $R_T = 22\ \Omega + 10\ \Omega + 47\ \Omega + 3\ \Omega = \mathbf{82.0\ \Omega}$

$$I_s = \frac{E}{R_T} = \frac{20.5\text{ V}}{82.0\ \Omega} = \mathbf{250\ mA}$$

$V_{R_1} = I_1R_1 = (250\text{ mA})(22\ \Omega) = \mathbf{5.50\ V}$
$V_{R_2} = I_2R_2 = (250\text{ mA})(10\ \Omega) = \mathbf{2.50\ V}$
$V_{R_3} = I_3R_3 = (250\text{ mA})(47\ \Omega) = \mathbf{11.75\ V}$
$V_{R_4} = I_4R_4 = (250\text{ mA})(3\ \Omega) = \mathbf{0.75\ V}$

b. $P_{R_1} = I_1^2R_1 = (250\text{ mA})^2 \cdot 22\ \Omega = \mathbf{1.38\ W}$
$P_{R_2} = I_2^2R_2 = (250\text{ mA})^2 \cdot 10\ \Omega = \mathbf{625.00\ mW}$
$P_{R_3} = I_3^2R_3 = (250\text{ mA})^2 \cdot 47\ \Omega = \mathbf{2.94\ W}$
$P_{R_4} = I_4^2R_4 = (250\text{ mA})^2 \cdot 3\ \Omega = \mathbf{187.50\ mW}$

c. $P_T = P_{R_1} + P_{R_2} + P_{R_3} + P_{R_4} = 1.38\text{ W} + 625.00\text{ mW} + 2.94\text{ W} + 187.50\text{ mW} = \mathbf{5.13\ W}$

d. $P = EI_s = (20.5\text{ V})(250\text{ mA}) = \mathbf{5.13\ W}$

e. the same

f. 47 Ω – the largest

g. dissipated

h. R_1: 2 W; R_2: 1/2 W, R_3: 5 W, R_4: 1/2 W

14. a. $P = 21\text{ W} = (1\text{ A})^2 \cdot R$, $\quad R = \mathbf{21\ \Omega}$
$V_1 = I_1R_1 = (1\text{ A})(2\ \Omega) = \mathbf{2\ V}$, $V_2 = I_2R_2 = (1\text{ A})(1\ \Omega) = \mathbf{1\ V}$
$V_3 = I_3R_3 = (1\text{ A})(21\ \Omega) = \mathbf{21\ V}$
$E = V_1 + V_2 + V_3 = 2\text{ V} + 1\text{ V} + 21\text{ V} = \mathbf{24\ V}$

b. $P = 4\text{ W} = I^2 \cdot 1\ \Omega$, $I = \sqrt{4} = \mathbf{2\ A}$
$P = 8\text{ W} = I^2R_1 = (2\text{ A})^2R_1$, $\quad R_1 = \mathbf{2\ \Omega}$
$R_T = 16\ \Omega = 2\ \Omega + R_2 + 1\ \Omega = 3\ \Omega + R_2$, $\quad R_2 = \mathbf{13\ \Omega}$
$E = IR_T = (2\text{ A})(16\ \Omega) = \mathbf{32\ V}$

15. a. $R_T = NR_1 = 8\left(28\frac{1}{8}\ \Omega\right) = 225\ \Omega$

$$I = \frac{E}{R_T} = \frac{120\text{ V}}{225\ \Omega} = \mathbf{0.53\ A}$$

b. $P = I^2R = \left(\frac{8}{15}\text{ A}\right)^2\left(28\frac{1}{8}\ \Omega\right) = \left(\frac{64}{\cancel{225}}\right)\left(\frac{\cancel{225}}{8}\right) = \mathbf{8\ W}$

c. $V = IR = \left(\frac{\cancel{8}}{15}\text{ A}\right)\left(\frac{225}{\cancel{8}}\ \Omega\right) = \mathbf{15\ V}$

d. All go out!

16. $P_s = P_{R_1} + P_{R_2} + P_{R_3}$

$E{\cdot}I = I^2R_1 + I^2R_2 + 24$

$(R_1 + R_2)I^2 - E{\cdot}I + 24 = 0$

$6I^2 - 24\,I + 24 = 0$

$I^2 - 4\,I + 4 = 0$

$$I = \frac{-(-4) \pm \sqrt{(-4)^2 - 4(1)(4)}}{2(1)} = \frac{4 \pm \sqrt{16-16}}{2} = \frac{4}{2} = 2\text{ A}$$

$P = 24\text{ W} = (2\text{ A})^2R,\quad R = \frac{24\ \Omega}{4} = \mathbf{6\ \Omega}$

17. a. $V_{ab} = -4\text{ V} - 8\text{ V} + 12\text{ V} = \mathbf{0\ V}$

b. $V_{ab} = -4\text{ V} - 8\text{ V} + 6\text{ V} = \mathbf{-6\ V}$

c. $V_{ab} = -10\text{ V} + 18\text{ V} - 6\text{ V} + 12\text{ V} = \mathbf{14\ V}$

18. a. $E_T = 16\text{ V} - 4\text{ V} - 8\text{V} = \mathbf{4\ V}$, $I = \frac{4\text{ V}}{10.3\ \Omega} = \mathbf{388.35\ mA}$ (CCW)

b. $E_T = 18\text{ V} - 12\text{ V} - 4\text{ V} = \mathbf{2\ V}$, $I = \frac{2\text{ V}}{11.5\ \Omega} = \mathbf{173.91\ mA}$ (CW)

19. a. $P = 8\text{ mW} = I^2R,\ R = \frac{8\text{ mW}}{I^2} = \frac{8\text{ mW}}{(2\text{ mA})^2} = \mathbf{2\ k\Omega}$

$$I = \frac{E}{R_T} = \frac{20\text{ V} - E}{3\text{ k}\Omega + 2\text{ k}\Omega} = 2\text{ mA (CW)},\quad E = \mathbf{10\ V}$$

b. $I = \frac{16\text{ V}}{2\text{ k}\Omega} = 8\text{ mA},\ R = \frac{V}{I} = \frac{12\text{ V}}{8\text{ mA}} = \mathbf{1.5\ k\Omega}$

$$I = \frac{E}{R_T} = \frac{E - 4\text{ V} - 10\text{ V}}{2\text{ k}\Omega + 1.5\text{ k}\Omega} = \frac{E - 14\text{ V}}{3.5\text{ k}\Omega} = 8\text{ mA (CCW)}$$

$E = \mathbf{42\ V}$

20. a. $+10\text{ V} + 4\text{ V} - 3\text{ V} - V = 0$
$V = 14\text{ V} - 3\text{ V} = \mathbf{11\text{ V}}$

b. $+30\text{ V} + 20\text{ V} - 8\text{ V} - V = 0$
$V = 50\text{ V} - 8\text{ V} = \mathbf{42\text{ V}}$

c. $+16\text{ V} - 10\text{ V} - 4\text{ V} - V + 60\text{ V} = 0$
$V = 76\text{ V} - 14\text{ V} = \mathbf{62\text{ V}}$

21. a. $+60\text{ V} - 12\text{ V} - V - 20\text{ V} = 0$
$V = 60\text{ V} - 32\text{ V} = \mathbf{28\text{ V}}$

b. $+E - 14\text{ V} - 6\text{ V} - 2\text{ V} + 18\text{ V} = 0$
$E = 22\text{ V} - 18\text{ V} = \mathbf{4\text{ V}}$

22. a. $+10\text{ V} - V_2 = 0$
$V_2 = \mathbf{10\text{ V}}$
$+10\text{ V} - 6\text{ V} - V_1 = 0$
$V_1 = \mathbf{4\text{ V}}$

b. $+24\text{ V} - 10\text{ V} - V_1 = 0$
$V_1 = \mathbf{14\text{ V}}$
$+10\text{ V} - V_2 + 8\text{ V} = 0$
$V_2 = \mathbf{18\text{ V}}$

23. a. $+20\text{ V} - V_1 - 10\text{ V} - 1\text{ V} = 0,\ V_1 = \mathbf{9\text{ V}}$
$+10\text{ V} - 2\text{ V} - V_2 = 0,\ V_2 = \mathbf{8\text{ V}}$

b. $+10\text{ V} - V_1 + 6\text{ V} - 2\text{ V} - 3\text{ V} = 0,\ V_1 = \mathbf{11\text{ V}}$
$+10\text{ V} - V_2 - 3\text{ V} = 0,\ V_2 = \mathbf{7\text{ V}}$

24. $$\frac{1\text{ V}}{2\,\Omega} = \frac{50\text{ V}}{R_2},\ R_2 = \frac{(50\text{ V})(2\,\Omega)}{1\text{ V}} = \mathbf{100\,\Omega}$$
$$\frac{1\text{ V}}{2\,\Omega} = \frac{100\text{ V}}{R_3},\ R_3 = \frac{(100\text{ V})(2\,\Omega)}{1\text{ V}} = \mathbf{200\,\Omega}$$

25. a. **8.2 kΩ**

b. $V_3 : V_2 = 8.2\text{ k}\Omega : 1\text{ k}\Omega = \mathbf{8.2:1}$
$V_3 : V_1 = 8.2\text{ k}\Omega : 100\,\Omega = \mathbf{82:1}$

c. $$V_3 = \frac{R_3 E}{R_T} = \frac{(8.2\text{ k}\Omega)(60\text{ V})}{0.1\text{ k}\Omega + 1\text{ k}\Omega + 8.2\text{ k}\Omega} = \mathbf{52.90\text{ V}}$$

d. $$V' = \frac{(R_2 + R_3)E}{R_T} = \frac{(1\text{ k}\Omega + 8.2\text{ k}\Omega)(60\text{ V})}{9.3\text{ k}\Omega} = \mathbf{59.35\text{ V}}$$

26. a. $V = \dfrac{40\ \Omega(30\ \text{V})}{40\ \Omega + 20\ \Omega} = \mathbf{20\ V}$

b. $V = \dfrac{(2\ \text{k}\Omega + 3\ \text{k}\Omega)(40\ \text{V})}{4\ \text{k}\Omega + 1\ \text{k}\Omega + 2\ \text{k}\Omega + 3\ \text{k}\Omega} = \dfrac{(5\ \text{k}\Omega)(40\ \text{V})}{10\ \text{k}\Omega} = \mathbf{20\ V}$

c. $\dfrac{(1.5\ \Omega + 0.6\ \Omega + 0.9\ \Omega)(0.72\ \text{V})}{(2.5\ \Omega + 1.5\ \Omega + 0.6\ \Omega + 0.9\ \Omega + 0.5\ \Omega)} = \dfrac{(3\ \Omega)(0.72\ \text{V})}{6\ \text{k}\Omega} = \mathbf{0.36\ V}$

27. a. $\dfrac{V_1}{6\ \Omega} = \dfrac{20\ \text{V}}{2\ \Omega},\ V_1 = \dfrac{(6\ \Omega)(20\ \text{V})}{2\ \Omega} = \mathbf{60\ V}$

$\dfrac{V_2}{4\ \Omega} = \dfrac{20\ \text{V}}{2\ \Omega},\ V_2 = \dfrac{(4\ \Omega)(20\ \text{V})}{2\ \Omega} = \mathbf{40\ V}$

$E = V_1 + 20\ \text{V} + V_2 = 60\ \text{V} + 20\ \text{V} + 40\ \text{V} = \mathbf{120\ V}$

b. $120\ \text{V} - V_1 - 80\ \text{V} = 0,\ V_1 = \mathbf{40\ V}$
$80\ \text{V} - 10\ \text{V} - V_3 = 0,\ V_3 = \mathbf{70\ V}$

c. $\dfrac{1000\ \text{V}}{100\ \Omega} = \dfrac{V_2}{2\ \Omega},\ V_2 = \dfrac{2\ \Omega(1000\ \text{V})}{100\ \Omega} = \mathbf{20\ V}$

$\dfrac{1000\ \text{V}}{100\ \Omega} = \dfrac{V_1}{1\ \Omega},\ V_1 = \dfrac{1\ \Omega(1000\ \text{V})}{100\ \Omega} = \mathbf{10\ V}$

$E = V_1 + V_2 + 1000\ \text{V} = 10\ \text{V} + 20\ \text{V} + 1000\ \text{V} = \mathbf{1030\ V}$

d. $16\ \text{V} - V_1 - 6\ \text{V} = 0,\ V_1 = \mathbf{10\ V}$

$V_2 = \dfrac{6\ \text{V}}{2} = \mathbf{3\ V}$

28. $\dfrac{2\ \text{V}}{1\ \text{k}\Omega} = \dfrac{V_2}{2\ \text{k}\Omega},\ V_2 = \dfrac{2\ \text{k}\Omega(2\ \text{V})}{1\ \text{k}\Omega} = \mathbf{4\ V}$

$\dfrac{2\ \text{V}}{1\ \text{k}\Omega} = \dfrac{V_4}{3\ \text{k}\Omega},\ V_4 = \dfrac{3\ \text{k}\Omega(2\ \text{V})}{1\ \text{k}\Omega} = \mathbf{6\ V}$

$I = \dfrac{2\ \text{V}}{1\ \text{k}\Omega} = \mathbf{2\ mA}$

$E = 2\ \text{V} + 4\ \text{V} + 12\ \text{V} + 6\ \text{V} = \mathbf{24\ V}$

29. a. $4\text{ V} = \dfrac{R(20\text{ V})}{2\text{ k}\Omega + 6\text{ k}\Omega}$, $R = \mathbf{1.6\text{ k}\Omega}$

b. $100\text{ V} = \dfrac{(6\ \Omega + R)140\text{ V}}{3\ \Omega + 6\ \Omega + R}$

$$300\ \Omega + 600\ \Omega + 100R = 840\ \Omega + 140\text{ R}$$
$$140R - 100R = -840\ \Omega + 900\ \Omega$$
$$40R = 60\ \Omega$$
$$R = \frac{60\ \Omega}{40} = \mathbf{1.5\ \Omega}$$

30. a. $\dfrac{4\text{ V}}{10\ \Omega} = \dfrac{V_2}{20\ \Omega} \Rightarrow V_2 = \dfrac{20\ \Omega(4\text{ V})}{10\ \Omega} = \mathbf{8\text{ V}}$

b. $V_3 = E - V_1 - V_2 = 40\text{ V} - 4\text{ V} - 8\text{ V} = \mathbf{28\text{ V}}$

c. $\dfrac{4\text{ V}}{10\ \Omega} = \dfrac{28\text{ V}}{R_3} \Rightarrow R_3 = \dfrac{(28\text{ V})(10\ \Omega)}{4\text{ V}} = \mathbf{70\ \Omega}$

31. a. $R_{\text{bulb}} = \dfrac{8\text{ V}}{50\text{ mA}} = 160\ \Omega$

$V_{\text{bulb}} = 8\text{ V} = \dfrac{R_{\text{bulb}}(12\text{ V})}{R_{\text{bulb}} + R_x} = \dfrac{160\ \Omega(12\text{ V})}{160\ \Omega + R_x}$, $R_x = \mathbf{80\ \Omega}$ in series with the bulb

b. $V_R = 12\text{ V} - 8\text{ V} = 4\text{ V}$, $P = \dfrac{V^2}{R} = \dfrac{(4\text{ V})^2}{80\ \Omega} = 0.2\text{ W}$, $\therefore$ **1/4 W okay**

32. $V_{R_1} + V_{R_2} = 72\text{ V}$

$\dfrac{1}{5}V_{R_2} + V_{R_2} = 72\text{ V}$

$V_{R_2}\left[1 + \dfrac{1}{5}\right] = 72\text{ V}$, $V_{R_2} = \dfrac{72\text{ V}}{1.2} = 60\text{ V}$

$R_2 = \dfrac{V_{R_2}}{I_{R_2}} = \dfrac{60\text{ V}}{4\text{ mA}} = \mathbf{15\text{ k}\Omega}$, $R_1 = \dfrac{V_{R_1}}{I_{R_1}} = \dfrac{72\text{ V} - 60\text{ V}}{4\text{ mA}} = \dfrac{12\text{ V}}{4\text{ mA}} = \mathbf{3\text{ k}\Omega}$

33. $R_T = R_1 + R_2 + R_3 = 2R_3 + 7R_3 + R_3 = 10R_3$

$V_{R_3} = \dfrac{R_3(60\text{ V})}{10R_3} = \mathbf{6\text{ V}}$, $V_{R_1} = 2V_{R_3} = 2\ (6\text{ V}) = \mathbf{12\text{ V}}$, $V_{R_2} = 7V_{R_3} = 7(6\text{ V}) = \mathbf{42\text{ V}}$

34. a. $V_{R_3} = 4V_{R_2} = 4(3V_{R_1}) = 12V_{R_1}$

$E = V_{R_1} + 3V_{R_1} + 12V_{R_1}$ $\therefore R_T = R_1 + 3R_1 + 12R_1 = 16R_1 = \dfrac{64\text{ V}}{10\text{ mA}} = 6.4\text{ k}\Omega$

$R_1 = \dfrac{6.4\text{ k}\Omega}{16} = \mathbf{400\ \Omega}$, $R_2 = 3R_1 = \mathbf{1.2\text{ k}\Omega}$, $R_3 = 12R_1 = \mathbf{4.8\text{ k}\Omega}$

b. $R_T = \dfrac{64\text{ V}}{10\ \mu\text{A}} = 6.4\text{ M}\Omega$, $R_1 = \dfrac{6.4\text{ M}\Omega}{16} = \mathbf{400\ k\Omega}$, $R_2 = \mathbf{1.2\ M\Omega}$, $R_3 = \mathbf{4.8\ M\Omega}$

$\dfrac{I_1}{I'} = \dfrac{10\text{ mA}}{10\ \mu\text{A}} = \mathbf{10^3}$ and $\dfrac{R_1'}{R_1} = \dfrac{400\text{ k}\Omega}{400\ \Omega} = \mathbf{10^3}$ also

35. a. $V_a = +12\text{ V} - 8\text{ V} = \mathbf{4\ V}$
$V_b = \mathbf{-8\ V}$
$V_{ab} = V_a - V_b = 4\text{ V} - (-8\text{ V}) = \mathbf{12\ V}$

b. $V_a = 20\text{ V} - 6\text{ V} = \mathbf{14\ V}$
$V_b = \mathbf{+4\ V}$
$V_{ab} = V_a - V_b = 14\text{ V} - 4\text{ V} = \mathbf{10\ V}$

c. $V_a = +10\text{ V} + 3\text{ V} = \mathbf{13\ V}$
$V_b = \mathbf{+6\ V}$
$V_{ab} = V_a - V_b = 13\text{ V} - 6\text{ V} = \mathbf{7\ V}$

36. a. $I(\text{CW}) = \dfrac{80\text{ V} - 26\text{ V}}{6\ \Omega + 3\ \Omega} = \dfrac{54\text{ V}}{9\ \Omega} = \mathbf{6\ A}$
$V = IR = (6\text{ A})(3\ \Omega) = \mathbf{18\ V}$

b. $I(\text{CW}) = \dfrac{70\text{ V} - 10\text{ V}}{10\ \Omega + 20\ \Omega + 30\ \Omega} = \dfrac{60\text{ V}}{60\ \Omega} = \mathbf{1\ A}$
$V = IR = (1\text{ A})(10\ \Omega) = \mathbf{10\ V}$

37. a. $I = \dfrac{16\text{ V} - 4\text{ V}}{10\ \Omega + 20\ \Omega} = \dfrac{12\text{ V}}{30\ \Omega} = 0.4\text{ A (CW)}$
$V_a = 16\text{ V} - I(10\ \Omega) = 16\text{ V} - (0.4\text{ A})(10\ \Omega) = 16\text{ V} - 4\text{ V} = \mathbf{12\ V}$
$V_1 = IR = (0.4\text{ A})(20\ \Omega) = \mathbf{8\ V}$

b. $I = \dfrac{12\text{ V} + 10\text{ V} + 8\text{ V}}{2.2\text{ k}\Omega + 3.3\text{ k}\Omega} = \dfrac{30\text{ V}}{5.5\text{ k}\Omega} = 5.455\text{ mA}$
$V_a = 12\text{ V} - I(2.2\text{ k}\Omega) + 10\text{ V}$
$= 12\text{ V} - (5.455\text{ mA})(2.2\text{ k}\Omega) + 10\text{ V}$
$= 12\text{ V} - 12\text{ V} + 10\text{ V} = \mathbf{10\ V}$
$V_1 = I(2.2\text{ k}\Omega) = (5.455\text{ mA})(2.2\text{ k}\Omega) = \mathbf{12\ V}$

38. $I = \dfrac{47\text{ V} - 20\text{ V}}{2\text{ k}\Omega + 3\text{ k}\Omega + 4\text{ k}\Omega} = \dfrac{27\text{ V}}{9\text{ k}\Omega} = 3\text{ mA (CCW)}$
$V_{2\text{k}\Omega} = 6\text{ V}$, $V_{3\text{k}\Omega} = 9\text{ V}$, $V_{4\text{k}\Omega} = 12\text{ V}$

a. $V_a = \mathbf{20\ V}$, $V_b = 20\text{ V} + 6\text{ V} = \mathbf{26\ V}$, $V_c = 20\text{ V} + 6\text{ V} + 9\text{ V} = \mathbf{35\ V}$
$V_d = \mathbf{-12\ V}$, $V_e = \mathbf{0\ V}$

b. $V_{ab} = \mathbf{-6\ V}$, $V_{dc} = \mathbf{-47\ V}$, $V_{cb} = \mathbf{9\ V}$

c. $V_{ac} = \mathbf{-15\ V}$, $V_{db} = -47\text{ V} + 9\text{ V} = \mathbf{-38\ V}$

39. $I_{R_2} = \dfrac{4\text{ V} + 4\text{ V}}{8\ \Omega} = \dfrac{8\text{ V}}{8\ \Omega} = 1\text{ A}$, $R_1 = \dfrac{V_{R_1}}{I} = \dfrac{12\text{ V} - 4\text{ V}}{1\text{ A}} = \dfrac{8\text{ V}}{1\text{ A}} = \mathbf{8\ \Omega}$,

$R_3 = \dfrac{V_{R_3}}{I} = \dfrac{8\text{ V} - 4\text{ V}}{1\text{ A}} = \dfrac{4\text{ V}}{1\text{ A}} = \mathbf{4\ \Omega}$

40. $V_{R_2} = 48\text{ V} - 12\text{ V} = 36\text{ V}$

$R_2 = \dfrac{V_{R_2}}{I} = \dfrac{36\text{ V}}{16\text{ mA}} = \mathbf{2.25\ k\Omega}$

$V_{R_3} = 12\text{ V} - 0\text{ V} = 12\text{ V}$

$R_3 = \dfrac{V_{R_3}}{I} = \dfrac{12\text{ V}}{16\text{ mA}} = \mathbf{0.75\ k\Omega}$

$V_{R_4} = 20\text{ V}$

$R_4 = \dfrac{V_{R_4}}{I} = \dfrac{20\text{ V}}{16\text{ mA}} = \mathbf{1.25\ k\Omega}$

$V_{R_1} = E - V_{R_2} - V_{R_3} - V_{R_4}$

$= 100\text{ V} - 36\text{ V} - 12\text{ V} - 20\text{ V} = 32\text{ V}$

$R_1 = \dfrac{V_{R_1}}{I} = \dfrac{32\text{ V}}{16\text{ mA}} = \mathbf{2\ k\Omega}$

41. $I = \dfrac{44\text{ V} - 20\text{ V}}{2\text{ k}\Omega + 4\text{ k}\Omega + 6\text{ k}\Omega} = \dfrac{24\text{ V}}{12\text{ k}\Omega} = 2\text{ mA (CW)}$

$V_{2k\Omega} = IR = (2\text{ mA})(2\text{ k}\Omega) = 4\text{ V}$

$V_{4k\Omega} = IR = (2\text{ mA})(4\text{ k}\Omega) = 8\text{ V}$

$V_{6k\Omega} = IR = (2\text{ mA})(6\text{ k}\Omega) = 12\text{ V}$

a. $V_a = \mathbf{44\ V}$, $V_b = 44\text{ V} - 4\text{ V} = \mathbf{40\ V}$, $V_c = 44\text{ V} - 4\text{ V} - 8\text{ V} = \mathbf{32\ V}$
$V_d = \mathbf{20\ V}$

b. $V_{ab} = V_{2k\Omega} = \mathbf{4\ V}$, $V_{cb} = -V_{4k\Omega} = \mathbf{-8\ V}$
$V_{cd} = V_{6k\Omega} = \mathbf{12\ V}$

c. $V_{ad} = V_a - V_d = 44\text{ V} - 20\text{ V} = \mathbf{24\ V}$
$V_{ca} = V_c - V_a = 32\text{ V} - 44\text{ V} = \mathbf{-12\ V}$

42. $V_0 = \mathbf{0\ V}$

$V_4 = -12\text{ V} + 2\text{ V} = 0$, $V_4 = \mathbf{+10\ V}$

$V_7 = \mathbf{4\ V}$

$V_{10} = \mathbf{20\ V}$

$V_{23} = \mathbf{+6\ V}$

$V_{30} = \mathbf{-8\ V}$

$V_{67} = \mathbf{0\ V}$

$V_{56} = \mathbf{-6\ V}$

$I = \dfrac{V_4}{4\ \Omega} = \dfrac{V_{23}}{4\ \Omega} = \dfrac{6\text{ V}}{4\ \Omega} = 1.5\text{ A}\uparrow$

43. $V_0 = \mathbf{0\ V}$, $V_{03} = V_0 - V_3 = \mathbf{0\ V}$, $V_2 = (2\text{ mA})(3\text{ k}\Omega + 1\text{ k}\Omega) = (2\text{ mA})(4\text{ k}\Omega) = \mathbf{8\ V}$
$V_{23} = V_2 - V_3 = 8\text{ V} - 0\text{ V} = \mathbf{8\ V}$, $V_{12} = 20\text{ V} - 8\text{ V} = \mathbf{12\ V}$,
$\Sigma I_i = \Sigma I_o \Rightarrow I_i = 2\text{ mA} + 5\text{ mA} + 10\text{ mA} = \mathbf{17\ mA}$

44. a. $V_L = I_L R_L = (2\text{ A})(28\ \Omega) = 56\text{ V}$
$V_{\text{int}} = 60\text{ V} - 56\text{ V} = 4\text{ V}$
$$R_{\text{int}} = \frac{V_{\text{int}}}{I} = \frac{4\text{ V}}{2\text{ A}} = \mathbf{2\ \Omega}$$

b. $$VR = \frac{V_{NL} - V_{FL}}{V_{FL}} \times 100\% = \frac{60\text{ V} - 56\text{ V}}{56\text{ V}} \times 100\% = \mathbf{7.14\%}$$

45. a. $$V_L = \frac{3.3\ \Omega(12\text{ V})}{3.3\ \Omega + 0.05\ \Omega} = \mathbf{11.82\ V}$$

b. $$VR = \frac{V_{NL} - V_{FL}}{V_{FL}} \times 100\% = \frac{12\text{ V} - 11.82\text{ V}}{11.82\text{ V}} \times 100\% = \mathbf{1.52\%}$$

c. $$I_s = I_L = \frac{11.82\text{ V}}{3.3\ \Omega} = 3.58\text{ A}$$
$P_s = EI_s = (12\text{ V})(3.58\text{ A}) = \mathbf{42.96\ W}$
$P_{\text{int}} = I^2 R_{\text{int}} = (3.58\text{ A})^2\ 0.05\ \Omega = \mathbf{0.64\ W}$

46. a. $$I = \frac{E}{R_T} = \frac{12\text{ V}}{2\text{ k}\Omega + 8\text{ k}\Omega} = \frac{12\text{ V}}{10\text{ k}\Omega} = \mathbf{1.2\ mA}$$

b. $$I = \frac{E}{R_T} = \frac{12\text{ V}}{10\text{ k}\Omega + 0.25\text{ k}\Omega} = \frac{12\text{ V}}{10.25\text{ k}\Omega} = \mathbf{1.17\ mA}$$

c. not for most applications.

Chapter 6

1. a. R_2 and R_3
   b. E and R_3
   c. E and R_1
   d. R_2, R_3 and R_4
   e. E, R_1, R_2, R_3, and R_4
   f. E, R_1, R_2, and R_3
   g. R_2 and R_3

2. a. R_3 and R_4, R_5 and R_6
   b. E and R_1

3. a. $R_T = \dfrac{(9.1\ \Omega)(18\ \Omega)}{9.1\ \Omega + 18\ \Omega} = \mathbf{6.04\ \Omega}$

   b. $R_T = \dfrac{1}{\dfrac{1}{1\text{ k}\Omega} + \dfrac{1}{2\text{ k}\Omega} + \dfrac{1}{3\text{ k}\Omega}} = \dfrac{1}{1\times10^{-3}\text{S} + 0.5\times10^{-3}\text{ S} + 0.333\times10^{-3}\text{S}}$

   $= \dfrac{1}{1.833\times10^{-3}\text{S}} = \mathbf{545.55\ \Omega}$

   c. $R_T = \dfrac{1}{\dfrac{1}{100\ \Omega} + \dfrac{1}{1\text{ k}\Omega} + \dfrac{1}{10\text{ k}\Omega}} = \dfrac{1}{10\times10^{-3}\text{S} + 1\times10^{-3}\text{S} + 0.1\times10^{-3}\text{S}} = \dfrac{1}{11.1\times10^{-3}\text{S}}$

   $= \mathbf{90.09\ \Omega}$

   d. $R_T' = \dfrac{18\text{ k}\Omega}{3} = 6\text{ k}\Omega$

   $R_T = \dfrac{(6\text{ k}\Omega)(6\text{ M}\Omega)}{6\text{ k}\Omega + 6\text{ M}\Omega} = \mathbf{5.99\text{ k}\Omega}$

   e. $R_T' = \dfrac{22\ \Omega}{4} = 5.5\ \Omega,\ R_T'' = \dfrac{10\ \Omega}{2} = 5\ \Omega$

   $R_T = \dfrac{(5.5\ \Omega)(5\ \Omega)}{5.5\ \Omega + 5\ \Omega} = \mathbf{2.62\ \Omega}$

   f. $R_T = \dfrac{1}{\dfrac{1}{1\ \Omega} + \dfrac{1}{1\text{ k}\Omega} + \dfrac{1}{1\text{ M}\Omega}} = \dfrac{1}{1000\times10^{-3}\text{S} + 1\times10^{-3}\text{S} + 0.001\times10^{-3}\text{S}}$

   $= \dfrac{1}{1001.001\times10^{-3}\text{S}} = \mathbf{0.99\ \Omega}$

4. a. $R_T = \dfrac{1}{\dfrac{1}{1\text{ k}\Omega} + \dfrac{1}{1.2\text{ k}\Omega} + \dfrac{1}{0.3\text{ k}\Omega}} = \dfrac{1}{1\times10^{-3}\text{S} + 0.833\times10^{-3}\text{S} + 3.333\times10^{-3}\text{S}}$

   $= \dfrac{1}{5.166\times10^{-3}\text{S}} = \mathbf{193.57\ \Omega}$

b. $R_T = \dfrac{1}{\dfrac{1}{1\,\text{k}\Omega}+\dfrac{1}{1.2\,\text{k}\Omega}+\dfrac{1}{2.2\,\text{k}\Omega}+\dfrac{1}{1\,\text{k}\Omega}} = \dfrac{1}{1\times10^{-3}\text{S}+0.833\times10^{-3}\text{S}+0.455\times10^{-3}\text{S}+1\times10^{-3}\text{S}}$

$= \dfrac{1}{3.288\times10^{-3}\text{S}} = \mathbf{304.14\ \Omega}$

5. a. $R'_T = 3\ \Omega \parallel 6\ \Omega = 2\ \Omega$

$R_T = 1.6\ \Omega = \dfrac{(2\ \Omega)(R)}{2\ \Omega + R}, \quad R = \mathbf{8\ \Omega}$

b. $R'_T = \dfrac{6\ \text{k}\Omega}{3} = 2\ \text{k}\Omega$

$R_T = 1.8\ \text{k}\Omega = \dfrac{(2\ \text{k}\Omega)(R)}{2\ \text{k}\Omega + R}, \quad R = \mathbf{18\ k\Omega}$

c. $R_T = 10\ \text{k}\Omega = \dfrac{(20\ \text{k}\Omega)(R)}{20\ \text{k}\Omega + R}, \quad R = \mathbf{20\ k\Omega}$

d. $R_T = 628.93\ \Omega = \dfrac{1}{\dfrac{1}{1.2\ \text{k}\Omega}+\dfrac{1}{R}+\dfrac{1}{2.2\ \text{k}\Omega}} = \dfrac{1}{833.33\times10^{-3}\text{S}+\dfrac{1}{R}+454.55\times10^{-3}\ \text{S}}$

$811.32\times10^{-3} + \dfrac{628.93\ \Omega}{R} = 1$

$R = \dfrac{628.93\ \Omega}{1-811.32\times10^{-3}} = \mathbf{3.3\ k\Omega}$

e. $R' = R_1 \parallel R_2 = \dfrac{R_1}{2}, R_3 = \dfrac{R_1}{2}$

$R_T = 1.6\ \text{k}\Omega = \dfrac{R'R_3}{R'+R_3} = \dfrac{\left(\dfrac{R_1}{2}\right)\left(\dfrac{R_1}{2}\right)}{\dfrac{R_1}{2}+\dfrac{R_1}{2}} = \dfrac{R_1}{4} \qquad R_1 = 4(1.6\ \text{k}\Omega) = \mathbf{6.4\ k\Omega} = R_2$

$R_3 = \dfrac{6.4\ \text{k}\Omega}{2} = \mathbf{3.2\ k\Omega}$

6. a. 1.2 kΩ

b. about 1 kΩ

c. $R_T = \dfrac{1}{\dfrac{1}{1.2\,\text{k}\Omega}+\dfrac{1}{22\,\text{k}\Omega}+\dfrac{1}{220\,\text{k}\Omega}+\dfrac{1}{2.2\,\text{M}\Omega}}$

$= \dfrac{1}{833.333\times10^{-6}\text{S}+45.455\times10^{-6}\text{S}+4.545\times10^{-6}\text{S}+0.455\times10^{-6}\text{S}}$

$= \dfrac{1}{883.788\times10^{-6}\text{S}} = \mathbf{1.131\ k\Omega}$

d. 220 kΩ, 2.2 MΩ: $R_T = \dfrac{(1.2\,\text{k}\Omega)(22\,\text{k}\Omega)}{1.2\,\text{k}\Omega + 22\,\text{k}\Omega} = \mathbf{1.138\ k\Omega}$

e. R_T reduced.

7. a. $R_T = \dfrac{(2\ \Omega)(8\ \Omega)}{2\ \Omega + 8\ \Omega} = \mathbf{1.6\ \Omega}$

b. $\infty\ \Omega$

c. $\infty\ \Omega$

d. $R_T = \dfrac{1}{\dfrac{1}{4\ \Omega} + \dfrac{1}{2\ \Omega} + \dfrac{1}{10\ \Omega}} = \dfrac{1}{0.25\text{ S} + 0.50\text{ S} + 0.10\text{ S}} = \dfrac{1}{0.85\text{ S}} = \mathbf{1.18\ \Omega}$

8. $\dfrac{1}{R_T} = \dfrac{1}{R_1} + \dfrac{1}{R_2} + \dfrac{1}{R_3}$

$$\frac{1}{20\ \Omega} = \frac{1}{R_1} + \frac{1}{5R_1} + \frac{1}{\frac{R_1}{2}} = 1\left[\frac{1}{R_1}\right] + \frac{1}{5}\left[\frac{1}{R_1}\right] + 2\left[\frac{1}{R_1}\right] = 3.2\left[\frac{1}{R_1}\right]$$

and $R_1 = 3.2(20\ \Omega) = \mathbf{64\ \Omega}$

$R_2 = 5R_1 = 5(64\ \Omega) = \mathbf{320\ \Omega}$

$R_3 = \dfrac{1}{2}R_1 = \dfrac{64\ \Omega}{2} = \mathbf{32\ \Omega}$

9. $24\ \Omega \parallel 24\ \Omega = 12\ \Omega$

$\dfrac{1}{R_T} = \dfrac{1}{R_1} + \dfrac{1}{12\ \Omega} + \dfrac{1}{120\ \Omega}$

$0.1\text{ S} = \dfrac{1}{R_1} + 0.08333\text{ S} + 0.00833\text{ S}$

$0.1\text{ S} = \dfrac{1}{R_1} + 0.09167\text{ S}$

$\dfrac{1}{R_1} = 0.1\text{ S} - 0.09167\text{ S} = 0.00833\text{ S}$

$R_1 = \dfrac{1}{0.00833\text{ S}} = \mathbf{120\ \Omega}$

10. a. $R_T = \dfrac{(8\ \Omega)(24\ \Omega)}{8\ \Omega + 24\ \Omega} = \mathbf{6\ \Omega}$

b. $V_{R_1} = V_{R_2} = \mathbf{36\ V}$

c. $I_s = \dfrac{E}{R_T} = \dfrac{36\text{ V}}{6\ \Omega} = \mathbf{6\ A}$

$I_1 = \dfrac{V_{R_1}}{R_1} = \dfrac{36\text{ V}}{8\ \Omega} = \mathbf{4.5\ A}$

$I_2 = \dfrac{V_{R_2}}{R_2} = \dfrac{36\text{ V}}{24\ \Omega} = \mathbf{1.5\ A}$

d. $I_s = I_1 + I_2$

6 A = 4.5 A + 1.5 A = 6 A (checks)

11. a. $R_T = \dfrac{1}{\dfrac{1}{3\,\Omega} + \dfrac{1}{9\,\Omega} + \dfrac{1}{36\,\Omega}} = \dfrac{1}{0.333\,\text{S} + 0.111\,\text{S} + 0.028\,\text{S}}$

$= \dfrac{1}{472 \times 10^{-3}\,\text{S}} = \mathbf{2.12\ \Omega}$

b. $V_{R_1} = V_{R_2} = V_{R_3} = \mathbf{18\ V}$

c. $I_s = \dfrac{E}{R_T} = \dfrac{18\text{ V}}{2.12\,\Omega} = \mathbf{8.5\ A}$

$I_1 = \dfrac{V_{R_1}}{R_1} = \dfrac{18\text{ V}}{3\,\Omega} = \mathbf{6\ A},\ I_2 = \dfrac{V_{R_2}}{R_2} = \dfrac{18\text{ V}}{9\,\Omega} = \mathbf{2\ A},\ I_3 = \dfrac{V_{R_3}}{R_3} = \dfrac{18\text{ V}}{36\,\Omega} = \mathbf{0.5\ A}$

d. I_s = 8.5 A = 6 A + 2 A + 0.5 A = 8.5 A (checks)

12. a. $R_T = \dfrac{1}{\dfrac{1}{10\text{ k}\Omega} + \dfrac{1}{1.2\text{ k}\Omega} + \dfrac{1}{6.8\text{ k}\Omega}} = \dfrac{1}{100 \times 10^{-6}\text{S} + 833.333 \times 10^{-6}\text{S} + 147.059 \times 10^{-6}\text{S}}$

$= \dfrac{1}{1.080 \times 10^{-3}\text{S}} = \mathbf{925.93\ \Omega}$

b. $V_{R_1} = V_{R_2} = V_{R_3} = \mathbf{24\ V}$

c. $I_s = \dfrac{E}{R_T} = \dfrac{24\text{ V}}{925.93\,\Omega} = \mathbf{25.92\ mA}$

$I_{R_1} = \dfrac{V_{R_2}}{R_1} = \dfrac{24\text{ V}}{10\text{ k}\Omega} = \mathbf{2.4\ mA},\ I_{R_2} = \dfrac{V_{R_2}}{R_2} = \dfrac{24\text{ V}}{1.2\text{ k}\Omega} = \mathbf{20\ mA},$

$I_{R_3} = \dfrac{V_{R_3}}{R_3} = \dfrac{24\text{ V}}{6.8\text{ k}\Omega} = \mathbf{3.53\ mA}$

d. I_T = **25.92 mA** = 2.4 mA + 20 mA + 3.53 mA = **25.93 mA** (checks)

13. a. $R_T \cong 1\text{ k}\Omega$

b. $R_T = \dfrac{1}{\dfrac{1}{10\text{ k}\Omega} + \dfrac{1}{22\text{ k}\Omega} + \dfrac{1}{1.2\text{ k}\Omega} + \dfrac{1}{56\text{ k}\Omega}}$

$= \dfrac{1}{100 \times 10^{-6}\text{S} + 45.46 \times 10^{-6}\text{S} + 833.333 \times 10^{-6}\text{S} + 17.86 \times 10^{-6}\text{S}}$

$= \dfrac{1}{996.65 \times 10^{-6}\text{S}} = \mathbf{1.003\ k\Omega}$, very close

c. I_3 the most, I_4 the least

d. $I_{R_1} = \dfrac{V_{R_1}}{R_1} = \dfrac{44\text{ V}}{10\text{ k}\Omega} = \mathbf{4.4\ mA},\ I_{R_2} = \dfrac{V_{R_2}}{R_2} = \dfrac{44\text{ V}}{22\text{ k}\Omega} = \mathbf{2\ mA}$

$I_{R_3} = \dfrac{V_{R_3}}{R_3} = \dfrac{44\text{ V}}{1.2\text{ k}\Omega} = \mathbf{36.67\ mA},\ I_{R_4} = \dfrac{V_{R_4}}{R_4} = \dfrac{44\text{ V}}{56\text{ k}\Omega} = \mathbf{0.79\ mA}$

e. $I_s = \dfrac{E}{R_T} = \dfrac{44\text{ V}}{1.003\text{ k}\Omega} = \mathbf{43.87\text{ mA}}$

$I_s = \mathbf{43.87\text{ mA}} = 4.4\text{ mA} + 2\text{ mA} + 36.67\text{ mA} + 0.79\text{ mA} = \mathbf{43.86\text{ mA}}$ (checks)

f. always greater

14. –

15. $R'_T = 3\,\Omega \parallel 6\,\Omega = 2\,\Omega,\ R_T = R'_T \parallel R_3 = 2\,\Omega \parallel 2\,\Omega = 1\,\Omega$

$I_s = I' = \dfrac{E}{R_T} = \dfrac{12\text{ V}}{1\,\Omega} = \mathbf{12\text{ A}}$

$I_{R_1} = \dfrac{E}{R_1} = \dfrac{12\text{ V}}{3\,\Omega} = 4\text{ A}$

$I'' = I' - I_{R_1} = 12\text{ A} - 4\text{ A} = \mathbf{8\text{ A}}$

$V = E = \mathbf{12\text{ V}}$

16. $I_3 = \dfrac{(20\,\Omega)(10.8\text{ A})}{20\,\Omega + 4\,\Omega} = \mathbf{9\text{ A}}$

$E = V_{R_3} = I_3R_3 = (9\text{ A})(4\,\Omega) = \mathbf{36\text{ V}}$

$I_{R_1} = 12.3\text{ A} - 10.8\text{ A} = 1.5\text{ A}$

$R_1 = \dfrac{V_{R_1}}{I_{R_1}} = \dfrac{36\text{ V}}{1.5\text{ A}} = \mathbf{24\,\Omega}$

17. a. $R_T = 20\,\Omega \parallel 5\,\Omega = 4\,\Omega$

$I_s = \dfrac{E}{R_T} = \dfrac{30\text{ V}}{4\,\Omega} = \mathbf{7.5\text{ A}}$

CDR: $I_1 = \dfrac{5\,\Omega\, I_s}{5\,\Omega + 20\,\Omega} = \dfrac{1}{5}(7.5\text{ A}) = \mathbf{1.5\text{ A}}$

b. $10\text{ k}\Omega \parallel 10\text{ k}\Omega = 5\text{ k}\Omega$

$R_T = 1\text{ k}\Omega \parallel 5\text{ k}\Omega = 0.833\text{ k}\Omega$

$I_s = \dfrac{E}{R_T} = \dfrac{8\text{ V}}{0.833\text{ k}\Omega} = \mathbf{9.6\text{ mA}}$

$R'_T = 10\text{ k}\Omega \parallel 1\text{ k}\Omega = 0.9091\text{ k}\Omega$

$I_1 = \dfrac{R'_T I_s}{R'_T + 10\text{ k}\Omega} = \dfrac{(0.9091\text{ k}\Omega)(9.6\text{ mA})}{0.9091\text{ k}\Omega + 10\text{ k}\Omega} = \dfrac{8.727\text{ mA}}{10.9091} = \mathbf{0.8\text{ mA}}$

18. a. $I = \dfrac{24\text{ V} - 8\text{ V}}{4\text{ k}\Omega} = \dfrac{16\text{ V}}{4\text{ k}\Omega} = \mathbf{4\text{ mA}}$

b. $V = \mathbf{24\text{ V}}$

c. $I_s = \dfrac{24\text{ V}}{10\text{ k}\Omega} + 4\text{ mA} + \dfrac{24\text{ V}}{2\text{ k}\Omega} = 2.4\text{ mA} + 4\text{ mA} + 12\text{ mA} = \mathbf{18.4\text{ mA}}$

19. a. $R_T = \dfrac{1}{\dfrac{1}{1\,\text{k}\Omega}+\dfrac{1}{33\,\text{k}\Omega}+\dfrac{1}{8.2\,\text{k}\Omega}} = \dfrac{1}{1000\times10^{-6}\text{S}+30.303\times10^{-6}\text{S}+121.951\times10^{-6}\text{S}}$

$= \dfrac{1}{1.152\times10^{-3}\text{S}} = \mathbf{867.86\ \Omega}$

$I_{R_1} = \dfrac{V_{R_1}}{R_1} = \dfrac{100\text{ V}}{1\,\text{k}\Omega} = \mathbf{100\ mA},\ I_{R_2} = \dfrac{V_{R_2}}{R_2} = \dfrac{100\text{ V}}{33\,\text{k}\Omega} = \mathbf{3.03\ mA}$

$I_{R_3} = \dfrac{V_{R_3}}{R_3} = \dfrac{100\text{ V}}{8.2\,\text{k}\Omega} = \mathbf{12.2\ mA}$

b. $P_{R_1} = V_{R_1}\cdot I_{R_1} = (100\text{ V})(100\text{ mA}) = \mathbf{10\ W}$

$P_{R_2} = V_{R_2}\cdot I_{R_2} = (100\text{ V})(3.03\text{ mA}) = \mathbf{0.30\ W}$

$P_{R_3} = V_{R_3}\cdot I_{R_3} = (100\text{ V})(12.2\text{ mA}) = \mathbf{1.22\ W}$

c. $I_s = \dfrac{E}{R_T} = \dfrac{100\text{ V}}{867.86\ \Omega} = 115.23\text{ mA}$

$P_s = E_sI_s = (100\text{ V})(115.23\text{ mA}) = \mathbf{11.52\ W}$

d. $P_s = \mathbf{11.52\ W} = 10\text{ W} + 0.30\text{ W} + 1.22\text{ W} = \mathbf{11.52\ W}$ (checks)

e. R_1 = the smallest parallel resistor

20. a. $I_{\text{bulb}} = \dfrac{E}{R_{\text{bulb}}} = \dfrac{120\text{ V}}{1.8\,\text{k}\Omega} = \mathbf{66.667\ mA}$

b. $R_T = \dfrac{R}{N} = \dfrac{1.8\,\text{k}\Omega}{8} = \mathbf{225\ \Omega}$

c. $I_s = \dfrac{E}{R_T} = \dfrac{120\text{ V}}{225\ \Omega} = \mathbf{0.533\ A}$

d. $P = \dfrac{V^2}{R} = \dfrac{(120\text{ V})^2}{1.8\,\text{k}\Omega} = \mathbf{8\ W}$

e. $P_s = 8(8\text{ W}) = \mathbf{64\ W}$

f. none, I_s drops by 66.667 mA

21. $R_T = \dfrac{1}{\dfrac{1}{5\ \Omega}+\dfrac{1}{10\ \Omega}+\dfrac{1}{20\ \Omega}} = \dfrac{1}{200\times10^{-3}\text{S}+100\times10^{-3}\text{S}+50\times10^{-3}\text{S}}$

$= \dfrac{1}{350\times10^{-3}\text{S}} = 2.86\ \Omega$

$I_s = \dfrac{E}{R_T} = \dfrac{60\text{ V}}{2.86\ \Omega} = 20.98\text{ A}$

$P = E\cdot I_s = (60\text{ V})(20.98\text{ A}) = \mathbf{1.26\ kW}$

22. a. $P_1 = 10(60\text{ W}) = 600\text{ W} = E \cdot I_1 = 120\text{ V} \cdot I_1, I_1 = \dfrac{600\text{ W}}{120\text{ V}} = \mathbf{5\text{ A}}$

$P_2 = 400\text{ W} = 120\text{ V} \cdot I_2, \quad I_2 = \dfrac{400\text{ W}}{120\text{ V}} = \mathbf{3.33\text{ A}}$

$P_3 = 200\text{ W} = 120\text{ V} \cdot I_3, \quad I_3 = \dfrac{200\text{ W}}{120\text{ V}} = \mathbf{1.67\text{ A}}$

$P_4 = 110\text{ W} = 120\text{ V} \cdot I_4, \quad I_4 = \dfrac{110\text{ W}}{120\text{ V}} = \mathbf{0.92\text{ A}}$

b. $I_s = 5\text{ A} + 3.33\text{ A} + 1.67\text{ A} + 0.92\text{ A} = \mathbf{10.92\text{ A}}$ (no)

c. $R_T = \dfrac{E}{I_s} = \dfrac{120\text{ V}}{10.92\text{ A}} = \mathbf{10.99\ \Omega}$

d. $P_s = E \cdot I_s = (120\text{ V})(10.92\text{ A}) = 1.31\text{ kW}$
$P_s = \mathbf{1.31\text{ kW}} = 600\text{ W} + 400\text{ W} + 200\text{ W} + 110\text{ W} = \mathbf{1.31\text{ kW}}$ (the same)

23. a. $8\ \Omega \parallel 12\ \Omega = 4.8\ \Omega,\ 4.8\ \Omega \parallel 4\ \Omega = 2.182\ \Omega$

$I_1 = \dfrac{24\text{ V} + 8\text{ V}}{2.182\ \Omega} = \mathbf{14.67\text{ A}}$

b. $P_4 = \dfrac{V^2}{R} = \dfrac{(24\text{ V} + 8\text{ V})^2}{4\ \Omega} = \mathbf{256\text{ W}}$

c. $I_2 = I_1 = \mathbf{14.67\text{ A}}$

24. $I_1 = 12.6\text{ mA} - 8.5\text{ mA} = \mathbf{4.1\text{ mA}}$
$I_2 = 8.5\text{ mA} - 4\text{ mA} = \mathbf{4.5\text{ mA}}$

25. a. $9\text{ A} + 2\text{ A} + I_1 = 12\text{ A}, \quad I_1 = 12\text{ A} - 11\text{ A} = \mathbf{1\text{ A}}$
$I_2 + 1\text{ A} = 1\text{ A} + 3\text{ A}, \quad I_2 = 4\text{ A} - 1\text{ A} = \mathbf{3\text{ A}}$

b. $6\text{ A} = 2\text{ A} + I_1, \quad I_1 = 6\text{ A} - 2\text{ A} = \mathbf{4\text{ A}}$
$4\text{ A} + 5\text{ A} = I_2, \quad I_2 = \mathbf{9\text{ A}}$
$9\text{ A} = I_3 + 3\text{ A}, \quad I_3 = 9\text{ A} - 3\text{ A} = \mathbf{6\text{ A}}$
$3\text{ A} + 10\text{ A} = I_4, \quad I_4 = \mathbf{13\text{ A}}$

26. a. $I_1 + 5\text{ mA} = 8\text{ mA}, \quad I_1 = \mathbf{3\text{ mA}}$
$5\text{ mA} = I_2 + 3.5\text{ mA}, \quad I_2 = \mathbf{1.5\text{ mA}}$
$I_1 = 3\text{ mA} = I_3 + 1\text{ mA}, \quad I_3 = \mathbf{2\text{ mA}}$
$I_4 = \mathbf{5\text{ mA}}$

b. $I_3 = 1.5\ \mu\text{A} + 0.5\ \mu\text{A} = \mathbf{2.0\ \mu A}$
$6\ \mu\text{A} = I_2 + I_3 = I_2 + 2\ \mu\text{A}, \quad I_2 = \mathbf{4\ \mu A}$
$I_2 + 1.5\ \mu\text{A} = I_4, \quad I_4 = 4\ \mu\text{A} + 1.5\ \mu\text{A} = \mathbf{5.5\ \mu A}$
$I_1 = \mathbf{6\ \mu A}$

27. $I_{R_2} = 5 \text{ mA} - 2 \text{ mA} = 3 \text{ mA}$

$E = V_{R_2} = (3 \text{ mA})(4 \text{ k}\Omega) = \mathbf{12\ V}$

$$R_1 = \frac{V_{R_1}}{I_{R_1}} = \frac{12 \text{ V}}{(9 \text{ mA} - 5 \text{ mA})} = \frac{12 \text{ V}}{4 \text{ mA}} = \mathbf{3\ k\Omega}$$

$$R_3 = \frac{V_{R_3}}{I_{R_3}} = \frac{12 \text{ V}}{2 \text{ mA}} = \mathbf{6\ k\Omega}$$

$$R_T = \frac{E}{I_T} = \frac{12 \text{ V}}{9 \text{ mA}} = \mathbf{1.33\ k\Omega}$$

28. a. $R_1 = \frac{E}{I_1} = \frac{10 \text{ V}}{2 \text{ A}} = \mathbf{5\ \Omega}$

$I_2 = I - I_1 = 3 \text{ A} - 2 \text{ A} = \mathbf{1\ A}$

$R = \frac{E}{I_2} = \frac{10 \text{ V}}{1 \text{ A}} = \mathbf{10\ \Omega}$

b. $E = I_1 R_1 = (2 \text{ A})(6\ \Omega) = \mathbf{12\ V}$

$I_2 = \frac{E}{R_2} = \frac{12 \text{ V}}{9\ \Omega} = \mathbf{1.33\ A}$

$I_3 = \frac{P}{V} = \frac{12 \text{ W}}{12 \text{ V}} = \mathbf{1\ A}$

$R_3 = \frac{E}{I_3} = \frac{12 \text{ V}}{1 \text{ A}} = \mathbf{12\ \Omega}$

$I = I_1 + I_2 + I_3 = 2 \text{ A} + 1.33\text{A} + 1 \text{ A} = \mathbf{4.33\ A}$

c. $I_1 = \frac{64 \text{ V}}{1 \text{ k}\Omega} = \mathbf{64\ mA}$

$I_3 = \frac{64 \text{ V}}{4 \text{ k}\Omega} = \mathbf{16\ mA}$

$I_s = I_1 + I_2 + I_3$

$I_2 = I_s - I_1 - I_3 = 100 \text{ mA} - 64 \text{ mA} - 16 \text{ mA} = \mathbf{20\ mA}$

$R = \frac{E}{I_2} = \frac{64 \text{ V}}{20 \text{ mA}} = \mathbf{3.2\ k\Omega}$

$I = I_2 + I_3 = 20 \text{ mA} + 16 \text{ mA} = \mathbf{36\ mA}$

d. $P = \dfrac{V_1^2}{R_1} \Rightarrow V_1 = \sqrt{PR_1} = \sqrt{(30\text{ W})(30\ \Omega)} = \mathbf{30\ V}$

$E = V_1 = \mathbf{30\ V}$

$I_1 = \dfrac{E}{R_1} = \dfrac{30\text{ V}}{30\ \Omega} = \mathbf{1\ A}$

Because $R_3 = R_2$, $I_3 = I_2$, and $I_s = I_1 + I_2 + I_3 = I_1 + 2I_2$

$$2\text{ A} = 1\text{ A} + 2I_2$$

$$I_2 = \frac{1}{2}(1\text{ A}) = 0.5\text{ A}$$

$$I_3 = \mathbf{0.5\ A}$$

$$R_2 = R_3 = \frac{E}{I_2} = \frac{30\text{ V}}{0.5\text{ A}} = \mathbf{60\ \Omega}$$

$$P_{R_2} = I_2^2 R_2 = (0.5\text{ A})^2 \cdot 60\ \Omega = \mathbf{15\ W}$$

29. $I_2 = \dfrac{4\ \Omega}{12\ \Omega} I_1 = \dfrac{1}{3} I_1 = \mathbf{2\ A}$

$I_3 = \dfrac{4\ \Omega}{2\ \Omega} I_1 = 2I_1 = \mathbf{12\ A}$

$I_4 = \dfrac{4\ \Omega}{40\ \Omega} I_1 = \dfrac{1}{10} I_1 = \mathbf{0.6\ A}$

$I_T = I_1 + I_2 + I_3 + I_4 = 6\text{ A} + 2\text{ A} + 12\text{ A} + 0.6\text{ A} = \mathbf{20.6\ A}$

30. a. $I_1 = \dfrac{8\text{ k}\Omega(20\text{ mA})}{2\text{ k}\Omega + 8\text{ k}\Omega} = \mathbf{16\ mA}$

$I_2 = 20\text{ mA} - 16\text{ mA} = \mathbf{4\ mA}$

b. $R_T = \dfrac{1}{\dfrac{1}{2.2\text{ k}\Omega} + \dfrac{1}{1.2\text{ k}\Omega} + \dfrac{1}{0.2\text{ k}\Omega}} = \dfrac{1}{454.55\times10^{-6}\text{S} + 833.33\times10^{-6}\text{S} + 5000\times10^{-6}\text{S}}$

$= \dfrac{1}{6{,}288\times10^{-6}\text{S}} = 159.03\ \Omega$

$I_x = \dfrac{R_T}{R_x} I$, $\quad I_1 = \dfrac{159.03\ \Omega}{2.2\text{ k}\Omega}(18\text{ mA}) = \mathbf{1.30\ mA}$

$I_2 = \dfrac{159.03\ \Omega}{1.2\text{ k}\Omega}(18\text{ mA}) = \mathbf{2.39\ mA}$

$I_3 = \dfrac{159.03\ \Omega}{0.2\text{ k}\Omega}(18\text{ mA}) = \mathbf{14.31\ mA}$

$I_4 = \mathbf{18\ mA}$

c. $R_T = \dfrac{1}{\dfrac{1}{4\,\Omega}+\dfrac{1}{8\,\Omega}+\dfrac{1}{12\,\Omega}} = \dfrac{1}{250\times10^{-3}\text{S}+125\times10^{-3}\text{S}+83.333\times10^{-3}\text{S}}$

$= \dfrac{1}{458.333\times10^{-3}} = 2.18\,\Omega$

$I_x = \dfrac{R_T}{R_x}I, \quad I_1 = \dfrac{2.18\,\Omega}{4\,\Omega}(6\text{ A}) = \mathbf{3.27\text{ A}}$

$I_2 = \dfrac{2.18\,\Omega}{8\,\Omega}(6\text{ A}) = \mathbf{1.64\text{ A}}$

$I_3 = \dfrac{2.18\,\Omega}{12\,\Omega}(6\text{ A}) = \mathbf{1.09\text{ A}}$

$I_4 = \mathbf{6\text{ A}}$

d. $I_1 = I_2 = \dfrac{20\,\Omega(9\text{ A})}{20\,\Omega+10\,\Omega} = \mathbf{6\text{ A}}$

$I_3 = 9\text{ A} - I_1 = 9\text{ A} - 6\text{ A} = \mathbf{3\text{ A}}$

$I_4 = \mathbf{9\text{ A}}$

31. a. $I_1 \cong \dfrac{9}{10}(10\text{ A}) = \mathbf{9\text{ A}}$

b. $I_1/I_2 = 10\,\Omega/1\,\Omega = 10, \qquad I_2 = \dfrac{I_1}{10} = \dfrac{9\text{ A}}{10} \cong \mathbf{0.9\text{ A}}$

c. $I_1/I_3 = 1\text{ k}\Omega/1\,\Omega = 1000,\ I_3 = I_1/1000 = 9\text{ A}/1000 \cong \mathbf{9\text{ mA}}$

d. $I_1/I_4 = 100\text{ k}\Omega/1\,\Omega = 100{,}000, \quad I_4 = I_1/100{,}000 = 9\text{ A}/100{,}000 \cong \mathbf{90\ \mu\text{A}}$

e. very little effect, 1/100,000

f. $R_T = \dfrac{1}{\dfrac{1}{1\,\Omega}+\dfrac{1}{10\,\Omega}+\dfrac{1}{1\text{ k}\Omega}+\dfrac{1}{100\text{ k}\Omega}}$

$= \dfrac{1}{1\text{ S}+0.1\text{ S}+1\times10^{-3}\text{ S}+10\times10^{-6}\text{ S}}$

$= \dfrac{1}{1.10\text{ S}} = 0.91\,\Omega$

$I_x = \dfrac{R_T}{R_x}I, \quad I_1 = \dfrac{0.91\,\Omega}{1\,\Omega}(10\text{ A}) = \mathbf{9.1\text{ A}}$ excellent (9 A)

g. $I_2 = \dfrac{0.91\,\Omega}{10\,\Omega}(10\text{ A}) = \mathbf{0.91\text{ A}}$ excellent (0.9 A)

h. $I_3 = \dfrac{0.91\,\Omega}{1\text{ k}\Omega}(10\text{ A}) = \mathbf{9.1\text{ mA}}$ excellent (9 mA)

i. $I_4 = \dfrac{0.91\,\Omega}{100\text{ k}\Omega}(10\text{ A}) = \mathbf{91\ \mu\text{A}}$ excellent (90 μA)

32. a. CDR: $I_{6\Omega} = \dfrac{2\,\Omega\, I}{2\,\Omega + 6\,\Omega} = 1\text{ A}$

$$I = \frac{1\text{ A}(8\,\Omega)}{2\,\Omega} = \mathbf{4\ A} = I_2$$

$$I_1 = I - 1\text{ A} = 3\text{ A}$$

b. $I_3 = I = \mathbf{7\ \mu A}$

By inspection: $I_2 = \mathbf{2\ \mu A}$

$$I_1 = I - 2(2\ \mu\text{A}) = 7\ \mu\text{A} - 4\ \mu\text{A} = \mathbf{3\ \mu A}$$

$$V_R = (2\ \mu\text{A})(9\ \Omega) = 18\ \mu\text{V}$$

$$R = \frac{V_R}{I_R} = \frac{18\ \mu\text{V}}{3\ \mu\text{A}} = \mathbf{6\ \Omega}$$

33. a. $R = 3(2\text{ k}\Omega) = \mathbf{6\ k\Omega}$

b. $I_1 = \dfrac{6\text{ k}\Omega(32\text{ mA})}{6\text{ k}\Omega + 2\text{ k}\Omega} = \mathbf{24\ mA}$

$$I_2 = \frac{I_1}{3} = \frac{24\text{ mA}}{3} = \mathbf{8\ mA}$$

34. $84\text{ mA} = I_1 + I_2 + I_3 = I_1 + 2I_1 + 2I_2 = I_1 + 2I_1 + 2(2I_1)$

$84\text{ mA} = I_1 + 2I_1 + 4I_1 = 7I_1$

and $I_1 = \dfrac{84\text{ mA}}{7} = 12\text{ mA}$

$$I_2 = 2I_1 = 2(12\text{ mA}) = 24\text{ mA}$$

$$I_3 = 2I_2 = 2(24\text{ mA}) = 48\text{ mA}$$

$$R_1 = \frac{V_{R_1}}{I_1} = \frac{24\text{ V}}{12\text{ mA}} = \mathbf{2\ k\Omega}$$

$$R_2 = \frac{V_{R_2}}{I_2} = \frac{24\text{ V}}{24\text{ mA}} = \mathbf{1\ k\Omega}$$

$$R_3 = \frac{V_{R_3}}{I_3} = \frac{24\text{ V}}{48\text{ mA}} = \mathbf{0.5\ k\Omega}$$

35. a. $P_L = V_L I_L$

$72\text{ W} = 12\text{ V} \cdot I_L$

$$I_L = \frac{72\text{ W}}{12\text{ V}} = 6\text{ A}$$

$$I_1 = I_2 = \frac{I_L}{2} = \frac{6\text{ A}}{2} = \mathbf{3\ A}$$

b. $P_{\text{source}} = EI = (12\text{ V})(3\text{ A}) = \mathbf{36\ W}$

c. $P_{s_1} + P_{s_2} = 36\text{ W} + 36\text{ W} = \mathbf{72\ W}$ (the same)

d. $I_{\text{drain}} = \mathbf{6\ A}$ (twice as much)

36. $R_T = 8\ \Omega \parallel 56\ \Omega = 7\ \Omega$

$$I_2 = I_3 = \frac{E}{R_T} = \frac{12\text{ V}}{7\ \Omega} = \mathbf{1.71\ A}$$

$$I_1 = \frac{1}{2}I_2 = \frac{1}{2}(1.71\text{ A}) = \mathbf{0.86\ A}$$

37. $I_{8\,\Omega} = \dfrac{16\text{ V}}{8\ \Omega} = 2\text{ A}, \quad I = 5\text{ A} - 2\text{ A} = \mathbf{3\ A}$

$$I_R = 5\text{ A} + 3\text{ A} = 8\text{ A}, \quad R = \frac{V_R}{I_R} = \frac{16\text{ V}}{8\text{ A}} = \mathbf{2\ \Omega}$$

38. a. $I_s = \dfrac{E}{R_T} = \dfrac{12\text{ V}}{0.1\text{ k}\Omega + 10\text{ k}\Omega} = \dfrac{12\text{ V}}{10.1\text{ k}\Omega} = \mathbf{1.188\ mA}$

$V_L = I_s R_L = (1.19\text{ mA})(10\text{ k}\Omega) = \mathbf{11.90\ V}$

b. $I_s = \dfrac{12\text{ V}}{100\ \Omega} = \mathbf{120\ mA}$

c. $V_L = E = \mathbf{12\ V}$

39. a. $V_L = \dfrac{4.7\text{ k}\Omega(9\text{ V})}{4.7\text{ k}\Omega + 2.2\text{ k}\Omega} = \dfrac{42.3\text{V}}{6.9} = \mathbf{6.13\ V}$

b. $V_L = E = \mathbf{9\ V}$

c. $V_L = E = \mathbf{9\ V}$

40. a. $I_1 = \dfrac{20\text{ V}}{4\ \Omega} = \mathbf{5\ A},\ I_2 = \mathbf{0\ A}$

b. $V_1 = \mathbf{0\ V},\ V_2 = \mathbf{20\ V}$

c. $I_s = I_1 = \mathbf{5\ A}$

41. a. $V_2 = \dfrac{22\text{ k}\Omega(20\text{ V})}{22\text{ k}\Omega + 4.7\text{ k}\Omega} = \mathbf{16.48\ V}$

b. $R_T' = 11\text{ M}\Omega \parallel 22\text{ k}\Omega = 21.956\text{ k}\Omega$

$V_2 = \dfrac{21.956\text{ k}\Omega(20\text{ V})}{21.956\text{ k}\Omega + 4.7\text{ k}\Omega} = \mathbf{16.47\ V}$ (very close to ideal)

c. $R_m = 20\text{ V}[20{,}000\ \Omega/\text{V}] = 400\text{ k}\Omega$

$R_T' = 400\text{ k}\Omega \parallel 22\text{ k}\Omega = 20.853\text{ k}\Omega$

$V_2 = \dfrac{20.853\text{ k}\Omega(20\text{ V})}{20.853\text{ k}\Omega + 4.7\text{ k}\Omega} = \mathbf{16.32\ V}$ (still very close to ideal)

d: a. $V_2 = \dfrac{200\text{ k}\Omega(20\text{ V})}{200\text{ k}\Omega + 100\text{ k}\Omega} = \mathbf{13.33\ V}$

b. $R_T' = 200\text{ k}\Omega \parallel 11\text{ M}\Omega = 196.429\text{ k}\Omega$

$V_2 = \dfrac{(196.429\text{ k}\Omega)(20\text{ V})}{196.429\text{ k}\Omega + 100\text{ k}\Omega} = \mathbf{13.25\ V}$ (very close to ideal)

c. $R_m = 400\text{ k}\Omega$

$R'_i = 400\text{ k}\Omega \,\|\, 200\text{ k}\Omega = 133.333\text{ k}\Omega$

$V_2 = \dfrac{(133.333\text{ k}\Omega)(20\text{ V})}{133.333\text{ k}\Omega + 100\text{ k}\Omega} = \mathbf{11.43\text{ V}}$ (a 1.824 V drop from $R_{mt} = 11\text{ M}\Omega$ level)

e. DMM level of 11 MΩ not a problem for most situations
VOM level of 400 kΩ can be a problem for some situations.

42. a. $V_{ab} = \mathbf{20\text{ V}}$

b. $V_{ab} = \dfrac{11\text{ M}\Omega(20\text{ V})}{11\text{ M}\Omega + 1\text{ M}\Omega} = \mathbf{18.33\text{ V}}$

c. $R_m = 200\text{ V}[20{,}000\ \Omega/\text{V}] = 4\text{ M}\Omega$

$V_{ab} = \dfrac{4\text{ M}\Omega(20\text{ V})}{4\text{ M}\Omega + 1\text{ M}\Omega} = 16.0\text{ V}$ (significant drop from ideal)

$R_m = 20\text{ V}[20{,}000\ \Omega/\text{V}] = 400\text{ k}\Omega$

$V_{ab} = \dfrac{400\text{ k}\Omega(20\text{ V})}{400\text{ k}\Omega + 1\text{ M}\Omega} = \mathbf{5.71\text{ V}}$ (significant error)

43. not operating properly, 6 kΩ not connected at both ends

$R_T = \dfrac{6\text{ V}}{3.5\text{ mA}} = 1.71\text{ k}\Omega$

$R_T = 3\text{ k}\Omega \,\|\, 4\text{ k}\Omega = 1.71\text{ k}\Omega$

44. $V_{ab} = E + I_{4\text{ k}\Omega} \cdot R_{4\text{ k}\Omega}$

$I_{4\text{ k}\Omega} = \dfrac{12\text{ V} - 4\text{ V}}{1\text{ k}\Omega + 4\text{ k}\Omega} = \dfrac{8\text{ V}}{5\text{ k}\Omega} = 1.6\text{ mA}$

$V_{ab} = 4\text{ V} + (1.6\text{ mA})(4\text{ k}\Omega) = 4\text{ V} + 6.4\text{ V} = 10.4\text{ V}$

4 V supply connected in reverse so that

$I = \dfrac{12\text{ V} + 4\text{ V}}{1\text{ k}\Omega + 4\text{ k}\Omega} = \dfrac{16\text{ V}}{5\text{ k}\Omega} = 3.2\text{ mA}$

and $V_{ab} = 12\text{ V} - (3.2\text{ mA})(1\text{ k}\Omega) = 12\text{ V} - 3.2\text{ V} = 8.8\text{ V}$ obtained

Chapter 7

1. a. E and R_1 in series; R_2, R_3 and R_4 in parallel
   b. E and R_1 in series; R_2, R_3 and R_4 in parallel
   c. R_1 and R_2 in series; E, R_3 and R_4 in parallel
   d. E and R_1 in series, R_4 and R_5 in series; R_2 and R_3 in parallel
   e. E and R_1 in series, R_2 and R_3 in parallel
   f. E, R_1 and R_4 in parallel; R_6 and R_7 in series; R_2 and R_5 in parallel

2. a. $R_T = 4\ \Omega + 10\ \Omega + 4\ \Omega = \mathbf{18\ \Omega}$
   b. $R_T = 10\ \Omega + \dfrac{10\ \Omega}{2} = 10\ \Omega + 5\ \Omega = \mathbf{15\ \Omega}$
   c. $R_T = 4\ \Omega \parallel (4\ \Omega + 4\ \Omega) + 10\ \Omega = 4\ \Omega \parallel 8\ \Omega + 10\ \Omega = 2.67\ \Omega + 10\ \Omega = \mathbf{12.67\ \Omega}$
   d. $R_T = \mathbf{10\ \Omega}$

3. a. **yes**
   b. $I_2 = I_s - I_1 = 10\text{ A} - 4\text{ A} = \mathbf{6\ A}$
   c. yes
   d. $V_3 = E - V_2 = 14\text{ V} - 8\text{ V} = \mathbf{6\ V}$
   e. $R'_T = 4\ \Omega \parallel 2\ \Omega = 1.33\ \Omega$, $R''_T = 4\ \Omega \parallel 6\ \Omega = 2.4\ \Omega$

      $R_T = R'_T + R''_T = 1.33\ \Omega + 2.4\ \Omega = \mathbf{3.73\ \Omega}$
   f. $R'_T = R''_T = \dfrac{20\ \Omega}{2} = 10\ \Omega$, $R_T = R'_T + R''_T = 10\ \Omega + 10\ \Omega = 20\ \Omega$

      $I_s = \dfrac{E}{R_T} = \dfrac{20\text{ V}}{20\ \Omega} = \mathbf{1\ A}$
   g. $P_s = EI_s = P_{\text{absorbed}} = (20\text{ V})(1\text{ A}) = \mathbf{20\ W}$

4. a. $R'_T = R_3 \parallel R_4 = \dfrac{12\ \Omega}{2} = 6\ \Omega$, $R''_T = R_2 \parallel R'_T = \dfrac{6\ \Omega}{2} = 3\ \Omega$

      $R_T = R_1 + R''_T = 4\ \Omega + 3\ \Omega = \mathbf{7\ \Omega}$
   b. $I_s = \dfrac{E}{R_T} = \dfrac{14\text{ V}}{7\ \Omega} = \mathbf{2\ A}$, $I_2 = \dfrac{1}{2}I_s = \dfrac{2\text{ A}}{2} = \mathbf{1\ A}$

      $I_3 = \dfrac{1\text{ A}}{2} = \mathbf{0.5\ A}$
   c. $I_5 = \mathbf{1\ A}$
   d. $V_2 = I_2R_2 = (1\text{ A})(6\ \Omega) = \mathbf{6\ V}$

      $V_4 = V_2 = \mathbf{6\ V}$

5. a. $R'_T = R_1 \parallel R_2 = 10\ \Omega \parallel 15\ \Omega = 6\ \Omega$

      $R_T = R'_T \parallel (R_3 + R_4) = 6\ \Omega \parallel (10\ \Omega + 2\ \Omega) = 6\ \Omega \parallel 12\ \Omega = \mathbf{4\ \Omega}$
   b. $I_s = \dfrac{E}{R_T} = \dfrac{36\text{ V}}{4\ \Omega} = \mathbf{9\ A}$, $I_1 = \dfrac{E}{R'_T} = \dfrac{36\text{ V}}{6\ \Omega} = \mathbf{6\ A}$

      $I_2 = \dfrac{E}{R_3 + R_4} = \dfrac{36\text{ V}}{10\ \Omega + 2\ \Omega} = \dfrac{36\text{ V}}{12\ \Omega} = \mathbf{3\ A}$
   c. $V_4 = I_4 R_4 = I_2R_4 = (3\text{ A})(2\ \Omega) = \mathbf{6\ V}$

6. a. $R'_T = 1.2\text{ k}\Omega + 6.8\text{ k}\Omega = 8\text{ k}\Omega,\quad R''_T = 2\text{ k}\Omega \parallel R'_T = 2\text{ k}\Omega \parallel 8\text{ k}\Omega = 1.6\text{ k}\Omega$

$R'''_T = R''_T + 2.4\text{ k}\Omega = 1.6\text{ k}\Omega + 2.4\text{ k}\Omega = 4\text{ k}\Omega$

$R_T = 1\text{ k}\Omega \parallel R'''_T = 1\text{ k}\Omega \parallel 4\text{ k}\Omega = \mathbf{0.8\text{ k}\Omega}$

b. $I_s = \dfrac{E}{R_T} = \dfrac{48\text{ V}}{0.8\text{ k}\Omega} = \mathbf{60\text{ mA}}$

c. $V = \dfrac{R''_T E}{R''_T + 2.4\text{ k}\Omega} = \dfrac{(1.6\text{ k}\Omega)(48\text{ V})}{1.6\text{ k}\Omega + 2.4\text{ k}\Omega} = \mathbf{19.2\text{ V}}$

7. a. $R_T = (R_1 \parallel R_2 \parallel R_3) \parallel (R_6 + R_4 \parallel R_5)$

$= (12\text{ k}\Omega \parallel 12\text{ k}\Omega \parallel 3\text{ k}\Omega) \parallel (10.4\text{ k}\Omega + 9\text{ k}\Omega \parallel 6\text{ k}\Omega)$

$= (6\text{ k}\Omega \parallel 3\text{ k}\Omega) \parallel (10.4\text{ k}\Omega + 3.6\text{ k}\Omega)$

$= 2\text{ k}\Omega \parallel 14\text{ k}\Omega = 1.75\text{ k}\Omega$

$I_s = \dfrac{E}{R_T} = \dfrac{28\text{ V}}{1.75\text{ k}\Omega} = \mathbf{16\text{ mA}},\quad I_2 = \dfrac{E}{R_2} = \dfrac{28\text{ V}}{12\text{ k}\Omega} = \mathbf{2.33\text{ mA}}$

$R' = R_1 \parallel R_2 \parallel R_3 = 2\text{ k}\Omega$

$R'' = R_6 + R_4 \parallel R_5 = 14\text{ k}\Omega$

$I_6 = \dfrac{R'(I_s)}{R' + R''} = \dfrac{2\text{ k}\Omega(16\text{ mA})}{2\text{ k}\Omega + 14\text{ k}\Omega} = \mathbf{2\text{ mA}}$

b. $V_1 = E = \mathbf{28\text{ V}}$

$R' = R_4 \parallel R_5 = 6\text{ k}\Omega \parallel 9\text{ k}\Omega = 3.6\text{ k}\Omega$

$V_5 = I_6 R' = (2\text{ mA})(3.6\text{ k}\Omega) = \mathbf{7.2\text{ V}}$

c. $P = \dfrac{V_{R_3}^2}{R_3} = \dfrac{(28\text{ V})^2}{3\text{ k}\Omega} = \mathbf{261.33\text{ mW}}$

8. a. $R' = R_4 \parallel R_5 \parallel (R_7 + R_8) = 4\ \Omega \parallel 8\ \Omega \parallel (6\ \Omega + 2\ \Omega) = 4\ \Omega \parallel 8\ \Omega \parallel 8\ \Omega$

$= 4\ \Omega \parallel 4\ \Omega = 2\ \Omega$

$R'' = (R_3 + R') \parallel (R_6 + R_9) = (8\ \Omega + 2\ \Omega) \parallel (6\ \Omega + 4\ \Omega)$

$= 10\ \Omega \parallel 10\ \Omega = 5\ \Omega$

$R_T = R_1 \parallel (R_2 + R'') = 10\ \Omega \parallel (5\ \Omega + 5\ \Omega) = 10\ \Omega \parallel 10\ \Omega = \mathbf{5\ \Omega}$

$I = \dfrac{E}{R_T} = \dfrac{80\text{ V}}{5\ \Omega} = \mathbf{16\text{ A}}$

b. $I_{R_2} = \dfrac{I}{2} = \dfrac{16\text{ A}}{2} = \mathbf{8\text{ A}}$

$I_3 = I_9 = \dfrac{8\text{ A}}{2} = \mathbf{4\text{ A}}$

c. $I_8 = \dfrac{(R_4 \parallel R_5)(I_3)}{(R_4 \parallel R_5) + (R_7 + R_8)}$

$= \dfrac{(4\ \Omega \parallel 8\ \Omega)(4\text{ A})}{(4\ \Omega \parallel 8\ \Omega) + (6\ \Omega + 2\ \Omega)}$

$= \dfrac{(2.67)(4\text{ A})}{2.67\ \Omega + 8\ \Omega} = \mathbf{1\text{ A}}$

d. $-I_8R_8 - V_x + I_9R_9 = 0$

$V_x = I_9R_9 - I_8R_8 = (4\text{ A})(4\ \Omega) - (1\text{ A})(2\ \Omega) = 16\text{ V} - 2\text{ V} = \mathbf{14\ V}$

9. $I_1 = \dfrac{20\text{ V}}{5\ \Omega} = \mathbf{4\ A}$

$R_T = 16\ \Omega \parallel 25\ \Omega = 9.756\ \Omega$

$I_2 = \dfrac{7\text{ V}}{9.756\ \Omega} = \mathbf{0.72\ A}$

10. a, b. $I_1 = \dfrac{24\text{ V}}{4\ \Omega} = \mathbf{6\ A}\downarrow,\ I_3 = \dfrac{8\text{ V}}{10\ \Omega} = \mathbf{0.8\ A}\uparrow$

$I_2 = \dfrac{24\text{ V} + 8\text{ V}}{2\ \Omega} = \dfrac{32\text{ V}}{2\ \Omega} = \mathbf{16\ A}$

$I = I_1 + I_2 = 6\text{ A} + 16\text{ A} = \mathbf{22\ A}\downarrow$

11. a. $R' = R_4 + R_5 = 14\ \Omega + 6\ \Omega = 20\ \Omega$

$R'' = R_2 \parallel R' = 20\ \Omega \parallel 20\ \Omega = 10\ \Omega$

$R''' = R'' + R_1 = 10\ \Omega + 10\ \Omega = 20\ \Omega$

$R_T = R_3 \parallel R''' = 5\ \Omega \parallel 20\ \Omega = \mathbf{4\ \Omega}$

$I_s = \dfrac{E}{R_T} = \dfrac{20\text{ V}}{4\ \Omega} = \mathbf{5\ A}$

$I_1 = \dfrac{20\text{ V}}{R_1 + R''} = \dfrac{20\text{ V}}{10\ \Omega + 10\ \Omega} = \dfrac{20\text{ V}}{20\ \Omega} = \mathbf{1\ A}$

$I_3 = \dfrac{20\text{ V}}{5\ \Omega} = \mathbf{4\ A}$

$I_4 = \dfrac{I_1}{2} = (\text{since } R' = R_2) = \dfrac{1\text{ A}}{2} = \mathbf{0.5\ A}$

b. $V_a = I_3R_3 - I_4R_5 = (4\text{ A})(5\ \Omega) - (0.5\text{ A})(6\ \Omega) = 20\text{ V} - 3\text{ V} = \mathbf{17\ V}$

$V_{bc} = \left(\dfrac{I_1}{2}\right)R_2 = (0.5\text{ A})(20\ \Omega) = \mathbf{10\ V}$

12. a. $I_1 = \dfrac{E}{R_1 + R_4 \parallel (R_2 + R_3 \parallel R_5)} = \dfrac{20\text{ V}}{3\ \Omega + 3\ \Omega \parallel (3\ \Omega + 6\ \Omega \parallel 6\ \Omega)}$

$= \dfrac{20\text{ V}}{3\ \Omega + 3\ \Omega \parallel (3\ \Omega + 3\ \Omega)} = \dfrac{20\text{ V}}{3\ \Omega + 3\ \Omega \parallel 6\ \Omega} = \dfrac{20\text{ V}}{3\ \Omega + 2\ \Omega}$

$= \mathbf{4\ A}$

b. CDR: $I_2 = \dfrac{R_4(I_1)}{R_4 + R_2 + R_3 \parallel R_5} = \dfrac{3\ \Omega(4\ \text{A})}{3\ \Omega + 3\ \Omega + 6\ \Omega \parallel 6\ \Omega}$

$= \dfrac{12\ \text{A}}{6+3} = \mathbf{1.33\ A}$

$I_3 = \dfrac{I_2}{2} = \mathbf{0.67\ A}$

c. $I_4 = I_1 - I_2 = 4\ \text{A} - 1.33\ \text{A} = 2.67\ \text{A}$

$V_a = I_4R_4 = (2.67\ \text{A})(3\ \Omega) = \mathbf{8\ V}$

$V_b = I_3R_3 = (0.67\ \text{A})(6\ \Omega) = \mathbf{4\ V}$

13. a. $I_E = \dfrac{V_E}{R_E} = \dfrac{2\ \text{V}}{1\ \text{k}\Omega} = \mathbf{2\ mA}$

$I_C = I_E = \mathbf{2\ mA}$

b. $I_B = \dfrac{V_{R_B}}{R_B} = \dfrac{V_{CC} - (V_{BE} + V_E)}{R_B} = \dfrac{8\ \text{V} - (0.7\ \text{V} + 2\ \text{V})}{220\ \text{k}\Omega}$

$= \dfrac{8\ \text{V} - 2.7\ \text{V}}{220\ \text{k}\Omega} = \dfrac{5.3\ \text{V}}{220\ \text{k}\Omega} = \mathbf{24\ \mu A}$

c. $V_B = V_{BE} + V_E = \mathbf{2.7\ V}$

$V_C = V_{CC} - I_CR_C = 8\ \text{V} - (2\ \text{mA})(2.2\ \text{k}\Omega) = 8\ \text{V} - 4.4\ \text{V} = \mathbf{3.6\ V}$

d. $V_{CE} = V_C - V_E = 3.6\ \text{V} - 2\ \text{V} = \mathbf{1.6\ V}$

$V_{BC} = V_B - V_C = 2.7\ \text{V} - 3.6\ \text{V} = \mathbf{-0.9\ V}$

14. a. $I_G = 0 \therefore V_G = \dfrac{270\ \text{k}\Omega(16\ \text{V})}{270\ \text{k}\Omega + 2000\ \text{k}\Omega} = \mathbf{1.9\ V}$

$V_G - V_{GS} - V_S = 0$

$V_S = V_G - V_{GS} = 1.9\ \text{V} - (-1.75\ \text{V}) = \mathbf{3.65\ V}$

b. $I_1 = I_2 = \dfrac{16\ \text{V}}{270\ \text{k}\Omega + 2000\ \text{k}\Omega} = \mathbf{7.05\ \mu A}$

$I_D = I_S = \dfrac{V_S}{R_S} = \dfrac{3.65\ \text{V}}{1.5\ \text{k}\Omega} = \mathbf{2.43\ mA}$

c. $V_{DS} = V_{DD} - I_DR_D - I_SR_S = V_{DD} - I_D(R_D + R_S)$ since $I_D = I_S$

$= 16\ \text{V} - (2.43\ \text{mA})(4\ \text{k}\Omega) = 16\ \text{V} - 9.72\ \text{V} = \mathbf{6.28\ V}$

d. $V_{DD} - I_DR_D - V_{DG} - V_G = 0$

$V_{DG} = V_{DD} - I_DR_D - V_G$

$= 16\ \text{V} - (2.43\ \text{mA})(2.5\ \text{k}\Omega) - 1.9\ \text{V} = 16\ \text{V} - 6.08\ \text{V} - 1.9\ \text{V} = \mathbf{8.02\ V}$

15. a. Network redrawn:

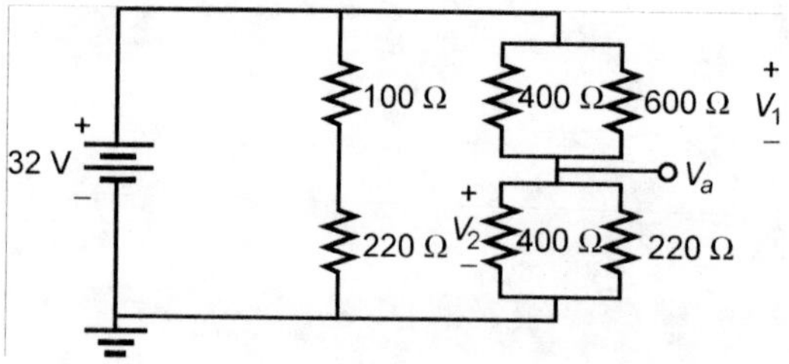

$100\ \Omega + 220\ \Omega = 320\ \Omega$
$400\ \Omega \parallel 600\ \Omega = 240\ \Omega$
$400\ \Omega \parallel 220\ \Omega = 141.94\ \Omega$
$240\ \Omega + 141.94\ \Omega = 381.94\ \Omega$

$R_T = 320\ \Omega \parallel 381.94\ \Omega = \mathbf{174.12\ \Omega}$

b. $V_a = \dfrac{141.94\ \Omega(32\ \text{V})}{141.94\ \Omega + 240\ \Omega} = \mathbf{11.89\ V}$

c. $V_1 = 32\ \text{V} - V_a = 32\ \text{V} - 11.89\ \text{V} = \mathbf{20.11\ V}$

d. $V_2 = V_a = \mathbf{11.89\ V}$

e. $I_{600\Omega} = \dfrac{20.11\ \text{V}}{600\ \Omega} = 33.52\ \text{mA}$

$I_{220\Omega} = \dfrac{11.89\ \text{V}}{220\ \Omega} = 54.05\ \text{mA}$

$I + I_{600\Omega} = I_{220\Omega}$
$I = I_{200\Omega} - I_{600\Omega}$
$= 54.05\ \text{mA} - 33.52\ \text{mA}$
$= \mathbf{20.53\ mA} \rightarrow$

16. a. $I = \dfrac{E_1}{R_2 + R_3} = \dfrac{9\ \text{V}}{7\ \Omega + 8\ \Omega} = \mathbf{0.6\ A}$

b. $E_1 - V_1 + E_2 = 0$
$V_1 = E_1 + E_2 = 9\ \text{V} + 19\ \text{V} = \mathbf{28\ V}$

17. a. R_8 "shorted out"
$R' = R_3 + R_4 \parallel R_5 + R_6 \parallel R_7$
$= 10\ \Omega + 6\ \Omega \parallel 6\ \Omega + 6\ \Omega \parallel 3\ \Omega$
$= 10\ \Omega + 3\ \Omega + 2\ \Omega$
$= 15\ \Omega$

$R_T = R_1 + R_2 \parallel R'$
$= 10\ \Omega + 30\ \Omega \parallel 15\ \Omega = 10\ \Omega + 10\ \Omega$
$= 20\ \Omega$

$I = \dfrac{E}{R_T} = \dfrac{100\ \text{V}}{20\ \Omega} = 5\ \text{A}$

$I_2 = \dfrac{R'(I)}{R' + R_2} = \dfrac{(15\ \Omega)(5\ \text{A})}{15\ \Omega + 30\ \Omega} = \mathbf{1.67\ A}$

$I_3 = I - I_2 = 5\text{ A} - 1\frac{2}{3}\text{ A} = 3\frac{1}{3}\text{ A}$

$$I_6 = \frac{R_7 I_3}{R_7 + R_6} = \frac{3\,\Omega\left(\frac{10}{3}\text{ A}\right)}{3\,\Omega + 6\,\Omega} = \mathbf{1.11\text{ A}}$$

$I_8 = \mathbf{0\text{ A}}$

b. $V_4 = I_3(R_4 \parallel R_5) = \left(\frac{10}{3}\text{ A}\right)(3\,\Omega) = \mathbf{10\text{ V}}$

$V_8 = \mathbf{0\text{ V}}$

18. $8\,\Omega \parallel 8\,\Omega = 4\,\Omega$

$$I = \frac{30\text{ V}}{4\,\Omega + 6\,\Omega} = \frac{30\text{ V}}{10\,\Omega} = \mathbf{3\text{ A}}$$

$V = I(8\,\Omega \parallel 8\,\Omega) = (3\text{ A})(4\,\Omega) = \mathbf{12\text{ V}}$

19. a. All resistors in parallel (between terminals a & b)

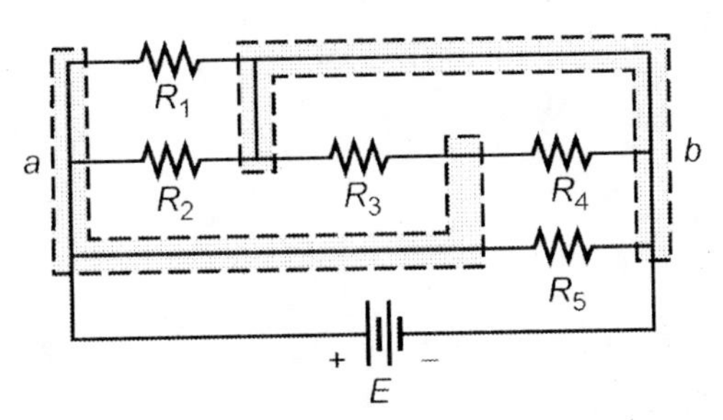

$R_T = \underbrace{16\,\Omega \parallel 16\,\Omega} \parallel 8\,\Omega \parallel 4\,\Omega \parallel 32\,\Omega$

$\underbrace{8\,\Omega \parallel 8\,\Omega} \parallel 4\,\Omega \parallel 32\,\Omega$

$\underbrace{4\,\Omega \parallel 4\,\Omega} \parallel 32\,\Omega$

$2\,\Omega \parallel 32\,\Omega = \mathbf{1.88\,\Omega}$

b. All in parallel. Therefore, $V_1 = V_4 = E = \mathbf{32\text{ V}}$

c. $I_3 = V_3/R_3 = 32\text{ V}/4\,\Omega = \mathbf{8\text{ A}} \leftarrow$

d. $I_s = I_1 + I_2 + I_3 + I_4 + I_5$

$$= \frac{32\text{ V}}{16\,\Omega} + \frac{32\text{ V}}{8\,\Omega} + \frac{32\text{ V}}{4\,\Omega} + \frac{32\text{ V}}{32\,\Omega} + \frac{32\text{ V}}{16\,\Omega}$$

$= 2\text{ A} + 4\text{ A} + 8\text{ A} + 1\text{ A} + 2\text{ A}$

$= 17\text{ A}$

$R_T = \frac{E}{I_s} = \frac{32\text{ V}}{17\text{ A}} = \mathbf{1.88\,\Omega}$ as above

20. a.

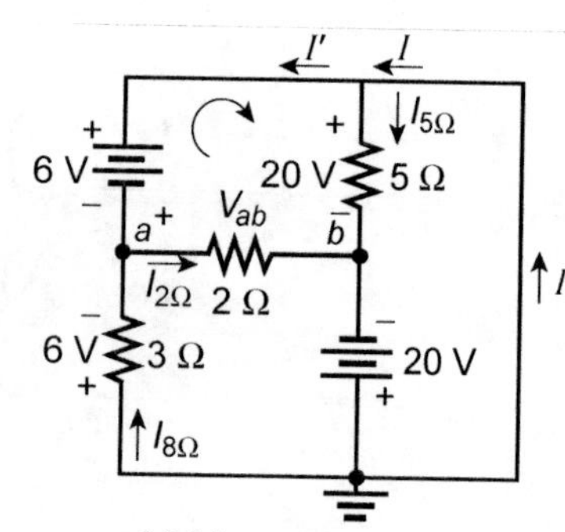

KVL: $+6\text{ V} - 20\text{ V} + V_{ab} = 0$
$V_{ab} = +20\text{ V} - 6\text{ V} = \mathbf{14\text{ V}}$

b. $I_{5\Omega} = \dfrac{20\text{ V}}{5\,\Omega} = 4\text{ A}$

$I_{2\Omega} = \dfrac{V_{ab}}{2\,\Omega} = \dfrac{14\text{ V}}{2\,\Omega} = 7\text{ A}$

$I_{3\Omega} = \dfrac{6\text{ V}}{3\,\Omega} = 2\text{ A}$

$I' + I_{3\Omega} = I_{2\Omega}$

and $I' = I_{2\Omega} - I_{3\Omega} = 7\text{ A} - 2\text{ A} = 5\text{ A}$

$I = I' + I_{5\Omega} = 5\text{ A} + 4\text{ A} = \mathbf{9\text{ A}}$

21. a. Applying Kirchoff's voltage law in the CCW direction in the upper "window":

$+18\text{ V} + 20\text{ V} - V_{8\Omega} = 0$

$V_{8\Omega} = 38\text{ V}$

$I_{8\Omega} = \dfrac{38\text{ V}}{8\,\Omega} = 4.75\text{ A}$

$I_{3\Omega} = \dfrac{18\text{ V}}{3\,\Omega + 6\,\Omega} = \dfrac{18\text{ V}}{9\,\Omega} = 2\text{ A}$

KCL: $I_{18\text{V}} = 4.75\text{ A} + 2\text{ A} = \mathbf{6.75\text{ A}}$

b. $V = (I_{3\Omega})(6\,\Omega) + 20\text{ V} = (2\text{ A})(6\,\Omega) + 20\text{ V} = 12\text{ V} + 20\text{ V} = \mathbf{32\text{ V}}$

22. $I_2R_2 = I_3R_3$ and $I_2 = \dfrac{I_3R_3}{R_2} = \dfrac{2R_3}{20} = \dfrac{R_3}{10}$ (since the voltage across parallel elements is the same)

$I_1 = I_2 + I_3 = \dfrac{R_3}{10} + 2$

KVL: $120 = I_1 12 + I_3R_3 = \left(\dfrac{R_3}{10} + 2\right)12 + 2R_3$

and $120 = 1.2R_3 + 24 + 2R_3$

$3.2R_3 = 96\,\Omega$

$R_3 = \dfrac{96\,\Omega}{3.2} = \mathbf{30\,\Omega}$

23. Assuming $I_s = 1$ A, the current I_s will divide as determined by the load appearing in each branch. Since balanced I_s will split equally between all three branches.

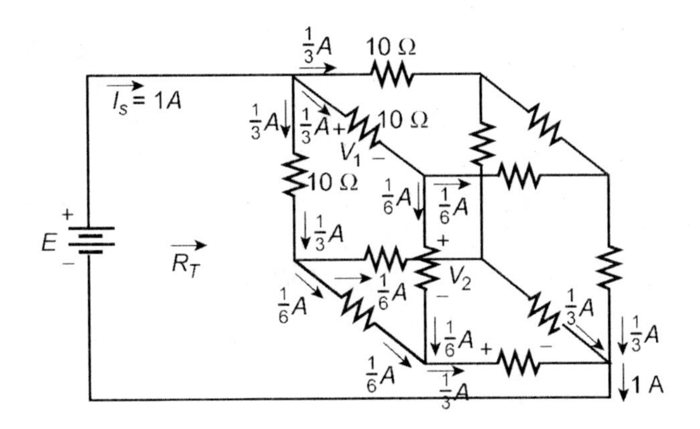

$$V_1 = \left(\frac{1}{3}\text{ A}\right)(10\,\Omega) = \frac{10}{3}\text{ V}$$

$$V_2 = \left(\frac{1}{6}\text{ A}\right)(10\,\Omega) = \frac{10}{6}\text{ V}$$

$$V_3 = \left(\frac{1}{3}\text{ A}\right)(10\,\Omega) = \frac{10}{3}\text{ V}$$

$$E = V_1 + V_2 + V_3 = \frac{10}{3}\text{ V} + \frac{10}{6}\text{ V} + \frac{10}{3}\text{ V} = 8.33\text{ V}$$

$$R_T = \frac{E}{I} = \frac{8.33\text{ V}}{1\text{ A}} = \mathbf{8.33\,\Omega}$$

24. $36\text{ k}\Omega \parallel 6\text{ k}\Omega \parallel 12\text{ k}\Omega = 3.6\text{ k}\Omega$

$$V = \frac{3.6\text{ k}\Omega(45\text{ V})}{3.6\text{ k}\Omega + 6\text{ k}\Omega} = 16.88\text{ V} \neq 27\text{ V}.$$ Therefore, **not** operating properly!

6 kΩ resistor "open"

$$R' = 12\text{ k}\Omega \parallel 36\text{ k}\Omega = 9\text{ k}\Omega,\ V = \frac{R'(45\text{ V})}{R' + 6\text{ k}\Omega} = \frac{9\text{ k}\Omega(45\text{ V})}{9\text{ k}\Omega + 6\text{ k}\Omega} = \mathbf{27\text{ V}}$$

25. a. $R'_T = R_5 \parallel (R_6 + R_7) = 6\,\Omega \parallel 3\,\Omega = 2\,\Omega$

$R''_T = R_3 \parallel (R_4 + R'_T) = 4\,\Omega \parallel (2\,\Omega + 2\,\Omega) = 2\,\Omega$

$R_t = R_1 + R_2 + R''_T = 3\,\Omega + 5\,\Omega + 2\,\Omega = 10\,\Omega$

$$I = \frac{240\text{ V}}{10\,\Omega} = \mathbf{24\text{ A}}$$

b. $$I_4 = \frac{4\,\Omega(I)}{4\,\Omega + 4\,\Omega} = \frac{4\,\Omega(24\text{ A})}{8\,\Omega} = 12\text{ A}$$

$$I_7 = \frac{6\,\Omega(12\text{ A})}{6\,\Omega + 3\,\Omega} = \frac{72\text{ A}}{9} = \mathbf{8\text{ A}}$$

c. $V_3 = I_3R_3 = (I - I_4)R_3 = (24\text{ A} - 12\text{ A})4\ \Omega = \mathbf{48\ V}$
$V_5 = I_5R_5 = (I_4 - I_7)R_5 = (4\text{ A})6\ \Omega = \mathbf{24\ V}$
$V_7 = I_7R_7 = (8\text{ A})2\ \Omega = \mathbf{16\ V}$

d. $P = I_7^2R_7 = (8\text{ A})^2 2\ \Omega = \mathbf{128\ W}$
$P = EI = (240\text{ V})(24\text{ A}) = \mathbf{5760\ W}$

26. a. $R'_T = R_4 \parallel (R_6 + R_7 + R_8) = 2\ \Omega \parallel 7\ \Omega = 1.56\ \Omega$
$R''_T = R_2 \parallel (R_3 + R_5 + R'_T) = 2\ \Omega \parallel (4\ \Omega + 1\ \Omega + 1.56\ \Omega) = 1.53\ \Omega$
$R_T = R_1 + R''_T = 4\ \Omega + 1.53\ \Omega = \mathbf{5.53\ \Omega}$

b. $I = 2\text{ V}/5.53\ \Omega = \mathbf{361.66\ mA}$

c. $$I_3 = \frac{2\ \Omega(I)}{2\ \Omega + 6.56\ \Omega} = \frac{2\ \Omega(361.66\text{ mA})}{2\ \Omega + 6.56\ \Omega} = \mathbf{84.50\ mA}$$
$$I_8 = \frac{2\ \Omega(84.5\text{ mA})}{2\ \Omega + 7\ \Omega} = \mathbf{18.78\ mA}$$

27. The 12 Ω resistors are in parallel.

Network redrawn:

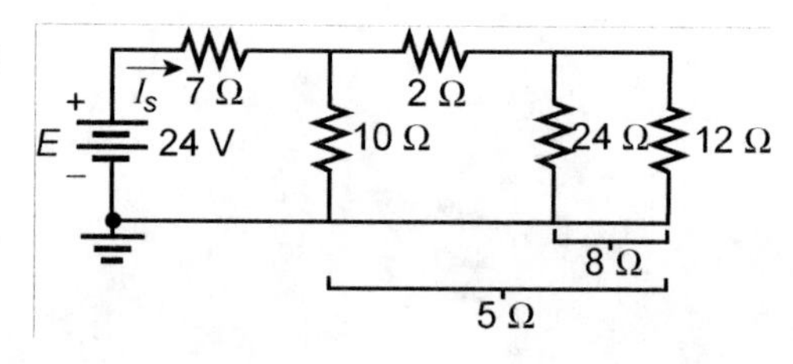

$R_T = 12\ \Omega$
$$I_s = \frac{E}{R_T} = \frac{24\text{ V}}{12\ \Omega} = 2\text{ A}$$
$$I_{2\Omega} = \frac{I_s}{2} = \frac{2\text{ A}}{2} = 1\text{ A}$$
$$I_{12\Omega} = \frac{24\ \Omega(I_{2\Omega})}{24\ \Omega + 12\ \Omega} = \frac{2}{3}\text{ A}$$
$$P_{10\Omega} = (I_{10\Omega})^2\ 10\ \Omega = \left(\frac{2}{3}\text{ A}\right)^2 \cdot 10\ \Omega = \mathbf{4.44\ W}$$

28. a. $R_{10} + R_{11} \parallel R_{12} = 1\ \Omega + 2\ \Omega \parallel 2\ \Omega = 2\ \Omega$
$R_4 \parallel (R_5 + R_6) = 10\ \Omega \parallel 10\ \Omega = 5\ \Omega$
$R_1 + R_2 \parallel (R_3 + 5\ \Omega) = 3\ \Omega + 6\ \Omega \parallel 6\ \Omega = 6\ \Omega$
$R_T = 2\ \Omega \parallel 3\ \Omega \parallel 6\ \Omega = 2\ \Omega \parallel 2\ \Omega = 1\ \Omega$
$I = 12\text{ V}/1\ \Omega = \mathbf{12\ A}$

b. $I_1 = 12\text{ V}/6\ \Omega = 2\text{ A}$
$$I_3 = \frac{6\ \Omega(2\text{ A})}{6\ \Omega + 6\ \Omega} = 1\text{ A}$$
$$I_4 = \frac{1\text{ A}}{2} = \mathbf{0.5\ A}$$

c. $I_6 = I_4 = \mathbf{0.5\ A}$

d. $$I_{10} = \frac{12\text{ A}}{2} = \mathbf{6\ A}$$

29. a. $E = (40 \text{ mA})(1.6 \text{ k}\Omega) = \mathbf{64 \text{ V}}$

b. $R_{L_2} = \dfrac{48 \text{ V}}{12 \text{ mA}} = \mathbf{4 \text{ k}\Omega}$

$R_{L_3} = \dfrac{24 \text{ V}}{8 \text{ mA}} = \mathbf{3 \text{ k}\Omega}$

c. $I_{R_1} = 72 \text{ mA} - 40 \text{ mA} = 32 \text{ mA}$

$I_{R_2} = 32 \text{ mA} - 12 \text{ mA} = 20 \text{ mA}$

$I_{R_3} = 20 \text{ mA} - 8 \text{ mA} = 12 \text{ mA}$

$$R_1 = \frac{V_{R_1}}{I_{R_1}} = \frac{64 \text{ V} - 48 \text{ V}}{32 \text{ mA}} = \frac{16 \text{ V}}{32 \text{ mA}} = \mathbf{0.5 \text{ k}\Omega}$$

$$R_2 = \frac{V_{R_2}}{I_{R_2}} = \frac{48 \text{ V} - 24 \text{ V}}{20 \text{ mA}} = \frac{24 \text{ V}}{20 \text{ mA}} = \mathbf{1.2 \text{ k}\Omega}$$

$$R_3 = \frac{V_{R_3}}{I_{R_3}} = \frac{24 \text{ V}}{12 \text{ mA}} = \mathbf{2 \text{ k}\Omega}$$

30. $I_{R_1} = 40 \text{ mA}$

$I_{R_2} = 40 \text{ mA} - 10 \text{ mA} = 30 \text{ mA}$

$I_{R_3} = 30 \text{ mA} - 20 \text{ mA} = 10 \text{ mA}$

$I_{R_5} = 40 \text{ mA}$

$I_{R_4} = 40 \text{ mA} - 4 \text{ mA} = 36 \text{ mA}$

$$R_1 = \frac{V_{R_1}}{I_{R_1}} = \frac{120 \text{ V} - 100 \text{ V}}{40 \text{ mA}} = \frac{20 \text{ V}}{40 \text{ mA}} = \mathbf{0.5 \text{ k}\Omega}$$

$$R_2 = \frac{V_{R_2}}{I_{R_2}} = \frac{100 \text{ V} - 40 \text{ V}}{30 \text{ mA}} = \frac{60 \text{ V}}{30 \text{ mA}} = \mathbf{2 \text{ k}\Omega}$$

$$R_3 = \frac{V_{R_3}}{I_{R_3}} = \frac{40 \text{ V}}{10 \text{ mA}} = \mathbf{4 \text{ k}\Omega}$$

$$R_4 = \frac{V_{R_4}}{I_{R_4}} = \frac{36 \text{ V}}{36 \text{ mA}} = \mathbf{1 \text{ k}\Omega}$$

$$R_5 = \frac{V_{R_5}}{I_{R_5}} = \frac{60 \text{ V} - 36 \text{ V}}{40 \text{ mA}} = \frac{24 \text{ V}}{40 \text{ mA}} = \mathbf{0.6 \text{ k}\Omega}$$

$P_1 = I_1^2 R_1 = (40\text{ mA})^2 0.5\text{ k}\Omega = \mathbf{0.8\text{ W}}$ (1 watt resistor)

$P_2 = I_2^2 R_2 = (30\text{ mA})^2 2\text{ k}\Omega = \mathbf{1.8\text{ W}}$ (2 watt resistor)

$P_3 = I_3^2 R_3 = (10\text{ mA})^2 4\text{ k}\Omega = \mathbf{0.4\text{ W}}$ (1/2 watt or 1 watt resistor)

$P_4 = I_4^2 R_4 = (36\text{ mA})^2 1\text{ k}\Omega = \mathbf{1.3\text{ W}}$ (2 watt resistor)

$P_5 = I_5^2 R_5 = (40\text{ mA})^2 0.6\text{ k}\Omega = \mathbf{0.96\text{ W}}$ (1 watt resistor)

All power levels less than **2 W**. Four less than **1 W**.

31. a. **yes,** $R_L \gg R_{\max}$ (potentiometer)

b. VDR: $V_{R_2} = 3\text{ V} = \dfrac{R_2(12\text{ V})}{R_1 + R_2} = \dfrac{R_2(12\text{ V})}{1\text{ k}\Omega}$

$$R_2 = \frac{3\text{ V}(1\text{ k}\Omega)}{12\text{ V}} = 0.25\text{ k}\Omega = \mathbf{250\ \Omega}$$

$$R_1 = 1\text{ k}\Omega - 0.25\text{ k}\Omega = 0.75\text{ k}\Omega = \mathbf{750\ \Omega}$$

c. $V_{R_1} = E - V_L = 12\text{ V} - 3\text{ V} = 9\text{ V}$ (Chose V_{R_1} rather than $V_{R_2 \| R_L}$ since numerator of VDR equation "cleaner")

$$V_{R_1} = 9\text{ V} = \frac{R_1(12\text{ V})}{R_1 + (R_2 \| R_L)}$$

$$9R_1 + 9(R_2 \| R_L) = 12R_1$$

$$\left.\begin{aligned} R_1 &= 3(R_2 \| R_L) \\ R_1 + R_2 &= 1\text{ k}\Omega \end{aligned}\right\} 2\text{ eq. } 2\text{ unk} (R_L = 10\text{ k}\Omega)$$

$$R_1 = \frac{3R_2 R_L}{R_2 + R_L} \Rightarrow \frac{3R_2\ 10\text{ k}\Omega}{R_2 + 10\text{ k}\Omega}$$

and $R_1(R_2 + 10\text{ k}\Omega) = 30\text{ k}\Omega\ R_2$

$R_1 R_2 + 10\text{ k}\Omega\ R_1 = 30\text{ k}\Omega\ R_2$

$R_1 + R_2 = 1\text{ k}\Omega$: $(1\text{ k}\Omega - R_2)R_2 + 10\text{ k}\Omega\,(1\text{ k}\Omega - R_2) = 30\text{ k}\Omega\ R_2$

$$R_2^2 + 39\text{ k}\Omega\ R_2 - 10\text{ k}\Omega^2 = 0$$

$$R_2 = 0.255\text{ k}\Omega,\ \cancel{-39.255}\text{ k}\Omega$$

$$R_2 = \mathbf{255\ \Omega}$$

$$R_1 = 1\text{ k}\Omega - R_2 = \mathbf{745\ \Omega}$$

32. a. $V_{ab} = \dfrac{80\ \Omega(40\text{ V})}{100\ \Omega} = \mathbf{32\text{ V}}$

$V_{bc} = 40\text{ V} - 32\text{ V} = \mathbf{8\text{ V}}$

b. $80\ \Omega \| 1\text{ k}\Omega = 74.07\ \Omega$

$20\ \Omega \| 10\text{ k}\Omega = 19.96\ \Omega$

$V_{ab} = \dfrac{74.07\ \Omega(40\text{ V})}{74.07\ \Omega + 19.96\ \Omega} = \mathbf{31.51\text{ V}}$

$V_{bc} = 40\text{ V} - 31.51\text{ V} = \mathbf{8.49\text{ V}}$

c. $P = \frac{(31.51\text{ V})^2}{80\,\Omega} + \frac{(8.49\text{ V})^2}{20\,\Omega} = 12.411\text{ W} + 3.604\text{ W} = \mathbf{16.02\text{ W}}$

d. $P = \frac{(32\text{ V})^2}{80\,\Omega} + \frac{(8\text{ V})^2}{20\,\Omega} = 12.8\text{ W} + 3.2\text{ W} = \mathbf{16\text{ W}}$

The applied loads dissipate less than 20 mW of power.

33. a. $I_{CS} = \mathbf{1\text{ mA}}$

b. $R_{\text{shunt}} = \frac{R_m I_{CS}}{I_{\max} - I_{CS}} = \frac{(100\,\Omega)(1\text{ mA})}{20\text{ A} - 1\text{ mA}} \cong \frac{0.1}{20}\,\Omega = \mathbf{5\text{ m}\Omega}$

34. 25 mA: $R_{\text{shunt}} = \frac{(1\text{ k}\Omega)(50\,\mu\text{A})}{25\text{ mA} - 0.05\text{ mA}} \cong \mathbf{2\,\Omega}$

50 mA: $R_{\text{shunt}} = \frac{(1\text{ k}\Omega)(50\,\mu\text{A})}{50\text{ mA} - 0.05\text{ mA}} = \mathbf{1\,\Omega}$

100 mA: $R_{\text{shunt}} \cong \mathbf{0.5\,\Omega}$

35. a. $R_s = \frac{V_{\max} - V_{VS}}{I_{CS}} = \frac{15\text{ V} - (50\,\mu\text{A})(1\text{ k}\Omega)}{50\,\mu\text{A}} = \mathbf{300\text{ k}\Omega}$

b. $\Omega/\text{V} = 1/I_{CS} = 1/50\,\mu\text{A} = \mathbf{20{,}000}$

36. 5 V: $R_s = \frac{5\text{ V} - (1\text{ mA})(100\,\Omega)}{1\text{ mA}} = \mathbf{4.9\text{ k}\Omega}$

50 V: $R_s = \frac{50\text{ V} - 0.1\text{ V}}{1\text{ mA}} = \mathbf{49.9\text{ k}\Omega}$

500 V: $R_s = \frac{500\text{ V} - 0.1\text{ V}}{1\text{ mA}} = \mathbf{499.9\text{ k}\Omega}$

37. $10\text{ M}\Omega = (0.5\text{ V})(\Omega/\text{V}) \Rightarrow \Omega/\text{V} = 20 \times 10^6$

$I_{CS} = 1/(\Omega/\text{V}) = \frac{1}{20 \times 10^6} = \mathbf{0.05\,\mu\text{A}}$

38. a. $R_s = \frac{E}{I_m} - R_m - \frac{\text{zero adjust}}{2} = \frac{3\text{ V}}{100\,\mu\text{A}} - 1\text{ k}\Omega - \frac{2\text{ k}\Omega}{2} = \mathbf{28\text{ k}\Omega}$

b. $xI_m = \dfrac{E}{R_{\text{series}}} + R_m + \dfrac{\text{zero adjust}}{2} + R_{\text{unk}}$

$$R_{\text{unk}} = \frac{E}{xI_m} - \left(R_{\text{series}} + R_m + \frac{\text{zero adjust}}{2}\right)$$

$$= \frac{3\text{ V}}{x100\ \mu\text{A}} - 30\text{ k}\Omega \Rightarrow \frac{30 \times 10^3}{x} - 30 \times 10^3$$

$x = \frac{3}{4}$, $R_{\text{unk}} = \mathbf{10\ k\Omega}$; $x = \frac{1}{2}$, $R_{\text{unk}} = \mathbf{30\ k\Omega}$; $x = \frac{1}{4}$, $R_{\text{unk}} = \mathbf{90\ k\Omega}$

39. –

40. a. Carefully redrawing the network will reveal that all three resistors are in parallel and $R_T = \dfrac{R}{N} = \dfrac{12\ \Omega}{3} = \mathbf{4\ \Omega}$

b. Again, all three resistors are in parallel and $R_T = \dfrac{R}{N} = \dfrac{18\ \Omega}{3} = \mathbf{6\ \Omega}$

Chapter 8

1. a. $I_2 = I_3 = \mathbf{10\ mA}$
   b. $V_1 = I_1R_1 = (10\ \text{mA})(1\ \text{k}\Omega) = \mathbf{10\ V}$
   c. $R_T = 1\ \text{k}\Omega + 2.2\ \text{k}\Omega + 0.56\ \text{k}\Omega = 3.76\ \text{k}\Omega$
   $V_s = IR_T = (10\ \text{mA})(3.76\ \text{k}\Omega) = \mathbf{37.6\ V}$

2. a. $I_2 = \dfrac{R_s(I)}{R_s + R_1 + R_2} = \dfrac{10\ \text{k}\Omega(4\ \text{A})}{10\ \text{k}\Omega + 10\ \Omega} = \mathbf{3.996\ A}, \boldsymbol{I_2 \cong I}$
   b. $V_2 = I_2R_2 = (3.996\ \text{A})(6\ \Omega) = \mathbf{23.98\ V}$
   c. $V_s = I_2(R_1 + R_2) = (3.996\ \text{A})(10\ \Omega) = \mathbf{39.96\ V}$

3. $V_{R_1} = IR_1 = (6\ \text{A})(3\ \Omega) = 18\ \text{V}$
   $E + V_{R_1} - V_s = 0,\quad V_s = E + V_{R_1} = 10\ \text{V} + 18\ \text{V} = \mathbf{28\ V}$

4. a. $V_s = E = \mathbf{24\ V}$
   b. $I_2 = \dfrac{E}{R_1 + R_2} = \dfrac{24\ \text{V}}{1\ \Omega + 3\ \Omega} = \dfrac{24\ \text{V}}{4\ \Omega} = \mathbf{6\ A}$
   c. $I + I_s = I_2,\quad I_s = I_2 - I = 6\ \text{A} - 2\ \text{A} = \mathbf{4\ A}$

5. $V_1 = V_2 = V_s = IR_T = 0.6\ \text{A}[6\ \Omega \,||\, 24\ \Omega \,||\, 24\ \Omega] = 0.6\ \text{A}[6\ \Omega \,||\, 12\ \Omega] = 2.4\ \text{V}$
   $I_2 = \dfrac{V_2}{R_2} = \dfrac{2.4\ \text{V}}{24\ \Omega} = \mathbf{0.1\ A}$
   $V_3 = \dfrac{R_3V_s}{R_3 + R_4} = \dfrac{16\ \Omega(2.4\ \text{V})}{24\ \Omega} = \mathbf{1.6\ V}$

6. a. $I_1 = \dfrac{E}{R_1} = \dfrac{24\ \text{V}}{2\ \Omega} = \mathbf{12\ A},\ I_{R_2} = \dfrac{E}{R_2 + R_3} = \dfrac{24\ \text{V}}{6\ \Omega + 2\ \Omega} = \dfrac{24\ \Omega}{8\ \Omega} = 3\ \text{A}$
   KCL: $I + I_s - I_1 - I_{R_2} = 0$
   $I_s = I_1 + I_{R_2} - I = 12\ \text{A} + 3\ \text{A} - 4\ \text{A} = \mathbf{11\ A}$

   b. $V_s = E = 24\ \text{V}$
   VDR: $V_3 = \dfrac{R_3E}{R_2 + R_3} = \dfrac{2\ \Omega(24\ \text{V})}{6\ \Omega + 2\ \Omega} = \dfrac{48\ \text{V}}{8\ \Omega} = \mathbf{6\ V}$

7. a. $I = \dfrac{E}{R_s} = \dfrac{18\ \text{V}}{6\ \Omega} = \mathbf{3\ A},\ R_p = R_s = \mathbf{6\ \Omega}$

   b. $I = \dfrac{E}{R_s} = \dfrac{9\ \text{V}}{2.2\ \text{k}\Omega} = \mathbf{4.09\ mA},\ R_p = R_s = \mathbf{2.2\ k\Omega}$

8. a. $E = IR_s = (1.5\text{ A})(3\ \Omega) = \mathbf{4.5\ V}$, $R_s = \mathbf{3\ \Omega}$

b. $E = IR_s = (6\text{ mA})(4.7\text{ k}\Omega) = \mathbf{28.2\ V}$, $R_s = \mathbf{4.7\ k\Omega}$

9. a. CDR: $I_L = \dfrac{R_s(I)}{R_s + R_L} = \dfrac{100\ \Omega(12\text{ A})}{100\ \Omega + 2\ \Omega} = \mathbf{11.76\ A},\ \boldsymbol{I_L \cong I}$

b. $E_s = IR = (12\text{ A})(100\ \Omega) = \mathbf{1.2\ kV}$
$R_s = 100\ \Omega$
$$I = \frac{E_s}{R_s + R_L} = \frac{1.2\text{ kV}}{100\ \Omega + 2\ \Omega} = \mathbf{11.76\ A}$$

10. a. $E = IR_2 = (2\text{ A})(6.8\ \Omega) = \mathbf{13.6\ V}$, $R = \mathbf{6.8\ \Omega}$

b. $I_1\text{(CW)} = (12\text{ V} + 13.6\text{ V})/(10\ \Omega + 6.8\ \Omega + 39\ \Omega) = \dfrac{25.6\text{ V}}{55.8\ \Omega} = \mathbf{458.78\ mA}$

c. $\underset{+-}{V_{ab}} = I_1R_3 = (458.78\text{ mA})(39\ \Omega) = \mathbf{17.89\ V}$

11. a. $I_T = 6.8\text{ A} - 1.2\text{ A} - 3.6\text{ A} = \mathbf{2\ A}$

b. $V_s = I_T \cdot R = (2\text{ A})(4\ \Omega) = \mathbf{8\ V}$

12. $I_T\uparrow = 7\text{ A} - 3\text{ A} = 4\text{ A}$
CDR: $I_1 = \dfrac{R_2(I_T)}{R_1 + R_2} = \dfrac{6\ \Omega(4\text{ A})}{4\ \Omega + 6\ \Omega} = \mathbf{2.4\ A}$
$V_2 = I_1R_1 = (2.4\text{ A})(4\ \Omega) = \mathbf{9.6\ V}$

13. a. Conversions: $I_1 = E_1/R_1 = 9\text{ V}/3\ \Omega = \mathbf{3\ A},\ R_1 = \mathbf{3\ \Omega}$
$I_2 = E_2/R_2 = 20\text{ V}/2\ \Omega = \mathbf{10\ A},\ R_2 = \mathbf{2\ \Omega}$

b. $I_T\downarrow = 10\text{ A} - 3\text{A} = 7\text{ A}$, $R_T = 3\ \Omega \parallel 6\ \Omega \parallel 2\ \Omega \parallel 12\ \Omega$
$= 2\ \Omega \parallel 2\ \Omega \parallel 12\ \Omega$
$= 1\ \Omega \parallel 12\ \Omega$
$= 0.92\ \Omega$
$\underset{+-}{V_{ab}}$ $V_{ab} = -I_TR_T = -(7\text{ A})(0.92\ \Omega) = \mathbf{-6.44\ V}$

c. $I_3\uparrow = \dfrac{6.44\text{ V}}{6\ \Omega} = \mathbf{1.07\ A}$

14. a. $I = \dfrac{E}{R_2} = \dfrac{12\text{ V}}{2.2\text{ k}\Omega} = \mathbf{5.45\ mA}$, $R_p = \mathbf{2.2\ k\Omega}$

b. $I_T\uparrow = 8\text{ mA} + 5.45\text{ mA} - 3\text{ mA} = 10.45\text{ mA}$
$R' = 6.8\text{ k}\Omega \parallel 2.2\text{ k}\Omega = 1.66\text{ k}\Omega$
$V_1 = I_T R' = (10.45\text{ mA})(1.66\text{ k}\Omega) = \mathbf{17.35\ V}$

c. $V_1 = V_2 + 12\text{ V} \Rightarrow V_2 = V_1 - 12\text{ V} = 17.35\text{ V} - 12\text{ V}$
$= \mathbf{5.35\ V}$

d. $I_2 = \dfrac{V_2}{R_2} = \dfrac{5.35\text{ V}}{2.2\text{ k}\Omega} = \mathbf{2.43\ mA}$

15. a. $I_1 \downarrow I_3\ I_2$

$4 - 4I_1 - 8I_3 = 0$
$6 - 2I_2 - 8I_3 = 0$
$I_1 + I_2 = I_3$

$I_1 = -\dfrac{\mathbf{1}}{\mathbf{7}}\ \mathbf{A},\ I_2 = \dfrac{\mathbf{5}}{\mathbf{7}}\ \mathbf{A},\ I_3 = \dfrac{\mathbf{4}}{\mathbf{7}}\ \mathbf{A}$

$I_{R_1} = I_1 = -\dfrac{\mathbf{1}}{\mathbf{7}}\ \mathbf{A},\ I_{R_2} = I_2 = \dfrac{\mathbf{5}}{\mathbf{7}}\ \mathbf{A},\ I_{R_3} = I_3 = \dfrac{\mathbf{4}}{\mathbf{7}}\ \mathbf{A}$

b. $I_1 \uparrow I_3\ I_2$

$10 + 12 - 3I_3 - 4I_1 = 0$
$12 - 3I_3 - 12I_2 = 0$
$I_1 + I_2 = I_3$

$I_1 = \mathbf{3.06\ A}$
$I_2 = \mathbf{0.19\ A}$
$I_3 = \mathbf{3.25\ A}$

$I_{R_1} = I_1 = \mathbf{3.06\ A},\ I_{R_2} = I_2 = \mathbf{0.19\ A}$
$I_{R_3} = I_3 = \mathbf{3.25\ A}$

16. (I): $I_1 \downarrow I_3\ I_2$

$10 - I_1\, 5.6\text{ k}\Omega - I_3\, 2.2\text{ k}\Omega + 20 = 0$
$-20 + I_3\, 2.2\text{ k}\Omega + I_2\, 3.3\text{ k}\Omega - 30 = 0$
$I_1 + I_2 = I_3$

$I_1 = I_{R_1} = \mathbf{1.45\ mA},\ I_2 = I_{R_2} = \mathbf{8.51\ mA},\ I_3 = I_{R_3} = \mathbf{9.96\ mA}$

(II): I_1, I_3, $\uparrow I_2$

$-1.2\text{ k}\Omega\, I_1 + 9 - 8.2\text{ k}\Omega\, I_3 = 0$
$-10.2\text{ k}\Omega\, I_2 + 8.2\text{ k}\Omega\, I_3 + 6 = 0$
$I_2 + I_3 = I_1$

$I_1 = \mathbf{2.03\ mA},\ I_2 = \mathbf{1.23\ mA},\ I_3 = \mathbf{0.8\ mA}$

$I_{R_1} = I_1 = \mathbf{2.03\ mA}$
$I_{R_2} = I_3 = \mathbf{0.8\ mA}$
$I_{R_3} = I_{R_4} = I_2 = \mathbf{1.23\ mA}$

17. (I): $\overrightarrow{I_1} \downarrow I_3 \downarrow I_2$

$$-25 - 2I_1 - 3I_3 + 60 = 0$$
$$-60 + 3I_3 + 6 - 5I_2 - 20 = 0$$
$$I_1 = I_2 + I_3$$

$I_2 = \mathbf{-8.55\ A}$

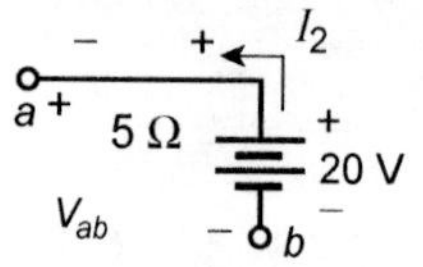

$V_{\underset{+-}{ab}} = 20\ \text{V} - I_2\ 5\ \Omega = 20\ \text{V} - (8.55\ \text{A})(5\ \Omega) = \mathbf{-22.75\ V}$

(II): Source conversion: $E = IR_1 = (3\ \text{A})(3\ \Omega) = 9\ \text{V},\ R_1 = 3\ \Omega$

$\overrightarrow{I_2} \downarrow I_4 \downarrow I_3$

$$9 + 6 - 3I_2 - 4I_2 - 6I_4 = 0$$
$$+ 6I_4 - 8I_3 - 4 = 0$$
$$I_2 = I_3 + I_4$$

$I_2 = \mathbf{1.27\ A}$

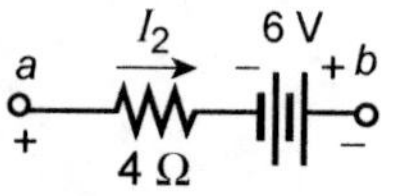

$V_{\underset{+-}{ab}} = I_2\ 4\ \Omega - 6\ \text{V} = (1.27\ \text{A})4\ \Omega - 6\ \text{V} = \mathbf{-0.92\ V}$

18. $I_1 = I_{R_1}$ (CW), $I_2 = I_{R_2}$ (down), $I_3 = I_{R_3}$ (right), $I_4 = I_{R_4}$ (down)
$I_5 = I_{R_5}$ (CW)

a.
$$E_1 - I_1R_1 - I_2R_2 = 0$$
$$I_2R_2 - I_3R_3 - I_4R_4 = 0$$
$$I_4R_4 - I_5R_5 - E_2 = 0$$
$$I_1 = I_2 + I_3$$
$$I_3 = I_4 + I_5$$

b.
$$E_1 - I_2(R_1 + R_2) - I_3R_1 = 0$$
$$I_2R_2 - I_3(R_3 + R_4) + I_5R_4 = 0$$
$$I_3R_4 - I_5(R_4 + R_5) - E_2 = 0$$

c.
$$I_2(R_1 + R_2) + I_3R_1 + 0 = E_1$$
$$I_2(R_2) - I_3(R_3 + R_4) + I_5R_4 = 0$$
$$0 + I_3R_4 - I_5(R_4 + R_5) = E_2$$

$$3I_2 + 2I_3 + 0 = 10$$
$$1I_2 - 9I_3 + 5I_5 = 0$$
$$0 + 5I_3 - 8I_5 = 6$$

d. $I_3 = I_{R_3} = \mathbf{-63.69\ mA}$

19. a. $20\text{ V} - I_B(270\text{ k}\Omega) - 0.7\text{ V} - I_E(0.51\text{ k}\Omega) = 0$
$I_E(0.51\text{ k}\Omega) + 8\text{ V} + I_C(2.2\text{ k}\Omega) - 20\text{ V} = 0$
$I_E = I_B + I_C$

$I_B = \mathbf{63.02\ \mu A}$, $I_C = \mathbf{4.42\ mA}$, $I_E = \mathbf{4.48\ mA}$

b. $V_B = 20\text{ V} - I_B(270\text{ k}\Omega) = 20\text{ V} - (63.02\ \mu\text{A})(270\text{ k}\Omega) = 20\text{ V} - 17.02\text{ V} = \mathbf{2.98\ V}$
$V_E = I_E R_E = (4.48\text{ mA})(510\ \Omega) = \mathbf{2.28\ V}$
$V_C = 20\text{ V} - I_C(2.2\text{ k}\Omega) = 20\text{ V} - (4.42\text{ mA})(2.2\text{ k}\Omega) = 20\text{ V} - 9.72\text{ V} = \mathbf{10.28\ V}$

c. $\beta \cong I_C/I_B = 4.42\text{ mA}/63.02\ \mu\text{A} = \mathbf{70.14}$

20. a. $I_1 \curvearrowright\ I_2 \curvearrowright$

$4 - 4I_1 - 8(I_1 - I_2) = 0$
$-8(I_2 - I_1) - 2I_2 - 6 = 0$

$$I_1 = -\frac{1}{7}\text{ A},\ I_2 = -\frac{5}{7}\text{ A}$$
$$I_{R_1} = I_1 = -\frac{1}{7}\text{ A}$$
$$I_{R_2} = I_2 = -\frac{5}{7}\text{ A}$$
$$I_{R_3} = I_1 - I_2 = \left(-\frac{1}{7}\text{A}\right) - \left(-\frac{5}{7}\text{A}\right) = \frac{4}{7}\text{ A (dir. of } I_1)$$

b. $I_1 \curvearrowright\ I_2 \curvearrowright$

$-10 - 4I_1 - 3(I_1 - I_2) - 12 = 0$
$12 - 3(I_2 - I_1) - 12I_2 = 0$

$I_1 = \mathbf{-3.06\ A}$, $I_2 = \mathbf{0.19\ A}$

$I_{R_1} = I_1 = \mathbf{-3.06\ A}$
$I_{R_3} = I_2 = \mathbf{0.19\ A}$
$I_{R_2} = I_1 - I_2 = (-3.06\text{ A}) - (0.19\text{ A}) = \mathbf{-3.25\ A}$

21. (I): $I_1 \curvearrowright\ I_2 \curvearrowright$

$10 - I_1(5.6\text{ k}\Omega) - 2.2\text{ k}\Omega(I_1 - I_2) + 20 = 0$
$-20 - 2.2\text{ k}\Omega(I_2 - I_1) - I_2\,3.3\text{ k}\Omega - 30 = 0$

$I_1 = \mathbf{1.45\ mA}$, $I_2 = \mathbf{8.51\ mA}$
$I_{R_1} = I_1 = \mathbf{1.45\ mA}$, $I_{R_2} = I_2 = \mathbf{8.51\ mA}$
$I_{R_3} = I_2 - I_1 = \mathbf{7.06\ mA}$ (direction of I_2)

(II): $I_1 \curvearrowright$ $\quad -I_1(1.2\text{ k}\Omega) + 9 - 8.2\text{ k}\Omega(I_1 - I_2) = 0$

$I_2 \curvearrowright$ $\quad -I_2(1.1\text{ k}\Omega) + 6 - I_2(9.1\text{ k}\Omega) - 8.2\text{ k}\Omega(I_2 - I_1) = 0$

$I_1 = \mathbf{2.03\text{ mA}}, I_2 = \mathbf{1.23\text{ mA}}$

$I_{R_1} = I_1 = \mathbf{2.03\text{ mA}},\ I_{R_3} = I_{R_4} = I_2 = \mathbf{1.23\text{ mA}}$

$I_{R_2} = I_1 - I_2 = 2.03\text{ mA} - 1.23\text{ mA} = \mathbf{0.80\text{ mA}}$ (direction of I_1)

22. (I): $I_1 \curvearrowright I_2 \curvearrowright$

$-25 - 2I_1 - 3(I_1 - I_2) + 60 = 0$

$-60 - 3(I_2 - I_1) + 6 - 5I_2 - 20 = 0$

$I_1 = \mathbf{1.87\text{ A}}, I_2 = \mathbf{-8.55\text{ A}}$

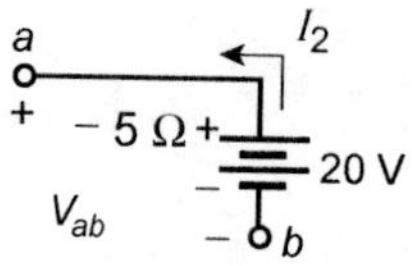

$V_{ab} = 20 - I_2 5 = 20 - (8.55\text{ A})(5) = 20\text{ V} - 42.75\text{ V}$

$= \mathbf{-22.75\text{ V}}$

(II): Source conversion: $E = 9\text{ V}, R = 3\ \Omega$

$I_2 \curvearrowright I_3 \curvearrowright$

$9 - 3I_2 - 4I_2 + 6 - 6(I_2 - I_3) = 0$

$-6(I_3 - I_2) - 8I_3 - 4 = 0$

$I_2 = \mathbf{1.27\text{ A}}, I_3 = \mathbf{0.26\text{ A}}$

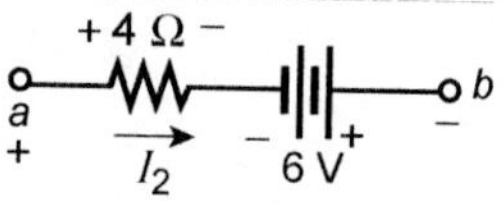

$V_{ab} = I_2 4 - 6 = (1.27\text{ A})(4\ \Omega) - 6\text{ V}$

$= 5.08\text{ V} - 6\text{ V}$

$= \mathbf{-0.92\text{ V}}$

23. (a): $I_1 \curvearrowright I_2 \curvearrowright I_3 \curvearrowright$

$10 - I_1 2 - 1(I_1 - I_2) = 0$

$-1(I_2 - I_1) - I_2 4 - 5(I_2 - I_3) = 0$

$-5(I_3 - I_2) - I_3 3 - 6 = 0$

$3I_1 - 1I_2 + 0 = 10$

$-1I_1 + 10I_2 - 5I_3 = 0$

$0 - 5I_2 + 8I_3 = -6$

$I_2 = I_{R_3} = \mathbf{-63.69\text{ mA}}$

24. a. $I_1 \curvearrowright I_2 \curvearrowright$

$-1I_1 - 4 - 5I_1 + 6 - 1(I_1 - I_2) = 0$

$-1(I_2 - I_1) - 6 - 3I_2 - 15 - 10I_2 = 0$

$I_1 = I_{5\Omega} = \mathbf{72.16\text{ mA}}$

$V_a = -4 - (72.16\text{ mA})(6\ \Omega)$

$= -4 - 0.433\text{ V}$

$= \mathbf{-4.43\text{ V}}$

b. Network redrawn:

V_a 5 Ω 6 Ω 4 Ω 2 Ω 3 Ω I_1 I_2 I_3 12 V 16 V

$$-6I_1 - 4(I_1 - I_2) - 12 = 0$$
$$12 - 4(I_2 - I_1) - 5I_2 - 2(I_2 - I_3) + 16 = 0$$
$$-16 - 2(I_3 - I_2) - 3I_3 = 0$$

$I_2 = I_{5\Omega} = \mathbf{1.95\ A}$

$V_a = (I_3)(3\ \Omega)$
$= (-2.42\ \text{mA})(3\ \Omega)$
$= \mathbf{-7.26\ V}$

25. (I): I_1 I_2 I_3

$$I_1(2.2\ \text{k}\Omega + 9.1\ \text{k}\Omega) - 9.1\ \text{k}\Omega\ I_2 = 18$$
$$I_2(9.1\ \text{k}\Omega + 7.5\ \text{k}\Omega + 6.8\ \text{k}\Omega) - 9.1\ \text{k}\Omega\ I_1 - 6.8\ \text{k}\Omega\ I_3 = -18$$
$$I_3(6.8\ \text{k}\Omega + 3.3\ \text{k}\Omega) - I_2\ 6.8\ \text{k}\Omega = -3$$

$I_1 = \mathbf{1.21\ mA}$, $I_2 = \mathbf{-0.48\ mA}$, $I_3 = \mathbf{-0.62\ mA}$

(II): I_1 I_3 I_2

$$16 - 4I_1 - 3(I_1 - I_2) - 12 - 4(I_1 - I_3) = 0$$
$$12 - 3(I_2 - I_1) - 10\ I_2 - 15 - 4(I_2 - I_3) = 0$$
$$-16 - 4(I_3 - I_1) - 4(I_3 - I_2) - 7I_3 = 0$$

$I_1 = \mathbf{-0.24\ A}$, $I_2 = \mathbf{-0.52\ A}$, $I_3 = \mathbf{-1.28\ A}$

26. a. I_1 I_2 I_4 I_3

$$-6.8\ \text{k}\Omega\ I_1 - 4.7\ \text{k}\Omega(I_1 - I_2) + 6 - 2.2\ \text{k}\Omega(I_1 - I_4) = 0$$
$$-6 - 4.7\ \text{k}\Omega(I_2 - I_1) - 2.7\ \text{k}\Omega\ I_2 - 8.2\ \text{k}\Omega\ (I_2 - I_3) = 0$$
$$-1.1\ \text{k}\Omega\ I_3 - 22\ \text{k}\Omega(I_3 - I_4) - 8.2\ \text{k}\Omega(I_3 - I_2) - 9 = 0$$
$$5 - 1.2\ \text{k}\Omega\ I_4 - 2.2\ \text{k}\Omega(I_4 - I_1) - 22\ \text{k}\Omega(I_4 - I_3) = 0$$

$I_1 = \mathbf{0.03\ mA}$, $I_2 = \mathbf{-0.88\ mA}$, $I_3 = \mathbf{-0.97\ mA}$, $I_4 = \mathbf{-0.64\ mA}$

b. Network redrawn:

$$-2I_1 - 6 - 4I_1 + 4I_2 = 0$$
$$-4I_2 + 4I_1 - 1I_2 + 1I_3 - 6 = 0$$
$$-1I_3 + 1I_2 + 6 - 8I_3 = 0$$

$I_1 = \mathbf{-3.8\ A}$, $I_2 = \mathbf{-4.20\ A}$, $I_3 = \mathbf{0.20\ A}$

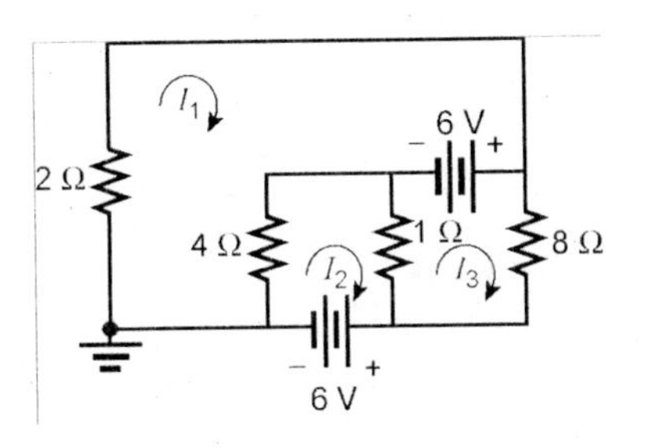

27. a.

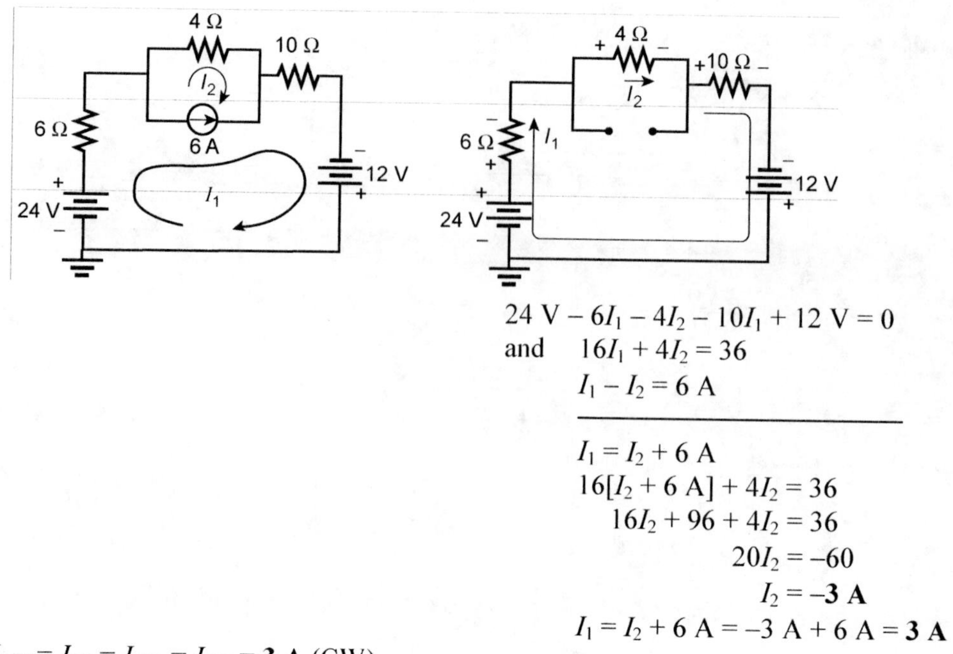

$$24\text{ V} - 6I_1 - 4I_2 - 10I_1 + 12\text{ V} = 0$$

and $16I_1 + 4I_2 = 36$

$I_1 - I_2 = 6\text{ A}$

$I_1 = I_2 + 6\text{ A}$

$16[I_2 + 6\text{ A}] + 4I_2 = 36$

$16I_2 + 96 + 4I_2 = 36$

$20I_2 = -60$

$I_2 = \mathbf{-3\text{ A}}$

$I_1 = I_2 + 6\text{ A} = -3\text{ A} + 6\text{ A} = \mathbf{3\text{ A}}$

$I_{24\text{V}} = I_{6\Omega} = I_{10\Omega} = I_{12\text{V}} = \mathbf{3\text{ A}}$ (CW)

$I_{4\Omega} = \mathbf{3\text{ A}}$ (CCW)

b.

$$20\text{ V} - 4I_1 - 6(I_1 - I_2) - 8(I_3 - I_2) - 1I_3 = 0$$

$10I_1 - 14I_2 + 9I_3 = 20$

$I_3 - I_1 = 3\text{ A}$

$I_2 = 8\text{ A}$

$10I_1 - 14(8\text{ A}) + 9[I_1 + 3\text{ A}] = 20$

$19I_1 = 105$

$I_1 = 5.526\text{ A}$

$I_3 = I_1 + 3\text{ A} = 5.526\text{ A} + 3\text{ A} = 8.526\text{ A}$

$I_2 = 8\text{ A}$

$I_{20\text{V}} = I_{4\Omega} = \mathbf{5.53\text{ A}}$ (dir. of I_1)

$I_{6\Omega} = I_2 - I_1 = \mathbf{2.47\text{ A}}$ (dir. of I_2)

$I_{8\Omega} = I_3 - I_2 = \mathbf{0.53\text{ A}}$ (dir. of I_3)

$I_{1\Omega} = \mathbf{8.53\text{ A}}$ (dir. of I_3)

28. a. $I_1 \curvearrowright I_2 \curvearrowright$

$(4 + 8)I_1 - 8I_2 = 4$
$(8 + 2)I_2 - 8I_1 = -6$

---

b. $I_1 \curvearrowright I_2 \curvearrowright$

$I_1 = -\frac{1}{7}\text{A}, I_2 = -\frac{5}{7}\text{A}$

$(4 + 3)I_1 - 3I_2 = -10 - 12$
$(3 + 12)I_2 - 3I_1 = 12$

$I_1 = \mathbf{-3.06\ A}, I_2 = \mathbf{0.19\ A}$

29. (I): $I_1 \curvearrowright I_2 \curvearrowright$

a. $I_1(5.6\ \text{k}\Omega + 2.2\ \text{k}\Omega) - 2.2\ \text{k}\Omega\ (I_2) = 10 + 20$
$I_2(2.2\ \text{k}\Omega + 3.3\ \text{k}\Omega) - 2.2\ \text{k}\Omega\ (I_1) = -20 - 30$

---

b. $I_1 = \mathbf{1.45\ mA}, I_2 = \mathbf{-8.51\ mA}$

c. $I_{R_1} = I_1 = \mathbf{1.45\ mA}, I_{R_2} = I_2 = \mathbf{-8.51\ mA}$
$I_{R_3} = I_1 + I_2 = 8.51\ \text{mA} + 1.44\ \text{mA} = \mathbf{9.96\ mA}$ (direction of I_1)

(II): $I_1 \curvearrowright$
$I_2 \curvearrowright$

a. $I_1(1.2\ \text{k}\Omega + 8.2\ \text{k}\Omega) - 8.2\ \text{k}\Omega\ I_2 = 9$
$I_2(8.2\ \text{k}\Omega + 1.1\ \text{k}\Omega + 9.1\ \text{k}\Omega) - 8.2\ \text{k}\Omega\ I_1 = 6$

---

b. $I_1 = \mathbf{2.03\ mA}, I_2 = \mathbf{1.23\ mA}$

c. $I_{R_1} = I_1 = \mathbf{2.03\ mA}, I_{R_3} = I_{R_4} = I_2 = \mathbf{1.23\ mA}$
$I_{R_2} = I_1 - I_2 = 2.03\ \text{mA} - 1.23\ \text{mA} = \mathbf{0.80\ mA}$ (direction of I_1)

30. (I): $I_1 \curvearrowright I_2 \curvearrowright$

$(2 + 3)I_1 - 3I_2 = -25 + 60$
$(3 + 5)I_2 - 3I_1 = -60 + 6 - 20$

---

b. $I_1 = \mathbf{1.87\ A}, I_2 = \mathbf{-8.55\ A}$

c. $I_{R_1} = I_1 = \mathbf{1.87\ A}, I_{R_2} = I_2 = \mathbf{-8.55\ A}$
$I_{R_3} = I_1 - I_2 = 1.87\ \text{A} - (-8.55\ \text{A}) = \mathbf{10.42\ A}$ (direction of I_1)

(II): a. $I_2 \curvearrowright I_3 \curvearrowright$

$(3 + 4 + 6)I_2 - 6I_3 = 9 + 6$
$(6 + 8)I_3 - 6I_2 = -4$

---

b. $I_2 = \mathbf{1.27\ A}$, $I_3 = \mathbf{0.26\ A}$

c. $I_{R_2} = I_2 = \mathbf{1.27\ A}$, $I_{R_3} = I_3 = \mathbf{0.26\ A}$
$I_{R_4} = I_2 - I_3 = 1.27\ \text{A} - 0.26\ \text{A} = \mathbf{1.01\ A}$
$I_{R_1} = 3\ \text{A} - I_2 = 3\ \text{A} - 1.27\ \text{A} = \mathbf{1.73\ A}$

31. I_1 I_2 I_3 (clockwise)
$I_1(2 + 1) - 1I_2 = 10$
$I_2(1 + 4 + 5) - 1I_1 - 5I_3 = 0$
$I_3(5 + 3) - 5I_2 = -6$

$I_2 = I_{R_3} = \mathbf{-63.69\ mA}$ (exact match with problem 18)

32. From Sol. 24(b)
I_1 I_2 I_3 (clockwise)
$I_1(6 + 4) - 4I_2 = -12$
$I_2(4 + 5 + 2) - 4I_1 - 2I_3 = 12 + 16$
$I_3(2 + 3) - 2I_2 = -16$

$I_{5\Omega} = I_2 = \mathbf{1.95\ A}$
$I_3 = -2.42\ \text{A}$, $\therefore$ $V_a = (I_3)(3\ \Omega) = (-2.42\ \text{A})(3\ \Omega) = \mathbf{-7.26\ V}$

33. (I): I_1 I_2 I_3 (clockwise)

$(2.2\ \text{k}\Omega + 9.1\ \text{k}\Omega)I_1 - 9.1\ \text{k}\Omega I_2 = 18$
$(9.1\ \text{k}\Omega + 7.5\ \text{k}\Omega + 6.8\ \text{k}\Omega)I_2 - 9.1\ \text{k}\Omega\ I_1 - 6.8\ \text{k}\Omega I_3 = -18$
$(6.8\ \text{k}\Omega + 3.3\ \text{k}\Omega)I_3 - 6.8\ \text{k}\Omega I_2 = -3$

$I_1 = \mathbf{1.21\ mA}$, $I_2 = \mathbf{-0.48\ mA}$, $I_3 = \mathbf{-0.62\ mA}$

(II): I_1, I_3 I_2 (clockwise)
$(4\ \Omega + 4\ \Omega + 3\ \Omega)I_1 - 3\ \Omega\ I_2 - 4\ \Omega\ I_3 = 16 - 12$
$(4\ \Omega + 3\ \Omega + 10\ \Omega)I_2 - 3I_1 - 4\ \Omega\ I_3 = 12 - 15$
$(4\ \Omega + 4\ \Omega + 7\ \Omega)I_3 - 4I_1 - 4I_2 = -16$

$I_1 = \mathbf{-0.24\ A}$, $I_2 = \mathbf{-0.52\ A}$, $I_3 = \mathbf{-1.28\ A}$

34. a. I_1 I_2, I_4 I_3 (clockwise)
$I_1(6.8\ \text{k}\Omega + 4.7\ \text{k}\Omega + 2.2\ \text{k}\Omega) - 4.7\ \text{k}\Omega\ I_2 - 2.2\ \text{k}\Omega\ I_4 = 6$
$I_2(2.7\ \text{k}\Omega + 8.2\ \text{k}\Omega + 4.7\ \text{k}\Omega) - 4.7\ \text{k}\Omega\ I_1 - 8.2\ \text{k}\Omega\ I_3 = -6$
$I_3(8.2\ \text{k}\Omega + 1.1\ \text{k}\Omega + 22\ \text{k}\Omega) - 22\ \text{k}\Omega\ I_4 - 8.2\ \text{k}\Omega\ I_2 = -9$
$I_4(2.2\ \text{k}\Omega + 22\ \text{k}\Omega + 1.2\ \text{k}\Omega) - 2.2\ \text{k}\Omega\ I_1 - 22\ \text{k}\Omega\ I_3 = 5$

$I_1 = \mathbf{0.03\ mA}$, $I_2 = \mathbf{-0.88\ mA}$, $I_3 = \mathbf{-0.97\ mA}$, $I_4 = \mathbf{-0.64\ mA}$

b. From Sol. 26(b):
$I_1(2 + 4) - 4I_2 = -6$
$I_2(4 + 1) - 4I_1 - 1I_3 = -6$
$I_3(1 + 8) - 1I_2 = 6$

$I_1 = \mathbf{3.8\ A}$, $I_2 = \mathbf{-4.20\ A}$, $I_3 = \mathbf{0.20\ A}$

35. a. V_1 V_2

$$V_1\left[\frac{1}{2}+\frac{1}{5}+\frac{1}{2}\right]-\frac{1}{2}V_2=5$$

$$V_2\left[\frac{1}{2}+\frac{1}{4}\right]-\frac{1}{2}V_1=3$$

$V_1 = \mathbf{8.08\ V}$
$V_2 = \mathbf{9.39\ V}$

Symmetry is present

b. V_1 V_2

$$V_1\left[\frac{1}{2}+\frac{1}{4}\right]-\frac{1}{4}V_2=4-2$$

$$V_2\left[\frac{1}{4}+\frac{1}{20}+\frac{1}{5}\right]-\frac{1}{4}V_1=2$$

$V_1 = \mathbf{4.80\ V}$
$V_2 = \mathbf{6.40\ V}$

Symmetry is present

36. (I): V_1 V_2

$$V_1\left[\frac{1}{3}+\frac{1}{6}+\frac{1}{4}\right]-\frac{1}{4}V_2=-5-3$$

$$V_2\left[\frac{1}{8}+\frac{1}{4}\right]-\frac{1}{4}V_1=3-4$$

$V_1 = \mathbf{-14.86\ V}$, $V_2 = \mathbf{-12.57\ V}$
$V_{R_1} = V_{R_4} = \mathbf{-14.86\ V}$
$V_{R_2} = \mathbf{-12.57\ V}$
$V_{R_3} = 12\text{ V} + 12.57\text{ V} - 14.86\text{ V} = \mathbf{9.71\ V}$

(II): V_1 V_2

$$V_1\left[\frac{1}{5}+\frac{1}{3}+\frac{1}{2}\right]-\frac{1}{3}V_2-\frac{1}{2}V_2=-6$$

$$V_2\left[\frac{1}{2}+\frac{1}{3}+\frac{1}{4}+\frac{1}{8}\right]-\frac{1}{3}V_1-\frac{1}{2}V_1=7$$

$V_1 = \mathbf{-2.56\ V}$, $V_2 = \mathbf{4.03\ V}$
$V_{R_1} = \mathbf{-2.56\ V}$
$V_{R_2} = V_{R_5} = \mathbf{4.03\ V}$
$V_{R_4} = V_{R_3} = 4.03\text{ V} + 2.56\text{ V} = \mathbf{6.59\ V}$

37. (I): a. V_1 V_2

$$V_1\left[\frac{1}{2.2\,\text{k}\Omega}+\frac{1}{9.1\,\text{k}\Omega}+\frac{1}{7.5\,\text{k}\Omega}\right]-\frac{1}{7.5\,\text{k}\Omega}V_2=-1.98\text{ mA}$$

$$V_2\left[\frac{1}{7.5\,\text{k}\Omega}+\frac{1}{6.8\,\text{k}\Omega}+\frac{1}{3.3\,\text{k}\Omega}\right]-\frac{1}{7.5\,\text{k}\Omega}V_1=0.91\text{ mA}$$

b. $V_1 = \mathbf{-2.65\ V}$, $V_2 = \mathbf{0.95\ V}$

c. $V_{R_3} = V_1 = \mathbf{-2.65\ V}$, $V_{R_5} = V_2 = \mathbf{0.95\ V}$, $V_{R_4} = \overset{(+)}{V_2} - \overset{(-)}{V_1} = \mathbf{3.60\ V}$

R_1 (+ top, − bottom): $V_{R_1} = 18\text{ V} - 2.65\text{ V} = \mathbf{15.35\ V}$

R_2 (− top, + bottom): $V_{R_2} = 3\text{ V} - 0.95\text{ V} = \mathbf{2.05\ V}$

(II): a. V_1 V_2 V_3

$$V_1\left[\frac{1}{4}+\frac{1}{4}+\frac{1}{7}\right]-\frac{1}{4}V_2-\frac{1}{4}V_3=4$$

$$V_2\left[\frac{1}{4}+\frac{1}{3}+\frac{1}{10}\right]-\frac{1}{4}V_1-\frac{1}{3}V_3=4+1.5$$

$$V_3\left[\frac{1}{4}+\frac{1}{3}+\frac{1}{4}\right]-\frac{1}{4}V_1-\frac{1}{3}V_3=-4-4$$

b. $V_1 = \mathbf{8.88\ V}$, $V_2 = \mathbf{9.83\ V}$, $V_3 = \mathbf{-3.01\ V}$

c. $V_{R_6} = V_1 = \mathbf{8.88\ V}$, $V_{R_4} = V_3 = \mathbf{-3.01\ V}$, $V_{R_5} = \underset{V_2}{(+)}\ \underset{V_1}{(-)} = \mathbf{0.95\ V}$

$-V_{R_1}+$ R_1: $V_{R_1} = 16\text{ V} - V_1 + V_3 = \mathbf{4.12\ V}$

$-V_{R_2}+$ R_2: $V_{R_2} = V_2 - V_3 - 12\text{ V} = \mathbf{0.84\ V}$

R_3 (- top, + bottom): $V_{R_3} = 15\text{ V} - V_2 = \mathbf{5.17\ V}$

38. (I): V_1 V_2 V_3

$$V_1\left[\frac{1}{3}+\frac{1}{6}+\frac{1}{6}\right]-\frac{1}{6}V_2-\frac{1}{6}V_3=5$$

$$V_2\left[\frac{1}{6}+\frac{1}{4}+\frac{1}{5}\right]-\frac{1}{6}V_1-\frac{1}{5}V_3=-3$$

$$V_3\left[\frac{1}{6}+\frac{1}{5}+\frac{1}{7}\right]-\frac{1}{5}V_2-\frac{1}{6}V_1=0$$

V_1 = **7.24 V**, V_2 = **–2.45 V**, V_3 = **1.41 V**

(II): Source conversion: $I = 4$ A, $R = 4\ \Omega$

V_1 V_2 V_3

$$V_1\left[\frac{1}{9}+\frac{1}{20}+\frac{1}{20}\right]-\frac{1}{20}V_2-\frac{1}{20}V_3=-2$$

$$V_2\left[\frac{1}{20}+\frac{1}{20}+\frac{1}{18}\right]-\frac{1}{20}V_1-\frac{1}{20}V_3=0$$

$$V_3\left[\frac{1}{20}+\frac{1}{20}+\frac{1}{4}\right]-\frac{1}{20}V_2-\frac{1}{20}V_1=4$$

V_1 = **–6.64 V**, V_2 = **1.29 V**, V_3 = **10.66 V**

39. (I) V_1 V_2 V_3

$$\left[\frac{1}{2}+\frac{1}{2}\right]V_1-\frac{1}{2}V_2+0=-5$$

$$\left[\frac{1}{2}+\frac{1}{9}+\frac{1}{7}+\frac{1}{2}\right]V_2-\frac{1}{2}V_1-\frac{1}{2}V_3=0$$

$$\left[\frac{1}{2}+\frac{1}{2}+\frac{1}{4}\right]V_3-\frac{1}{2}V_2=5$$

V_1 = **–5.31 V**, V_2 = **–0.62 V**, V_3 = **3.75 V**

(II) V_1 V_2 V_3

$$V_1\left[\frac{1}{2}+\frac{1}{6}\right]-\frac{1}{6}V_3=-5$$

$$V_2\left[\frac{1}{4}\right]=5-2$$

$$V_3\left[\frac{1}{6}+\frac{1}{5}\right]-\frac{1}{6}V_1=2$$

$V_1 = \mathbf{-6.92\ V}$, $V_2 = \mathbf{12\ V}$, $V_3 = \mathbf{2.3\ V}$

40. a.

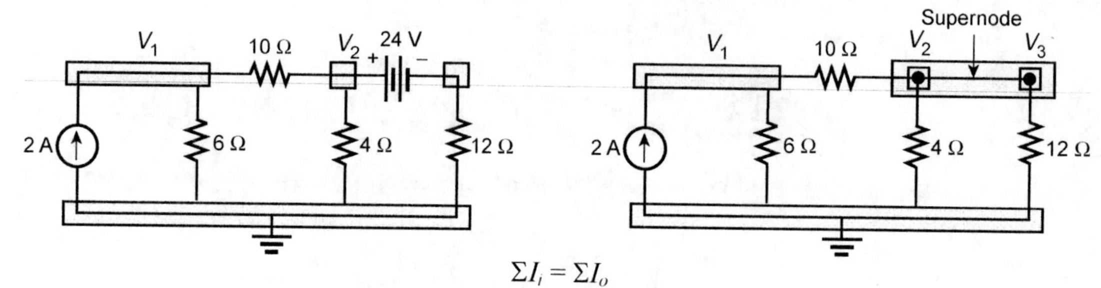

$$\Sigma I_i = \Sigma I_o$$

Node V_1:

$$2\text{ A} = \frac{V_1}{6\,\Omega}+\frac{V_1-V_2}{10\,\Omega}$$

Supernode V_2, V_3:

$$0 = \frac{V_2-V_1}{10\,\Omega}+\frac{V_2}{4\,\Omega}+\frac{V_3}{12\,\Omega}$$

Independent source:

$$V_2 - V_3 = 24\text{ V or } V_3 = V_2 - 24\text{ V}$$

2 eq. 2 unknowns:

$$\frac{V_1}{6\,\Omega}+\frac{V_1-V_2}{10\,\Omega}=2\text{ A}$$

$$\frac{V_2-V_1}{10\,\Omega}+\frac{V_2}{4\,\Omega}+\frac{V_2-24\text{ V}}{12\,\Omega}=0$$

$0.267V_1 - 0.1V_2 = 2$

$+0.1V_1 - 0.433V_2 = -2$

$V_1 = \mathbf{10.08\ V}$, $V_2 = \mathbf{6.94\ V}$

$V_3 = V_2 - 24\text{ V} = \mathbf{-17.06\ V}$

b.

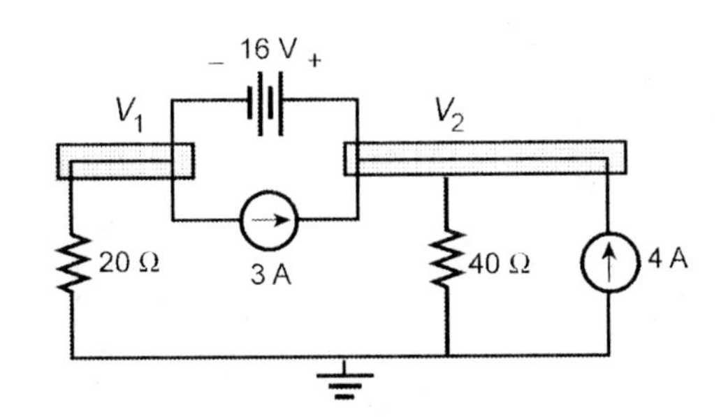

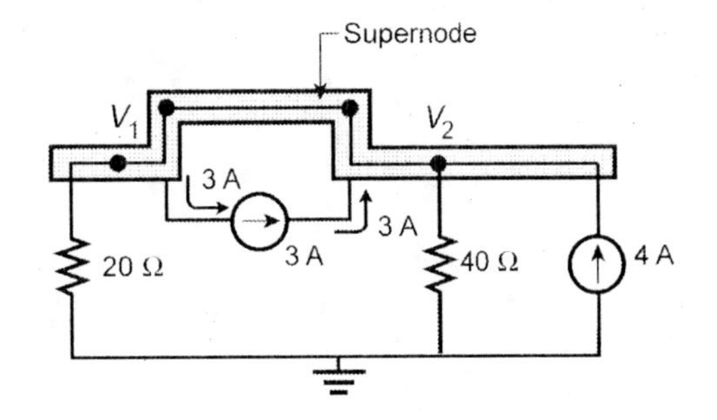

$$\Sigma I_i = \Sigma I_o$$

Supernode:

$$3\text{ A} + 4\text{ A} = 3\text{ A} + \frac{V_1}{20\,\Omega} + \frac{V_2}{40\,\Omega}$$

2 eq. 2 unk. $\begin{cases} 4\text{ A} = \dfrac{V_1}{20\,\Omega} + \dfrac{V_2}{40\,\Omega} \\ V_2 - V_1 = 16\text{ V} \end{cases}$

Subt. $V_2 = 16\text{ V} + V_1$

$$4\text{ A} = \frac{V_1}{20\,\Omega} + \frac{(16\text{ V} + V_1)}{40\,\Omega}$$

and $V_1 = \mathbf{48\ V}$

$V_2 = 16\text{ V} + V_1 = \mathbf{64\ V}$

41. a. V_1 V_2

$$V_1\left[\frac{1}{2} + \frac{1}{5} + \frac{1}{2}\right] - \frac{1}{2}V_2 = 5$$

$$V_2\left[\frac{1}{2} + \frac{1}{4}\right] - \frac{1}{2}V_1 = 3$$

$V_1 = \mathbf{8.08\ V}$, $V_2 = \mathbf{9.39\ V}$

Symmetry present

b. V_1 V_2

$$V_1\left[\frac{1}{2} + \frac{1}{4}\right] - \frac{1}{4}V_2 = 4 - 2$$

$$V_2\left[\frac{1}{4} + \frac{1}{20} + \frac{1}{5}\right] - \frac{1}{4}V_1 = 2$$

$V_1 = \mathbf{4.8\ V}$, $V_2 = \mathbf{6.4\ V}$

Symmetry present

42. (I): a. Note the solution to problem 36(I).

b. $V_1 = \mathbf{-14.86\ V}$, $V_2 = \mathbf{-12.57\ V}$

c. $V_{R_1} = V_{R_4} = V_1 = \mathbf{-14.86\ V}$, $V_{R_2} = V_2 = \mathbf{-12.57\ V}$

$+V_{R_3}-$ (R_3)

$V_{R_3} = V_1 - V_2 + 12\text{ V} = (-14.86\text{ V}) - (-12.57\text{ V}) + 12\text{ V} = \mathbf{9.71\ V}$

(II): a. Note the solution to problem 36(II).

b. $V_1 = \mathbf{-2.56\ V}$, $V_2 = \mathbf{4.03\ V}$

c. $V_{R_1} = V_1 = \mathbf{-2.56\ V}$, $V_{R_2} = V_{R_5} = V_2 = \mathbf{4.03\ V}$

(+) (−)

$V_{R_3} = V_{R_4} = V_2 - V_1 = \mathbf{6.59\ V}$

43. (I): a. Source conversion: $I = 5$ A, $R = 3\ \Omega$

V_1, V_2, V_3

$$V_1\left[\frac{1}{3}+\frac{1}{6}+\frac{1}{6}\right]-\frac{1}{6}V_2-\frac{1}{6}V_3 = 5$$

$$V_2\left[\frac{1}{6}+\frac{1}{4}+\frac{1}{5}\right]-\frac{1}{6}V_1-\frac{1}{5}V_3 = -3$$

$$V_3\left[\frac{1}{6}+\frac{1}{5}+\frac{1}{7}\right]-\frac{1}{5}V_2-\frac{1}{6}V_1 = 0$$

b. $V_1 = \mathbf{7.24\ V}$, $V_2 = \mathbf{-2.45\ V}$, $V_3 = \mathbf{1.41\ V}$

c. R_1 (− V_{R_1} +) $V_{R_1} = 15\text{ V} - 7.24\text{ V} = \mathbf{7.76\ V}$

$V_{R_2} = V_2 = \mathbf{-2.45\ V}$, $V_{R_3} = V_3 = \mathbf{1.41\ V}$

(+) (−)

$V_{R_4} = V_3 - V_2 = 1.41\text{ V} - (-2.45\text{ V}) = \mathbf{3.86\ V}$

$V_{R_5} = V_1 - V_2 = 7.24\text{ V} - (-2.45\text{ V}) = \mathbf{9.69\ V}$

$V_{R_6} = V_1 - V_3 = 7.24\text{ V} - 1.41\text{ V} = \mathbf{5.83\ V}$

(II): a. Source conversion: $I = 4$ A, $R = 4\ \Omega$

$$V_1\left[\frac{1}{9}+\frac{1}{20}+\frac{1}{20}\right]-\frac{1}{20}V_2-\frac{1}{20}V_3=-2$$

V_1 V_2 V_3

$$V_2\left[\frac{1}{20}+\frac{1}{20}+\frac{1}{18}\right]-\frac{1}{20}V_1-\frac{1}{20}V_3=0$$

$$V_3\left[\frac{1}{20}+\frac{1}{20}+\frac{1}{4}\right]-\frac{1}{20}V_2-\frac{1}{20}V_1=4$$

b. $V_1 = \mathbf{-6.64\ V}$, $V_2 = \mathbf{1.29\ V}$, $V_3 = \mathbf{10.66\ V}$

c. $V_{R_1} = V_1 = \mathbf{-6.64\ V}$, R_2 (− V_{R_2} +) $= 16\text{ V} - 10.66\text{ V} = \mathbf{5.34\ V}$

$V_{R_3} = V_2 = \mathbf{1.29\ V}$, $V_{R_4} = \overset{(+)}{V_2} - \overset{(-)}{V_1} = 1.29\text{ V} - (-6.64\text{ V}) = \mathbf{7.93\ V}$

$V_{R_5} = \overset{(+)}{V_3} - \overset{(-)}{V_2} = 10.66\text{ V} - 1.29\text{ V} = \mathbf{9.37\ V}$

$V_{R_6} = \overset{(+)}{V_3} - \overset{(-)}{V_1} = 10.66\text{ V} - (-6.64\text{ V}) = \mathbf{17.30\ V}$

44. a. Note the solution to problem 39(I).
$V_1 = \mathbf{-5.31\ V}$, $V_2 = \mathbf{-0.62\ V}$, $V_3 = \mathbf{3.75\ V}$
$V_{5A} = V_1 = \mathbf{-5.31\ V}$

b. Note the solution to problem 39(II).
$V_1 = \mathbf{-6.92\ V}$, $V_2 = \mathbf{12\ V}$, $V_3 = \mathbf{2.3\ V}$
$V_{2A} = \overset{(+)}{V_2} - \overset{(-)}{V_3} = \mathbf{9.7\ V}$, $V_{5A} = \overset{(+)}{V_2} - \overset{(-)}{V_1} = \mathbf{18.92\ V}$

45. a. (I_1, I_2, I_3 clockwise)

$I_1(6 + 5 + 10) - 5I_2 - 10I_3 = 6$
$I_2(5 + 5 + 5) - 5I_1 - 5I_3 = 0$
$I_3(5 + 10 + 20) - 10I_1 - 5I_2 = 0$

$I_1 = \mathbf{0.39\ A}$, $I_2 = \mathbf{0.18\ A}$, $I_3 = \mathbf{0.14\ A}$

b. $I_5 = I_2 - I_3 = \mathbf{40\ mA}$ (direction of I_2)

c, d. no

46. Source conversion: $I = 1$ A, $R = 6\ \Omega$

V_1

V_3 V_2

$$\left[\frac{1}{6}+\frac{1}{5}+\frac{1}{5}\right]V_1 - \frac{1}{5}V_2 - \frac{1}{5}V_3 = 1$$
$$\left[\frac{1}{5}+\frac{1}{5}+\frac{1}{20}\right]V_2 - \frac{1}{5}V_1 - \frac{1}{5}V_3 = 0$$
$$\left[\frac{1}{5}+\frac{1}{5}+\frac{1}{10}\right]V_3 - \frac{1}{5}V_1 - \frac{1}{5}V_2 = 0$$

V_{R_5} **= 196.70 mV, no**

47. a. I_2 I_1 I_3

$I_1(2\text{ k}\Omega + 33\text{ k}\Omega + 3.3\text{ k}\Omega) - 33\text{ k}\Omega\, I_2 - 3.3\text{ k}\Omega\, I_3 = 24$
$I_2(33\text{ k}\Omega + 56\text{ k}\Omega + 36\text{ k}\Omega) - 33\text{ k}\Omega\, I_1 - 36\text{ k}\Omega\, I_3 = 0$
$I_3(3.3\text{ k}\Omega + 36\text{ k}\Omega + 5.6\text{ k}\Omega) - 36\text{ k}\Omega\, I_2 - 3.3\text{ k}\Omega\, I_1 = 0$

I_1 **= 0.97 mA,** $I_2 = I_3$ **= 0.36 mA**

b. $I_5 = I_2 - I_3 = 0.36\text{ mA} - 0.36\text{ mA} = \mathbf{0}$

c, d. yes

48. Source conversion: $I = 12$ A, $R = 2\text{ k}\Omega$

V_1

V_3 V_2

$$\left[\frac{1}{2\text{ k}\Omega}+\frac{1}{33\text{ k}\Omega}+\frac{1}{56\text{ k}\Omega}\right]V_1 - \frac{1}{56\text{ k}\Omega}V_2 - \frac{1}{33\text{ k}\Omega}V_3 = 12$$
$$\left[\frac{1}{56\text{ k}\Omega}+\frac{1}{36\text{ k}\Omega}+\frac{1}{5.6\text{ k}\Omega}\right]V_2 - \frac{1}{56\text{ k}\Omega}V_1 - \frac{1}{36\text{ k}\Omega}V_3 = 0$$
$$\left[\frac{1}{33\text{ k}\Omega}+\frac{1}{3.3\text{ k}\Omega}+\frac{1}{36\text{ k}\Omega}\right]V_3 - \frac{1}{33\text{ k}\Omega}V_1 - \frac{1}{36\text{ k}\Omega}V_2 = 0$$

I_{R_5} **= 0 A, yes**

49. Source conversion: $I = 9$ mA, $R = 1\text{ k}\Omega$

V_1

V_2 V_3

$$V_1\left[\frac{1}{1\text{ k}\Omega}+\frac{1}{100\text{ k}\Omega}+\frac{1}{200\text{ k}\Omega}\right] - \frac{1}{100\text{ k}\Omega}V_2 - \frac{1}{200\text{ k}\Omega}V_3 = 4\text{ mA}$$
$$V_2\left[\frac{1}{100\text{ k}\Omega}+\frac{1}{200\text{ k}\Omega}+\frac{1}{1\text{ k}\Omega}\right] - \frac{1}{100\text{ k}\Omega}V_1 - \frac{1}{1\text{ k}\Omega}V_3 = -9\text{ mA}$$
$$V_3\left[\frac{1}{200\text{ k}\Omega}+\frac{1}{100\text{ k}\Omega}+\frac{1}{1\text{ k}\Omega}\right] - \frac{1}{200\text{ k}\Omega}V_1 - \frac{1}{1\text{ k}\Omega}V_2 = 9\text{ mA}$$

---

50. a. 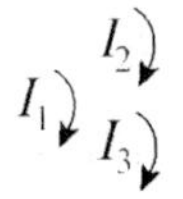 I_1, I_2, I_3

$$(1\text{ k}\Omega + 2\text{ k}\Omega + 2\text{ k}\Omega)I_1 - 2\text{ k}\Omega\, I_2 - 2\text{ k}\Omega\, I_3 = 10$$
$$(2\text{ k}\Omega + 2\text{ k}\Omega + 2\text{ k}\Omega)I_2 - 2\text{ k}\Omega\, I_1 - 2\text{ k}\Omega\, I_3 = 0$$
$$(2\text{ k}\Omega + 2\text{ k}\Omega + 2\text{ k}\Omega)I_3 - 2\text{ k}\Omega\, I_1 - 2\text{ k}\Omega\, I_2 = 0$$

$I_1 = I_{10V} = \mathbf{3.33\text{ mA}}$

Source conversion: $I = 10\text{ V}/1\text{ k}\Omega = 10\text{ mA},\ R = 1\text{ k}\Omega$

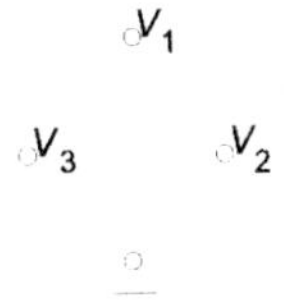

V_1, V_2, V_3

$$V_1\left[\frac{1}{1\text{ k}\Omega} + \frac{1}{2\text{ k}\Omega} + \frac{1}{2\text{ k}\Omega}\right] - \frac{1}{2\text{ k}\Omega}V_2 - \frac{1}{2\text{ k}\Omega}V_3 = 10\text{ mA}$$
$$V_2\left[\frac{1}{2\text{ k}\Omega} + \frac{1}{2\text{ k}\Omega} + \frac{1}{2\text{ k}\Omega}\right] - \frac{1}{2\text{ k}\Omega}V_1 - \frac{1}{2\text{ k}\Omega}V_3 = 0$$
$$V_3\left[\frac{1}{2\text{ k}\Omega} + \frac{1}{2\text{ k}\Omega} + \frac{1}{2\text{ k}\Omega}\right] - \frac{1}{2\text{ k}\Omega}V_2 - \frac{1}{2\text{ k}\Omega}V_1 = 0$$

$$V_1 = 6.67\text{ V} = E - IR_s = 10\text{ V} - I(1\text{ k}\Omega)$$
$$I = \frac{10 - 6.67\text{ V}}{1\text{ k}\Omega} = \mathbf{3.33\text{ mA}}$$

b. 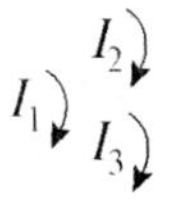 I_1, I_2, I_3

Source conversion: $E = 20\text{ V},\ R = 10\ \Omega$

$$(10 + 10 + 20)I_1 - 10I_2 - 20I_3 = 20$$
$$(10 + 20 + 20)I_2 - 10I_1 - 20I_3 = 0$$
$$(20 + 20 + 10)I_3 - 20I_1 - 20I_2 = 0$$

$I_1 = I_{20V} = 0.83\text{ A}$

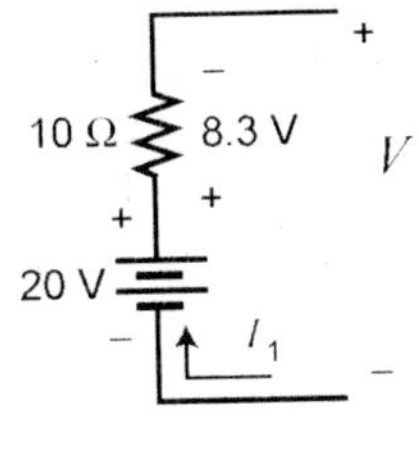

$$V = 20\text{ V} - 8.3\text{ V} = 11.7\text{ V}$$

$$I_s = \frac{V}{R_s} = \frac{11.70\text{ V}}{10\ \Omega} = \mathbf{1.17A}$$

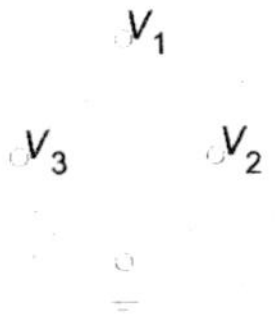

V_1, V_2, V_3

$$V_1\left[\frac{1}{10} + \frac{1}{10} + \frac{1}{20}\right] - \left[\frac{1}{20}\right]V_2 - \left[\frac{1}{10}\right]V_3 = 2$$
$$V_2\left[\frac{1}{20} + \frac{1}{20} + \frac{1}{10}\right] - \left[\frac{1}{20}\right]V_1 - \left[\frac{1}{20}\right]V_3 = 0$$
$$V_3\left[\frac{1}{10} + \frac{1}{20} + \frac{1}{20}\right] - \left[\frac{1}{10}\right]V_1 - \left[\frac{1}{20}\right]V_2 = 0$$

$$I_{R_s} = \frac{V_1}{R_s} = \mathbf{1.17\text{ A}}$$

51. a.

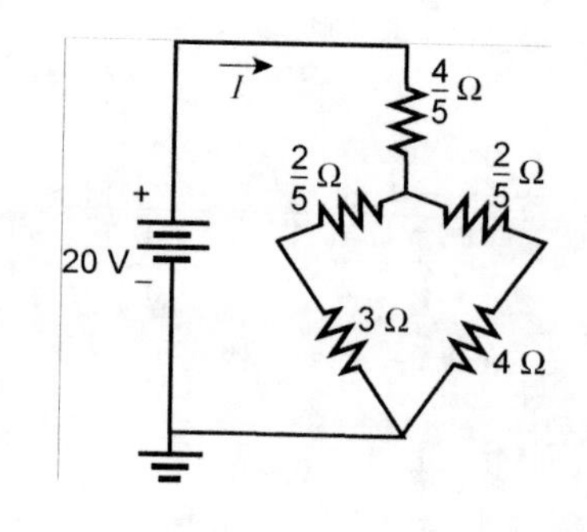

$$I = \frac{20\text{ V}}{\frac{4}{5}\Omega + \left[\frac{2}{5}\Omega + 3\Omega\right] \| \left[\frac{2}{5}\Omega + 4\Omega\right]}$$

$$= \frac{20\text{ V}}{\frac{4}{5}\Omega + (3.14\,\Omega) \| (4.4\,\Omega)}$$

$= \mathbf{7.36\ A}$

b.

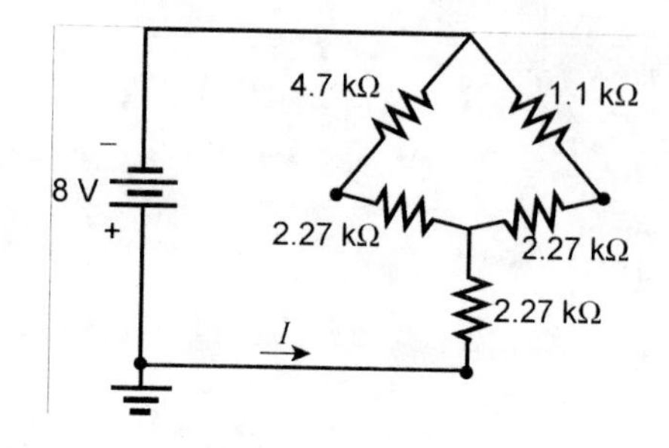

$R_T = 2.27\text{ k}\Omega + [4.7\text{ k}\Omega + 2.27\text{ k}\Omega] \| [1.1\text{ k}\Omega + 2.27\text{ k}\Omega]$
$= 2.27\text{ k}\Omega + [6.97\text{ k}\Omega] \| [3.37\text{ k}\Omega]$
$= 2.27\text{ k}\Omega + 2.27\text{ k}\Omega$
$= 4.54\text{ k}\Omega$

$I = \dfrac{8\text{ V}}{4.54\text{ k}\Omega} = \mathbf{1.76\ mA}$

52. a.

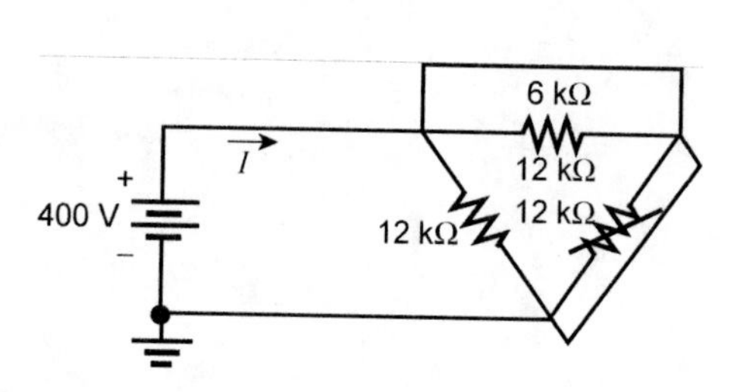

(Y-Δ conversion)

$I = \dfrac{400\text{ V}}{12\text{ k}\Omega \| 12\text{ k}\Omega \| 6\text{ k}\Omega} = \dfrac{400\text{ V}}{3\text{ k}\Omega}$

$= \mathbf{133.33\ mA}$

b. $I = \dfrac{42\text{ V}}{(18\,\Omega \| 18\,\Omega) \| [(18\,\Omega \| 18\,\Omega) + (18\,\Omega \| 18\,\Omega)]} = \dfrac{42\text{ V}}{9\,\Omega \| [9\,\Omega + 9\,\Omega]}$

$= \mathbf{7\ A}$ (Y–Δ conversion)

53.

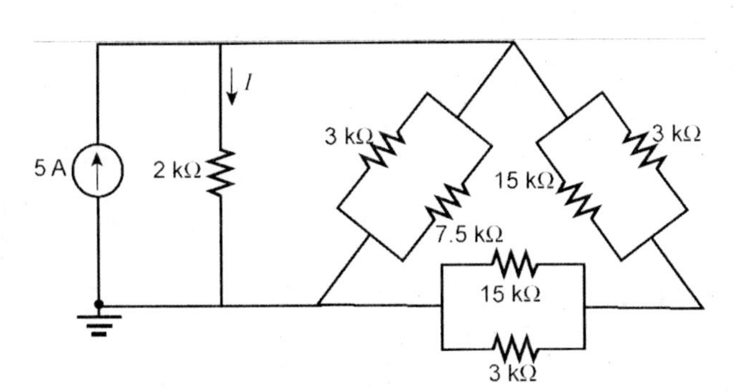

$3\text{ k}\Omega \parallel 7.5\text{ k}\Omega = 2.14\text{ k}\Omega$
$3\text{ k}\Omega \parallel 15\text{ k}\Omega = 2.5\text{ k}\Omega$

$R'_T = 2.14\text{ k}\Omega \parallel (2.5\text{ k}\Omega + 2.5\text{ k}\Omega) = 1.5\text{ k}\Omega$

CDR: $I = \dfrac{(1.5\text{ k}\Omega)(5\text{ A})}{1.5\text{ k}\Omega + 2\text{ k}\Omega} = \mathbf{2.14\text{ A}}$

54.

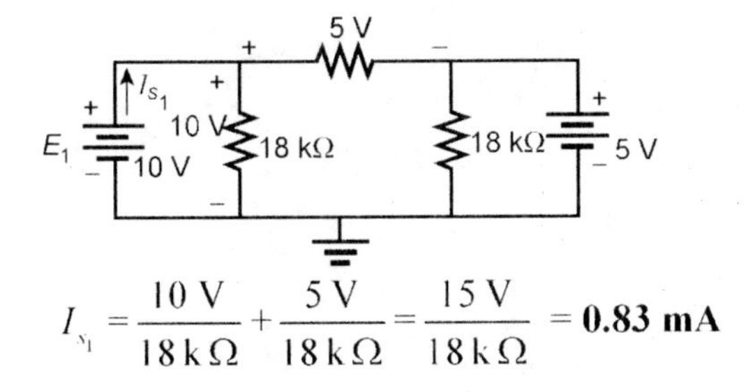

$I_{s_1} = \dfrac{10\text{ V}}{18\text{ k}\Omega} + \dfrac{5\text{ V}}{18\text{ k}\Omega} = \dfrac{15\text{ V}}{18\text{ k}\Omega} = \mathbf{0.83\text{ mA}}$

55.

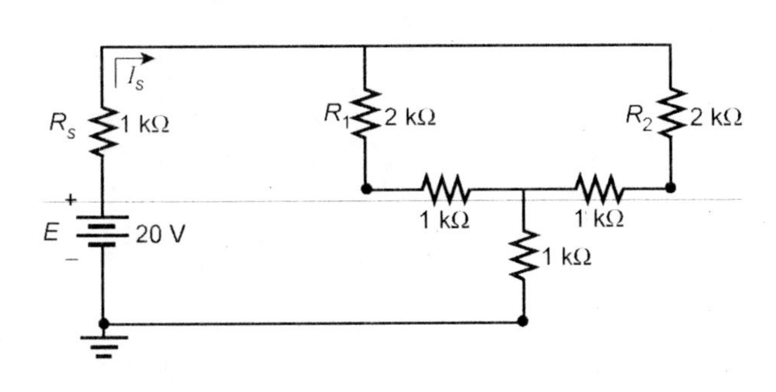

$R' = R_1 + 1\text{ k}\Omega = 3\text{ k}\Omega$
$R'' = R_2 + 1\text{ k}\Omega = 3\text{ k}\Omega$
$R'_T = \dfrac{3\text{ k}\Omega}{2} = 1.5\text{ k}\Omega$

$R_T = 1\text{ k}\Omega + 1.5\text{ k}\Omega + 1\text{ k}\Omega = 3.5\text{ k}\Omega$

$I_s = \dfrac{E}{R_T} = \dfrac{20\text{ V}}{3.5\text{ k}\Omega} = \mathbf{5.71\text{ mA}}$

56.

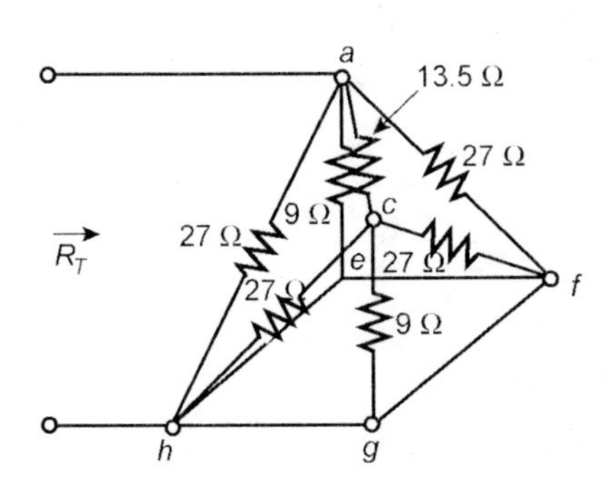

c – g: $27\ \Omega \parallel 9\ \Omega \parallel 27\ \Omega = 5.4\ \Omega$

a – h: $27\ \Omega \parallel 9\ \Omega \parallel 27\ \Omega = 5.4\ \Omega$

$R_T = 5.4\ \Omega \parallel (13.5\ \Omega + 5.4\ \Omega)$
$= 5.4\ \Omega \parallel 18.9\Omega$
$= \mathbf{4.2\ \Omega}$

Chapter 9

1. a. E_1:

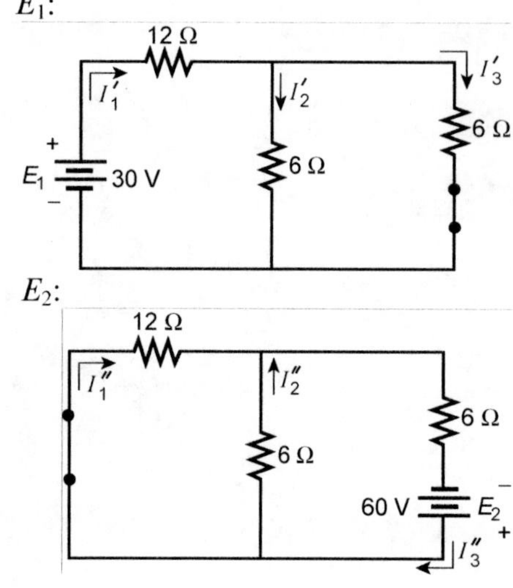

$$I'_1 = \frac{30 \text{ V}}{12\,\Omega + 6\,\Omega \| 6\,\Omega} = \frac{30 \text{ V}}{12\,\Omega + 3\,\Omega} = 2 \text{ A}$$

$$I'_2 = I'_3 = \frac{I'_1}{2} = 1 \text{ A}$$

$$I''_3 = \frac{60 \text{ V}}{6\,\Omega + 6\,\Omega \| 12\,\Omega} = \frac{60 \text{ V}}{6\,\Omega + 4\,\Omega} = 6 \text{ A}$$

$$I''_1 = \frac{6\,\Omega(I''_3)}{6\,\Omega + 12\,\Omega} = 2 \text{ A}$$

$$I''_2 = \frac{12\,\Omega(I''_3)}{12\,\Omega + 6\,\Omega} = 4 \text{ A}$$

$I_1 = I'_1 + I''_1 = 2 \text{ A} + 2 \text{ A} =$ **4 A** (dir. of I'_1)

$I_2 = I''_2 - I'_2 = 4 \text{ A} - 1 \text{ A} =$ **3 A** (dir. of I''_2)

$I_3 = I'_3 + I''_3 = 1 \text{ A} + 6 \text{ A} =$ **7 A** (dir. of I'_3)

b. E_1: $P'_1 = I'^2_1 R_1 = (2 \text{ A})^2\, 12\,\Omega =$ **48 W**

E_2: $P''_1 = I''^2_1 R_1 I''R_1 = (2 \text{ A})^2\, 12\,\Omega =$ **48 W**

c. $P_1 = I_1^2 R_1 = (4 \text{ A})^2\, 12\,\Omega =$ **192 W**

d. $P'_1 + P''_1 = 48 \text{ W} + 48 \text{ W} = 96 \text{ W} \neq 192 \text{ W} = P_1$

2. I:

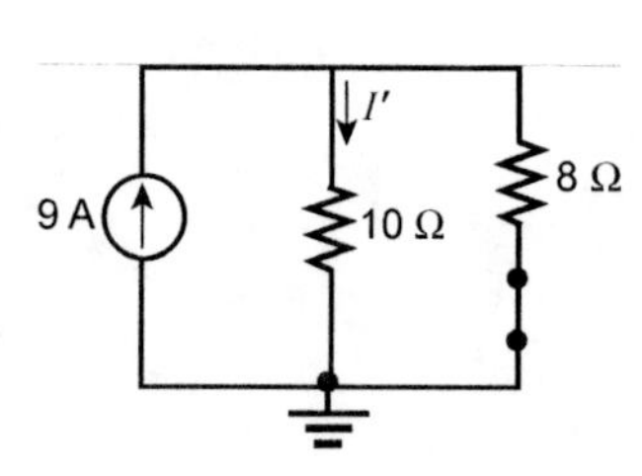

$$I' = \frac{8\,\Omega(9 \text{ A})}{8\,\Omega + 10\,\Omega} = 4 \text{ A}$$

E:

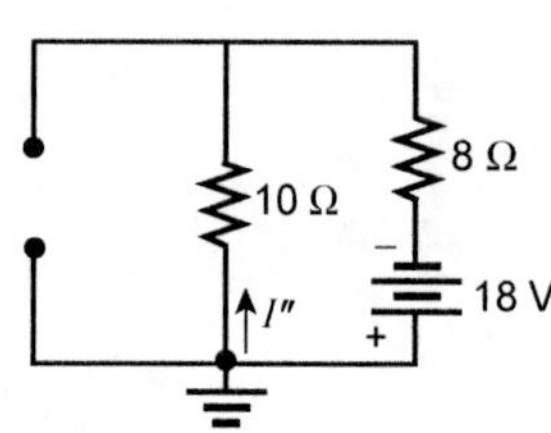

$$I'' = \frac{18 \text{ V}}{10\,\Omega + 8\,\Omega} = 1 \text{ A}$$

$I = I' - I'' = 4 \text{ A} - 1 \text{ A} =$ **3 A (dir of I')**

3.

E_1:

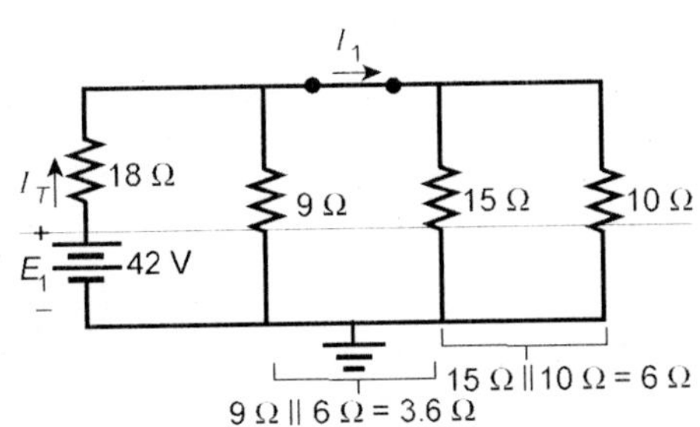

$$I_T = \frac{42\text{ V}}{18\,\Omega + 3.6\,\Omega} = 1.944\text{ A}$$

$$I_1 = \frac{9\,\Omega(I_T)}{9\,\Omega + 6\,\Omega} = \frac{9\,\Omega(1.944\text{ A})}{15\,\Omega}$$
$$= 1.17\text{ A}$$

E_2:

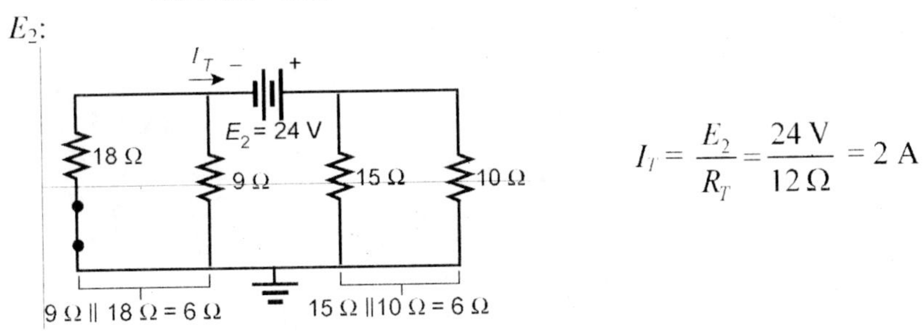

$$I_T = \frac{E_2}{R_T} = \frac{24\text{ V}}{12\,\Omega} = 2\text{ A}$$

$I_{24\text{V}} = I_T + I_1 = 2\text{ A} + 1.17\text{ A} =$ **3.17 A (dir. of I_1)**

4.

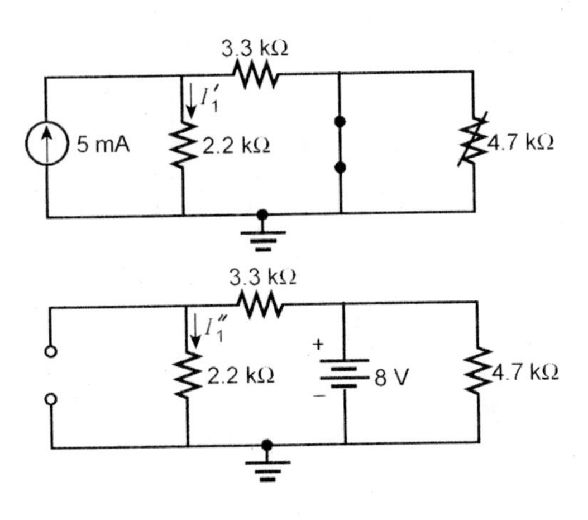

$$I'_1 = \frac{3.3\text{ k}\Omega(5\text{ mA})}{2.2\text{ k}\Omega + 3.3\text{ k}\Omega} = \frac{16.5\text{ mA}}{5.5}$$

$$= 3\text{ mA}$$

$$I''_1 = \frac{8\text{ V}}{3.3\text{ k}\Omega + 2.2\text{ k}\Omega} = \frac{8\text{ V}}{5.5\text{ k}\Omega}$$

$$= 1.45\text{ mA}$$

$I_1 = I'_1 + I''_1 = 3\text{ mA} + 1.45\text{ mA} =$ **4.45 mA**

5. E_1:

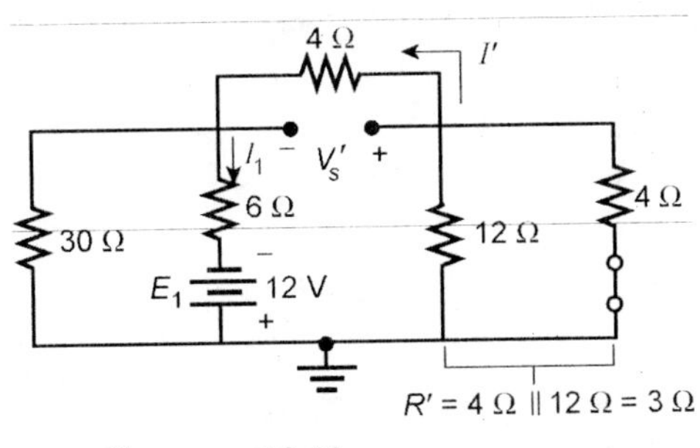

$$I_1 = \frac{E_1}{R_T} = \frac{12\text{ V}}{6\,\Omega + 5.88\,\Omega} = 1.03\text{ A}$$

$$I' = \frac{30\ \Omega(I_1)}{30\ \Omega + 7\ \Omega} = \frac{30\ \Omega(1.03\ \text{A})}{37\ \Omega}$$
$$= 835.14\ \text{mA}$$
$$V_s' = I'(4\ \Omega) = (835.14\ \text{mA})(4\ \Omega)$$
$$= 3.34\ \text{V}$$

I:

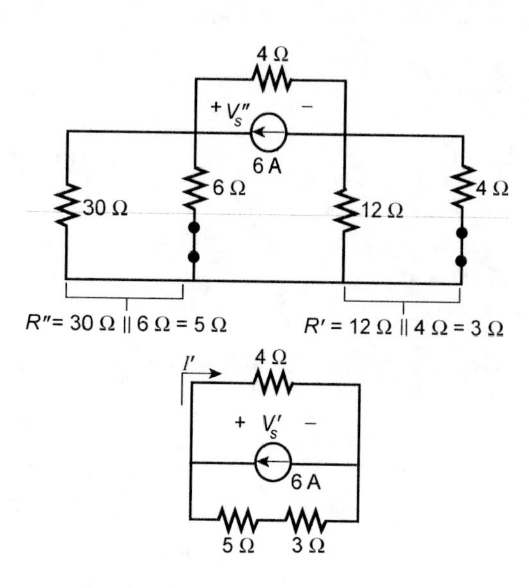

$$I' = \frac{8\ \Omega(6\ \text{A})}{8\ \Omega + 4\ \Omega} = 4\ \text{A}$$
$$V_s'' = I'(4\ \Omega) = 4\ \text{A}(4\ \Omega) = 16\ \text{V}$$

E_2:

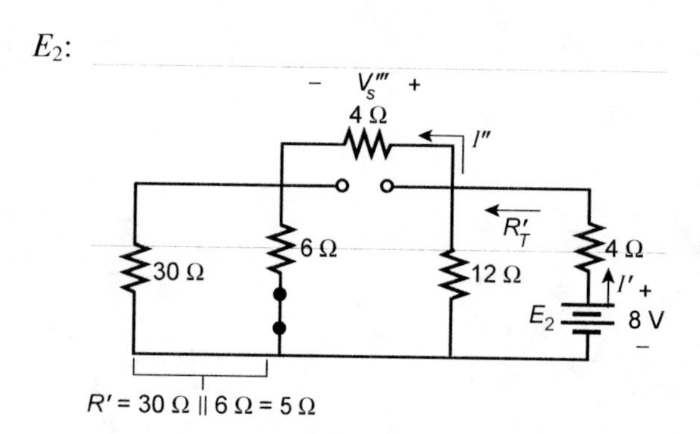

$$R'_T = 12\ \Omega \parallel (4\ \Omega + 5\ \Omega) = 12\ \Omega \parallel 9\ \Omega = 5.14\ \Omega$$
$$I' = \frac{E_2}{R_T} = \frac{8\ \text{V}}{4\ \Omega + 5.14\ \Omega} = 0.875\ \text{A}$$
$$I'' = \frac{12\ \Omega(I')}{12\ \Omega + 9\ \Omega} = \frac{12\ \Omega(0.875\ \text{A})}{21\ \Omega} = 0.5\ \text{A}$$
$$V_s''' = I''(4\ \Omega) = 0.5\ \text{A}(4\ \Omega) = 2\ \text{V}$$
$$V_s = V_s'' - V_s' - V_s''' = 16\ \text{V} - 3.34\ \text{V} - 2\ \text{V} = \mathbf{10.66\ V}$$

6. E:

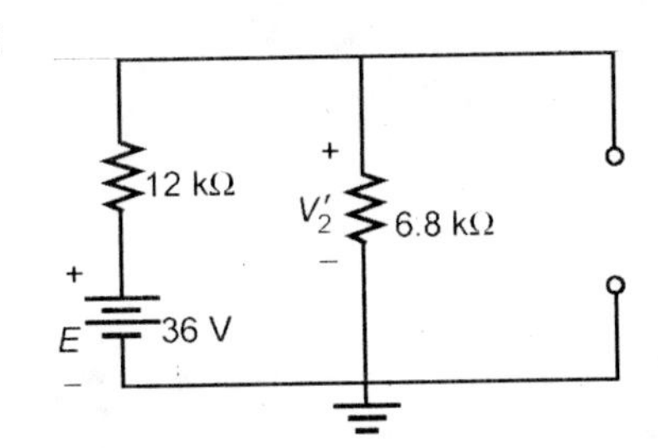

$$V'_2 = \frac{6.8\text{ k}\Omega(36\text{ V})}{6.8\text{ k}\Omega + 12\text{ k}\Omega} = 13.02\text{ V}$$

I:

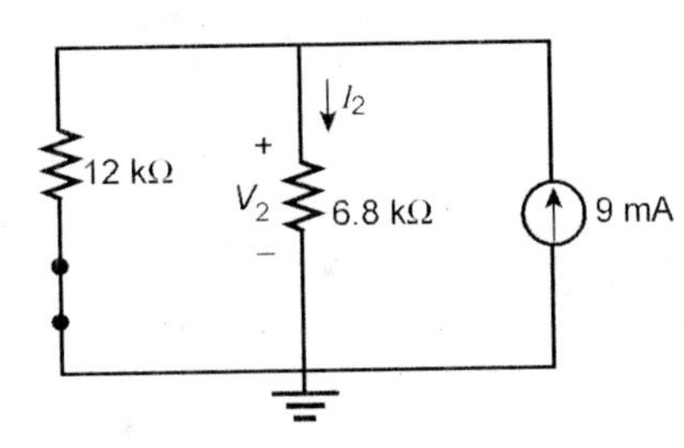

$$I_2 = \frac{12\text{ k}\Omega(9\text{ mA})}{12\text{ k}\Omega + 6.8\text{ k}\Omega} = 5.75\text{ mA}$$

$V_2'' = I_2R_2 = (5.75\text{ mA})(6.8\text{ k}\Omega) = 39.10\text{ V}$

$V_2 = V_2' + V_2'' = 13.02\text{ V} + 39.10\text{ V} = \mathbf{52.12\text{ V}}$

7. a. $R_{Th} = R_3 + R_1 \parallel R_2 = 4\ \Omega + 6\ \Omega \parallel 3\ \Omega = 4\ \Omega + 2\ \Omega = \mathbf{6\ \Omega}$

$$E_{Th} = \frac{R_2E}{R_2 + R_1} = \frac{3\ \Omega(18\text{ V})}{3\ \Omega + 6\ \Omega} = 6\text{ V}$$

b. $$I_1 = \frac{E_{Th}}{R_{Th} + R} = \frac{6\text{ V}}{6\ \Omega + 2\ \Omega} = \mathbf{0.75\text{ A}}$$

$$I_2 = \frac{6\text{ V}}{6\ \Omega + 30\ \Omega} = \mathbf{166.67\text{ mA}}$$

$$I_3 = \frac{6\text{ V}}{6\ \Omega + 100\ \Omega} = \mathbf{56.60\text{ mA}}$$

8. a.

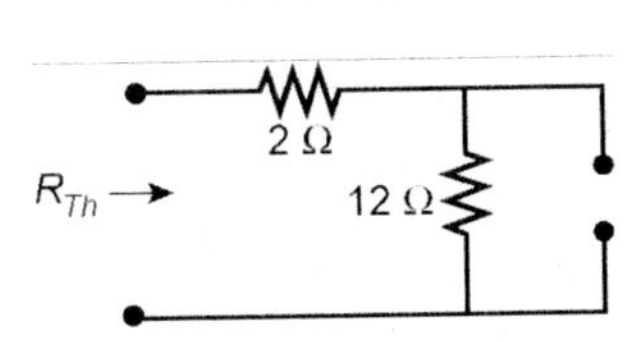

$R_{Th} = 2\ \Omega + 12\ \Omega = \mathbf{14\ \Omega}$

$E_{Th} = IR = (3\text{ A})(12\ \Omega) = \mathbf{36\text{ V}}$

b. $R = 2\ \Omega$: $P = \left(\dfrac{E_{Th}}{R_{Th} + R}\right)^2 R = \left(\dfrac{36\text{ V}}{14\ \Omega + 2\ \Omega}\right)^2 2\ \Omega = \mathbf{10.13\ W}$

$R = 100\ \Omega$: $P = \left(\dfrac{36\text{ V}}{14\ \Omega + 100\ \Omega}\right)^2 100\ \Omega = \mathbf{9.97\ W}$

9. a. R_{Th}:

$\leftarrow R_{Th} = 5\ \Omega + 5\ \Omega \parallel 5\ \Omega = \mathbf{7.5\ \Omega}$

E_{Th}:

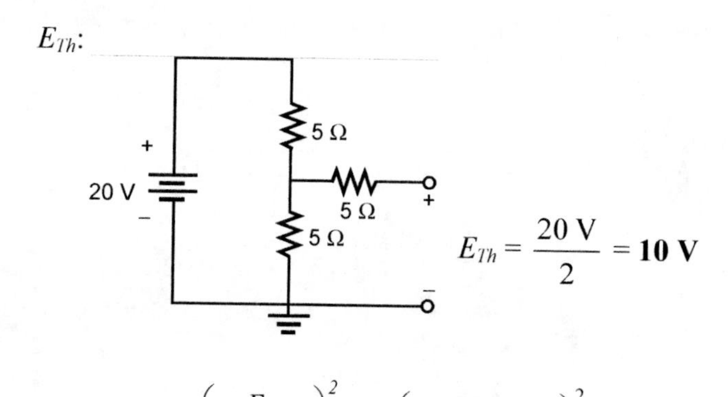

$E_{Th} = \dfrac{20\text{ V}}{2} = \mathbf{10\ V}$

b. $R = 2\ \Omega$: $P = \left(\dfrac{E_{Th}}{R_{Th} + R}\right)^2 R = \left(\dfrac{10\text{ V}}{7.5\ \Omega + 2\ \Omega}\right)^2 2\ \Omega = \mathbf{2.22\ W}$

$R = 100\ \Omega$: $P = \left(\dfrac{10\text{ V}}{7.5\ \Omega + 100\ \Omega}\right)^2 100\ \Omega = \mathbf{0.87\ W}$

10. R_{Th}:

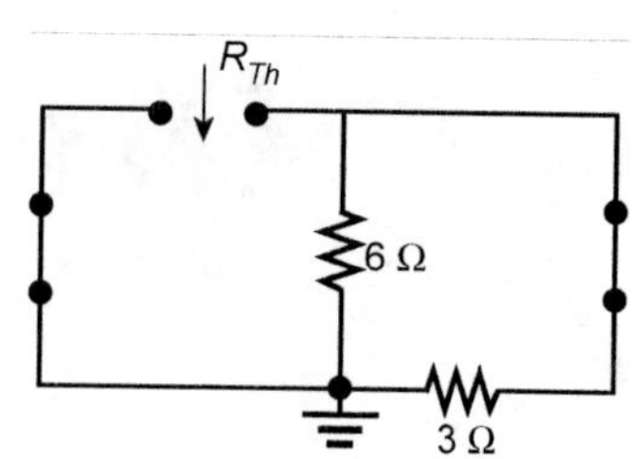

$R_{Th} = 6\ \Omega \parallel 3\ \Omega = \mathbf{2\ \Omega}$

E_{Th}:

$V_{6\Omega} = \dfrac{6\ \Omega(18\text{ V})}{6\ \Omega + 3\ \Omega} = 12\text{ V}$

$E_{Th} = 72\text{ V} + 12\text{ V} = \mathbf{84\ V}$

11. R_{Th}:

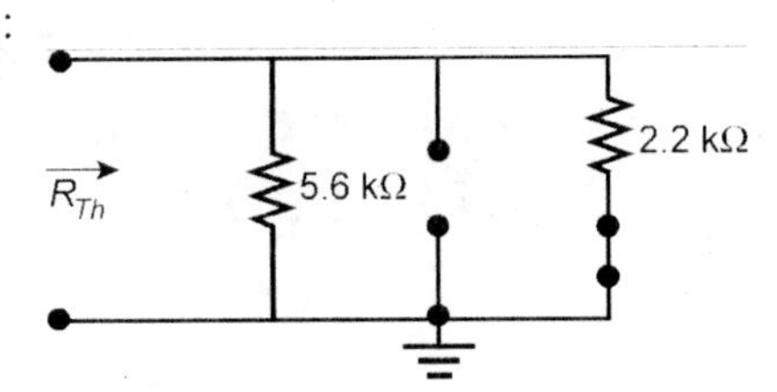

$R_{Th} = 5.6\text{ k}\Omega \parallel 2.2\text{ k}\Omega = \mathbf{1.58\text{ k}\Omega}$

E_{Th}: Superposition:

I:

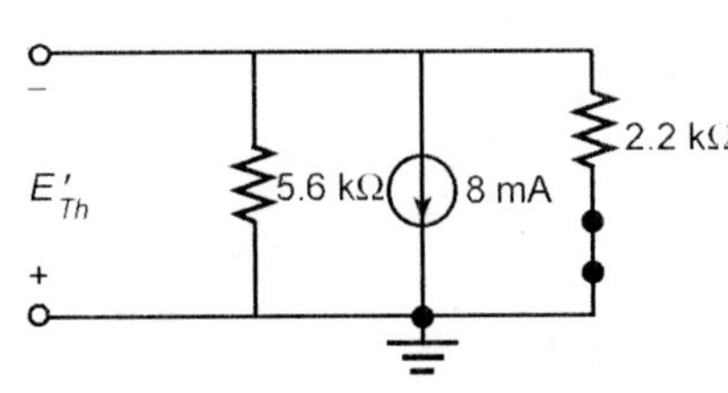

$E'_{Th} = IR_T$
$= 8\text{ mA}(5.6\text{ k}\Omega \parallel 2.2\text{ k}\Omega)$
$= 8\text{ mA}(1.579\text{ k}\Omega)$
$= 12.64\text{ V}$

E:

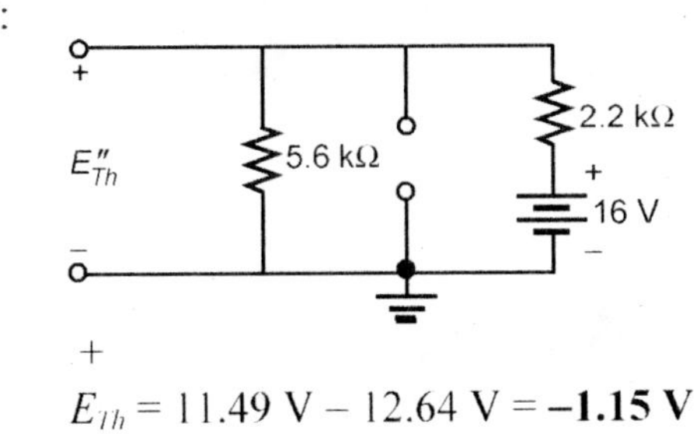

$$E''_{Th} = \frac{5.6\text{ k}\Omega(16\text{ V})}{5.6\text{ k}\Omega + 2.2\text{ k}\Omega}$$
$= 11.49\text{ V}$

+
$E_{Th} = 11.49\text{ V} - 12.64\text{ V} = \mathbf{-1.15\text{ V}}$
–

12. a. R_{Th}:

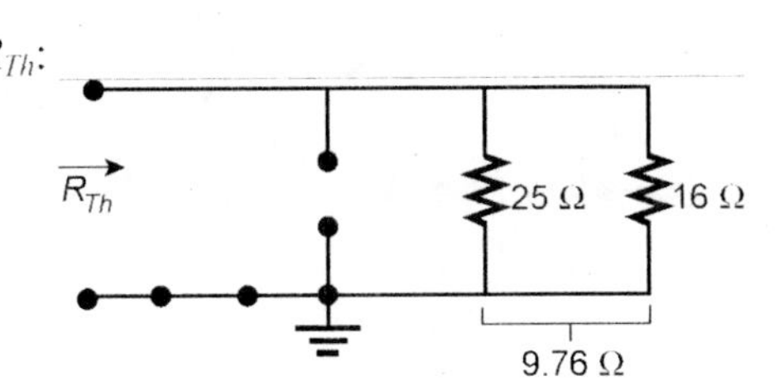

$R_{Th} = 25\ \Omega \parallel 16\ \Omega = \mathbf{9.76\ \Omega}$

E_{Th}: Superposition:

E:

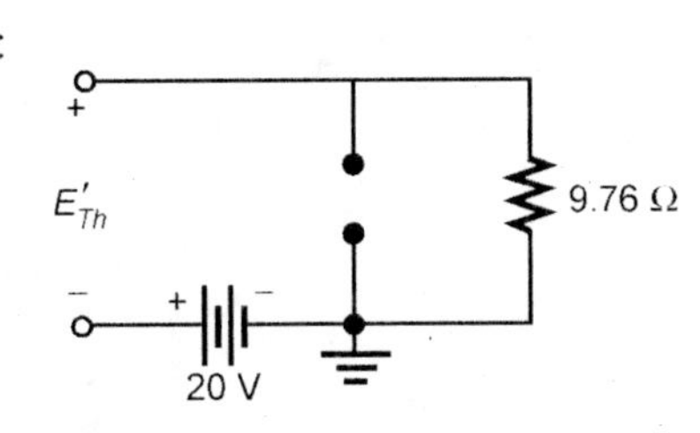

$E'_{Th} = -20\text{ V}$

I:

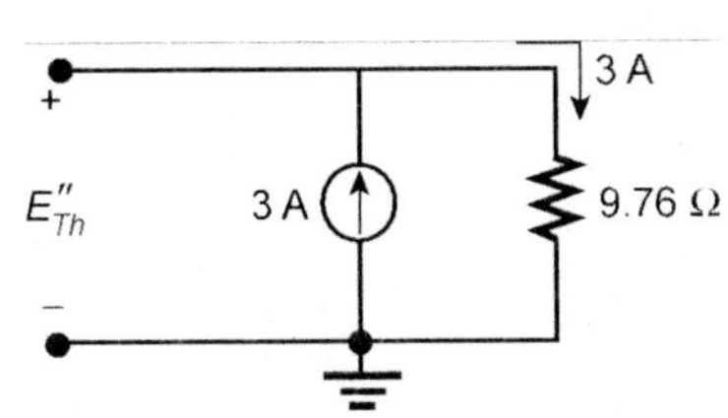

$E''_{Th} = (3\text{ A})(9.76\ \Omega) = 29.28\text{ V}$

$E_{Th} = E''_{Th} - E'_{Th} = 29.28\text{ V} - 20\text{ V} = \mathbf{9.28\text{ V}}$

b. R_{Th}:

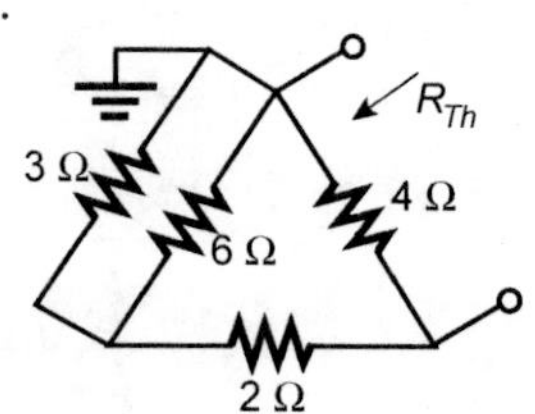

$$R_{Th} = 4\ \Omega \parallel (2\ \Omega + 6\ \Omega \parallel 3\ \Omega) = \mathbf{2\ \Omega}$$

E_{Th}:

$$I_T = \frac{72\ \text{V}}{6\ \Omega + 3\ \Omega \parallel (2\ \Omega + 4\ \Omega)} = 9\ \text{A}$$

$$I_2 = \frac{3\ \Omega(I_T)}{3\ \Omega + 6\ \Omega} = \frac{3\ \Omega(9\ \text{A})}{9\ \Omega} = 3\ \text{A}$$

$$E_{Th} = V_6 + V_2 = (I_T)(6\ \Omega) + I_2(2\ \Omega)$$
$$= (9\ \text{A})(6\ \Omega) + (3\ \text{A})(2\ \Omega) = \mathbf{60\ V}$$

13. (I): R_{Th}:

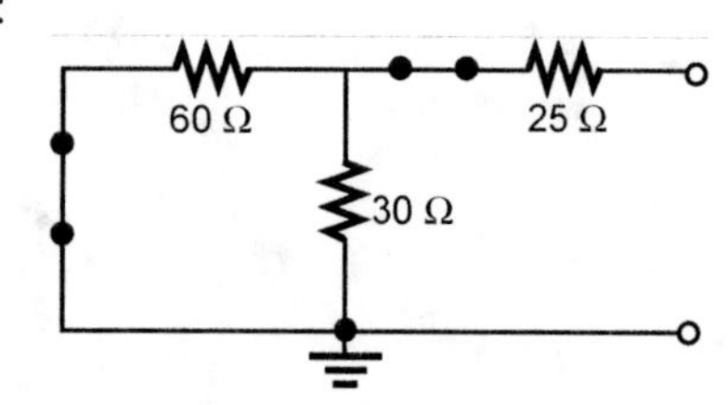

$$\leftarrow R_{Th} = 25\ \Omega + 60\ \Omega \parallel 30\ \Omega = \mathbf{45\ \Omega}$$

E_{Th}:

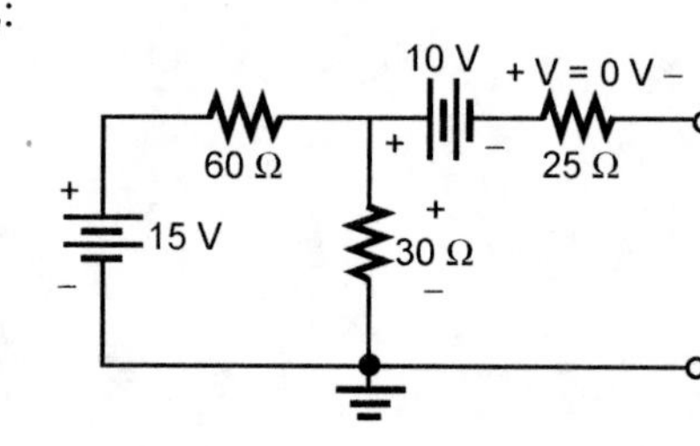

$$E_{Th} = V_{30\Omega} - 10\ \text{V} - 0$$
$$= \frac{30\ \Omega(15\ \text{V})}{30\ \Omega + 60\ \Omega} - 10\ \text{V}$$
$$= 5\ \text{V} - 10\ \text{V} = \mathbf{-5\ V}$$

(II): R_{Th}:

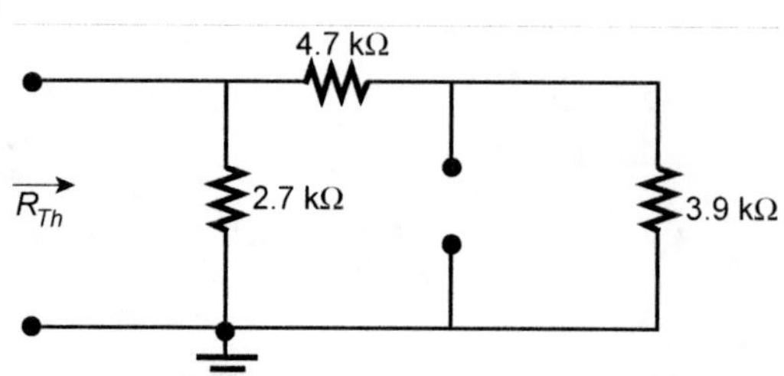

$$R_{Th} = 2.7\ \text{k}\Omega \parallel (4.7\ \text{k}\Omega + 3.9\ \text{k}\Omega) = 2.7\ \text{k}\Omega \parallel 8.6\ \text{k}\Omega = \mathbf{2.06\ k\Omega}$$

E_{Th}:

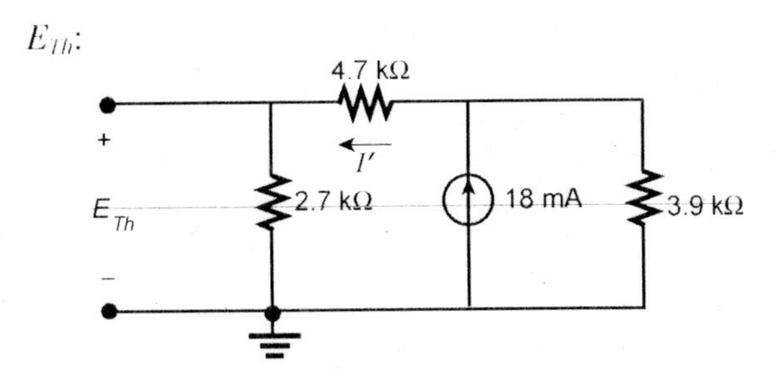

$$I' = \frac{3.9\text{ k}\Omega(18\text{ mA})}{3.9\text{ k}\Omega + 7.4\text{ k}\Omega} = 6.21\text{ mA}$$

$E_{Th} = I'(2.7\text{ k}\Omega) = (6.21\text{ mA})(2.7\text{ k}\Omega) = \mathbf{16.77\text{ V}}$

14. (I): R_{Th}:

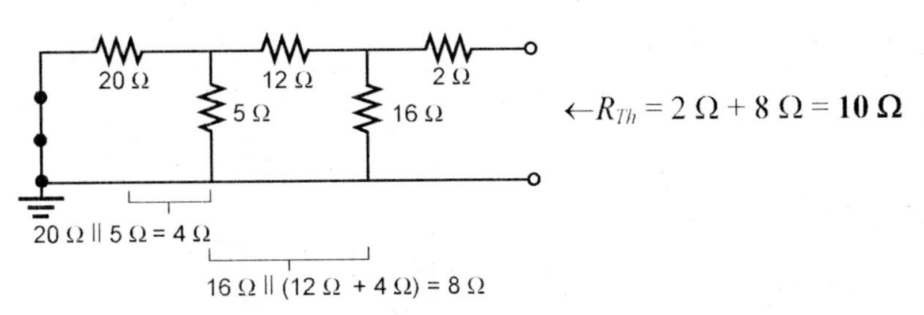

$\leftarrow R_{Th} = 2\ \Omega + 8\ \Omega = \mathbf{10\ \Omega}$

E_{Th}:

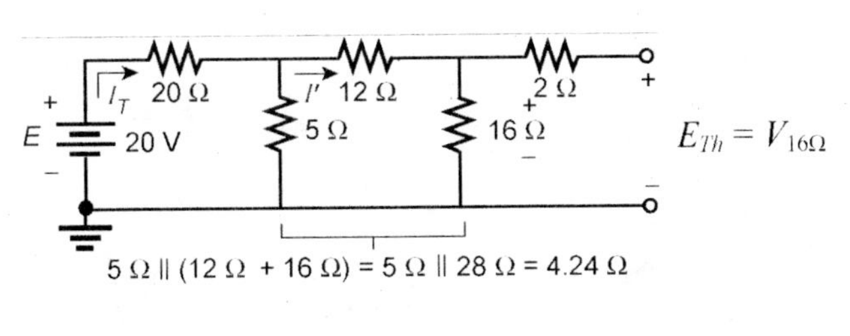

$E_{Th} = V_{16\Omega}$

$$I_T = \frac{20\text{ V}}{20\ \Omega + 4.24\ \Omega} = 825.08\text{ mA}$$

$$I' = \frac{5\ \Omega(I_T)}{5\ \Omega + 28\ \Omega} = \frac{5\ \Omega(825.08\text{ mA})}{33\ \Omega} = 125.01\text{ mA}$$

$E_{Th} = V_{16\Omega} = (I')(16\ \Omega) = (125.01\text{ mA})(16\ \Omega) = \mathbf{2\text{ V}}$

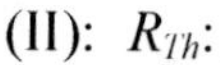

(II): R_{Th}:

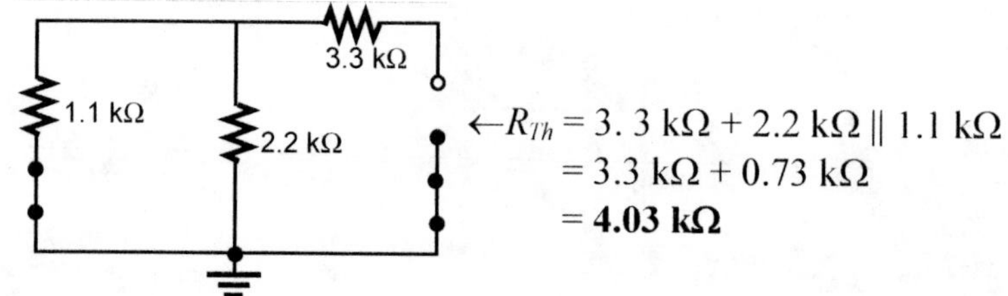

$\leftarrow R_{Th} = 3.\ 3\text{ k}\Omega + 2.2\text{ k}\Omega \parallel 1.1\text{ k}\Omega$
$= 3.3\text{ k}\Omega + 0.73\text{ k}\Omega$
$= \mathbf{4.03\text{ k}\Omega}$

E_{Th}: Superposition:

E_1:

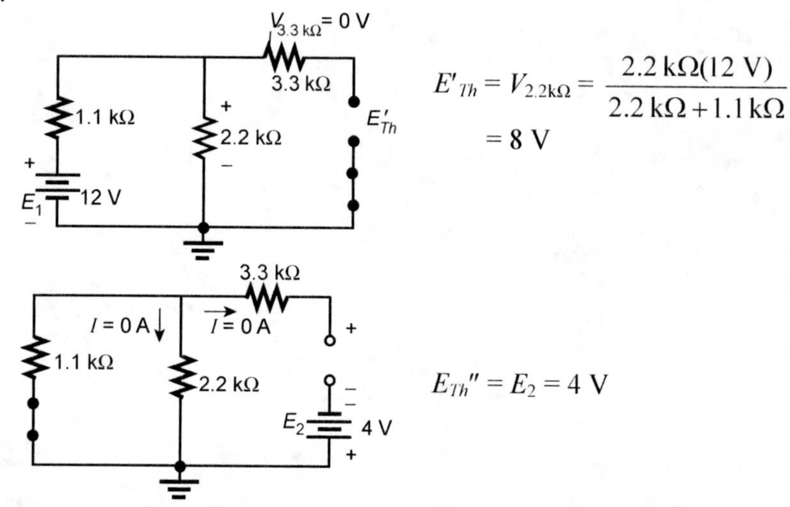

$$E'_{Th} = V_{2.2\text{k}\Omega} = \frac{2.2\text{ k}\Omega(12\text{ V})}{2.2\text{ k}\Omega + 1.1\text{ k}\Omega}$$
$$= 8\text{ V}$$

$$E_{Th}'' = E_2 = 4\text{ V}$$

$E_{Th} = E'_{Th} + E''_{Th} = 8\text{ V} + 4\text{ V} = \mathbf{12\text{ V}}$

15. R_{Th}:

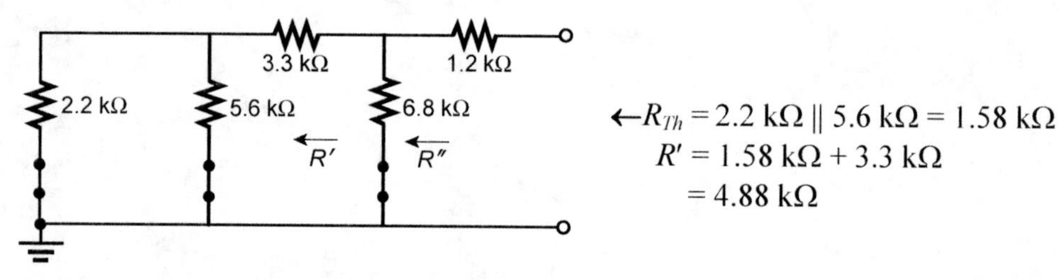

$\leftarrow R_{Th} = 2.2\text{ k}\Omega \parallel 5.6\text{ k}\Omega = 1.58\text{ k}\Omega$
$R' = 1.58\text{ k}\Omega + 3.3\text{ k}\Omega$
$= 4.88\text{ k}\Omega$

$R'' = 4.88\text{ k}\Omega \parallel 6.8\text{ k}\Omega = 2.84\text{ k}\Omega$
$R_{Th} = 1.2\text{ k}\Omega + R'' = 1.2\text{ k}\Omega + 2.84\text{ k}\Omega = \mathbf{4.04\text{ k}\Omega}$

E_{Th}: Source conversions:

$$I_1 = \frac{22\text{ V}}{2.2\text{ k}\Omega} = 10\text{ mA},\ R_s = 2.2\text{ k}\Omega$$

$$I_2 = \frac{12\text{ V}}{5.6\text{ k}\Omega} = 2.14\text{ mA},\ R_s = 5.6\text{ k}\Omega$$

Combining parallel current sources: $I'_T = I_1 - I_2 = 10\text{ mA} - 2.14\text{ mA} = 7.86\text{ mA}$

$$2.2\text{ k}\Omega \parallel 5.6\text{ k}\Omega = 1.58\text{ k}\Omega$$

Source conversion:

$E = (7.86\text{ mA})(1.58\text{ k}\Omega) = 12.42\text{ V}$

$R' = R_s + 3.3\text{ k}\Omega = 1.58\text{ k}\Omega + 3.3\text{ k}\Omega = 4.88\text{ k}\Omega$

$$I = \frac{12.42\text{ V} - 6\text{ V}}{4.88\text{ k}\Omega + 6.8\text{ k}\Omega} = \frac{6.42\text{ V}}{11.68\text{ k}\Omega} = 549.66\ \mu\text{A}$$

$$V_{6.8\text{k}\Omega} = I(6.8\text{ k}\Omega) = (549.66\ \mu\text{A})(6.8\text{ k}\Omega) = 3.74\text{ V}$$

$$E_{Th} = 6\text{ V} + V_{6.8\text{k}\Omega} = 6\text{ V} + 3.74\text{ V} = \mathbf{9.74\text{ V}}$$

16. a. R_{Th}:

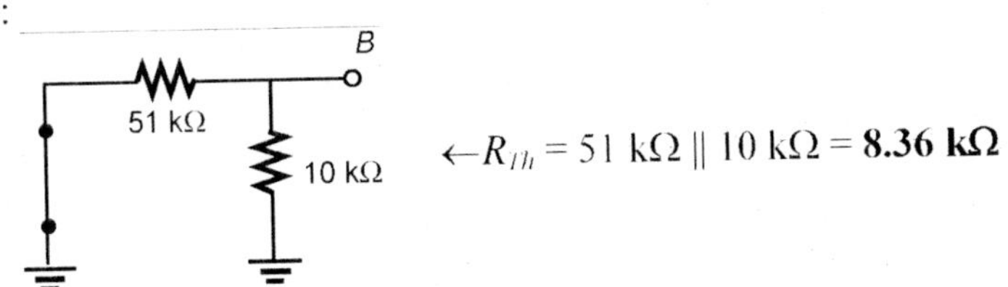

$\leftarrow R_{Th} = 51\text{ k}\Omega \parallel 10\text{ k}\Omega = \mathbf{8.36\text{ k}\Omega}$

E_{Th}:

$$E_{Th} = \frac{10\text{ k}\Omega(20\text{ V})}{10\text{ k}\Omega + 51\text{ k}\Omega} = 3.28\text{ V}$$

b. $I_E R_E + V_{CE} + I_C R_C = 20\text{ V}$

but $I_C \cong I_E$

and $I_E(R_C + R_E) + V_{CE} = 20\text{ V}$

$$\text{or } I_E = \frac{20\text{ V} - V_{CE}}{R_C + R_E} = \frac{20\text{ V} - 8\text{ V}}{2.2\text{ k}\Omega + 0.5\text{ k}\Omega} = \frac{12\text{ V}}{2.7\text{ k}\Omega} = \mathbf{4.44\text{ mA}}$$

c.

$$E_{Th} - I_B R_{Th} - V_{BE} - V_E = 0$$

$$\text{and } I_B = \frac{E_{Th} - V_{BE} - V_E}{R_{Th}} = \frac{3.28\text{ V} - 0.7\text{ V} - (4.44\text{ mA})(0.5\text{ k}\Omega)}{8.36\text{ k}\Omega}$$

$$= \frac{2.58\text{ V} - 2.22\text{ V}}{8.36\text{ k}\Omega} = \frac{0.36\text{ V}}{8.36\text{ k}\Omega} = \mathbf{43.06\ \mu A}$$

d. $V_C = 20\text{ V} - I_C R_C = 20\text{ V} - (4.44\text{ mA})(2.2\text{ k}\Omega)$
$= 20\text{ V} - 9.77\text{ V}$
$= \mathbf{10.23\text{ V}}$

17. a. $E_{Th} = \mathbf{20\text{ V}}$

$$I = 1.6\text{ mA} = \frac{E_{Th}}{R_{Th}} = \frac{20\text{ V}}{R_{Th}}, R_{Th} = \frac{20\text{ V}}{1.6\text{ mA}} = \mathbf{12.5\text{ k}\Omega}$$

b. $E_{Th} = \mathbf{60\text{ mV}}$, $R_{Th} = \mathbf{2.72\text{ k}\Omega}$

c. $E_{Th} = \mathbf{16\text{ V}}$, $R_{Th} = \mathbf{2.2\text{ k}\Omega}$

18. R_N:

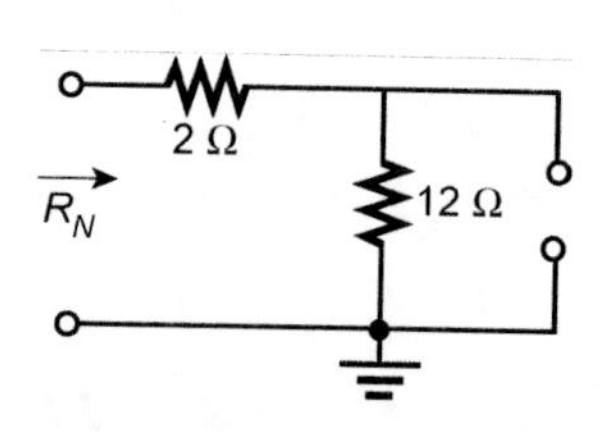

$R_N = 2\ \Omega + 12\ \Omega = \mathbf{14\ \Omega}$

I_N:

$$I_N = \frac{12\ \Omega(3\text{ A})}{12\ \Omega + 2\ \Omega} = 2.57\text{ A}$$

19. a. R_N:

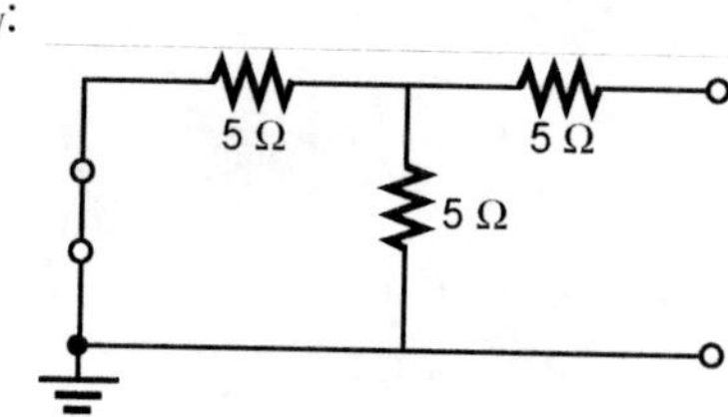

$$\leftarrow R_N = 5\ \Omega + \frac{5\ \Omega}{2} = \mathbf{7.5\ \Omega}$$

I_N:

$$I_T = \frac{20\text{ V}}{5\ \Omega + \frac{5\ \Omega}{2}} = 2.67\text{ A}$$

$$I_N = \frac{I_T}{2} = \mathbf{1.34\text{ A}}$$

b. $E_{Th} = I_N R_N = (1.34\text{ A})(7.5\ \Omega) = 10.05\text{ V} \cong \mathbf{10\text{ V}}$, $R_{Th} = R_N = \mathbf{7.5\ \Omega}$

20. R_N:

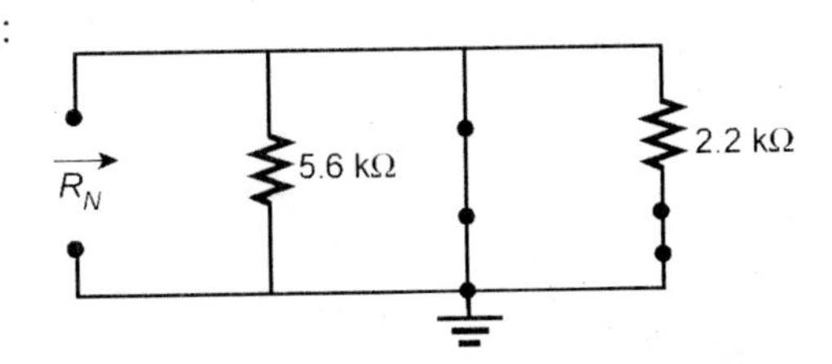

$R_N = 5.6\text{ k}\Omega \parallel 2.2\text{ k}\Omega = \mathbf{1.58\text{ k}\Omega}$

I_N:

I:

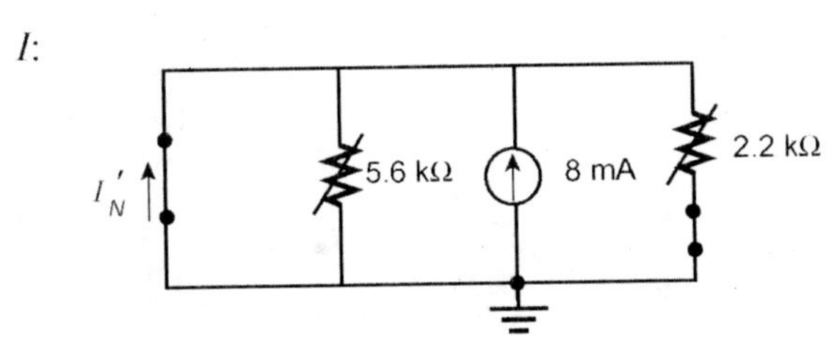

$I'_N = 8\text{ mA}$

E:

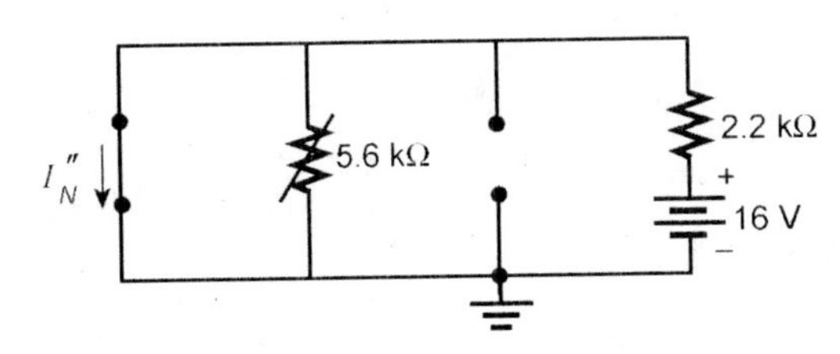

$$I''_N = \frac{16\text{ V}}{2.2\text{ k}\Omega} = 7.27\text{ mA}$$

$I_N\uparrow = 8\text{ mA} - 7.27\text{ mA} = \mathbf{0.73\text{ mA}}$

21. (I): (a)

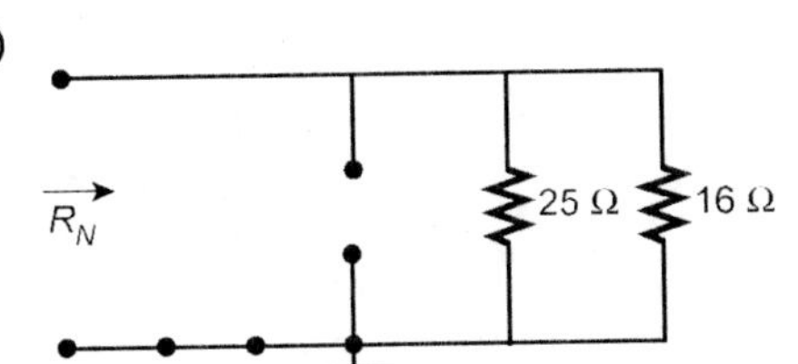

$R_N = 25\ \Omega \parallel 16\ \Omega = \mathbf{9.76\ \Omega}$

I_N: Superposition:

I:

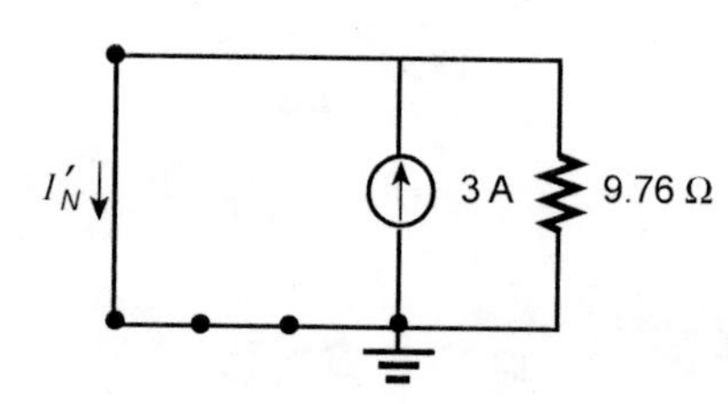

$I'_N = 3$ A

E:

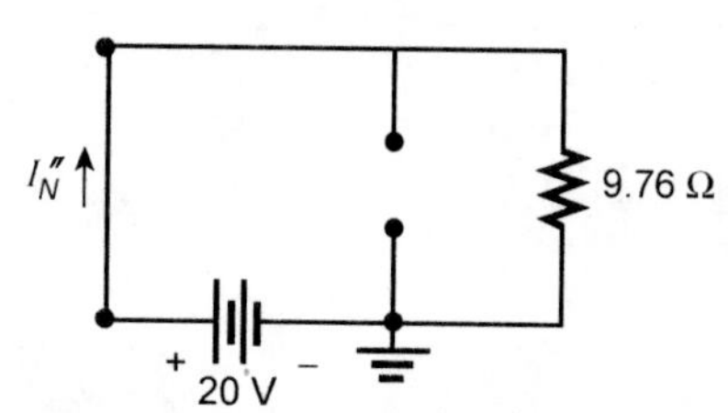

$$I''_N = \frac{20\text{ V}}{9.76\,\Omega} = 2.05\text{ A}$$

$I_N = I'_N - I''_N = 3\text{ A} - 2.05\text{ A} = \mathbf{0.95\text{ A}}$ (direction of I'_N)

b. $E_{Th} = I_N R_N = (0.95\text{ A})(9.76\,\Omega) = \mathbf{9.27\text{ V}} \cong 9.28\text{ V}$, $R_{Th} = R_N = \mathbf{9.76\,\Omega}$

(II): a. R_N:

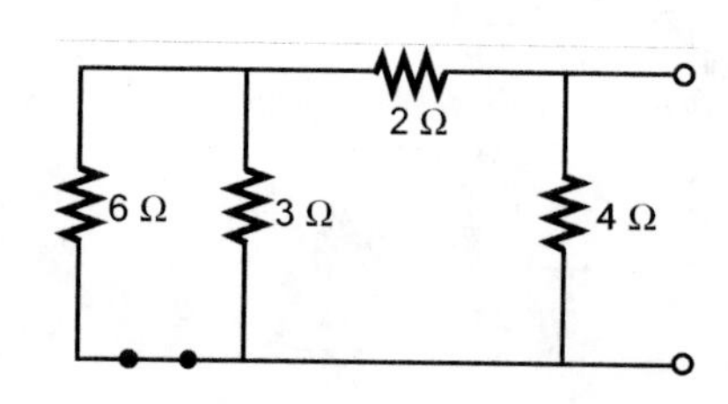

$\leftarrow R_N = 4\,\Omega \parallel (2\,\Omega + 2\,\Omega) = \mathbf{2\,\Omega}$

I_N:

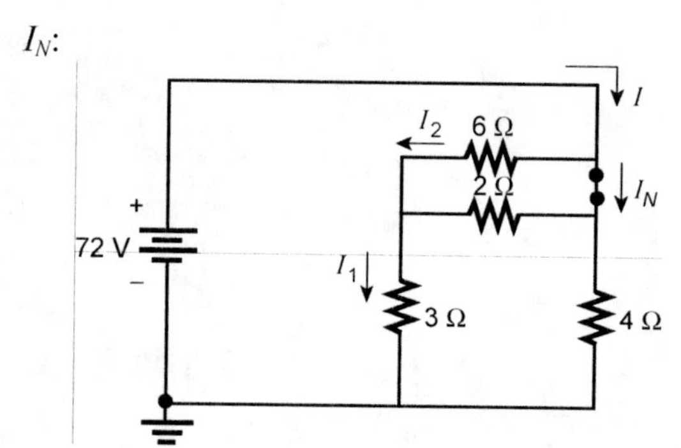

$$I = \frac{72\text{ V}}{4\,\Omega \parallel (3\,\Omega + 6\,\Omega \parallel 2\,\Omega)}$$

$$= \frac{72\text{ V}}{2.118\,\Omega} \cong 34\text{ A}$$

$$I_1 = \frac{4\,\Omega(I)}{4\,\Omega + 4.5\,\Omega} = 16\text{ A}$$

$$I_2 = \frac{2\,\Omega(I_1)}{2\,\Omega + 6\,\Omega} = 4\text{ A}$$

$I_N = I - I_2 = 34\text{ A} - 4\text{ A} = \mathbf{30\text{ A}}$

b. $E_{Th} = I_N R_N = (30\text{ A})(2\,\Omega) = \mathbf{60\text{ V}}$, $R_{Th} = R_N = \mathbf{2\,\Omega}$

22. (I) R_N:

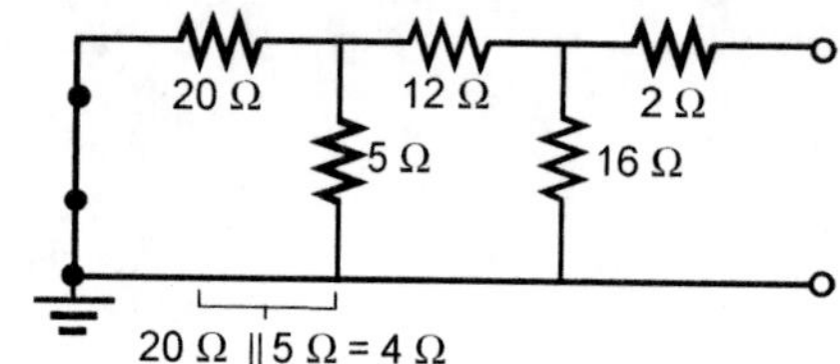

$\leftarrow R_N = 2\,\Omega + 16\,\Omega \parallel (12\,\Omega + 4\,\Omega)$
$= 2\,\Omega + 16\,\Omega \parallel 16\,\Omega$
$= 2\,\Omega + 8\,\Omega = \mathbf{10\,\Omega}$

I_N:

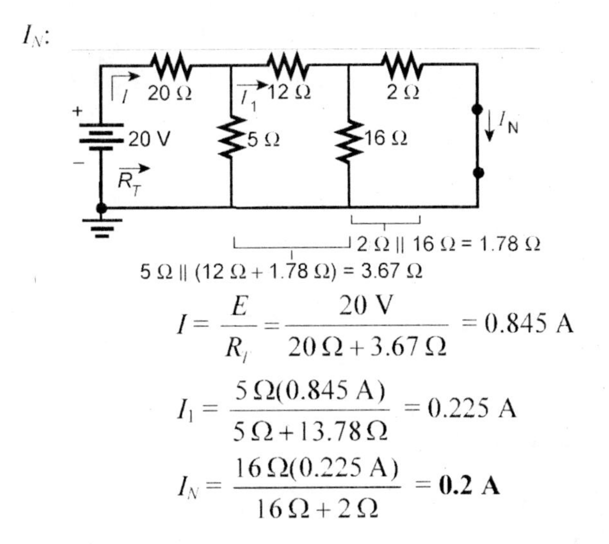

$$I = \frac{E}{R_I} = \frac{20\text{ V}}{20\,\Omega + 3.67\,\Omega} = 0.845\text{ A}$$

$$I_1 = \frac{5\,\Omega(0.845\text{ A})}{5\,\Omega + 13.78\,\Omega} = 0.225\text{ A}$$

$$I_N = \frac{16\,\Omega(0.225\text{ A})}{16\,\Omega + 2\,\Omega} = \mathbf{0.2\text{ A}}$$

(II): R_N:

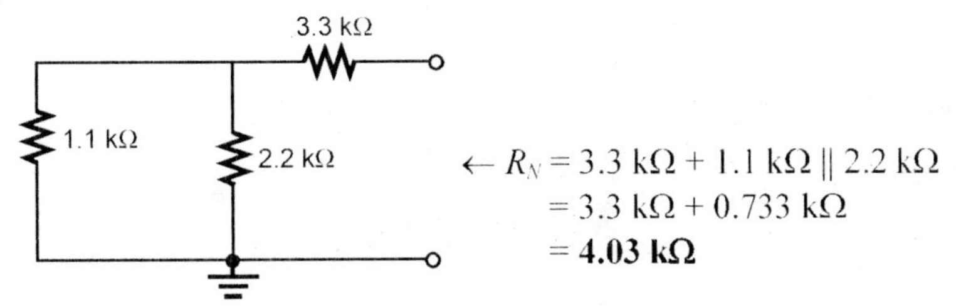

$\leftarrow R_N = 3.3\text{ k}\Omega + 1.1\text{ k}\Omega \parallel 2.2\text{ k}\Omega$
$= 3.3\text{ k}\Omega + 0.733\text{ k}\Omega$
$= \mathbf{4.03\text{ k}\Omega}$

I_N: Superposition:

E_1:

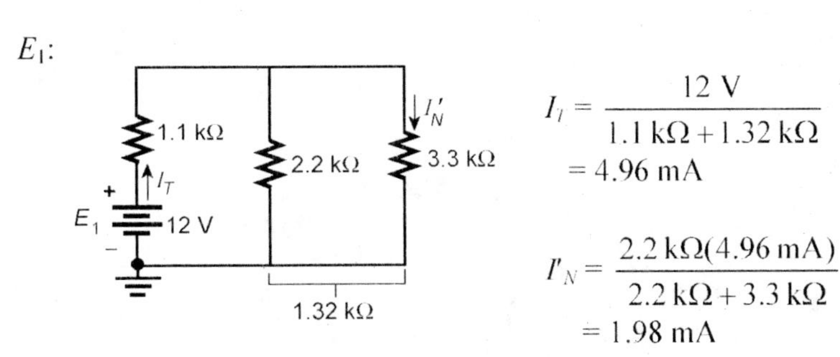

$$I_I = \frac{12\text{ V}}{1.1\text{ k}\Omega + 1.32\text{ k}\Omega} = 4.96\text{ mA}$$

$$I'_N = \frac{2.2\text{ k}\Omega(4.96\text{ mA})}{2.2\text{ k}\Omega + 3.3\text{ k}\Omega} = 1.98\text{ mA}$$

E_2:

1.1 kΩ   2.2 kΩ   3.3 kΩ I''_N 4 V   0.73 kΩ

$$I''_N = \frac{4\text{ V}}{3.3\text{ k}\Omega + 0.73\text{ k}\Omega} = 0.99\text{ mA}$$

$I_N = I'_N + I''_N = 1.98\text{ mA} + 0.99\text{ mA} = \mathbf{2.97\text{ mA}}$

23. a. R_N:

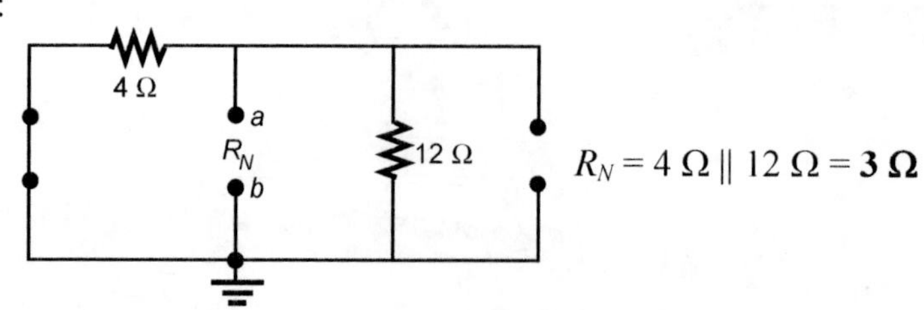

$R_N = 4\ \Omega \parallel 12\ \Omega = \mathbf{3\ \Omega}$

$E = 12$ V:

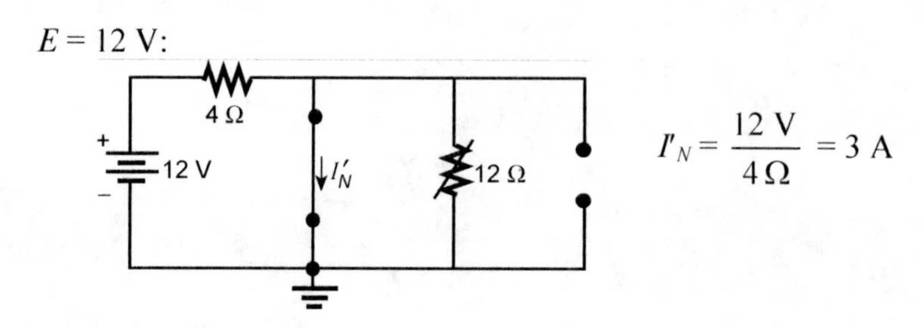

$$I'_N = \frac{12\text{ V}}{4\ \Omega} = 3\text{ A}$$

$I = 2$ A:

$I''_N = 2$ A

$I_N = I'_N + I''_N = 3\text{ A} + 2\text{ A} = \mathbf{5\ A}$

b. R_N:

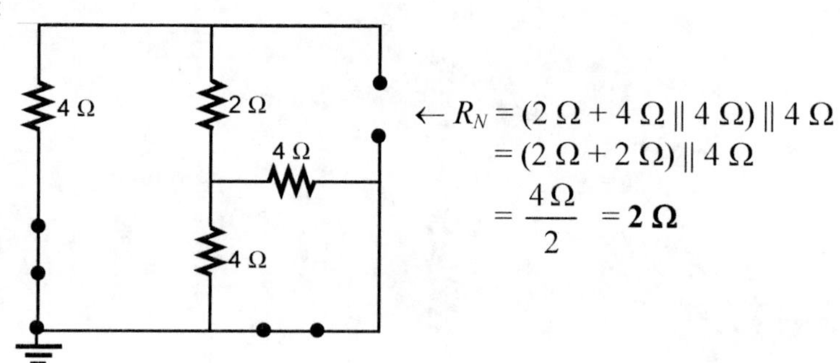

$$\leftarrow R_N = (2\ \Omega + 4\ \Omega \parallel 4\ \Omega) \parallel 4\ \Omega$$
$$= (2\ \Omega + 2\ \Omega) \parallel 4\ \Omega$$
$$= \frac{4\ \Omega}{2} = \mathbf{2\ \Omega}$$

I_N:

$$I = \frac{V_{4\Omega}}{4\ \Omega} = \frac{6\text{ V} - 2\text{ V}}{4\ \Omega} = \frac{4\text{ V}}{4\ \Omega}$$
$$= 1\text{ A}$$
$$V = \frac{(4\ \Omega \parallel 2\ \Omega)(2\text{ V})}{(4\ \Omega \parallel 2\ \Omega) + 4\ \Omega}$$
$$= 0.5\text{ V}$$
$$I_2 = \frac{V}{R} = \frac{0.5\text{ V}}{2\ \Omega} = 0.25\text{ A}$$

$I_N = I - I_2 = 1\text{ A} - 0.25\text{ A} = \mathbf{0.75\text{ A}}$

24. (I): (a) $R = R_{Th} = \mathbf{9.76\ \Omega}$ (from problem 12)

(II): (a) $R = R_{Th} = \mathbf{2\ \Omega}$ (from problem 12)

(I): (b) $P_{\max} = E_{Th}^2/4R_{Th} = (9.28\text{ V})^2/4(9.76\ \Omega) = \mathbf{2.21\text{ W}}$

(II): (b) $P_{\max} = E_{Th}^2/4R_{Th} = (60\text{ V})^2/4(2\ \Omega) = \mathbf{450\text{ W}}$

25. (I): (a) $R = R_{Th} = \mathbf{10\ \Omega}$ (from problem 14)

(II): (a) $R = R_{Th} = \mathbf{4.03\text{ k}\Omega}$ (from problem 14)

(I): (b) $P_{\max} = E_{Th}^2/4R_{Th} = (2\text{ V})^2/4(10\ \Omega) = \mathbf{100\text{ mW}}$

(II): (b) $P_{\max} = E_{Th}^2/4R_{Th} = (12\text{ V})^2/4(4.03\text{ k}\Omega) = \mathbf{8.93\text{ mW}}$

26. $R_L = R_{Th} = \mathbf{4.04\text{ k}\Omega}$ (from problem 15)
$E_{Th} = \mathbf{9.74\text{ V}}$ (from problem 15)
$P_{\max} = E_{Th}^2/4R_{Th} = (9.74\text{ V})^2/4(4.04\text{ k}\Omega) = \mathbf{5.87\text{ mW}}$

27. a.

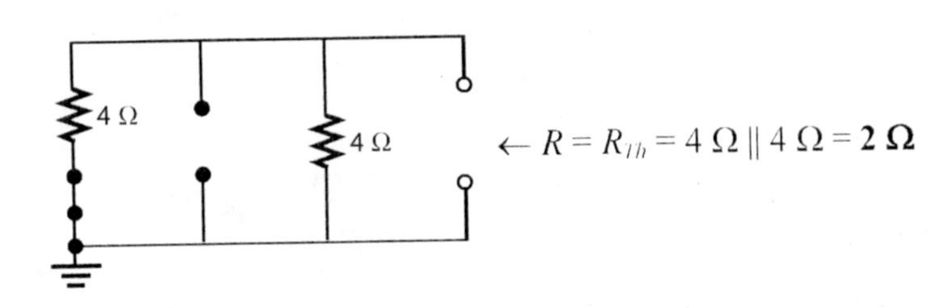

$\leftarrow R = R_{Th} = 4\ \Omega \parallel 4\ \Omega = \mathbf{2\ \Omega}$

b. E_{Th}:

E:

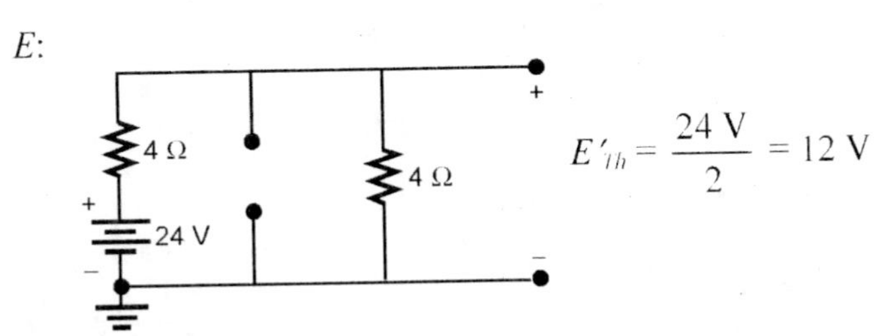

$$E'_{Th} = \frac{24\text{ V}}{2} = 12\text{ V}$$

I:

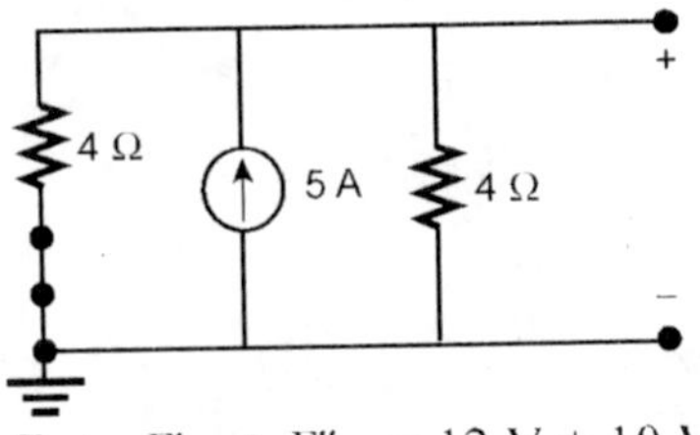

$E''_{Th} = IR_T = (5\text{ A})(4\ \Omega \parallel 4\ \Omega)$
$= (5\text{ A})(2\ \Omega) = 10\text{ V}$

$E_{Th} = E'_{Th} + E''_{Th} = 12\text{ V} + 10\text{ V} = \mathbf{22\text{ V}}$

$$P_{\max} = \frac{E_{Th}^2}{4R_{Th}} = \frac{(22\text{ V})^2}{4(2\ \Omega)} = \mathbf{60.5\text{ W}}$$

c.

$$P = I^2R = \left(\frac{E_{Th}}{R_{Th} + R}\right)^2 R$$

$R = \frac{1}{4}(2\,\Omega) = 0.5\,\Omega$, P = **38.72 W**

$R = \frac{1}{2}(2\,\Omega) = 1\,\Omega$, P = **53.78 W**

$R = \frac{3}{4}(2\,\Omega) = 1.5\,\Omega$, P = **59.27 W**

R = **2 Ω**, P = **60.5 W**

$R = \frac{5}{4}(2\,\Omega) = 2.5\,\Omega$, P = **59.75 W**

$R = \frac{3}{2}(2\,\Omega) = 3\,\Omega$, P = **58 W**

$R = \frac{7}{4}(2\,\Omega) = 3.5\,\Omega$, P = **56 W**

$R = 2(2\,\Omega) = 4\,\Omega$, P = **53.78 W**

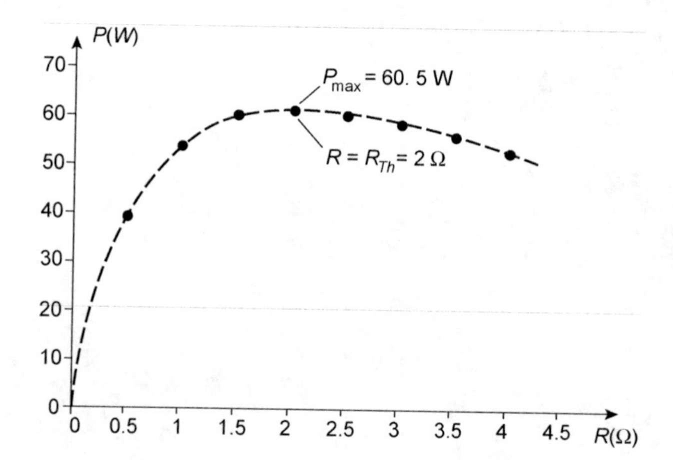

28. $$P_{max} = \left(\frac{E_{Th}}{R_{Th} + R_4}\right)^2 R_4$$

with R_1 = **0 Ω** $\quad$ E_{Th} is a maximum and R_{Th} a minimum

$\therefore P_{max}$ a **maximum**

29. a.

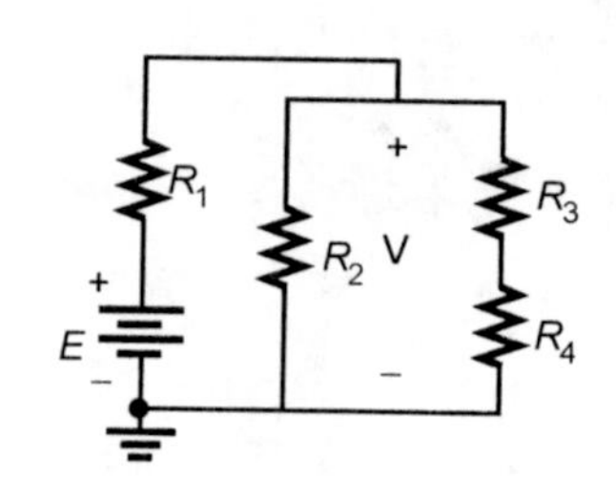

V, and therefore V_4, will be its largest value when R_2 is as large as possible. Therefore choose R_2 = open-circuit (∞ Ω).

Then $P_4 = \frac{V_4^2}{R_4}$ will be a maximum.

b. No, examine each individually.

30.

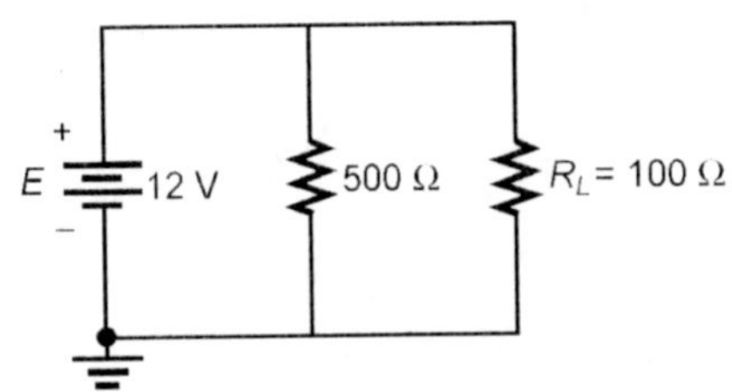

Since R_l fixed, maximum power to R_L when V_{R_l} a maximum as defined by $P_l = \dfrac{V_{R_l}^2}{R_L}$

$$\therefore\ R = \mathbf{500\ \Omega} \text{ and } P_{\max} = \frac{(12\ \text{V})^2}{100\ \Omega} = \mathbf{1.44\ W}$$

31.

$I_T\!\uparrow = 4\ \text{A} + 7\ \text{A} = 11\ \text{A}$

$R_l = 10\ \Omega \parallel 6\ \Omega \parallel 3\ \Omega = 1.67\ \Omega$

$V_L = I_l R_l = (11\ \text{A})(1.67\ \Omega) = \mathbf{18.37\ V}$

$$I_L = \frac{V_L}{R_L} = \frac{18.37\ \text{V}}{3\ \Omega} = \mathbf{6.12\ A}$$

32. $$E_{\text{eq}} = \frac{-5\ \text{V}/2.2\ \text{k}\Omega + 20\ \text{V}/8.2\ \text{k}\Omega}{1/2.2\ \text{k}\Omega + 1/8.2\ \text{k}\Omega} = 0.2879\ \text{V}$$

$$R_{\text{eq}} = \frac{1}{1/2.2\ \text{k}\Omega + 1/8.2\ \text{k}\Omega} = 1.7346\ \text{k}\Omega$$

$$I_L = \frac{E_{\text{eq}}}{R_{\text{eq}} + R_L} = \frac{0.2879\ \text{V}}{1.7346\ \text{k}\Omega + 5.6\ \text{k}\Omega} = \mathbf{39.3\ \mu A}$$

$V_L = I_L R_L = (39.3\ \mu\text{A})(5.6\ \text{k}\Omega) = \mathbf{220\ mV}$

33. $I_T\!\downarrow = 5\ \text{A} - 0.4\ \text{A} - 0.2\ \text{A} = 4.40\ \text{A}$

$R_T = 200\ \Omega \parallel 80\ \Omega \parallel 50\ \Omega \parallel 50\ \Omega = 17.39\ \Omega$

$V_L = I_T R_T = (4.40\ \text{A})(17.39\ \Omega) = \mathbf{75.52\ V}$

$$I_L = \frac{V_L}{R_L} = \frac{76.52\ \text{V}}{200\ \Omega} = \mathbf{0.38\ A}$$

34. $$I_{\text{eq}} = \frac{(4\ \text{A})(4.7\ \Omega) + (1.6\ \text{A})(3.3\ \Omega)}{4.7\ \Omega + 3.3\ \Omega} = \frac{18.8\ \text{V} + 5.28\ \text{V}}{8\ \Omega} = 3.01\ \text{A}$$

$R_{\text{eq}} = 4.7\ \Omega + 3.3\ \Omega = 8\ \Omega$

$$I_L = \frac{R_{\text{eq}}(I_{\text{eq}})}{R_{\text{eq}} + R_L} = \frac{8\ \Omega(3.01\ \text{A})}{8\ \Omega + 2.7\ \Omega} = \mathbf{2.25\ A}$$

$V_L = I_l R_l = (2.25\ \text{A})(2.7\ \Omega) = \mathbf{6.08\ V}$

35. $$\overleftarrow{I}_{eq} = \frac{(4\text{ mA})(8.2\text{ k}\Omega) + (8\text{ mA})(4.7\text{ k}\Omega) - (10\text{ mA})(2\text{ k}\Omega)}{8.2\text{ k}\Omega + 4.7\text{ k}\Omega + 2\text{ k}\Omega}$$

$$= \frac{32.8\text{ V} + 37.6\text{ V} - 20\text{ V}}{14.9\text{ k}\Omega} = 3.38\text{ mA}$$

$$R_{eq} = 8.2\text{ k}\Omega + 4.7\text{ k}\Omega + 2\text{ k}\Omega = 14.9\text{ k}\Omega$$

$$I_L = \frac{R_{eq}I_{eq}}{R_{eq} + R_L} = \frac{(14.9\text{ k}\Omega)(3.38\text{ mA})}{14.9\text{ k}\Omega + 6.8\text{ k}\Omega} = \mathbf{2.32\text{ mA}}$$

$$V_L = I_L R_L = (2.32\text{ mA})(6.8\text{ k}\Omega) = \mathbf{15.78\text{ V}}$$

36. $15\text{ k}\Omega \parallel (8\text{ k}\Omega + 7\text{ k}\Omega) = 15\text{ k}\Omega \parallel 15\text{ k}\Omega = 7.5\text{ k}\Omega$

$$V_{ab} = \frac{7.5\text{ k}\Omega(60\text{ V})}{7.5\text{ k}\Omega + 2.5\text{ k}\Omega} = 45\text{ V}$$

$$I_{ab} = \frac{45\text{ V}}{15\text{ k}\Omega} = 3\text{ mA}$$

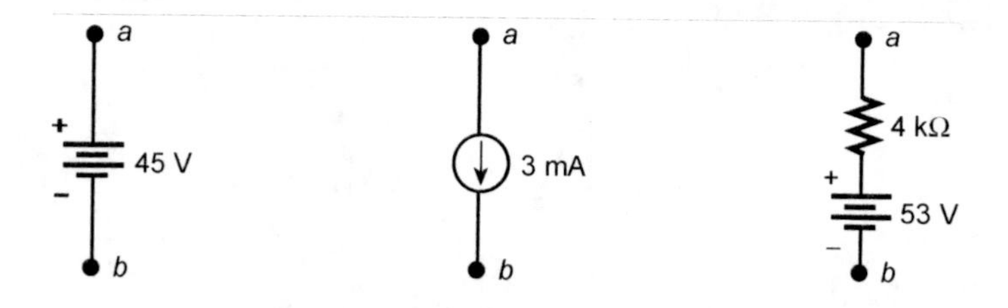

37.

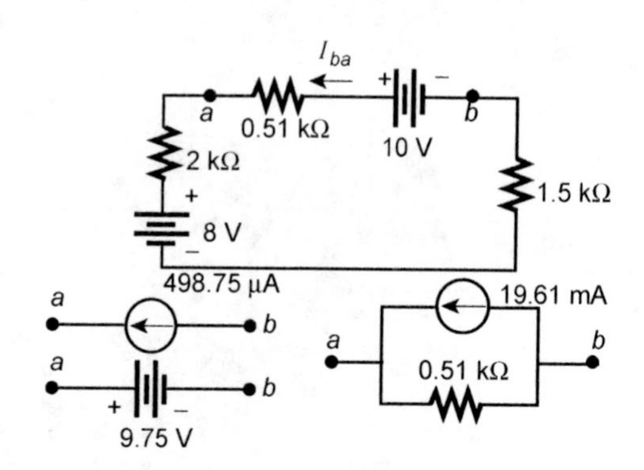

$$I_{ba} = \frac{10\text{ V} - 8\text{ V}}{2\text{ k}\Omega + 0.51\text{ k}\Omega + 1.5\text{ k}\Omega}$$

$$= \mathbf{498.75\ \mu A}$$

$$V_{0.51\text{k}\Omega} = (498.75\ \mu\text{A})(0.51\text{ k}\Omega) = 0.25\text{ V}$$

$$V_{\underset{+-}{ab}} = 10\text{ V} - 0.25\text{ V} = 9.75\text{ V}$$

38.

$V_{ab} = 0$ V (short)
$I_{ab} = 0$ A (open)

R_2 any resistive value

$\therefore R_2$ = short-circuit, open-circuit, any value

39. a. $I_s = \dfrac{24\text{ V}}{8\text{ k}\Omega + \dfrac{24\text{ k}\Omega}{3}} = 1.5\text{ mA},\ I = \dfrac{I_s}{3} = \mathbf{0.5\text{ mA}}$

b.

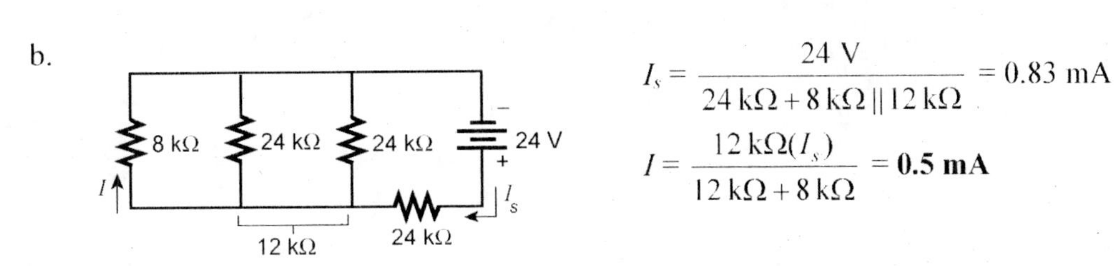

$$I_s = \frac{24\text{ V}}{24\text{ k}\Omega + 8\text{ k}\Omega \,\|\, 12\text{ k}\Omega} = 0.83\text{ mA}$$

$$I = \frac{12\text{ k}\Omega(I_s)}{12\text{ k}\Omega + 8\text{ k}\Omega} = \mathbf{0.5\text{ mA}}$$

c. yes

40. (a)

$$I_T = \frac{10\text{ V}}{4\text{ k}\Omega \,\|\, 8\text{ k}\Omega + 4\text{ k}\Omega \,\|\, 4\text{ k}\Omega} = \frac{10\text{ V}}{2.67\text{ k}\Omega + 2\text{ k}\Omega} = \frac{10\text{ V}}{4.67\text{ k}\Omega} = 2.14\text{ mA}$$

$$I_1 = \frac{8\,\Omega(I_T)}{8\,\Omega + 4\,\Omega} = 1.43\text{ mA},\ I_2 = I_T/2 = 1.07\text{ mA}$$

$$I = I_1 - I_2 = 1.43\text{ mA} - 1.07\text{ mA} = \mathbf{0.36\text{ mA}}$$

(b)

$$V_1 = \frac{(8\text{ k}\Omega \,\|\, 4\text{ k}\Omega)(10\text{ V})}{8\text{ k}\Omega \,\|\, 4\text{ k}\Omega + 4\text{ k}\Omega \,\|\, 4\text{ k}\Omega} = 5.72\text{ V}$$

$$I_1 = \frac{V_1}{8\text{ k}\Omega} = 0.71\text{ mA}$$

$$V_2 = E - V_1 = 10\text{ V} - 5.72\text{ V} = 4.28\text{ V}$$

$$I_2 = \frac{V_2}{4\text{ k}\Omega} = 1.07\text{ mA}$$

$$I = I_2 - I_1 = 1.07\text{ mA} - 0.71\text{ mA} = \mathbf{0.36\text{ mA}}$$

41. a. $I_{R_2} = \dfrac{R_1(I)}{R_1 + R_2 + R_3} = \dfrac{3\,\Omega(6\text{ A})}{3\,\Omega + 2\,\Omega + 4\,\Omega} = 2\text{ A}$

$V = I_{R_2}R_2 = (2\text{ A})(2\,\Omega) = \mathbf{4\text{ V}}$

b. $I_{R_1} = \dfrac{R_2(I)}{R_1 + R_2 + R_3} = \dfrac{2\,\Omega(6\text{ A})}{3\,\Omega + 2\,\Omega + 4\,\Omega} = 1.33\text{ A}$

$V = I_{R_1}R_1 = (1.33\text{ A})(3\,\Omega) = \mathbf{4\text{ V}}$

Chapter 10

1. (a) $\mathscr{E} = k\dfrac{Q_1}{r^2} = \dfrac{(9\times10^9)(4\ \mu C)}{(2\ m)^2}$ = **9 × 10³ N/C**

   (b) $\mathscr{E} = k\dfrac{Q_1}{r^2} = \dfrac{(9\times10^9)(4\ \mu C)}{(1\ mm)^2}$ = **36 × 10⁹ N/C**

   $\mathscr{E}(1\ mm) : \mathscr{E}(2\ m) = 4 \times 10^6 : 1$

2. $\mathscr{E} = \dfrac{kQ}{r^2} \Rightarrow r = \sqrt{\dfrac{kQ}{\mathscr{E}}} = \sqrt{\dfrac{(9\times10^9)(2\ \mu C)}{72\ N/C}}$ = **15.81 m**

3. $C = \dfrac{Q}{V} = \dfrac{1200\ \mu C}{10\ V}$ = **120 μF**

4. $Q = CV = (0.15\ \mu F)(45\ V)$ = **6.75 μC**

5. $\mathscr{E} = \dfrac{V}{d} = \dfrac{100\ mV}{2\ mm}$ = **50 V/m**

6. $d = 10\ \text{mils}\left[\dfrac{10^{-3}\ \text{in.}}{1\ \text{mil}}\right]\left[\dfrac{1\ m}{39.37\ \text{in.}}\right] = 0.254\ mm$

   $\mathscr{E} = \dfrac{V}{d} = \dfrac{100\ mV}{0.254\ mm}$ = **393.70 V/m**

7. $V = \dfrac{Q}{C} = \dfrac{160\ \mu C}{4\ \mu F} = 40\ V$

   $\mathscr{E} = \dfrac{V}{d} = \dfrac{40\ V}{5\ mm}$ = **8 × 10³ V/m**

8. $C = 8.85 \times 10^{-12}\varepsilon_r\dfrac{A}{d} = 8.85 \times 10^{-12}(1)\dfrac{(0.1\ m^2)}{2\ mm}$ = **442.50 pF**

9. $C = 8.85 \times 10^{-12}\ \varepsilon_r\dfrac{A}{d} = 8.85 \times 10^{-12}(2.5)\dfrac{(0.1\ m^2)}{2\ mm}$ = **1.11 nF**

10. $C = 8.85 \times 10^{-12}\varepsilon_r\dfrac{A}{d} \Rightarrow d = \dfrac{8.85\times10^{-12}(4)(0.15\ m^2)}{2\ \mu F}$ = **2.66 μm**

11. $C = \varepsilon_r C_o \Rightarrow \varepsilon_r = \dfrac{C}{C_o} = \dfrac{6\ nF}{1200\ pF}$ = **5 (mica)**

12. a. $C = 8.85 \times 10^{-12}(1)\dfrac{(0.08\text{ m}^2)}{0.2\text{ mm}} = \mathbf{3.54\ nF}$

b. $\mathscr{E} = \dfrac{V}{d} = \dfrac{200\text{ V}}{0.2\text{ mm}} = \mathbf{10^6\ V/m}$

c. $Q = CV = (3.54\text{ nF})(200\text{ V}) = \mathbf{0.71\ \mu C}$

13. a. $\mathscr{E} = \dfrac{V}{d} = \dfrac{200\text{ V}}{0.2\text{ mm}} = \mathbf{10^6\ V/m}$

b. $Q = \varepsilon\mathscr{E}A = \varepsilon_r\varepsilon_o\mathscr{E}A = (7)(8.85\times10^{-12})(10^6\text{ V/m})(0.08\text{ m}^2) = \mathbf{4.96\ \mu C}$

c. $C = \dfrac{Q}{V} = \dfrac{4.96\ \mu\text{C}}{200\text{ V}} = \mathbf{24.80\ nF}$

14. a. $C = \dfrac{1}{2}(5\ \mu\text{F}) = \mathbf{2.5\ \mu F}$

b. $C = 2(5\ \mu\text{F}) = \mathbf{10\ \mu F}$

c. $C = 20(5\ \mu\text{F}) = \mathbf{100\ \mu F}$

d. $C = \dfrac{(4)\left(\dfrac{1}{3}\right)}{\left(\dfrac{1}{4}\right)}(5\ \mu\text{F}) = \mathbf{26.67\ \mu F}$

15. $d = \dfrac{8.85\times10^{-12}\varepsilon_r A}{C} = \dfrac{(8.85\times10^{-12})(5)(0.02\text{ m}^2)}{0.006\ \mu\text{F}} = 0.1475\text{ mm} = 147.5\ \mu\text{m}$

$d = 0.1475\ \cancel{\text{mm}}\left[\dfrac{10^{-3}\ \cancel{\text{m}}}{1\ \cancel{\text{mm}}}\right]\left[\dfrac{39.37\ \cancel{\text{in.}}}{1\ \cancel{\text{m}}}\right]\left[\dfrac{1000\text{ mils}}{1\ \cancel{\text{in.}}}\right] = 5.807\text{ mils}$

$5.807\ \cancel{\text{mils}}\left[\dfrac{5000\text{ V}}{\cancel{\text{mil}}}\right] = \mathbf{29.04\ kV}$

16. mica: $\dfrac{1200\text{ V}}{\dfrac{5000\text{ V}}{\cancel{\text{mil}}}} = 1200\text{ V}\left[\dfrac{\cancel{\text{mil}}}{5000\text{ V}}\right] = 0.24\text{ mils}$

$0.24\text{ mils}\left[\dfrac{\cancel{1}}{1000\text{ mils}}\right]\left[\dfrac{1\text{ m}}{39.37\ \cancel{\text{in.}}}\right] = \mathbf{6.10\ \mu m}$

17. $\dfrac{200}{1\times10^6}(22\ \mu\text{F})/°\text{C} = 4400\text{ pF}/°\text{C}$

$\dfrac{4400\text{ pF}}{°\text{C}}[\Delta T] = \dfrac{4400\text{ pF}}{°\text{C}}[80°\text{C}] = \mathbf{0.35\ \mu F}$

18. J = ±5%, Size ⇒ 40 pF ± 2 pF, **38 pF → 42 pF**

19. M = ±20%, Size ⇒ 220 μF ± 44 μF, **176 μF → 264 μF**

20. K = ±10%, Size ⇒ 33,000 pF ± 3300 pF, **29,700 pF → 36,300 pF**

21. a. $\tau = RC = (10^5\ \Omega)(5.1\ \mu\text{F}) = \mathbf{0.51\ s}$

b. $\upsilon_C = E(1 - e^{-t/\tau}) = \mathbf{20\ V(1 - e^{-t/0.51\ s})}$

c. $1\tau = 0.632(20\text{ V}) = \mathbf{12.64\ V}$, $3\tau = 0.95(20\text{ V}) = \mathbf{19\ V}$
$5\tau = 0.993(20\text{ V}) = \mathbf{19.87\ V}$

d. $i_C = \dfrac{20\text{ V}}{100\text{ k}\Omega} e^{-t/\tau} = \mathbf{0.2\ mA}\boldsymbol{e^{-t/0.51\ s}}$
$\upsilon_R = Ee^{-t/\tau} = \mathbf{20\ V}\boldsymbol{e^{-t/0.51\ s}}$

e.

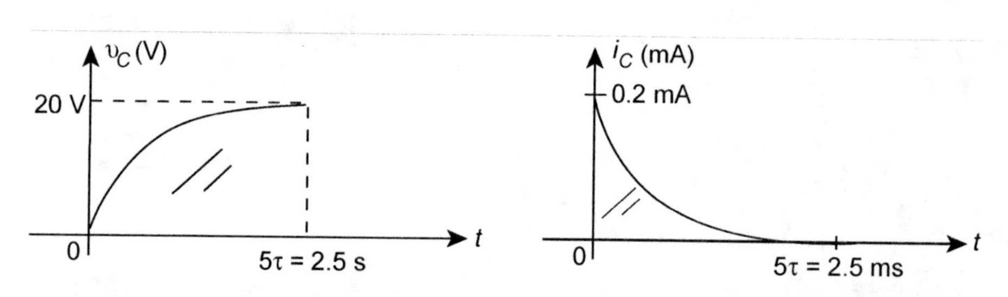

22. a. $\tau = RC = (10^6\ \Omega)(5.1\ \mu\text{F}) = \mathbf{5.1\ s}$

b. $\upsilon_C = E(1 - e^{-t/\tau}) = \mathbf{20\ V(1 - e^{-t/5.1s})}$

c. $1\tau = \mathbf{12.64\ V}$, $3\tau = \mathbf{19\ V}$, $5\tau = \mathbf{19.87\ V}$

d. $i_C = \dfrac{20\text{ V}}{1\text{ M}\Omega} e^{-t/\tau} = \mathbf{20\ \mu A}\ \boldsymbol{e^{-t/5.1s}}$
$\upsilon_R = Ee^{-t/\tau} = \mathbf{20V}\ \boldsymbol{e^{-t/5.1s}}$

e. Same as problem 21 with $5\tau = 25$ s and $I_m = 20\ \mu$A

23. a. $\tau = RC = (2.2\text{ k}\Omega + 3.3\text{ k}\Omega)1\ \mu\text{F} = (5.5\text{ k}\Omega)(1\ \mu\text{F}) = \mathbf{5.5\ ms}$

b. $\upsilon_C = E(1 - e^{-t/\tau}) = \mathbf{100\ V(1 - e^{-t/5.5\ ms})}$

c. $1\tau = \mathbf{63.21\ V}$, $3\tau = \mathbf{95.02\ V}$, $5\tau = \mathbf{99.33\ V}$

d. $i_C = \dfrac{E}{R_T} e^{-t/\tau} = \dfrac{100\text{ V}}{5.5\text{ k}\Omega} e^{-t/\tau} = \mathbf{18.18\ mA}\boldsymbol{e^{-t/5.5\ ms}}$
$V_{R_2} = \dfrac{3.3\text{ k}\Omega(100\text{ V})}{3.3\text{ k}\Omega + 2.2\text{ k}\Omega} = 60\text{ V}$
$\upsilon_R = \upsilon_{R_2} = \mathbf{60\ V}\boldsymbol{e^{-t/5.5\ ms}}$

e.

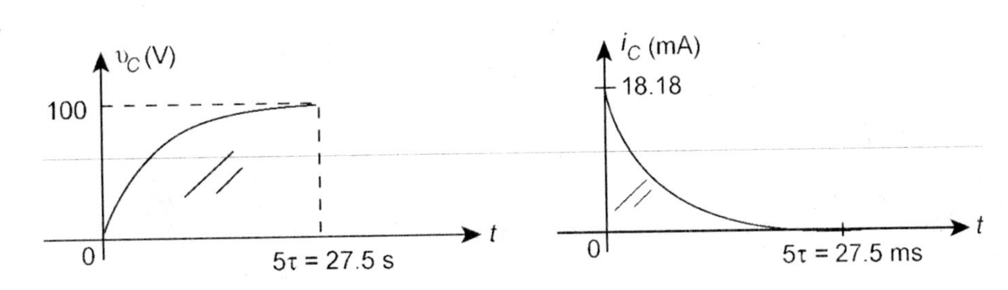

24. a. $\tau = RC = (56\text{ k}\Omega)(0.1\ \mu\text{F}) = \mathbf{5.6\ ms}$

b. $\upsilon_C = E(1 - e^{-t/\tau}) = 25\text{ V}(1 - e^{-t/5.6\text{ms}})$

c. $i_C = \dfrac{E}{R}e^{-t/\tau} = \dfrac{25\text{ V}}{56\text{ k}\Omega}e^{-t/\tau} = \mathbf{0.45\ mA}e^{-t/5.6\text{ms}}$

d.

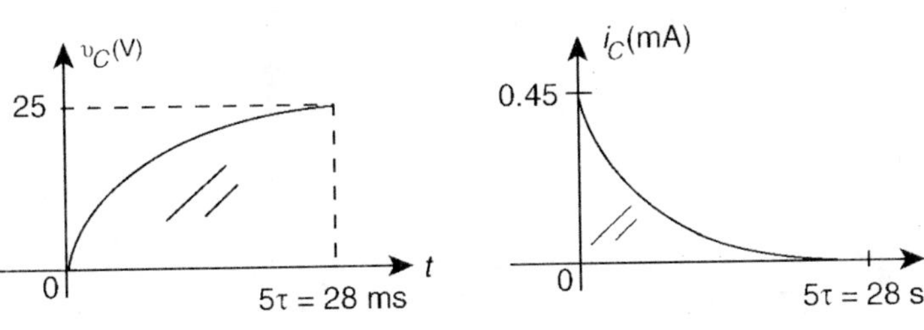

25. a. **5 ms**

b. $\upsilon_C = 60\text{ mV}(1 - e^{-2\text{ms}/5\text{ms}}) = 60\text{ mV}(1 - e^{-0.4}) = 60\text{ mV}(1 - 0.670)$
$= 60\text{ mV}(0.330) = \mathbf{19.8\ mV}$

c. $\upsilon_C = 60\text{ mV}(1 - e^{-100\text{ms}/5\text{ms}}) = 60\text{ mV}(1 - e^{-20}) = 60\text{ mV}(1 - 2.06 \times 10^{-9})$
$\cong 60\text{ mV}(1) = \mathbf{60\ mV}$

26. a. $\tau = 40\text{ ms},\ 5\tau = 5(40\text{ ms}) = \mathbf{200\ ms}$

b. $\tau = RC,\ R = \dfrac{\tau}{C} = \dfrac{40\text{ ms}}{10\ \mu\text{F}} = \mathbf{4\ k\Omega}$

c. $\upsilon_C(20\text{ ms}) = 12\text{ V}(1 - e^{-20\text{ ms}/40\text{ms}}) = 12\text{ V}(1 - e^{-0.5})$
$= 12\text{ V}(1 - 0.607) = 12\text{ V}(0.393) = \mathbf{4.72\ V}$

d. $\upsilon_C = 12\text{ V}(1 - e^{-10}) = 12\text{ V}(1 - 45 \times 10^{-6}) \cong \mathbf{12.0\ V}$

e. $Q = CV = (10\ \mu\text{F})(12\text{ V}) = \mathbf{120\ \mu C}$

f. $\tau = RC = (1000 \times 10^6\ \Omega)(10\ \mu\text{F}) = 10 \times 10^3\text{ s}$

$$5\tau = 50 \times 10^3\ \cancel{\text{s}}\left[\frac{1\ \cancel{\text{min}}}{60\ \cancel{\text{s}}}\right]\left[\frac{1\text{ h}}{60\ \cancel{\text{min}}}\right] = \mathbf{13.89\ h}$$

27. a. $\tau = RC = (2\text{ k}\Omega)(100\ \mu\text{F}) = \mathbf{200\ ms}$

b. $\upsilon_C = E(1 - e^{-t/\tau}) = \mathbf{8\ V(1 - e^{-t/200ms})}$

$i_C = \dfrac{E}{R}e^{-t/\tau} = \dfrac{8\text{ V}}{2\text{ k}\Omega}e^{-t/200\text{ms}} = \mathbf{4\ mA}e^{-t/200\text{ms}}$

c. $\upsilon_C(1\text{ s}) = 8\text{ V}(1 - e^{-1\text{s}/200\text{ms}}) = 8\text{ V}(1 - e^{-5})$
$= 8\text{ V}(1 - 6.738 \times 10^{-3}) = 8\text{ V}(0.9933) = \mathbf{7.95\ V}$
$i_C(1\text{ s}) = 4\text{ mA}e^{-5} = 4\text{ mA}(6.738 \times 10^{-3}) = \mathbf{26.95\ \mu A}$

d. $\upsilon_C = \mathbf{7.95\ V}\boldsymbol{e}^{-t/200\text{ms}}$

$i_C = \dfrac{7.95\text{ V}}{2\text{ k}\Omega}e^{-t/200\text{ms}} = \mathbf{3.98\ mA}\boldsymbol{e}^{-t/200\text{ms}}$

e.

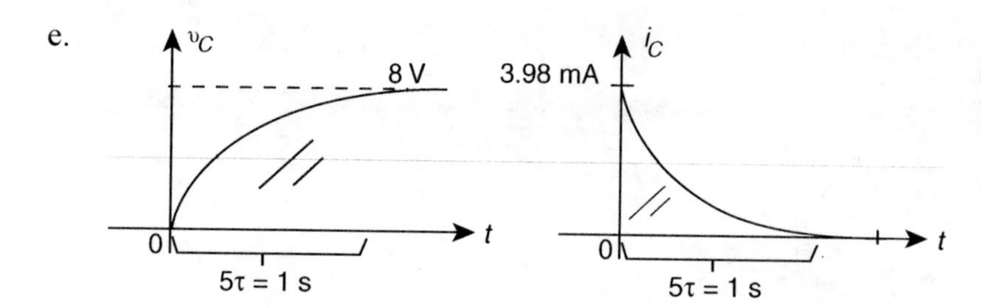

28. a. $\tau = RC = (3\text{ k}\Omega + 2\text{ k}\Omega)(2\ \mu\text{F}) = 10\text{ ms}$

$\upsilon_C = \mathbf{50\ V(1 - e^{-t/10ms})}$

$i_C = \dfrac{50\text{ V}}{5\text{ k}\Omega}e^{-t/10\text{ms}} = \mathbf{10\ mA^{-t/10ms}}$

$\upsilon_{R_1} = i_C \cdot R_1 = (10\text{ mA})(3\text{ k}\Omega)e^{-t/10\text{ms}} = \mathbf{30\ V}\boldsymbol{e}^{-t/10\text{ms}}$

b. 100ms: $e^{-10} = 45.4 \times 10^{-6}$

$\upsilon_C = 50\text{ V}(1 - 45.4 \times 10^{-6}) = \mathbf{50\ V}$

$i_C = 10\text{ mA}(45.4 \times 10^{-6}) = \mathbf{0.45\ \mu A}$

$\upsilon_{R_1} = 30\text{ V}(45.4 \times 10^{-6}) = \mathbf{1.36\ mV}$

c. 200 ms: $\tau' = R_2C = (2\text{ k}\Omega)(2\ \mu\text{F}) = 4\text{ ms}$

$\upsilon_C = \mathbf{50\ V}\boldsymbol{e}^{-t/4\text{ms}}$

$i_C = -\dfrac{50\text{ V}}{2\text{ k}\Omega}e^{-t/4\text{ms}} = \mathbf{-25\ mA}\boldsymbol{e}^{-t/4\text{ms}}$

$\upsilon_{R_2} = \upsilon_C = \mathbf{-50\ V}\boldsymbol{e}^{-t/4\text{ms}}$

d.

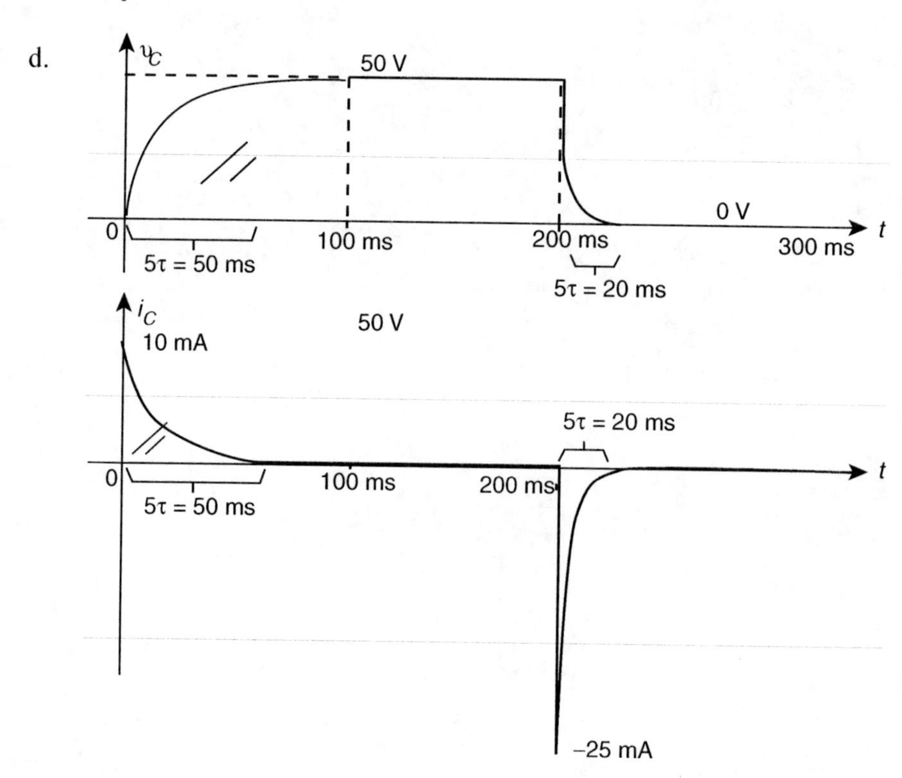

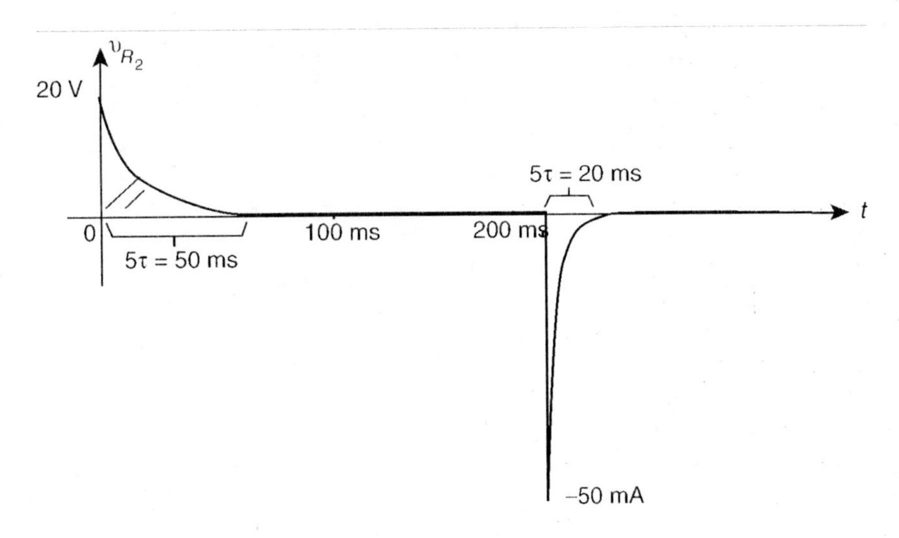

29. a. $\tau = RC = (5\text{ k}\Omega)(20\ \mu\text{F}) = 100\text{ ms}$

$\upsilon_C = \mathbf{50\ V(1 - e^{-t/100ms})}$

$i_C = \dfrac{50\text{ V}}{5\text{ k}\Omega}e^{-t/100\text{ms}} = \mathbf{10\ mAe^{-t/100ms}}$

$\upsilon_{R_1} = i_C \cdot R_1 = (10\text{ mA})(3\text{ k}\Omega)\,e^{-t/100\text{ms}} = \mathbf{30\ Ve^{-t/100ms}}$

b. 100 ms: $e^{-1} = 0.368$

$\upsilon_C = 50\text{ V}(1 - 0.368) = 50\text{ V}(0.632) = \mathbf{31.6\ V}$

$i_C = 10\text{ mA}(0.368) = \mathbf{3.68\ mA}$

$\upsilon_{R_1} = 30\text{ V}(0.368) = \mathbf{11.04\ V}$

c. 200 ms: $\tau' = R_2C = (2\text{ k}\Omega)(20\ \mu\text{F}) = 40\text{ ms}$

$\upsilon_C = \mathbf{31.6\ Ve^{-t/40ms}}$

$i_C = -\dfrac{31.6\text{ V}}{2\text{ k}\Omega}e^{-t/40\text{ms}} = \mathbf{-15.8\ mAe^{-t/40ms}}$

$\upsilon_{R_2} = -\upsilon_C = \mathbf{-31.6\ Ve^{-t/40ms}}$

d.

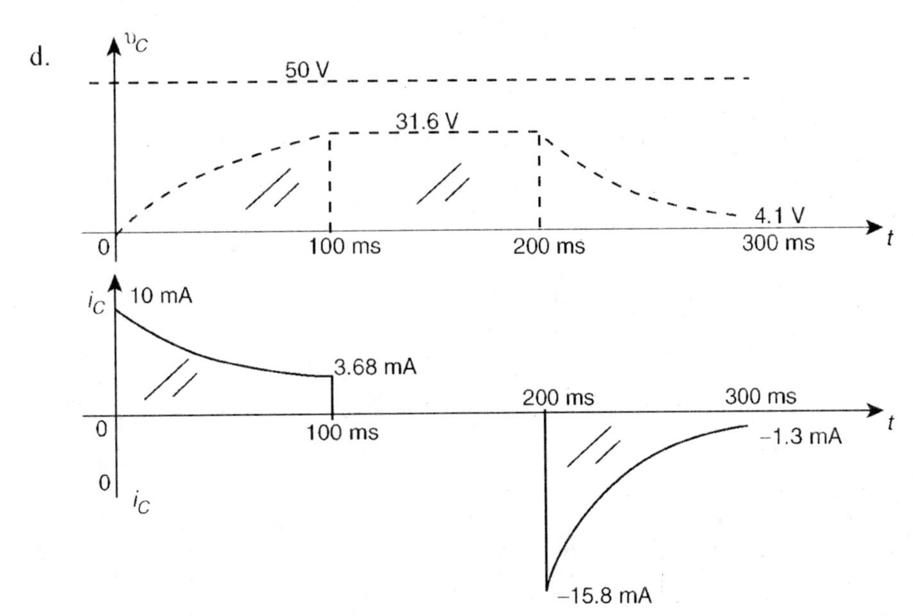

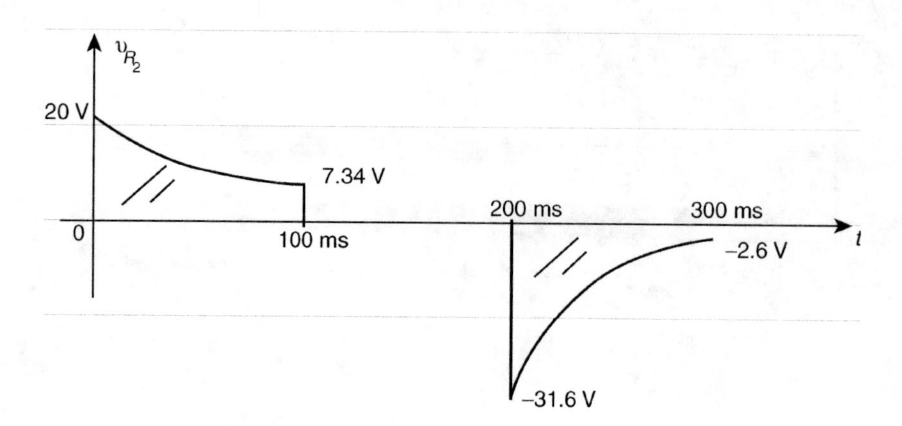

30. a. $\tau = R_1C = (10^5\ \Omega)(10\ \text{pF}) = 1\ \mu\text{s}$

$$\boldsymbol{\upsilon_C = 80\ \text{V}\left(1 - e^{-t/1\mu s}\right)}$$

$$i_C = \frac{80\ \text{V}}{100\ \text{k}\Omega}e^{-t/\tau} = \mathbf{0.8\ mA}e^{-t/1\mu s}$$

b. $\tau' = R'C = (490\ \text{k}\Omega)(10\ \text{pF}) = 4.9\ \mu\text{s}$

$$\upsilon_C = 80\ \text{V}e^{-t/\tau'} = \mathbf{80\ V}e^{-t/4.9\times10^{-6}}$$

$$i_C = \frac{80\ \text{V}}{490\ \text{k}\Omega}e^{-t/\tau'} = \mathbf{0.16\ mA}e^{-t/4.9\times10^{-6}}$$

c.

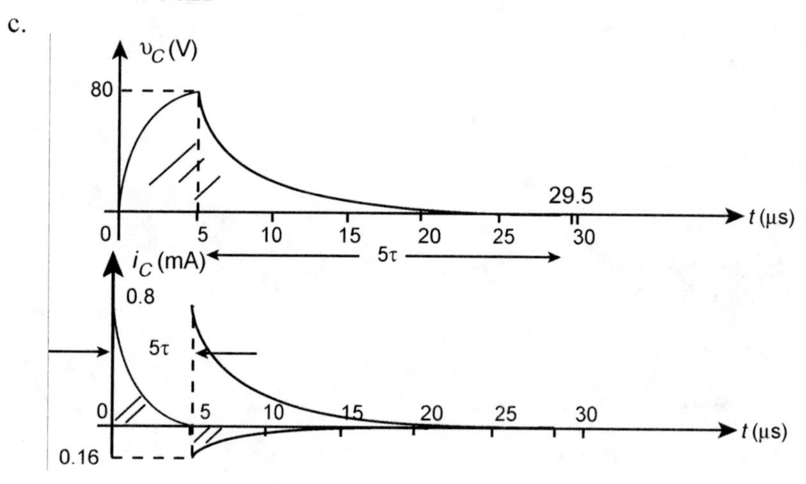

31. a. $\tau = RC = (2\ \text{m}\Omega)(1000\ \mu\text{F}) = 2\ \mu\text{s}$

$5\tau = \mathbf{10\ \mu s}$

b. $I_m = \dfrac{V}{R} = \dfrac{6\ \text{V}}{2\ \text{m}\Omega} = \mathbf{3\ kA}$

c. yes

32. a. $\upsilon_C = V_f + (V_i - V_f)e^{-t/\tau}$

$\tau = RC = (10\text{ k}\Omega)(2\ \mu\text{F}) = 20\text{ ms},\ V_f = 50\text{ V},\ V_i = -10\text{ V}$

$\upsilon_C = 50\text{ V} + (-10\text{ V} - (+50\text{ V}))e^{-t/20\text{ms}}$

$\upsilon_C = \mathbf{50\ V - 60\ V}e^{-t/20\text{ms}}$

b. Initially $V_R = E + \upsilon_C = 50\text{ V} + 10\text{ V} = 60\text{ V}$

$$i_C = \frac{V_R}{R}e^{-t/\tau} = \frac{60\text{ V}}{10\text{ k}\Omega}e^{-t/20\text{ms}} = \mathbf{6\ mA}\ e^{-t/20\text{ms}}$$

c.

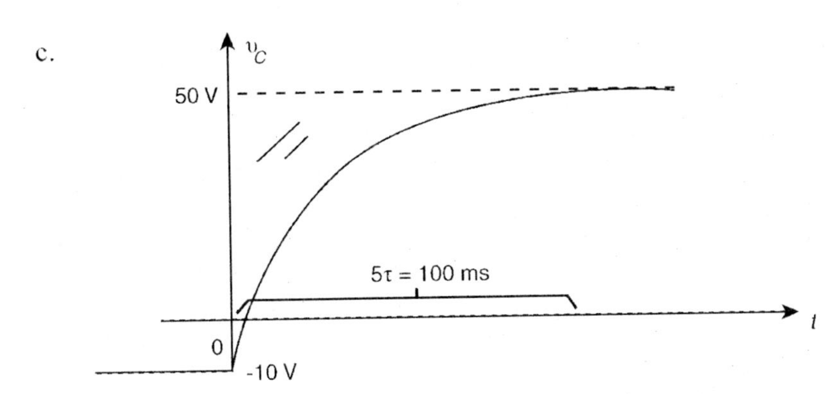

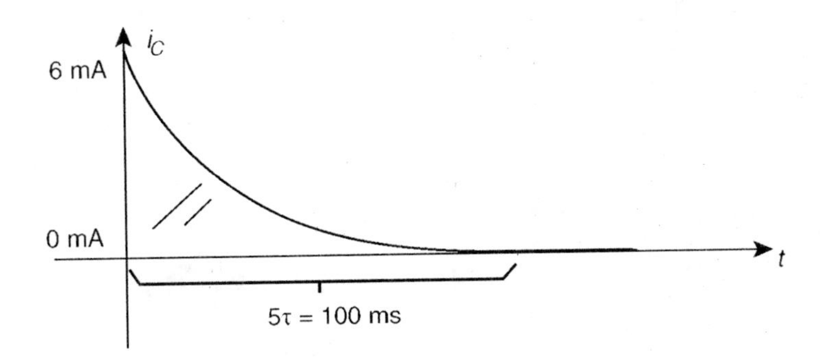

33. $\tau = RC = (2.2\text{ k}\Omega)(2000\ \mu\text{F}) = 4.4\text{ s}$

$\upsilon_C = V_C e^{-t/\tau} = \mathbf{40\ V}e^{-t/4.4\text{ s}}$

$$I_C = \frac{V_C}{R}e^{-t/\tau} = \frac{40\text{ V}}{2.2\text{ k}\Omega}e^{-t/4.4\text{ s}} = \mathbf{18.18\ mA}e^{-t/4.4\text{ s}}$$

$\upsilon_R = \upsilon_C = \mathbf{40\ V}e^{-t/4.4\text{s}}$

34. $\upsilon_C = V_f + (V_i - V_f)e^{-t/\tau}$

$\tau = RC = (860\ \Omega)(4000\text{ pF}) = 3.44\ \mu\text{s},\ V_f = -30\text{ V},\ V_i = 20\text{ V}$

$\upsilon_C = -30\text{ V} + (20\text{ V} - (-30\text{ V}))e^{-t/3.44\mu\text{s}}$

$\upsilon_C = \mathbf{-30\ V + 50\ V}e^{-t/3.44\mu\text{s}}$

$$I_m = \frac{20\text{ V} + 30\text{ V}}{860\ \Omega} = 58.14\text{ mA}$$

$i_C = \mathbf{-58.14\ mA}e^{-t/3.44\mu\text{s}}$

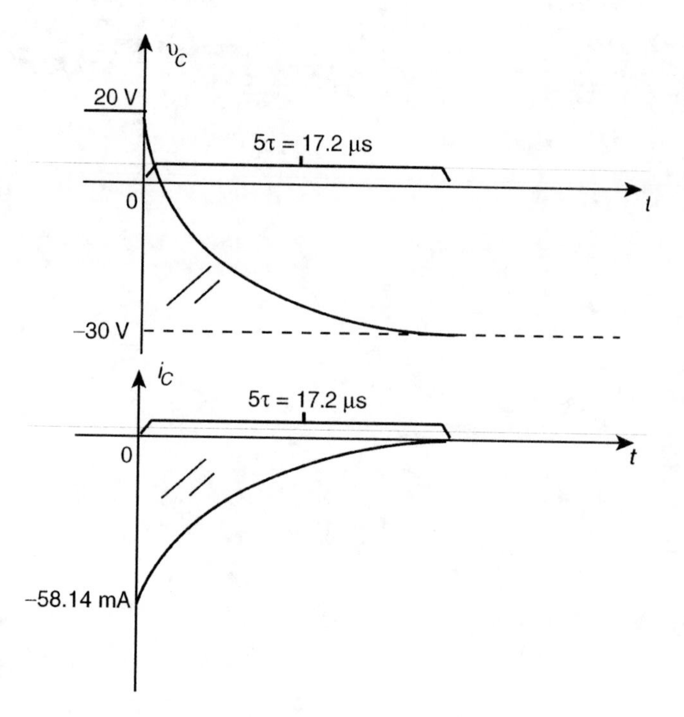

35. a. 18.2 kΩ, 52 V, i_C, 12 V, 6.8 μF, υ_C

$\tau = RC = (18.2\text{ k}\Omega)(6.8\ \mu\text{F}) = 123.8\text{ ms}$

$\upsilon_C = V_f + (V_i - V_f)\,e^{-t/\tau}$

$= 52\text{ V} + (12\text{ V} - 52\text{ V})e^{-t/123.8\text{ ms}}$

$\upsilon_C = \mathbf{52\ V - 40\ V}\boldsymbol{e^{-t/123.8\text{ ms}}}$

$\upsilon_R(0+) = 52\text{ V} - 12\text{ V} = 40\text{ V}$

$i_C = \dfrac{40\text{ V}}{18.2\text{ k}\Omega}\,e^{-t/123.8\text{ ms}}$

$= \mathbf{2.20\ mA}\boldsymbol{e^{-t/123.8\text{ ms}}}$

b.

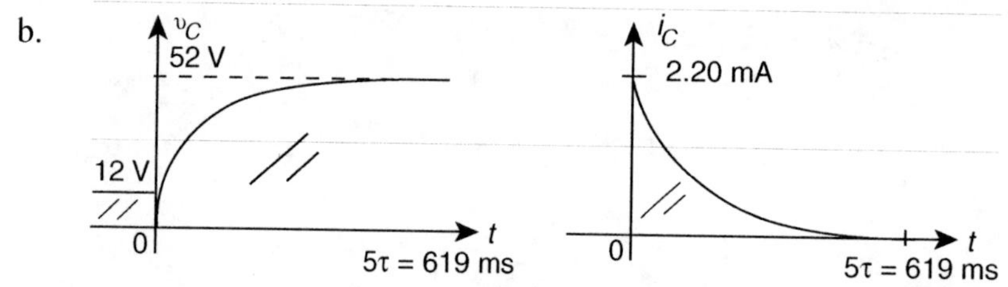

36. a. $\upsilon_C = 12\text{ V}(1 - e^{-10\mu s/20\ \mu s}) = 12\text{ V}(1 - e^{-0.5}) = 12\text{ V}(1 - 0.607)$

$= 12\text{ V}(0.393) = \mathbf{4.72\ V}$

b. $\upsilon_C = 12\text{ V}(1 - e^{-10\tau/\tau}) = 12\text{ V}(1 - e^{-10}) = 12\text{ V}(1 - 45.4 \times 10^{-6})$

$\cong \mathbf{12\ V}$

c. $6\text{ V} = 12\text{ V}(1 - e^{-t/20\ \mu s})$

$0.5 = 1 - e^{-t/20\ \mu s}$

$-0.5 = -e^{-t/20\ \mu s}$

$0.5 = e^{-t/20\ \mu s}$

$\log_e 0.5 = \log_e e^{-t/20\ \mu s}$

$-0.693 = -t/20\ \mu s$

$t = 0.693\ (20\ \mu s) = \mathbf{13.86\ \mu s}$

d. $\upsilon_C = 11.98 \text{ V} = 12 \text{ V}(1 - e^{t/20\ \mu\text{s}})$

$0.998 = 1 - e^{-t/20\ \mu\text{s}}$

$-0.002 = -e^{-t/20\ \mu\text{s}}$

$0.002 = -e^{-t/20\ \mu\text{s}}$

$\log_e 0.002 = -t/20\ \mu\text{s}$

$-6.215 = -t/20\ \mu\text{s}$

$t = (6.215)(20\ \mu\text{s}) = \mathbf{124.3\ \mu s}$

37. $\tau = RC = (33\text{ k}\Omega)(20\ \mu\text{F}) = 0.66\text{ s}$

$\upsilon_C = 12\text{ V}(1 - e^{-t/0.66\text{ s}})$

$8\text{ V} = 12\text{ V}(1 - e^{-t/0.66\text{ s}})$

$8\text{ V} = 12\text{ V} - 12\text{ V}e^{-t/0.66\text{ s}}$

$-4\text{ V} = -12\text{ V}e^{-t/0.66\text{ s}}$

$0.333 = e^{-t/0.66\text{ s}}$

$\log_e 0.333 = -t/0.66\text{ s}$

$-1.0996 = -t/0.66\text{ s}$

$t = 1.0996(0.66\text{ s}) = \mathbf{0.73\ s}$

38. $t = -\tau \log_e\left(1 - \dfrac{\upsilon_C}{E}\right)$

$10\text{ s} = -\tau \log_e\left(1 - \dfrac{12\text{ V}}{20\text{ V}}\right)$

$\left(1 - \dfrac{12\text{ V}}{20\text{ V}}\right) = .4$

$\log_e(.4) = -916.29 \times 10^{-3}$

$$\tau = \frac{10\text{ s}}{0.916} = 10.92\text{ s}$$

$$\tau = RC \Rightarrow R = \frac{\tau}{C} = \frac{10.92\text{ s}}{200\ \mu\text{F}} = \mathbf{54.60\ k\Omega}$$

39. a. $\tau = (R_1 + R_2)C = (20\text{ k}\Omega)(6\ \mu\text{F}) = 0.12\text{ s}$

$\upsilon_C = E(1 - e^{-t/\tau})$

$60\text{ V} = 80\text{ V}(1 - e^{-t/0.12\text{s}})$

$0.75 = 1 - e^{-t/0.12\text{s}}$

$0.25 = e^{-t/0.12\text{s}}$

$t = -(0.12\text{ s})(-1.39)$

$= \mathbf{166.80\ ms}$

b. $i_C = \dfrac{E}{R}e^{-t/\tau}$

$$i_C = \frac{80\text{ V}}{20\text{ k}\Omega}e^{-\frac{166.80\text{ ms}}{0.12\text{s}}} = 4\text{ mA}e^{-1.39}$$

$= (4\text{ mA})(249.08 \times 10^{-3})$

$\cong \mathbf{1\ mA}$

c. $i_s = i_C = 4\text{ mA}e^{-t/\tau} = 4\text{ mA}e^{-2\tau/\tau} = 4\text{ mA}e^{-2}$
$= 4\text{ mA}(135.34 \times 10^{-3})$
$= 0.54\text{ mA}$
$P_s = EI_s = (80\text{ V})(0.54\text{ mA})$
$= \mathbf{43.20\text{ mW}}$

40. a. $\tau = RC = (1\text{ M}\Omega)(0.2\ \mu\text{F}) = 0.2\text{ s}$
$\upsilon_C = \mathbf{60\text{ V}(1 - e^{-t/0.2\text{s}})}$
$i_C = \dfrac{E}{R}e^{-t/\tau} = \dfrac{60\text{ V}}{1\text{ M}\Omega}e^{-t/0.2\text{s}} = \mathbf{60\ \mu\text{A}e^{-t/0.2\text{s}}}$
$\upsilon_{R_1} = Ee^{-t/\tau} = \mathbf{60\text{ V}e^{-t/0.2\text{s}}}$

υ_C: 0.5 s = **55.07 V**
1 s = **59.58 V**

i_C: 0.5 s = **4.93 V**
1 s = **0.40 V**

b. 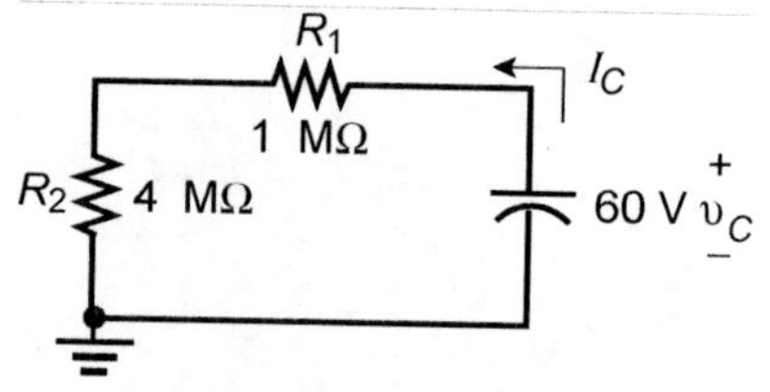 $\tau' = RC = (1\text{ M}\Omega + 4\text{ M}\Omega)(0.2\ \mu\text{F})$
$= (5\text{ M}\Omega)(0.2\ \mu\text{F})$
$= 1\text{ s}$
$i_C = \dfrac{60\text{ V}}{5\text{ M}\Omega}e^{-t} = \mathbf{12\ \mu\text{A}e^{-t}}$

$8\ \mu\text{A} = 12\ \mu\text{A}e^{-t}$
$0.667 = e^{-t}$
$\log_e 0.667 = -t$
$-0.41 = -t$
$t = \mathbf{0.41\text{ s}}$

$\upsilon_C = 60\text{ V}e^{-t/\tau'}$
$10\text{ V} = 60\text{ V}e^{-t}$
$0.167 = e^{-t}$
$\log_e 0.167 = -t$
$-1.79 = -t$
$t = 1.79\text{ s}$
Longer = 1.79 s – 0.41 s = **1.38 s**

41. a. $\upsilon_m = \upsilon_R = Ee^{-t/\tau} = 60\text{ V}e^{-1\tau/\tau} = 60\text{ V}e^{-1}$
$= 60\text{ V}(0.3679)$
$= \mathbf{22.07\text{ V}}$

b. $i_C = \dfrac{E}{R}e^{-t/\tau} = \dfrac{60\text{ V}}{10\text{ M}\Omega}e^{-2\tau/\tau} = 6\ \mu\text{A}e^{-2}$
$= 6\ \mu\text{A}(0.1353)$
$= \mathbf{0.81\ \mu\text{A}}$

c. $\upsilon_C = E(1 - e^{-t/\tau})$ $\tau = RC = (10\ \text{M}\Omega)(0.2\ \mu\text{F}) = 2\ \text{s}$

$$50\ \text{V} = 60\ \text{V}(1 - e^{-t/2\ \text{s}})$$
$$0.8333 = 1 - e^{-t/2\ \text{s}}$$
$$\log_e 0.1667 = -t/2\ \text{s}$$
$$t = -(2\ \text{s})(-1.792)$$
$$= \mathbf{3.58\ s}$$

42. a. Thevenin's theorem:

R_{Th}: E_{Th}:

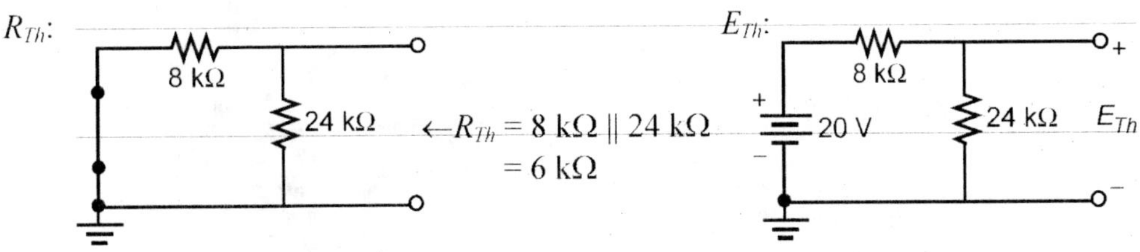

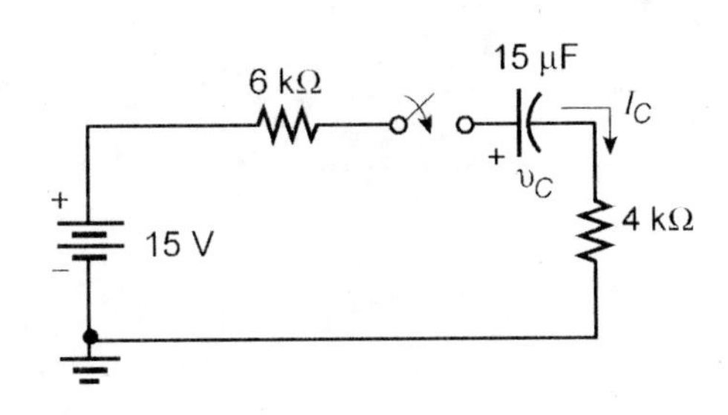

$$E_{Th} = \frac{24\ \text{k}\Omega(20\ \text{V})}{24\ \text{k}\Omega + 8\ \text{k}\Omega} = 15\ \text{V}$$

$\tau = RC = (10\ \text{k}\Omega)(15\ \mu\text{F}) = 0.15\ \text{s}$

$\upsilon_C = E(1 - e^{-t/\tau})$

$= \mathbf{15\ V(1 - e^{-t/0.15\ s})}$

$$i_C = \frac{E}{R}e^{-t/\tau} = \frac{15\ \text{V}}{10\ \text{k}\Omega}e^{-t/0.15} = \mathbf{1.5\ mA}e^{-t/0.15\ \text{s}}$$

b.

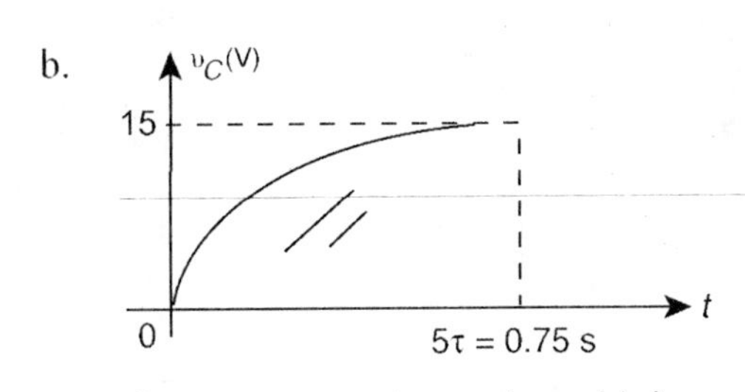

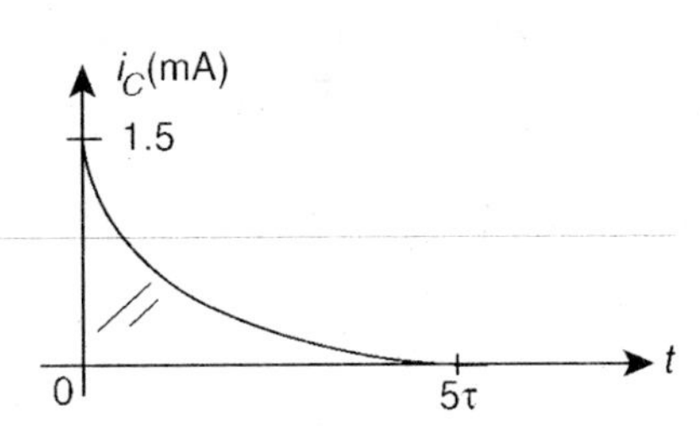

43. a. Source conversion and combining series resistors:

$\tau = RC = (8.3\ \text{k}\Omega)(2.2\ \mu\text{F}) = 18.26\ \text{ms}$

$\upsilon_C = V_f + (V_i - V_f)e^{-t/\tau}$

$= 27.2\ \text{V} + (2\ \text{V} - 27.2\ \text{V})e^{-t/18.26\ \text{ms}}$

$\upsilon_C = \mathbf{27.2\ V - 25.2\ V}e^{-t/18.26\ \text{ms}}$

$\upsilon_R(0+) = 27.2\ \text{V} - 2\ \text{V} = 25.2\ \text{V}$

$i_C = \dfrac{25.2\ \text{V}}{8.3\ \text{k}\Omega}e^{-t/18.26\text{ms}}$

$i_C = \mathbf{3.04\ mA}e^{-t/18.26\ \text{ms}}$

b.

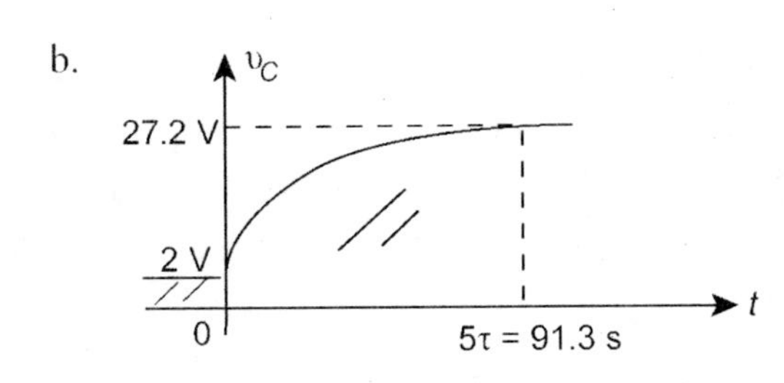

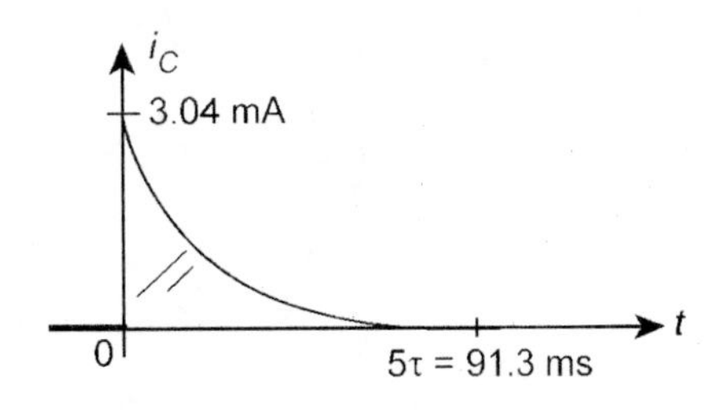

44. a. $R_{Th} = 3.9\text{ k}\Omega + 0\text{ }\Omega \parallel 1.8\text{ k}\Omega = 3.9\text{ k}\Omega$
$E_{Th} = 36\text{ V}$

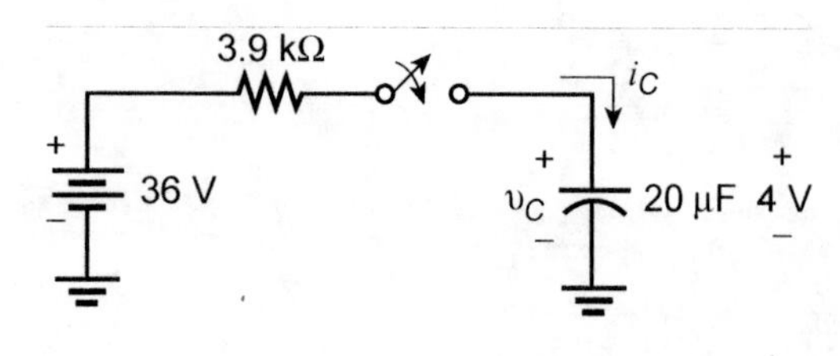

$\tau = RC = (3.9\text{ k}\Omega)(20\text{ }\mu\text{F}) = 78\text{ ms}$

$\upsilon_C = V_f + (V_i - V_f)e^{-t/\tau}$

$= 36\text{ V} + (-4\text{ V} - 36\text{ V})e^{-t/78\text{ ms}}$

$\upsilon_C = \mathbf{36\text{ V} - 40\text{ V}e^{-t/78\text{ ms}}}$

$\upsilon_R(0+) = 36\text{ V} + 4\text{ V} = 40\text{ V}$

$$i_C = \frac{40\text{ V}}{3.9\text{ k}\Omega}e^{-t/78\text{ ms}}$$

$i_C = \mathbf{10.26\text{ mA}e^{-t/78\text{ ms}}}$

b.

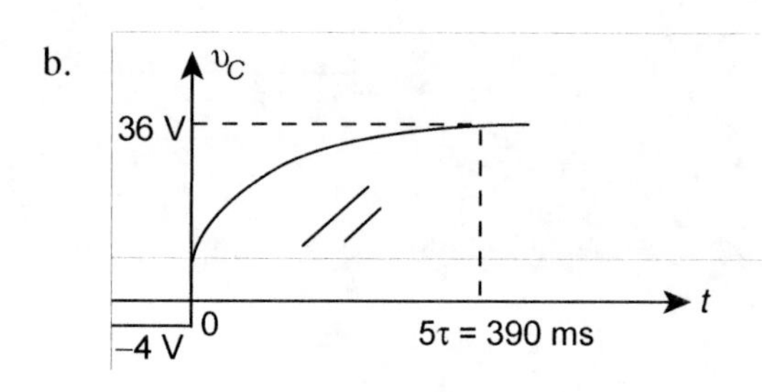

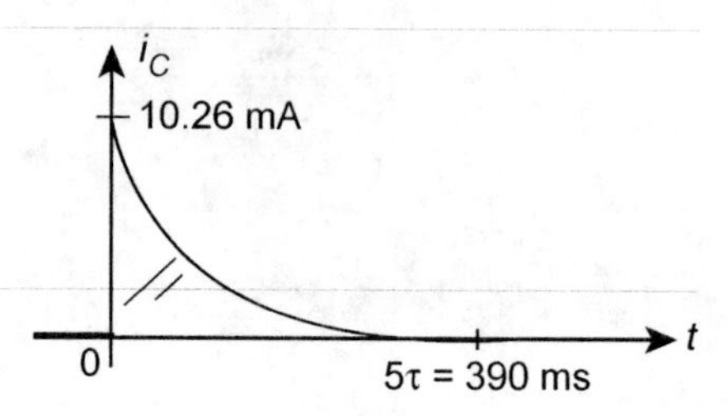

45. Source conversion:

$E = IR_1 = (5\text{ mA})(0.56\text{ k}\Omega) = 2.8\text{ V}$

$R' = R_1 + R_2 = 0.56\text{ k}\Omega + 3.9\text{ k}\Omega = 4.46\text{ k}\Omega$

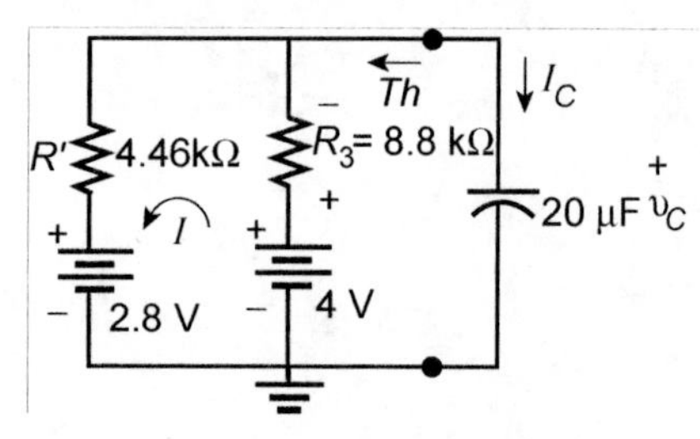

$R_{Th} = 4.46\text{ k}\Omega \parallel 6.8\text{ k}\Omega = 2.69\text{ k}\Omega$

$$I = \frac{4\text{ V} - 2.8\text{ V}}{6.8\text{ k}\Omega + 4.46\text{ k}\Omega} = \frac{1.2\text{ V}}{11.26\text{ k}\Omega} = 0.107\text{ mA}$$

$E_{Th} = 4\text{ V} - (0.107\text{ mA})(6.8\text{ k}\Omega)$

$= 4\text{ V} - 0.727\text{ V}$

$= 3.27\text{ V}$

$\upsilon_C = 3.27\text{ V}(1 - e^{-t/\tau})$

$\tau = RC = (2.69\text{ k}\Omega)(20\text{ }\mu\text{F})$

$= 53.80\text{ ms}$

$\upsilon_C = \mathbf{3.27\text{ V}(1 - e^{-t/53.80\text{ ms}})}$

$$i_C = \frac{3.27\text{ V}}{2.69\text{ k}\Omega}e^{-t/\tau}$$

$= \mathbf{1.22\text{ mA }e^{-t/53.80\text{ ms}}}$

46. a.

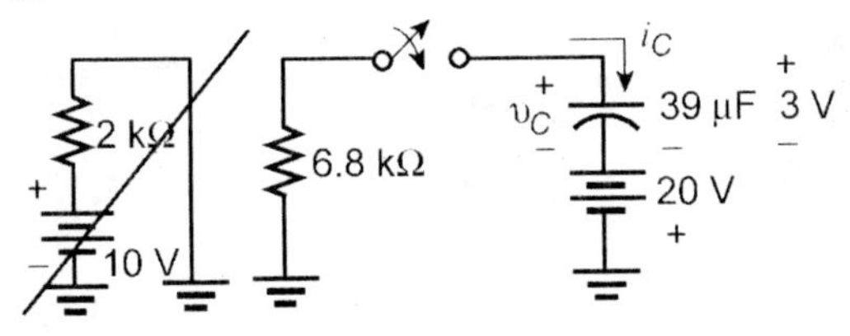

$\tau = RC = (6.8\ \text{k}\Omega)(39\ \mu\text{F}) = 265.2\ \text{ms}$

$\upsilon_C = V_f + (V_i - V_f)e^{-t/\tau}$

$= 20\ \text{V} + (3\ \text{V} - 20\ \text{V})e^{-t/265.2\ \text{ms}}$

$\upsilon_C = \mathbf{20\ V - 17\ V}e^{-t/265.2\ \text{ms}}$

$\upsilon_R(0+) = 20\ \text{V} - 3\ \text{V} = 17\ \text{V}$

$i_C = \dfrac{17\ \text{V}}{6.8\ \text{k}\Omega}e^{-t/265.2\ \text{ms}}$

$i_C = \mathbf{2.5\ mA}e^{-t/265.2\ \text{ms}}$

b.

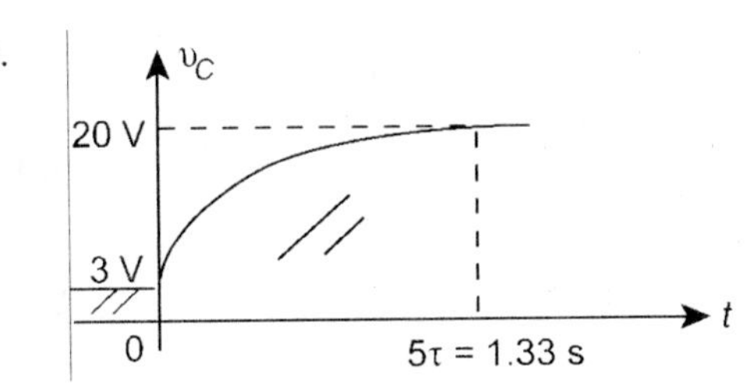

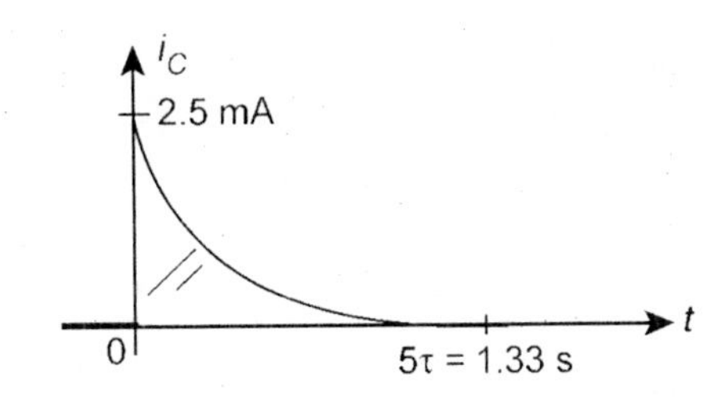

47. a.

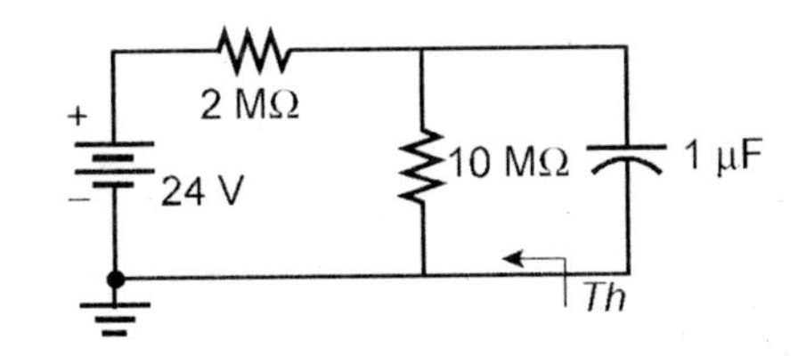

$R_{Th} = 2\ \text{M}\Omega \parallel 10\ \text{M}\Omega = 1.67\ \text{M}\Omega$

$E_{Th} = \dfrac{10\ \text{M}\Omega(24\ \text{V})}{10\ \text{M}\Omega + 2\ \text{M}\Omega} = 20\ \text{V}$

$\upsilon_C = E_{Th}(1 - e^{-t/\tau})$

$= 20\ \text{V}(1 - e^{-4\tau/\tau})$

$= 20\ \text{V}(1 - e^{-4})$

$= 20\ \text{V}(1 - 0.0183)$

$= \mathbf{19.63\ V}$

$\tau = R_{Th}C = (1.67\ \text{M}\Omega)(1\ \mu\text{F}) = 1.67\ \text{s}$

$i_C = \dfrac{E}{R}e^{-t/\tau}$

$3\ \mu\text{A} = \dfrac{20\ \text{V}}{1.67\ \text{M}\Omega}e^{-t/1.67\text{s}}$

$0.25 = e^{-t/1.67\text{s}}$

$\log_e 0.25 = -t/1.67\ \text{s}$

$t = -(1.67\ \text{s})(-1.39)$

$= \mathbf{2.32\ s}$

c. $\upsilon_{\text{meter}} = \upsilon_C$

$\upsilon_C = E_{Th}(1 - e^{-t/\tau})$

$10\ \text{V} = 20\ \text{V}(1 - e^{-t/1.67\text{s}})$

$0.5 = 1 - e^{-t/1.67\text{s}}$

$-0.5 = -e^{-t/1.67\text{s}}$

$\log_e 0.5 = -t/1.67\ \text{s}$

$t = -(1.67\ \text{s})(-0.69)$

$= \mathbf{1.15\ s}$

48. $i_{C_{av}} = C\dfrac{\Delta \upsilon_C}{\Delta t}$

$$0 \rightarrow 4 \text{ ms: } i_C = 2 \times 10^{-6}\frac{(20\text{ V})}{4\text{ ms}} = \mathbf{10\ mA}$$

$$4 \rightarrow 6 \text{ ms: } i_C = 2 \times 10^{-6}\frac{(0\text{ V})}{2\text{ ms}} = \mathbf{0\ mA}$$

$$6 \rightarrow 7 \text{ ms: } i_C = 2 \times 10^{-6}\frac{(20\text{ V})}{1\text{ ms}} = \mathbf{40\ mA}$$

$$7 \rightarrow 9 \text{ ms: } i_C = 2 \times 10^{-6}\frac{(0\text{ V})}{2\text{ ms}} = \mathbf{0\ mA}$$

$$9 \rightarrow 11 \text{ ms: } i_C = -2 \times 10^{-6}\frac{(40\text{ V})}{2\text{ ms}} = \mathbf{-40\ mA}$$

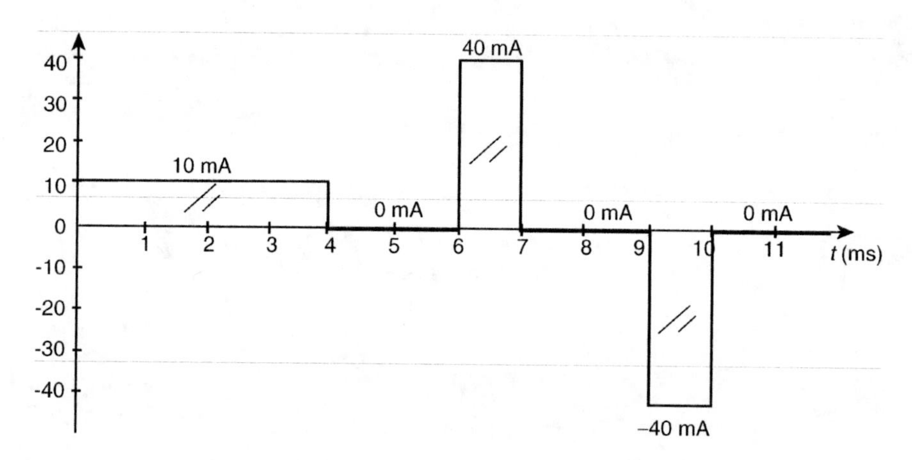

49. $i_{C_{av}} = C\dfrac{\Delta \upsilon_C}{\Delta t}$

$$0 \rightarrow 20\ \mu\text{s: } i_C = 4.7\ \mu\text{F}\frac{(-5\text{ V})}{20\ \mu\text{s}} = \mathbf{-1.18\ A}$$

$$20 \rightarrow 30\ \mu\text{s: } i_C = 4.7\ \mu\text{F}\frac{(0\text{ V})}{10\ \mu\text{s}} = \mathbf{0\ A}$$

$$30 \rightarrow 50\ \mu\text{s: } i_C = 4.7\ \mu\text{F}\frac{(+10\text{ V})}{20\ \mu\text{s}} = \mathbf{+2.35\ A}$$

$$50 \rightarrow 80\ \mu\text{s: } i_C = 4.7\ \mu\text{F}\frac{(-15\text{ V})}{30\ \mu\text{s}} = \mathbf{-2.35\ A}$$

$$80 \rightarrow 90\ \mu\text{s: } i_C = 4.7\ \mu\text{F}\frac{(+10\text{ V})}{10\ \mu\text{s}} = \mathbf{+4.7\ A}$$

$$90\ \mu\text{s} \rightarrow 100\ \mu\text{s: } i_C = 4.7\ \mu\text{F}\frac{(0\text{ V})}{10\ \mu\text{s}} = \mathbf{0\ A}$$

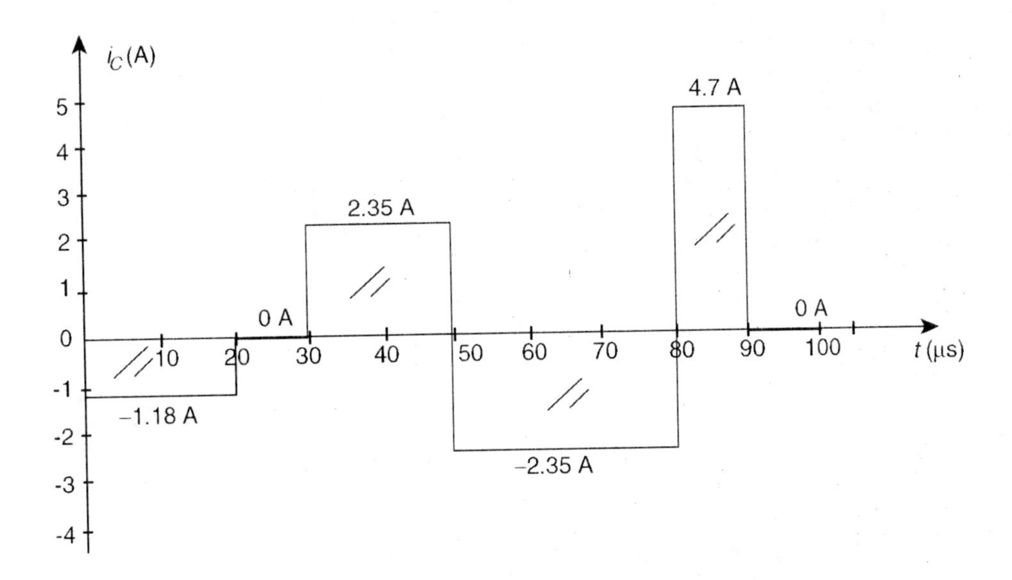

50. $i_C = C\dfrac{\Delta v_C}{\Delta t} \Rightarrow \Delta v_C = \dfrac{\Delta t}{C}(i_C)$

$0 \to 2$ ms: $i_C = 0$ mA $\Delta v_C = \mathbf{0\ V}$

$2 \to 6$ ms: $i_C = -80$ mA $\Delta v_C = \dfrac{(2\text{ ms})}{20\ \mu\text{F}}(-80\text{ mA}) = \mathbf{-8\ V}$

$6 \to 16$ ms: $i_C = +40$ mA $\Delta v_C = \dfrac{(10\text{ ms})}{20\ \mu\text{F}}(40\text{ mA}) = \mathbf{+20\ V}$

$16 \to 18$ ms: $i_C = 0$ mA $\Delta v_C = \mathbf{0\ V}$

$18 \to 20$ ms: $i_C = -120$ mA $\Delta v_C = \dfrac{(2\text{ ms})}{20\ \mu\text{F}}(-120\text{ mA}) = \mathbf{-12\ V}$

$20 \to 25$ ms: $i_C = 0$ mA $\Delta v_C = \mathbf{0\ V}$

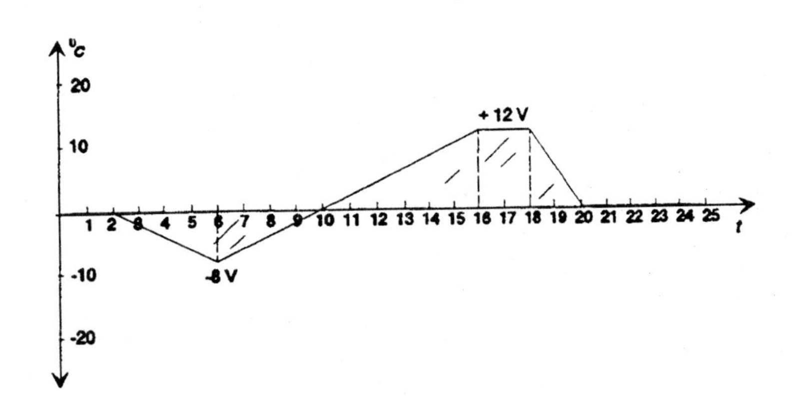

51. $C_T = 6\ \mu\text{F} + 4\ \mu\text{F} + 3\ \mu\text{F} \parallel 6\ \mu\text{F} = 10\ \mu\text{F} + 2\ \mu\text{F} = \mathbf{12\ \mu F}$

52. $C_T' = 6\ \mu\text{F} \parallel 12\ \mu\text{F} = 4\ \mu\text{F}$

$C_T'' = C_T' + 12\ \mu\text{F} = 4\ \mu\text{F} + 12\ \mu\text{F} = 16\ \mu\text{F}$

$C_T = 6\ \mu\text{F} \parallel C_T'' = \dfrac{6\ \mu\text{F} \cdot C_T''}{6\ \mu\text{F} + C_T''} = \dfrac{(6\ \mu\text{F})(16\ \mu\text{F})}{6\ \mu\text{F} + 16\ \mu\text{F}} = \mathbf{4.36\ \mu F}$

53. $V_1 = \mathbf{10\ V}$, $Q_1 = V_1C_1 = (10\ \text{V})(6\ \mu\text{F}) = \mathbf{60\ \mu C}$

$C_T = 6\ \mu\text{F} \parallel 12\ \mu\text{F} = 4\ \mu\text{F}$, $Q_T = C_TE = (4\ \mu\text{F})(10\ \text{V}) = 40\ \mu\text{C}$

$Q_2 = Q_3 = \mathbf{40\ \mu C}$

$$V_2 = \frac{Q_2}{C_2} = \frac{40\mu\text{C}}{6\mu\text{F}} = \mathbf{6.67\ V}$$

$$V_3 = \frac{Q_3}{C_3} = \frac{40\mu\text{C}}{12\mu\text{F}} = \mathbf{3.33\ V}$$

54. $C_T = 1200\ \text{pF} \parallel (200\ \text{pF} + 400\ \text{pF}) \parallel 600\ \text{pF}$
$= 1200\ \text{pF} \parallel 600\ \text{pF} \parallel 600\ \text{pF} = 1200\ \text{pF} \parallel 300\ \text{pF}$
$= 240\ \text{pF}$

$Q_T = C_TE = (240\ \text{pF})(40\ \text{V}) = 9.60\ \text{nC}$

$Q_1 = Q_4 = Q_T = \mathbf{9.60\ nC}$

$$V_1 = \frac{Q_1}{C_1} = \frac{9.60\ \text{nC}}{1200\ \text{pF}} = \mathbf{8.00\ V},\ V_4 = \frac{Q_4}{C_4} = \frac{9.60\ \text{nC}}{600\ \text{pF}} = \mathbf{16.00\ V}$$

$V_2 = V_3 = E - V_1 - V_4 = 40\ \text{V} - 8\ \text{V} - 16\ \text{V} = \mathbf{16\ V}$

$Q_2 = C_2V_2 = (200\ \text{pF})(16\ \text{V}) = \mathbf{3.20\ nC}$, $Q_3 = C_3V_3 = (400\ \text{pF})(16\ \text{V}) = \mathbf{6.40\ nC}$

55.

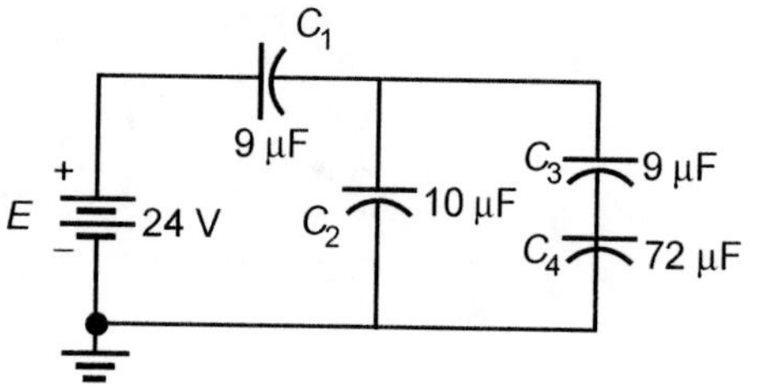

$$\frac{(9\ \mu\text{F})(72\ \mu\text{F})}{9\ \mu\text{F} + 72\ \mu\text{F}} = 8\ \mu\text{F}$$

$8\ \mu\text{F} + 10\ \mu\text{F} = 18\ \mu\text{F}$

$$\frac{(9\ \mu\text{F})(18\ \mu\text{F})}{9\ \mu\text{F} + 18\ \mu\text{F}} = 6\ \mu\text{F}$$

$$C_T = \frac{Q}{V} = \frac{Q}{E} \Rightarrow Q = C_TE = (6\ \mu\text{F})(24\ \text{V}) = 144\ \mu\text{C}$$

$Q_1 = \mathbf{144\ \mu C}$

$$V_1 = \frac{Q_1}{C_1} = \frac{144\ \mu\text{C}}{9\ \mu\text{F}} = \mathbf{16\ V}$$

$V_2 = E - V_1 = 24\ \text{V} - 16\ \text{V} = \mathbf{8\ V}$

$Q_2 = C_2V_2 = 10\ \mu\text{F}(8\ \text{V}) = \mathbf{80\ \mu C}$

$Q_{3\text{-}4} = C'V = (8\ \mu\text{F})(8\ \text{V}) = 64\ \mu\text{C}$

$Q_3 = Q_4 = \mathbf{64\ \mu C}$

$$V_3 = \frac{Q_3}{C_3} = \frac{64\ \mu\text{C}}{9\ \mu\text{F}} = \mathbf{7.11\ V}$$

$$V_4 = \frac{Q_4}{C_4} = \frac{64\ \mu\text{C}}{72\ \mu\text{F}} = \mathbf{0.89\ V}$$

56. $$V_{4\text{k}\Omega} = \frac{4\ \text{k}\Omega(48\ \text{V})}{4\ \text{k}\Omega + 2\ \text{k}\Omega} = \mathbf{32\ V} = V_{0.08\mu\text{F}}$$

$Q_{0.08\mu\text{F}} = (0.08\ \mu\text{F})(32\ \text{V}) = \mathbf{2.56\ \mu C}$

$V_{0.04\mu\text{F}} = \mathbf{48\ V}$

$Q_{0.04\mu\text{F}} = (0.04\ \mu\text{F})(48\ \text{V}) = \mathbf{1.92\ \mu C}$

57. $W_C = \frac{1}{2}CV^2 = \frac{1}{2}(120 \text{ pF})(12 \text{ V})^2 = \mathbf{8{,}640 \text{ pJ}}$

58. $W = \frac{Q^2}{2C} \Rightarrow Q = \sqrt{2CW} = \sqrt{2(6 \,\mu\text{F})(1200 \text{ J})} = \mathbf{0.12 \text{ C}}$

59. a. $V_{6\mu F} = V_{12\mu F} = \frac{3 \text{ k}\Omega(24 \text{ V})}{3 \text{ k}\Omega + 6 \text{ k}\Omega} = 8 \text{ V}$

$W_{6\mu F} = \frac{1}{2}CV^2 = \frac{1}{2}(6 \,\mu\text{F})(8 \text{ V})^2 = \mathbf{0.19 \text{ mJ}}$

$W_{12\mu F} = \frac{1}{2}CV^2 = \frac{1}{2}(12 \,\mu\text{F})(8 \text{ V})^2 = \mathbf{0.38 \text{ mJ}}$

b. $C_T = \frac{(6 \,\mu\text{F})(12 \,\mu\text{F})}{6 \,\mu\text{F} + 12 \,\mu\text{F}} = 4 \,\mu\text{F}$

$Q_T = C_T V = (4 \,\mu\text{F})(8 \text{ V}) = 32 \,\mu\text{C}$

$Q_{6\mu F} = Q_{12\mu F} = 32 \,\mu\text{C}$

$V_{6\mu F} = \frac{Q}{C} = \frac{32 \,\mu\text{C}}{6 \,\mu\text{F}} = 5.33 \text{ V}$

$V_{12\mu F} = \frac{Q}{C} = \frac{32 \,\mu\text{C}}{12 \,\mu\text{F}} = 2.67 \text{ V}$

$W_{6\mu F} = \frac{1}{2}CV^2 = \frac{1}{2}(6 \,\mu\text{F})(5.33 \text{ V})^2 = \mathbf{85.23 \,\mu J}$

$W_{12\mu F} = \frac{1}{2}CV^2 = \frac{1}{2}(12 \,\mu\text{F})(2.67 \text{ V})^2 = \mathbf{42.77 \,\mu J}$

60. a. $W_C = \frac{1}{2}CV^2 = \frac{1}{2}(1000 \,\mu\text{F})(100 \text{ V})^2 = \mathbf{5 \text{ pJ}}$

b. $Q = CV = (1000 \,\mu\text{F})(100 \text{ V}) = \mathbf{0.1 \text{ C}}$

c. $I = Q/t = 0.1 \text{ C}/(1/2000) = \mathbf{200 \text{ A}}$

d. $P = V_{av}I_{av} = W/t = 5 \text{ J}(1/2000 \text{ s}) = \mathbf{10{,}000 \text{ W}}$

e. $t = Q/I = 0.1 \text{ C}/10 \text{ mA} = \mathbf{10 \text{ s}}$

Chapter 11

1. a. $B = \dfrac{\Phi}{A} = \dfrac{4\times10^{-4}\text{ Wb}}{0.01\text{ m}^2} = 4\times10^{-2}\text{ Wb/m}^2 = \mathbf{0.04\ Wb/m^2}$

   b. **0.04 T**

   c. $F = NI = (40\text{ t})(2.2\text{ A}) = \mathbf{88\ At}$

   d. $0.04\cancel{T}\left[\dfrac{10^4\text{ gauss}}{1\cancel{T}}\right] = \mathbf{0.4\times10^3\ gauss}$

2. $A = \dfrac{\pi d^2}{4} = \dfrac{\pi(5\text{ mm})^2}{4} = 19.63\times10^{-6}\text{ m}^2$

   $L = \dfrac{N^2\mu A}{\ell} = \dfrac{(200\text{ t})^2(4\pi\times10^{-7})(19.63\times10^{-6}\text{ m}^2)}{100\text{ mm}} = \mathbf{9.87\ \mu H}$

3. $d = 0.2\ \cancel{\text{in.}}\left[\dfrac{1\text{ m}}{39.37\ \cancel{\text{in.}}}\right] = 5.08\text{ mm}$

   $A = \dfrac{\pi d^2}{4} = \dfrac{(\pi)(5.08\text{ mm})^2}{4} = 20.27\times10^{-6}\text{ m}^2$

   $\ell = 1.6\ \cancel{\text{in.}}\left(\dfrac{1\text{ m}}{39.37\ \cancel{\text{in.}}}\right) = 40.64\text{ mm}$

   $L = \dfrac{N^2\mu_r\mu_o A}{\ell} = \dfrac{(200\text{ t})^2(500)(4\pi\times10^{-7})(20.27\times10^{-6}\text{ m}^2)}{40.64\text{ mm}} = \mathbf{12.54\ mH}$

4. $L = N^2\dfrac{\mu_r\mu_o}{\ell} = \dfrac{(200\text{ t})^2(1000)(4\pi\times10^{-7})(1.5\times10^{-4}\text{ m}^2)}{0.15\text{ m}} = \mathbf{50.27\ mH}$

5. $L = \dfrac{N^2\mu_r\mu_o A}{\ell}$

   a. $L' = (3)^2L_o = 9L_o = 9(5\text{ mH}) = \mathbf{45\ mH}$

   b. $L' = \dfrac{1}{3}L_o = \dfrac{1}{3}(5\text{ mH}) = \mathbf{1.67\ mH}$

   c. $L' = \dfrac{(2)(2)^2}{\frac{1}{2}}L_o = 16\,(5\text{ mH}) = \mathbf{80\ mH}$

   d. $L' = \dfrac{\left(\frac{1}{2}\right)^2\frac{1}{2}(1500)L_o}{\frac{1}{2}} = 375(5\text{ mH}) = \mathbf{1875\ mH}$

6. a. $12\times10^3\ \mu\text{H}\pm5\% \Rightarrow 12{,}000\ \mu\text{H}\pm600\ \mu\text{H} \Rightarrow \mathbf{11{,}400\ \mu H \to 12{,}600\ \mu H}$

   b. $47\ \mu\text{H}\pm10\% \Rightarrow 47\ \mu\text{H}\pm4.7\ \mu\text{H} \Rightarrow \mathbf{42.3\ \mu F \to 51.7\ \mu F}$

7. $e = N\frac{d\phi}{dt} = (50\ \text{t})(120\ \text{mWb/s}) = \mathbf{6.0\ V}$

8. $e = N\frac{d\phi}{dt} \Rightarrow \frac{d\phi}{dt} = \frac{e}{N} = \frac{20\ \text{V}}{200\ \text{t}} = \mathbf{100\ mWb/s}$

9. $e = N\frac{d\phi}{dt} \Rightarrow N = e\left(\frac{1}{\frac{d\phi}{dt}}\right) = 42\ \text{mV}\left(\frac{1}{3\ \text{m Wb/s}}\right) = \mathbf{14\ turns}$

10. a. $e = L\frac{di_L}{dt} = (5\ \text{H})(1\ \text{A/s}) = \mathbf{5\ V}$

b. $e = L\frac{di_L}{dt} = (5\ \text{H})(60\ \text{mA/s}) = \mathbf{0.3\ V}$

$e = L\frac{di_L}{dt} = (5\ \text{H})\left[\frac{0.5\ \text{A}}{\cancel{\text{ms}}}\right]\left[\frac{1000\ \cancel{\text{ms}}}{1\ \text{s}}\right] = \mathbf{2.5\ kV}$

11. $e = L\frac{di_L}{dt} = (50\ \text{mH})\left(\frac{0.1\ \text{mA}}{\mu\text{s}}\right) = \mathbf{5\ V}$

12. a. $\tau = \frac{L}{R} = \frac{250\ \text{mH}}{20\ \text{k}\Omega} = \mathbf{12.5\ \mu s}$

b. $i_L = \frac{E}{R}(1 - e^{-t/\tau}) = \frac{40\ \text{mV}}{20\ \text{k}\Omega}(1 - e^{-t/\tau})$
$= \mathbf{2\ \mu A(1 - e^{-t/12.5\mu s})}$

c. $\upsilon_L = Ee^{-t/\tau} = \mathbf{40\ mVe^{-t/12.5\ \mu s}}$
$\upsilon_R = i_R R = i_L R = E(1 - e^{-t/\tau}) = \mathbf{40\ mV(1 - e^{-t/12.5\ \mu s})}$

d. i_L: $1\tau = \mathbf{1.26\ \mu A}$, , $3\tau = \mathbf{1.9\ \mu A}$, $5\tau = \mathbf{1.99\ \mu A}$
υ_L: $1\tau = \mathbf{14.72\ V}$, $3\tau = \mathbf{1.99\ V}$, $5\tau = \mathbf{0.27\ V}$

e.

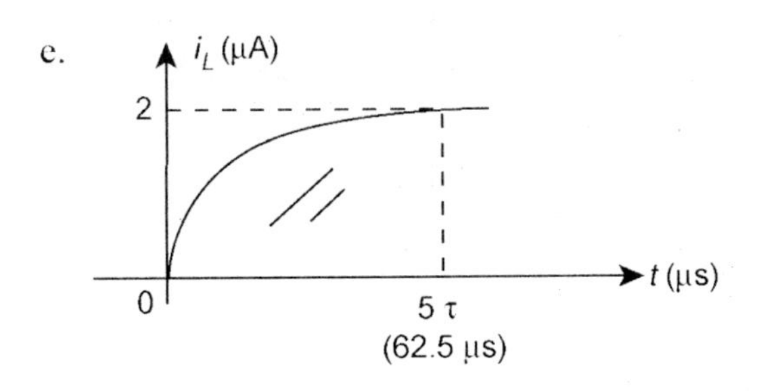

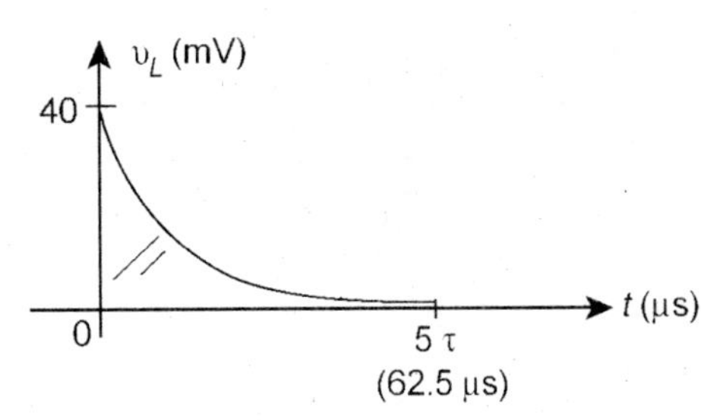

13. a. $\tau = \frac{L}{R} = \frac{5\text{ mH}}{2.2\text{ k}\Omega} = \mathbf{2.27\ \mu s}$

b. $i_L = \frac{E}{R}(1 - e^{-t/\tau}) = \frac{12\text{ V}}{2.2\text{ k}\Omega}(1 - e^{-t/\tau}) = \mathbf{5.45\text{ mA}(1 - e^{-t/2.27\,\mu s})}$

c. $\upsilon_L = Ee^{-t/\tau} = \mathbf{12\text{ V}e^{-t/2.27\,\mu s}}$
$\upsilon_R = i_R R = i_L R = E(1 - e^{-t/\tau}) = \mathbf{12\text{ V}(1 - e^{-t/2.27\,\mu s})}$

d. i_L: $1\tau = \mathbf{3.45\text{ mA}}$, , $3\tau = \mathbf{5.18\text{ mA}}$, $5\tau = \mathbf{5.41\text{ mA}}$
υ_L: $1\tau = \mathbf{4.42\text{ V}}$, $3\tau = \mathbf{0.60\text{ V}}$, $5\tau = \mathbf{0.08\text{ V}}$

e.

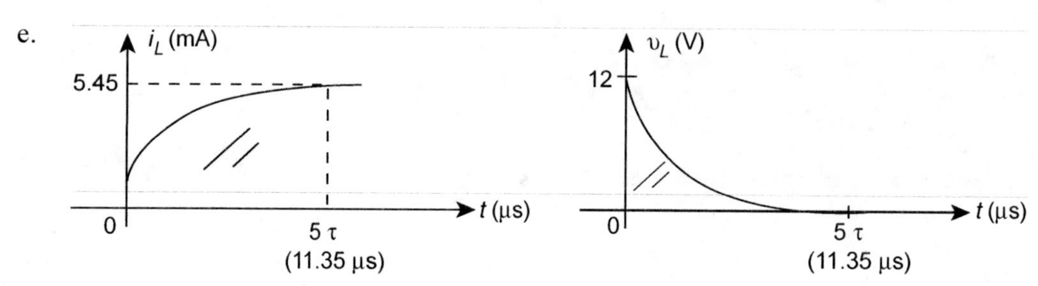

14. a. $\tau = \frac{L}{R} = \frac{2\text{ H}}{(20\ \Omega + 10\ \Omega)} = \frac{2\text{ H}}{30\ \Omega} = \mathbf{66.67\text{ ms}}$

b. $\upsilon_L = -E(1 - e^{-t/\tau}) = \mathbf{-12\text{ V}(1 - e^{-t/66.67ms})}$
$i_L = -\frac{E}{R}e^{-t/\tau} = -\frac{12\text{ V}}{30\ \Omega}e^{-t/66.67\text{ms}} = \mathbf{-400\text{ mA}e^{-t/66.67\text{ ms}}}$

c.

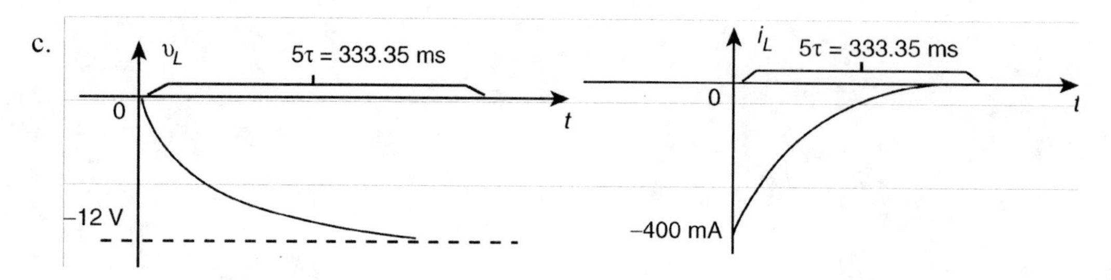

15. a. $i_L = I_f + (I_i - I_f)e^{-t/\tau}$
$I_i = 8\text{ mA},\ I_f = \frac{E}{R} = \frac{36\text{ V}}{3.9\text{ k}\Omega} = \mathbf{9.23\text{ mA}},\ \tau = \frac{L}{R} = \frac{120\text{ mH}}{3.9\text{ k}\Omega} = 30.77\ \mu s$
$i_L = 9.23\text{ mA} + (8\text{ mA} - 9.23\text{ mA})e^{-t/30.77\,\mu s}$
$i_L = \mathbf{9.23\text{ mA} - 1.23\text{ mA}e^{-t/30.77\,\mu s}}$
$+E - \upsilon_L - \upsilon_R = 0$ and $\upsilon_L = E - \upsilon_R$
$\upsilon_R = i_R R = i_L R = (8\text{ mA})(3.9\text{ k}\Omega) = 31.2\text{ V}$
$\upsilon_L = E - \upsilon_R = 36\text{ V} - 31.2\text{ V} = 4.8\text{ V}$
$\upsilon_L = \mathbf{4.8\text{ V}e^{-t/30.77\,\mu s}}$

b.

i_L

9.23 mA

8 mA

0

5τ = 153.85 μs

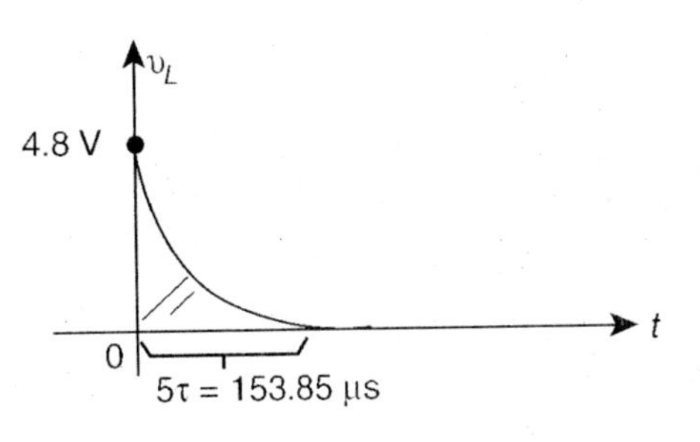

16. a. $I_i = -8$ mA, $I_f = 9.23$ mA, $\tau = \dfrac{L}{R} = \dfrac{120 \text{ mH}}{3.9 \text{ k}\Omega} = 30.77\ \mu s$

$i_L = I_f + (I_i - I_f)e^{-t/\tau}$

$= 9.23 \text{ mA} + (-8 \text{ mA} - 9.23 \text{ mA})e^{-t/30.77\ \mu s}$

$i_L = \mathbf{9.23\ mA - 17.23\ mA}\ e^{-t/30.77\ \mu s}$

$+E - \upsilon_L - \upsilon_R = 0$ (at $t = 0^-$)

but, $\upsilon_R = i_R R = -i_i R = (-8 \text{ mA})(3.9 \text{ k}\Omega) = -31.2$ V

$\upsilon_L = E - \upsilon_R = 36 \text{ V} - (-31.2 \text{ V}) = 67.2$ V

$\upsilon_L = \mathbf{67.2\ V}\ e^{-t/30.77\ \mu s}$

b.

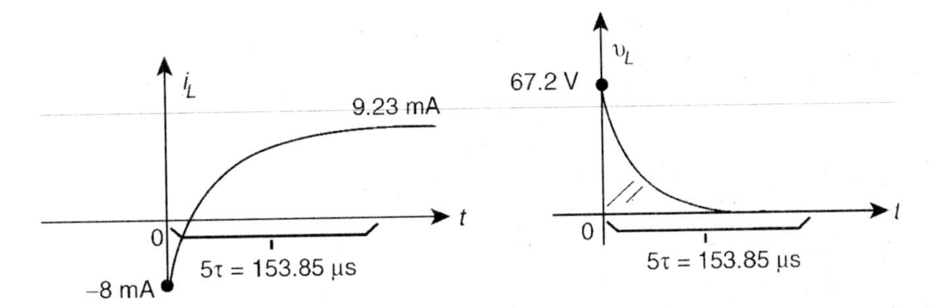

c. Final levels are the same. Transition period defined by 5τ is also the same.

17. a. Source conversion:

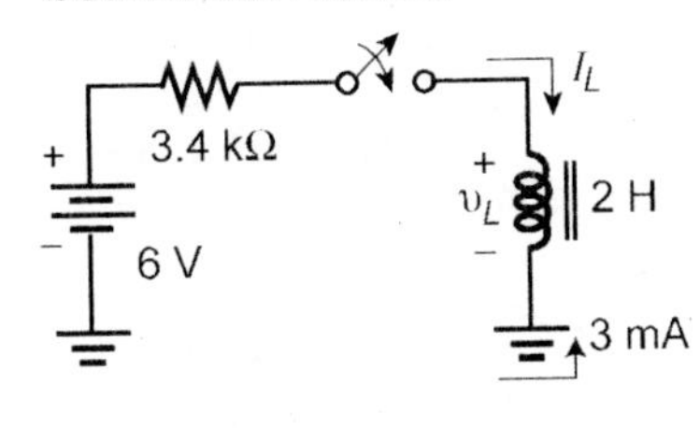

$\tau = \dfrac{L}{R} = \dfrac{2 \text{ H}}{3.4 \text{ k}\Omega} = 588.2\ \mu s$

$i_L = I_f + (I_i - I_f)e^{-t/\tau}$

$I_f = \dfrac{6 \text{ V}}{3.4 \text{ k}\Omega} = 1.76$ mA

$i_L = 1.76 \text{ mA} + (-3 \text{ mA} - 1.76 \text{ mA})e^{-t/588.2\mu s}$

$i_L = \mathbf{1.76\ mA - 4.76\ mA}\ e^{-t/588.2\mu s}$

– 10.2 V +

6 V

υ_L

$\upsilon_R(0+) = 3 \text{ mA}(3.4 \text{ k}\Omega) = 10.2$ V

KVL: $+6 \text{ V} + 10.2 \text{ V} - \upsilon_L(0+) = 0$

$\upsilon_L(0+) = 16.2$ V

$\upsilon_L = \mathbf{16.2\ V}e^{-t/588.2\mu s}$

b.

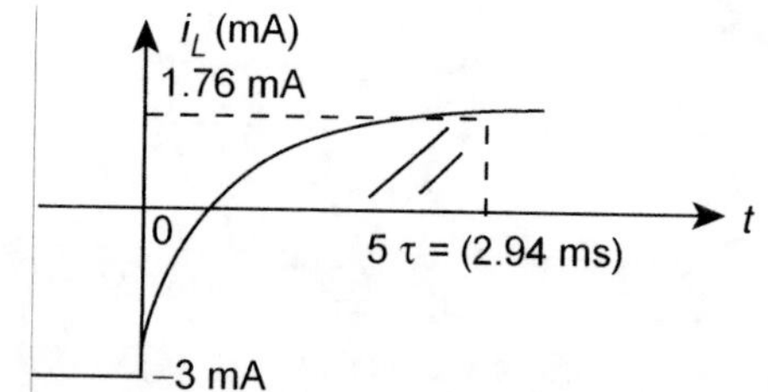

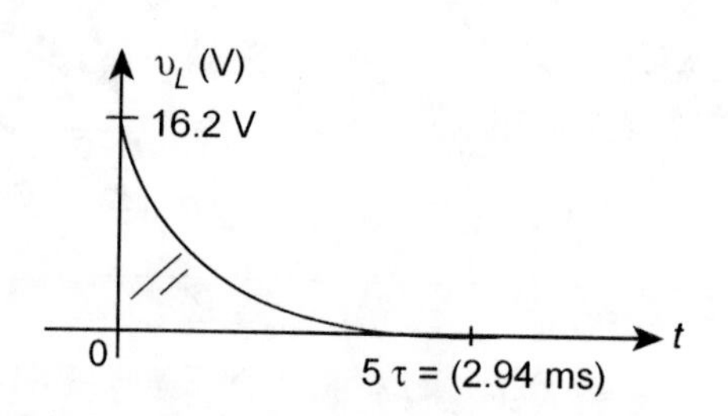

18. a.

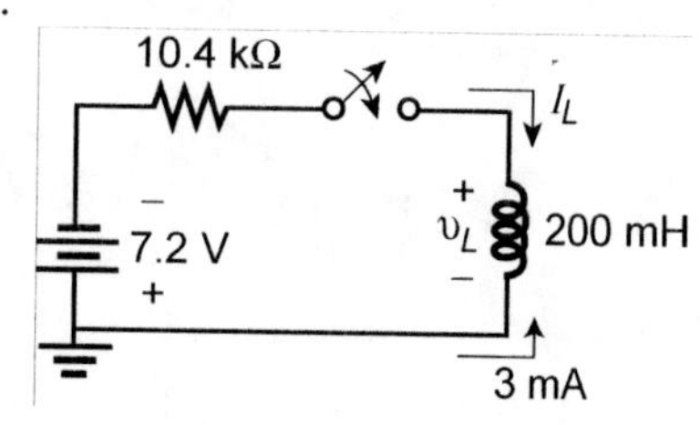

$$I_f = -\frac{7.2\text{ V}}{10.4\text{ k}\Omega} = -0.69\text{ mA}$$

$$\tau = \frac{L}{R} = \frac{200\text{ mH}}{10.4\text{ k}\Omega} = 19.23\ \mu\text{s}$$

$$i_L = I_f + (I_i - I_f)e^{-t/\tau}$$

$$= -0.69\text{ mA} + (-3\text{ mA} - (-0.69\text{ mA}))e^{-t/19.23\ \mu\text{s}}$$

$$i_L = \mathbf{-0.69\ mA - 2.31\ mA}e^{-t/19.23\ \mu\text{s}}$$

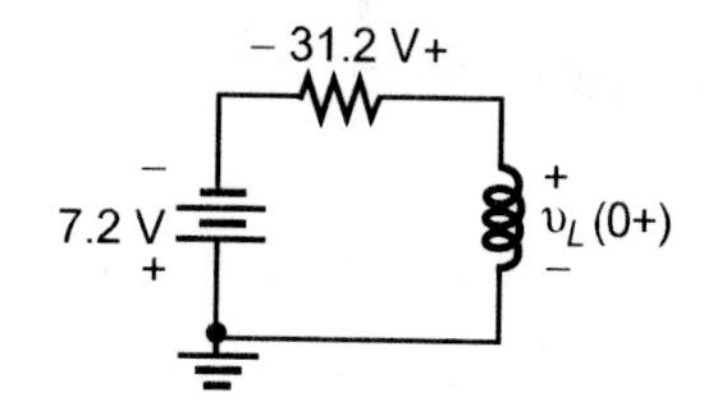

KVL: $-7.2\text{ V} + 31.2\text{ V} - \upsilon_L(0+) = 0$

$$\upsilon_L(0+) = 24\text{ V}$$

$$\upsilon_L = \mathbf{24\ V}e^{-t/19.23\ \mu\text{s}}$$

b.

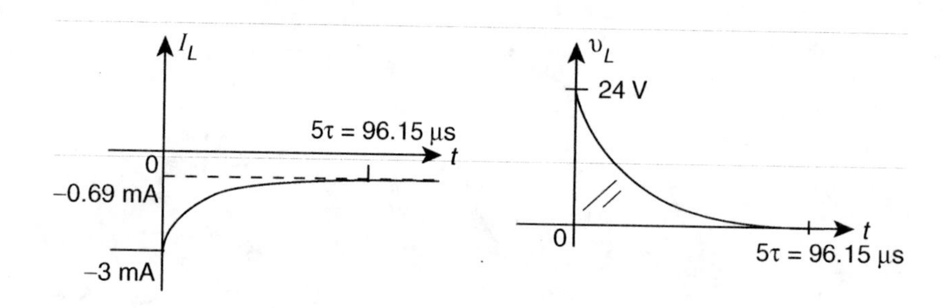

19. a.

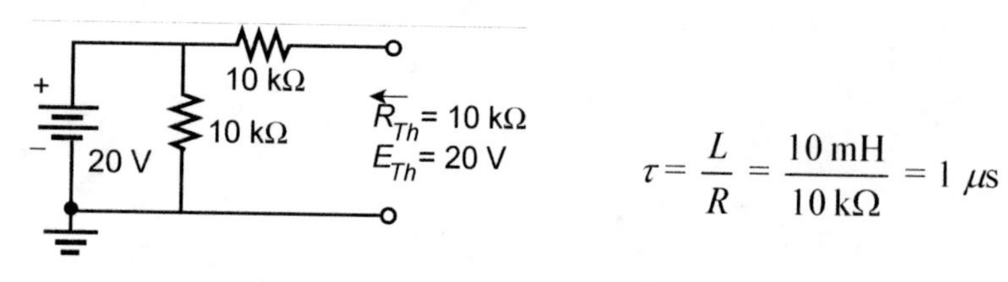

$$\tau = \frac{L}{R} = \frac{10\text{ mH}}{10\text{ k}\Omega} = 1\ \mu\text{s}$$

$$\upsilon_L = \mathbf{20\ V}e^{-t/1\mu s},\ i_L = \frac{E}{R}(1 - e^{-t/\tau}) = \mathbf{2\ mA}(1 - e^{-t/1\mu s})$$

b. $5\tau \Rightarrow$ steady state

$$\tau' = \frac{L}{R} = \frac{10 \text{ mH}}{10 \text{ k}\Omega} = 1 \ \mu\text{s}$$

$$i_L = I_m e^{-t/\tau'} = \mathbf{2\ mA}\boldsymbol{e^{-t/1\mu s}}$$

$$\upsilon_L = -(2 \text{ mA})(20 \text{ k}\Omega)e^{-t/\tau} = \mathbf{-40\ V}\boldsymbol{e^{-t/1\mu s}}$$

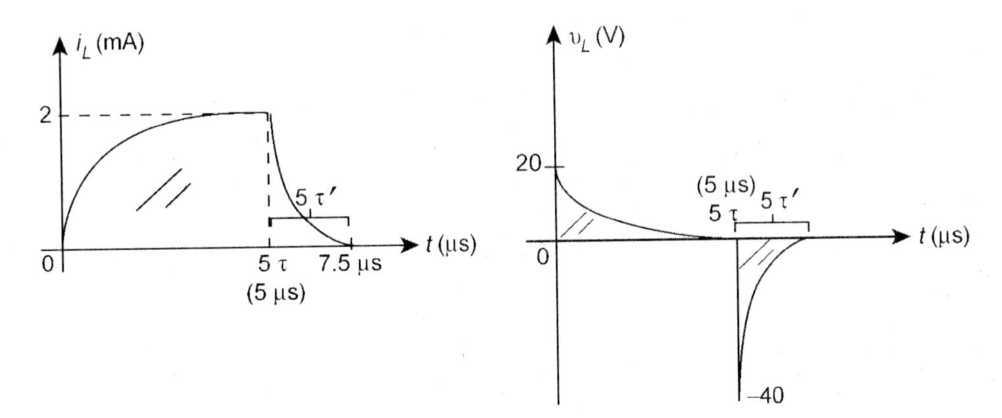

20. a. $$\tau = \frac{L}{R} = \frac{1 \text{ mH}}{2 \text{ k}\Omega} = 0.5 \ \mu\text{s}$$

$$i_L = \frac{E}{R}(1 - e^{-t/\tau}) = \frac{12 \text{ V}}{2 \text{ k}\Omega}(1 - e^{-t/\tau}) = \mathbf{6\ mA(1 - }\boldsymbol{e^{-t/0.5\mu s}}\mathbf{)}$$

$$\upsilon_L = Ee^{-t/\tau} = \mathbf{12\ V}\ \boldsymbol{e^{-t/0.5\mu s}}$$

b. $$i_L = 6 \text{ mA}(1 - e^{-t/0.5\mu s}) = 6 \text{ mA}(1 - e^{-1\mu s/0.5\mu s})$$

$$= 6 \text{ mA}(1 - e^{-2}) = 5.19 \text{ mA}$$

$$i_L = I'_m e^{-t/\tau'} \qquad \tau' = \frac{L}{R} = \frac{1 \text{ mH}}{12 \text{ k}\Omega} = 83.3 \text{ ns}$$

$$i_L = \mathbf{5.19\ mA}\boldsymbol{e^{-t/83.3ns}}$$

$t = 1\ \mu\text{s}$: $\upsilon_L = 12 \text{ V}e^{-t/0.5\mu s} = 12 \text{ V}e^{-2} = 12 \text{ V}(0.1353) = 1.62 \text{ V}$

$$V'_L = (5.19 \text{ mA})(12 \text{ k}\Omega) = 62.28 \text{ V}$$

$$\upsilon_L = \mathbf{-62.28\ V}\boldsymbol{e^{-t/83.3ns}}$$

c.

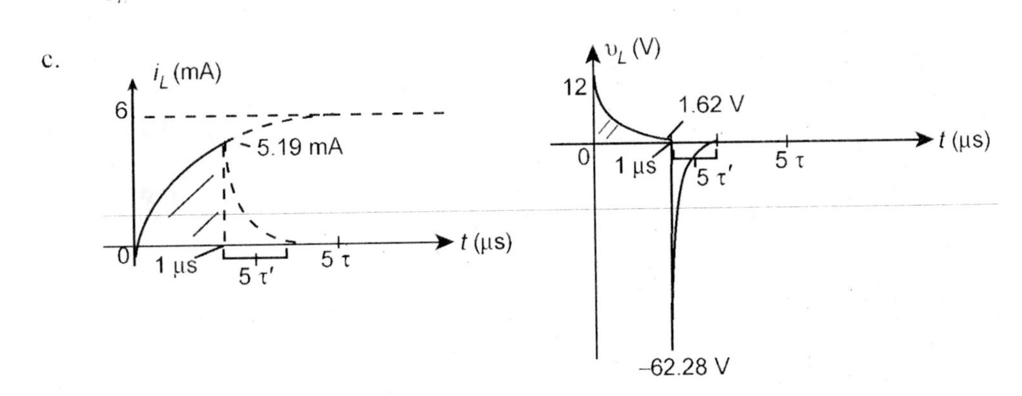

21. a.

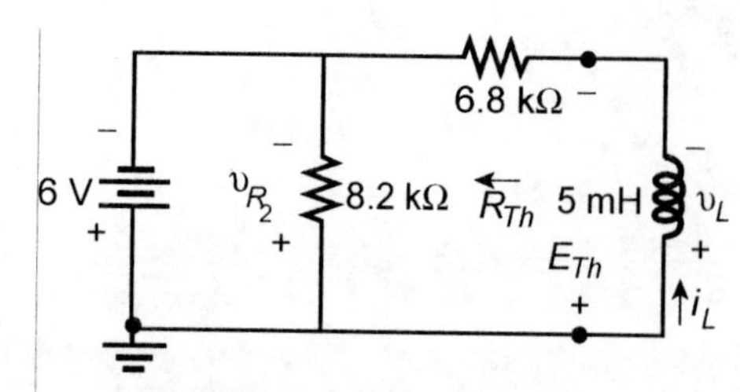

$R_{Th} = 6.8\text{ k}\Omega$
$E_{Th} = 6\text{ V}$

$$\tau = \frac{L}{R} = \frac{5\text{ mH}}{6.8\text{ k}\Omega} = 0.74\ \mu\text{s}$$

$$i_L = \frac{E}{R}(1 - e^{-t/\tau}) = \frac{6\text{ V}}{6.8\text{ k}\Omega}(1 - e^{-t/\tau}) = \mathbf{0.88\text{ mA}(1 - e^{-t/0.74\mu s})}$$

$$v_L = Ee^{-t/\tau} = \mathbf{6\text{ V}e^{-t/0.74\mu s}}$$

b. Assume steady state and $I_L = 0.88$ mA

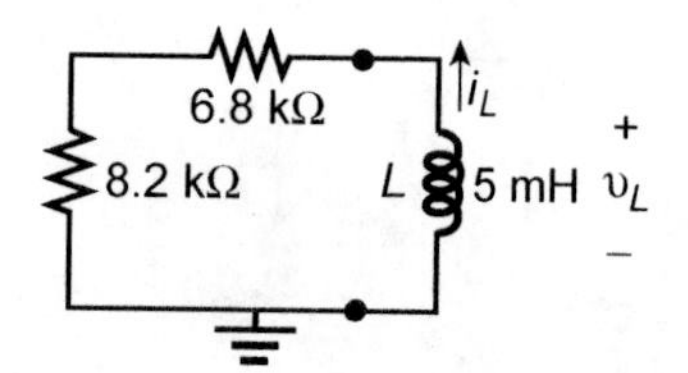

$$\tau' = \frac{L}{R} = \frac{5\text{ mH}}{15\text{ k}\Omega} = 0.33\ \mu\text{s}$$

$$i_L = I_m e^{-t/\tau'} = \mathbf{0.88\text{ mA } e^{-t/0.33\mu s}}$$

$$v_L = -V_m e^{-t/\tau'}$$

$$V_m = I_m R = (0.88\text{ mA})(15\text{ k}\Omega) = 13.23\text{ V}$$

$$v_L = \mathbf{-13.23\text{ V}e^{-t/0.33\mu s}}$$

c.

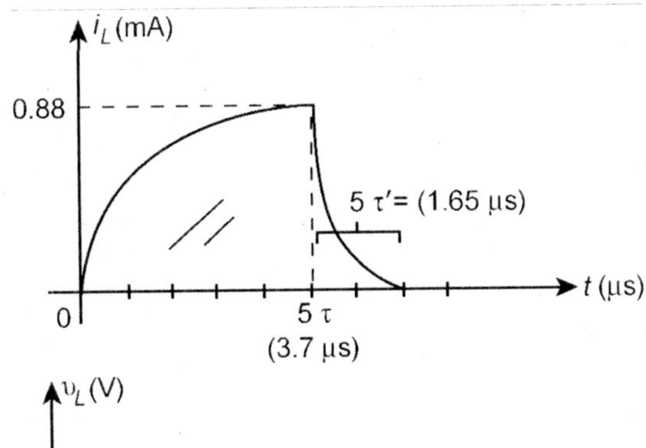

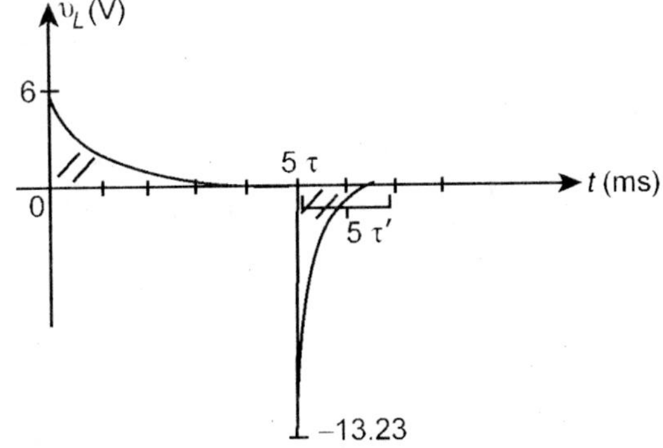

d. $V_{R_{2\,max}} = I_m R_2 = (0.88 \text{ mA})(8.2 \text{ k}\Omega) = 7.22 \text{ V}$

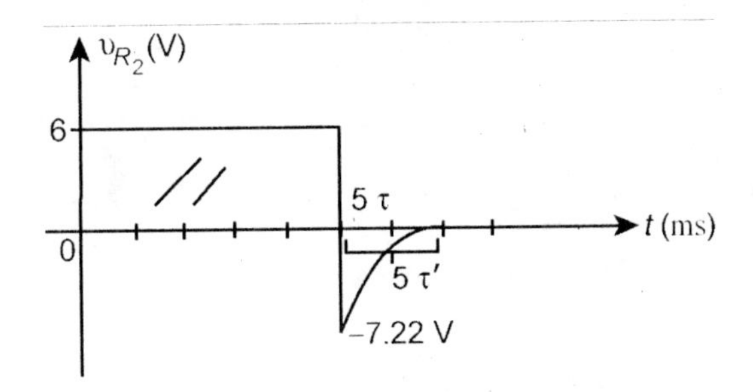

22. a. $R_{Th} = 2 \text{ k}\Omega + 3 \text{ k}\Omega \parallel 6 \text{ k}\Omega = 2 \text{ k}\Omega + 2 \text{ k}\Omega = 4 \text{ k}\Omega$

$E_{Th} = \dfrac{6 \text{ k}\Omega(12 \text{ V})}{6 \text{ k}\Omega + 3 \text{ k}\Omega} = 8 \text{ V}, \quad \tau = \dfrac{L}{R} = \dfrac{100 \text{ mH}}{4 \text{ k}\Omega} = 25 \ \mu\text{s}$

$I_f = \dfrac{E_{Th}}{R_{Th}} = \dfrac{8 \text{ V}}{4 \text{ k}\Omega} = 2 \text{ mA}$

$i_L = \mathbf{2 \text{ mA}(1 - e^{-t/25\mu s})}$

$\boldsymbol{\upsilon_L = 8 \text{ V}e^{-t/25\mu s}}$

b. $i_L = 2 \text{ mA}(1 - e^{-1}) = \mathbf{1.26 \text{ mA}}$

$\upsilon_L = 8 \text{ V}e^{-1} = \mathbf{2.94 \text{ V}}$

23. a. Source conversion: $E = IR = (4\text{ mA})(12\text{ k}\Omega) = 48\text{ V}$

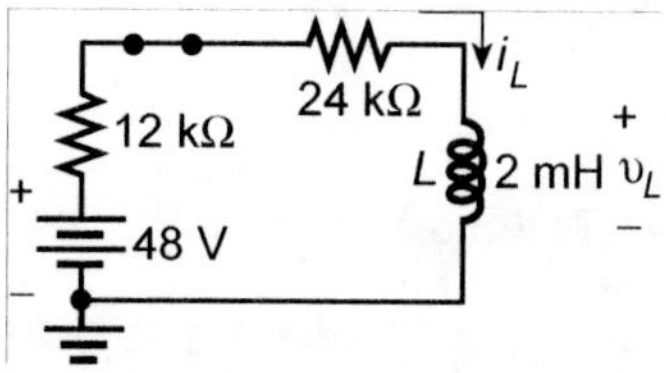

$$\tau = \frac{L}{R} = \frac{2\text{ mH}}{36\text{ k}\Omega} = 55.56\text{ ns}$$

$$i_L = \frac{E}{R}(1 - e^{-t/\tau}) = \frac{48\text{ V}}{36\text{ k}\Omega}(1 - e^{-t/\tau}) = \mathbf{1.33\text{ mA}(1 - e^{-t/55.56\text{ns}})}$$

$$\upsilon_L = Ee^{-t/\tau} = \mathbf{48\text{ V}e^{-t/55.56\text{ns}}}$$

b. $t = 100\text{ ns}$:

$$i_L = 1.33\text{ mA}(1 - e^{-100\text{ns}/55.56\text{ns}}) = 1.33\text{ mA}(1 - \underbrace{e^{-1.8}}_{0.165}) = \mathbf{1.11\text{ mA}}$$

$$\upsilon_L = \mathbf{48\text{ V}e^{-1.8} = 7.93\text{ V}}$$

24. a.

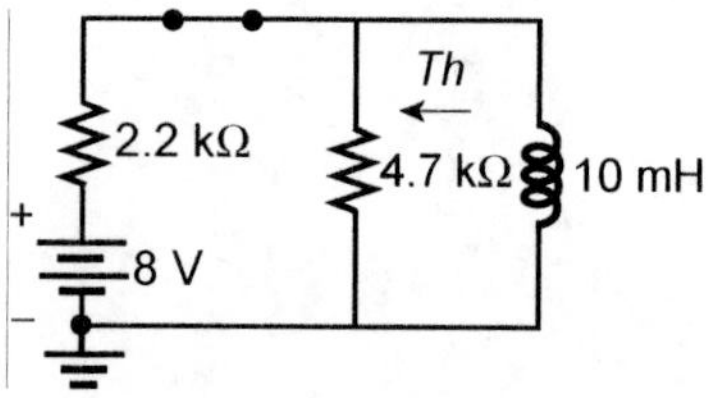

$$R_{Th} = 2.2\text{ k}\Omega \parallel 4.7\text{ k}\Omega = 1.50\text{ k}\Omega$$

$$E_{Th} = \frac{4.7\text{ k}\Omega(8\text{ V})}{4.7\text{ k}\Omega + 2.2\text{ k}\Omega} = 5.45\text{ V}$$

$$\tau = \frac{L}{R} = \frac{10\text{ mH}}{1.50\text{ k}\Omega} = 6.67\ \mu\text{s}$$

$$i_L = \frac{E}{R}(1 - e^{-t/\tau}) = \frac{5.45\text{ V}}{1.5\text{ k}\Omega}(1 - e^{-t/\tau}) = \mathbf{3.63\text{ mA}(1 - e^{-t/6.67\mu\text{s}})}$$

$$\upsilon_L = Ee^{-t/\tau} = \mathbf{5.45\text{ V}e^{-t/6.67\mu\text{s}}}$$

b. $t = 10\ \mu\text{s}$:

$$i_L = 3.63\text{ mA}(1 - e^{-10\mu\text{s}/6.67\mu\text{s}}) = 3.63\text{ mA}(1 - \underbrace{e^{-1.4}}_{0.246})$$

$= \mathbf{2.74\text{ mA}}$

$\upsilon_L = 5.45\text{ V}(0.246) = \mathbf{1.34\text{ V}}$

c. $\tau' = \frac{L}{R} = \frac{10\text{ mH}}{4.7\text{ k}\Omega} = 2.13\ \mu\text{s}$

$i_L = \mathbf{2.74\text{ mA}e^{-t/2.13\mu\text{s}}}$

At $t = 10\ \mu\text{s}$

$V_L = (2.74\text{ mA})(4.7\text{ k}\Omega) = 12.88\text{ V}$

$\upsilon_L = \mathbf{-12.88\text{ V}e^{-t/2.13\mu\text{s}}}$

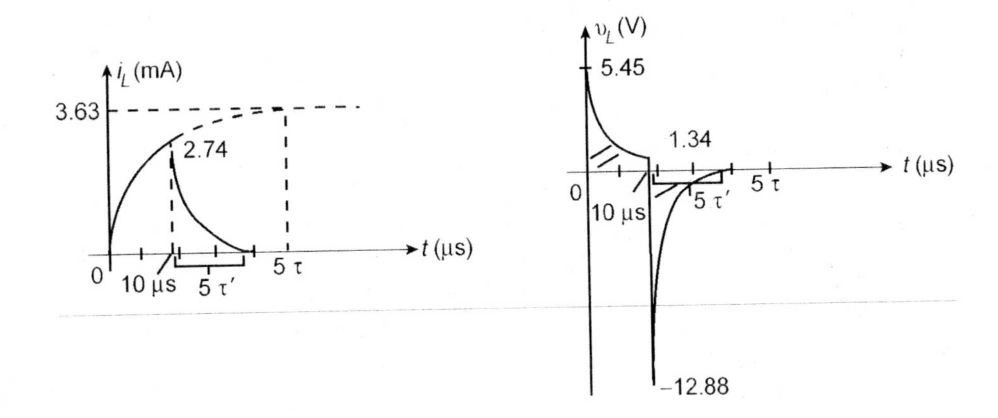

25. a. $\upsilon_L = Ee^{-t/\tau}$ $\qquad \tau = \dfrac{L}{R_1 + R_3} = \dfrac{0.6\text{ H}}{100\ \Omega + 20\ \Omega} = \dfrac{0.6\text{ H}}{120\ \Omega} = 5\text{ ms}$

$\upsilon_L = 36\text{ V}e^{-t/5\text{ ms}}$

$\upsilon_L = 36\text{ V}e^{-25\text{ ms}/5\text{ ms}} = 36\text{ V}e^{-5} = 36\text{ V}(0.00674) = \mathbf{0.24\ V}$

b. $\upsilon_L = 36\text{ V}e^{-1\text{ ms}/5\text{ ms}} = 36\text{ V}e^{-0.2} = 36\text{ V}(0.819) = \mathbf{29.47\ V}$

c. $\upsilon_{R_1} = i_{R_1}R_1 = i_L R_1 = \left(\dfrac{E}{R_1 + R_3}(1 - e^{-t/\tau})\right)R_1$

$= \left(\dfrac{36\text{ V}}{120\ \Omega}(1 - e^{-t/5\text{ms}})\right)100\ \Omega$

$= (300\text{ mA}(1 - e^{-t/5\text{ ms}}))100\ \Omega$

$= 30\text{ V}(1 - e^{-5\text{ ms}/5\text{ ms}}) = 30\text{ V}(1 - e^{-1})$

$= 30\text{ V}(1 - 0.368) = \mathbf{18.96\ V}$

d. $i_L = 300\text{ mA}(1 - e^{-t/5\text{ ms}})$

$100\text{ mA} = 300\text{ mA}(1 - e^{-t/5\text{ ms}})$

$0.333 = 1 - e^{-t/5\text{ ms}}$

$0.667 = e^{-t/5\text{ ms}}$

$\log_e 0.667 = -t/5\text{ ms}$

$0.405 = t/5\text{ ms}$

$t = 0.405(5\text{ ms}) = \mathbf{2.03\ ms}$

26. a. $I_i = \dfrac{16\text{ V}}{4.7\text{ k}\Omega + 3.3\text{ k}\Omega} = 2\text{ mA}$

$t = 0$ s: Thevenin:

$R_{Th} = 3.3\text{ k}\Omega + 1\text{ k}\Omega \parallel 4.7\text{ k}\Omega = 3.3\text{ k}\Omega + 0.82\text{ k}\Omega = 4.12\text{ k}\Omega$

$E_{Th} = \dfrac{1\text{ k}\Omega(16\text{ V})}{1\text{ k}\Omega + 4.7\text{ k}\Omega} = 2.81\text{ V}$

$i_L = I_f + (I_i - I_f)e^{-t/\tau}$

$$I_f = \frac{2.81\text{ V}}{4.12\text{ k}\Omega} = 0.68\text{ mA},\ \tau = \frac{L}{R} = \frac{2\text{ H}}{4.12\text{ k}\Omega} = 0.49\text{ ms}$$

$$i_L = 0.68\text{ mA} + (2\text{ mA} - 0.68\text{ mA})e^{-t/0.49\text{ ms}}$$

$$i_L = \mathbf{0.68\text{ mA} + 1.32\text{ mA}e^{-t/0.49\text{ ms}}}$$

$$\upsilon_R(0+) = 2\text{ mA}(4.12\text{ k}\Omega) = 8.24\text{ V}$$

KVL(0+): $2.81\text{ V} - 8.24\text{ V} - \upsilon_L = 0$

$$\upsilon_L = -5.43\text{ V}$$

$$\upsilon_L = \mathbf{-5.43\text{ V}e^{-t/0.49\text{ ms}}}$$

b.

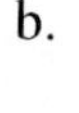

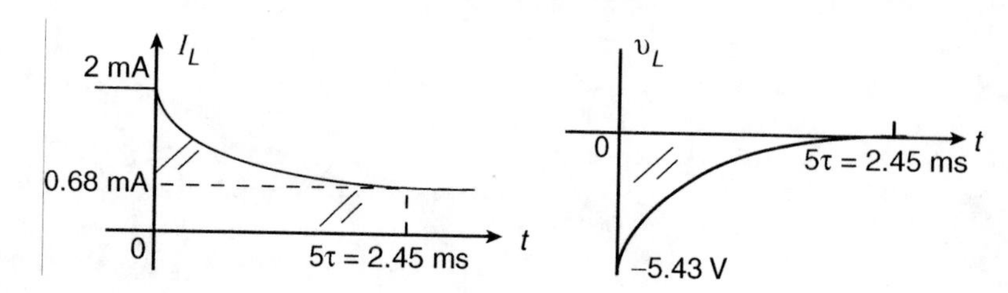

27. a. Redrawn:

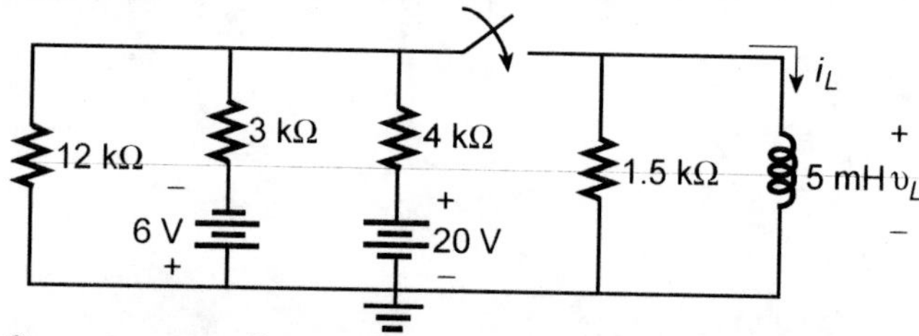

Source conversions:

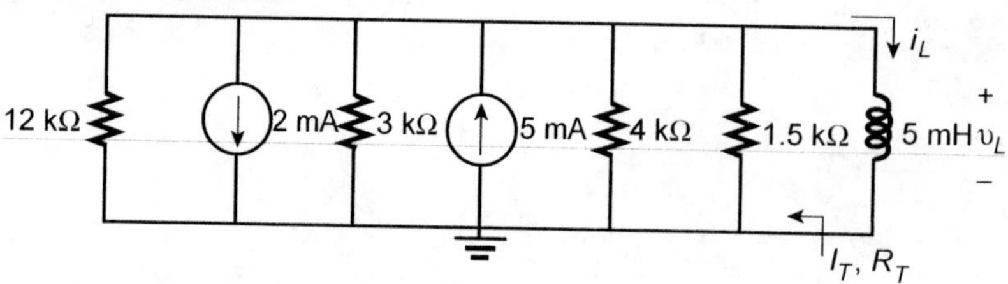

$I_T = 5\text{ mA} - 2\text{ mA} = 3\text{ mA}\uparrow$

$$\frac{1}{R_T} = \frac{1}{12\text{ k}\Omega} + \frac{1}{3\text{ k}\Omega} + \frac{1}{4\text{ k}\Omega} + \frac{1}{1.5\text{ k}\Omega}$$

and $R_T = 0.75\text{ k}\Omega$

Source conversion:

$E_T = I_T R_T = (3\text{ mA})(0.75\text{ k}\Omega) = 2.25\text{ V}$

$$\tau = \frac{L}{R} = \frac{5\text{ mH}}{0.75\text{ k}\Omega} = 6.67\ \mu\text{s}$$

$$i_L = \frac{2.25\text{ V}}{0.75\text{ k}\Omega}(1 - e^{-t/\tau}) = \mathbf{3\text{ mA}(1 - e^{-t/6.67\ \mu\text{s}})}$$

$$\upsilon_L = \mathbf{2.25\text{ V}e^{-t/6.67\ \mu\text{s}}}$$

b. 2τ: $0.865\ I_m$, $0.135\ V_m$

i_L: $0.865(3\text{ mA}) = \mathbf{2.60\ mA}$

υ_L: $0.135(2.25\text{ V}) = \mathbf{0.30\ V}$

c.

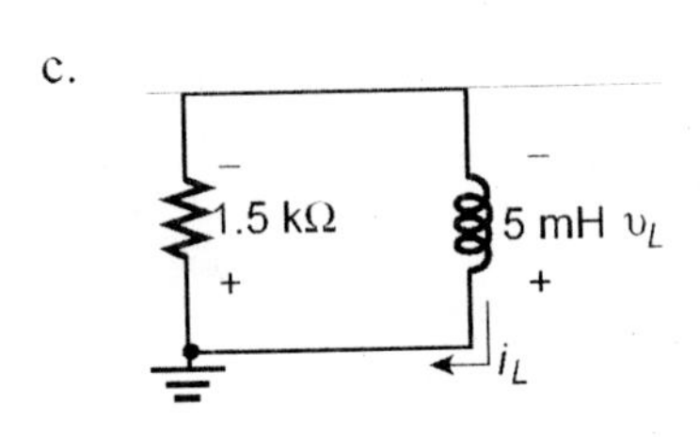

$$\tau' = \frac{L}{R} = \frac{5\text{ mH}}{1.5\text{ k}\Omega} = 3.33\ \mu\text{s}$$

$i_L = \mathbf{2.60\ mA}\ \boldsymbol{e^{-t/3.33\ \mu s}}$

$i_L(0+) = 2.60\text{ mA}$

$\upsilon_R(0+) = (2.60\text{ mA})(1.5\text{ k}\Omega) = 3.90\text{ V}$

$\upsilon_L = \mathbf{-3.90\ V}\boldsymbol{e^{-t/3.33\ \mu s}}$

d.

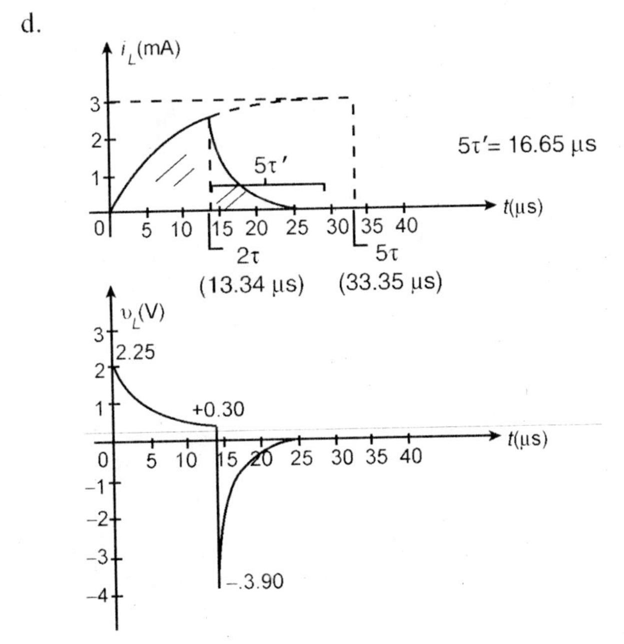

28. a.

2 MΩ

E 24 V

10 MΩ

i_L

υ_L

$R_{Th} = 2\text{ M}\Omega \parallel 10\text{ M}\Omega = 1.67\text{ M}\Omega$

$$E_{Th} = \frac{10\text{ M}\Omega(24\text{ V})}{10\text{ M}\Omega + 2\text{ M}\Omega} = 20\text{ V}$$

$$I_L(0^-) = \frac{E_{Th}}{R_{Th}} = \frac{20\text{ V}}{1.67\text{ M}\Omega} = \mathbf{12\ \mu A}$$

$$\tau' = \frac{L}{R_{\text{meter}}} = \frac{5\text{ H}}{10\text{ M}\Omega} = 5\,\mu\text{s}$$

$i_L = 12\ \mu\text{A}e^{-t/5\ \mu s}$

$10\ \mu\text{A} = 12\ \mu\text{A}e^{-t/5\ \mu s}$

$0.833 = e^{-t/5\ \mu s}$

$\log_e 0.833 = -t/5\ \mu\text{s}$

$0.183 = t/5\ \mu s$

$t = 0.183(5\ \mu s) = \mathbf{0.92\ \mu s}$

b. $\upsilon_L(0^+) = i_L(0^+)R_m = (12\ \mu A)(10\ M\Omega) = 120\ V$

$\upsilon_L = 120\ Ve^{-t/5\mu s} = 120\ Ve^{-10\mu s/5\mu s} = 120\ Ve^{-2} = 120\ V(0.135) = \mathbf{16.2\ V}$

c. $\upsilon_L = 120\ Ve^{-5\tau/\tau} = 120\ Ve^{-5} = 120\ V(6.74 \times 10^{-3}) = \mathbf{0.81\ V}$

29. a. $I_i = -\dfrac{24\ V}{2.2\ k\Omega} = -10.91\ mA$

Switch open: $I_f = -\dfrac{24\ V}{2.2\ k\Omega + 4.7\ k\Omega} = -\dfrac{24\ V}{6.9\ k\Omega} = -3.48\ mA$

$i_L = I_f + (I_i - I_f)e^{-t/\tau}$

$\tau = \dfrac{L}{R} = \dfrac{1.2\ H}{6.9\ k\Omega} = 173.9\ \mu s$

$i_L = -3.48\ mA + (-10.91\ mA - (-3.48\ mA))e^{-t/173.9\ \mu s}$

$i_L = \mathbf{-3.48\ mA - 7.43\ mAe^{-t/173.9\ \mu s}}$

$t = 0+$:

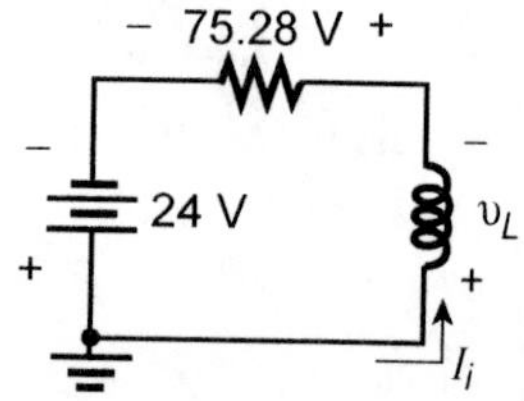

− 75.28 V +

24 V

υ_L

I_i

$\upsilon_R(0+) = (10.91\ mA)(6.9\ k\Omega) = 75.28\ V$

KVL: $-24\ V + 75.28\ V - \upsilon_L = 0$

$\upsilon_L = 51.28\ V$

$\upsilon_L = \mathbf{51.28\ Ve^{-t/173.9\ \mu s}}$

30. a. $i_L = 100\ mA(1 - e^{-1ms/20ms}) = 100\ mA(1 - e^{-1/20})$

$= 100\ mA(1 - e^{-0.05}) = 100\ mA(1 - 951.23 \times 10^{-3}) = 100\ mA(48.77 \times 10^{-3})$

$= \mathbf{4.88\ mA}$

b. $i_L = 100\ mA(1 - e^{-100ms/20ms}) = 100\ mA(1 - e^{-5})$

$= \mathbf{99.33\ mA}$

c. $50\ mA = 100\ mA(1 - e^{-t/\tau})$

$0.5 = 1 - e^{-t/\tau}$

$-0.5 = -e^{-t/\tau}$

$0.5 = e^{-t/\tau}$

$\log_e 0.5 = -t/\tau$

$t = -(\tau)(\log_e 0.5) = -(20\ ms)(\log_e 0.5) = -(20\ ms)(-693.15 \times 10^{-3})$

$= \mathbf{13.86\ ms}$

d. $99 \text{ mA} = 100 \text{ mA}(1 - e^{-t/20 \text{ ms}})$

$$0.99 = 1 - e^{-t/20\text{ms}}$$
$$-0.01 = -e^{-t/20\text{ms}}$$
$$0.01 = e^{-t/20\text{ms}}$$
$$\log_e 0.01 = -t/20 \text{ ms}$$
$$t = -(20 \text{ ms})(\log_e 0.01) = -(20 \text{ ms})(-4.605) = \mathbf{92.1ms}$$

31. a. $L \Rightarrow$ open circuit equivalent

$$V_L = \frac{10 \text{ M}\Omega(24 \text{ V})}{10 \text{ M}\Omega + 2 \text{ M}\Omega} = \mathbf{20 \text{ V}}$$

b.

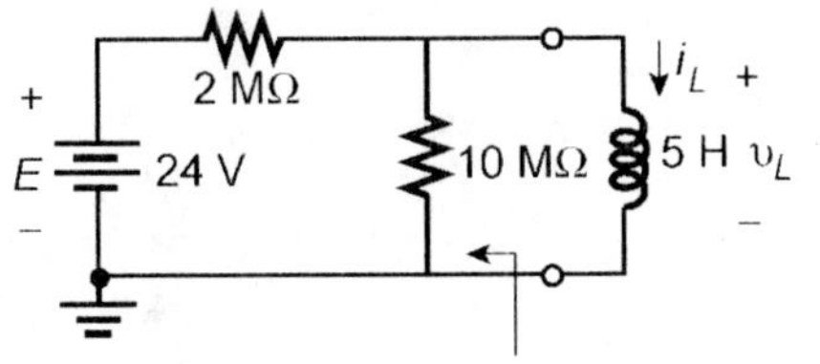

+ 2 MΩ i_L +

E 24 V 10 MΩ 5 H υ_L

– –

$$R_{Th} = 2 \text{ M}\Omega \parallel 10 \text{ M}\Omega = 1.67 \text{ M}\Omega$$
$$E_{Th} = \frac{10 \text{ M}\Omega(24 \text{ V})}{10 \text{ M}\Omega + 2 \text{ M}\Omega} = 20 \text{ V}$$

$$I_{L_{\text{final}}} = \frac{E_{Th}}{R_{Th}} = \frac{20 \text{ V}}{1.67 \text{ M}\Omega} = \mathbf{12\ \mu A}$$

c. $i_L = 12\ \mu\text{A}(1 - e^{-t/3\ \mu\text{s}})$ $\tau = \frac{L}{R} = \frac{5 \text{ H}}{1.67 \text{ M}\Omega} = 3\ \mu\text{s}$

$$10\ \mu\text{A} = 12\ \mu\text{A}(1 - e^{-t/3\ \mu\text{s}})$$
$$0.8333 = 1 - e^{-t/3\ \mu\text{s}}$$
$$0.1667 = e^{-t/3\ \mu\text{s}}$$
$$\log_e(0.1667) = -t/3\ \mu\text{s}$$
$$1.792 = t/3\ \mu\text{s}$$
$$t = 1.792(3\ \mu\text{s}) = \mathbf{5.38\ \mu s}$$

d. $\upsilon_L = 20 \text{ V } e^{-t/3\ \mu\text{s}} = 20 \text{ V } e^{-12\ \mu\text{s}/3\ \mu\text{s}} = 20 \text{ V } e^{-4}$
$= 20 \text{ V}(0.0183) = \mathbf{0.37 \text{ V}}$

32. $e_L = L\frac{\Delta i}{\Delta t}$: 0 – 3 ms, $e_L = \mathbf{0 \text{ V}}$

$$3 - 8 \text{ ms}, e_L = (200 \text{ mH})\left(\frac{40 \times 10^{-3} \text{ A}}{5 \times 10^{-3} \text{ s}}\right) = \mathbf{1.6 \text{ V}}$$

$$8 - 13 \text{ ms}, e_L = -(200 \text{ mH})\left(\frac{40 \times 10^{-3} \text{ A}}{5 \times 10^{-3} \text{ s}}\right) = \mathbf{-1.6 \text{ V}}$$

13 – 14 ms, $e_L = \mathbf{0 \text{ V}}$

$$14 - 15 \text{ ms}, e_L = (200 \text{ mH})\left(\frac{40 \times 10^{-3} \text{ A}}{5 \times 10^{-3} \text{ s}}\right) = \mathbf{8 \text{ V}}$$

$15 - 16$ ms, $e_L =$ **–8 V**

$16 - 17$ ms, $e_L =$ **0 V**

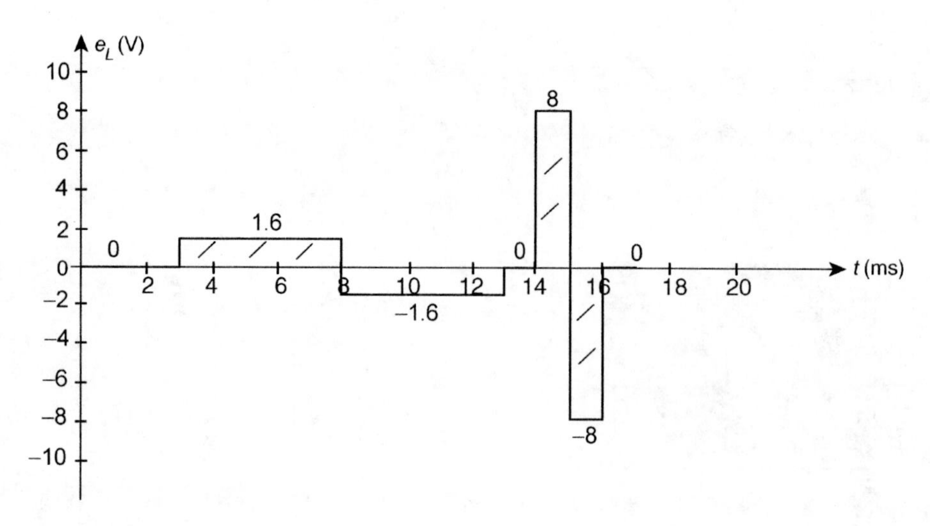

33. $\upsilon_L = L\dfrac{\Delta i_L}{\Delta t}$

$0 \rightarrow 2$ ms: $\upsilon_L = (5\text{ mH})\left(-\dfrac{20\text{ mA}}{2\text{ ms}}\right) = \mathbf{-50\ mV}$

$2 \rightarrow 5$ ms: $\Delta i_L = 0$ mA, $\upsilon_L = 0$ V

$5 \rightarrow 11$ ms: $\upsilon_L = (5\text{ mH})\left(\dfrac{+30\text{ mA}}{6\text{ ms}}\right) = \mathbf{+25\ mV}$

$11 \rightarrow 18$ ms: $\upsilon_L = (5\text{ mH})\left(\dfrac{-10\text{ mA}}{7\text{ ms}}\right) = \mathbf{-7.14\ V}$

$18 \rightarrow$: $\Delta i_L = 0$ mA, $\upsilon_L = \mathbf{0\ V}$

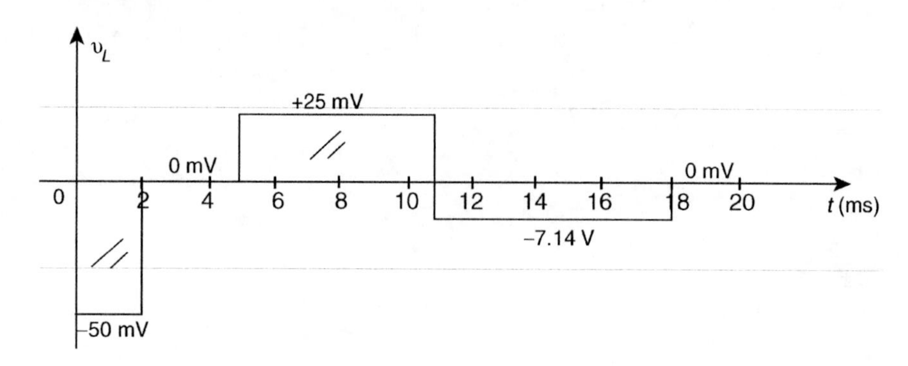

34. $L = 10$ mH, 4 mA at $t = 0$ s

$$\upsilon_L = L\frac{\Delta i}{\Delta t} \Rightarrow \Delta i = \frac{\Delta t}{L}\upsilon_L$$

$0 - 5\ \mu$s: $\upsilon_L = 0$ V, $\Delta i_L = 0$ mA and $i_L =$ **4 mA**

$5 - 10\ \mu$s: $\Delta i_L = \dfrac{5\ \mu\text{s}}{10\text{ mH}}(-24\text{ V}) = \mathbf{-12\ mA}$

$10 - 12\ \mu s$: $\Delta i_L = \dfrac{2\ \mu s}{10\ mH}(+60\ V) = \mathbf{+12\ mA}$

$12 - 16\ \mu s$: $\upsilon_L = 0\ V$, $\Delta i_L = 0\ mA$ and $i_L = \mathbf{4\ mA}$

$16 - 24\ \mu s$: $\Delta i_L = \dfrac{8\ \mu s}{10\ mH}(-5\ V) = \mathbf{-4\ mA}$

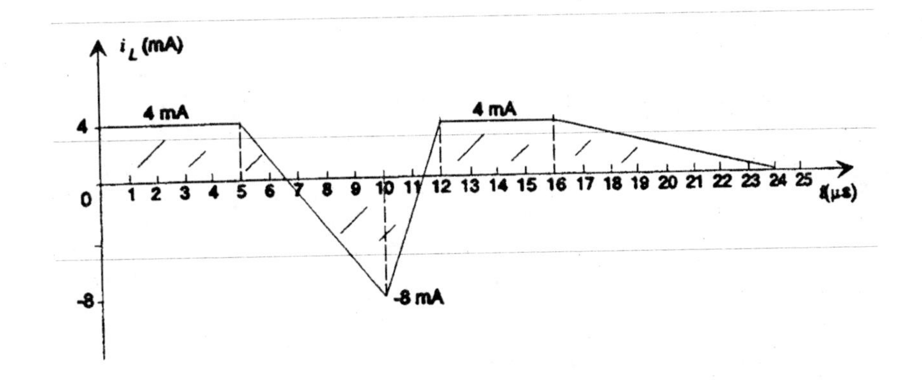

35. a. $L_T = L_1 + L_2 \parallel (L_3 + L_4) = 6\ H + 6\ H \parallel (6\ H + 6\ H)$
$= 6\ H + 6\ H \parallel 12\ H = 6\ H + 4\ H = \mathbf{10\ H}$

b. $L_T = (L_1 + L_2 \parallel L_3) \parallel L_4 = (4\ H + 4\ H \parallel 4\ H) \parallel 4\ H$
$= (4\ H + 2\ H) \parallel 4\ H = 6\ H \parallel 4\ H = \mathbf{2.4\ H}$

36. $L'_T = 6\ H \parallel (1\ H + 2\ H) = 6\ H \parallel 3\ H = 2\ H$

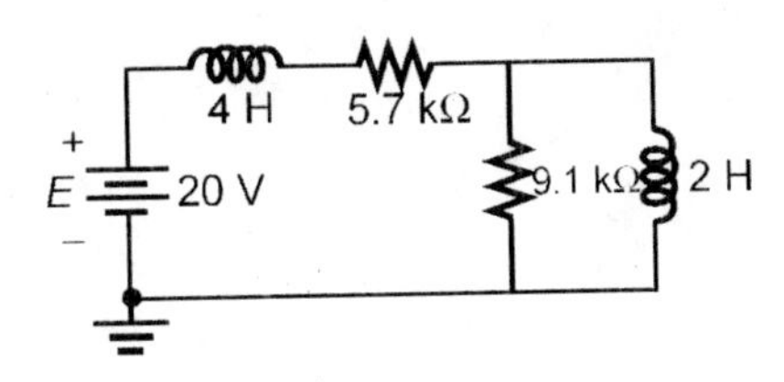

37. $L'_T = 6\ mH + 14\ mH \parallel 35\ mH = 6\ mH + 10\ mH = \mathbf{16\ mH}$
$C'_T = 9\ \mu F + 10\ \mu F \parallel 90\ \mu F = 9\ \mu F + 9\ \mu F = \mathbf{18\ \mu F}$
16 mH in series with 18 μF

38. a. $R'_T = 2\ k\Omega \parallel 8\ k\Omega = 1.6\ k\Omega$, $L'_T = 4\ H \parallel 6\ H = 2.4\ H$

$$\tau = \frac{L'_T}{R'_T} = \frac{2.4\ H}{1.6\ k\Omega} = 1.5\ ms$$

$$i_L = \frac{E}{R'_T}(1 - e^{-t/\tau})$$

$$= \frac{36\ V}{1.6\ k\Omega}(1 - e^{-t/1.5ms}) = \mathbf{22.5\ mA(1 - e^{-t/1.5ms})}$$

$\upsilon_L = Ee^{-t/\tau} = \mathbf{36\ Ve}^{-t/1.5ms}$

b.

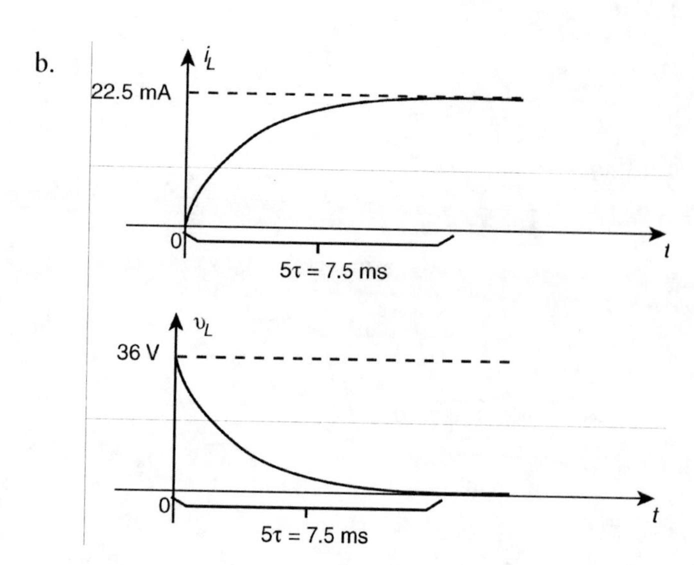

39. a. Source conversion: $E = 16$ V, $R_s = 2$ kΩ

$R_{Th} = 2\text{ k}\Omega + 2\text{ k}\Omega \parallel 8\text{ k}\Omega = 2\text{ k}\Omega + 16\text{ k}\Omega = 3.6\text{ k}\Omega$

$$E_{Th} = \frac{8\text{ k}\Omega(16\text{ V})}{8\text{ k}\Omega + 2\text{ k}\Omega} = 12.8\text{ V}$$

$$I_m = \frac{E_{Th}}{R_{Th}} = \frac{12.8\text{ V}}{3.6\text{ k}\Omega} = 3.56\text{ mA}, \quad \tau = \frac{L}{R} = \frac{30\text{ mH}}{3.6\text{ k}\Omega} = 8.33\ \mu\text{s}$$

$i_L = \mathbf{3.56\ mA(1 - e^{-t/8.33\mu s})}$

$\upsilon_L = E_{Th}e^{-t/\tau} = \mathbf{12.8\ V}e^{-t/8.33\mu s}$

b.

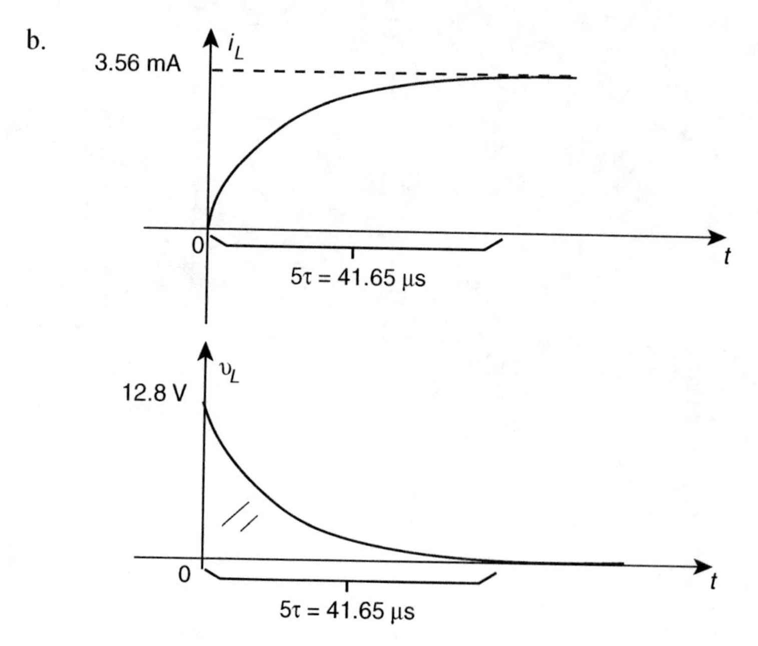

40. a.

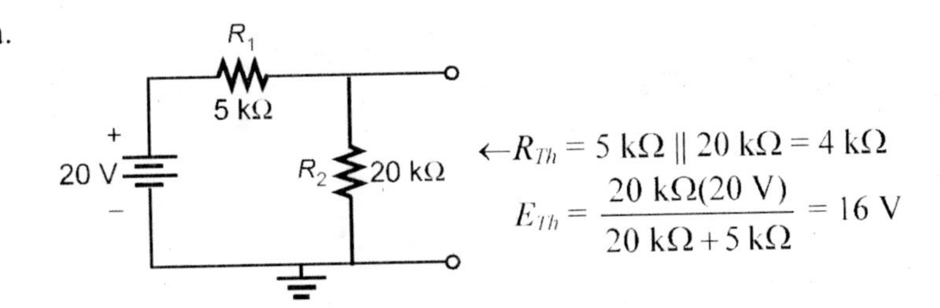

$\leftarrow R_{Th} = 5\text{ k}\Omega \parallel 20\text{ k}\Omega = 4\text{ k}\Omega$

$$E_{Th} = \frac{20\text{ k}\Omega(20\text{ V})}{20\text{ k}\Omega + 5\text{ k}\Omega} = 16\text{ V}$$

$$L_T = 5\text{ H} + 6\text{ H} \parallel 30\text{ H} = 5\text{ H} + 5\text{ H} = \mathbf{10\text{ H}}$$

$$\tau = \frac{L_T}{R} = \frac{10\text{ H}}{4\text{ k}\Omega} = 2.5\text{ ms}$$

$$\upsilon_L = \mathbf{16 V}\boldsymbol{e^{-t/2.5\text{ ms}}}$$

$$i_L = \frac{16\text{ V}}{4\text{ k}\Omega}(1 - e^{-t/\tau}) = \mathbf{4\text{ mA}(1 - e^{-t/2.5\text{ ms}})}$$

b.

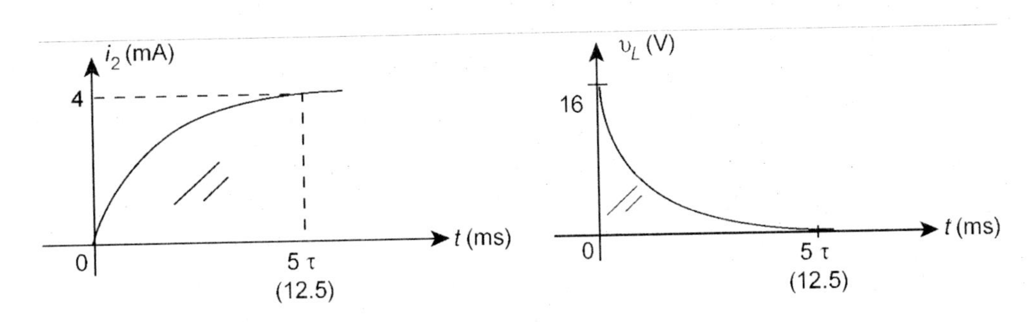

c.

5 H
+
υ_L
+
υ_{L_3}
5 H
–
–

$$\upsilon_{L_3} = \frac{\upsilon_L}{2} = \mathbf{8\text{ V}}\ \boldsymbol{e^{-t/2.5\text{ ms}}}$$

41. $$I_{R_1} = \frac{E}{R_1} = \frac{20\text{ V}}{4\,\Omega} = 5\text{ A}$$

$$I_2 = I_{R_2} = \frac{E}{R_2 + R_3} = \frac{20\text{ V}}{6\,\Omega + 4\,\Omega} = \frac{20\text{ V}}{10\,\Omega} = \mathbf{2\text{ A}}$$

$$I_1 = I_{R_1} + I_2 = 5\text{ A} + 2\text{ A} = \mathbf{7\text{ A}}$$

42. $I_1 = I_2 = \mathbf{0\text{ A}}$
$V_1 = V_2 = E = \mathbf{60\text{ V}}$

43. $I_1 = \dfrac{12\text{ V}}{4\,\Omega} = \mathbf{3\text{ A}}$, $I_2 = \mathbf{0\text{ A}}$
$V_1 = \mathbf{12\text{ V}}$, $V_2 = \mathbf{0\text{ V}}$

44. $$V_1 = \frac{(3\ \Omega + 3\ \Omega \parallel 6\ \Omega)(50\ \text{V})}{(3\ \Omega + 3\ \Omega \parallel 6\ \Omega) + 20\ \Omega} = \frac{(3\ \Omega + 2\ \Omega)(50\ \text{V})}{(3\ \Omega + 2\ \Omega) + 20\ \Omega} = \mathbf{10\ V}$$

$$R_T = 20\ \Omega + 3\ \Omega + 3\ \Omega \parallel 6\ \Omega = 23\ \Omega + 2\ \Omega = 25\ \Omega$$

$$I_s = I_1 = \frac{50\ \text{V}}{25\ \Omega} = \mathbf{2\ A}$$

$$I_{5\Omega} = 0\ \text{A},\ \therefore\ I_2 = \frac{6\ \Omega(I_s)}{6\ \Omega + 3\ \Omega} = \frac{6\ \Omega(2\ \text{A})}{6\ \Omega + 3\ \Omega} = \mathbf{1.33\ A}$$

$$V_2 = \frac{(3\ \Omega \parallel 6\ \Omega)(50\ \text{V})}{(3\ \Omega \parallel 6\ \Omega) + 20\ \Omega + 3\ \Omega} = \frac{2\ \Omega(50\ \text{V})}{2\ \Omega + 23\ \Omega}$$

$$= \mathbf{4\ V}$$

Chapter 12

1. Φ: CGS: **5×10^4 Maxwells**, English: **5×10^4 lines**
   B: CGS: **8 Gauss**, English: **51.62 lines/in.^{2}**

2. Φ: SI **6×10^{-4} Wb**, English **60,000 lines**
   B: SI **0.465 T**, CGS **4.65×10^3 Gauss**, English **30,000 lines/in.^{2}**

3. a. $B = \dfrac{\Phi}{A} = \dfrac{4\times10^{-4}\text{ Wb}}{0.01\text{ m}^2} = \mathbf{0.04\ T}$

4. a. $\Re = \dfrac{l}{\mu A} = \dfrac{0.06\text{ m}}{\mu 2\times10^{-4}\text{ m}^2} = \dfrac{300}{\mu\text{m}}$

   b. $\Re = \dfrac{l}{\mu A} = \dfrac{0.0762\text{ m}}{\mu 5\times10^{-4}\text{ m}^2} = \dfrac{152.4}{\mu\text{m}}$

   c. $\Re = \dfrac{l}{\mu \text{A}} = \dfrac{0.1\text{ m}}{\mu 1\times10^{-4}\text{ m}^2} = \dfrac{1000}{\mu\text{m}}$

   from the above $\Re_{(c)} > \Re_{(a)} > \Re_{(b)}$

5. $\Re = \dfrac{\mathcal{F}}{\Phi} = \dfrac{400\text{ At}}{4.2\times10^{-4}\text{ Wb}} = \mathbf{952.4 \times 10^3\ At/Wb}$

6. $\Re = \dfrac{\mathcal{F}}{\Phi} = \dfrac{120\text{ gilberts}}{72{,}000\text{ maxwells}} = \mathbf{1.67 \times 10^{-3}\ rels\ (CGS)}$

7. $6\text{ in.}\left[\dfrac{1\text{ m}}{39.37\text{ in.}}\right] = 0.1524\text{ m}$

   $H = \dfrac{\mathcal{F}}{l} = \dfrac{400\text{ At}}{0.1524\text{ m}} = \mathbf{2624.67\ At/m}$

8. $\mu = \dfrac{2B}{H} = \dfrac{2(1200\times10^{-4}\text{ T})}{600\text{ At/m}} = \mathbf{4 \times 10^{-4}\ Wb/Am}$

9. $B = \dfrac{\Phi}{A} = \dfrac{10\times10^{-4}\text{ Wb}}{3\times10^{-3}\text{ m}^2} = 0.33\text{ T}$

   Fig. 12.7: $H \cong 800$ At/m

   $NI = Hl \Rightarrow I = Hl/N = (800\text{ At/m})(0.2\text{ m})/75\text{ t} = \mathbf{2.13\ A}$

10. $B = \dfrac{\Phi}{A} = \dfrac{3\times10^{-4}\text{ Wb}}{5\times10^{-4}\text{ m}^2} = 0.6\text{ T}$

Fig. 12.7, $H_{iron} = 2500$ At/m

Fig. 12.8, $H_{steel} = 70$ At/m

$NI = Hl_{(iron)} + Hl_{(steel)}$

$(100\text{ t})I = (H_{iron} + H_{steel})l$

$(100\text{ t})I = (2500\text{ At/m} + 70\text{ At/m})0.3\text{ m}$

$I = \dfrac{771\text{ A}}{100} = \mathbf{7.71\ A}$

11. a. $N_1I_1 + N_2I_2 = Hl$

$B = \dfrac{\Phi}{A} = \dfrac{12\times10^{-4}\text{ Wb}}{12\times10^{-4}\text{ m}^2} = 1\text{ T}$

Fig. 12.7: $H \cong 750$ At/m

$N_1(2\text{ A}) + 30\text{ At} = (750\text{ At/m})(0.2\text{ m})$

$N_1 = \mathbf{60\ t}$

b. $\mu = \dfrac{B}{H} = \dfrac{1\text{T}}{750\text{ At/m}} = \mathbf{13.34\times10^{-4}\ Wb/Am}$

12. a. $80{,}000\text{ lines}\left[\dfrac{1\text{ Wb}}{10^8\text{ lines}}\right] = 8\times10^4\times10^{-8}\text{ Wb} = 8\times10^{-4}\text{ Wb}$

$l_{(cast\ steel)} = 5.5\text{ in.}\left[\dfrac{1\text{ m}}{39.37\text{ in.}}\right] = 0.14\text{ m}$

$l_{(sheet\ steel)} = 0.5\text{ in.}\left[\dfrac{1\text{ m}}{39.37\text{ in.}}\right] = 0.013\text{ m}$

$\text{Area} = 1\text{ in.}^2\left[\dfrac{1\text{ m}}{39.37\text{ in.}}\right]\left[\dfrac{1\text{ m}}{39.37\text{ in.}}\right] = 6.45\times10^{-4}\text{ m}^2$

$B = \dfrac{\Phi}{A} = \dfrac{8\times10^{-4}\text{ Wb}}{6.45\times10^{-4}\text{ m}^2} = 1.24\text{ T}$

Fig 12.8: $H_{sheet\ steel} \cong 460$ At/m, Fig. 12.7: $H_{cast\ steel} \cong 1275$ At/m

$NI = Hl_{(sheet\ steel)} + Hl_{(cast\ iron)}$

$= (460\text{ At/m})(0.013\text{ m}) + (1275\text{ At/m})(0.14\text{ m})$

$= 5.98\text{ At} + 178.50\text{ At}$

$NI = \mathbf{184.48\ At}$

b. Cast steel: $\mu = \dfrac{B}{H} = \dfrac{1.24\text{ T}}{1275\text{ At/m}} = \mathbf{9.73\times10^{-4}\ Wb/Am}$

Sheet steel: $\mu = \dfrac{B}{H} = \dfrac{1.24\text{ T}}{460\text{ At/m}} = \mathbf{26.96\times10^{-4}\ Wb/Am}$

13. $N_1I + N_2 = \underbrace{Hl}_{\text{cast steel}} + \underbrace{Hl}_{\text{cast iron}}$

$(20\text{ t})I + (30\text{ t})I = $ "

$(50\text{ t})I = $ "

$$B = \frac{\Phi}{A} \text{ with } 0.25\ \cancel{\text{in.}}^2\left[\frac{1\text{ m}}{39.37\ \cancel{\text{in.}}}\right]\left[\frac{1\text{ m}}{39.37\ \cancel{\text{in.}}}\right] = 1.6 \times 10^{-4}\text{ m}^2$$

$$B = \frac{0.8 \times 10^{-4}\text{ Wb}}{1.6 \times 10^{-4}\text{ m}^2} = 0.5\text{ T}$$

Fig. 12.8: $H_{\text{cast steel}} \cong 280$ At/m

Fig. 12.7: $H_{\text{cast iron}} \cong 1500$ At/m

$$l_{\text{cast steel}} = 5.5\ \cancel{\text{in.}}\left[\frac{1\text{ m}}{39.37\ \cancel{\text{in.}}}\right] = 0.14\text{ m}$$

$$l_{\text{cast iron}} = 2.5\ \cancel{\text{in.}}\left[\frac{1\text{ m}}{39.37\ \cancel{\text{in.}}}\right] = 0.064\text{ m}$$

$(50\text{ t})I = (280\text{ At/m})(0.14\text{ m}) + (1500\text{ At/m})(0.064\text{ m})$

$50I = 39.20 + 96.00 = 135.20$

$I = \mathbf{2.70\ A}$

14. a. $l_{ab} = l_{ef} = 0.05$ m, $l_{af} = 0.02$ m, $l_{bc} = l_{de} = 0.0085$ m

$NI = 2H_{ab}l_{ab} + 2H_{bc}l_{bc} + H_{fa}l_{fa} + H_gl_g$

$$B = \frac{\Phi}{A} = \frac{2.4 \times 10^{-4}\text{ Wb}}{2 \times 10^{-4}\text{ m}^2} = 1.2\text{ T} \Rightarrow H \cong 360\text{ At/m (Fig. 12.8)}$$

$100I = 2(360\text{ At/m})(0.05\text{ m}) + 2(360\text{ At/m})(0.0085\text{ m})$
$+ (360\text{ At/m})(0.02\text{ m}) + 7.97 \times 10^5(1.2\text{ T})(0.003\text{ m})$

$= 36\text{ At} + 6.12\text{ At} + 7.2\text{ At} + 2869\text{ At}$

$100I = 2918.32$ At

$I \cong \mathbf{29.18\ A}$

b. air gap: metal = 2869 At:49.72 At = **58.17:1**

$$\mu_{\text{sheet steel}} = \frac{B}{H} = \frac{1.2\text{ T}}{360\text{ At/m}} = \mathbf{3.33 \times 10^{-3}\ Wb/Am}$$

$\mu_{\text{air}} = \mathbf{4\pi \times 10^{-7}\ Wb/Am}$

$\mu_{\text{sheet steel}}: \mu_{\text{air}} = 3.33 \times 10^{-3}\text{ Wb/Am}:4\pi \times 10^{-7} \cong \mathbf{2627:1}$

15. $4\ \cancel{\text{cm}}\left[\frac{1\text{ m}}{100\ \cancel{\text{cm}}}\right] = 0.04\text{ m}$

$$f = \frac{1}{2}NI\frac{d\phi}{dx} = \frac{1}{2}(80\text{ t})(0.9\text{ A})\frac{(8 \times 10^{-4}\text{ Wb} - 0.5 \times 10^{-4}\text{ Wb})}{\frac{1}{2}(0.04\text{ m})} = \frac{36(7.5 \times 10^{-4})}{0.02}$$

$= \mathbf{1.35\ N}$

16. $C = 2\pi r = (6.28)(0.3 \text{ m}) = 1.88 \text{ m}$

$$B = \frac{\Phi}{A} = \frac{2\times10^{-4} \text{ Wb}}{1.3\times10^{-4} \text{ m}^2} = 1.54 \text{ T}$$

Fig. 12.7: $H_{\text{sheet steel}} \cong 2100$ At/m

$H_g = 7.97 \times 10^5 B_g = (7.97 \times 10^5)(1.54 \text{ T}) = 1.23 \times 10^6$ At/m

$N_1I_1 + N_2I_2 = H_gl_g + Hl_{\text{(sheet steel)}}$

$(200 \text{ t})I_1 + (40 \text{ t})(0.3 \text{ A}) = (1.23 \times 10^6 \text{ At/m})(2 \text{ mm}) + (2100 \text{ At/m})(1.88 \text{ m})$

$I_1 = \mathbf{31.98\ A}$

17. a. $0.2 \text{ cm}\left[\frac{1 \text{ m}}{100 \text{ cm}}\right] = 2 \times 10^{-3}$ m

$$A = \frac{\pi d^2}{4} = \frac{(3.14)(0.01 \text{ m})^2}{4} = 0.79 \times 10^{-4} \text{ m}^2$$

$NI = H_gl_g,\ H_g = 7.96 \times 10^5 B_g$

$$(200 \text{ t})I = \left[(7.96\times10^5)\left(\frac{0.2\times10^{-4} \text{ Wb}}{0.79\times10^{-4} \text{ m}^2}\right)\right]2 \times 10^{-3} \text{ m}$$

$I = \mathbf{2.02\ A}$

b. $$B_g = \frac{\Phi}{A} = \frac{2\times10^{-4} \text{ Wb}}{0.79\times10^{-4} \text{ m}^2} = 0.25 \text{ T}$$

$$F \cong \frac{1}{2}\frac{B_g^2A}{\mu_o} = \frac{1}{2}\frac{(0.25 \text{ T})^2(0.79\times10^{-4} \text{ m}^2)}{4\pi\times10^{-7}}$$

$\cong \mathbf{2\ N}$

18. **Table:**

Section	Φ(Wb)	A(m²)	*B*(T)	*H*	*l*(m)	*Hl*
a–b, g–h		5×10^{-4}			0.2	
b–c, f–g	2×10^{-4}	5×10^{-4}			0.1	
c–d, e–f	2×10^{-4}	5×10^{-4}			0.099	
a–h		5×10^{-4}			0.2	
b–g		2×10^{-4}			0.2	
d–e	2×10^{-4}	5×10^{-4}			0.002	

$$B_{bc} = B_{cd} = B_g = B_{ef} = B_{fg} = \frac{\Phi}{A} = \frac{2\times10^{-4}\ \text{Wb}}{5\times10^{-4}\ \text{m}^2} = 0.4\ \text{T}$$

Air gap: $H_g = 7.97 \times 10^5(0.4\ \text{T}) = 3.19 \times 10^5\ \text{At/m}$

$H_g l_g = (3.19 \times 10^5\ \text{At/m})(2\ \text{mm}) = 638\ \text{At}$

Fig 12.8: $H_{bc} = H_{cd} = H_{ef} = H_{fg} = 55\ \text{At/m}$

$H_{bc}l_{bc} = H_{fg}l_{fg} = (55\ \text{At/m})(0.1\ \text{m}) = 5.5\ \text{At}$

$H_{cd}l_{cd} = H_{ef}l_{ef} = (55\ \text{At/m})(0.099\ \text{m}) = 5.45\ \text{At}$

For loop 2: $\sum \mathscr{F} = 0$

$H_{bc}l_{bc} + H_{cd}l_{cd} + H_g l_g + H_{ef}l_{ef} + H_{fg}l_{fg} - H_{gh}l_{gh} = 0$

$5.5\ \text{At} + 5.45\ \text{At} + 638\ \text{At} + 5.45\ \text{At} + 5.50\ \text{At} - H_{gh}l_{gh} = 0$

$H_{gh}l_{gh} = 659.90\ \text{At}$

and $H_{gh} = \dfrac{659.90\ \text{At}}{0.2\ \text{m}} = 3300\ \text{At/m}$

Fig 12.7: $B_{gh} \cong 1.55\ \text{T}$

with $\Phi_2 = B_{gh}A = (1.55\ \text{T})(2 \times 10^{-4}\ \text{m}^2) = 3.1 \times 10^{-4}\ \text{Wb}$

$\Phi_T = \Phi_1 + \Phi_2$

$= 2 \times 10^{-4}\ \text{Wb} + 3.1 \times 10^{-4}\ \text{Wb}$

$= 5.1 \times 10^{-4}\ \text{Wb} = \Phi_{ab} = \Phi_{ha} = \Phi_{gh}$

$$B_{ab} = B_{ha} = B_{gh} = \frac{\Phi_T}{A} = \frac{5.1\times10^{-4}\ \text{Wb}}{5\times10^{-4}\ \text{m}^2} = 1.02\ \text{T}$$

B–H curve: (Fig 12.8):

$H_{ab} = H_{ha} = H_{gh} \cong 180\ \text{At/m}$

$H_{ab}l_{ab} = (180\ \text{At/m})(0.2\ \text{m}) = 36\ \text{At}$

$H_{ha}l_{ha} = (180\ \text{At/m})(0.2\ \text{m}) = 36\ \text{At}$

$H_{gh}l_{gh} = (180\ \text{At/m})(0.2\ \text{m}) = 36\ \text{At}$

which **completes** the table!

Loop #1: $\sum \mathscr{F} = 0$

$NI = H_{ab}l_{ab} + H_{bg}l_{bg} + H_{gh}l_{gh} + H_{ah}l_{ah}$

$(200\ \text{t})I = 36\ \text{At} + 659.49\ \text{At} + 36\ \text{At} + 36\ \text{At}$

$(200\ \text{t})I = 767.49\ \text{At}$

$I \cong \mathbf{3.84\ A}$

19. $NI = Hl$

$l = 2\pi r = (6.28)(0.08\ \text{m}) = 0.50\ \text{m}$

$(100\ \text{t})(2\ \text{A}) = H(0.50\ \text{m})$

$H = 400\ \text{At/m}$

Fig. 12.8: $B \cong 0.68\ \text{T}$

$\Phi = BA = (0.68\ \text{T})(0.009\ \text{m}^2)$

$\Phi = \mathbf{6.12\ mWb}$

20. $NI = H_{ab}(l_{ab} + l_{bc} + l_{de} + l_{ef} + l_{fa}) + H_g l_g$

$300\text{ At} = H_{ab}(0.8\text{ m}) + 7.97 \times 10^5\, B_g(0.8\text{ mm})$

$300\text{ At} = H_{ab}(0.8\text{ m}) + 637.6\, B_g$

Assuming $637.6\, B_g \gg H_{ab}(0.8\text{ m})$

then $300\text{ At} = 637.6\, B_g$

and $B_g = 0.47\text{ T}$

$\Phi = BA = (0.47\text{ T})(2 \times 10^{-4}\text{ m}^2) = 0.94 \times 10^{-4}\text{ Wb}$

$B_{ab} = B_g = 0.47\text{ T} \Rightarrow H \cong 270\text{ At/m}$ (Fig. 12.8)

$300\text{ At} = (270\text{ At/m})(0.8\text{ m}) + 637.6(0.47\text{ T})$

$300\text{ At} \neq 515.67\text{ At}$

$\therefore$ Poor approximation!

$$\frac{300\text{ At}}{515.67\text{ At}} \times 100\% \cong 58\%$$

Reduce Φ to 58%

$0.58(0.94 \times 10^{-4}\text{ Wb}) = 0.55 \times 10^{-4}\text{ Wb}$

$$B = \frac{\Phi}{A} = \frac{0.55 \times 10^{-4}\text{ Wb}}{2 \times 10^{-4}\text{ m}^2} = 0.28\text{ T} \Rightarrow H \cong 190\text{ At/m}\ \text{(Fig. 12.8)}$$

$300\text{ At} = (190\text{ At/m})(0.8\text{ m}) + 637.6(0.28\text{ T})$

$300\text{ At} \neq 330.53\text{ At}$

Reduce Φ another $10\% = 0.55 \times 10^{-4}\text{ Wb} - 0.1(0.55 \times 10^{-4}\text{ Wb})$

$= 0.495 \times 10^{-4}\text{ Wb}$

$$B = \frac{\Phi}{A} = \frac{0.495 \times 10^{-4}\text{ Wb}}{2 \times 10^{-4}\text{m}^2} = 0.25\text{ T} \Rightarrow H \cong 175\text{ At/m}\ \text{(Fig. 12.7)}$$

$300\text{ At} = (175\text{ At/m})(0.8) + 637.6(0.28\text{ T})$

$300\text{ At} \neq 318.53\text{ At}$ but within 5% $\therefore$ OK

$\mathbf{\Phi \cong 0.55 \times 10^{-4}\ Wb}$

21. a. $1\tau = 0.632\ T_{max}$

$T_{max} \cong 1.5\text{ T}$ for cast steel

$0.632(1.5\text{ T}) = 0.945\text{ T}$

At 0.945 T, $H \cong 700\text{ At/m}$ (Fig. 12.7)

$\therefore \boldsymbol{B = 1.5\ \mathrm{T}(1 - e^{-H/700\ \mathrm{At/m}})}$

b. $H = 900\text{ At/m}$:

$$B = 1.5\text{ T}\left(1 - e^{-\frac{900\text{ At/m}}{700\text{ At/m}}}\right) = \mathbf{1.09\ T}$$

Graph: $\cong$ **1.1 T**

$H = 1800\text{ At/m}$:

$$B = 1.5\text{ T}\left(1 - e^{-\frac{1800\text{ At/m}}{700\text{ At/m}}}\right) = \mathbf{1.39\ T}$$

Graph: $\cong$ **1.38 T**

$H = 2700\text{ At/m}$:

$$B = 1.5\left(1 - e^{-\frac{2700\text{ At/m}}{700\text{ At/m}}}\right) = \mathbf{1.47\ T}$$

Graph: $\cong$ **1.47 T**

Excellent comparison!

c. $B = 1.5\text{ T}(1 - e^{-H/700\text{ At/m}}) = 1.5\text{ T} - 1.5\text{ T}e^{-H/700\text{ At/m}}$

$B - 1.5\text{ T} = -1.5\text{ T}e^{-H/700\text{ At/m}}$

$1.5 - B = 1.5\text{ T}e^{-H/700\text{ At/m}}$

$$\frac{1.5\text{ T} - B}{1.5\text{ T}} = e^{-H/700\text{ At/m}}$$

$$\log_e\left(1 - \frac{B}{1.5\text{ T}}\right) = \frac{-H}{700\text{ At/m}}$$

and $H = -700\log_e\left(1 - \dfrac{B}{1.5\text{ T}}\right)$

d. $B = 1\text{ T}$:

$$H = -700\log_e\left(1 - \frac{1\text{ T}}{1.5\text{ T}}\right) = \mathbf{769.03\ At/m}$$

Graph: $\cong$ **750 At/m**

$B = 1.4\text{ T}$:

$$H = -700\log_e\left(1 - \frac{1.4\text{ T}}{1.5\text{ T}}\right) = \mathbf{1895.64\ At/m}$$

Graph: $\cong$ **1920 At/m**

e. $H = -700\log_e\left(1 - \dfrac{B}{1.5\text{ T}}\right)$

$= -700\log_e\left(1 - \dfrac{0.2\text{ T}}{1.5\text{ T}}\right)$

$= 100.2\text{ At/m}$

$$I = \frac{Hl}{N} = \frac{(100.2\text{ At/m})(0.16\text{ m})}{400\text{ t}} = \mathbf{40.1\ mA}$$

vs 44 mA for Ex. 12.1

Chapter 13

1. a. **20 mA**
   b. 15 ms: **−20 mA**, 20 ms: **0 mA**
   c. **40 mA**
   d. **20 ms**
   e. **2.5 cycles**

2. a. **40 V**
   b. 5 μs: **40 V**, 11 μs: **−40 V**
   c. **80 V**
   d. **4 μs**
   e. **3 cycles**

3. a. **8 mV**
   b. 3 μs: **−8 mV**, 9 μs: **0 mV**
   c. **16 mV**
   d. **4.5 μs**
   e. $\dfrac{10\ \mu\text{S}}{4.5\ \mu\text{S/cycle}} = \mathbf{2.22\ cycles}$

4. a. $T = \dfrac{1}{f} = \dfrac{1}{25\ \text{Hz}} = \mathbf{40\ ms}$

   b. $T = \dfrac{1}{f} = \dfrac{1}{40\ \text{mHz}} = \mathbf{25\ ns}$

   c. $T = \dfrac{1}{f} = \dfrac{1}{25\ \text{kHz}} = \mathbf{40\ \mu s}$

   d. $T = \dfrac{1}{f} = \dfrac{1}{1\ \text{Hz}} = \mathbf{1\ s}$

5. a. $f = \dfrac{1}{T} = \dfrac{0}{\dfrac{1}{60}\text{s}} = \mathbf{60\ Hz}$

   b. $f = \dfrac{1}{T} = \dfrac{1}{0.01\ \text{s}} = \mathbf{100\ Hz}$

   c. $f = \dfrac{1}{T} = \dfrac{1}{40\ \text{ms}} = \mathbf{25\ Hz}$

   d. $f = \dfrac{1}{T} = \dfrac{1}{25\ \mu\text{s}} = \mathbf{40\ kHz}$

6. $T = \dfrac{1}{20\ \text{Hz}} = 0.05\ \text{s},\ 5(0.05\ \text{s}) = \mathbf{0.25\ s}$

7. $T = \dfrac{24 \text{ ms}}{80 \text{ cycles}} = \mathbf{0.3 \text{ ms}}$

8. $f = \dfrac{42 \text{ cycles}}{6 \text{ s}} = \mathbf{7 \text{ Hz}}$

9. a. $V_{\text{peak}} = (3 \text{ div.})(50 \text{ mV/div}) = \mathbf{150 \text{ mV}}$

b. $T = (4 \text{ div.})(10 \ \mu\text{s/div.}) = \mathbf{40 \ \mu s}$

c. $f = \dfrac{1}{T} = \dfrac{1}{40 \ \mu\text{s}} = \mathbf{25 \text{ kHz}}$

10. a. $\text{Radians} = \left(\dfrac{\pi}{180°}\right)45° = \dfrac{\pi}{4} \textbf{ rad}$

b. $\text{Radians} = \left(\dfrac{\pi}{180°}\right)60° = \dfrac{\pi}{3} \textbf{ rad}$

c. $\text{Radians} = \left(\dfrac{\pi}{180°}\right)270° = \mathbf{1.5\pi \text{ rad}}$

d. $\text{Radians} = \left(\dfrac{\pi}{180°}\right)170° = \mathbf{0.94\pi \text{ rad}}$

11. a. $\text{Degrees} = \left(\dfrac{180°}{\pi}\right)\dfrac{\pi}{4} = \mathbf{45°}$

b. $\text{Degrees} = \left(\dfrac{180°}{\pi}\right)\dfrac{\pi}{6} = \mathbf{30°}$

c. $\text{Degrees} = \left(\dfrac{180°}{\pi}\right)\dfrac{1}{10}\pi = \mathbf{18°}$

d. $\text{Degrees} = \left(\dfrac{180°}{\pi}\right)0.6\,\pi = \mathbf{108°}$

12. a. $\omega = \dfrac{2\pi}{T} = \dfrac{2\pi}{2 \text{ s}} = \mathbf{3.14 \text{ rad/s}}$

b. $\omega = \dfrac{2\pi}{0.3 \times 10^{-3} \text{ s}} = \mathbf{20.94 \times 10^3 \text{ rad/s}}$

c. $\omega = \dfrac{2\pi}{4 \times 10^{-6} \text{ s}} = \mathbf{1.57 \times 10^6 \text{ rad/s}}$

d. $\omega = \dfrac{2\pi}{1/25 \text{ s}} = \mathbf{157.1 \text{ rad/s}}$

13. a. $\omega = 2\pi f = 2\pi(50 \text{ Hz}) = \mathbf{314.16 \text{ rad/s}}$
b. $\omega = 2\pi f = 2\pi(600 \text{ Hz}) = \mathbf{3769.91 \text{ rad/s}}$
c. $\omega = 2\pi f = 2\pi(2 \text{ kHz}) = \mathbf{12.56 \times 10^3 \text{ rad/s}}$
d. $\omega = 2\pi f = 2\pi(0.004 \text{ MHz}) = \mathbf{25.13 \times 10^3 \text{ rad/s}}$

14. a. $\omega = 2\pi f = \dfrac{2\pi}{T} \Rightarrow f = \dfrac{\omega}{2\pi}$

$T = \dfrac{2\pi}{\omega} = \dfrac{1}{f}$

$f = \dfrac{\omega}{2\pi} = \dfrac{754 \text{ rad/s}}{2\pi}$ $= \mathbf{120\ Hz},\ \boldsymbol{T} = \mathbf{8.33\ ms}$

b. $f = \dfrac{\omega}{2\pi} = \dfrac{8.4 \text{ rad/s}}{2\pi}$ $= \mathbf{1.34\ Hz},\ \boldsymbol{T} = \mathbf{746.27\ ms}$

c. $f = \dfrac{\omega}{2\pi} = \dfrac{6000 \text{ rad/s}}{2\pi}$ $= \mathbf{954.93\ Hz},\ \boldsymbol{T} = \mathbf{1.05\ ms}$

d. $f = \dfrac{\omega}{2\pi} = \dfrac{1/16 \text{ rad/s}}{2\pi}$ $= \mathbf{9.95 \times 10^{-3}\ Hz},\ \boldsymbol{T} = \mathbf{100.5\ ms}$

15. $(45°)\left(\dfrac{\pi}{180°}\right) = \dfrac{\pi}{4}$ radians

$t = \dfrac{\theta}{\omega} = \dfrac{\pi/4 \text{ rad}}{2\pi f} = \dfrac{\pi/4 \text{ rad}}{2\pi(60 \text{ Hz})} = \dfrac{1}{(8)(60)} = \dfrac{1}{480}$ $= \mathbf{2.08\ ms}$

16. $(30°)\left(\dfrac{\pi}{180°}\right) = \dfrac{\pi}{6},\ \alpha = \omega t \Rightarrow \omega = \dfrac{\alpha}{t} = \dfrac{\pi/6}{5 \times 10^{-3} \text{ s}}$ $= \mathbf{104.7\ rad/s}$

17. a. Amplitude = **20**, $f = \dfrac{\omega}{2\pi} = \dfrac{377 \text{ rad/s}}{2\pi}$ $= \mathbf{60\ Hz}$

b. Amplitude = **5**, $f = \dfrac{\omega}{2\pi} = \dfrac{754 \text{ rad/s}}{2\pi}$ $= \mathbf{120\ Hz}$

c. Amplitude = $\mathbf{10^6}$, $f = \dfrac{\omega}{2\pi} = \dfrac{10{,}000 \text{ rad/s}}{2\pi}$ $= \mathbf{1591.55\ Hz}$

d. Amplitude = **–6.4**, $f = \dfrac{\omega}{2\pi} = \dfrac{942 \text{ rad/s}}{2\pi}$ $= \mathbf{149.92\ Hz}$

18. –

19. –

20. $T = \dfrac{2\pi}{\omega} = \dfrac{2\pi}{157}$ $= 40$ ms, $\dfrac{1}{2}$ cycle = **20 ms**

21. $i = 0.5 \sin 72° = 0.5(0.9511) =$ **0.48 A**

22. $1.2\pi\left(\frac{180°}{\pi}\right) = 216°$

$\upsilon = 20 \sin 216° = 20(-0.588) = \mathbf{-11.76\ V}$

23. $6 \times 10^{-3} = 30 \times 10^{-3} \sin \alpha$

$0.2 = \sin \alpha$

$\alpha = \sin^{-1} 0.2 = \mathbf{11.54°}$ and $180° - 11.54° = \mathbf{168.46°}$

24. $\upsilon = V_m \sin \alpha$

$40 = V_m \sin 30° = V_m (0.5)$

$\therefore V_m = \frac{40}{0.5} = \mathbf{80\ V}$

$\frac{30°}{360°} = \frac{1\text{ ms}}{T}$

$T = 1\text{ ms}\left(\frac{360}{30}\right) = \mathbf{12\ ms}$

$f = \frac{1}{T} = \frac{1}{12 \times 10^{-3}\text{ s}} = \mathbf{83.33\ Hz}$

$\omega = 2\pi f = (2\pi)(83.33\text{ Hz}) = \mathbf{523.58\ rad/s}$

and $\upsilon = \mathbf{80 \sin 523.58}\boldsymbol{t}$

25. –

26. –

27. a. $\omega = 2\pi f = 377$ rad/s

$\upsilon = \mathbf{25 \sin (\omega t + 30°)}$

b. $\pi - \frac{2}{3}\pi = \frac{\pi}{3} = 60°$, $\omega = 2\pi f = 6.28 \times 10^3$ rad/s

$i = \mathbf{3 \times 10^{-3} \sin(6.28 \times 10^3 t - 60°)}$

28. a. $\omega = 2\pi f = 2\pi(40\text{ Hz}) = 251.33$ rad/s

$\upsilon = \mathbf{0.01 \sin (251.33t - 110°)}$

b. $\omega = 2\pi f = 2\pi(10\text{ kHz}) = 62.83 \times 10^3$ rad/s, $\frac{3}{4}\pi\left(\frac{180°}{\pi}\right) = 135°$

$i = \mathbf{2 \times 10^{-3} \sin (62.83 \times 10^3 t + 135°)}$

29. **υ leads i by 10°**

30. **i leads υ by 70°**

31. **i leads υ by 80°**

32. $\upsilon = 2 \sin (\omega t \underbrace{- 30° + 90°}_{+60°})$

$i = 5 \sin(\omega t + 60°)$

} **in phase**

33. $\upsilon = 4 \sin(\omega t + 90° + 90° + 180° = 4 \sin \omega t$

$i = \sin(\omega t + 10° + 180°) = \sin(\omega t + 190°)$

} **i leads υ by 190°**

34. $T = \dfrac{1}{f} = \dfrac{1}{1000\text{ Hz}} = 1\text{ ms}$

$t_1 = \dfrac{120°}{180°}\left(\dfrac{T}{2}\right) = \dfrac{2}{3}\left(\dfrac{1\text{ ms}}{2}\right) = \mathbf{\dfrac{1}{3}\text{ ms}}$

35. $\omega = 2\pi f = 50{,}000\text{ rad/s}$

$f = \dfrac{50{,}000}{2\pi} = 7957.75\text{ Hz}$

$T = \dfrac{1}{f} = 125.66\ \mu\text{s}$

$t_1 = \dfrac{40°}{180°}\left(\dfrac{T}{2}\right) = 0.222(62.83\ \mu\text{s}) = \mathbf{13.95\ \mu s}$

36. a. $T = (8\text{ div.})(1\text{ ms/div.}) = \mathbf{8\text{ ms}}$ (both waveforms)

b. $f = \dfrac{1}{T} = \dfrac{1}{8\text{ ms}} = \mathbf{125\text{ Hz (both)}}$

c. Peak = (2.5 div)(0.5 V/div.) = 1.25 V
$V_{\text{rms}} = 0.707(1.25\text{ V}) = \mathbf{0.884\text{ V}}$

d. Phase shift = 4.6 div., $T = 8$ div.
$\theta = \dfrac{4.6\text{ div.}}{8\text{ div.}} \times 360° = \mathbf{207°\ \textit{i}\ leads\ \textit{e}}$
or ***e* leads *i* by 153°**

37. $G = \dfrac{(6\text{ V})(1\text{ s}) + (3\text{ V})(1\text{ s}) - (3\text{ V})(1\text{ s})}{3\text{ s}} = \dfrac{6\text{ V}}{3} = \mathbf{2\text{ V}}$

38. $G = \dfrac{\left[\dfrac{1}{2}(4\text{ ms})(20\text{ mA})\right] - (2\text{ ms})(5\text{ mA})}{8\text{ ms}} = \dfrac{40\text{ mA} - 10\text{ mA}}{8} = \dfrac{30\text{ mA}}{8} = \mathbf{3.87\text{ mA}}$

39. $G = \dfrac{2A_m - (5\text{ mA})(\pi)}{2\pi} = \dfrac{2(20\text{ mA}) - (5\text{ mA})(\pi)}{2\pi} = \dfrac{40\text{ mA} - 15.708\text{ mA}}{2\pi} = \mathbf{3.87\text{ mA}}$

40. a. $T = (2\text{ div.})(50\ \mu\text{s}) = \mathbf{100\ \mu s}$

b. $f = \dfrac{1}{T} = \dfrac{1}{100\ \mu\text{s}} = \mathbf{10\text{ kHz}}$

c. Average = (–1.5 div.)(0.2 V/div.) = **–0.3 V**

41. a. $T = (4\text{ div.})(10\ \mu\text{s/div.}) = \mathbf{40\ \mu s}$

b. $f = \dfrac{1}{T} = \dfrac{1}{40\ \mu\text{s}} = \mathbf{25\text{ kHz}}$

c. $G = \dfrac{(2.5\text{ div.})(1.5\cancel{\text{div.}}) + (1\text{ div.})(0.5\cancel{\text{div.}}) + (1\text{ div.})(0.6\cancel{\text{div.}}) + (2.5\text{ div.})(0.4\cancel{\text{div.}}) + (1\text{ div.})(1\cancel{\text{div.}})}{4\cancel{\text{div.}}}$

$= \dfrac{3.75\text{ div.} + 0.5\text{ div.} + 0.6\text{ div.} + 1\text{ div.} + 1\text{ div.}}{4}$

$= \dfrac{6.85\text{ div.}}{4} = 1.713\text{ div.}$

$1.713\ \cancel{\text{div.}}(10\text{ mV}/\cancel{\text{div.}}) = \mathbf{17.13\ mV}$

42. a. $V_{rms} = 0.7071(140\text{ V}) = \mathbf{98.99\ V}$
    b. $I_{rms} = 0.7071(6\text{ mA}) = \mathbf{4.24\ mA}$
    c. $V_{rms} = 0.7071(40\ \mu\text{V}) = \mathbf{28.28\ \mu V}$

43. a. $\upsilon = \mathbf{14.14\sin 377}t$
    b. $i = \mathbf{70.7\times10^{-3}\sin 377}t$
    c. $\upsilon = \mathbf{2.83\times10^{3}\sin 377}t$

44. $V_{rms} = \dfrac{\sqrt{(2\text{ V})^2(4\text{ s}) + (-2\text{ V})^2(1\text{ s}) + (3\text{ V})^2\left(\frac{1}{2}\text{s}\right)}}{12\text{ s}} = \mathbf{1.43\ V}$

45. $V_{rms} = \sqrt{\dfrac{(3\text{ V})^2(2\text{ s}) + (2\text{ V})^2(2\text{ s}) + (1\text{ V})^2(2\text{ s}) + (-1\text{ V})^2(2\text{ s}) + (-3\text{ V})^2(2\text{ s}) + (-2\text{ V})^2(2\text{ s})}{12\text{ s}}}$

$= \mathbf{+2.16\ V}$

46. $G = \dfrac{(10\text{ V})(4\text{ ms}) - (10\text{ V})(4\text{ ms})}{8\text{ ms}} = \dfrac{0}{8\text{ ms}} = \mathbf{0\ V}$

$V_{rms} = \sqrt{\dfrac{(10\text{ V})^2(4\text{ ms}) + (-10\text{ V})^2(4\text{ ms})}{8\text{ ms}}} = \mathbf{10\ V}$

47. a. $T = (4\text{ div.})(10\ \mu\text{s/div.}) = \mathbf{40\ \mu s}$

$f = \dfrac{1}{T} = \dfrac{1}{40\ \mu\text{s}} = \mathbf{25\ kHz}$

Av. = (1 div.)(20 mV/div.) = **20 mV**

Peak = (2 div.)(20 mV/div.) = **40 mV**

$\text{rms} = \sqrt{V_0^2 + \dfrac{V_{max}^2}{2}} = \sqrt{(20\text{ mV})^2 + \dfrac{(40\text{ mV})^2}{2}} = \mathbf{34.64\ mV}$

b. $T = (2 \text{ div.})(50\ \mu s) = \mathbf{100\ \mu s}$

$$f = \frac{1}{T} = \frac{1}{100\ \mu s} = \mathbf{10\ kHz}$$

Av. = (–1.5 div.)(0.2 V/div.) = **–0.3 V**

Peak = (1.5 div.)(0.2 V/div.) = **0.3 mV**

$$\text{rms} = \sqrt{V_0^2 + \frac{V_{\text{max}}^2}{2}} = \sqrt{(.3\text{ V})^2 + \frac{(.3\text{ V})^2}{2}} = \mathbf{367.42\ mV}$$

48. a. $V_{dc} = IR = (4\text{ mA})(2\text{ k}\Omega) = 8\text{ V}$

Meter indication = 2.22(8 V) = **17.76 V**

b. $V_{\text{rms}} = 0.707(16\text{ V}) = \mathbf{11.31\ V}$

Chapter 14

1. –

2. –

3. a. $(377)(10) \cos 377t =$ **$3770 \cos 377t$**

   b. $(754)(0.6) \cos(754t + 20°) =$ **$452.4 \cos(754t + 20°)$**

   c. $(\sqrt{2}\ 20)(157) \cos(157t - 20°) =$ **$4440.63 \cos(157t - 20°)$**

   d. $(-200)(1) \cos(t + 180°) = -200 \cos(t + 180°) =$ **$200 \cos t$**

4. a. $I_m = V_m/R = 150\text{ V}/5\ \Omega = 30\text{ A}$, $i =$ **$30 \sin 200t$**

   b. $I_m = V_m/R = 30\text{ V}/5\ \Omega = 6\text{ A}$, $i =$ **$6 \sin(377t + 20°)$**

   c. $I_m = V_m/R = 40\text{ V}/5\ \Omega = 8\text{ A}$, $i =$ **$8 \sin(\omega t + 100°)$**

   d. $I_m = V_m/R = 80\text{ V}/5\ \Omega = 16\text{ A}$, $i =$ **$16 \sin(\omega t + 220°)$**

5. a. $V_m = I_mR = (0.1\text{ A})(7 \times 10^3\ \Omega) = 700\text{ V}$
   $\upsilon =$ **$700 \sin 1000t$**

   b. $V_m = I_mR = (2 \times 10^{-3}\text{ A})((7 \times 10^3\ \Omega) = 14.8\text{ V}$
   $\upsilon =$ **$14.8 \sin(400t - 120°)$**

   c. $i = 6 \times 10^{-6} \sin(\omega t - 2° + 90°) = 6 \times 10^{-6} \sin(\omega t + 88°)$
   $V_m = I_mR = (6 \times 10^{-6}\text{ A})((7 \times 10^3\ \Omega) = 42 \times 10^{-3}\text{ V}$
   $\upsilon =$ **$42 \times 10^{-3} \sin(\omega t + 88°)$**

   d. $i = 0.004 \sin(\omega t + 90° + 90° + 180°) = 0.004 \sin(\omega t + 360°) = 0.0004 \sin \omega t$
   $V_m = I_mR = (4 \times 10^{-3}\text{ A})((7 \times 10^3\ \Omega) = 28\text{ V}$
   $\upsilon =$ **$28 \sin \omega t$**

6. a. **$0\ \Omega$**

   b. $X_L = 2\pi fL = 2\pi Lf = (6.28)(2\text{ H})f = 12.56f = 12.56(10\text{ Hz}) =$ **$125.6\ \Omega$**

   c. $X_L = 12.56f = 12.56(60\text{ Hz}) =$ **$753.6\ \Omega$**

   d. $X_L = 12.56f = 12.56(2000\text{ Hz}) =$ **$25.13\text{ k}\Omega$**

   e. $X_L = 12.56f = 12.56(10^5\text{ Hz}) =$ **$1.256\text{ M}\Omega$**

7. a. $L = \frac{X_L}{2\pi f} = \frac{20\ \Omega}{2\pi(2\text{ Hz})} = \mathbf{1.59\ H}$

b. $L = \frac{X_L}{2\pi f} = \frac{1000\ \Omega}{2\pi(60\text{ Hz})} = \mathbf{2.65\ H}$

c. $L = \frac{X_L}{2\pi f} = \frac{5280\ \Omega}{2\pi(500\text{ Hz})} = \mathbf{1.68\ H}$

8. a. $X_L = 2\pi fL \Rightarrow f = \frac{X_L}{2\pi L} = \frac{X_L}{(6.28)(10\text{ H})} = \frac{X_L}{62.8}$

$f = \frac{100\ \Omega}{62.8} = \mathbf{1.59\ Hz}$

b. $f = \frac{X_L}{62.8} = \frac{3770\ \Omega}{62.8} = \mathbf{60.03\ Hz}$

c. $f = \frac{X_L}{62.8} = \frac{15{,}700\ \Omega}{62.8} = \mathbf{250\ Hz}$

d. $f = \frac{X_L}{62.8} = \frac{243\ \Omega}{62.8} = \mathbf{3.87\ Hz}$

9. a. $V_m = I_m X_L = (5\text{ A})(20\ \Omega) = 100\text{ V}$
$\upsilon = \mathbf{100\ sin(\omega t + 90°)}$

b. $V_m = I_m X_L = (40 \times 10^{-3}\text{ A})(20\ \Omega) = 0.8\text{ V}$
$\upsilon = \mathbf{0.8\ sin(\omega t + 150°)}$

c. $i = 6\sin(\omega t + 150°)$, $V_m = I_m X_L = (6\text{ A})(20\ \Omega) = 120\text{ V}$
$\upsilon = 120\sin(\omega t + 240°) = \mathbf{120\ sin(\omega t - 120°)}$

d. $i = 3\sin(\omega t + 100°)$, $V_m = I_m X_L = (3\text{ A})(20\ \Omega) = 60\text{ V}$
$\upsilon = \mathbf{60\ sin(\omega t + 190°)}$

10. a. $X_L = \omega L = (100\text{ rad/s})(0.1\text{ H}) = 10\ \Omega$
$V_m = I_m X_L = (10\text{ A})(10\ \Omega) = 100\text{ V}$
$\upsilon = \mathbf{100\ sin(100t + 90°)}$

b. $X_L = \omega L = (377\text{ rad/s})(0.1\text{ H}) = 37.7\ \Omega$
$V_m = I_m X_L = (6 \times 10^{-3}\text{ A})(37.7\ \Omega) = 226.2\text{ mV}$
$\upsilon = \mathbf{226.2 \times 10^{-3}\ sin(377t + 90°)}$

c. $X_L = \omega L = (400\text{ rad/s})(0.1\text{ H}) = 40\ \Omega$
$V_m = I_m X_L = (5 \times 10^{-6}\text{ A})(40\ \Omega) = 200\ \mu\text{V}$
$\upsilon = \mathbf{200 \times 10^{-6}\ sin(400t + 110°)}$

d. $i = 4 \sin(20t + 200°)$
$X_L = \omega L = (20 \text{ rad/s})(0.1 \text{ H}) = 2\ \Omega$
$V_m = I_m X_L = (4 \text{ A})(2\ \Omega) = 8 \text{ V}$
$\upsilon = 8 \sin(20t + 290°) = \mathbf{8 \sin(20t - 70°)}$

11. a. $I_m = \dfrac{V_m}{X_L} = \dfrac{120 \text{ V}}{50\ \Omega} = 2.4 \text{ A}, \; i = \mathbf{2.4 \sin(\omega t - 90°)}$

b. $I_m = \dfrac{V_m}{X_L} = \dfrac{30 \text{ V}}{50\ \Omega} = 0.6 \text{ A}, \; i = \mathbf{0.6 \sin(\omega t - 70°)}$

c. $\upsilon = 40 \sin(\omega t + 100°)$
$I_m = \dfrac{V_m}{X_L} = \dfrac{40 \text{ V}}{50\ \Omega} = 0.8 \text{ A}, \; i = \mathbf{0.8 \sin(\omega t + 10°)}$

d. $\upsilon = 80 \sin(377t + 220°)$
$I_m = \dfrac{V_m}{X_L} = \dfrac{80 \text{ V}}{50\ \Omega} = 1.6 \text{ A}, \; i = \mathbf{1.6 \sin(377t + 130°)}$

12. a. $X_L = \omega L = (60 \text{ rad/s})(0.2 \text{ H}) = 12\ \Omega$
$I_m = V_m/X_L = 1.5 \text{ V}/12\ \Omega = 0.125 \text{ A}$
$i = \mathbf{0.125 \sin(60t - 90°)}$

b. $X_L = \omega L = (10 \text{ rad/s})(0.2 \text{ H}) = 2\ \Omega$
$I_m = V_m/X_L = 16 \text{ mV}/2\ \Omega = 8 \text{ mA}$
$i = 8 \times 10^{-3} \sin(t + 2° - 90°) = \mathbf{8 \times 10^{-3} \sin(t - 88°)}$

c. $\upsilon = 4.8 \sin(0.05t + 230°)$
$X_L = \omega L = (0.05 \text{ rad/s})(0.2 \text{ H}) = 0.01\ \Omega$
$I_m = V_m/X_L = 4.8 \text{ V}/0.01\ \Omega = 480 \text{ A}$
$i = 480 \sin(0.05t + 230° - 90°) = \mathbf{480 \sin(0.05t + 140°)}$

d. $\upsilon = 9 \times 10^{-3} \sin(377t + 90°)$
$X_L = \omega L = (377 \text{ rad/s})(0.2 \text{ H}) = 75.4\ \Omega$
$I_m = V_m/X_L = 9 \text{ mV}/75.4\ \Omega = 0.119 \text{ mA}$
$i = \mathbf{0.119 \times 10^{-3} \sin 377t}$

13. a. $X_C = \dfrac{1}{2\pi fC} = \dfrac{1}{2\pi(0 \text{ Hz})(5 \times 10^{-6} \text{ F})} = \mathbf{\infty\ \Omega}$

b. $X_C = \dfrac{1}{2\pi fC} = \dfrac{1}{2\pi(60 \text{ Hz})(5 \times 10^{-6} \text{ F})} = \mathbf{530.79\ \Omega}$

c. $X_C = \dfrac{1}{2\pi fC} = \dfrac{1}{2\pi(120 \text{ Hz})(5 \times 10^{-6} \text{ F})} = \mathbf{265.39\ \Omega}$

d. $X_C = \dfrac{1}{2\pi fC} = \dfrac{1}{2\pi(2\text{ kHz})(5\times10^{-6}\text{ F})} = \mathbf{15.92\ \Omega}$

e. $X_C = \dfrac{1}{2\pi fC} = \dfrac{1}{2\pi(2\times10^{6}\text{ Hz})(5\times10^{-6}\text{ F})} = \mathbf{62.83\ \Omega}$

14. a. $C = \dfrac{1}{2\pi fX_C} = \dfrac{1}{6.28(60\text{ Hz})(250\ \Omega)} = \mathbf{10.62\ \mu F}$

b. $C = \dfrac{1}{2\pi fX_C} = \dfrac{1}{6.28(312\text{ Hz})(55\ \Omega)} = \mathbf{9.28\ \mu F}$

c. $C = \dfrac{1}{2\pi fX_C} = \dfrac{1}{6.28(25\text{ Hz})(10\ \Omega)} = \mathbf{636.94\ \mu F}$

15. a. $f = \dfrac{1}{2\pi CX_C} = \dfrac{1}{2\pi(50\times10^{-6}\text{ F})(100\ \Omega)} = \mathbf{31.83\ Hz}$

b. $f = \dfrac{1}{2\pi CX_C} = \dfrac{1}{2\pi(50\times10^{-6}\text{ F})(684\ \Omega)} = \mathbf{4.66\ Hz}$

c. $f = \dfrac{1}{2\pi CX_C} = \dfrac{1}{2\pi(50\times10^{-6}\text{ F})(342\ \Omega)} = \mathbf{9.31\ Hz}$

d. $f = \dfrac{1}{2\pi CX_C} = \dfrac{1}{2\pi(50\times10^{-6}\text{ F})(2000\ \Omega)} = \mathbf{1.59\ Hz}$

16. a. $I_m = V_m/X_C = 120\text{ V}/2.5\ \Omega = 48\text{ A}$
$i = \mathbf{48\ sin(\omega t + 90°)}$

b. $I_m = V_m/X_C = 0.4\text{ V}/2.5\ \Omega = 0.16\text{ A}$
$i = \mathbf{0.16\ sin(\omega t + 110°)}$

c. $\upsilon = 8\sin(\omega t + 100°)$
$I_m = V_m/X_C = 8\text{ V}/2.5\ \Omega = 3.2\text{ A}$
$i = \mathbf{3.2\ sin(\omega t + 190°)}$

d. $\upsilon = -70\sin(\omega t + 40°) = 70\sin(\omega t + 220°)$
$I_m = V_m/X_C = 70\text{ V}/2.5\ \Omega = 28\text{ A}$
$i = 28\sin(\omega t + 310°) = \mathbf{28\ sin(\omega t - 50°)}$

17. a. $\upsilon = 30 \sin 200t$, $X_C = \dfrac{1}{\omega C} = \dfrac{1}{(200)(1\times 10^{-6})} = 5\text{ k}\Omega$

$$I_m = \frac{V_m}{X_C} = \frac{30\text{ V}}{5\text{ k}\Omega} = 6\text{ mA},\ i = \mathbf{6 \times 10^{-3} \sin(200t + 90°)}$$

b. $\upsilon = 60 \times 10^{-3} \sin 377t$, $X_C = \dfrac{1}{\omega C} = \dfrac{1}{(377)(1\times 10^{-6})} = 2.65\text{ k}\Omega$

$$I_m = \frac{V_m}{X_C} = \frac{60\times 10^{-3}\text{ V}}{2{,}650\ \Omega} = 22.64\ \mu\text{A},\ i = \mathbf{22.64 \times 10^{-6} \sin(377t + 90°)}$$

c. $\upsilon = 120 \sin(374t + 210°)$, $X_C = \dfrac{1}{\omega C} = \dfrac{1}{(374)(1\times 10^{-6})} = 2.67\text{ k}\Omega$

$$I_m = \frac{V_m}{X_C} = \frac{120\text{ V}}{2{,}670\ \Omega} = 44.94\text{ mA},\ i = \mathbf{44.94 \times 10^{-3} \sin(374t + 300°)}$$

d. $\upsilon = 70 \sin(800t + 70°)$, $X_C = \dfrac{1}{\omega C} = \dfrac{1}{(800)(1\times 10^{-6})} = 1.25\text{ k}\Omega$

$$I_m = \frac{V_m}{X_C} = \frac{70\text{ V}}{1250\ \Omega} = 56\text{ mA},\ i = \mathbf{56 \times 10^{-3} \sin(\omega t + 160°)}$$

18. a. $V_m = I_m X_C = (50 \times 10^{-3}\text{ A})(10\ \Omega) = 0.5\text{ V}$
$\upsilon = \mathbf{0.5 \sin(\omega t - 90°)}$

b. $V_m = I_m X_C = (2 \times 10^{-6})(10\ \Omega) = 20\ \mu\text{V}$
$\upsilon = \mathbf{20 \times 10^{-6} \sin(\omega t - 30°)}$

c. $i = -6 \sin(\omega t - 30°) = 6 \sin(\omega t + 150°)$
$V_m = I_m X_C = (6\text{ A})(10\ \Omega) = 60\text{ V}$
$\upsilon = \mathbf{60 \sin(\omega t + 60°)}$

d. $i = 3 \sin(\omega t + 100°)$
$V_m = I_m X_C = (3\text{ A})(10\ \Omega) = 30\text{ V}$
$\upsilon = \mathbf{30 \sin(\omega t + 10°)}$

19. a. $i = 0.2 \sin 300t$, $X_C = \dfrac{1}{\omega C} = \dfrac{1}{(300)(0.5\times 10^{-6})} = 6.67\text{ k}\Omega$

$V_m = I_m X_C = (0.2\text{ A})(6{,}670\ \Omega) = 1334\text{ V}$, $\upsilon = \mathbf{1334 \sin(300t - 90°)}$

b. $i = 8 \times 10^{-3} \sin 377t$, $X_C = \dfrac{1}{\omega C} = \dfrac{1}{(377)(0.5\times 10^{-6})} = 5.31\text{ k}\Omega$

$V_m = I_m X_C = (8 \times 10^{-3}\text{ A})(5.31 \times 10^{3}\ \Omega) = 42.48\text{ V}$
$\upsilon = \mathbf{42.48 \sin(377t - 90°)}$

c. $i = 60 \times 10^{-3} \sin(754t + 90°)$, $X_C = \dfrac{1}{\omega C} = \dfrac{1}{(754)(0.5 \times 10^{-6})} = 2.65\text{ k}\Omega$

$V_m = I_m X_C = (60 \times 10^{-3}\text{ A})(2.65 \times 10^3\ \Omega) = 159\text{ V}$

$\upsilon = \mathbf{159 \sin 754}t$

d. $i = 80 \times 10^{-3} \sin(1600t - 80°)$, $X_C = \dfrac{1}{\omega C} = \dfrac{1}{(1600)(0.5 \times 10^{-6})} = 1.25\text{ k}\Omega$

$V_m = I_m X_C = (80 \times 10^{-3}\text{ A})(1.25 \times 10^3\ \Omega) = 100\text{ V}$

$\upsilon = \mathbf{100 \sin(1600}t\mathbf{ - 170°)}$

20. a. υ leads i by 90° $\Rightarrow L$, $X_L = V_m/I_m = 550\text{ V}/11\text{ A} = 50\ \Omega$

$$L = \frac{X_L}{\omega} = \frac{50\ \Omega}{377\text{ rad/s}} = \mathbf{132.63\text{ mH}}$$

b. υ leads i by 90° $\Rightarrow L$, $X_L = V_m/I_m = 36\text{ V}/4\text{ A} = 9\ \Omega$

$$L = \frac{1}{\omega X_L} = \frac{1}{(754\text{ rad/s})(9\ \Omega)} = \mathbf{147.36\ \mu H}$$

c. υ and i are in phase $\Rightarrow R$

$$R = \frac{V_m}{I_m} = \frac{10.5\text{ V}}{1.5\text{ A}} = \mathbf{7\ \Omega}$$

21. a. $\left.\begin{array}{l} i = 5\sin(\omega t + 90°) \\ \upsilon = 2000 \sin \omega t \end{array}\right\}$ i leads υ by 90° $\Rightarrow \boldsymbol{C}$

$$X_C = \frac{V_m}{I_m} = \frac{2000\text{ V}}{5\text{ A}} = 400\ \Omega$$

b. $\left.\begin{array}{l} i = 2\sin(157t + 60°) \\ \upsilon = 80 \sin(157t + 150°) \end{array}\right\}$ υ leads i by 90° $\Rightarrow \boldsymbol{L}$

$$X_L = \frac{V_m}{I_m} = \frac{80\text{ V}}{2\text{ A}} = 40\ \Omega,\ L = \frac{X_L}{\omega} = \frac{40\ \Omega}{157\text{ rad/s}} = \mathbf{254.78\text{ mH}}$$

c. $\left.\begin{array}{l} \upsilon = 35\sin(\omega t - 20°) \\ i = 7 \sin(\omega t - 20°) \end{array}\right\}$ in phase $\Rightarrow \boldsymbol{R}$

$$R = \frac{V_m}{I_m} = \frac{35\text{ V}}{7\text{ A}} = \mathbf{5\ \Omega}$$

22. –

23. –

24. $X_C = \dfrac{1}{2\pi fC} = R \Rightarrow f = \dfrac{1}{2\pi RC} = \dfrac{1}{2\pi(2\times10^3\ \Omega)(1\times10^{-6}\ \text{F})} = \dfrac{1}{12.56\times10^{-3}}$

$\cong$ **79.62 Hz**

25. $X_L = 2\pi fL = R$

$$L = \frac{R}{2\pi f} = \frac{10{,}000\ \Omega}{2\pi(5\times10^3\ \text{Hz})} = \mathbf{318.47\ mH}$$

26. $X_C = X_L$

$$\frac{1}{2\pi fC} = 2\pi fL$$

$$f^2 = \frac{1}{4\pi^2 LC}$$

and $f = \dfrac{1}{2\pi\sqrt{LC}} = \dfrac{1}{2\pi\sqrt{(10\times10^{-3}\ \text{H})(1\times10^{-6}\text{F})}} = \mathbf{1.59\ kHz}$

27. $X_C = X_L$

$$\frac{1}{2\pi fC} = 2\pi fL \Rightarrow C = \frac{1}{4\pi^2 f^2 L} = \frac{1}{4(9.86)(2500\times10^6)(2\times10^{-3})} = \mathbf{5.07\ nF}$$

28. a. $P = \dfrac{V_m I_m}{2}\cos\theta = \dfrac{(550\ \text{V})(11\ \text{A})}{2}\cos 90° = (\ )(0) = \mathbf{0\ W}$

b. $P = \dfrac{V_m I_m}{2}\cos\theta = \dfrac{(36\ \text{V})(4\ \text{A})}{2}\cos 90° = (\ )(0) = \mathbf{0\ W}$

c. $P = \dfrac{V_m I_m}{2}\cos\theta = \dfrac{(10.5\ \text{V})(1.5\ \text{A})}{2}\cos 0° = \mathbf{7.88\ W}$

29. a. $P = \dfrac{V_m I_m}{2}\cos\theta = \dfrac{(5\ \text{A})(2000\ \text{V})}{2}\cos 90° = \mathbf{0\ W}$

b. $\cos\theta = 0 \Rightarrow \mathbf{0\ W}$

c. $P = \dfrac{(35\ \text{V})(7\ \text{A})}{2}\cos 0° = \mathbf{122.5\ W}$

30. a. $P = \dfrac{(60\ \text{V})(15\ \text{A})}{2}\cos 30° = \mathbf{389.7\ W}$, $F_p = \mathbf{0.866}$

b. $P = \dfrac{(50\ \text{V})(2\ \text{A})}{2}\cos 0° = \mathbf{50\ W}$, $F_p = \mathbf{1.0}$

c. $P = \dfrac{(50\text{ V})(3\text{ A})}{2}\cos 10° = \mathbf{73.86\text{ W}},\ F_p = \mathbf{0.985}$

d. $P = \dfrac{(75\text{ V})(0.08\text{ A})}{2}\cos 40° = \mathbf{2.30\text{ W}},\ F_p = \mathbf{0.766}$

31. $R = \dfrac{V_m}{I_m} = \dfrac{48\text{ V}}{8\text{ A}} = 6\ \Omega,\ P = I^2R = \left(\dfrac{8\text{ A}}{\sqrt{2}}\right)^2 6\ \Omega = \mathbf{192\text{ W}}$

$$P = \frac{V_m I_m}{2}\cos\theta = \frac{(48\text{ V})(8\text{ A})}{2}\cos 0° = \mathbf{192\text{ W}}$$

$$P = VI\cos\theta = \left(\frac{48\text{ V}}{\sqrt{2}}\right)\left(\frac{8\text{ A}}{\sqrt{2}}\right)\cos 0° = \mathbf{192\text{ W}}$$

All the same!

32. $P = 100$ W: $F_p = \cos\theta = P/VI = 100\text{ W}/(150\text{ V})(2\text{ A}) = \mathbf{0.333}$
$P = 0$ W: $F_p = \cos\theta = \mathbf{0}$
$P = 300$ W: $F_p = \dfrac{300}{300} = \mathbf{1}$

33. $P = \dfrac{V_m I_m}{2}\cos\theta$

$500\text{ W} = \dfrac{(50\text{ V})I_m}{2}(0.5) \Rightarrow I_m = 40\text{ A}$

$i = \mathbf{40\sin(\omega t - 50°)}$

34. a. $I_m = E_m/R = 30\text{ V}/6.8\ \Omega = 4.41\text{ A},\ i = \mathbf{4.41\sin(377t + 20°)}$

b. $P = I^2R = \left(\dfrac{4.41\text{ A}}{\sqrt{2}}\right)^2 3\ \Omega = \mathbf{29.18\text{ W}}$

c. $T = \dfrac{2\pi}{\omega} = \dfrac{6.28}{377\text{ rad/s}} = \mathbf{16.67\text{ ms}}$
$6(16.67\text{ ms}) = 100.02\text{ ms} \cong \mathbf{0.1\text{ s}}$

35. a. $I_m = \dfrac{V_m}{X_L} = \dfrac{100\text{ V}}{25\ \Omega} = 4\text{ A},\ i = \mathbf{4\sin(314t - 30°)}$

b. $L = \dfrac{X_L}{\omega} = \dfrac{25\ \Omega}{314\text{ rad/s}} = \mathbf{79.62\text{ mH}}$

c. $L \Rightarrow \mathbf{0\text{ W}}$

36. a. $E_m = I_m X_C = (30 \times 10^{-3}\ \text{A})(2.4\ \text{k}\Omega) = 72\ \text{V}$

$e = 72 \sin(377t - 20° - 90°) = \mathbf{72 \sin(377t - 110°)}$

b. $C = \dfrac{1}{\omega X_C} = \dfrac{1}{(377\ \text{rad/s})(2.4\ \text{k}\Omega)} = \mathbf{1.11\ \mu F}$

c. $P = 0\ \text{W}$

37. a. $X_{C_1} = \dfrac{1}{2\pi f C_1} = \dfrac{1}{\omega C_1} = \dfrac{1}{(10^4\ \text{rad/s})(2\ \mu\text{F})} = 50\ \Omega$

$X_{C_2} = \dfrac{1}{\omega C_2} = \dfrac{1}{(10^4)(10\ \mu F)} = 10\ \Omega$

$\mathbf{E} = 100\ \text{V} \angle 60°$

$\mathbf{I}_1 = \dfrac{\mathbf{E}}{\mathbf{Z}_{C_1}} = \dfrac{120\ \text{V} \angle 60°}{50\ \Omega \angle -90°} = 2.4\ \text{A} \angle 150°$

$\mathbf{I}_2 = \dfrac{\mathbf{E}}{\mathbf{Z}_{C_2}} = \dfrac{120\ \text{V} \angle 60°}{10\ \Omega \angle -90°} = 12\ \text{A} \angle 150°$

$i_1 = \sqrt{2}\ 2.4 \sin(10^4 t + 150°) = \mathbf{3.39 \sin(10^4 t + 150°)}$

$i_2 = \sqrt{2}\ 12 \sin(10^4 t + 150°) = \mathbf{16.97 \sin(10^4 t + 150°)}$

b. $\mathbf{I}_s = \mathbf{I}_1 + \mathbf{I}_2 = 2.4\ \text{A} \angle 150° + 12\ \text{A} \angle 150° = 14.4\ \text{A} \angle 150°$

$i_s = \sqrt{2}\ 14.4 \sin(10^4 t + 150°) = \mathbf{20.36 \sin(10^4 t + 150°)}$

38. a. $L_1 \parallel L_2 = 60\ \text{mH} \parallel 120\ \text{mH} = 40\ \text{mH}$

$X_{L_T} = 2\pi f L_T = 2\pi(10^3\ \text{Hz})(40\ \text{mH}) = 251.33\ \Omega$

$V_m = I_m X_{L_T} = \left(\sqrt{2}\ 24\ \text{A}\right)(251.33\ \Omega) = \sqrt{2}\ 6.03\ \text{kV}$

and $\upsilon_s = \sqrt{2}\ 6.03\ \text{kV} \sin(10^3 t + 30° + 90°)$

or $\upsilon_s = \mathbf{8..53 \times 10^3 \sin(10^3 t + 120°)}$

b. $I_{m_1} = \dfrac{V_m}{X_{L_1}}$, $X_{L_1} = 2\pi f L_1 = 2\pi(10^3\ \text{Hz})(60\ \text{mH}) = 376.99\ \Omega$

$I_{m_1} = \dfrac{8.53 \times 10^3}{376.99\ \Omega} = 22.63\ \text{A}$

and $i_1 = \mathbf{22.63 \sin(10^3 t + 30°)}$

$X_{L_2} = 2\pi f L_2 = 2\pi(10^3\ \text{Hz})(120\ \text{mH}) = 753.98\ \Omega$

$I_{m_2} = \dfrac{8.53 \times 10^3}{753.98\ \Omega} = 11.31\ \text{A}$

and $i_2 = \mathbf{11.31 \sin(10^3 t + 30°)}$

39. a. $\mathbf{5.0 \angle 36.87°}$ b. $\mathbf{2.83 \angle 45°}$
c. $\mathbf{17.09 \angle 69.44°}$ d. $\mathbf{1.0 \times 10^{3} \angle 84.29°}$
e. $\mathbf{1077.03 \angle 21.80°}$ f. $\mathbf{6.58 \times 10^{-3} \angle 81.25°}$
g. $\mathbf{11.78 \angle -49.82°}$ h. $\mathbf{8.94 \angle -153.43°}$
i. $\mathbf{61.85 \angle -104.04°}$ j. $\mathbf{101.73 \angle -39.94°}$
k. $\mathbf{4{,}326.66 \angle 123.69°}$ l. $\mathbf{25.5 \times 10^{-3} \angle -78.69°}$

40. a. $\mathbf{5.196 + j3.0}$ b. $\mathbf{6.946 + j39.39}$
c. $\mathbf{2530.95 + j6953.73}$ d. $\mathbf{3.96 \times 10^{-4} + j5.57 \times 10^{-5}}$
e. $\mathbf{j0.04}$ f. $\mathbf{6.91 \times 10^{-3} + j6.22 \times 10^{-3}}$
g. $\mathbf{-56.29 + j32.50}$ h. $\mathbf{-0.85 + j0.85}$
i. $\mathbf{-469.85 - j171.01}$ j. $\mathbf{5177.04 - j3625.0}$
k. $\mathbf{-4.31 - j6.16}$ l. $\mathbf{-6.93 \times 10^{-3} - j4.00 \times 10^{-3}}$

41. a. $\mathbf{15.03 \angle 86.19}$ b. $\mathbf{60.21 \angle 4.76°}$
c. $\mathbf{0.30 \angle 88.09°}$ d. $\mathbf{223.61 \angle -63.43°}$
e. $\mathbf{86.18 \angle 93.73°}$ f. $\mathbf{38.69 \angle -94.0°}$

42. a. $\mathbf{12.95 + j1.13}$ b. $\mathbf{8.37 + j159.78}$
c. $\mathbf{7.00 \times 10^{-6} + j2.44 \times 10^{-7}}$ d. $\mathbf{-8.69 + j0.46}$
e. $\mathbf{75.82 - j5.30}$ f. $\mathbf{-34.51 - j394.49}$

43. a. $\mathbf{11.8 + j7.0}$ b. $\mathbf{151.90 + j49.90}$
c. $\mathbf{4.72 \times 10^{-6} + j71}$ d. $\mathbf{5.20 + j1.60}$
e. $\mathbf{209.30 + j311.0}$ f. $\mathbf{-21.20 + j12.0}$

g. $6 \angle 20° + 8 \angle 80° = (5.64 + j2.05) + (1.39 + j7.88) = \mathbf{7.03 + j9.93}$

h. $(29.698 + j29.698) + (31.0 + j53.69) - (-35 + j60.62) = \mathbf{95.7 + j22.77}$

44. a. $\mathbf{-12.0 + j34.0}$ b. $\mathbf{86.80 + j312.40}$
c. $\mathbf{56. \times 10^{-3} - j\,8 \times 10^{-3}}$ d. $\mathbf{698.00 \angle -114°}$
e. $\mathbf{8.00 \angle 20°}$ f. $\mathbf{49.68 \angle -64.0°}$
g. $\mathbf{40 \times 10^{-3} \angle 40°}$ h. $\mathbf{-16{,}740 \angle 160°}$

45. a. $\mathbf{6.0 \angle -50°}$ b. $\mathbf{200 \times 10^{-6} \angle 60°}$

c. $\mathbf{109 \angle -170.0°}$ d. $\mathbf{76.47 \angle -80}$

e. $\mathbf{4 \angle 0°}$

f. $\mathbf{5.93 \angle -134.47°}$

g. $(0.05 + j0.25)/(8 - j60) = 0.255\angle 78.69°/60.53 \angle -82.41° = \mathbf{4.21 \times 10^{-3} \angle 161.10°}$

h. $\mathbf{9.30 \angle -43.99°}$

46. a. $\dfrac{10 - j5}{1 + j0} = \mathbf{10.0 - j5.0}$

b. $\dfrac{8 \angle 60°}{102 + j400} = \dfrac{8 \angle 60°}{412.80 \angle 75.69°} = \mathbf{19.38 \times 10^{-3} \angle -15.69°}$

c. $\dfrac{(6 \angle 20°)(120 \angle -40°)(8.54 \angle 69.44°)}{2 \angle -30°} = \dfrac{6.15 \times 10^{3} \angle 49.44°}{2 \angle -30°} = \mathbf{3.07 \times 10^{3} \angle 79.44°}$

d. $\dfrac{(0.16 \angle 120°)(300 \angle 40°)}{9.487 \angle 71.565°} = \dfrac{48 \angle 160°}{9.487 \angle 71.565°} = \mathbf{5.06 \angle 88.44°}$

e. $\left(\dfrac{1}{4 \times 10^{-4} \angle 20°}\right)\left(\dfrac{8}{j(j^2)}\right)\left(\dfrac{1}{36 - j30}\right)$

$(2500 \angle -20°)\left(\dfrac{8}{-j}\right)\left(\dfrac{1}{46.861 \angle -39.81°}\right)$

$(2500 \angle -20°)(8j)(0.0213 \angle 39.81°) = \mathbf{426 \angle 109.81°}$

47. a.
$x + j4 + 3x + jy - j7 = 16$
$(x + 3x) + j(4 + y - 7) = 16 + j0$

$x + 3x = 16$ $4 + y - 7 = 0$
$4x = 16$ $y = +7 - 4$
$x = \mathbf{4}$ $y = \mathbf{3}$

b. $(10 \angle 20°)(x \angle -60°) = 30.64 - j25.72$
$10x \angle -40° = 40 \angle -40°$
$10\,x = 40$
$x = \mathbf{4}$

c. $5x + j10$
$\quad 2 - jy$

$$10x + j20 - j5xy - j^2 10y = 90 - j70$$
$$(10x + 10y) + j(20 - 5xy) = 90 - j70$$
$$10x + 10y = 90$$
$$x + y = 9$$
$$x = 9 - y \Rightarrow$$

$$20 - 5xy = -70$$
$$20 - 5(9 - y)y = -70$$
$$5y(9 - y) = 90$$
$$y^2 - 9y + 18 = 0$$
$$y = \frac{-(-9) \pm \sqrt{(-9)^2 - 4(1)(18)}}{2}$$
$$y = \frac{9 \pm 3}{2} = 6, 3$$

For $y = 6, x = 3$
$\quad y = 3, x = 6$
($x = 3, y = 6$) or ($x = 6, y = 3$)

d. $\dfrac{80 \angle 0°}{40 \angle \theta} = 4 \angle -\theta = 3.464 - j2 = 4 \angle -30°$
$\quad$ **$\theta = 30°$**

48. a. **$160.0 \angle 30°$** b. **$25 \times 10^{-3} \angle -40°$**
c. **$70.71 \angle -90°$** d. **$14.14 \angle 0°$**
e. **$4.24 \times 10^{-6} \angle 90°$** f. **$2.55 \times 10^{-6} \angle 70°$**

49. a. **$56.57 \sin(377t + 20°)$** b. **$169.68 \sin(377t + 10°)$**
c. **$11.31 \times 10^{-3} \sin(377t + 120°)$** d. **$7.07 \sin(377t + 90°)$**
e. **$1696.8 \sin(377t - 50°)$** f. **$6000 \sin(377t - 180°)$**

50. (Using peak values)
$$e_{in} = \upsilon_a + \upsilon_b \Rightarrow \upsilon_a = e_{in} - \upsilon_b$$
$$= 60 \text{ V} \angle 20° - 20 \text{ V} \angle -20°$$
$$= 46.49 \text{ V} \angle 36.05°$$
and e_{in} = $46.49 \sin(377t + 36.05°)$

51. $i_s = i_1 + i_2 \Rightarrow i_1 = i_s - i_2$
(Using peak values) = $(20 \times 10^{-6} \text{ A} \angle 60°) - (6 \times 10^{-6} \text{ A} \angle -30°) = 20.88 \times 10^{-6} \text{ A} \angle 76.70°$
i_1 = **20.88×10^{-6}** $\sin(\omega t + 76.70°)$

52.
$$e = \upsilon_a + \upsilon_b + \upsilon_c$$
$$= 60 \text{ V} \angle 30° + 30 \text{ V} \angle 60° + 40 \text{ V} \angle 120°$$
$$= 102.07 \text{ V} \angle 62.61°$$
and e = **$102.07 \sin(\omega t + 62.61°)$**

53. (Using effective values)

$\mathbf{I}_s = \mathbf{I}_1 + \mathbf{I}_2 + \mathbf{I}_3 = 4.24 \text{ mA} \angle 180° + 5.66 \text{ mA} \angle -180° + 11.31 \text{ mA} \angle -180°$

$= -4.24 \text{ mA} - 5.66 \text{ mA} - 11.31 \text{ mA}$

$= 21.21 \times 10^{-3} \sin (377t + 180°)$

$i_s = \mathbf{-21.21 \times 10^{-3} \sin 377}t$

Chapter 15

1. a. $R \angle 0° = \mathbf{6.8\ \Omega \angle 0° = 6.8\ \Omega}$

b. $X_L = \omega L = (377 \text{ rads/s})(1.2 \text{ H}) = 452.4\ \Omega$
$X_L \angle 90° = \mathbf{452.4\ \Omega \angle 90° = +j452.4\ \Omega}$

c. $X_L = 2\pi fL = (6.28)(50 \text{ Hz})(0.05 \text{ H}) = 15.7\ \Omega$
$X_L \angle 90° = \mathbf{15.7\ \Omega \angle 90° = +j15.7\ \Omega}$

d. $X_C = \dfrac{1}{\omega C} = \dfrac{1}{(100 \text{ rad/s})(10 \times 10^{-6} \text{ F})} = 1 \text{ k}\Omega$
$X_C \angle -90° = \mathbf{1\ k\Omega \angle -90° = -j1\ k\Omega}$

e. $X_C = \dfrac{1}{2\pi fC} = \dfrac{1}{2\pi(10 \times 10^3 \text{ Hz})(0.05 \times 10^{-6} \text{ F})} = 318.47\ \Omega$
$X_C \angle -90° = \mathbf{318.47\ \Omega \angle -90° = -j318.47\ \Omega}$

f. $R \angle 0° = \mathbf{220\ \Omega \angle 0° = 220\ \Omega}$

2. a. $\mathbf{V} = 10.61 \text{ V} \angle 10°, \mathbf{I} = \dfrac{V\angle\theta}{R\angle 0°} = \dfrac{10.61 \text{ V} \angle 10°}{3\ \Omega \angle 0°} = 3.54 \text{ A} \angle 10°$
$\boldsymbol{i = 5 \sin (\omega t + 10°)}$

b. $\mathbf{V} = 39.60 \text{ V} \angle 10°, \mathbf{I} = \dfrac{V\angle\theta}{X_L\angle 90°} = \dfrac{39.60 \text{ V} \angle 10°}{7\ \Omega \angle 90°} = 5.66 \text{ A} \angle -80°$
$\boldsymbol{i = 8 \sin (\omega t - 80°)}$

c. $\mathbf{V} = 17.68 \text{ V} \angle -20°, \mathbf{I} = \dfrac{V\angle\theta}{X_C\angle -90°} = \dfrac{17.68 \text{ V} \angle -20°}{100\ \Omega \angle -90°} = 0.1768 \text{ A} \angle 70°$
$\boldsymbol{i = 0.25 \sin (\omega t + 70°)}$

d. $\mathbf{V} = 2.828 \text{ mV} \angle -120°, \mathbf{I} = \dfrac{V\angle\theta}{R\angle 0°} = \dfrac{2.828 \text{ mV} \angle -120°}{5.1 \text{ k}\Omega \angle 0°} = 0.555\ \mu\text{A} \angle -120°$
$\boldsymbol{i = 0.785 \times 10^{-6} \sin (\omega t - 120°)}$

e. $\mathbf{V} = 11.312 \text{ V} \angle 60°, \mathbf{I} = \dfrac{V\angle\theta}{X_L\angle 90°} = \dfrac{11.312 \text{ V} \angle 60°}{(377 \text{ rad/s})(0.2 \text{ H} \angle 90°)} = 150.03 \text{ mA} \angle -30°$
$\boldsymbol{i = 106.09 \times 10^{-3} \sin (377t - 30°)}$

f. $\mathbf{V} = 84.84 \text{ V} \angle 0°, X_C = \dfrac{1}{2\pi fC} = \dfrac{1}{2\pi(5 \text{ kHz})(2\ \mu\text{F})} = 15.924\ \Omega$
$\mathbf{I} = \dfrac{V\angle\theta}{X_C\angle -90°} = \dfrac{84.84 \text{ V} \angle 0°}{15.924\ \Omega \angle -90°} = 5.328 \text{ A} \angle 90°$
$\boldsymbol{i = 7.534 \sin (\omega t + 90°)}$

3. a. $\mathbf{I} = (0.707)(4 \text{ mA} \angle 0°) = 2.828 \text{ mA} \angle 0°$

$\mathbf{V} = (I \angle 0°)(R \angle 0°) = 2.828 \text{ mA} \angle 0°)(22 \ \Omega \angle 0°) = 62.216 \text{ mV} \angle 0°$

$\upsilon = \mathbf{88 \times 10^{-3} \sin \omega t}$

b. $\mathbf{I} = (0.707)(1.5 \text{ A} \angle 60°) = 1.061 \text{ A} \angle 60°$

$X_L = \omega L = (1000 \text{ rad/s})(0.016 \text{ H}) = 16 \ \Omega$

$\mathbf{V} = (I \angle \theta)(X_L \angle 90°) = (1.061 \text{ A} \angle 60°)(16 \ \Omega \angle 90°) = 16.98 \text{ V} \angle 150°$

$\upsilon = \mathbf{16.98 \sin(1000t + 150°)}$

c. $\mathbf{I} = (0.707)(2 \text{ mA} \angle 40°) = 1.414 \text{ mA} \angle 40°$

$$X_C = \frac{1}{\omega C} = \frac{1}{(157 \text{rad/s})(0.05 \times 10^{-6} \text{ F})} = 127.39 \text{ k}\Omega$$

$\mathbf{V} = (I \angle \theta)(X_C \angle -90°) = 1.414 \text{ mA} \angle 40°)(127.39 \text{ k}\Omega \angle -90°) = 180.13 \text{ V} \angle -50°$

$V_p = \sqrt{2}(180.13 \text{ V}) = 254.7 \text{ V}$

and $\upsilon = \mathbf{254.7 \sin(157t - 50°)}$

4. a. $\mathbf{Z}_T = \mathbf{6.8 \ \Omega + j8.2 \ \Omega = 10.65 \ \Omega \angle 50.33°}$

b. $\mathbf{Z}_T = 2 \ \Omega - j6 \ \Omega + 10 \ \Omega = \mathbf{12 \ \Omega - j6 \ \Omega = 13.42 \ \Omega \angle -26.57°}$

c. $\mathbf{Z}_T = 1 \text{ k}\Omega + j3 \text{ k}\Omega + 4 \text{ k}\Omega + j7 \text{ k}\Omega = \mathbf{5 \text{ k}\Omega + j10 \text{ k}\Omega = 11.18 \text{ k}\Omega \angle 63.44°}$

5. a. $\mathbf{Z}_T = \mathbf{3 \ \Omega + j4 \ \Omega - j5 \ \Omega = 3 \ \Omega - j1 \ \Omega = 3.16 \ \Omega \angle -18.43°}$

b. $\mathbf{Z}_T = 1 \text{ k}\Omega + j8 \text{ k}\Omega - j4 \text{ k}\Omega = \mathbf{1 \text{ k}\Omega + j4 \text{ k}\Omega = 4.12 \text{ k}\Omega \angle 75.96°}$

c. $L_T = 240 \text{ mH}$

$X_L = \omega L = 2\pi f L = 2\pi(10^3 \text{ Hz})(240 \times 10^{-3} \text{ H}) = 1.51 \text{ k}\Omega$

$$X_C = \frac{1}{2\pi f C} = \frac{1}{2\pi(10^3 \text{ Hz})(0.1 \times 10^{-6} \text{ F})} = 1.59 \text{ k}\Omega$$

$= 470 \ \Omega + j1.51 \text{ k}\Omega - j1.59 \text{ k}\Omega$

$= \mathbf{470 \ \Omega - j80 \ \Omega = 476.76 \ \Omega \angle -9.66°}$

6. a. $$\mathbf{Z}_T = \frac{\mathbf{E}}{\mathbf{I}} = \frac{120 \text{ V} \angle 0°}{60 \text{ A} \angle 70°} = 2 \ \Omega \angle -70° = \mathbf{0.684 \ \Omega - j1.879 \ \Omega = R - jX_C}$$

b. $$\mathbf{Z}_T = \frac{\mathbf{E}}{\mathbf{I}} = \frac{80 \text{ V} \angle 320°}{20 \text{ mA} \angle 40°} = 4 \text{ k}\Omega \angle 280° = \mathbf{4 \text{ k}\Omega \angle -80° = 0.695 \text{ k}\Omega - j3.939 \ \Omega}$$

$= \mathbf{R - jX_C}$

c. $$\mathbf{Z}_T = \frac{\mathbf{E}}{\mathbf{I}} = \frac{8 \text{ kV} \angle 0°}{0.2 \text{ A} \angle -60°} = 40 \text{ k}\Omega \angle 60° = \mathbf{20 \text{ k}\Omega + j34.64 \text{ k}\Omega = R + jX_L}$$

7. a. $\mathbf{Z}_T = 8\ \Omega + j6\ \Omega = \mathbf{10\ \Omega \angle 36.87°}$

c. $\mathbf{I} = \mathbf{E}/\mathbf{Z}_T = 100\text{ V} \angle 0°/10\ \Omega \angle 36.87° = \mathbf{10\ A \angle -36.87°}$
$\mathbf{V}_R = (I \angle \theta)(R \angle 0°) = (10\text{ A} \angle -36.87°)(8\ \Omega \angle 0°) = \mathbf{80\ V \angle -36.87°}$
$\mathbf{V}_L = (I \angle \theta)(X_L \angle 90°) = (10\text{ A} \angle -36.87°)(6\ \Omega \angle 90°) = \mathbf{60\ V \angle 53.13°}$

f. $P = I^2R = (10\text{ A})^2\ 8\ \Omega = \mathbf{800\ W}$

g. $F_p = \cos\theta_T = R/Z_T = 8\ \Omega/10\ \Omega = \mathbf{0.8}$ **lagging**

h. $\upsilon_R = \mathbf{113.12\ sin(\omega t - 36.87°)}$
$\upsilon_L = \mathbf{84.84\ sin(\omega t + 53.13°)}$
$i = \mathbf{14.14\ sin\ (\omega t - 36.87°)}$

8. a. $\mathbf{Z}_T = 6\ \Omega - j30\ \Omega = \mathbf{30.59\ \Omega \angle -78.69°}$

c. $\mathbf{I} = \dfrac{\mathbf{E}}{\mathbf{Z}_T} = \dfrac{120\text{ V} \angle 20°}{30.59\ \Omega \angle -78.69°} = \mathbf{3.92\ A \angle 98.69°}$

$\mathbf{V}_R = (I \angle \theta)(R \angle 0°) = (3.92\text{ A} \angle 98.69°)(6\ \Omega \angle 0°) = \mathbf{23.52\ V \angle 98.69°}$
$\mathbf{V}_C = (I \angle \theta)(X_C \angle -90°) = (3.92\text{ A} \angle 98.69°)(30\ \Omega \angle -90°) = \mathbf{117.60\ V \angle 8.69°}$

f. $P = I^2R = (3.92\text{ A})^2\ 6\ \Omega = \mathbf{92.2\ \ W}$

g. $F_p = R/Z_T = 6\ \Omega/30.59\ \Omega = \mathbf{0.196}$ **leading**

h. $i = \mathbf{5.54\ sin(377\mathit{t} + 98.69°)}$
$\upsilon_R = \mathbf{33.26\ sin(377\mathit{t} + 98.69°)}$
$\upsilon_C = \mathbf{166.29\ sin(377\mathit{t} + 8.69°)}$

9. a. $X_C = \dfrac{1}{2\pi fC} = \dfrac{1}{2\pi(10^3\text{ Hz})(0.2 \times 10^{-6}\text{ F})} = 795.77\ \Omega$

$\mathbf{Z}_T = 2.2\text{ k}\Omega - j795.77\ \Omega = \mathbf{2.34\ k\Omega \angle -19.89°}$

b. $\mathbf{I} = \mathbf{E}/\mathbf{Z}_T = 14.14\text{ V} \angle 0°/2.34\text{ k}\Omega \angle -19.89° = \mathbf{6.04\ mA \angle 19.89°}$

c. $\mathbf{V}_R = (I \angle \theta)(R \angle 0°) = (6.04\text{ mA} \angle 19.89°)(2.2 \times 10^3\ \Omega \angle 0°) = \mathbf{13.29\ V \angle 19.89°}$
$\mathbf{V}_C = (I \angle \theta)(X_C \angle -90°) = (6.04\text{ mA} \angle 19.89°)(795.77\ \Omega \angle -90°)$
$= \mathbf{4.81\ V \angle -70.11°}$

d. $P = I^2R = (6.04\text{ mA})^2\ 2.2\text{ k}\Omega = \mathbf{80.26\ mW}$
$F_p = \cos\theta_T = \cos 19.89° = \mathbf{0.94}$ **leading**

10. a. $\mathbf{Z}_T = 4\ \Omega + j6\ \Omega - j10\ \Omega = 4\ \Omega - j4\ \Omega = \mathbf{5.66\ \Omega\ \angle{-45^\circ}}$

c. $X_L = \omega L \Rightarrow L = \dfrac{X_L}{\omega} = \dfrac{6\ \Omega}{377\text{ rad/s}} = \mathbf{16\ mH}$

$X_C = \dfrac{1}{\omega C} \Rightarrow C = \dfrac{1}{\omega X_C} = \dfrac{1}{(377\text{ rad/s})(10\ \Omega)} = \mathbf{265\ \mu F}$

d. $\mathbf{I} = \dfrac{\mathbf{E}}{\mathbf{Z}_T} = \dfrac{50\text{ V}\ \angle 0^\circ}{5.66\ \Omega\ \angle -45^\circ} = \mathbf{8.83\ A\ \angle 45^\circ}$

$\mathbf{V}_R = (I\ \angle\theta)(R\ \angle 0^\circ) = (8.83\text{ A}\ \angle 45^\circ)(4\ \Omega\ \angle 0^\circ) = \mathbf{35.32\ V\ \angle 45^\circ}$

$\mathbf{V}_L = (I\ \angle\theta)(X_L\ \angle 90^\circ) = (8.83\text{ A}\ \angle 45^\circ)(6\ \Omega\ \angle 90^\circ) = \mathbf{52.98\ V\ \angle 135^\circ}$

$\mathbf{V}_C = (I\ \angle\theta)(X_C\ \angle{-90^\circ}) = (8.83\text{ A}\ \angle 45^\circ)(10\ \Omega\ \angle{-90^\circ}) = \mathbf{88.30\ V\ \angle{-45^\circ}}$

f. $\mathbf{E} = \mathbf{V}_R + \mathbf{V}_L + \mathbf{V}_C$

$50\text{ V}\ \angle 0^\circ = 35.32\text{ V}\ \angle 45^\circ + 52.98\text{ V}\ \angle 135^\circ + 88.30\text{ V}\ \angle{-45^\circ}$

$50\text{ V}\ \angle 0^\circ = 49.95\text{ V}\ \angle 0^\circ \cong 50\text{ V}\ \angle 0^\circ$

g. $P = I^2R = (8.83\text{ A})^2\ 4\ \Omega = \mathbf{311.88\ W}$

h. $F_p = \cos\theta_T = \dfrac{R}{Z_T} = 4\ \Omega/5.66\ \Omega = \mathbf{0.707\ leading}$

i. $i = \mathbf{12.49\ sin(377\mathit{t} + 45^\circ)}$

$e = \mathbf{70.7\ sin\ 377\mathit{t}}$

$\upsilon_R = \mathbf{49.94\ sin(377\mathit{t} + 45^\circ)}$

$\upsilon_L = \mathbf{74.91\ sin(377\mathit{t} + 135^\circ)}$

$\upsilon_C = \mathbf{124.86\ sin(377\mathit{t} - 45^\circ)}$

11. a. $\mathbf{Z}_T = 1.8\text{ k}\Omega + j2\text{ k}\Omega - j0.6\text{ k}\Omega = \mathbf{1.8\ k\Omega + \mathit{j}1.2\ k\Omega} = \mathbf{2.16\ k\Omega\ \angle 33.69^\circ}$

c. $X_C = \dfrac{1}{\omega C} \Rightarrow C = \dfrac{1}{\omega X_C} = \dfrac{1}{(314\text{ rad/s})(0.6\text{ k}\Omega)} = \mathbf{5.31\ \mu F}$

$X_L = \omega L \Rightarrow L = \dfrac{X_L}{\omega} = \dfrac{2\times 10^3\ \Omega}{314\text{ rad/s}} = \mathbf{6.37\ H}$

d. $\mathbf{I} = \mathbf{E}/\mathbf{Z}_T = 4.242\text{ V}\ \angle 60^\circ/2.16\text{ k}\Omega\ \angle 33.69^\circ = \mathbf{1.96\ mA\ \angle 26.31^\circ}$

$\mathbf{V}_R = (I\ \angle\theta)(R\ \angle 0^\circ) = (1.96\text{ mA}\ \angle 26.31^\circ)(1.8\text{ k}\Omega\ \angle 0^\circ) = \mathbf{3.53\ V\ \angle 26.31^\circ}$

$\mathbf{V}_L = (I\ \angle\theta)(X_L\ \angle 90^\circ) = (1.96\text{ mA}\ \angle 26.31^\circ)(2\text{ k}\Omega\ \angle 90^\circ) = \mathbf{2.68\ V\ \angle 116.31^\circ}$

$\mathbf{V}_C = (I\ \angle\theta)(X_C\ \angle{-90^\circ}) = (1.96\text{ mA}\ \angle 26.31^\circ)(0.6\text{ k}\Omega\ \angle{-90^\circ}) = \mathbf{1.18\ V\ \angle{-63.69^\circ}}$

g. $P = I^2R = (1.96\text{ mA})^2\ 1.8\text{ k}\Omega = \mathbf{6.91\ mW}$

h. $F_p = \cos\theta_T = \cos 33.69^\circ = \mathbf{0.832\ lagging}$

i. $i = \mathbf{2.77 \times 10^{-3} \sin(\omega t + 26.31°)}$
$\upsilon_R = \mathbf{4.99 \sin(\omega t + 26.31°)}$
$\upsilon_L = \mathbf{3.79 \sin(\omega t + 116.31°)}$
$\upsilon_C = \mathbf{1.67 \sin(\omega t - 63.69°)}$

12. $V_{80\Omega}(\text{rms}) = 0.7071\left(\dfrac{45.27\text{ V}}{2}\right) = 16\text{ V}$

$$V_{\text{scope}} = \frac{80\,\Omega\ (20\text{ V})}{80\,\Omega + R} = 16\text{ V}$$
$$1600 = 1280 + 16R$$
$$R = \frac{320}{16} = \mathbf{20\,\Omega}$$

13. a. $V_L(\text{rms}) = 0.7071\left(\dfrac{21.28\text{ V}}{2}\right) = 7.524\text{ V}$

$$X_L = \frac{V_L}{I_L} = \frac{7.524\text{ V}}{29.94\text{ mA}} = 251.303\,\Omega$$
$$X_L = 2\pi fL \Rightarrow L = \frac{X_L}{2\pi f} = \frac{251.303\,\Omega}{2\pi(1\text{ kHz})} = 39.996\text{ mH} \cong \mathbf{40\text{ mH}}$$

b.

E, 10 V, V_L, 7.524 V, V_R, I

$$E^2 = V_R^2 + V_L^2$$
$$V_R = \sqrt{E^2 - V_L^2}$$
$$= \sqrt{(100\text{ V}) - (56.611)} = \sqrt{43.389} = 6.587\text{ V}$$

$$R = \frac{V_R}{I_R} = \frac{6.587\text{ V}}{29.94\text{ mA}} = \mathbf{220\,\Omega}$$

14. $V_R(\text{rms}) = 0.7071\left(\dfrac{8.27\text{ V}}{2}\right) = 2.924\text{ V}$

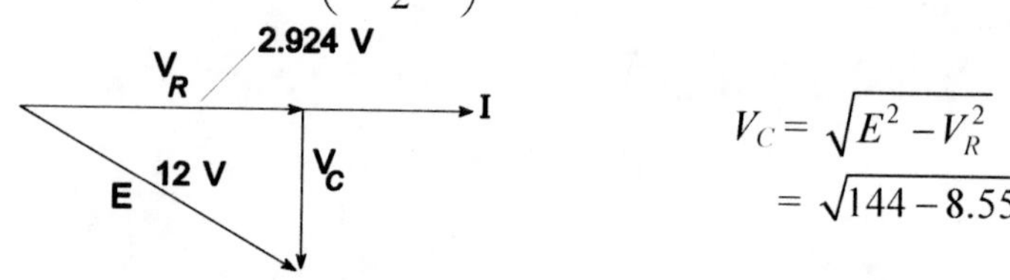

$$V_C = \sqrt{E^2 - V_R^2}$$
$$= \sqrt{144 - 8.55} = \sqrt{135.45} = 11.638\text{ V}$$

$$I_C = I_R = \frac{2.924\text{ V}}{10\text{ k}\Omega} = 292.4\,\mu\text{A}$$
$$X_C = \frac{V_C}{I_C} = \frac{11.638\text{ V}}{292.4\,\mu\text{A}} = 39.802\text{ k}\Omega$$
$$X_C = \frac{1}{2\pi fC} \Rightarrow C = \frac{1}{2\pi f X_C} = \frac{1}{2\pi(40\text{ kHz})(39.802\text{ k}\Omega)} = 99.967\text{ pF} \cong \mathbf{100\text{ pF}}$$

15. a. $\mathbf{V}_1 = \dfrac{(2\text{ k}\Omega \angle 0°)(120\text{ V} \angle 60°)}{2\text{ k}\Omega + j8\text{ k}\Omega} = \dfrac{240\text{ V} \angle 60°}{8.25 \angle 75.96°} = \mathbf{29.09\ V \angle{-15.96°}}$

$\mathbf{V}_2 = \dfrac{(8\text{ k}\Omega \angle 90°)(120\text{ V} \angle 60°)}{8.25\text{ k}\Omega \angle 75.96°} = \mathbf{116.36\ V \angle 74.04°}$

b. $\mathbf{V}_1 = \dfrac{(40\,\Omega \angle 90°)(60\text{ V} \angle 5°)}{6.8\,\Omega + j40\,\Omega + 22\,\Omega} = \dfrac{2400\text{ V} \angle 95°}{28.8 + j40} = \mathbf{48.69\ V \angle 40.75°}$

$\mathbf{V}_2 = \dfrac{(22\,\Omega \angle 0°)(60\text{ V} \angle 5°)}{49.29\,\Omega \angle 54.25°} = \dfrac{1.32\text{ kV} \angle 5°}{49.29\,\Omega \angle 54.25°} = \mathbf{26.78\ V \angle{-49.25°}}$

16. a. $\mathbf{V}_1 = \dfrac{(20\,\Omega \angle 90°)(20\text{ V} \angle 70°)}{20\,\Omega + j20\,\Omega - j40\,\Omega} = \mathbf{14.14\ V \angle{-155°}}$

$\mathbf{V}_2 = \dfrac{(40\,\Omega \angle -90°)(20\text{ V} \angle 70°)}{28.28\,\Omega \angle -45°} = \mathbf{28.29\ V \angle 25°}$

b. $\mathbf{Z}_T = 4.7\text{ k}\Omega + j30\text{ k}\Omega + 3.3\text{ k}\Omega - j10\text{ k}\Omega = 8\text{ k}\Omega + j20\text{ k}\Omega = 21.541\text{ k}\Omega \angle 68.199°$

$\mathbf{Z}'_T = 3.3\text{ k}\Omega + j30\text{ k}\Omega - j10\text{ k}\Omega = 3.3\text{ k}\Omega + j20\text{ k}\Omega = 20.27\text{ k}\Omega \angle 80.631°$

$\mathbf{V}_1 = \dfrac{\mathbf{Z}'_T\mathbf{E}}{\mathbf{Z}_T} = \dfrac{(20.27\text{ k}\Omega \angle 80.631°)(120\text{ V} \angle 0°)}{21.541\text{ k}\Omega \angle 68.199°} = \mathbf{112.92\ V \angle 12.432°}$

$\mathbf{V}_2 = \dfrac{\mathbf{Z}''_T\mathbf{E}}{\mathbf{Z}_T}$ $\qquad \mathbf{Z}''_T = 3.3\text{ k}\Omega - j10\text{ k}\Omega = 10.53\text{ k}\Omega \angle{-71.737°}$

$= \dfrac{(10.53\text{ k}\Omega \angle -71.737°)(120\text{ V} \angle 0°)}{21.541\text{ k}\Omega \angle 68.199°} = \mathbf{58.66\ V \angle{-139.94°}}$

17. a. $X_L = \omega L = (377\text{ rad/s})(0.4\text{ H}) = 150.8\,\Omega$

$X_C = \dfrac{1}{\omega C} = \dfrac{1}{(377\text{ rad/s})(4\,\mu\text{F})} = 663\,\Omega$

$\mathbf{Z}_T = 30\,\Omega + j150.8\,\Omega - j663\,\Omega = 30\,\Omega - j512.2\,\Omega = \mathbf{513.08\,\Omega \angle{-86.65°}}$

$\mathbf{I} = \dfrac{\mathbf{E}}{\mathbf{Z}_T} = \dfrac{20\text{ V} \angle 40°}{513.08\,\Omega \angle -86.65°} = \mathbf{39\ mA \angle 126.65°}$

$\mathbf{V}_R = (I \angle \theta)(R \angle 0°) = (39\text{ mA} \angle 126.65°)(30\,\Omega \angle 0°) = \mathbf{1.17\ V \angle 126.65°}$

$\mathbf{V}_C = (39\text{ mA} \angle 126.65°)(0.663\text{ k}\Omega \angle{-90°}) = \mathbf{25.86\ V \angle 36.65°}$

b. $\cos\theta_T = \dfrac{R}{Z_T} = \dfrac{30\,\Omega}{513.08\,\Omega} = \mathbf{0.058\ leading}$

c. $P = I^2R = (39\text{ mA})^2\, 30\,\Omega = \mathbf{45.63\ mW}$

f. $\mathbf{V}_R = \dfrac{(30\,\Omega \angle 0°)(20\text{ V} \angle 40°)}{\mathbf{Z}_T} = \dfrac{600\text{ V} \angle 40°}{513.08\,\Omega \angle -86.65°} = \mathbf{1.17\ V \angle 126.65°}$

$\mathbf{V}_C = \dfrac{(0.663\text{ k}\Omega \angle -90°)(20\text{ V} \angle 40°)}{513.08\,\Omega \angle -86.65°} = \mathbf{25.84\ V \angle 36.65°}$

g. $\mathbf{Z}_T = \mathbf{30\,\Omega - \mathit{j}512.2\,\Omega} = R - jX_C$

18. a. $X_L = \omega L = (377 \text{ rad/s})(0.4 \text{ H}) = 150.8\ \Omega$

$$X_C = \frac{1}{\omega C} = \frac{1}{(377 \text{ rad/s})(220 \times 10^{-6} \text{ F})} = 12.06\ \Omega$$

$\mathbf{Z}_T = 30\ \Omega + j150.8\ \Omega - j12.06\ \Omega$

$= 30\ \Omega + j138.74\ \Omega = 141.95\ \Omega\ \angle 77.80°$

$\mathbf{I} = \mathbf{E}/\mathbf{Z}_T = 20 \text{ V} \angle 40°/141.95\ \Omega\ \angle 77.80° = \mathbf{140.89\ mA\ \angle{-37.80°}}$

$\mathbf{V}_R = (I \angle \theta)(R \angle 0°) = (140.89 \text{ mA} \angle{-37.80°})(30\ \Omega \angle 0°) = \mathbf{4.23\ V\ \angle{-37.80°}}$

$\mathbf{V}_C = (I \angle \theta)(X_C \angle{-90°}) = (140.89 \text{ mA} \angle{-37.80°})(12.06\ \Omega \angle{-90°})$

$= \mathbf{1.70\ V\ \angle{-127.80°}}$

b. $F_p = \cos\theta_T = R/Z_T = 30\ \Omega/141.95\ \Omega = \mathbf{0.211}$ **lagging**

c. $P = I^2R = (140.89 \text{ mA})^2\, 30\ \Omega = \mathbf{595.50\ mW}$

f. $$\mathbf{V}_R = \frac{(30\ \Omega \angle 0°)(20 \text{ V} \angle 40°)}{141.95\ \Omega \angle 77.80°} = \mathbf{4.23\ V\ \angle{-37.80°}}$$

$$\mathbf{V}_C = \frac{(12.06\ \Omega \angle{-90°})(20 \text{ V} \angle 40°)}{141.95\ \Omega \angle 77.80°} = \mathbf{1.70\ V\ \angle{-127.80°}}$$

g. $\mathbf{Z}_T = 30\ \Omega + j138.74\ \Omega = R + jX_L$

19. $P = VI\cos\theta \Rightarrow 8000 \text{ W} = (200 \text{ V})(I)(0.8)$

$$I = \frac{8000 \text{ A}}{160} = 50 \text{ A}$$

$0.8 = \cos\theta$

$\theta = 36.87°$

$\mathbf{V} = 200 \text{ V} \angle 0°,\ I = 50 \text{ A} \angle{-36.87°}$

$$\mathbf{Z}_T = \frac{\mathbf{V}}{\mathbf{I}} = \frac{200 \text{ V} \angle 0°}{50 \text{ A} \angle{-36.87°}} = 4\ \Omega \angle 36.87° = \mathbf{3.2\ \Omega + \mathit{j}2.4\ \Omega}$$

20. $P = VI\cos\theta \Rightarrow 300 \text{ W} = (120 \text{ V})(3 \text{ A})\cos\theta$

$\cos\theta = 0.833 \Rightarrow \theta = \mathbf{33.59°}$

$\mathbf{V} = 120 \text{ V} \angle 0°,\ \mathbf{I} = 3 \text{ A} \angle{-33.59°}$

$$\mathbf{Z}_T = \frac{\mathbf{V}}{\mathbf{I}} = \frac{120 \text{ V} \angle 0°}{3 \text{ A} \angle{-33.59°}} = 40\ \Omega \angle 33.59° = \mathbf{33.34\ \Omega + \mathit{j}22.10\ \Omega}$$

$R_T = 33.34\ \Omega = 2\ \Omega + R \Rightarrow R = 31.34\ \Omega$

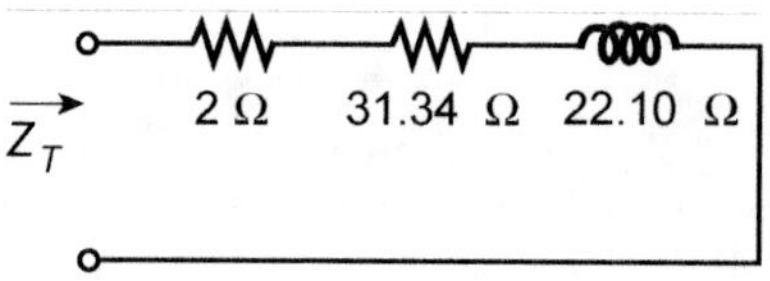

2 Ω 31.34 Ω 22.10 Ω
Z_T

21. a. $\mathbf{Z}_T = \sqrt{R^2 + X_L^2} \angle \tan^{-1} X_L/R$

f	Z_T	θ_T
0 Hz	1.0 kΩ	0.0°
1 kHz	1.008 kΩ	7.16°
5 kHz	1.181 kΩ	32.14°
10 kHz	1.606 kΩ	51.49°
15 kHz	2.134 kΩ	62.05°
20 kHz	2.705 kΩ	68.3°

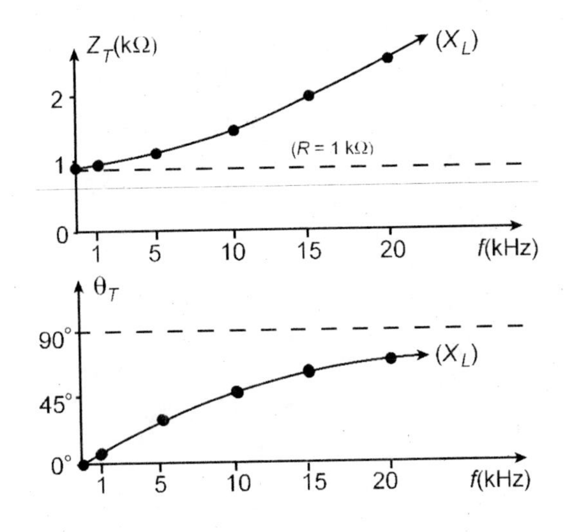

b. $V_L = \dfrac{X_L E}{Z_T}$

f	V_L
0 Hz	0.0 V
1 kHz	0.623 V
5 kHz	2.66 V
10 kHz	3.888 V
15 kHz	4.416 V
20 kHz	4.646 V

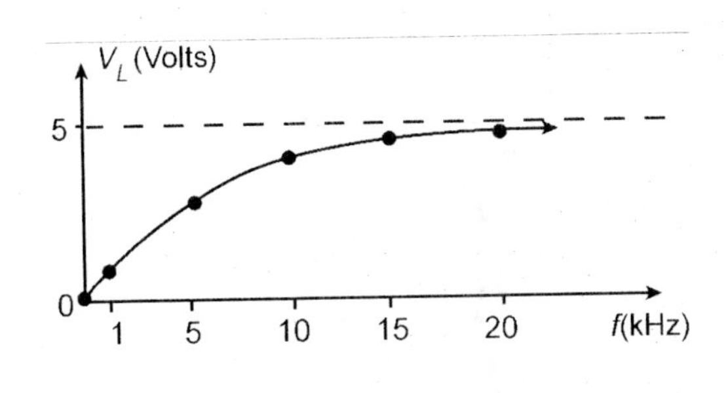

c.

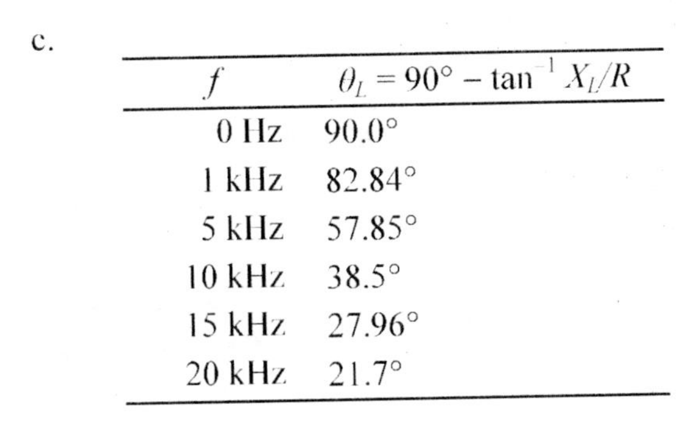

f	$\theta_L = 90° - \tan^{-1} X_L/R$
0 Hz	90.0°
1 kHz	82.84°
5 kHz	57.85°
10 kHz	38.5°
15 kHz	27.96°
20 kHz	21.7°

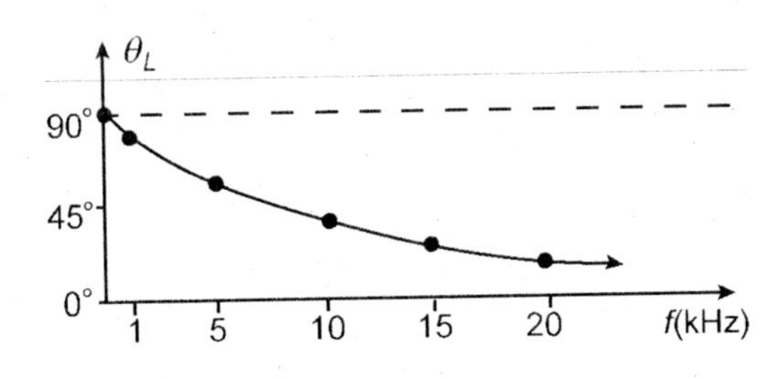

d.

f	$V_R = RE/Z_T$
0 Hz	5.0 V
1 kHz	4.96 V
5 kHz	4.23 V
10 kHz	3.11 V
15 kHz	2.34 V
20 kHz	1.848 V

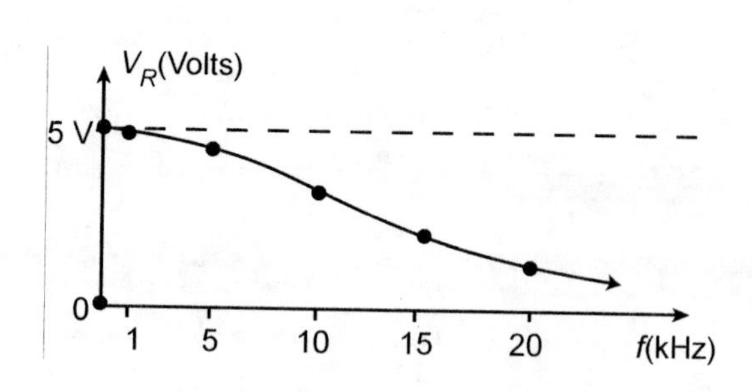

22. a. $\mathbf{Z}_T = \sqrt{R^2 + X_C^2} \angle -\tan^{-1} X_C/R$

$|Z_T| = \sqrt{R^2 + X_C^2}$, $\theta_T = -\tan^{-1} X_C/R$

f	$\|\mathbf{Z}_T\|$	θ_T
0 kHz	$\infty\ \Omega$	–90.0°
1 kHz	333.64 Ω	–72.56°
3 kHz	145.8 Ω	–46.7°
5 kHz	118.54 Ω	–32.48°
7 kHz	109.85 Ω	–24.45°
10 kHz	104.94 Ω	–17.66°

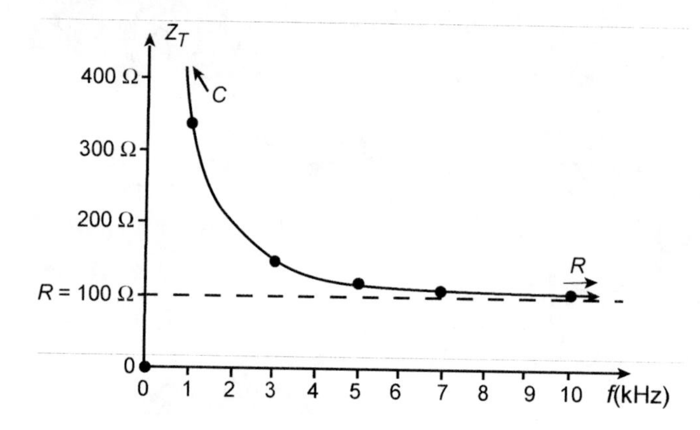

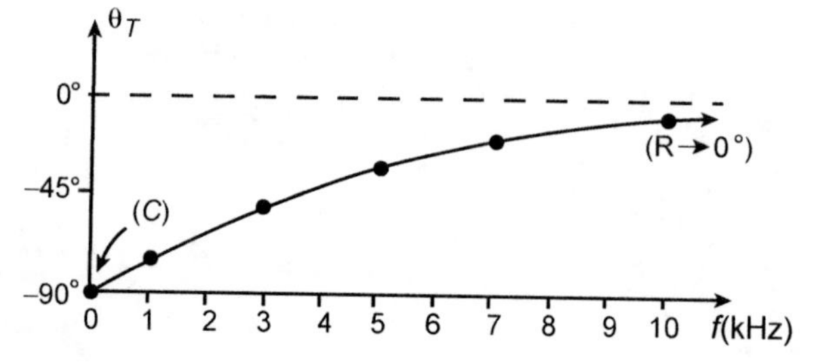

b. $\mathbf{V}_C = \dfrac{(X_C\angle -90°)(E\angle 0°)}{R - jX_C} = \dfrac{X_C E}{\sqrt{R^2 + X_C^2}} \angle -90° + \tan^{-1} X_C/R$

$$|V_C| = \frac{X_C E}{\sqrt{R^2 + X_C^2}}$$

f	$\lvert V_C \rvert$
0 Hz	10.0 V
1 kHz	9.54 V
3 kHz	7.28 V
5 kHz	5.37 V
7 kHz	4.14 V
10 kHz	3.03 V

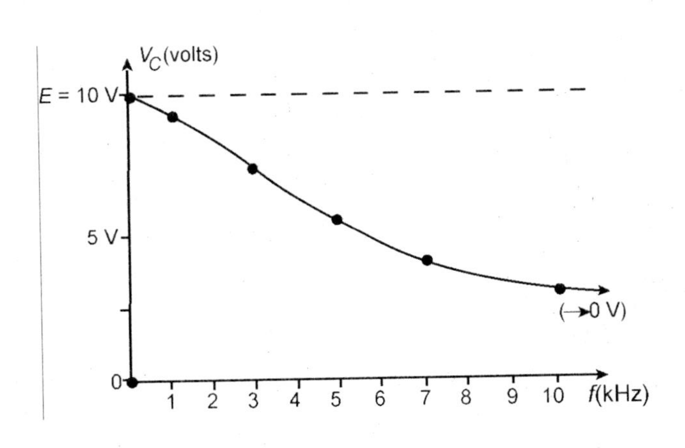

c. $\theta_C = -90° + \tan^{-1} X_C/R$

f	θ_C
0 Hz	0.0°
1 kHz	−17.44°
3 kHz	−43.3°
5 kHz	−57.52°
7 kHz	−65.55°
10 kHz	−72.34°

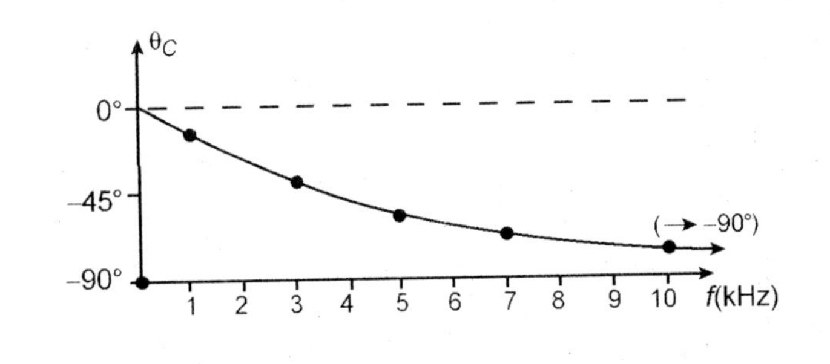

d. $$|V_R| = \frac{RE}{\sqrt{R^2 + X_C^2}}$$

f	$\lvert V_R \rvert$
0 Hz	0.0 V
1 kHz	3.0 V
3 kHz	6.86 V
5 kHz	8.44 V
7 kHz	9.10 V
10 kHz	9.53 V

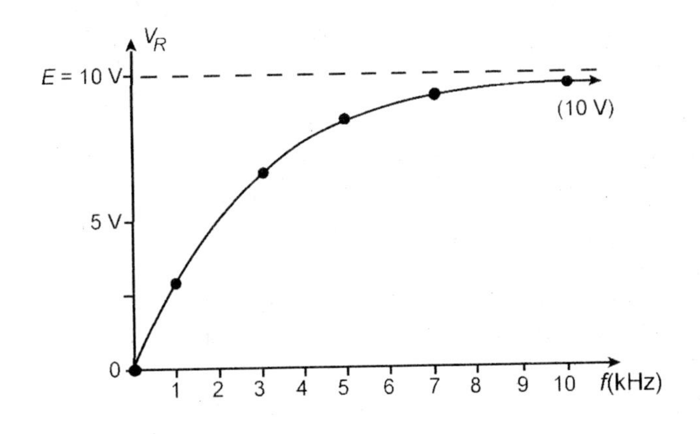

23. a. $\mathbf{Z}_T = \sqrt{R^2 + (X_L - X_C)^2} \angle \tan^{-1}(X_L - X_C)/R$

f	Z_T	θ_T
0 Hz	∞ Ω	−90.0°
1 kHz	19,793.97 Ω	−87.1°
5 kHz	3,496.6 Ω	−73.38°
10 kHz	1,239.76 Ω	−36.23°
15 kHz	1,145.47 Ω	+29.19°
20 kHz	1,818.24 Ω	+56.63°

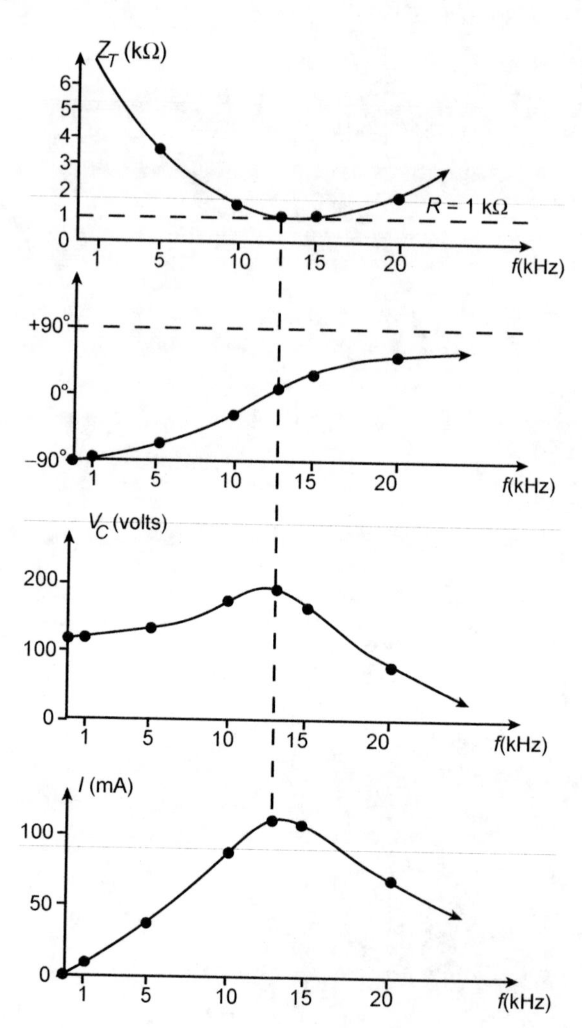

b. $|V_C| = \dfrac{X_C E}{Z_T}$

f	$\lvert V_C \rvert$
0 Hz	120.0 V
1 kHz	120.61 V
5 kHz	136.55 V
10 kHz	192.57 V
15 kHz	138.94 V
20 kHz	65.65 V

c. $|I| = \dfrac{E}{Z_T}$

f	I
0 Hz	0.0 mA
1 kHz	6.062 mA
5 kHz	34.32 mA
10 kHz	96.79 mA
15 kHz	104.76 mA
20 kHz	66.0 mA

24. a. $X_C = \dfrac{1}{2\pi fC} = R \Rightarrow f = \dfrac{1}{2\pi RC} = \dfrac{1}{2\pi(220\ \Omega)(0.47\ \mu\text{F})} = \mathbf{1.54\ kHz}$

b. Low frequency: X_C very large resulting in large Z_T
High frequency: X_C approaches zero ohms and Z_T approaches R

c. $f = 100\text{ Hz}$: $X_C = \dfrac{1}{2\pi fC} = \dfrac{1}{2\pi(100\text{ Hz})(0.47\ \mu\text{F})} = 3.39\text{ k}\Omega$

$Z_T \cong X_C$

$f = 10\text{ kHz}$: $X_C = \dfrac{1}{2\pi fC} = \dfrac{1}{2\pi(10\text{ kHz})(0.47\ \mu\text{F})} = 33.86\ \Omega$

$Z_T \cong R$

d. –

e. $f = 40\text{ kHz}$: $X_C = \dfrac{1}{2\pi fC} = \dfrac{1}{2\pi(40\text{ kHz})(0.47\ \mu\text{F})} = 8.47\text{ k}\Omega$

$\theta = -\tan^{-1}\dfrac{X_C}{R} = -\tan^{-1}\dfrac{8.47\ \Omega}{220\ \Omega} = \mathbf{-2.2°}$

25. a. $\mathbf{Z}_T = \mathbf{91\ \Omega\ \angle 0°} = R\ \angle 0°$, $\mathbf{Y}_T = \mathbf{10.99\ mS\ \angle 0°} = G\ \angle 0°$

b. $\mathbf{Z}_T = \mathbf{200\ \Omega\ \angle 90°} = X_L\ \angle 90°$, $\mathbf{Y}_T = \mathbf{5\ mS\ \angle{-90°}} = B_L\ \angle{-90°}$

c. $\mathbf{Z}_T = \mathbf{0.2\ k\Omega\ \angle{-90°}} = X_C\ \angle{-90°}$, $\mathbf{Y}_T = \mathbf{5.00\ mS\ \angle 90°} = B_C\ \angle 90°$

d. $\mathbf{Z}_T = \dfrac{(10\ \Omega\angle 0°)(60\ \Omega\ \angle 90°)}{10\ \Omega + j60\ \Omega} = \mathbf{9.86\ \Omega\ \angle 9.46° = 9.73\ \Omega + \mathit{j}1.62\ \Omega} = R + jX_L$

$\mathbf{Y}_T = \mathbf{0.10\ S\ \angle{-9.46°} = 0.1\ S - \mathit{j}0.02\ S} = G - jB_L$

e. $22\ \Omega \parallel 2.2\ \Omega = 2\ \Omega$

$\mathbf{Z}_T = \dfrac{(2\ \Omega\angle 0°)(6\ \Omega\ \angle -90°)}{2\ \Omega - j6\ \Omega} = \dfrac{12\ \Omega\ \angle -90°}{6.32\ \Omega\ \angle -71.57°} = \mathbf{1.90\ \Omega\ \angle{-18.43°}}$

$= \mathbf{1.80\ \Omega - \mathit{j}0.6\ \Omega} = R - jX_C$

$\mathbf{Y}_T = \mathbf{0.53\ S\ \angle 18.43°} = \mathbf{0.5\ S + \mathit{j}0.17\ S} = G + jB_C$

f. $\mathbf{Y}_T = \dfrac{1}{3\text{ k}\Omega\ \angle 0°} + \dfrac{1}{6\text{ k}\Omega\ \angle 90°} + \dfrac{1}{9\text{ k}\Omega\ \angle -90°}$

$= 0.333 \times 10^{-3}\ \angle 0° + 0.167 \times 10^{-3}\ \angle{-90°} + 0.111 \times 10^{-3}\ \angle 90°$

$= \mathbf{0.333 \times 10^{-3}\ S - \mathit{j}0.056 \times 10^{-3}\ S = 0.34\ mS\ \angle{-9.55°}}$

$= G - jB_L$

$\mathbf{Z}_T = \dfrac{1}{\mathbf{Y}_T} = \mathbf{2.94\ k\Omega\ \angle 9.55° = 2.90\ k\Omega + \mathit{j}0.49\ k\Omega}$

26. a. $\mathbf{Z}_T = 4.7\ \Omega + j8\ \Omega = \mathbf{9.28\ \Omega \angle 59.57°}$, $\mathbf{Y}_T = \mathbf{0.108\ S \angle{-59.57°}}$

$\mathbf{Y}_T = \mathbf{54.7\ mS - j93.12\ mS} = G - jB_L$

b. $\mathbf{Z}_T = 33\ \Omega + 20\ \Omega - j70\ \Omega = \mathbf{53\ \Omega - j70\ \Omega} = \mathbf{87.80\ \Omega \angle{-52.87°}}$

$\mathbf{Y}_T = \mathbf{11.39\ mS \angle 52.87° = 6.88\ mS + j9.08\ mS} = G + jB_C$

c. $\mathbf{Z}_T = 200\ \Omega + j500\ \Omega - j600\ \Omega = \mathbf{200\ \Omega - j100\ \Omega} = \mathbf{223.61\ \Omega \angle{-26.57°}}$

$\mathbf{Y}_T = \mathbf{4.47\ mS \angle 26.57°} = \mathbf{4\ mS + j2\ mS} = G + jB_C$

27. a. $\mathbf{Y}_T = \dfrac{\mathbf{I}}{\mathbf{E}} = \dfrac{60\ \text{A} \angle 70°}{120\ \text{V} \angle 0°} = 0.5\ \text{S} \angle 70° = 0.171\ \text{S} + j0.470\ \text{S} = G + jB_C$

$R = \dfrac{1}{G} = \mathbf{5.85\ \Omega}$, $X_C = \dfrac{1}{B_C} = \mathbf{2.13\ \Omega}$

b. $\mathbf{Y}_T = \dfrac{\mathbf{I}}{\mathbf{E}} = \dfrac{20\ \text{mA} \angle 40°}{80\ \text{V} \angle 320°} = 0.25\ \text{mS} \angle{-280°} = 0.25\ \text{mS} \angle 80°$

$= 0.043\ \text{mS} + j0.246\ \text{mS} = G + jB_C$

$R = \dfrac{1}{G} = \mathbf{23.26\ k\Omega}$, $X_C = \dfrac{1}{B_C} = \mathbf{4.07\ k\Omega}$

c. $\mathbf{Y}_T = \dfrac{\mathbf{I}}{\mathbf{E}} = \dfrac{0.2\ \text{A} \angle -60°}{8\ \text{kV} \angle 0°} = 0.25\ \text{mS} \angle{-60°} = 0.0125\ \text{mS} - j0.02165\ \text{mS} = G - jB_L$

$R = \dfrac{1}{G} = \mathbf{80\ k\Omega}$, $X_L = \dfrac{1}{B_L} = \mathbf{46.19\ k\Omega}$

28. a. $\mathbf{Y}_T = \dfrac{1}{10\,\Omega \angle 0°} + \dfrac{1}{20\,\Omega \angle 90°} = 0.1\ \text{S} - j0.05\ \text{S} = \mathbf{111.8\ mS \angle{-26.57°}}$

c. $\mathbf{E} = \mathbf{I}_s/\mathbf{Y}_T = 2\ \text{A} \angle 0°/111.8\ \text{mS} \angle{-26.57°} = \mathbf{17.89\ V \angle 26.57°}$

$\mathbf{I}_R = \dfrac{E \angle \theta}{R \angle 0°} = 17.89\ \text{V} \angle 26.57°/10\ \Omega \angle 0° = \mathbf{1.79\ A \angle 26.57°}$

$\mathbf{I}_L = \dfrac{E \angle \theta}{X_L \angle 90°} = 17.89\ \text{V} \angle 26.57°/20\ \Omega \angle 90° = \mathbf{0.89\ A \angle{-63.43°}}$

f. $P = I^2R = (1.79\ \text{A})^2\ 10\ \Omega = \mathbf{32.04\ W}$

g. $F_p = \dfrac{G}{Y_T} = \dfrac{0.1\ \text{S}}{111.8\ \text{mS}} = \mathbf{0.894\ lagging}$

h. $e = \mathbf{25.30\ sin(377\mathit{t} + 26.57°)}$
$i_R = \mathbf{2.53\ sin(377\mathit{t} + 26.57°)}$
$i_L = \mathbf{1.26\ sin(377\mathit{t} - 63.43°)}$
$i_s = \mathbf{2.83\ sin\ 377\mathit{t}}$

29. a. $\mathbf{Y}_T = \dfrac{1}{10\,\text{k}\Omega\,\angle 0°} + \dfrac{1}{20\,\text{k}\Omega\,\angle -90°} = 0.1\text{ mS }\angle 0° + 0.05\text{ mS }\angle -90°$

$= \mathbf{0.112\ mS\ \angle 26.57°}$

c. $\mathbf{E} = \dfrac{\mathbf{I}_s}{\mathbf{Y}_T} = \dfrac{2\text{ mA }\angle 20°}{0.1118\text{ mS }\angle 26.565°} = \mathbf{17.89\ V\ \angle{-6.57°}}$

$\mathbf{I}_R = \dfrac{\mathbf{E}}{\mathbf{Z}_R} = \dfrac{17.89\text{ V }\angle -6.57°}{10\,\text{k}\Omega\,\angle 0°} = \mathbf{1.79\ mA\ \angle{-6.57°}}$

$\mathbf{I}_C = \dfrac{\mathbf{E}}{\mathbf{Z}_C} = \dfrac{17.89\text{ V }\angle -6.57°}{20\,\text{k}\Omega\,\angle -90°} = \mathbf{0.90\ mA\ \angle 83.44°}$

e. $\mathbf{I}_s = \mathbf{I}_R + \mathbf{I}_C$

$2\text{ mA }\angle 20° = 1.79\text{ mA }\angle -6.57° + 0.90\text{ mA }\angle 83.44°$

$= 1.88\text{ mA} + j0.69\text{ mA}$

$2\text{ mA }\angle 20° \overset{\checkmark}{=} 2\text{ mA }\angle 20.15°$

f. $P = I^2R = (1.79\text{ mA})^2\ 10\text{ k}\Omega = \mathbf{32.04\ mW}$

g. $F_p = \dfrac{G}{Y_T} = \dfrac{0.1\text{ mS}}{0.1118\text{ mS}} = \mathbf{0.894\ leading}$

h. $\omega = 2\pi f = 377\text{ rad/s}$

$\boldsymbol{i_s = 2.83 \times 10^{-3}\sin(\omega t + 20°)}$

$\boldsymbol{i_R = 2.53 \times 10^{-3}\sin(\omega t - 6.57°)}$

$\boldsymbol{i_C = 1.27 \times 10^{-3}\sin(\omega t + 83.44°)}$

$\boldsymbol{e = 25.3\sin(\omega t - 6.57°)}$

30. a. $\mathbf{Y}_T = \dfrac{1}{12\,\Omega\,\angle 0°} + \dfrac{1}{10\,\Omega\,\angle 90°} = 0.083\text{ S} - j0.1\text{ S} = \mathbf{129.96\ mS\ \angle{-50.31°}}$

c. $\mathbf{I}_s = \mathbf{E}\mathbf{Y}_T = (60\text{ V }\angle 0°)(0.13\text{ S}\angle -50.31°) = \mathbf{7.8\ A\ \angle{-50.31°}}$

$\mathbf{I}_R = \dfrac{E\angle\theta}{R\angle 0°} = 60\text{ V }\angle 0°/12\ \Omega\ \angle 0° = \mathbf{5\ A\ \angle 0°}$

$\mathbf{I}_L = \dfrac{E\angle\theta}{X_L\angle 90°} = 60\text{ V }\angle 0°/10\ \Omega\ \angle 90° = \mathbf{6\ A\ \angle{-90°}}$

f. $P = I^2R = (5\text{ A})^2\ 12\ \Omega = \mathbf{300\ W}$

g. $F_p = G/Y_T = 0.083\text{ S}/0.13\text{ S} = \mathbf{0.638\ lagging}$

h. $\boldsymbol{e = 84.84\sin 377t}$

$\boldsymbol{i_R = 7.07\sin 377t}$

$\boldsymbol{i_L = 8.484\sin(377t - 90°)}$

$\boldsymbol{i_s = 11.03\sin(377t - 50.31°)}$

31. a. $\mathbf{Y}_T = \dfrac{1}{1.2\,\Omega\angle 0°} + \dfrac{1}{2\,\Omega\angle 90°} + \dfrac{1}{5\,\Omega\angle -90°}$

$= 0.833\text{ S}\angle 0° + 0.5\text{ S}\angle -90° + 0.2\text{ S}\angle 90°$

$= 0.833\text{ S} - j0.3\text{ S} = \mathbf{0.89\text{ S}\angle -19.81°}$

$\mathbf{Z}_T = 1.12\,\Omega\angle 19.81°$

c. $X_C = \dfrac{1}{\omega C} \Rightarrow C = \dfrac{1}{\omega X_C} = \dfrac{1}{(377\text{ rad/s})(5\,\Omega)} = \mathbf{531\ \mu F}$

$X_L = \omega L \Rightarrow L = \dfrac{X_L}{\omega} = \dfrac{2\,\Omega}{377\text{ rad/s}} = \mathbf{5.31\text{ mH}}$

d. $\mathbf{E} = \dfrac{\mathbf{I}_s}{\mathbf{Y}_T} = \dfrac{(0.707)(3\text{ A})\angle 60°}{0.885\text{ S}\angle -19.81°} = \dfrac{2.121\text{ A}\angle 60°}{0.885\text{ S}\angle -19.81°} = \mathbf{2.40\text{ V}\angle 79.81°}$

$\mathbf{I}_R = \dfrac{E\angle\theta}{R\angle 0°} = \dfrac{2.397\text{ V}\angle 79.81°}{1.2\,\Omega\angle 0°} = \mathbf{2.00\text{ A}\angle 79.81°}$

$\mathbf{I}_L = \dfrac{E\angle\theta}{X_L\angle 90°} = \dfrac{2.397\text{ V}\angle 79.81°}{2\,\Omega\angle 90°} = \mathbf{1.20\text{ A}\angle -10.19°}$

$\mathbf{I}_C = \dfrac{E\angle\theta}{X_C\angle -90°} = \dfrac{2.397\text{ V}\angle 79.81°}{5\,\Omega\angle -90°} = \mathbf{0.48\text{ A}\angle 169.81°}$

f. $\mathbf{I}_s = \mathbf{I}_R + \mathbf{I}_L + \mathbf{I}_C$

$2.121\text{ A}\angle 60° = 2.00\text{ A}\angle 79.81° + 1.20\text{ A}\angle -10.19° + 0.48\text{ A}\angle 169.81°$

$2.121\text{ A}\angle 60° \overset{\checkmark}{=} 2.13\text{ A}\angle 60.01°$

g. $P = I^2R = (2.00\text{ A})^2\, 1.2\,\Omega = \mathbf{4.8\text{ W}}$

h. $F_p = \dfrac{G}{Y_T} = \dfrac{0.833\text{ S}}{0.885\text{ S}} = \mathbf{0.941\text{ lagging}}$

i. $e = \mathbf{3.39\sin(377t + 79.81°)}$

$i_R = \mathbf{2.83\sin(377t + 79.81°)}$

$i_L = \mathbf{1.70\sin(377t - 10.19°)}$

$i_C = \mathbf{0.68\sin(377t + 169.81°)}$

32. a. $\mathbf{Y}_T = \dfrac{1}{3\text{ k}\Omega\angle 0°} + \dfrac{1}{4\text{ k}\Omega\angle 90°} + \dfrac{1}{8\text{ k}\Omega\angle -90°}$

$= 0.333\text{ mS}\angle 0° + 0.25\text{ mS}\angle -90° + 0.125\text{ mS}\angle 90°$

$= \mathbf{0.333\text{ mS} + j0.125\text{ mS} = 0.356\text{ mS}\angle 20.57°}$

c. $X_L = \omega L \Rightarrow L = X_L/\omega = 4000\,\Omega/377\text{ rad/s} = \mathbf{10.61\text{ H}}$

$X_C = \dfrac{1}{\omega C} \Rightarrow C = \dfrac{1}{\omega X_C} = \dfrac{1}{(377\text{ rad/s})(8\text{ k}\Omega)} = \mathbf{0.332\ \mu F}$

d. $\mathbf{E} = \mathbf{I}/\mathbf{Y}_T = 3.535 \text{ mA} \angle -20° / 0.356 \text{ mS} \angle 20.57° = \mathbf{9.93 \text{ V} \angle -40.57°}$

$\mathbf{I}_R = \dfrac{E \angle \theta}{R \angle 0°} = 9.93 \text{ V}\angle -40.57°/3 \text{ k}\Omega \angle 0° = \mathbf{3.31 \text{ mA} \angle -40.57°}$

$\mathbf{I}_L = \dfrac{E \angle \theta}{X_L \angle 90°} = 9.93 \text{ V}\angle -40.57°/4 \text{ k}\Omega \angle 90° = \mathbf{2.48 \text{ mA} \angle -130.57°}$

$\mathbf{I}_C = \dfrac{E \angle \theta}{X_C \angle -90°} = 9.93 \text{ V}\angle -40.57°/8 \text{ k}\Omega \angle -90° = \mathbf{1.24 \text{ mA} \angle 49.43°}$

g. $P = I^2R = (3.31 \text{ mA})^2 3 \text{ k}\Omega = \mathbf{32.87 \text{ mW}}$

h. $F_p = G/Y_T = 0.333 \text{ mS}/0.356 \text{ mS} = \mathbf{0.935 \text{ leading}}$

i. $e = \mathbf{14.04 \sin(377t - 40.57°)}$
$i_R \cong \mathbf{4.68 \times 10^{-3} \sin(377t - 40.57°)}$
$i_L \cong \mathbf{3.51 \times 10^{-3} \sin(377t - 130.57°)}$
$i_C = \mathbf{1.75 \times 10^{-3} \sin(377t + 49.43°)}$

33. a. $\mathbf{Y}_T = \dfrac{1}{5\ \Omega \angle -90°} + \dfrac{1}{22\ \Omega \angle 0°} + \dfrac{1}{10\ \Omega \angle 90°}$
$= 0.2 \text{ S} \angle 90° + 0.045 \text{ S} \angle 0° + 0.1 \text{ S} \angle -90°$
$= 0.045 \text{ S} + j0.1 \text{ S} = \mathbf{0.110 \text{ S} \angle 65.77°}$
$\mathbf{Z}_T = \mathbf{9.09\ \Omega \angle -65.77°}$

c. $C = \dfrac{1}{\omega X_C} = \dfrac{1}{(377 \text{ rad/s})(5\ \Omega)} = \mathbf{636.9\ \mu F}$

$L = \dfrac{X_L}{\omega} = \dfrac{10\ \Omega}{314 \text{ rad/s}} = \mathbf{31.8 \text{ mH}}$

d. $\mathbf{E} = (0.707)(35.4 \text{ V}) \angle 60° = \mathbf{25.03 \text{ V} \angle 60°}$
$\mathbf{I}_s = \mathbf{E}\mathbf{Y}_T = (25.03 \text{ V} \angle 60°)(0.11 \text{ S} \angle 65.77°) = \mathbf{2.75 \text{ A} \angle 125.77°}$

$\mathbf{I}_C = \dfrac{E \angle \theta}{X_C \angle -90°} = \dfrac{25.03 \text{ V} \angle 60°}{5 \angle -90°} = \mathbf{5 \text{ A} \angle 150°}$

$\mathbf{I}_R = \dfrac{E \angle \theta}{R \angle 0°} = \dfrac{25.03 \text{ V} \angle 60°}{22\ \Omega \angle 0°} = \mathbf{1.14 \text{ A} \angle 60°}$

$\mathbf{I}_L = \dfrac{E \angle \theta}{X_L \angle 90°} = \dfrac{25.03 \text{ V} \angle 60°}{10\ \Omega \angle 90°} = \mathbf{2.50 \text{ A} \angle -30°}$

f. $\mathbf{I}_s = \mathbf{I}_C + \mathbf{I}_R + \mathbf{I}_L$
$2.75 \text{ A} \angle 125.77° = 5 \text{ A} \angle 150° + 1.14 \text{ A} \angle 60° + 2.50 \text{ A} \angle -30°$
$= (-4.33 + j2.5) + (0.57 + j0.9) + (2.17 - j1.25)$
$= -1.59 + j2.24$
$\overset{\checkmark}{=} 2.75 \angle 125.4°$

g. $P = I^2R = (1.14 \text{ A})^2\ 22\ \Omega = \mathbf{28.59 \text{ W}}$

h. $F_p = \dfrac{G}{Y_T} = \dfrac{0.045\,\text{S}}{0.110\,\text{S}} = \mathbf{0.409\ leading}$

i. $e = \mathbf{35.4\,\sin(314t + 60°)}$
$i_s = \mathbf{3.89\,\sin(314t + 125.77°)}$
$i_C = \mathbf{7.07\,\sin(314t + 150°)}$
$i_R = \mathbf{1.61\,\sin(314t + 60°)}$
$i_L = \mathbf{3.54\,\sin(314t - 30°)}$

34. a. $\mathbf{I}_1 = \dfrac{(80\,\Omega\,\angle 90°)(20\text{ A}\,\angle 40°)}{22\,\Omega + j80\,\Omega} = \dfrac{1600\text{ A}\,\angle 130°}{82.97\,\angle 74.62°} = \mathbf{19.28\ A\ \angle 55.38°}$

$\mathbf{I}_2 = \dfrac{(22\,\Omega\,\angle 0°)(20\text{ A}\,\angle 40°)}{82.97\,\Omega\,\angle 74.62°} = \dfrac{440\text{ A}\,\angle 40°}{82.97\,\angle 74.62°} = \mathbf{5.30\ A\ \angle{-34.62°}}$

b. $\mathbf{I}_1 = \dfrac{(12\,\Omega - j6\,\Omega)(6\text{ A}\,\angle 30°)}{12\,\Omega - j6\,\Omega + j4\,\Omega} = \dfrac{(13.42\,\angle -26.57°)(6\text{ A}\,\angle 30°)}{12 - j2}$

$= \dfrac{80.52\text{ A}\angle 3.43°}{12.17\angle -9.46°} = \mathbf{6.62\ A\ \angle 12.89°}$

$\mathbf{I}_2 = \dfrac{(4\,\Omega\,\angle 90°)(6\text{ A}\,\angle 30°)}{12.17\,\Omega\angle -9.46°} = \dfrac{24\text{ A}\,\angle 120°}{12.17\,\angle -9.46°} = \mathbf{1.97\ A\ \angle 129.46°}$

35. a. $\mathbf{Z}_T = \dfrac{(R\,\angle 0°)(X_C\,\angle -90°)}{R - jX_C} = \dfrac{RX_C}{\sqrt{R^2 + X_C^2}}\,\angle -90° + \tan^{-1} X_C/R$

$|Z_T| = \dfrac{RX_C}{\sqrt{R^2 + X_C^2}}$ $\quad \theta_T = -90° + \tan^{-1} X_C/\text{R}$

f	$\lvert Z_T \rvert$	θ_T
0 Hz	40.0 Ω	0.0°
1 kHz	35.74 Ω	–26.67°
2 kHz	28.22 Ω	–45.14°
3 kHz	22.11 Ω	–56.44°
4 kHz	17.82 Ω	–63.55°
5 kHz	14.79 Ω	–68.30°
10 kHz	7.81 Ω	–78.75°
20 kHz	3.959 Ω	–89.86°

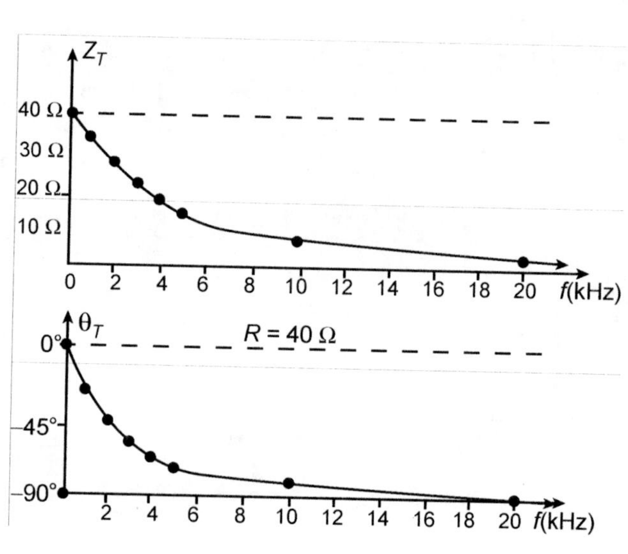

b. $|V_C| = \dfrac{IRX_C}{\sqrt{R^2 + X_C^2}} = I[Z_T(f)]$

f	$\lvert V_C \rvert$
0 kHz	2.0 V
1 kHz	1.787 V
2 kHz	1.411 V
3 kHz	1.105 V
4 kHz	0.891 V
5 kHz	0.740 V
10 kHz	0.391 V
20 kHz	0.198 V

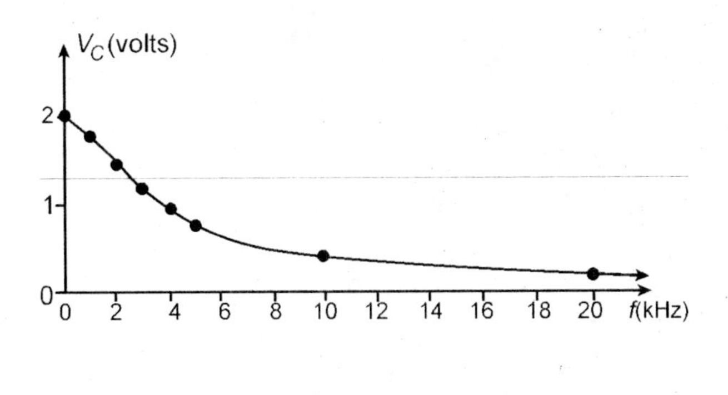

c. $|I_R| = \left|\dfrac{V_C}{R}\right|$

f	$\lvert I_R \rvert$
0 kHz	50.0 mA
1 kHz	44.7 mA
2 kHz	35.3 mA
3 kHz	27.64 mA
4 kHz	22.28 mA
5 kHz	18.50 mA
10 kHz	9.78 mA
20 kHz	4.95 mA

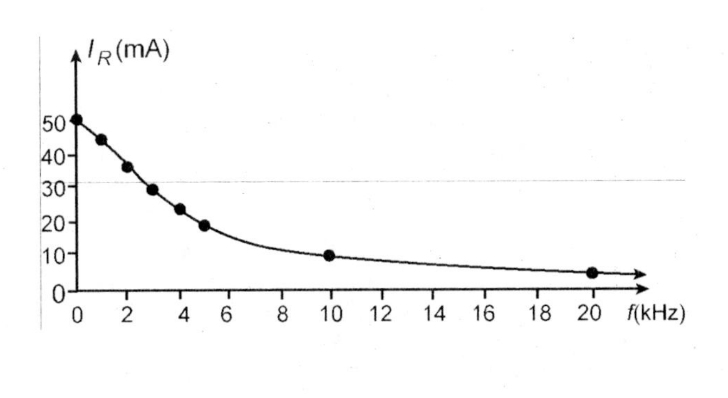

36. a. $\mathbf{Z}_T = \dfrac{\mathbf{Z}_R\mathbf{Z}_L}{\mathbf{Z}_R + \mathbf{Z}_L} = \dfrac{(R\angle 0^\circ)(X_L\angle 90^\circ)}{R + jX_L} = \dfrac{RX_L}{\sqrt{R^2 + X_L^2}}\angle 90^\circ - \tan^{-1}X_L/R$

$|\mathbf{Z}_T| = \dfrac{RX_L}{\sqrt{R^2 + X_L^2}}\ \theta_T = 90^\circ - \tan^{-1}X_L/R$

f	$\lvert Z_T \rvert$	θ_T
0 Hz	0.0 kΩ	90.0°
1 kHz	1.22 kΩ	75.86°
5 kHz	3.91 kΩ	38.53°
7 kHz	4.35 kΩ	29.6°
10 kHz	4.65 kΩ	21.69°

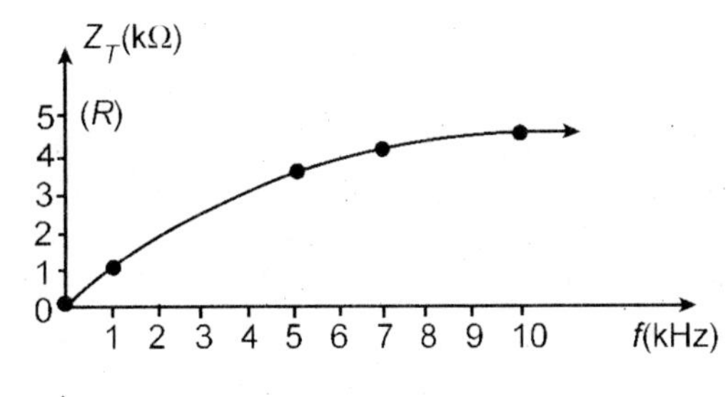

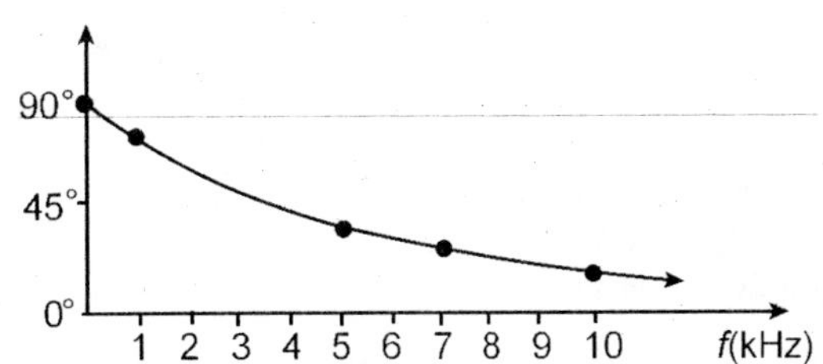

b. $|I_L| = \dfrac{E}{X_L}$

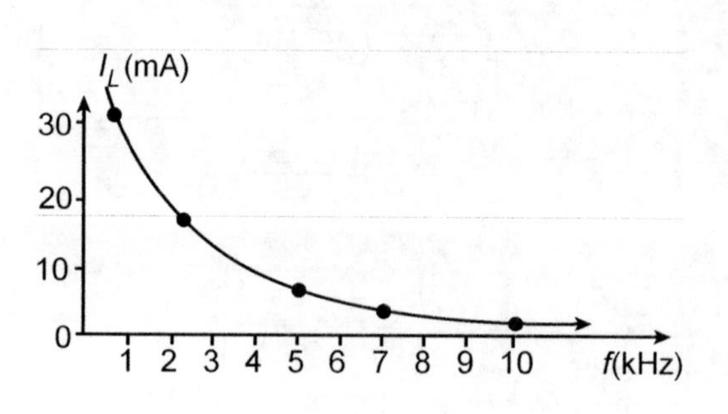

f	$\lvert I_L \rvert$
0 Hz	∞
1 kHz	31.75 mA
5 kHz	6.37 mA
7 kHz	4.55 mA
10 kHz	3.18 mA

c. $I_R = \dfrac{E}{R} = \dfrac{40\text{ V}}{5\text{ k}\Omega} = 8\text{ mA (constant)}$

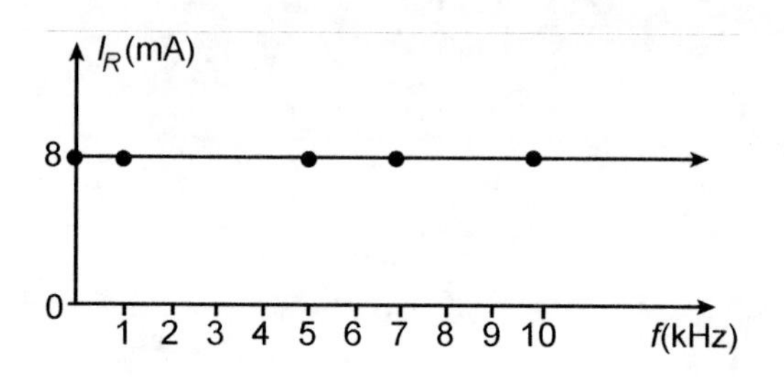

37. $\mathbf{Y}_T = \dfrac{\sqrt{R^2 + X_C^2}}{RX_C} \angle 90° - \tan^{-1} X_C/R$

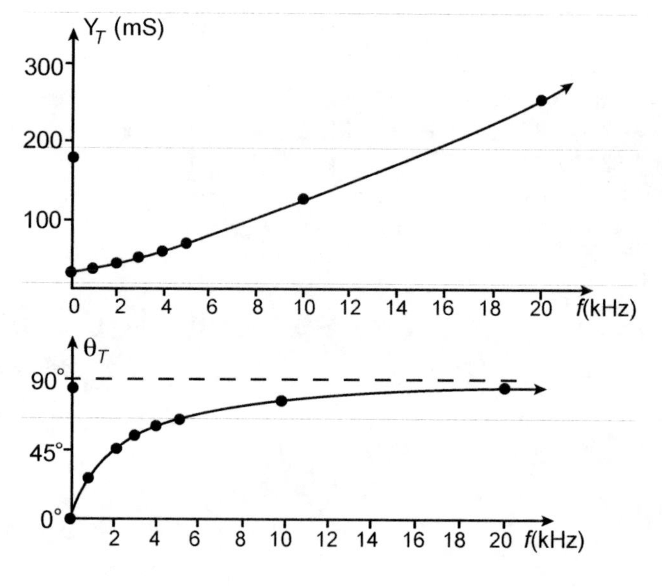

f	$\lvert Y_T \rvert$	θ_T
0 Hz	25.0 mS	0.0°
1 kHz	27.98 mS	26.67°
2 kHz	35.44 mS	45.14°
3 kHz	45.23 mS	56.44°
4 kHz	56.12 mS	63.55°
5 kHz	67.61 mS	68.30°
10 kHz	128.04 mS	78.75°
20 kHz	252.59 mS	89.86°

38. 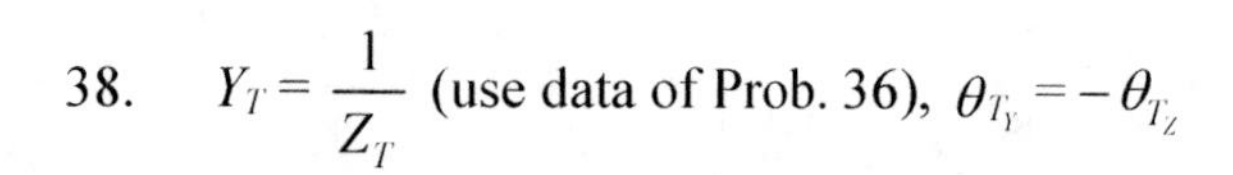

$Y_T = \dfrac{1}{Z_T}$ (use data of Prob. 36), $\theta_{T_Y} = -\theta_{T_Z}$

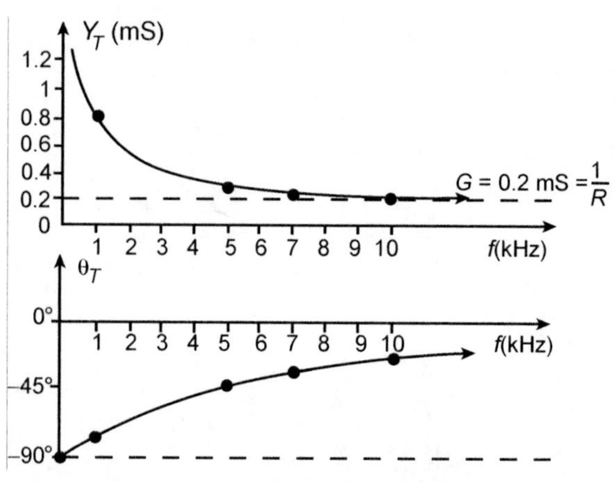

f	Y_T	θ_T
0 Hz	∞	–90.0°
1 kHz	0.82 mS	–75.86°
5 kHz	0.256 mS	–38.53°
7 kHz	0.23 mS	–29.6°
10 kHz	0.215 mS	–21.69°

39. a. $\mathbf{Y}_T = G \angle 0° + B_L \angle -90° + B_C \angle 90°$

$$= \sqrt{G^2 + (B_C - B_L)^2} \angle \tan^{-1} \frac{B_C - B_L}{G}$$

f	$\lvert Y_T \rvert$
0 Hz	$X_L \Rightarrow 0\ \Omega$, $Z_T = 0\ \Omega$, $Y_T = \infty\ \Omega$
1 kHz	1.857 mS
5 kHz	1.018 mS
10 kHz	1.004 mS
15 kHz	1.036 mS
20 kHz	1.086 mS

f	$\lvert \theta_T \rvert$
0 Hz	−90.0°
1 kHz	−57.42°
5 kHz	−10.87°
10 kHz	+5.26°
15 kHz	+15.16°
20 kHz	+22.95°

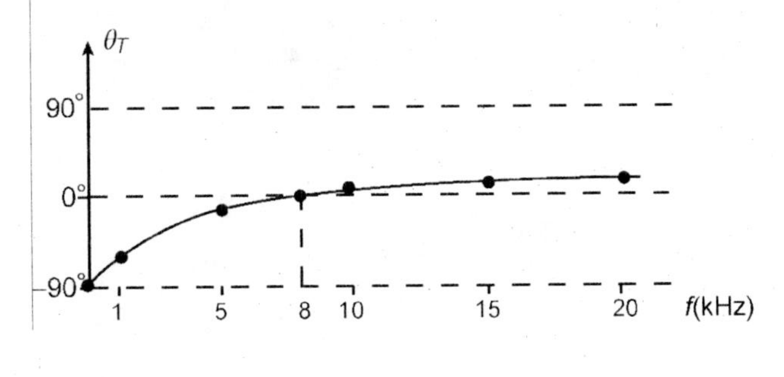

b. $Z_T = \dfrac{1}{Y_T}$, $\theta_{T_Z} = -\theta_{T_Y}$

f	Z_T	θ_T
0 kHz	0.0 Ω	90.0°
1 kHz	538.5 Ω	57.42°
5 kHz	982.32 Ω	10.87°
10 kHz	996.02 Ω	−5.26°
15 kHz	965.25 Ω	−15.16°
20 kHz	921.66 Ω	−22.95°

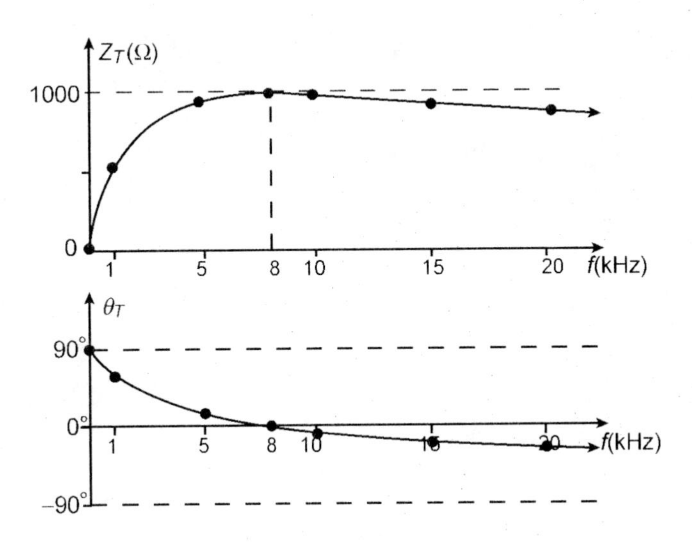

c. $V_C(f) = I[Z_T(f)]$

f	$\lvert V_C \rvert$
0 kHz	0.0 V
1 kHz	5.39 V
5 kHz	9.82 V
10 kHz	9.96 V
15 kHz	9.65 V
20 kHz	9.22 V

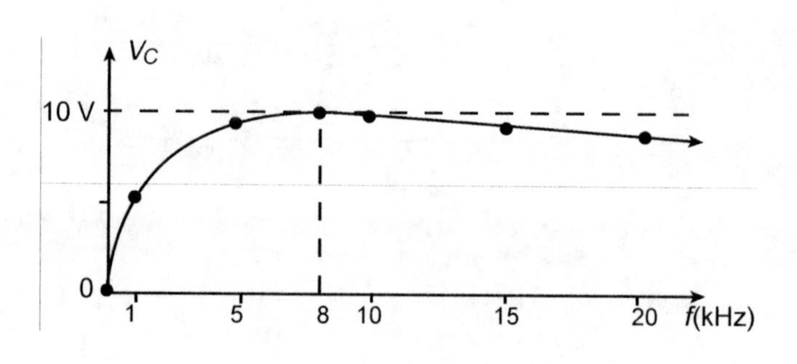

d. $I_L = \dfrac{V_C(f)}{X_L}$

f	I_L
0 kHz	10.0 mA
1 kHz	8.57 mA
5 kHz	3.13 mA
10 kHz	1.59 mA
15 kHz	1.02 mA
20 kHz	0.733 mA

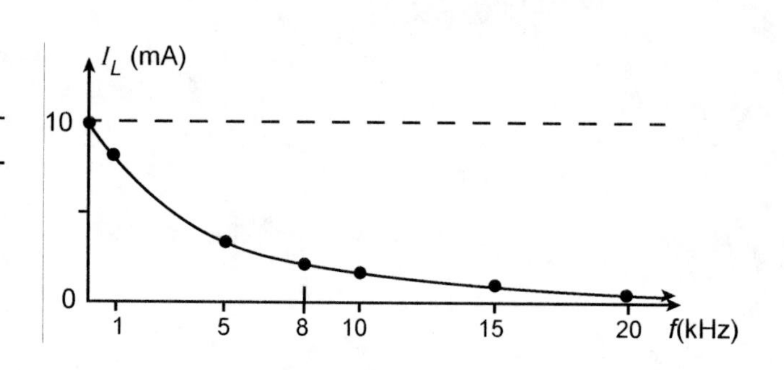

40. a. $$R_p = \frac{R_s^2 + X_s^2}{R_s} = \frac{(20\,\Omega)^2 + (40\,\Omega)^2}{20\,\Omega} = \mathbf{100\,\Omega}\ (R)$$

$$X_p = \frac{R_s^2 + X_s^2}{X_s} = \frac{2000\,\Omega}{40} = \mathbf{50\,\Omega}\ (C)$$

b. $$R_p = \frac{R_s^2 + X_s^2}{R_s} = \frac{(2\,\text{k}\Omega)^2 + (3\,\text{k}\Omega)^2}{2\,\text{k}\Omega} = \mathbf{6.5\,k\Omega}\ (R)$$

$$X_p = \frac{R_s^2 + X_s^2}{X_s} = \frac{(2\,\text{k}\Omega)^2 + (3\,\text{k}\Omega)^2}{3\,\text{k}\Omega} = \mathbf{4.33\,k\Omega}\ (C)$$

41. a. $$R_s = \frac{R_p X_p^2}{X_p^2 + R_p^2} = \frac{(8.2\,\text{k}\Omega)(20\,\text{k}\Omega)^2}{(20\,\text{k}\Omega)^2 + (8.2\,\text{k}\Omega)^2} = \mathbf{7.02\,k\Omega}$$

$$X_s = \frac{R_p^2 X_p}{X_p^2 + R_p^2} = \frac{(8.2\,\text{k}\Omega)^2(20\,\text{k}\Omega)}{467.24\,\text{k}\Omega} = \mathbf{2.88\,k\Omega}$$

$\mathbf{Z}_T = \mathbf{7.02\,k\Omega - \mathit{j}2.88\,k\Omega}$

b. $$R_s = \frac{R_p X_p^2}{X_p^2 + R_p^2} = \frac{(68\,\Omega)(40\,\Omega)^2}{(40\,\Omega)^2 + (68\,\Omega)^2} = \mathbf{17.48\,\Omega}$$

$$X_s = \frac{R_p^2 X_p}{X_p^2 + R_p^2} = \frac{(68\,\Omega)^2(40\,\Omega)}{6224\,\Omega^2} = \mathbf{29.72\,\Omega}$$

$\mathbf{Z}_T = \mathbf{17.48\,\Omega + \mathit{j}29.72\,\Omega}$

42. a. $C_T = 2\ \mu F$

$$X_C = \frac{1}{\omega C} = \frac{1}{2\pi(10^3\ \text{Hz})(2\ \mu\text{F})} = 79.62\ \Omega$$

$$X_L = \omega L = 2\pi(10^3\ \text{Hz})(10\ \text{mH}) = 62.80\ \Omega$$

$$\mathbf{Y}_T = \frac{1}{220\ \Omega\ \angle 0^\circ} + \frac{1}{79.62\ \Omega\ \angle -90^\circ} + \frac{1}{62.8\ \Omega\ \angle 90^\circ}$$

$= 4.55\ \text{mS}\ \angle 0^\circ + 12.56\ \text{mS}\ \angle 90^\circ + 15.92\ \text{mS}\ \angle -90^\circ$
$= \mathbf{4.55\ mS - \mathit{j}3.36\ mS} = \mathbf{5.66\ mS\ \angle -36.44^\circ}$

$\mathbf{E} = \mathbf{I}/\mathbf{Y}_T = 1\ \text{A}\ \angle 0^\circ / 5.66\ \text{mS}\ \angle -36.44^\circ = \mathbf{176.68\ V\ \angle 36.44^\circ}$

$$\mathbf{I}_R = \frac{E\ \angle\theta}{R\ \angle 0^\circ} = 176.68\ \text{V}\ \angle 36.44^\circ / 220\ \Omega\ \angle 0^\circ = \mathbf{0.803\ A\ \angle 36.44^\circ}$$

$$\mathbf{I}_L = \frac{E\ \angle\theta}{X_L\ \angle 90^\circ} = 176.68\ \text{V}\ \angle 36.44^\circ / 62.80\ \angle 90^\circ = \mathbf{2.813\ A\ \angle -53.56^\circ}$$

b. $F_p = G/Y_T = 4.55\ \text{mS}/5.66\ \text{mS} = \mathbf{0.804\ lagging}$

e. $P = I^2R = (0.803\ \text{A})^2\ 220\ \Omega = \mathbf{141.86\ W}$

f. $\mathbf{I}_s = \mathbf{I}_R + 2\mathbf{I}_C + \mathbf{I}_L$

and $\mathbf{I}_C = \dfrac{\mathbf{I}_s - \mathbf{I}_R - \mathbf{I}_L}{2}$

$$= \frac{1\ \text{A}\ \angle 0^\circ - 0.803\ \text{A}\ \angle 36.44^\circ - 2.813\ \text{A}\ \angle -53.56^\circ}{2}$$

$$= \frac{1 - (0.646 + j0.477) - (1.671 - j2.263)}{2} = \frac{-1.317 + j1.786}{2}$$

$\mathbf{I}_C = -0.657 + j0.893 = \mathbf{1.11\ A\ \angle 126.43^\circ}$

g. $$\mathbf{Z}_T = \frac{1}{\mathbf{Y}_T} = \frac{1}{5.66\ \text{mS}\ \angle -36.44^\circ} = 176.7\ \Omega\ \angle 36.44^\circ$$

$= \mathbf{142.15\ \Omega + \mathit{j}104.96\ \Omega} = R + jX_L$

43. a. $(R = 220\ \Omega)\ \|\ (L = 1\ \text{H})\ \|\ (C = 2\ \mu\text{F})$

$$X_C = \frac{1}{\omega C} = \frac{1}{2\pi(10^3\ \text{Hz})(2\ \mu\text{F})} = 79.62\ \Omega$$

$$X_L = \omega L = 2\pi(10^3\ \text{Hz})(1\ \text{H}) = 6.28\ \text{k}\Omega$$

$$\mathbf{Y}_T = \frac{1}{220\ \Omega\ \angle 0^\circ} + \frac{1}{6.28\times 10^3\ \Omega\ \angle 90^\circ} + \frac{1}{79.62\ \Omega\ \angle -90^\circ}$$

$= 0.0045 - j0.1592 \times 10^{-3} + j0.0126$
$= 4.5 \times 10^{-3} - j0.1592 \times 10^{-3} + j12.6 \times 10^{-3}$
$= \mathbf{4.5\ mS + \mathit{j}12.44\ mS = 13.23\ mS\ \angle 70.11^\circ}$

$$\mathbf{E} = \mathbf{I}/\mathbf{Y}_T = 1\text{ A }\angle 0°/13.23\text{ mS }\angle 70.11° = \mathbf{75.6\text{ V }\angle{-70.11°}}$$

$$\mathbf{I}_R = \frac{E\angle\theta}{R\angle 0°} = 75.6\text{ V }\angle{-70.11°}/220\ \Omega\ \angle 0° = \mathbf{0.34\text{ A }\angle{-70.11°}}$$

$$\mathbf{I}_L = \frac{E\angle\theta}{X_L\angle 90°} = 75.6\text{ V }\angle{-70.11°}/6.28\text{ k}\Omega\ \angle 90° = \mathbf{12.04\text{ mA }\angle{-160.11°}}$$

b. $$F_p = \frac{G}{Y_T} = \frac{4.5\text{ mS}}{13.23\text{ mS}} = \mathbf{0.340\ leading}$$

c. $$P = I^2R = (0.34\text{A})^2\ 220\ \Omega = \mathbf{25.43\ W}$$

f. $$2\mathbf{I}_C = \mathbf{I}_s - \mathbf{I}_R - \mathbf{I}_L$$

$$\mathbf{I}_C = \frac{\mathbf{I}_s - \mathbf{I}_R - \mathbf{I}_L}{2} = \frac{1\text{ A }\angle 0° - 0.34\text{ A }\angle -70.11° - 12.04\text{ mA }\angle -160.11°}{2}$$

$$= \frac{1-(0.12-j0.32)-(-11.32\times10^{-3} - j4.1\times10^{-3})}{2}$$

$$= \frac{0.89+j0.32}{2}$$

$$\mathbf{I}_C = 0.45 + j0.16 = \mathbf{0.47\text{ A }\angle 19.63°}$$

g. $$\mathbf{Z}_T = \frac{1}{\mathbf{Y}_T} = \frac{1}{13.23\text{ mS}\angle 70.11°} = 75.59\ \Omega\ \angle{-70.11°} = \mathbf{25.72\ \Omega - j71.08\ \Omega}$$

$$R = \mathbf{25.72\ \Omega},\ X_C = \mathbf{71.08\ \Omega}$$

44. $$P = VI\cos\theta = 3000\text{ W}$$

$$\cos\theta = \frac{3000\text{ W}}{VI} = \frac{3000\text{ W}}{(100\text{ V})(40\text{ A})} = \frac{3000}{4000} = 0.75\ \text{(lagging)}$$

$$\theta = \cos^{-1} 0.75 = 41.41°$$

$$\mathbf{Y}_T = \frac{\mathbf{I}}{\mathbf{E}} = \frac{40\text{ A }\angle -41.41°}{100\text{ V }\angle 0°} = 0.4\text{ S }\angle{-41.41°} = 0.3\text{ S} - j0.265\text{ S} = G_T - jB_L$$

$$G_T = 0.3\text{ S} = \frac{1}{20\ \Omega} + \frac{1}{R'} = 0.05\text{ S} + \frac{I}{R'}$$

$$\text{and } R' = \frac{1}{0.25\text{S}} = 4\ \Omega$$

$$X_L = \frac{1}{B_L} = \frac{1}{0.265\text{ S}} = \mathbf{3.74\ \Omega}$$

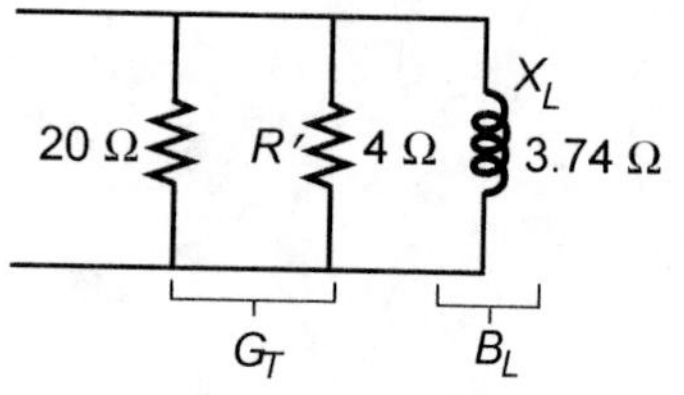

20 Ω
R′ 4 Ω
X_L 3.74 Ω
G_T
B_L

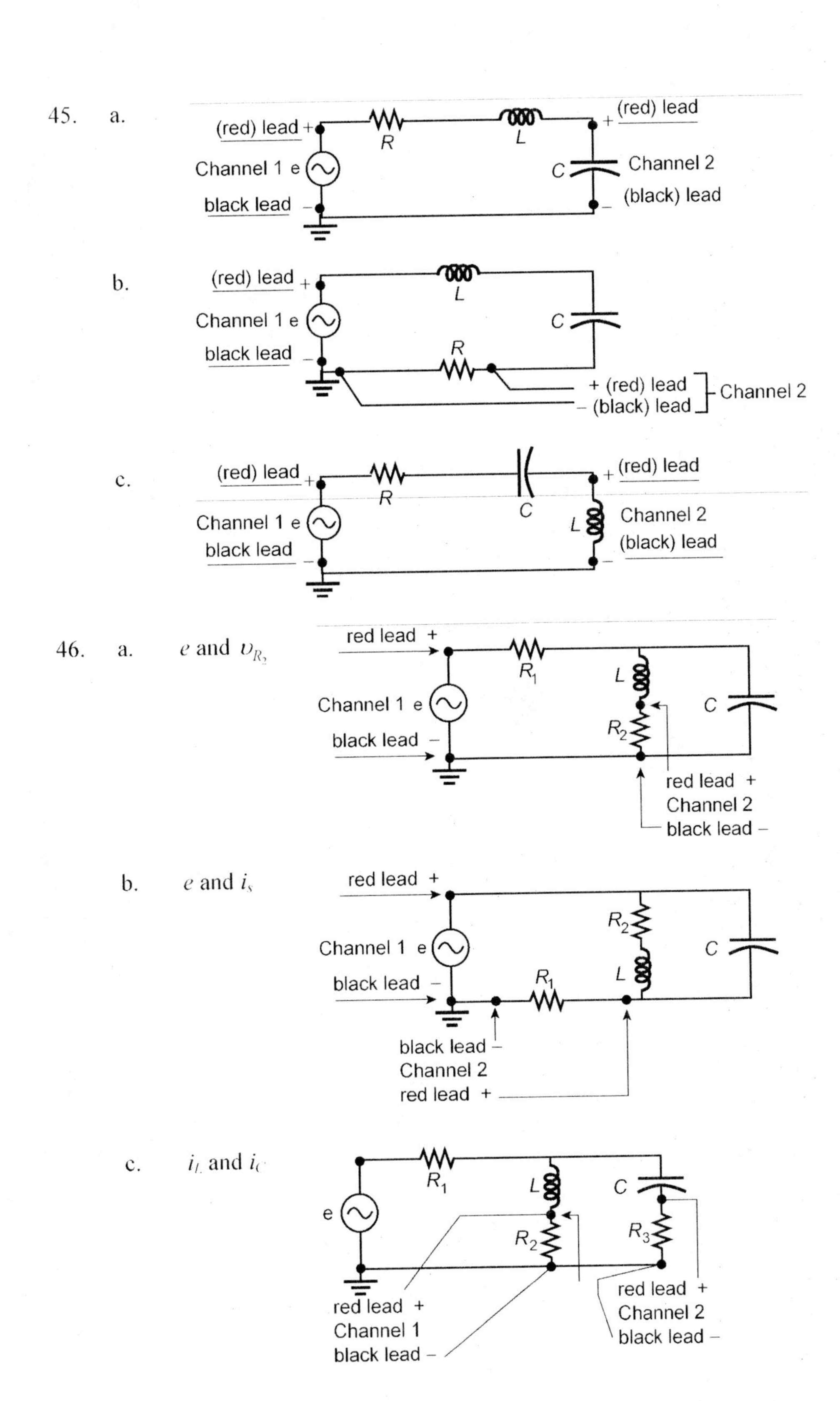
45.
a.
(red) lead +
R
L
(red) lead
Channel 1 e
C
Channel 2
black lead
(black) lead
b.
(red) lead
L
Channel 1 e
C
black lead
R
+ (red) lead
– (black) lead
Channel 2
c.
(red) lead
R
(red) lead
C
Channel 1 e
L
Channel 2
black lead
(black) lead
46.
a.
e and v_{R_2}
red lead +
R_1
L
Channel 1 e
C
black lead –
R_2
red lead +
Channel 2
black lead –
b.
e and i_s
red lead +
R_2
Channel 1 e
C
black lead –
R_1
L
black lead –
Channel 2
red lead +
c.
i_L and i_C
R_1
L
C
e
R_2
R_3
red lead +
Channel 2
black lead –
red lead +
Channel 1
black lead –

47. (I): (a) $\theta_{div.} = 0.8$ div., $\theta_T = 4$ div.

$$\theta = \frac{0.8\text{ div.}}{4\text{ div.}} \times 360° = 72°$$

υ_1 leads υ_2 by 72°

(b) υ_1: peak-to-peak = (5 div.)(0.5 V/div.) = **2.5 V**

$$V_1(\text{rms}) = 0.7071\left(\frac{2.5\text{ V}}{2}\right) = \mathbf{0.88\text{ V}}$$

υ_2: peak-to-peak = (2.4 div.)(0.5 V/div.) = **1.2 V**

$$V_2(\text{rms}) = 0.7071\left(\frac{1.2\text{ V}}{2}\right) = \mathbf{0.42\text{ V}}$$

(c) $T = (4\text{ div.})(0.2\text{ ms/div.}) = 0.8\text{ ms}$

$$f = \frac{1}{T} = \frac{1}{0.8\text{ ms}} = \mathbf{1.25\text{ kHz}}\text{ (both)}$$

(II): (a) $\theta_{div.} = 2.2$ div., $\theta_T = 6$ div.

$$\theta = \frac{2.2\text{ div.}}{6\text{ div.}} \times 360° = 132°$$

υ_1 leads υ_2 by 132°

(b) υ_1: peak-to-peak = (2.8 div.)(2 V/div.) = **5.6 V**

$$V_1(\text{rms}) = 0.7071\left(\frac{5.6\text{ V}}{2}\right) = \mathbf{1.98\text{ V}}$$

υ_2: peak-to-peak = (4 div.)(2 V/div.) = **8 V**

$$V_2(\text{rms}) = 0.7071\left(\frac{8\text{ V}}{2}\right) = \mathbf{2.83\text{ V}}$$

(c) $T = (6\text{ div.})(10\ \mu\text{s/div.}) = 60\ \mu\text{s}$

$$f = \frac{1}{T} = \frac{1}{60\ \mu\text{s}} = \mathbf{16.67\text{ kHz}}$$

Chapter 16

1. a. $\mathbf{Z}_T = 2\ \Omega + j6\ \Omega + 8\ \Omega\ \angle{-90°} \parallel 12\ \Omega\ \angle{-90°}$

$$= 2\ \Omega + j6\ \Omega + \frac{(8\ \Omega\ \angle -90°)(12\ \Omega\ \angle -90°)}{-j8\Omega - j12\Omega} = 2\ \Omega + j6\ \Omega + \frac{96\ \Omega\ \angle -180°}{20\ \angle -90°}$$

$$= 2\ \Omega + j6\ \Omega + 4.8\ \Omega\ \angle{-90°} = 2\ \Omega + j6\ \Omega - j4.8\ \Omega = 2\ \Omega + j\,1.2\ \Omega$$

$\mathbf{Z}_T = \mathbf{2.33\ \Omega\ \angle 30.96°}$

b. $\mathbf{I} = \dfrac{\mathbf{E}}{\mathbf{Z}_T} = \dfrac{12\ \text{V}\ \angle 0°}{2.33\ \Omega\ \angle 30.96°} = \mathbf{5.15\ A\ \angle{-30.96°}}$

c. $\mathbf{I}_1 = \mathbf{I} = \mathbf{5.15\ A\ \angle{-30.96°}}$

d. $(\text{CDR})\mathbf{I}_2 = \dfrac{(12\ \Omega\ \angle -90°)(5.15\ \text{A}\ \angle -30.96°)}{-j12\ \Omega - j8\ \Omega} = \dfrac{61.80\ \text{A}\ \angle -120.96°}{20\ \angle -90°} = \mathbf{3.09\ A\ \angle{-30.96°}}$

$\mathbf{I}_3 = \dfrac{(8\ \Omega\ \angle -90°)(5.15\ \text{A}\ \angle -30.96°)}{20\ \Omega\ \angle -90°} = \dfrac{41.2\ \text{A}\ \angle -120.96°}{20\ \angle -90°} = \mathbf{2.06\ A\ \angle{-30.96°}}$

e. $\mathbf{V}_L = (I\ \angle\theta)(X_L\ \angle 90°) = (5.15\ \text{A}\ \angle{-30.96°})(6\ \Omega\ \angle 90°) = \mathbf{30.9\ V\ \angle 59.04°}$

2. a. $\mathbf{Z}_T = 3\ \Omega + j6\ \Omega + 2\ \Omega\ \angle 0° \parallel 8\ \Omega\ \angle{-90°}$

$$= 3\ \Omega + j6\ \Omega + 1.94\ \Omega\ \angle{-14.04°}$$
$$= 3\ \Omega + j6\ \Omega + 1.88\ \Omega - j0.47\ \Omega$$
$$= 4.88\ \Omega + j5.53\ \Omega = \mathbf{7.38\ \Omega\ \angle 48.57°}$$

b. $\mathbf{I}_s = \dfrac{\mathbf{E}}{\mathbf{Z}_T} = \dfrac{30\ \text{V}\ \angle 0°}{7.38\ \Omega\ \angle 48.57°} = \mathbf{4.07\ A\ \angle{-48.57°}}$

c. $\mathbf{I}_C = \dfrac{\mathbf{Z}_{R_2}\mathbf{I}_s}{\mathbf{Z}_{R_2} + \mathbf{Z}_C} = \dfrac{(2\ \Omega\ \angle 0°)(4.07\ \text{A}\ \angle -48.57°)}{2\ \Omega - j8\ \Omega}$

$$= \frac{8.14\ \text{A}\ \angle -48.57°}{8.25\ \angle -75.96°} = \mathbf{0.987\ A\ \angle 27.39°}$$

d. $\mathbf{V}_L = \dfrac{\mathbf{Z}_L\mathbf{E}}{\mathbf{Z}_T} = \dfrac{(6\ \Omega\ \angle 90°)(30\ \text{V}\ \angle 0°)}{7.38\ \Omega\ \angle 48.57°} = \dfrac{180\ \text{V}\ \angle 90°}{7.38\ \Omega\ \angle 48.57°}$

$$= \mathbf{24.39\ V\ \angle 41.43°}$$

3. a. $\mathbf{Z}_T = 12\ \Omega\ \angle 90° \parallel (9.1\ \Omega - j12\ \Omega) = 12\ \Omega\ \angle 90° \parallel 15.06\ \Omega\ \angle{-52.826°}$

$$= \frac{180.72\ \Omega\angle 37.17°}{9.10\angle 0°}$$
$$= \mathbf{19.86\ \Omega\ \angle 37.17°}$$

$\mathbf{Y}_T = \dfrac{1}{\mathbf{Z}_T} = \dfrac{1}{19.86\ \Omega\ \angle 37.17°} = \mathbf{50.35\ mS\ \angle{-37.17°}}$

b. $\mathbf{I}_s = \dfrac{\mathbf{E}}{\mathbf{Z}_T} = \dfrac{60\text{ V}\angle 30^\circ}{19.86\ \Omega\ \angle 37.17^\circ} = \mathbf{3.02\ A\ \angle{-7.17^\circ}}$

c. $(\text{CDR})\ \mathbf{I}_2 = \dfrac{(12\ \Omega\ \angle 90^\circ)(3.02\text{ A}\angle -7.17^\circ)}{j12\,\Omega + 9.1\,\Omega - j12\,\Omega} = \dfrac{36.24\text{ A}\angle 82.83^\circ}{9.1\angle 0^\circ}$
$= \mathbf{3.98\ A\ \angle 82.83^\circ}$

d. $(\text{VDR})\ \mathbf{V}_C = \dfrac{(12\,\Omega\angle -90^\circ)(60\text{ V}\angle 30^\circ)}{9.1\,\Omega - j12\,\Omega} = \dfrac{720\text{ V}\angle -60^\circ}{15.06\angle -52.826^\circ}$
$= \mathbf{47.81\ V\ \angle{-7.17^\circ}}$

e. $P = EI\cos\theta = (60\text{ V})(3.02\text{ A})\cos(30^\circ - 7.17^\circ)$
$= 181.20(0.922) = \mathbf{167.07\ W}$

4. a. $\mathbf{Z}_T = 2\,\Omega + \dfrac{(4\,\Omega\angle -90^\circ)(6\Omega\angle 90^\circ)}{-j4\,\Omega + j6\,\Omega} + \dfrac{(4\,\Omega\angle 0^\circ)(3\,\Omega\angle 90^\circ)}{4\,\Omega + j3\,\Omega}$
$= 2\,\Omega + \dfrac{24\,\Omega\angle 0^\circ}{2\angle 90^\circ} + \dfrac{12\,\Omega\angle 90^\circ}{5\angle 36.87^\circ}$
$= 2\,\Omega + 12\,\Omega\ \angle -90^\circ + 2.4\ \angle 53.13^\circ$
$= 2\,\Omega - j12\,\Omega + 1.44\,\Omega + j1.92\,\Omega$
$= \mathbf{3.44\ \Omega - \mathit{j}10.08\ \Omega} = \mathbf{10.65\ \Omega\ \angle{-71.16^\circ}}$

b. $\mathbf{V}_2 = \mathbf{I}(2.4\,\Omega\ \angle 53.13^\circ) = (5\text{ A}\ \angle 0^\circ)(2.4\,\Omega\ \angle 53.13^\circ) = \mathbf{12\ V\ \angle 53.13^\circ}$
$\mathbf{I}_L = \dfrac{(4\,\Omega\ \angle 0^\circ)(\mathbf{I})}{4\,\Omega + j3\,\Omega} = \dfrac{(4\,\Omega\angle 0^\circ)(5\text{ A}\angle 0^\circ)}{5\,\Omega\angle 36.87^\circ} = \dfrac{20\text{ A}\ \angle 0^\circ}{5\angle 36.87^\circ} = \mathbf{4\ A\ \angle{-36.87^\circ}}$

c. $F_p = \dfrac{R}{\mathbf{Z}_T} = \dfrac{3.44\,\Omega}{10.65\,\Omega} = \mathbf{0.323\ (leading)}$

5. a. $400\ \Omega\ \angle -90^\circ \parallel 400\ \Omega\ \angle -90^\circ = \dfrac{400\,\Omega\angle -90^\circ}{2} = 200\ \Omega\ \angle -90^\circ$
$\mathbf{Z}' = 200\ \Omega - j200\ \Omega = 282.843\ \Omega\ \angle -45^\circ$
$\mathbf{Z}'' = -j200\ \Omega + j560\ \Omega = +j360\ \Omega = 360\ \Omega\ \angle 90^\circ$
$\mathbf{Z}_T = \mathbf{Z}' \parallel \mathbf{Z}'' = \dfrac{(282.843\,\Omega\angle -45^\circ)(360\,\Omega\angle 90^\circ)}{(200\,\Omega - j200\,\Omega) + j360\,\Omega} = \dfrac{101.83\text{ k}\Omega\angle 45^\circ}{256.12\ \angle 38.66^\circ}$
$= 397.59\ \Omega\ \angle 6.34^\circ$
$\mathbf{I} = \dfrac{\mathbf{E}}{\mathbf{Z}_T} = \dfrac{100\text{ V}\ \angle 0^\circ}{397.59\,\Omega\angle 6.34^\circ} = \mathbf{0.25\ A\ \angle{-6.34^\circ}}$

b. $\mathbf{V}_C = \dfrac{(200\,\Omega\angle -90^\circ)(100\text{ V}\ \angle 0^\circ)}{200\,\Omega - j200\,\Omega} = \dfrac{20{,}000\text{ V}\angle -90^\circ}{282.843\angle -45^\circ} = \mathbf{70.71\ V\ \angle{-45^\circ}}$

c. $P = EI\cos\theta = (100\text{ V})(0.25\text{ A})\cos 6.34^\circ$
$= (25)(0.994) = \mathbf{24.85\ W}$

6. a. $\mathbf{Z}_1 = 3\ \Omega + j4\ \Omega = 5\ \Omega \angle 53.13°$

$$\mathbf{I}_1 = \frac{\mathbf{E}}{\mathbf{Z}_1} = \frac{120\text{ V} \angle 60°}{5\,\Omega \angle 53.13°} = \mathbf{24\ A \angle 6.87°}$$

b. $$\mathbf{V}_C = \frac{(13\,\Omega \angle -90°)(120\text{ V} \angle 60°)}{-j13\,\Omega + j7\,\Omega} = \frac{1560\text{ V} \angle -30°}{6 \angle -90°} = \mathbf{260\ V \angle 60°}$$

c. $V_{R_1} = (I_1 \angle \theta)R \angle 0° = (24\text{ A} \angle 6.87°)(3\ \Omega \angle 0°) = 72\text{ V} \angle 6.87°$

$\mathbf{V}_{ab} + V_{R_1} - \mathbf{V}_C = 0$

$\mathbf{V}_{ab} = \mathbf{V}_C - V_{R_1} = 260\text{ V} \angle 60° - 72\text{ V} \angle 6.87°$

$= (130\text{ V} + j225.167\text{ V}) - (71.483\text{ V} + j8.612\text{ V})$

$= \mathbf{58.52\ V + \mathit{j}216.56\ V = 224.33\ V \angle 74.88°}$

7. a. $\mathbf{Z}_1 = 10\ \Omega \angle 0°$

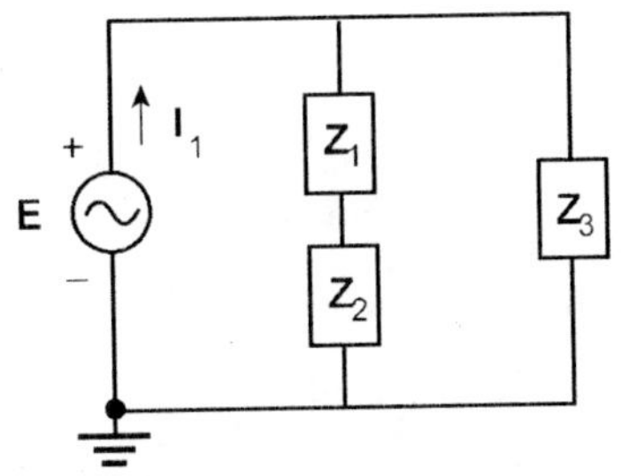

$\mathbf{Z}_2 = 80\ \Omega \angle 90° \parallel 20\ \Omega \angle 0°$

$$= \frac{1600\,\Omega \angle 90°}{20 + j80} = \frac{1600\,\Omega \angle 90°}{82.462 \angle 75.964°}$$

$= 19.403\ \Omega \angle 14.036°$

$\mathbf{Z}_3 = 60\ \Omega \angle -90°$

$\mathbf{Z}_T = (\mathbf{Z}_1 + \mathbf{Z}_2) \parallel \mathbf{Z}_3$

$= (10\ \Omega + 18.824\ \Omega + j4.706\ \Omega) \parallel 60\ \Omega \angle -90°$

$$= 29.206\ \Omega \angle 9.273° \parallel 6\ \Omega \angle -90° = \frac{1752.36\,\Omega \angle -80.727°}{28.824 + j4.706 - j60}$$

$$= \frac{1752.36\,\Omega \angle -80.727°}{62.356 \angle -62.468°} = \mathbf{28.103\ \Omega \angle -18.259°}$$

$$\mathbf{I}_1 = \frac{\mathbf{E}}{\mathbf{Z}_T} = \frac{40\text{ V} \angle 0°}{28.103\,\Omega \angle -18.259°} = \mathbf{1.42\ A \angle 18.26°}$$

b. $$\mathbf{V}_1 = \frac{\mathbf{Z}_2\mathbf{E}}{\mathbf{Z}_2 + \mathbf{Z}_1} = \frac{(19.403\,\Omega \angle 14.036°)(40\text{ V} \angle 0°)}{29.206\,\Omega \angle 9.273°} = \frac{776.12\text{ V} \angle 14.036°}{29.206 \angle 9.273°}$$

$= \mathbf{26.57\ V \angle 4.76°}$

c. $P = EI\cos\theta = (40\text{ V})(1.423\text{ A})\cos 18.259°$

$= \mathbf{54.07\ W}$

8. a. $\mathbf{Z}_1 = 2\ \Omega + j1\ \Omega = 2.236\ \Omega\ \angle 26.565°,\ \mathbf{Z}_2 = 3\ \Omega\ \angle 0°$

$\mathbf{Z}_3 = 16\ \Omega + j15\ \Omega - j7\ \Omega = 16\ \Omega + j8\ \Omega = 17.889\ \Omega\ \angle 26.565°$

$$\mathbf{Y}_T = \frac{1}{\mathbf{Z}_1} + \frac{1}{\mathbf{Z}_2} + \frac{1}{\mathbf{Z}_3} = \frac{1}{2.236\ \Omega\ \angle 26.565°} + \frac{1}{3\ \Omega\ \angle 0°} + \frac{1}{17.889\ \Omega\ \angle 26.565°}$$
$$= 0.447\ \text{S}\ \angle -26.565° + 0.333\ \text{S}\ \angle 0° + 0.056\ \text{S}\ \angle -26.565°$$
$$= (0.4\ \text{S} - j0.2\ \text{S}) + (0.333\ \text{S}) + (0.05\ \text{S} - j0.025\ \text{S})$$
$$= 0.783\ \text{S} - j0.225\ \text{S} = \mathbf{0.82\ S\ \angle -16.03°}$$
$$\mathbf{Z}_T = \frac{1}{\mathbf{Y}_T} = \frac{1}{0.82\ \text{S}\ \angle -16.03°} = \mathbf{1.23\ \Omega\ \angle 16.03°}$$

b $$\mathbf{I}_1 = \frac{\mathbf{E}}{\mathbf{Z}_1} = \frac{60\ \text{V}\ \angle 0°}{2.236\ \Omega\ \angle 26.565°} = \mathbf{26.83\ A\ \angle -26.57°}$$
$$\mathbf{I}_2 = \frac{\mathbf{E}}{\mathbf{Z}_2} = \frac{60\ \text{V}\ \angle 0°}{3\ \Omega\ \angle 0°} = \mathbf{20\ A\ \angle 0°}$$
$$\mathbf{I}_3 = \frac{\mathbf{E}}{\mathbf{Z}_3} = \frac{60\ \text{V}\ \angle 0°}{17.889\ \Omega\ \angle 26.565°} = \mathbf{3.35\ A\ \angle -26.57°}$$

c. $$\mathbf{I}_s = \frac{\mathbf{E}}{\mathbf{Z}_T} = \frac{60\ \text{V}\ \angle 0°}{1.227\ \Omega\ \angle 16.032°} = \mathbf{48.9\ A\ \angle -16.03°}$$

$$\mathbf{I}_s \overset{?}{=} \mathbf{I}_1 + \mathbf{I}_2 + \mathbf{I}_3$$
$$48.9\ \text{A}\ \angle -16.03° \overset{?}{=} 26.83\ \text{A}\ \angle -26.57° + 20\ \text{A}\ \angle 0° + 3.35\ \text{A}\ \angle -26.57°$$
$$= (24\ \text{A} - j12\ \text{A}) + (20\ \text{A}) + (3\ \text{A} - j1.5\ \text{A})$$
$$\overset{\checkmark}{=}\ 47\ \text{A} + j13.5\ \text{A} = \mathbf{48.9\ A\ \angle -16.03°}\ \text{(checks)}$$

d. $$F_p = \frac{G}{Y_T} = \frac{0.783\ \text{S}}{0.820\ \text{S}} = \mathbf{0.955\ (lagging)}$$

9. a.

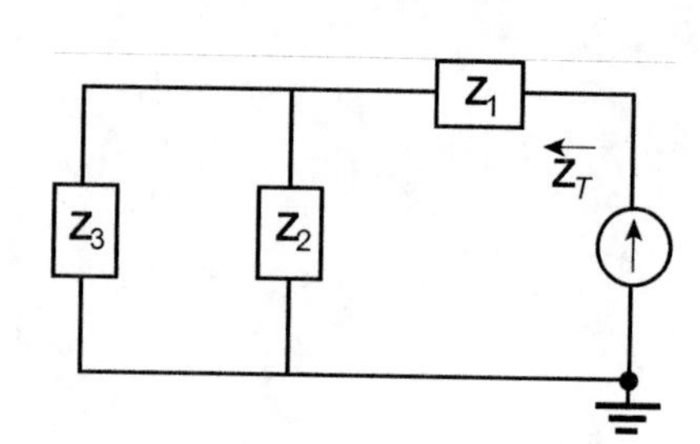

$$\mathbf{Z}' = 3\ \Omega\ \angle 0°\ \|\ 4\ \Omega\ \angle -90° = \frac{12\ \Omega\ \angle -90°}{3 - j4}$$
$$= \frac{12\ \Omega\ \angle -90°}{5\ \angle -53.13°} = 2.4\ \Omega\ \angle -36.87°$$
$$\mathbf{Z}_3 = 2\ \mathbf{Z}' + j7\ \Omega$$
$$= 4.8\ \Omega\ \angle -36.87° + j7\ \Omega$$
$$= 3.84\ \Omega - j2.88\ \Omega + j7\ \Omega$$
$$= 3.84\ \Omega + j4.12\ \Omega$$
$$= 5.63\ \Omega\ \angle 47.02°$$

$$\mathbf{Z}_T = \mathbf{Z}_1 + \mathbf{Z}_2 \parallel \mathbf{Z}_3 = 8.8\ \Omega + 8.2\ \Omega\ \angle 0° \parallel 5.63\ \Omega\ \angle 47.02°$$

$$= 8.8\ \Omega + \frac{46.18\ \Omega\ \angle 47.02°}{8.2 + 3.84 + j4.12} = 8.8\ \Omega + \frac{46.18\ \Omega\ \angle 47.02°}{12.73\ \angle 18.89°}$$

$$= 8.8\ \Omega + 3.63\ \Omega\ \angle 28.13° = 8.8\ \Omega + 3.20\ \Omega + j1.71\ \Omega$$

$$= 12\ \Omega + j1.71\ \Omega = \mathbf{12.12\ \Omega\ \angle 8.11°}$$

$$\mathbf{Y}_T = \frac{1}{\mathbf{Z}_T} = \mathbf{82.51\ mS\ \angle{-8.11°}}$$

b. $\mathbf{V}_1 = \mathbf{IZ}_1 = (3\ \text{A}\ \angle 30°)(6.8\ \Omega\ \angle 0°) = \mathbf{20.4\ V\ \angle 30°}$

$\mathbf{V}_2 = \mathbf{I}(\mathbf{Z}_2 \parallel \mathbf{Z}_3) = (3\ \text{A}\ \angle 30°)(3.63\ \Omega\ \angle 28.13°)$

$= \mathbf{10.89\ V\ \angle 58.13°}$

c. $\mathbf{I}_3 = \dfrac{\mathbf{V}_2}{\mathbf{Z}_3} = \dfrac{10.89\ \text{V}\ \angle 58.13°}{5.63\ \Omega\ \angle 47.02°} = \mathbf{1.93\ A\ \angle 11.11°}$

10. a. $X_{L_1} = \omega L_1 = 2\pi(10^3\ \text{Hz})(0.1\ \text{H}) = 628\ \Omega$

$X_{L_2} = \omega L_2 = 2\pi(10^3\ \text{Hz})(0.2\ \text{H}) = 1.256\ \text{k}\Omega$

$$X_C = \frac{1}{\omega C} = \frac{1}{2\pi(10^3\ \text{Hz})(1\ \mu\text{F})} = 0.159\ \text{k}\Omega$$

$$\mathbf{Z}_T = R\ \angle 0° + X_{L_1}\ \angle 90° + X_C\ \angle{-90°} \parallel X_{L_2}\ \angle 90°$$

$$= 300\ \Omega + j628\ \Omega + 0.159\ \text{k}\Omega\ \angle{-90°} \parallel 1.256\ \text{k}\Omega\ \angle 90°$$

$$= 300\ \Omega + j628\ \Omega - j182\ \Omega$$

$$= \mathbf{300\ \Omega + \mathit{j}446\ \Omega} = \mathbf{537.51\ \Omega\ \angle 56.07°}$$

$$\mathbf{Y}_T = \frac{1}{\mathbf{Z}_T} = \frac{1}{537.51\ \Omega\ \angle 56.07°} = \mathbf{1.86\ mS\ \angle{-56.07°}}$$

b. $\mathbf{I}_s = \dfrac{\mathbf{E}}{\mathbf{Z}_T} = \dfrac{50\ \text{V}\ \angle 0°}{537.51\ \Omega\ \angle 56.07°} = \mathbf{93\ mA\ \angle{-56.07°}}$

c. (CDR): $\mathbf{I}_1 = \dfrac{\mathbf{Z}_{L_2}\mathbf{I}_s}{\mathbf{Z}_{L_2} + \mathbf{Z}_C} = \dfrac{(1.256\ \text{k}\Omega\ \angle 90°)(93\ \text{mA}\ \angle -56.07°)}{+j1.256\ \text{k}\Omega - j0.159\ \text{k}\Omega}$

$$= \frac{116.81\ \text{mA}\ \angle 33.93°}{1.097\ \angle 90°} = \mathbf{106.48\ mA\ \angle{-56.07°}}$$

$$\mathbf{I}_2 = \frac{\mathbf{Z}_C\mathbf{I}_s}{\mathbf{Z}_{L_2} + \mathbf{Z}_C} = \frac{(0.159\ \text{k}\Omega\ \angle -90°)(93\ \text{mA}\ \angle -56.07°)}{1.097\ \text{k}\Omega\ \angle 90°}$$

$$= \frac{14.79\ \text{mA}\ \angle -146.07°}{1.097\ \angle 90°} = 13.48\ \text{mA}\ \angle{-236.07°}$$

$$= \mathbf{13.48\ mA\ \angle 123.93°}$$

d. $\mathbf{V}_1 = (I_2 \angle\theta)(X_{L_2} \angle 90°) = (13.48 \text{ mA} \angle 123.92°)(1.256 \text{ k}\Omega \angle 90°)$

$= \mathbf{16.93 \text{ V} \angle 213.93°}$

$\mathbf{V}_{ab} = \mathbf{E} - (I_s \angle\theta)(R \angle 0°) = 50 \text{ V} \angle 0° - (93 \text{ mA} \angle -56.07°)(300\ \Omega \angle 0°)$

$= 50 \text{ V} - 27.9 \text{ V} \angle -56.07°$

$= 50 \text{ V} - (15.573 \text{ V} - j23.149 \text{ V})$
$= 34.43 \text{ V} + j23.149 \text{ V} = \mathbf{41.49 \text{ V} \angle 33.92°}$

e. $P = I_s^2 R = (93 \text{ mA})^2 300\ \Omega = \mathbf{2.595 \text{ W}}$

f. $F_p = \dfrac{R}{Z_T} = \dfrac{300\ \Omega}{537.51\ \Omega} = \mathbf{0.558 \text{ (lagging)}}$

11.

$\mathbf{Z}_1 = 2\ \Omega - j2\ \Omega = 2.828\ \Omega \angle -45°$
$\mathbf{Z}_2 = 3\ \Omega - j9\ \Omega + j6\ \Omega$
$= 3\ \Omega - j3\ \Omega = 4.243\ \Omega \angle -45°$
$\mathbf{Z}_3 = 10\ \Omega \angle 0°$

$\mathbf{Y}_T = \dfrac{1}{\mathbf{Z}_1} + \dfrac{1}{\mathbf{Z}_2} + \dfrac{1}{\mathbf{Z}_3} = \dfrac{1}{2.828\ \Omega \angle -45°} + \dfrac{1}{4.243\ \Omega \angle -45°} + \dfrac{1}{10\ \Omega \angle 0°}$
$= 0.354 \text{ S} \angle 45° + 0.236 \text{ S} \angle 45° + 0.1 \text{ S} \angle 0° = 0.59 \text{ S} \angle 45° + 0.1 \text{ S} \angle 0°$
$= 0.417 \text{ S} + j0.417 \text{ S} + 0.1 \text{ S}$
$\mathbf{Y}_T = 0.517 \text{ S} + j\,0.417 \text{ S} = \mathbf{0.66 \text{ S} \angle 38.89°}$

$\mathbf{Z}_T = \dfrac{1}{\mathbf{Y}_T} = \dfrac{1}{0.66 \text{ S} \angle 38.89°} = \mathbf{1.52\ \Omega \angle -38.89°}$

$\mathbf{I} = \dfrac{\mathbf{E}}{\mathbf{Z}_T} = \dfrac{50 \text{ V} \angle 0°}{1.52\ \Omega \angle -38.89°} = \mathbf{32.89 \text{ A} \angle 38.89°}$

12. $\mathbf{Z}' = 12\ \Omega - j20\ \Omega = 23.32\ \Omega \angle -59.04°$
$X_L \angle 90° \parallel \mathbf{Z}' = 20\ \Omega \angle 90° \parallel 23.32\ \Omega \angle -59.04° = 33.34\ \Omega \angle 19.99°$
$\mathbf{Z}'' = R_3 \angle 0° + X_L \angle 90° \parallel \mathbf{Z}' = 12\ \Omega + 33.34\ \Omega \angle 19.99°$
$= 12\ \Omega + (31.33\ \Omega - j11.40\ \Omega)$
$= 43.33\ \Omega - j11.40\ \Omega = 44.80\ \Omega \angle 14.74°$
$R_2 \angle 0° \parallel \mathbf{Z}'' = 20\ \Omega \angle 0° \parallel 44.80\ \Omega \angle 14.74° = 13.93\ \Omega \angle 4.54°$
$\mathbf{Z}_T = R_1 \angle 0° + R_2 \angle 0° \parallel \mathbf{Z}'' = 12\ \Omega + 13.93 \angle 4.54°$
$= 12\ \Omega + (13.89\ \Omega + j1.10\ \Omega)$
$= 25.89\ \Omega + j1.10\ \Omega = \mathbf{25.91\ \Omega \angle 2.43°}$

$\mathbf{I}_s = \dfrac{\mathbf{E}}{\mathbf{Z}_T} = \dfrac{100 \text{ V} \angle 0°}{25.91\ \Omega \angle 2.43°} = \mathbf{3.86 \text{ A} \angle -2.43°}$

$\mathbf{I}_{R_1} = \mathbf{I}$

$$\mathbf{I}_{R_3} = \frac{R_2 \angle 0°\ \mathbf{I}_s}{R_2\angle 0° + \mathbf{Z}''} = \frac{(20\ \Omega \angle 0°)(3.86\ \text{A} \angle -2.43°)}{\underbrace{20\ \Omega + 43.33\ \Omega}_{63.33\ \Omega} + j11.40\ \Omega} = \frac{77.20\ \text{A} \angle -2.43°}{64.35 \angle 10.20°}$$

$$= 1.20\ \text{A} \angle -12.63°$$

$$\mathbf{I}_4 = \frac{X_L \angle 90° \mathbf{I}_{R_3}}{X_L \angle 90° + \mathbf{Z}'} = \frac{(20\ \Omega \angle 90°)(1.20\ \text{A} \angle -12.63°)}{j20\ \Omega + 12\ \Omega - j20\ \Omega} = \frac{24.00\ \text{A} \angle 77.37°}{12 \angle 0°}$$

$$= \mathbf{2.00\ A \angle 77.37°}$$

13. $R_3 + R_4 = 2.7\ \text{k}\Omega + 4.3\ \text{k}\Omega = 7\ \text{k}\Omega$
$R' = 3\ \text{k}\Omega \parallel 7\ \text{k}\Omega = 2.1\ \text{k}\Omega$
$Z' = 2.1\ \text{k}\Omega - j10\ \Omega$

(CDR) $$\mathbf{I}' \text{ (of } 10\ \Omega \text{ cap.)} = \frac{(40\ \text{k}\Omega \angle 0°)(20\ \text{mA} \angle 0°)}{40\ \text{k}\Omega + 2.1\ \text{k}\Omega - j10\ \Omega}$$

$$= 19\ \text{mA} \angle +0.014° \text{ as expected since } R_1 \gg \mathbf{Z}'$$

(CDR) $$\mathbf{I}_4 = \frac{(3\ \text{k}\Omega \angle 0°)(19\ \text{mA} \angle 0.014°)}{3\ \text{k}\Omega + 7\ \text{k}\Omega} = \frac{57\ \text{mA} \angle 0.014°}{10}$$

$$= 5.7\ \text{mA} \angle 0.014°$$

$$P = I^2R = (5.7\ \text{mA})^2\ 4.3\ \text{k}\Omega = \mathbf{139.71\ mW}$$

14. $$\mathbf{Z}' = X_{C_2} \angle -90° \parallel R_1 \angle 0° = 2\ \Omega \angle -90° \parallel 1\ \Omega \angle 0°$$

$$= \frac{2\ \Omega \angle -90°}{1 - j2} = \frac{2\ \Omega \angle -90°}{2.236 \angle -63.435°}$$

$$= 0.894\ \Omega \angle -26.565°$$

$$\mathbf{Z}'' = X_{L_2} \angle 90° + \mathbf{Z}' = +j8\ \Omega + 0.894\ \Omega \angle -26.565°$$

$$= +j8\ \Omega + (0.8\ \Omega - j4\ \Omega)$$

$$= 0.8\ \Omega + j4 = 4.079\ \Omega \angle 78.69°$$

$$\mathbf{I}_{X_{L_2}} = \frac{X_{C_1} \angle -90° \mathbf{I}}{X_{C_1} \angle -90° + \mathbf{Z}''} = \frac{(2\ \Omega \angle -90°)(0.5\ \text{A} \angle 0°)}{-j2\ \Omega + (0.8\ \Omega + j4\ \Omega)} = \frac{1\ \text{A} \angle -90°}{0.8 + j2}$$

$$= \frac{1\ \text{A} \angle -90°}{2.154 \angle 68.199°} = 0.464\ \text{A} \angle -158.99°$$

$$\mathbf{I}_1 = \frac{X_{C_2} \angle -90°\ \mathbf{I}_{X_{C_2}}}{X_{C_2} \angle -90° + R_1} = \frac{(2\ \Omega \angle -90°)(0.464\ \text{A} \angle -158.99°)}{-j2\ \Omega + 1\ \Omega} = \frac{0.928\ \text{A} \angle -248.99°}{2.236 \angle -63.435°}$$

$$= \mathbf{0.42\ A \angle 174.45°}$$

Chapter 17

1. –

2. a. $\mathbf{Z} = 2.2\ \Omega + 5.6\ \Omega + j8.2\ \Omega = 7.8\ \Omega + j8.2\ \Omega = \mathbf{11.32\ \Omega\ \angle 46.43^\circ}$

$$\mathbf{I} = \frac{\mathbf{E}}{\mathbf{Z}} = \frac{20\text{ V}\ \angle 20^\circ}{11.32\ \Omega\ \angle 46.43^\circ} = \mathbf{1.77\ A\ \angle{-26.43^\circ}}$$

b. $\mathbf{Z} = -j5\ \Omega + 2\ \Omega\ \angle 0^\circ \parallel 5\ \Omega\ \angle 90^\circ = -j5\ \Omega + 1.72\ \Omega + j0.69\ \Omega = \mathbf{4.64\ \Omega\ \angle{-68.24^\circ}}$

$$\mathbf{I} = \frac{\mathbf{E}}{\mathbf{Z}} = \frac{60\text{ V}\ \angle 30^\circ}{4.64\ \Omega\ \angle -68.24^\circ} = \mathbf{12.93\ A\ \angle 98.24^\circ}$$

3. a. $\mathbf{Z} = 15\ \Omega - j16\ \Omega = \mathbf{21.93\ \Omega\ \angle{-46.85^\circ}}$

$\mathbf{E} = \mathbf{IZ} = (0.5\text{ A}\ \angle 60^\circ)(21.93\ \Omega\ \angle{-46.85^\circ})$

$= \mathbf{10.97\ V\ \angle 13.15^\circ}$

b. $\mathbf{Z} = 10\ \Omega\ \angle 0^\circ \parallel 6\ \Omega\ \angle 90^\circ = \mathbf{5.15\ \Omega\ \angle 59.04^\circ}$

$\mathbf{E} = \mathbf{IZ} = (2\text{ A}\ \angle 120^\circ)(5.15\ \Omega\ \angle 59.04^\circ)$

$= \mathbf{10.30\ V\ \angle 179.04^\circ}$

4. a. $$\mathbf{I} = \frac{\mu \mathbf{V}}{R} = \frac{16\text{ V}}{4 \times 10^3} = \mathbf{4 \times 10^{-3}\ V}$$

$\mathbf{Z} = \mathbf{4\ k\Omega\ \angle 0^\circ}$

b. $\mathbf{V} = (h\mathbf{I})(R) = (50\ \mathbf{I})(50\text{ k}\Omega) = \mathbf{2.5 \times 10^6\ I}$

$\mathbf{Z} = \mathbf{50\ k\Omega\ \angle 0^\circ}$

5. a. Clockwise mesh currents:

$\mathbf{E} - \mathbf{I}_1\mathbf{Z}_1 - \mathbf{I}_1\mathbf{Z}_2 + \mathbf{I}_2\mathbf{Z}_2 = 0$

$-\mathbf{I}_2\mathbf{Z}_2 + \mathbf{I}_1\mathbf{Z}_2 - \mathbf{I}_2\mathbf{Z}_3 - \mathbf{E}_2 = 0$

$[\mathbf{Z}_1 + \mathbf{Z}_2]\mathbf{I}_1 - \mathbf{Z}_2\mathbf{I}_2 = \mathbf{E}_1$

$-\mathbf{Z}_2\mathbf{I}_1 + [\mathbf{Z}_2 + \mathbf{Z}_3]\mathbf{I}_2 = -\mathbf{E}_2$

$\mathbf{Z}_1 = R_1\ \angle 0^\circ = 4\ \Omega\ \angle 0^\circ$

$\mathbf{Z}_2 = X_L\ \angle 90^\circ = 6\ \Omega\ \angle 90^\circ$

$\mathbf{Z}_3 = X_C\ \angle{-90^\circ} = 8\ \Omega\ \angle{-90^\circ}$

$\mathbf{E}_1 = 10\text{ V}\ \angle 0^\circ$, $\mathbf{E}_2 = 40\text{ V}\ \angle 60^\circ$

$$\mathbf{I}_{R_1} = \mathbf{I}_1 = \frac{\begin{vmatrix} \mathbf{E}_1 & -\mathbf{Z}_2 \\ -\mathbf{E}_2 & [\mathbf{Z}_2 + \mathbf{Z}_3] \end{vmatrix}}{\begin{vmatrix} [\mathbf{Z}_1 + \mathbf{Z}_2] & -\mathbf{Z}_2 \\ -\mathbf{Z}_2 & [\mathbf{Z}_2 + \mathbf{Z}_3] \end{vmatrix}} = \frac{[\mathbf{Z}_2 + \mathbf{Z}_3]\mathbf{E}_1 - \mathbf{Z}_2\mathbf{E}_2}{\mathbf{Z}_1\mathbf{Z}_2 + \mathbf{Z}_1\mathbf{Z}_3 + \mathbf{Z}_2\mathbf{Z}_3} = \mathbf{5.15\ A\ \angle{-24.5^\circ}}$$

b. By interchanging the right two branches, the general configuration of part (a) will result and

$$\mathbf{I}_{50\Omega} = \mathbf{I}_1 = \frac{[\mathbf{Z}_2 + \mathbf{Z}_3]\mathbf{E}_1 - \mathbf{Z}_2\mathbf{E}_2}{\mathbf{Z}_1\mathbf{Z}_2 + \mathbf{Z}_1\mathbf{Z}_3 + \mathbf{Z}_2\mathbf{Z}_3}$$
$$= \mathbf{0.44\ A\ \angle 143.48°}$$

$\mathbf{Z}_1 = R_1 = 50\ \Omega\ \angle 0°$
$\mathbf{Z}_2 = X_C\ \angle -90° = 60\ \Omega\ \angle -90°$
$\mathbf{Z}_3 = X_L\ \angle 90° = 20\ \Omega\ \angle 90°$
$\mathbf{E}_1 = 5\ \text{V}\ \angle 30°$, $\mathbf{E}_2 = 20\ \text{V}\ \angle 0°$

6. a.

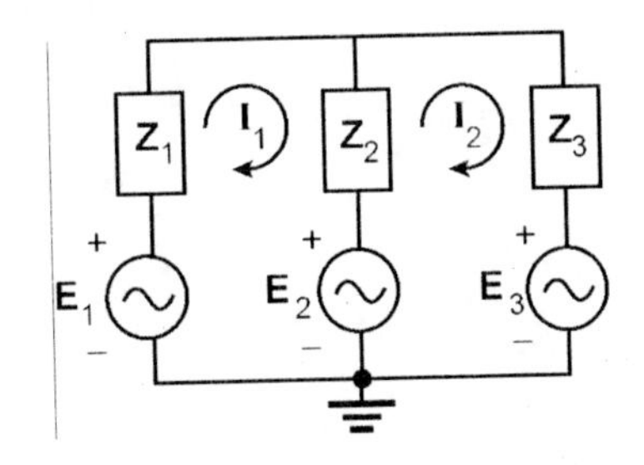

$\mathbf{Z}_1 = 12\ \Omega + j12\ \Omega = 16.971\ \Omega\ \angle 45°$
$\mathbf{Z}_2 = 3\ \Omega\ \angle 0°$
$\mathbf{Z}_3 = -j1\ \Omega$
$\mathbf{E}_1 = 20\ \text{V}\ \angle 50°$
$\mathbf{E}_2 = 60\ \text{V}\ \angle 70°$
$\mathbf{E}_3 = 40\ \text{V}\ \angle 0°$

$$\mathbf{I}_1[\mathbf{Z}_1 + \mathbf{Z}_2] - \mathbf{Z}_2\mathbf{I}_2 = \mathbf{E}_1 - \mathbf{E}_2$$
$$\mathbf{I}_2[\mathbf{Z}_2 + \mathbf{Z}_3] - \mathbf{Z}_2\mathbf{I}_1 = \mathbf{E}_2 - \mathbf{E}_3$$

$$(\mathbf{Z}_1 + \mathbf{Z}_2)\mathbf{I}_1 - \mathbf{Z}_2\mathbf{I}_2 = \mathbf{E}_1 - \mathbf{E}_2$$
$$-\mathbf{Z}_2\mathbf{I}_1 + (\mathbf{Z}_2 + \mathbf{Z}_3)\mathbf{I}_2 = \mathbf{E}_2 - \mathbf{E}_3$$

Using determinants:

$$\mathbf{I}_{R_1} = \mathbf{I}_1 = \frac{(\mathbf{E}_1 - \mathbf{E}_2)(\mathbf{Z}_2 + \mathbf{Z}_3) + \mathbf{Z}_2(\mathbf{E}_2 - \mathbf{E}_3)}{\mathbf{Z}_1\mathbf{Z}_2 + \mathbf{Z}_1\mathbf{Z}_3 + \mathbf{Z}_2\mathbf{Z}_3} = \mathbf{2.55\ A\ \angle 132.72°}$$

b.

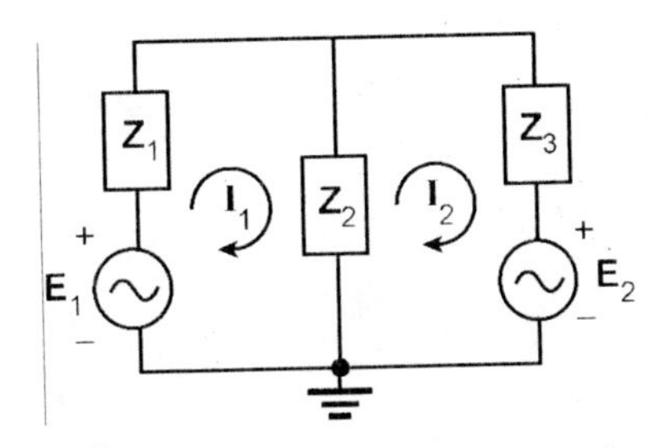

Source conversion:

$\mathbf{E}_1 = \mathbf{IZ} = (6\ \text{A}\ \angle 0°)(2\ \Omega\ \angle 0°)$
$= 12\ \text{V}\ \angle 0°$
$\mathbf{Z}_1 = 2\ \Omega + 20\ \Omega + j20\ \Omega = 22\ \Omega + j20\ \Omega$
$= 29.732\ \Omega\ \angle 42.274°$
$\mathbf{Z}_2 = -j10\ \Omega = 10\ \Omega\ \angle -90°$
$\mathbf{Z}_3 = 10\ \Omega\ \angle 0°$

$$\mathbf{I}_1[\mathbf{Z}_1 + \mathbf{Z}_2] - \mathbf{Z}_2\mathbf{I}_2 = \mathbf{E}_1$$
$$\mathbf{I}_2[\mathbf{Z}_2 + \mathbf{Z}_3] - \mathbf{Z}_2\mathbf{I}_1 = -\mathbf{E}_2$$

$$(\mathbf{Z}_1 + \mathbf{Z}_2)\mathbf{I}_1 - \mathbf{Z}_2\mathbf{I}_2 = \mathbf{E}_1$$
$$-\mathbf{Z}_2\mathbf{I}_1 + (\mathbf{Z}_2 + \mathbf{Z}_3)\mathbf{I}_2 = -\mathbf{E}_2$$

$$\mathbf{I}_{R_1} = \mathbf{I}_1 = \frac{\mathbf{E}_1(\mathbf{Z}_2 + \mathbf{Z}_3) - \mathbf{Z}_2\mathbf{E}_2}{\mathbf{Z}_1\mathbf{Z}_2 + \mathbf{Z}_1\mathbf{Z}_3 + \mathbf{Z}_2\mathbf{Z}_3} = \mathbf{0.495\ A\ \angle 72.26°}$$

7. a. Clockwise mesh currents:

$Z_1 = 4\ \Omega + j3\ \Omega$, $Z_2 = -j1\ \Omega$
$Z_3 = +j6\ \Omega$, $Z_4 = !j2\ \Omega$
$Z_5 = 8\ \Omega$
$E_1 = 60\ V\ \angle 0°$, $E_2 = 120\ V\ \angle 120°$

$$\begin{aligned} &\mathbf{E}_1 - \mathbf{I}_1\mathbf{Z}_1 - \mathbf{I}_1\mathbf{Z}_2 + \mathbf{I}_2\mathbf{Z}_2 = 0 \\ &-\mathbf{I}_2\mathbf{Z}_2 + \mathbf{I}_1\mathbf{Z}_2 - \mathbf{I}_2\mathbf{Z}_3 - \mathbf{I}_2\mathbf{Z}_4 + \mathbf{I}_3\mathbf{Z}_4 = 0 \\ &-\mathbf{I}_3\mathbf{Z}_4 + \mathbf{I}_2\mathbf{Z}_4 - \mathbf{I}_3\mathbf{Z}_5 - \mathbf{E}_2 = 0 \end{aligned}$$

$$\begin{aligned} &[\mathbf{Z}_1 + \mathbf{Z}_2]\mathbf{I}_1 \quad -\mathbf{Z}_2\ \mathbf{I}_2 \quad + 0 = \mathbf{E}_1 \\ &-\mathbf{Z}_2\ \mathbf{I}_1 + [\mathbf{Z}_2 + \mathbf{Z}_3 + \mathbf{Z}_4]\mathbf{I}_2 \quad - \mathbf{Z}_4\ \mathbf{I}_3 = 0 \\ &0 \quad - \mathbf{Z}_4\ \mathbf{I}_2 + [\mathbf{Z}_4 + \mathbf{Z}_5]\mathbf{I}_3 = -\mathbf{E}_2 \end{aligned}$$

$$\mathbf{I}_{R_1} = \mathbf{I}_3 = \frac{[\mathbf{Z}_2\mathbf{Z}_4]\mathbf{E}_1 + \left[\mathbf{Z}_2^2 - [\mathbf{Z}_1 + \mathbf{Z}_2]\ [\mathbf{Z}_2 + \mathbf{Z}_3 + \mathbf{Z}_4]\right]\mathbf{E}_2}{[\mathbf{Z}_1 + \mathbf{Z}_2][\mathbf{Z}_2 + \mathbf{Z}_3 + \mathbf{Z}_4][\mathbf{Z}_4 + \mathbf{Z}_5] - [\mathbf{Z}_1 + \mathbf{Z}_2]\mathbf{Z}_4^2 - [\mathbf{Z}_4 + \mathbf{Z}_5]\mathbf{Z}_2^2}$$
$$= \mathbf{13.07\ A\ \angle -33.71°}$$

b.

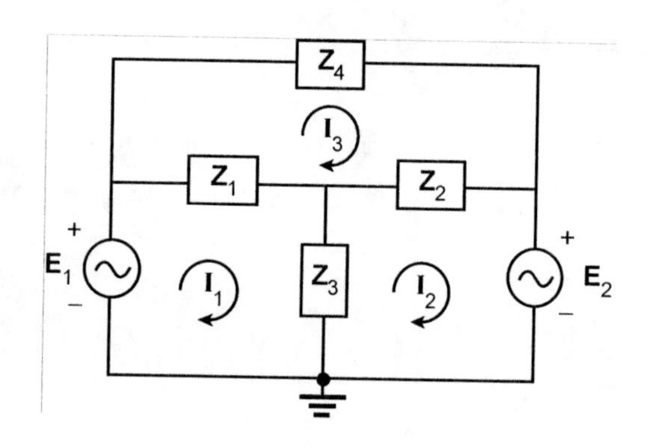

$Z_1 = 15\ \Omega\ \angle 0°$, $Z_2 = 15\ \Omega\ \angle 0°$
$Z_3 = -j10\ \Omega = 10\ \Omega\ \angle -90°$
$Z_4 = 3\ \Omega + j4\ \Omega = 5\ \Omega\ \angle 53.13°$
$E_1 = 220\ V\ \angle 0°$
$E_2 = 100\ V\ \angle 90°$

$$\begin{aligned} &\mathbf{I}_1(\mathbf{Z}_1 + \mathbf{Z}_3) - \mathbf{I}_2\mathbf{Z}_3 - \mathbf{I}_3\mathbf{Z}_1 = \mathbf{E}_1 \\ &\mathbf{I}_2(\mathbf{Z}_2 + \mathbf{Z}_3) - \mathbf{I}_1\mathbf{Z}_3 - \mathbf{I}_3\mathbf{Z}_2 = -\mathbf{E}_2 \\ &\mathbf{I}_3(\mathbf{Z}_1 + \mathbf{Z}_2 + \mathbf{Z}_4) - \mathbf{I}_1\mathbf{Z}_1 - \mathbf{I}_2\mathbf{Z}_2 = 0 \end{aligned}$$

$$\begin{aligned} &\mathbf{I}_1(\mathbf{Z}_1 + \mathbf{Z}_3) - \mathbf{I}_2\mathbf{Z}_3 \quad - \mathbf{I}_3\mathbf{Z}_1 = \mathbf{E}_1 \\ &-\mathbf{I}_1\mathbf{Z}_3 \quad + \mathbf{I}_2(\mathbf{Z}_2 + \mathbf{Z}_3) - \mathbf{I}_3\mathbf{Z}_2 = -\mathbf{E}_2 \\ &-\mathbf{I}_1\mathbf{Z}_1 \quad - \mathbf{I}_2\mathbf{Z}_2 \quad + \mathbf{I}_3(\mathbf{Z}_1 + \mathbf{Z}_2 + \mathbf{Z}_4) = 0 \end{aligned}$$

Applying determinants:

$$\mathbf{I}_3 = \frac{-(\mathbf{Z}_1 + \mathbf{Z}_3)(\mathbf{Z}_2)\mathbf{E}_2 - \mathbf{Z}_1\mathbf{Z}_3\mathbf{E}_2 + \mathbf{E}_1[\mathbf{Z}_2\mathbf{Z}_3 + \mathbf{Z}_1(\mathbf{Z}_2 + \mathbf{Z}_3)]}{(\mathbf{Z}_1 + \mathbf{Z}_3)\left[(\mathbf{Z}_2 + \mathbf{Z}_3)(\mathbf{Z}_1 + \mathbf{Z}_2 + \mathbf{Z}_4) - \mathbf{Z}_2^2\right] + \mathbf{Z}_3[\mathbf{Z}_3(\mathbf{Z}_1 + \mathbf{Z}_2 + \mathbf{Z}_4) - \mathbf{Z}_1\mathbf{Z}_2] - \mathbf{Z}_1[-\mathbf{Z}_2\mathbf{Z}_3 - \mathbf{Z}_1(\mathbf{Z}_2 + \mathbf{Z}_3)]}$$
$$= \mathbf{48.33\ A\ \angle -77.57°}$$

or $\mathbf{I}_3 = \dfrac{\mathbf{E}_1 - \mathbf{E}_2}{\mathbf{Z}_4}$ if one carefully examines the network!

8. a.

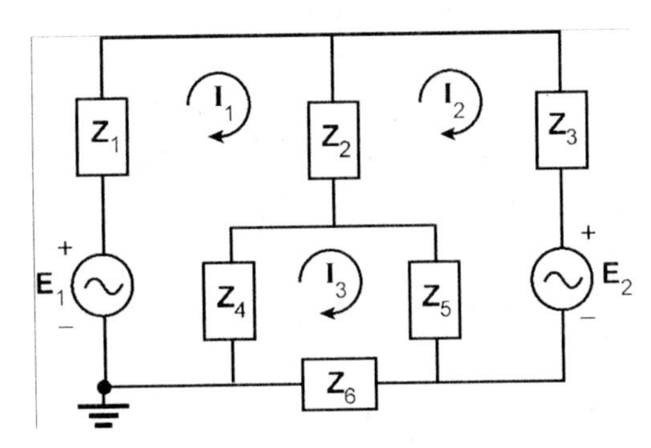

$\mathbf{Z}_1 = 5\ \Omega\ \angle 0°$, $\mathbf{Z}_2 = 5\ \Omega\ \angle 90°$
$\mathbf{Z}_3 = 4\ \Omega\ \angle 0°$, $\mathbf{Z}_4 = 6\ \Omega\ \angle -90°$
$\mathbf{Z}_5 = 4\ \Omega\ \angle 0°$, $\mathbf{Z}_6 = 6\ \Omega + j8\ \Omega$
$\mathbf{E}_1 = 20\ \text{V}\ \angle 0°$, $\mathbf{E}_2 = 40\ \text{V}\ \angle 60°$

$$\mathbf{I}_1(\mathbf{Z}_1 + \mathbf{Z}_2 + \mathbf{Z}_4) - \mathbf{I}_2\mathbf{Z}_2 - \mathbf{I}_3\mathbf{Z}_4 = \mathbf{E}_1$$
$$\mathbf{I}_2(\mathbf{Z}_2 + \mathbf{Z}_3 + \mathbf{Z}_5) - \mathbf{I}_1\mathbf{Z}_2 - \mathbf{I}_3\mathbf{Z}_5 = -\mathbf{E}_2$$
$$\mathbf{I}_3(\mathbf{Z}_4 + \mathbf{Z}_5 + \mathbf{Z}_6) - \mathbf{I}_1\mathbf{Z}_4 - \mathbf{I}_2\mathbf{Z}_5 = 0$$

$$(\mathbf{Z}_1 + \mathbf{Z}_2 + \mathbf{Z}_4)\,\mathbf{I}_1 \quad - \mathbf{Z}_2\mathbf{I}_2 \quad - \mathbf{Z}_4\mathbf{I}_3 = \mathbf{E}_1$$
$$-\mathbf{Z}_2\mathbf{I}_1 + (\mathbf{Z}_2 + \mathbf{Z}_3 + \mathbf{Z}_5)\mathbf{I}_2 \quad - \mathbf{Z}_5\mathbf{I}_3 = -\mathbf{E}_2$$
$$-\mathbf{Z}_4\mathbf{I}_1 \quad - \mathbf{Z}_5\mathbf{I}_2 + (\mathbf{Z}_4 + \mathbf{Z}_5 + \mathbf{Z}_6)\mathbf{I}_3 = 0$$

Using $\mathbf{Z}' = \mathbf{Z}_1 + \mathbf{Z}_2 + \mathbf{Z}_4$, $\mathbf{Z}'' = \mathbf{Z}_2 + \mathbf{Z}_3 + \mathbf{Z}_5$, $\mathbf{Z}''' = \mathbf{Z}_4 + \mathbf{Z}_5 + \mathbf{Z}_6$ and determinants:

$$\mathbf{I}_{R_1} = \mathbf{I}_1 = \frac{\mathbf{E}_1(\mathbf{Z}''\mathbf{Z}''' - \mathbf{Z}_5^2) - \mathbf{E}_2(\mathbf{Z}_2\mathbf{Z}''' + \mathbf{Z}_4\mathbf{Z}_5)}{\mathbf{Z}'(\mathbf{Z}''\mathbf{Z}''' - \mathbf{Z}_5^2) - \mathbf{Z}_2(\mathbf{Z}_2\mathbf{Z}''' + \mathbf{Z}_4\mathbf{Z}_5) - \mathbf{Z}_4(\mathbf{Z}_2\mathbf{Z}_5 + \mathbf{Z}_4\mathbf{Z}'')}$$
$$= \mathbf{3.04\ A\ \angle 169.12°}$$

b.

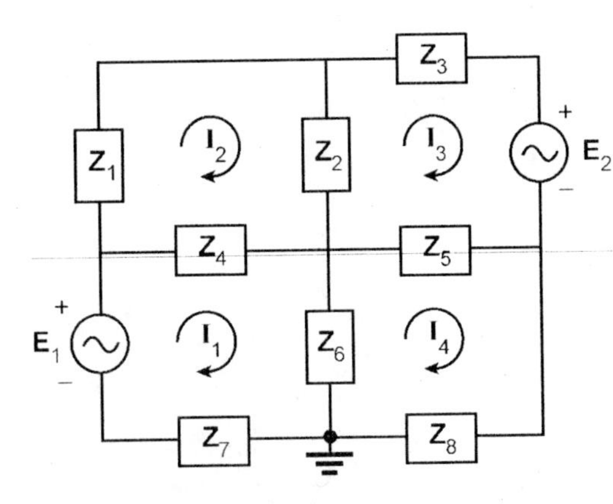

$\mathbf{Z}_1 = 10\ \Omega + j20\ \Omega$	$\mathbf{Z}_2 = -j20\ \Omega$
$\mathbf{Z}_3 = 80\ \Omega\ \angle 0°$	$\mathbf{Z}_4 = 6\ \Omega\ \angle 0°$
$\mathbf{Z}_5 = 15\ \Omega\ \angle 90°$	$\mathbf{Z}_6 = 10\ \Omega\ \angle 0°$
$\mathbf{Z}_7 = 5\ \Omega\ \angle 0°$	$\mathbf{Z}_8 = 5\ \Omega - j20\ \Omega$
$\mathbf{E}_1 = 25\ \text{V}\ \angle 0°$	$\mathbf{E}_2 = 75\ \text{V}\ \angle 20°$

$$\mathbf{I}_1(\mathbf{Z}_4 + \mathbf{Z}_6 + \mathbf{Z}_7) - \mathbf{I}_2\mathbf{Z}_4 - \mathbf{I}_4\mathbf{Z}_6 = \mathbf{E}_1$$
$$\mathbf{I}_2(\mathbf{Z}_1 + \mathbf{Z}_2 + \mathbf{Z}_4) - \mathbf{I}_1\mathbf{Z}_4 - \mathbf{I}_3\mathbf{Z}_2 = 0$$
$$\mathbf{I}_3(\mathbf{Z}_2 + \mathbf{Z}_3 + \mathbf{Z}_5) - \mathbf{I}_2\mathbf{Z}_2 - \mathbf{I}_4\mathbf{Z}_5 = -\mathbf{E}_2$$
$$\mathbf{I}_4(\mathbf{Z}_5 + \mathbf{Z}_6 + \mathbf{Z}_8) - \mathbf{I}_1\mathbf{Z}_6 - \mathbf{I}_3\mathbf{Z}_5 = 0$$

$$(\mathbf{Z}_4 + \mathbf{Z}_6 + \mathbf{Z}_7)\,\mathbf{I}_1 \quad - \mathbf{Z}_4\mathbf{I}_2 \quad + 0 \quad - \mathbf{Z}_6\mathbf{I}_4 = \mathbf{E}_1$$
$$-\mathbf{Z}_4\mathbf{I}_1 + (\mathbf{Z}_1 + \mathbf{Z}_2 + \mathbf{Z}_4)\mathbf{I}_2 \quad - \mathbf{Z}_2\mathbf{I}_3 \quad + 0 = 0$$
$$0 \quad - \mathbf{Z}_2\mathbf{I}_2 + (\mathbf{Z}_2 + \mathbf{Z}_3 + \mathbf{Z}_5)\mathbf{I}_3 \quad - \mathbf{Z}_5\mathbf{I}_4 = -\mathbf{E}_2$$
$$-\mathbf{Z}_6\mathbf{I}_1 \quad + 0 \quad - \mathbf{Z}_5\mathbf{I}_3 + (\mathbf{Z}_5 + \mathbf{Z}_6 + \mathbf{Z}_7)\mathbf{I}_4 = 0$$

Applying determinants:

$$\mathbf{I}_{R_1} = \mathbf{I}_{80\Omega} = \mathbf{0.68\ A\ \angle -162.9°}$$

9.

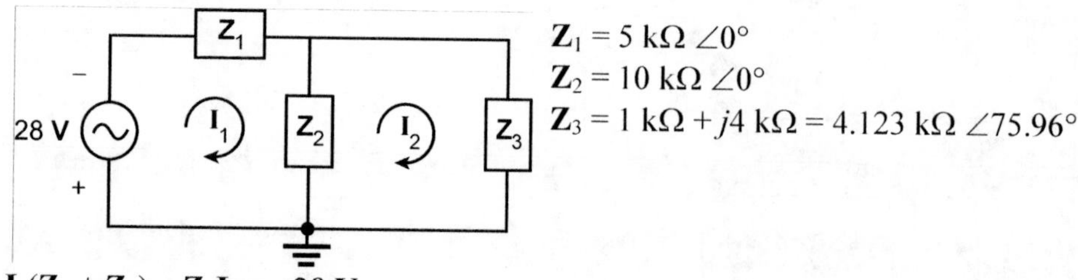

$\mathbf{Z}_1 = 5\text{ k}\Omega\ \angle 0°$
$\mathbf{Z}_2 = 10\text{ k}\Omega\ \angle 0°$
$\mathbf{Z}_3 = 1\text{ k}\Omega + j4\text{ k}\Omega = 4.123\text{ k}\Omega\ \angle 75.96°$

$\mathbf{I}_1(\mathbf{Z}_1 + \mathbf{Z}_2) - \mathbf{Z}_2\mathbf{I}_2 = -28\text{ V}$
$\mathbf{I}_2(\mathbf{Z}_2 + \mathbf{Z}_3) - \mathbf{Z}_2\mathbf{I}_1 = 0$

$(\mathbf{Z}_1 + \mathbf{Z}_2)\mathbf{I}_1 - \mathbf{Z}_2\mathbf{I}_2 = -28\text{ V}$
$-\mathbf{Z}_2\mathbf{I}_1 + (\mathbf{Z}_2 + \mathbf{Z}_3)\mathbf{I}_2 = 0$

$$\mathbf{I}_L = \mathbf{I}_2 = \frac{-\mathbf{Z}_2 28\text{ V}}{\mathbf{Z}_1\mathbf{Z}_2 + \mathbf{Z}_1\mathbf{Z}_3 + \mathbf{Z}_2\mathbf{Z}_3} = \mathbf{-3.17 \times 10^{-3}\ V\ \angle 137.29°}$$

10. a.

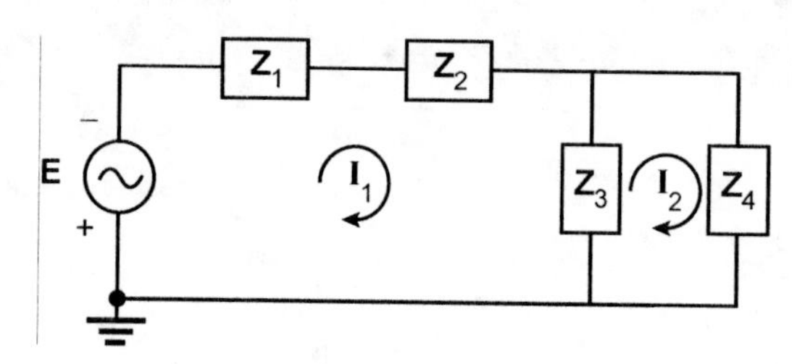

Source Conversion:

$\mathbf{E} = (I\ \angle\theta)(R_p\ \angle 0°)$
$= (50\ \mathbf{I})(40\text{ k}\Omega\ \angle 0°)$
$= 2 \times 10^6\ \mathbf{I}\ \angle 0°$
$\mathbf{Z}_1 = R_s = R_p = 40\text{ k}\Omega\ \angle 0°$
$\mathbf{Z}_2 = -j0.2\text{ k}\Omega$
$\mathbf{Z}_3 = 8\text{ k}\Omega\ \angle 0°$
$\mathbf{Z}_4 = 4\text{ k}\Omega\ \angle 90°$

$\mathbf{I}_1(\mathbf{Z}_1 + \mathbf{Z}_2 + \mathbf{Z}_3) - \mathbf{Z}_3\mathbf{I}_2 = -\mathbf{E}$
$\mathbf{I}_2(\mathbf{Z}_3 + \mathbf{Z}_4) - \mathbf{Z}_3\mathbf{I}_1 = 0$

$(\mathbf{Z}_1 + \mathbf{Z}_2 + \mathbf{Z}_3)\mathbf{I}_1 - \mathbf{Z}_3\mathbf{I}_2 = -\mathbf{E}$
$-\mathbf{Z}_3\mathbf{I}_1 + (\mathbf{Z}_3 + \mathbf{Z}_4)\mathbf{I}_2 = 0$

$$\mathbf{I}_L = \mathbf{I}_2 = \frac{-\mathbf{Z}_3\mathbf{E}}{(\mathbf{Z}_1 + \mathbf{Z}_2 + \mathbf{Z}_3)(\mathbf{Z}_3 + \mathbf{Z}_4) - \mathbf{Z}_3^2} = \mathbf{42.91\ I\ \angle 149.31°}$$

11. $6\mathbf{V}_x - \mathbf{I}_1\ 1\text{ k}\Omega - 10\text{ V}\ \angle 0° = 0$
$10\text{ V}\angle 0° - \mathbf{I}_2\ 4\text{ k}\Omega - \mathbf{I}_2\ 2\text{ k}\Omega = 0$

$\mathbf{V}_x = \mathbf{I}_2\ 2\text{ k}\Omega$

$-\mathbf{I}_1\ 1\text{ k}\Omega + \mathbf{I}_2\ 12\text{ k}\Omega = 10\text{ V}\ \angle 0°$
$-\mathbf{I}_2\ 6\text{ k}\Omega = -10\text{ V}\ \angle 0°$

$$\mathbf{I}_2 = \mathbf{I}_{2\text{k}\Omega} = \frac{10\text{ V}\ \angle 0°}{6\text{ k}\Omega} = \mathbf{1.67\ mA\ \angle 0°} = \mathbf{I}_{2\text{k}\Omega}$$

$-\mathbf{I}_1\ 1\text{ k}\Omega + (1.667\text{ mA}\ \angle 0°)(12\text{ k}\Omega) = 10\text{ V}\ \angle 0°$
$-\mathbf{I}_1\ 1\text{ k}\Omega + 20\text{ V}\ \angle 0° = 10\text{ V}\ \angle 0°$
$-\mathbf{I}_1\ 1\text{ k}\Omega = -10\text{ V}\ \angle 0°$

$$\mathbf{I}_1 = \mathbf{I}_{1k\Omega} = \frac{10\text{ V }\angle 0°}{1\text{ k}\Omega} = \mathbf{10\ mA\ \angle 0°}$$

12.

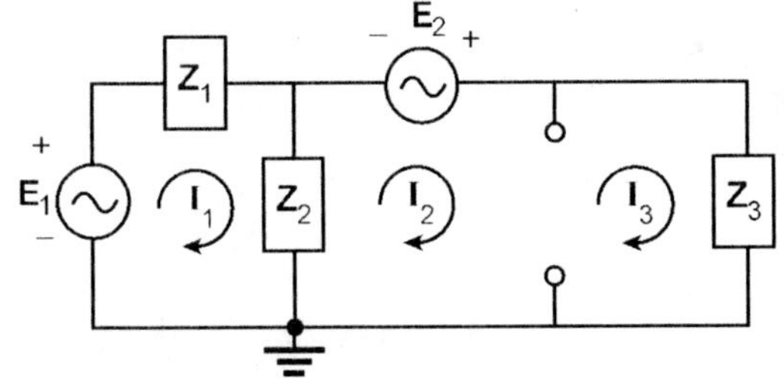

$\mathbf{E}_1 = 5\text{ V }\angle 0°$
$\mathbf{E}_2 = 20\text{ V }\angle 0°$
$\mathbf{Z}_1 = 2.2\text{ k}\Omega\ \angle 0°$
$\mathbf{Z}_2 = 5\text{ k}\Omega\ \angle 90°$
$\mathbf{Z}_3 = 10\text{ k}\Omega\ \angle 0°$
$\mathbf{I} = 4\text{ mA }\angle 0°$

$$\mathbf{E}_1 - \mathbf{I}_1\mathbf{Z}_1 - \mathbf{Z}_2(\mathbf{I}_1 - \mathbf{I}_2) = 0$$
$$-\mathbf{Z}_2(\mathbf{I}_2 - \mathbf{I}_1) + \mathbf{E}_2 - \mathbf{I}_3\mathbf{Z}_3 = 0$$

$$\mathbf{I}_3 - \mathbf{I}_2 = \mathbf{I}$$

Substituting, we obtain:

$$\mathbf{I}_1(\mathbf{Z}_1 + \mathbf{Z}_2) - \mathbf{I}_2\mathbf{Z}_2 = \mathbf{E}_1$$
$$\mathbf{I}_1\mathbf{Z}_2 - \mathbf{I}_2(\mathbf{Z}_2 + \mathbf{Z}_3) = \mathbf{I}\mathbf{Z}_3 - \mathbf{E}_2$$

Determinants:

$\mathbf{I}_1 = 1.39\text{ mA }\angle -126.48°$, $\mathbf{I}_2 = 1.341\text{ mA }\angle -10.56°$, $\mathbf{I}_3 = 2.693\text{ mA }\angle -174.8°$
$\mathbf{I}_{10k\Omega} = \mathbf{I}_3 = \mathbf{2.693\ mA\ \angle -174.8°}$

13.

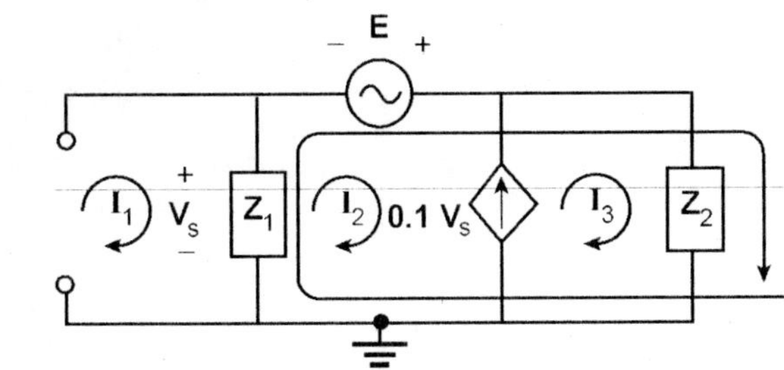

$\mathbf{Z}_1 = 1\text{ k}\Omega\ \angle 0°$
$\mathbf{Z}_2 = 4\text{ k}\Omega + j6\text{ k}\Omega$
$\mathbf{E} = 10\text{ V }\angle 0°$

$$-\mathbf{Z}_1(\mathbf{I}_2 - \mathbf{I}_1) + \mathbf{E} - \mathbf{I}_3\mathbf{Z}_3 = 0$$
$$\mathbf{I}_1 = 6\text{ mA }\angle 0°,\ 0.1\ \mathbf{V}_s = \mathbf{I}_3 - \mathbf{I}_2,\ \mathbf{V}_s = (\mathbf{I}_1 - \mathbf{I}_2)\mathbf{Z}_1$$

Substituting:

$$(1\text{ k}\Omega)\mathbf{I}_2 + (4\text{ k}\Omega + j6\text{ k}\Omega)\mathbf{I}_3 = 16\text{ V }\angle 0°$$
$$(99\ \Omega)\mathbf{I}_2 + \qquad \mathbf{I}_3 = 0.6\text{ V }\angle 0°$$

Determinants:

$$\mathbf{I}_3 = \mathbf{I}_{6\text{ k}\Omega} = \mathbf{1.38\ mA\ \angle -56.31°}$$

14. a.

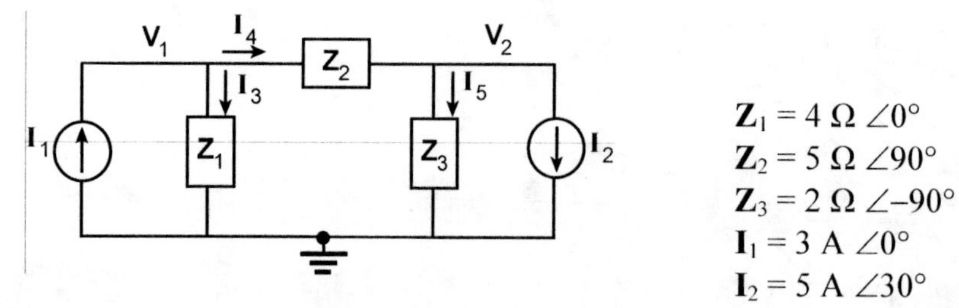

$\mathbf{Z}_1 = 4\ \Omega\ \angle 0°$
$\mathbf{Z}_2 = 5\ \Omega\ \angle 90°$
$\mathbf{Z}_3 = 2\ \Omega\ \angle -90°$
$\mathbf{I}_1 = 3\ \text{A}\ \angle 0°$
$\mathbf{I}_2 = 5\ \text{A}\ \angle 30°$

$\mathbf{I}_1 = \mathbf{I}_3 + \mathbf{I}_4$

$$\mathbf{I}_1 = \frac{\mathbf{V}_1}{\mathbf{Z}_1} + \frac{\mathbf{V}_1 - \mathbf{V}_2}{\mathbf{Z}_2} \Rightarrow \mathbf{V}_1\left[\frac{1}{\mathbf{Z}_1} + \frac{1}{\mathbf{Z}_2}\right] - \mathbf{V}_2\left[\frac{1}{\mathbf{Z}_2}\right] = \mathbf{I}_1$$

or $\mathbf{V}_1[\mathbf{Y}_1 + \mathbf{Y}_2] - \mathbf{V}_2[\mathbf{Y}_2] = \mathbf{I}_1$

$\mathbf{I}_4 = \mathbf{I}_5 + \mathbf{I}_2$

$$\frac{\mathbf{V}_1 - \mathbf{V}_2}{\mathbf{Z}_2} = \frac{\mathbf{V}_2}{\mathbf{Z}_3} + \mathbf{I}_2 \Rightarrow \mathbf{V}_2\left[\frac{1}{\mathbf{Z}_2} + \frac{1}{\mathbf{Z}_3}\right] - \mathbf{V}_1\left[\frac{1}{\mathbf{Z}_2}\right] = -\mathbf{I}_2$$

or $\mathbf{V}_2[\mathbf{Y}_2 + \mathbf{Y}_3] - \mathbf{V}_1[\mathbf{Y}_2] = -\mathbf{I}_2$

$$[\mathbf{Y}_1 + \mathbf{Y}_2]\mathbf{V}_1 \qquad - \mathbf{Y}_2\mathbf{V}_2 = \mathbf{I}_1$$
$$-\mathbf{Y}_2\mathbf{V}_1 + [\mathbf{Y}_2 + \mathbf{Y}_3]\mathbf{V}_2 = -\mathbf{I}_2$$

$$\mathbf{V}_1 = \frac{[\mathbf{Y}_2 + \mathbf{Y}_3]\mathbf{I}_1 - \mathbf{Y}_2\mathbf{I}_2}{\mathbf{Y}_1\mathbf{Y}_2 + \mathbf{Y}_1\mathbf{Y}_3 + \mathbf{Y}_2\mathbf{Y}_3} = \mathbf{14.68\ V\ \angle 68.89°}$$

$$\mathbf{V}_2 = \frac{-[\mathbf{Y}_1 + \mathbf{Y}_2]\mathbf{I}_2 + \mathbf{Y}_2\mathbf{I}_1}{\mathbf{Y}_1\mathbf{Y}_2 + \mathbf{Y}_1\mathbf{Y}_3 + \mathbf{Y}_2\mathbf{Y}_3} = \mathbf{12.97\ V\ \angle 155.88°}$$

b.

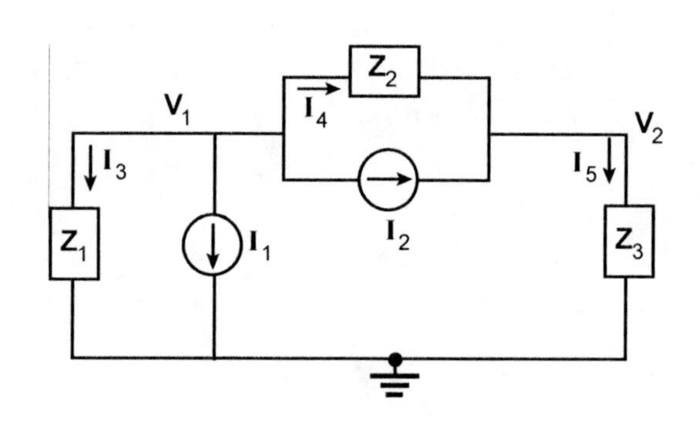

$\mathbf{Z}_1 = 3\ \Omega + j4\ \Omega = 5\ \angle 53.13°$
$\mathbf{Z}_2 = 2\ \Omega\ \angle 0°$
$\mathbf{Z}_3 = 6\ \Omega\ \angle 0° \parallel 8\ \Omega\ \angle -90°$
$= 4.8\ \Omega\ \angle -36.87°$
$\mathbf{I}_1 = 0.6\ \text{A}\ \angle 20°$
$\mathbf{I}_2 = 4\ \text{A}\ \angle 80°$

$0 = \mathbf{I}_1 + \mathbf{I}_3 + \mathbf{I}_4 + \mathbf{I}_2$

$$0 = \mathbf{I}_1 + \frac{\mathbf{V}_1}{\mathbf{Z}_1} + \frac{\mathbf{V}_1 - \mathbf{V}_2}{\mathbf{Z}_2} + \mathbf{I}_2$$

$$\mathbf{V}_1\left[\frac{1}{\mathbf{Z}_1} + \frac{1}{\mathbf{Z}_2}\right] - \mathbf{V}_2\left[\frac{1}{\mathbf{Z}_2}\right] = -\mathbf{I}_1 - \mathbf{I}_2$$

or $\quad \mathbf{V}_1[\mathbf{Y}_1 + \mathbf{Y}_2] - \mathbf{V}_2[\mathbf{Y}_2] = -\mathbf{I}_1 - \mathbf{I}_2$

$\mathbf{I}_2 + \mathbf{I}_4 = \mathbf{I}_5$

$$\mathbf{I}_2 + \frac{\mathbf{V}_1 - \mathbf{V}_2}{\mathbf{Z}_2} = \frac{\mathbf{V}_2}{\mathbf{Z}_3}$$

$$\mathbf{V}_2\left[\frac{1}{\mathbf{Z}_2}+\frac{1}{\mathbf{Z}_3}\right]-\mathbf{V}_1\left[\frac{1}{\mathbf{Z}_2}\right]=+\mathbf{I}_2$$

or $\mathbf{V}_2[\mathbf{Y}_2+\mathbf{Y}_3]-\mathbf{V}_1[\mathbf{Y}_2]=\mathbf{I}_2$

and $[\mathbf{Y}_1+\mathbf{Y}_2]\mathbf{V}_1-\mathbf{Y}_2\mathbf{V}_2=-\mathbf{I}_1-\mathbf{I}_2$

$-\mathbf{Y}_2\mathbf{V}_1+[\mathbf{Y}_2+\mathbf{Y}_3]\mathbf{V}_2=\mathbf{I}_2$

Applying determinants:

$$\mathbf{V}_1=\frac{-[\mathbf{Y}_2+\mathbf{Y}_3][\mathbf{I}_1+\mathbf{I}_2]+\mathbf{Y}_2\mathbf{I}_2}{\mathbf{Y}_1\mathbf{Y}_2+\mathbf{Y}_1\mathbf{Y}_3+\mathbf{Y}_2\mathbf{Y}_3}=\mathbf{5.12\ V\ \angle{-79.36^\circ}}$$

$$\mathbf{V}_2=\frac{\mathbf{Y}_1\mathbf{I}_2-\mathbf{I}_1\mathbf{Y}_2}{\mathbf{Y}_1\mathbf{Y}_2+\mathbf{Y}_1\mathbf{Y}_3+\mathbf{Y}_2\mathbf{Y}_3}=\mathbf{2.71\ V\ \angle 39.96^\circ}$$

15. a.

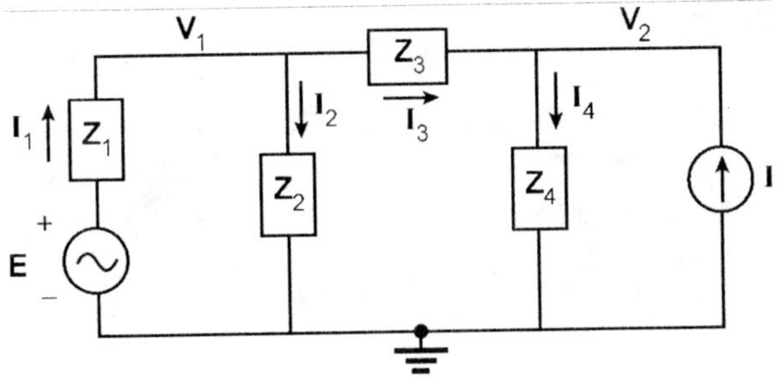

V1 V2 Z3 I1 Z1 I2 I3 I4 Z2 Z4 I + E −

$\mathbf{Z}_1 = 5\ \Omega\ \angle 0^\circ$
$\mathbf{Z}_2 = 6\ \Omega\ \angle 90^\circ$
$\mathbf{Z}_3 = 4\ \Omega\ \angle{-90^\circ}$
$\mathbf{Z}_4 = 2\ \Omega\ \angle 0^\circ$
$\mathbf{E} = 30\ \text{V}\ \angle 50^\circ$
$\mathbf{I} = 0.04\ \text{A}\ \angle 90^\circ$

$\mathbf{I}_1=\mathbf{I}_2+\mathbf{I}_3$

$$\frac{\mathbf{E}_1-\mathbf{V}_1}{\mathbf{Z}_1}=\frac{\mathbf{V}_1}{\mathbf{Z}_2}+\frac{(\mathbf{V}_1-\mathbf{V}_2)}{\mathbf{Z}_3}\Rightarrow \mathbf{V}_1\left[\frac{1}{\mathbf{Z}_1}+\frac{1}{\mathbf{Z}_2}+\frac{1}{\mathbf{Z}_3}\right]-\frac{\mathbf{V}_2}{\mathbf{Z}_3}=\frac{\mathbf{E}_1}{\mathbf{Z}_1}$$

or $\mathbf{V}_1[\mathbf{Y}_1+\mathbf{Y}_2+\mathbf{Y}_3]-\mathbf{Y}_3\mathbf{V}_2=\mathbf{E}_1\mathbf{Y}_1$

$\mathbf{I}_3+\mathbf{I}=\mathbf{I}_4$

$$\frac{\mathbf{V}_1-\mathbf{V}_2}{\mathbf{Z}_3}+\mathbf{I}=\frac{\mathbf{V}_2}{\mathbf{Z}_4}\Rightarrow \mathbf{V}_2\left[\frac{1}{\mathbf{Z}_3}+\frac{1}{\mathbf{Z}_4}\right]-\frac{\mathbf{V}_1}{\mathbf{Z}_3}=\mathbf{I}$$

or $\mathbf{V}_2[\mathbf{Y}_3+\mathbf{Y}_4]-\mathbf{V}_1\mathbf{Y}_3=\mathbf{I}$

resulting in

$$\mathbf{V}_1[\mathbf{Y}_1+\mathbf{Y}_2+\mathbf{Y}_3]-\mathbf{V}_2\mathbf{Y}_3=\mathbf{E}_1\mathbf{Y}_1$$
$$-\mathbf{V}_1[\mathbf{Y}_3]+\mathbf{V}_2[\mathbf{Y}_3+\mathbf{Y}_4]=+\mathbf{I}$$

Using determinants:

$\mathbf{V}_1 = \mathbf{19.86\ V\ \angle 43.8^\circ}$ and $\mathbf{V}_2 = \mathbf{8.94\ V\ \angle 106.9^\circ}$

b.

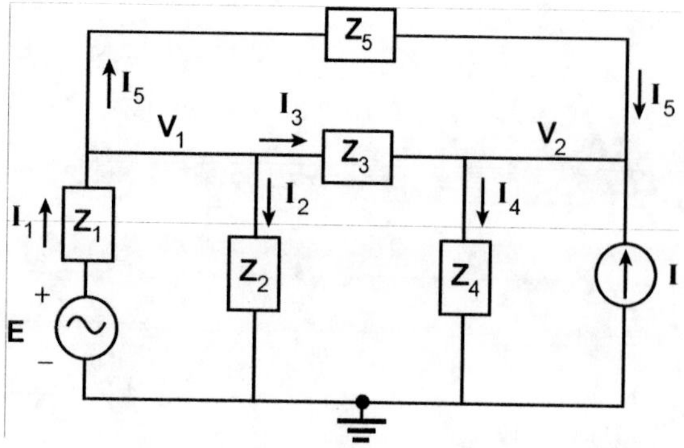

$\mathbf{Z}_1 = 10\ \Omega\ \angle 0°$
$\mathbf{Z}_2 = 10\ \Omega\ \angle 0°$
$\mathbf{Z}_3 = 4\ \Omega\ \angle 90°$
$\mathbf{Z}_4 = 2\ \Omega\ \angle 0°$
$\mathbf{Z}_5 = 8\ \Omega\ \angle -90°$
$\mathbf{E} = 50\ \text{V}\ \angle 120°$
$\mathbf{I} = 0.8\ \text{A}\ \angle 70°$

$\mathbf{I}_1 = \mathbf{I}_2 + \mathbf{I}_5$

$$\frac{\mathbf{E}-\mathbf{V}_1}{\mathbf{Z}_1} = \frac{\mathbf{V}_1}{\mathbf{Z}_2} + \frac{(\mathbf{V}_1-\mathbf{V}_2)}{\mathbf{Z}_5} + \frac{\mathbf{V}_1-\mathbf{V}_2}{\mathbf{Z}_3} \Rightarrow \mathbf{V}_1\left[\frac{1}{\mathbf{Z}_1}+\frac{1}{\mathbf{Z}_2}+\frac{1}{\mathbf{Z}_3}+\frac{1}{\mathbf{Z}_5}\right] - \mathbf{V}_2\left[\frac{1}{\mathbf{Z}_3}+\frac{1}{\mathbf{Z}_5}\right] = \frac{\mathbf{E}}{\mathbf{Z}_1}$$

or $\mathbf{V}_1[\mathbf{Y}_1 + \mathbf{Y}_2 + \mathbf{Y}_3 + \mathbf{Y}_5] - \mathbf{V}_2[\mathbf{Y}_3 + \mathbf{Y}_5] = \mathbf{E}_1\mathbf{Y}_1$

$\mathbf{I}_3 + \mathbf{I}_5 = \mathbf{I}_4 + \mathbf{I}$

$$\frac{\mathbf{V}_1-\mathbf{V}_2}{\mathbf{Z}_3} + \frac{\mathbf{V}_1-\mathbf{V}_2}{\mathbf{Z}_5} = \frac{\mathbf{V}_2}{\mathbf{Z}_4} + \mathbf{I} \Rightarrow \mathbf{V}_2\left[\frac{1}{\mathbf{Z}_3}+\frac{1}{\mathbf{Z}_4}+\frac{1}{\mathbf{Z}_5}\right] - \mathbf{V}_1\left[\frac{1}{\mathbf{Z}_3}+\frac{1}{\mathbf{Z}_5}\right] = -\mathbf{I}$$

or $\mathbf{V}_2[\mathbf{Y}_3 + \mathbf{Y}_4 + \mathbf{Y}_5] - \mathbf{V}_1[\mathbf{Y}_3 + \mathbf{Y}_5] = -\mathbf{I}$

resulting in

$$\mathbf{V}_1[\mathbf{Y}_1 + \mathbf{Y}_2 + \mathbf{Y}_3 + \mathbf{Y}_5] - \mathbf{V}_2[\mathbf{Y}_3 + \mathbf{Y}_5] = \mathbf{E}_1\mathbf{Y}_1$$
$$-\mathbf{V}_1[\mathbf{Y}_3 + \mathbf{Y}_5] + \mathbf{V}_2[\mathbf{Y}_3 + \mathbf{Y}_4 + \mathbf{Y}_5] = -\mathbf{I}$$

Applying determinants:

$\mathbf{V}_1 = \mathbf{19.78\ V\ \angle 132.48°}$ and $\mathbf{V}_2 = \mathbf{13.37\ V\ \angle 98.78°}$

16. $$\mathbf{I} = \frac{\mathbf{V}_1}{\mathbf{Z}_1} + \frac{\mathbf{V}_1-\mathbf{V}_2}{\mathbf{Z}_2}$$

$$0 = \frac{\mathbf{V}_2-\mathbf{V}_1}{\mathbf{Z}_2} + \frac{\mathbf{V}_2}{\mathbf{Z}_3} + \frac{\mathbf{V}_2-\mathbf{E}}{\mathbf{Z}_4}$$

$\mathbf{Z}_1 = 2\ \Omega\ \angle 0°$
$\mathbf{Z}_2 = 20\ \Omega + j\,20\ \Omega$
$\mathbf{Z}_3 = 10\ \Omega\ \angle -90°$
$\mathbf{Z}_4 = 10\ \Omega\ \angle 0°$
$\mathbf{I} = 6\ \text{A}\ \angle 0°$
$\mathbf{E} = 30\ \text{V}\ \angle 0°$

Rearranging:

$$\mathbf{V}_1\left[\frac{1}{\mathbf{Z}_1}+\frac{1}{\mathbf{Z}_2}\right] - \frac{1}{\mathbf{Z}_2}\mathbf{V}_2 = \mathbf{I}$$

$$\frac{-\mathbf{V}_1}{\mathbf{Z}_2} + \mathbf{V}_2\left[\frac{1}{\mathbf{Z}_2}+\frac{1}{\mathbf{Z}_3}+\frac{1}{\mathbf{Z}_4}\right] = \frac{\mathbf{E}}{\mathbf{Z}_4}$$

Determinants and substituting:

$\mathbf{V}_1 = \mathbf{11.74\ V\ \angle -4.61°}$, $\mathbf{V}_2 = \mathbf{22.53\ V\ \angle -36.48°}$

17.

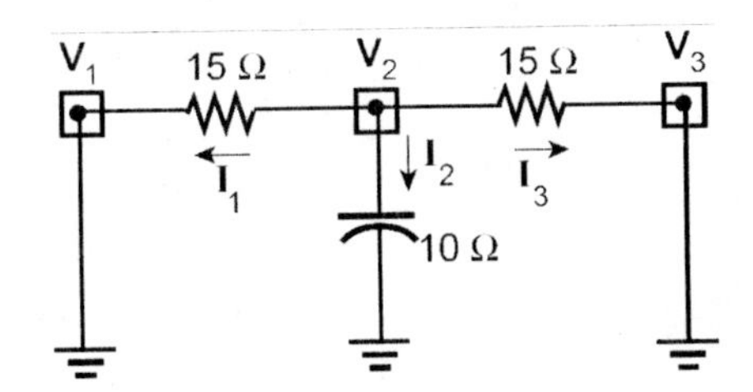

(Note that $3 + j4$ branch has no effect on nodal voltages)

$$\Sigma \mathbf{I}_i = \Sigma \mathbf{I}_o$$

$$0 = \mathbf{I}_1 + \mathbf{I}_2 + \mathbf{I}_3$$

$$= \frac{\mathbf{V}_2 - \mathbf{V}_1}{15\,\Omega} + \frac{\mathbf{V}_2}{10\,\Omega\angle -90°} + \frac{\mathbf{V}_2 - \mathbf{V}_3}{15\,\Omega}$$

Through manipulation:

$$\mathbf{V}_2[2 + j1.5] - \mathbf{V}_1 - \mathbf{V}_3 = 0$$

but $\mathbf{V}_1 = \mathbf{220\ V\ \angle 0°}$ and $\mathbf{V}_3 = \mathbf{100\ V\ \angle 90°}$

and $\mathbf{V}_2 = \dfrac{220 + j100}{2 + j1.5} = \mathbf{96.66\ V\angle{-12.43}°}$

with $\mathbf{V}_3 = 0\text{V}\ \angle 0°$

18.

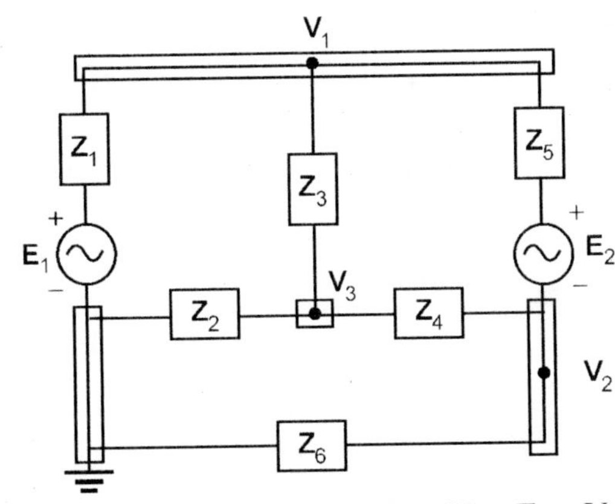

$\mathbf{Z}_1 = 5\ \Omega\ \angle 0°$
$\mathbf{Z}_2 = 6\ \Omega\ \angle{-90}°$
$\mathbf{Z}_3 = 5\ \Omega\ \angle 90°$
$\mathbf{Z}_4 = 4\ \Omega\ \angle 0°$
$\mathbf{Z}_5 = 4\ \Omega\ \angle 0°$
$\mathbf{Z}_6 = 6\ \Omega + j8\ \Omega$
$\mathbf{E}_1 = 20\ \text{V}\ \angle 0°$
$\mathbf{E}_2 = 40\ \text{V}\ \angle 60°$

node $\mathbf{V}_1$: $\dfrac{\mathbf{V}_1 - \mathbf{E}_1}{\mathbf{Z}_1} + \dfrac{\mathbf{V}_1 - \mathbf{V}_3}{\mathbf{Z}_3} + \dfrac{\mathbf{V}_1 - \mathbf{E}_2 - \mathbf{V}_2}{\mathbf{Z}_5} = 0$

node $\mathbf{V}_2$: $\dfrac{\mathbf{V}_2 + \mathbf{E}_2 - \mathbf{V}_1}{\mathbf{Z}_5} + \dfrac{\mathbf{V}_2 - \mathbf{V}_3}{\mathbf{Z}_4} + \dfrac{\mathbf{V}_2}{\mathbf{Z}_6} = 0$

node $\mathbf{V}_3$: $\dfrac{\mathbf{V}_3}{\mathbf{Z}_2} + \dfrac{\mathbf{V}_3 - \mathbf{V}_1}{\mathbf{Z}_3} + \dfrac{\mathbf{V}_3 - \mathbf{V}_2}{\mathbf{Z}_4} = 0$

Rearranging:

$$\mathbf{V}_1\left(\frac{1}{\mathbf{Z}_1} + \frac{1}{\mathbf{Z}_3} + \frac{1}{\mathbf{Z}_5}\right) - \frac{\mathbf{V}_2}{\mathbf{Z}_5} - \frac{\mathbf{V}_3}{\mathbf{Z}_3} = \frac{\mathbf{E}_1}{\mathbf{Z}_1} + \frac{\mathbf{E}_2}{\mathbf{Z}_5}$$

$$\mathbf{V}_2\left(\frac{1}{\mathbf{Z}_5} + \frac{1}{\mathbf{Z}_4} + \frac{1}{\mathbf{Z}_6}\right) - \frac{\mathbf{V}_1}{\mathbf{Z}_5} - \frac{\mathbf{V}_3}{\mathbf{Z}_4} = -\frac{\mathbf{E}_2}{\mathbf{Z}_5}$$

$$\mathbf{V}_3\left(\frac{1}{\mathbf{Z}_2} + \frac{1}{\mathbf{Z}_3} + \frac{1}{\mathbf{Z}_4}\right) - \frac{\mathbf{V}_1}{\mathbf{Z}_3} - \frac{\mathbf{V}_2}{\mathbf{Z}_4} = 0$$

Determinants: $\mathbf{V}_1 = \mathbf{5.84\ V\ \angle 29.4°}$, $\mathbf{V}_2 = \mathbf{28.06\ V\ \angle{-89.15}°}$, $\mathbf{V}_3 = \mathbf{31.96\ V\ \angle{-77.6}°}$

19.

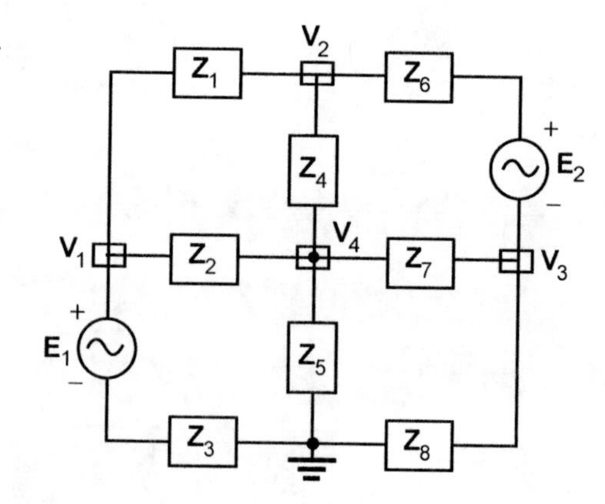

$\mathbf{E}_1 = 25\text{ V}\angle 0°$
$\mathbf{E}_2 = 75\text{ V}\angle 20°$

$\mathbf{Z}_1 = 10\ \Omega + j20\ \Omega$
$\mathbf{Z}_2 = 6\ \Omega\angle 0°$
$\mathbf{Z}_3 = 5\ \Omega\angle 0°$
$\mathbf{Z}_4 = 20\ \Omega\angle -90°$
$\mathbf{Z}_5 = 10\ \Omega\angle 0°$
$\mathbf{Z}_6 = 80\ \Omega\angle 0°$
$\mathbf{Z}_7 = 15\ \Omega\angle 90°$
$\mathbf{Z}_8 = 5\ \Omega - j20\ \Omega$

$$\mathbf{V}_1\text{:}\quad \frac{\mathbf{V}_1-\mathbf{V}_2}{\mathbf{Z}_1}+\frac{\mathbf{V}_1-\mathbf{V}_4}{\mathbf{Z}_2}+\frac{\mathbf{V}_1-\mathbf{E}_1}{\mathbf{Z}_3}=0$$

$$\mathbf{V}_2\text{:}\quad \frac{\mathbf{V}_2-\mathbf{V}_1}{\mathbf{Z}_1}+\frac{\mathbf{V}_2-\mathbf{V}_4}{\mathbf{Z}_4}+\frac{\mathbf{V}_2-\mathbf{E}_2-\mathbf{V}_3}{\mathbf{Z}_6}=0$$

$$\mathbf{V}_3\text{:}\quad \frac{\mathbf{V}_3+\mathbf{E}_2-\mathbf{V}_2}{\mathbf{Z}_6}+\frac{\mathbf{V}_3-\mathbf{V}_4}{\mathbf{Z}_7}+\frac{\mathbf{V}_3}{\mathbf{Z}_8}=0$$

$$\mathbf{V}_4\text{:}\quad \frac{\mathbf{V}_4-\mathbf{V}_1}{\mathbf{Z}_2}+\frac{\mathbf{V}_4-\mathbf{V}_2}{\mathbf{Z}_4}+\frac{\mathbf{V}_4-\mathbf{V}_3}{\mathbf{Z}_7}+\frac{\mathbf{V}_4}{\mathbf{Z}_5}=0$$

Rearranging:

$$\mathbf{V}_1\left(\frac{1}{\mathbf{Z}_1}+\frac{1}{\mathbf{Z}_2}+\frac{1}{\mathbf{Z}_3}\right)-\frac{\mathbf{V}_2}{\mathbf{Z}_1}-\frac{\mathbf{V}_4}{\mathbf{Z}_2}=\frac{\mathbf{E}_1}{\mathbf{Z}_3}$$

$$\mathbf{V}_2\left(\frac{1}{\mathbf{Z}_1}+\frac{1}{\mathbf{Z}_4}+\frac{1}{\mathbf{Z}_6}\right)-\frac{\mathbf{V}_1}{\mathbf{Z}_1}-\frac{\mathbf{V}_4}{\mathbf{Z}_4}-\frac{\mathbf{V}_3}{\mathbf{Z}_6}=\frac{\mathbf{E}_2}{\mathbf{Z}_6}$$

$$\mathbf{V}_3\left(\frac{1}{\mathbf{Z}_6}+\frac{1}{\mathbf{Z}_7}+\frac{1}{\mathbf{Z}_8}\right)-\frac{\mathbf{V}_2}{\mathbf{Z}_6}-\frac{\mathbf{V}_4}{\mathbf{Z}_7}=-\frac{\mathbf{E}_2}{\mathbf{Z}_6}$$

$$\mathbf{V}_4\left(\frac{1}{\mathbf{Z}_2}+\frac{1}{\mathbf{Z}_4}+\frac{1}{\mathbf{Z}_7}+\frac{1}{\mathbf{Z}_5}\right)-\frac{\mathbf{V}_1}{\mathbf{Z}_2}-\frac{\mathbf{V}_2}{\mathbf{Z}_4}-\frac{\mathbf{V}_3}{\mathbf{Z}_7}=0$$

Setting up and then using determinants:

$\mathbf{V}_1 = \mathbf{14.62\text{ V}\angle -5.86°}$, $\mathbf{V}_2 = \mathbf{35.03\text{ V}\angle -37.69°}$
$\mathbf{V}_3 = \mathbf{32.4\text{ V}\angle -73.34°}$, $\mathbf{V}_4 = \mathbf{5.67\text{ V}\angle 23.53°}$

20. a.

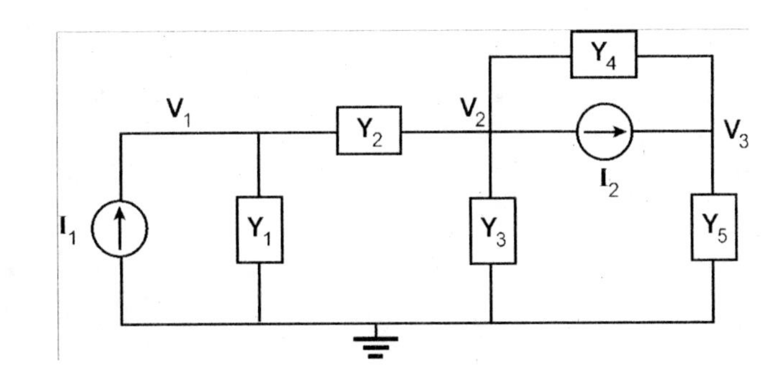

$$\mathbf{Y}_1 = \frac{1}{4\ \Omega\ \angle 0^\circ} = 0.25\text{ S }\angle 0^\circ$$

$$\mathbf{Y}_2 = \frac{1}{1\ \Omega\ \angle 90^\circ} = 1\text{ S }\angle -90^\circ$$

$$\mathbf{Y}_3 = \frac{1}{5\ \Omega\ \angle 0^\circ} = 0.2\text{ S }\angle 0^\circ$$

$$\mathbf{Y}_4 = \frac{1}{4\ \Omega\ \angle -90^\circ} = 0.25\text{ S }\angle 90^\circ$$

$$\mathbf{Y}_5 = \frac{1}{8\ \Omega\ \angle 90^\circ} = 0.125\text{ S }\angle -90^\circ$$

$\mathbf{I}_1 = 2\text{ A }\angle 30^\circ$
$\mathbf{I}_2 = 3\text{ A }\angle 150^\circ$

$$\mathbf{V}_1[\mathbf{Y}_1 + \mathbf{Y}_2] - \mathbf{Y}_2\mathbf{V}_2 = \mathbf{I}_1$$
$$\mathbf{V}_2[\mathbf{Y}_2 + \mathbf{Y}_3 + \mathbf{Y}_4] - \mathbf{Y}_2\mathbf{V}_1 - \mathbf{Y}_4\mathbf{V}_3 = -\mathbf{I}_2$$
$$\mathbf{V}_3[\mathbf{Y}_4 + \mathbf{Y}_5] - \mathbf{Y}_4\mathbf{V}_2 = \mathbf{I}_2$$

$$[\mathbf{Y}_1 + \mathbf{Y}_2]\mathbf{V}_1 \quad - \mathbf{Y}_2\mathbf{V}_2 \quad + 0 = \mathbf{I}_1$$
$$-\mathbf{Y}_2\mathbf{V}_1 + [\mathbf{Y}_2 + \mathbf{Y}_3 + \mathbf{Y}_4]\mathbf{V}_2 \quad - \mathbf{Y}_4\mathbf{V}_3 = -\mathbf{I}_2$$
$$0 \quad - \mathbf{Y}_4\mathbf{V}_2 + [\mathbf{Y}_4 + \mathbf{Y}_5]\mathbf{V}_3 = \mathbf{I}_2$$

$$\mathbf{V}_1 = \frac{\mathbf{I}_1\left[(\mathbf{Y}_2 + \mathbf{Y}_3 + \mathbf{Y}_4)(\mathbf{Y}_4 + \mathbf{Y}_5) - \mathbf{Y}_4^2\right] - \mathbf{I}_2[\mathbf{Y}_2\mathbf{Y}_5]}{\left[\mathbf{Y}_1 + \mathbf{Y}_2\right]\left[(\mathbf{Y}_2 + \mathbf{Y}_3 + \mathbf{Y}_4)(\mathbf{Y}_4 + \mathbf{Y}_5) - \mathbf{Y}_4^2\right] - \mathbf{Y}_2^2(\mathbf{Y}_4 + \mathbf{Y}_5) = \mathbf{Y}_\Delta}$$
$$= \mathbf{5.74\ V\ \angle 122.76^\circ}$$

$$\mathbf{V}_2 = \frac{\mathbf{I}_1\mathbf{Y}_2(\mathbf{Y}_4 + \mathbf{Y}_5) - \mathbf{I}_2\mathbf{Y}_5(\mathbf{Y}_1 + \mathbf{Y}_2)}{\mathbf{Y}_\Delta} = \mathbf{4.04\ V\ \angle 145.03^\circ}$$

$$\mathbf{V}_3 = \frac{\mathbf{I}_2\left[(\mathbf{Y}_1 + \mathbf{Y}_2)(\mathbf{Y}_3 + \mathbf{Y}_4) - \mathbf{Y}_2^2\right] - \mathbf{Y}_2\mathbf{Y}_4\mathbf{I}_1}{\mathbf{Y}_\Delta} = \mathbf{25.94\ V\ \angle 78.07^\circ}$$

b.

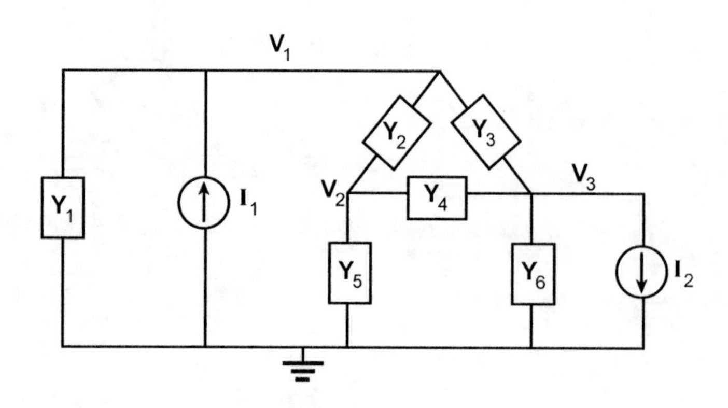

$$\mathbf{Y}_1 = \frac{1}{4\ \Omega\ \angle 0°} = 0.25\ \text{S}\ \angle 0°$$

$$\mathbf{Y}_2 = \frac{1}{6\ \Omega\ \angle 0°} = 0.167\ \text{S}\ \angle 0°$$

$$\mathbf{Y}_3 = \frac{1}{8\ \Omega\ \angle 0°} = 0.125\ \text{S}\ \angle 0°$$

$$\mathbf{Y}_4 = \frac{1}{2\ \Omega\ \angle -90°} = 0.5\ \text{S}\ \angle 90°$$

$$\mathbf{Y}_5 = \frac{1}{5\ \Omega\ \angle 90°} = 0.2\ \text{S}\ \angle -90°$$

$$\mathbf{Y}_6 = \frac{1}{4\ \Omega\ \angle 90°} = 0.25\ \text{S}\ \angle -90°$$

$\mathbf{I}_1 = 4\ \text{A}\ \angle 0°$

$\mathbf{I}_2 = 6\ \text{A}\ \angle 90°$

$$\mathbf{V}_1[\mathbf{Y}_1 + \mathbf{Y}_2 + \mathbf{Y}_3] - \mathbf{Y}_2\mathbf{V}_2 - \mathbf{Y}_3\mathbf{V}_3 = \mathbf{I}_1$$
$$\mathbf{V}_2[\mathbf{Y}_2 + \mathbf{Y}_4 + \mathbf{Y}_5] - \mathbf{Y}_2\mathbf{V}_1 - \mathbf{Y}_4\mathbf{V}_3 = 0$$
$$\mathbf{V}_3[\mathbf{Y}_3 + \mathbf{Y}_4 + \mathbf{Y}_6] - \mathbf{Y}_3\mathbf{V}_1 - \mathbf{Y}_4\mathbf{V}_2 = -\mathbf{I}_2$$

$$[\mathbf{Y}_1 + \mathbf{Y}_2 + \mathbf{Y}_3]\mathbf{V}_1 - \mathbf{Y}_2\mathbf{V}_2 - \mathbf{Y}_3\mathbf{V}_3 = \mathbf{I}_1$$
$$-\mathbf{Y}_2\mathbf{V}_1 + [\mathbf{Y}_2 + \mathbf{Y}_4 + \mathbf{Y}_5]\mathbf{V}_2 - \mathbf{Y}_4\mathbf{V}_3 = 0$$
$$-\mathbf{Y}_3\mathbf{V}_1 - \mathbf{Y}_4\mathbf{V}_2 + [\mathbf{Y}_3 + \mathbf{Y}_4 + \mathbf{Y}_6]\mathbf{V}_3 = -\mathbf{I}_2$$

$$\mathbf{V}_1 = \frac{\mathbf{I}_1\left[(\mathbf{Y}_2+\mathbf{Y}_4+\mathbf{Y}_5)(\mathbf{Y}_3+\mathbf{Y}_4+\mathbf{Y}_6)-\mathbf{Y}_4^2\right]-\mathbf{I}_2\left[\mathbf{Y}_2\mathbf{Y}_4+\mathbf{Y}_3(\mathbf{Y}_3+\mathbf{Y}_4+\mathbf{Y}_5)\right]}{\mathbf{Y}_\Delta=(\mathbf{Y}_1+\mathbf{Y}_2+\mathbf{Y}_3)\left[(\mathbf{Y}_2+\mathbf{Y}_4+\mathbf{Y}_5)(\mathbf{Y}_3+\mathbf{Y}_4+\mathbf{Y}_6)-\mathbf{Y}_4^2\right]-\mathbf{Y}_2\left[\mathbf{Y}_2(\mathbf{Y}_3+\mathbf{Y}_4+\mathbf{Y}_6)+\mathbf{Y}_3\mathbf{Y}_4\right]-\mathbf{Y}_3\left[\mathbf{Y}_2\mathbf{Y}_4+\mathbf{Y}_3(\mathbf{Y}_2+\mathbf{Y}_4+\mathbf{Y}_5)\right]}$$

$= \mathbf{15.13\ V\ \angle 1.29°}$

$$\mathbf{V}_2 = \frac{\mathbf{I}_1\left[(\mathbf{Y}_2)(\mathbf{Y}_3+\mathbf{Y}_4+\mathbf{Y}_6)+\mathbf{Y}_3\mathbf{Y}_4\right]+\mathbf{I}_2\left[\mathbf{Y}_4(\mathbf{Y}_1+\mathbf{Y}_2+\mathbf{Y}_3)-\mathbf{Y}_2\mathbf{Y}_3\right]}{\mathbf{Y}_\Delta} = \mathbf{17.24\ V\ \angle 3.73°}$$

$$\mathbf{V}_3 = \frac{\mathbf{I}_1\left[(\mathbf{Y}_3)(\mathbf{Y}_2+\mathbf{Y}_4+\mathbf{Y}_5)+\mathbf{Y}_2\mathbf{Y}_4\right]+\mathbf{I}_2\left[\mathbf{Y}_2^2-(\mathbf{Y}_1+\mathbf{Y}_2+\mathbf{Y}_3)(\mathbf{Y}_2+\mathbf{Y}_4+\mathbf{Y}_5)\right]}{\mathbf{Y}_\Delta}$$

$= \mathbf{10.59\ V\ \angle -0.11°}$

21. Left node: $\mathbf{V}_1$

$$\Sigma\mathbf{I}_i = \Sigma\mathbf{I}_o$$

$$4\mathbf{I}_x = \mathbf{I}_x + 5\ \text{mA}\ \angle 0° + \frac{\mathbf{V}_1 - \mathbf{V}_2}{2\ \text{k}\Omega}$$

Right node: $\mathbf{V}_2$

$$\Sigma\mathbf{I}_i = \Sigma\mathbf{I}_o$$

$$8\ \text{mA}\ \angle 0° = \frac{\mathbf{V}_2}{1\ \text{k}\Omega} + \frac{\mathbf{V}_2 - \mathbf{V}_1}{2\ \text{k}\Omega} + 4\mathbf{I}_x$$

Insert $\mathbf{I}_x = \dfrac{\mathbf{V}_1}{4\ \text{k}\Omega\ \angle -90°}$

Rearrange, reduce and 2 equations with 2 unknowns result:

$$\mathbf{V}_1[1.803\ \angle 123.69°] + \mathbf{V}_2 = 10$$
$$\mathbf{V}_1[2.236\ \angle 116.57°] + 3\ \mathbf{V}_2 = 16$$

Determinants: $\mathbf{V}_1 = \mathbf{4.37\ V\ \angle{-128.66°}}$
$\mathbf{V}_2 = \mathbf{V}_{1k\Omega} = \mathbf{2.25\ V\ \angle 17.63°}$

22.

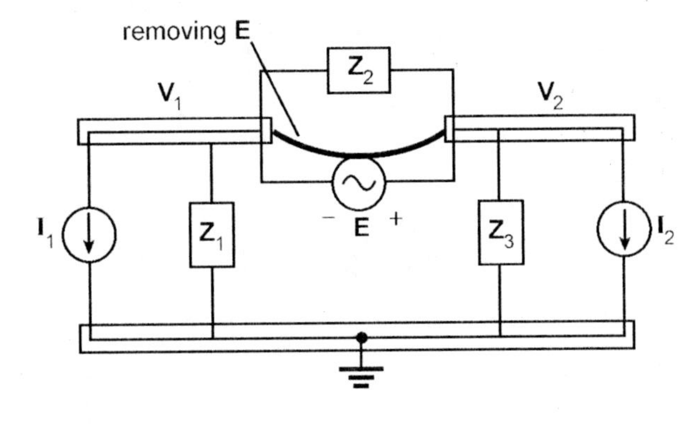

$\mathbf{Z}_1 = 1\ k\Omega\ \angle 0°$
$\mathbf{Z}_2 = 2\ k\Omega\ \angle 90°$
$\mathbf{Z}_3 = 3\ k\Omega\ \angle{-90°}$
$\mathbf{I}_1 = 12\ mA\ \angle 0°$
$\mathbf{I}_2 = 4\ mA\ \angle 0°$
$\mathbf{E} = 10\ V\ \angle 0°$

$$\Sigma \mathbf{I}_i = \Sigma \mathbf{I}_o$$

$$0 = \mathbf{I}_1 + \frac{\mathbf{V}_1}{\mathbf{Z}_1} + \frac{\mathbf{V}_2}{\mathbf{Z}_3} + \mathbf{I}_2$$

and $\dfrac{\mathbf{V}_1}{\mathbf{Z}_1} + \dfrac{\mathbf{V}_2}{\mathbf{Z}_3} = -\mathbf{I}_1 - \mathbf{I}_2$

with $\mathbf{V}_2 - \mathbf{V}_1 = \mathbf{E}$

Substituting and rearranging:

$$\mathbf{V}_1\left[\frac{1}{\mathbf{Z}_1} + \frac{1}{\mathbf{Z}_3}\right] = -\mathbf{I}_1 - \mathbf{I}_2 - \frac{\mathbf{E}}{\mathbf{Z}_3}$$

and solving for $\mathbf{V}_1$:

$\mathbf{V}_1 = \mathbf{15.4\ V\ \angle\ 178.2°}$

with $\mathbf{V}_2 = \mathbf{V}_C = \mathbf{5.41\ V\ \angle\ 174.87°}$

23. Left node: $\mathbf{V}_1$

$$\Sigma \mathbf{I}_i = \Sigma \mathbf{I}_o$$

$$2\ mA\ \angle 0° = 12\ mA\ \angle 0° + \frac{\mathbf{V}_1}{2\,k\Omega} + \frac{\mathbf{V}_1 - \mathbf{V}_2}{1\,k\Omega}$$

and $1.5\ \mathbf{V}_1 - \mathbf{V}_2 = -10$

Right node: $\mathbf{V}_2$

$$\Sigma \mathbf{I}_i = \Sigma \mathbf{I}_o$$

$$0 = 2\ mA\ \angle 0° + \frac{\mathbf{V}_2 - \mathbf{V}_1}{1\,k\Omega} - \frac{\mathbf{V}_2 - 6\ \mathbf{V}_x}{3.3\,k\Omega}$$

and $2.7\ \mathbf{V}_1 - 3.7\ \mathbf{V}_2 = -6.6$

Using determinants: $\mathbf{V}_1 = \mathbf{V}_{2k\Omega} = \mathbf{-10.67\ V\ \angle 0° = 10.67\ V\ \angle 180°}$
$\mathbf{V}_2 = \mathbf{-6\ V\ \angle 0° = 6\ V\ \angle 180°}$

24.

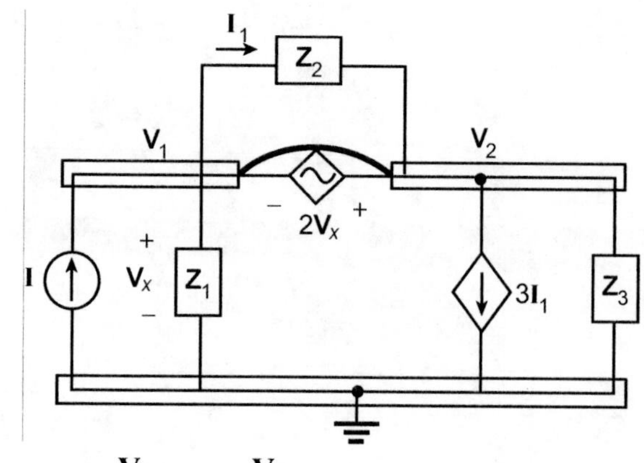

$\mathbf{Z}_1 = 2\text{ k}\Omega\ \angle 0°$
$\mathbf{Z}_2 = 1\text{ k}\Omega \angle 0°$
$\mathbf{Z}_3 = 1\text{ k}\Omega\ \angle 0°$
$\mathbf{I} = 5\text{ mA}\ \angle 0°$

$\mathbf{V}_1$: $\mathbf{I} = \dfrac{\mathbf{V}_1}{\mathbf{Z}_1} + 3\mathbf{I}_1 + \dfrac{\mathbf{V}_2}{\mathbf{Z}_3}$

with $\mathbf{I}_1 = \dfrac{\mathbf{V}_1 - \mathbf{V}_2}{\mathbf{Z}_2}$

and $\mathbf{V}_2 - \mathbf{V}_1 = 2\mathbf{V}_x = 2\mathbf{V}_1$ or $\mathbf{V}_2 = 3\mathbf{V}_1$

Substituting will result in:

$$\mathbf{V}_1\left[\frac{1}{\mathbf{Z}_1} + \frac{3}{\mathbf{Z}_2}\right] + 3\,\mathbf{V}_1\left[\frac{1}{\mathbf{Z}_3} - \frac{3}{\mathbf{Z}_2}\right] = \mathbf{I}$$

or $$\mathbf{V}_1\left[\frac{1}{\mathbf{Z}_1} - \frac{6}{\mathbf{Z}_2} + \frac{3}{\mathbf{Z}_3}\right] = \mathbf{I}$$

and $\mathbf{V}_1 = \mathbf{V}_x = \mathbf{-2\ V\ \angle 0°}$
with $\mathbf{V}_2 = \mathbf{-6\ V\ \angle 0°}$

25.

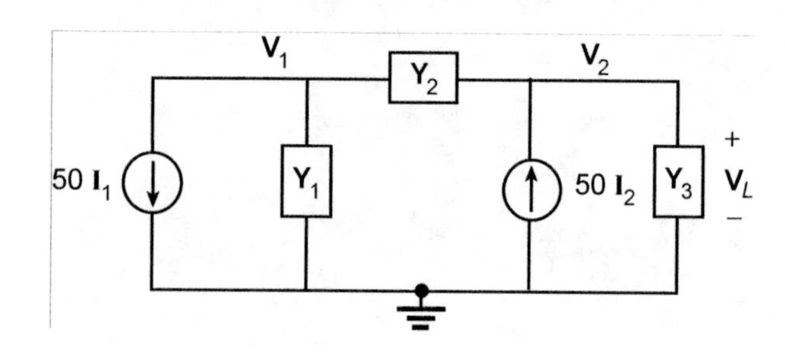

$\mathbf{I}_1 = \dfrac{E_i \angle \theta}{R_1\ \angle 0°} = 1 \times 10^{-3}\ \mathbf{E}_i$

$\mathbf{Y}_1 = \dfrac{1}{50\text{ k}\Omega} = 0.02\text{ mS}\ \angle 0°$

$\mathbf{Y}_2 = \dfrac{1}{1\text{ k}\Omega} = 1\text{ mS}\ \angle 0°$

$\mathbf{Y}_3 = 0.02\text{ mS}\ \angle 0°$
$\mathbf{I}_2 = (\mathbf{V}_1 - \mathbf{V}_2)\mathbf{Y}_2$

$\mathbf{V}_1(\mathbf{Y}_1 + \mathbf{Y}_2) - \mathbf{Y}_2\mathbf{V}_2 = -50\mathbf{I}_1$
$\mathbf{V}_2(\mathbf{Y}_2 + \mathbf{Y}_3) - \mathbf{Y}_2\mathbf{V}_1 = 50\mathbf{I}_2 = 50(\mathbf{V}_1 - \mathbf{V}_2)\mathbf{Y}_2 = 50\mathbf{Y}_2\mathbf{V}_1 - 50\mathbf{Y}_2\mathbf{V}_2$

$(\mathbf{Y}_1 + \mathbf{Y}_2)\mathbf{V}_1 - \mathbf{Y}_2\mathbf{V}_2 = -50\mathbf{I}_1$
$-51\mathbf{Y}_2\mathbf{V}_1 + (51\mathbf{Y}_2 + \mathbf{Y}_3)\mathbf{V}_2 = 0$

$$\mathbf{V}_L = \mathbf{V}_2 = \frac{-(50)(51)\mathbf{Y}_2\mathbf{I}_1}{(\mathbf{Y}_1 + \mathbf{Y}_2)(51\mathbf{Y}_2 + \mathbf{Y}_3) - 51\mathbf{Y}_2^2} = \mathbf{-2451.92\ E}_i$$

26. a. yes

$$\frac{\mathbf{Z}_1}{\mathbf{Z}_3} = \frac{\mathbf{Z}_2}{\mathbf{Z}_4}$$

$$\frac{5 \times 10^3 \angle 0°}{2.5 \times 10^3 \angle 90°} = \frac{8 \times 10^3 \angle 0°}{4 \times 10^3 \angle 90°}$$

$$2 \angle -90° = 2 \angle -90° \text{ (balanced)} ✓$$

b. $\mathbf{Z}_1 = 5 \text{ k}\Omega \angle 0°$, $\mathbf{Z}_2 = 8 \text{ k}\Omega \angle 0°$
$\mathbf{Z}_3 = 2.5 \text{ k}\Omega \angle 90°$, $\mathbf{Z}_4 = 4 \text{ k}\Omega \angle 90°$
$\mathbf{Z}_5 = 5 \text{ k}\Omega \angle -90°$, $\mathbf{Z}_6 = 1 \text{ k}\Omega \angle 0°$

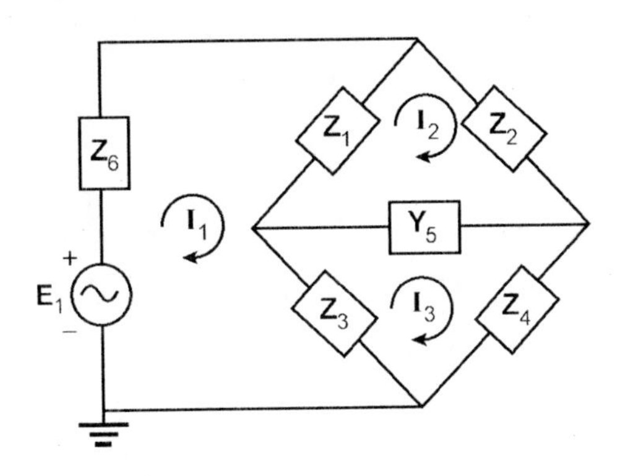

$$\mathbf{I}_1[\mathbf{Z}_1 + \mathbf{Z}_3 + \mathbf{Z}_6] - \mathbf{Z}_1\mathbf{I}_2 - \mathbf{Z}_3\mathbf{I}_3 = \mathbf{E}$$
$$\mathbf{I}_2[\mathbf{Z}_1 + \mathbf{Z}_2 + \mathbf{Z}_5] - \mathbf{Z}_1\mathbf{I}_1 - \mathbf{Z}_5\mathbf{I}_3 = 0$$
$$\mathbf{I}_3[\mathbf{Z}_3 + \mathbf{Z}_4 + \mathbf{Z}_5] - \mathbf{Z}_3\mathbf{I}_1 - \mathbf{Z}_5\mathbf{I}_2 = 0$$

$$[\mathbf{Z}_1 + \mathbf{Z}_3 + \mathbf{Z}_6]\mathbf{I}_1 - \mathbf{Z}_1\mathbf{I}_2 - \mathbf{Z}_3\mathbf{I}_3 = \mathbf{E}$$
$$-\mathbf{Z}_1\mathbf{I}_1 + [\mathbf{Z}_1 + \mathbf{Z}_2 + \mathbf{Z}_5]\mathbf{I}_2 - \mathbf{Z}_5\mathbf{I}_3 = 0$$
$$-\mathbf{Z}_3\mathbf{I}_1 - \mathbf{Z}_5\mathbf{I}_2 + [\mathbf{Z}_3 + \mathbf{Z}_4 + \mathbf{Z}_5]\mathbf{I}_3 = 0$$

$$\mathbf{I}_2 = \frac{\mathbf{E}[\mathbf{Z}_1(\mathbf{Z}_3 + \mathbf{Z}_4 + \mathbf{Z}_5) + \mathbf{Z}_3\mathbf{Z}_5]}{\mathbf{Z}_\Delta = (\mathbf{Z}_1 + \mathbf{Z}_3 + \mathbf{Z}_6)[(\mathbf{Z}_1 + \mathbf{Z}_2 + \mathbf{Z}_5)(\mathbf{Z}_3 + \mathbf{Z}_4 + \mathbf{Z}_5) - \mathbf{Z}_5^2] - \mathbf{Z}_1[\mathbf{Z}_1(\mathbf{Z}_3 + \mathbf{Z}_4 + \mathbf{Z}_5) - \mathbf{Z}_3\mathbf{Z}_5] - \mathbf{Z}_3[\mathbf{Z}_1\mathbf{Z}_5 + \mathbf{Z}_3(\mathbf{Z}_1 + \mathbf{Z}_2 + \mathbf{Z}_5)]}$$

$$\mathbf{I}_3 = \frac{\mathbf{E}[\mathbf{Z}_1\mathbf{Z}_5 + \mathbf{Z}_3(\mathbf{Z}_1 + \mathbf{Z}_2 + \mathbf{Z}_5)]}{\mathbf{Z}_\Delta}$$

$$\mathbf{I}_{Z_5} = \mathbf{I}_2 - \mathbf{I}_3 = \frac{\mathbf{E}[\mathbf{Z}_1\mathbf{Z}_4 - \mathbf{Z}_3\mathbf{Z}_2]}{\mathbf{Z}_\Delta} = \frac{E[20 \times 10^6 \angle 90° - 20 \times 10^6 \angle 90°]}{\mathbf{Z}_\Delta} = \mathbf{0\ A}$$

c.

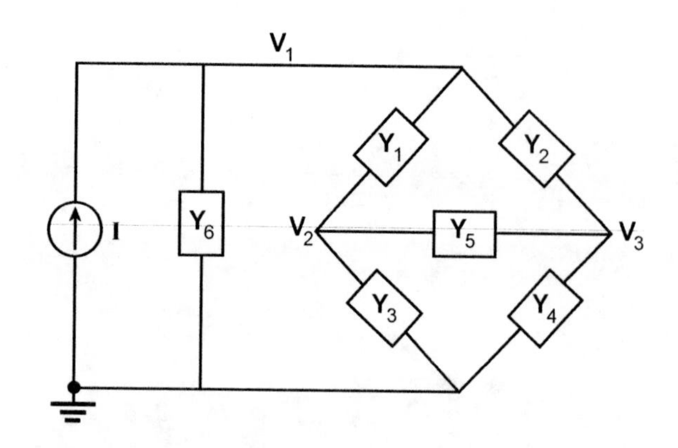

$$\mathbf{I} = \frac{\mathbf{E}_s}{\mathbf{R}_s} = \frac{10\text{ V}\angle 0^\circ}{1\text{ k}\Omega\angle 0^\circ} = 10\text{ mA}\angle 0^\circ$$

$$\mathbf{Y}_1 = \frac{1}{5\text{ k}\Omega\angle 0^\circ} = 0.2\text{ mS}\angle 0^\circ$$

$$\mathbf{Y}_2 = \frac{1}{8\text{ k}\Omega\angle 0^\circ} = 0.125\text{ mS}\angle 0^\circ$$

$$\mathbf{Y}_3 = \frac{1}{2.5\text{ k}\Omega\angle 90^\circ} = 0.4\text{ mS}\angle -90^\circ$$

$$\mathbf{Y}_4 = \frac{1}{4\text{ k}\Omega\angle 90^\circ} = 0.25\text{ mS}\angle -90^\circ$$

$$\mathbf{Y}_5 = \frac{1}{5\text{ k}\Omega\angle -90^\circ} = 0.2\text{ mS}\angle 90^\circ$$

$$\mathbf{Y}_6 = \frac{1}{1\text{ k}\Omega\angle 0^\circ}$$

$$\mathbf{V}_2 = 1\text{ mS}\angle 0^\circ$$

$$\mathbf{V}_1[\mathbf{Y}_1 + \mathbf{Y}_2 + \mathbf{Y}_6] - \mathbf{Y}_1\mathbf{V}_2 - \mathbf{Y}_2\mathbf{V}_3 = \mathbf{I}$$
$$\mathbf{V}_2[\mathbf{Y}_1 + \mathbf{Y}_3 + \mathbf{Y}_5] - \mathbf{Y}_1\mathbf{V}_1 - \mathbf{Y}_5\mathbf{V}_3 = 0$$
$$\mathbf{V}_3[\mathbf{Y}_2 + \mathbf{Y}_4 + \mathbf{Y}_5] - \mathbf{Y}_2\mathbf{V}_1 - \mathbf{Y}_5\mathbf{V}_2 = 0$$

$$[\mathbf{Y}_1 + \mathbf{Y}_2 + \mathbf{Y}_6]\mathbf{V}_1 - \mathbf{Y}_1\mathbf{V}_2 - \mathbf{Y}_2\mathbf{V}_3 = \mathbf{I}$$
$$-\mathbf{Y}_1\mathbf{V}_1 + [\mathbf{Y}_1 + \mathbf{Y}_3 + \mathbf{Y}_5]\mathbf{V}_2 - \mathbf{Y}_5\mathbf{V}_3 = 0$$
$$-\mathbf{Y}_2\mathbf{V}_1 - \mathbf{Y}_5\mathbf{V}_2 + [\mathbf{Y}_2 + \mathbf{Y}_4 + \mathbf{Y}_5]\mathbf{V}_3 = 0$$

$$\mathbf{V}_2 = \frac{\mathbf{I}[\mathbf{Y}_1(\mathbf{Y}_2+\mathbf{Y}_4+\mathbf{Y}_5)+\mathbf{Y}_2\mathbf{Y}_5]}{\mathbf{Y}_\Delta = (\mathbf{Y}_1+\mathbf{Y}_2+\mathbf{Y}_6)[(\mathbf{Y}_1+\mathbf{Y}_3+\mathbf{Y}_5)(\mathbf{Y}_2+\mathbf{Y}_4+\mathbf{Y}_5)-\mathbf{Y}_5^2]-\mathbf{Y}_1[\mathbf{Y}_1(\mathbf{Y}_2+\mathbf{Y}_4+\mathbf{Y}_5)+\mathbf{Y}_2\mathbf{Y}_5]-\mathbf{Y}_2[\mathbf{Y}_1\mathbf{Y}_5+\mathbf{Y}_2(\mathbf{Y}_1+\mathbf{Y}_3+\mathbf{Y}_5)]}$$

$$\mathbf{V}_3 = \frac{\mathbf{I}[\mathbf{Y}_1\mathbf{Y}_5 + \mathbf{Y}_2(\mathbf{Y}_1+\mathbf{Y}_3+\mathbf{Y}_5)]}{\mathbf{Y}_\Delta}$$

$$\mathbf{V}_{Z_5} = \mathbf{V}_2 - \mathbf{V}_3 = \frac{\mathbf{I}[\mathbf{Y}_1\mathbf{Y}_4 - \mathbf{Y}_4\mathbf{Y}_3]}{\mathbf{Y}_\Delta} = \frac{\mathbf{I}\left[0.05\times 10^{-3}\angle -90^\circ - 0.05\times 10^{-3}\angle -90^\circ\right]}{\mathbf{Y}_\Delta}$$

$$= \mathbf{0\ V}$$

27. a.

$$\frac{\mathbf{Z}_1}{\mathbf{Z}_3} = \frac{\mathbf{Z}_2}{\mathbf{Z}_4}$$

$$\frac{4\times 10^3\angle 0^\circ}{4\times 10^3\angle 90^\circ} \stackrel{?}{=} \frac{4\times 10^3\angle 0^\circ}{4\times 10^3\angle -90^\circ}$$

$1\angle -90^\circ \neq 1\angle 90^\circ$ **(not balanced)**

b. The solution to 26(b) resulted in

$$\mathbf{I}_3 = \mathbf{I}_{X_C} = \frac{\mathbf{E}(\mathbf{Z}_1\mathbf{Z}_5 + \mathbf{Z}_3(\mathbf{Z}_1 + \mathbf{Z}_2 + \mathbf{Z}_5))}{\mathbf{Z}_\Delta}$$

where $\mathbf{Z}_\Delta = (\mathbf{Z}_1 + \mathbf{Z}_3 + \mathbf{Z}_6)[(\mathbf{Z}_1 + \mathbf{Z}_2 + \mathbf{Z}_5)(\mathbf{Z}_3 + \mathbf{Z}_4 + \mathbf{Z}_5) - \mathbf{Z}_5^2] - \mathbf{Z}_1[\mathbf{Z}_1(\mathbf{Z}_3 + \mathbf{Z}_4 + \mathbf{Z}_5) - \mathbf{Z}_3\mathbf{Z}_5] - \mathbf{Z}_3[\mathbf{Z}_1\mathbf{Z}_5 + \mathbf{Z}_3(\mathbf{Z}_1 + \mathbf{Z}_2 + \mathbf{Z}_5)]$

and $\mathbf{Z}_1 = 5\text{ k}\Omega\angle 0^\circ$, $\mathbf{Z}_2 = 8\text{ k}\Omega\angle 0^\circ$, $\mathbf{Z}_3 = 2.5\text{ k}\Omega\angle 90^\circ$
$\mathbf{Z}_4 = 4\text{ k}\Omega\angle 90^\circ$, $\mathbf{Z}_5 = 5\text{ k}\Omega\angle -90^\circ$, $\mathbf{Z}_6 = 1\text{ k}\Omega\angle 0^\circ$

and $\mathbf{I}_{X_C} = \mathbf{1.76\ mA\angle -71.54^\circ}$

c. The solution to 26(c) resulted in

$$\mathbf{V}_3 = \mathbf{V}_{X_C} = \frac{\mathbf{I}[\mathbf{Y}_1\mathbf{Y}_5 + \mathbf{Y}_2(\mathbf{Y}_1 + \mathbf{Y}_3 + \mathbf{Y}_5)]}{\mathbf{Y}_\Delta}$$

where $\mathbf{Y}_\Delta = (\mathbf{Y}_1 + \mathbf{Y}_2 + \mathbf{Y}_6)[(\mathbf{Y}_1 + \mathbf{Y}_3 + \mathbf{Y}_5)(\mathbf{Y}_2 + \mathbf{Y}_4 + \mathbf{Y}_5) - \mathbf{Y}_5^2]$
$- \mathbf{Y}_1[\mathbf{Y}_1(\mathbf{Y}_2 + \mathbf{Y}_4 + \mathbf{Y}_5) + \mathbf{Y}_2\mathbf{Y}_5]$
$- \mathbf{Y}_2[\mathbf{Y}_1\mathbf{Y}_5 + \mathbf{Y}_2(\mathbf{Y}_1 + \mathbf{Y}_3 + \mathbf{Y}_5)]$

with $\mathbf{Y}_1 = 0.2\text{ mS }\angle 0°$, $\mathbf{Y}_2 = 0.125\text{ mS }\angle 0°$, $\mathbf{Y}_3 = 0.4\text{ mS }\angle -90°$
$\mathbf{Y}_4 = 0.25\text{ mS }\angle -90°$, $\mathbf{Y}_5 = 0.2\text{ mS }\angle 90°$

Source conversion: $\mathbf{Y}_6 = 1\text{ mS }\angle 0°$, $\mathbf{I} = 10\text{ mA }\angle 0°$
and $\mathbf{V}_3 = \mathbf{7.03\text{ V }\angle -18.46°}$

28. $\mathbf{Z}_1\mathbf{Z}_4 = \mathbf{Z}_3\mathbf{Z}_2$

$(R_1 - jX_C)(R_x + jX_{L_x}) = R_3R_2$ $\qquad X_C = \dfrac{1}{\omega C} = \dfrac{1}{(10^3\text{ rad/s})(1\,\mu\text{F})} = 1\text{ k}\Omega$

$(1\text{ k}\Omega - j1\text{ k}\Omega)(R_x + jX_{L_x}) = (0.1\text{ k}\Omega)(0.1\text{ k}\Omega) = 10\text{ k}\Omega$

$$\text{and } R_x + jX_{L_x} = \frac{10 \times 10^3\ \Omega}{1 \times 10^3 - j1 \times 10^3} = \frac{10 \times 10^3}{1.414 \times 10^3\ \angle -45°} = 5\ \Omega + j5\ \Omega$$

$$\therefore R_x = \mathbf{5\ \Omega},\ L_x = \frac{X_{L_x}}{\omega} = \frac{5\ \Omega}{10^3\text{ rad/s}} = \mathbf{5\text{ mH}}$$

29. $X_{C_1} = \dfrac{1}{\omega C} = \dfrac{1}{(1000\text{ rad/s})(3\,\mu\text{F})} = \dfrac{1}{3}\text{k}\Omega$

$\mathbf{Z}_1 = R_1 \parallel X_{C_1}\angle -90° = (2\text{ k}\Omega\ \angle 0°) \parallel 2\frac{1}{3}\text{ k}\Omega\ \angle -90° = 328.8\ \Omega\ \angle -80.54°$

$\mathbf{Z}_2 = R_2\ \angle 0° = 0.5\text{ k}\Omega\ \angle 0°$, $\mathbf{Z}_3 = R_3\ \angle 0° = 4\text{ k}\Omega\ \angle 0°$
$\mathbf{Z}_4 = R_x + jX_{L_x} = 1\text{ k}\Omega + j6\text{ k}\Omega$

$$\frac{\mathbf{Z}_1}{\mathbf{Z}_3} = \frac{\mathbf{Z}_2}{\mathbf{Z}_4}$$

$$\frac{328.8\ \Omega\ \angle -80.54°}{4\text{ k}\Omega\ \angle 0°} \stackrel{?}{=} \frac{0.5\text{ k}\Omega\ \angle 0°}{6.083\ \Omega\ \angle 80.54°}$$

$$82.2\ \angle -80.54° \stackrel{\checkmark}{=} 82.2\ \angle -80.54° \text{ \textbf{(balanced)}}$$

30. Apply Eq. **17.6.**

31. For balance:

$$R_1(R_x + jX_{L_x}) = R_2(R_3 + jX_{L_3})$$

$$R_1R_x + jR_1X_{L_x} = R_2R_3 + jR_2X_{L_3}$$

$$\therefore R_1R_x = R_2R_3 \text{ and } R_x = \frac{R_2R_3}{R_1}$$

$$R_1X_{L_x} = R_2X_{L_3} \text{ and } R_1\omega L_x = R_2\omega L_3$$

$$\text{so that } L_x = \mathbf{\frac{R_2L_3}{R_1}}$$

32. a.

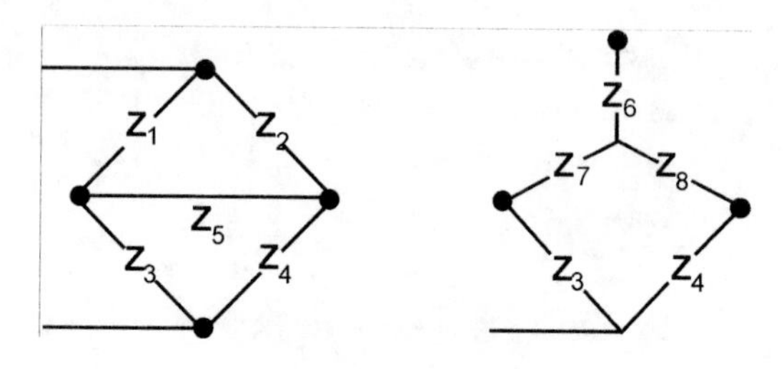

$\mathbf{Z}_1 = 8\ \Omega\ \angle{-90°} = -j8\ \Omega$
$\mathbf{Z}_2 = 4\ \Omega\ \angle 90° = +j4\ \Omega$
$\mathbf{Z}_3 = 8\ \Omega\ \angle 90° = +j8\ \Omega$
$\mathbf{Z}_4 = 6\ \Omega\ \angle{-90°} = -j6\ \Omega$
$\mathbf{Z}_5 = 5\ \Omega\ \angle 0°$

$$\mathbf{Z}_6 = \frac{\mathbf{Z}_1\mathbf{Z}_2}{\mathbf{Z}_1 + \mathbf{Z}_2 + \mathbf{Z}_5} = 5\ \Omega\ \angle 38.66°$$

$$\mathbf{Z}_7 = \frac{\mathbf{Z}_1\mathbf{Z}_5}{\mathbf{Z}_1 + \mathbf{Z}_2 + \mathbf{Z}_5} = 6.25\ \Omega\ \angle{-51.34°}$$

$$\mathbf{Z}_8 = \frac{\mathbf{Z}_2\mathbf{Z}_5}{\mathbf{Z}_1 + \mathbf{Z}_2 + \mathbf{Z}_5} = 3.125\ \Omega\ \angle 128.66°$$

$$\mathbf{Z}' = \mathbf{Z}_7 + \mathbf{Z}_3 = 3.9\ \Omega + j3.12\ \Omega = 4.99\ \Omega\ \angle 38.66°$$

$$\mathbf{Z}'' = \mathbf{Z}_8 + \mathbf{Z}_4 = -1.95\ \Omega - j3.56\ \Omega = 4.06\ \Omega\ \angle{-118.71°}$$

$$\mathbf{Z}' \parallel \mathbf{Z}'' = 10.13\ \Omega\ \angle{-67.33°} = 3.90\ \Omega - j9.35\ \Omega$$

$$\mathbf{Z}_T = \mathbf{Z}_6 + \mathbf{Z}' \parallel \mathbf{Z}'' = 7.80\ \Omega - j6.23\ \Omega = 9.98\ \Omega\ \angle{-38.61°}$$

$$\mathbf{I} = \frac{\mathbf{E}}{\mathbf{Z}_T} = \frac{120\text{ V}\ \angle 0°}{9.98\ \Omega\ \angle{-38.61°}} = \mathbf{12.02\ A\ \angle 38.61°}$$

b. $$\mathbf{Z}_Y = \frac{\mathbf{Z}_\Delta}{3} = \frac{12\ \Omega - j9\ \Omega}{3} = 4\ \Omega - j3\ \Omega$$

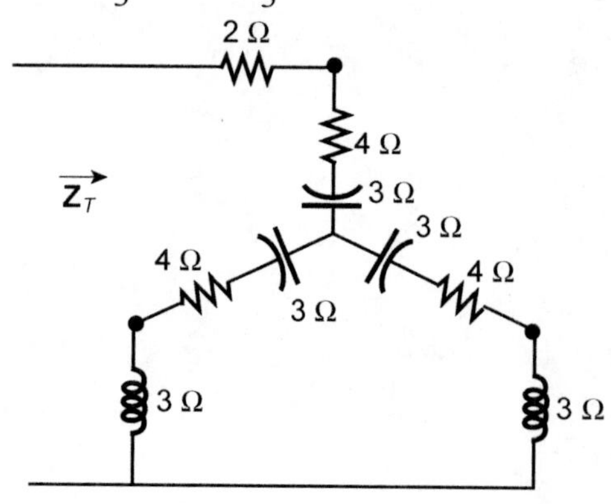

$$\mathbf{Z}_T = 2\,\Omega + 4\,\Omega + j3\,\Omega + [4\,\Omega - \cancel{j3}\,\Omega + \cancel{j3}\,\Omega] \parallel [4\,\Omega - \cancel{j3}\,\Omega + \cancel{j3}\,\Omega]$$
$$= 6\,\Omega - j3\,\Omega + 2\,\Omega$$
$$= 8\,\Omega - j3\,\Omega = 8.544\,\Omega \angle{-20.56^\circ}$$
$$\mathbf{I} = \frac{\mathbf{E}}{\mathbf{Z}_T} = \frac{60\text{ V}\angle 0^\circ}{8.544\,\Omega \angle -20.56^\circ} = \mathbf{7.02\text{ A}\angle 20.56^\circ}$$

33. a.

$$\mathbf{Z}_\Delta = 3\mathbf{Z}_Y = 3(3\,\Omega\angle 90^\circ) = 9\,\Omega\angle 90^\circ$$
$$\mathbf{Z} = 9\,\Omega\angle 90^\circ \parallel (12\,\Omega - j16\,\Omega)$$
$$= 9\,\Omega\angle 90^\circ \parallel 20\,\Omega\angle 53.13^\circ$$
$$= 12.96\,\Omega\angle 67.13^\circ$$

$$\mathbf{Z}_T = \mathbf{Z} \parallel 2\mathbf{Z} = \frac{2\mathbf{Z}^2}{\mathbf{Z} + 2\mathbf{Z}} = \frac{2}{3}\mathbf{Z} = \frac{2}{3}[12.96\,\Omega\angle 67.13^\circ] = 8.64\,\Omega\angle 67.13^\circ$$
$$\mathbf{I} = \frac{\mathbf{E}}{\mathbf{Z}_T} = \frac{100\text{ V}\angle 0^\circ}{8.64\,\Omega\angle 67.13^\circ} = \mathbf{11.57\text{ A}\angle{-67.13^\circ}}$$

b. $\mathbf{Z}_\Delta = 3\mathbf{Z}_Y = 3(5\,\Omega) = 15\,\Omega$

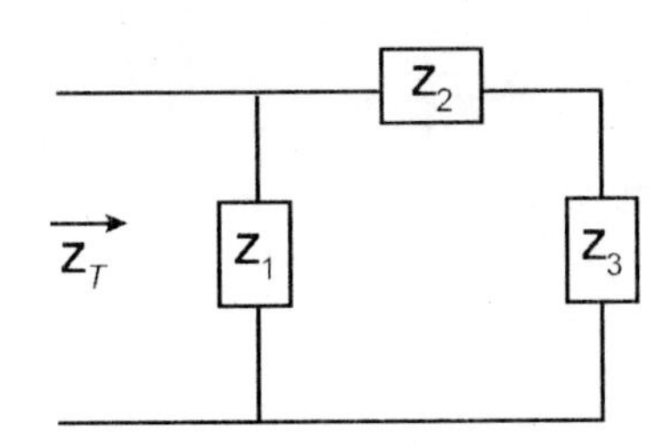

$$\mathbf{Z}_1 = 15\,\Omega\angle 0^\circ \parallel 5\,\Omega\angle{-90^\circ}$$
$$= 4.74\,\Omega\angle{-71.57^\circ}$$
$$\mathbf{Z}_2 = 15\,\Omega\angle 0^\circ \parallel 6\,\Omega\angle 90^\circ$$
$$= 5.57\,\Omega\angle 68.2^\circ = 2.07\,\Omega + j5.17\,\Omega$$
$$\mathbf{Z}_3 = \mathbf{Z}_1 = 4.74\,\Omega\angle{-71.57^\circ}$$
$$= 1.5\,\Omega - j4.5\,\Omega$$

$$\mathbf{Z}_T = \mathbf{Z}_1 \parallel (\mathbf{Z}_2 + \mathbf{Z}_3) = (4.74\,\Omega\angle{-71.57^\circ}) \parallel (2.07\,\Omega + j5.17\,\Omega + 1.5\,\Omega - j4.5\,\Omega)$$
$$= (4.74\,\Omega\angle{-7.57^\circ}) \parallel (3.63\,\Omega\angle 10.63^\circ)$$
$$= 2.71\,\Omega\angle{-23.87^\circ}$$
$$\mathbf{I} = \frac{\mathbf{E}}{\mathbf{Z}_T} = \frac{100\text{ V}\angle 0^\circ}{2.71\,\Omega\angle -23.87^\circ} = \mathbf{36.9\text{ A}\angle 23.87^\circ}$$

Chapter 18

1. a.

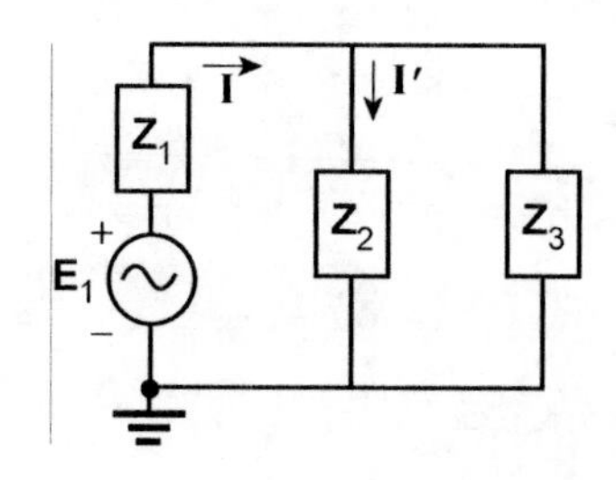

$\mathbf{Z}_1 = 3\ \Omega\ \angle 0°,\ \mathbf{Z}_2 = 8\ \Omega\ \angle 90°,\ \mathbf{Z}_3 = 6\ \Omega\ \angle -90°$

$\mathbf{Z}_2 \parallel \mathbf{Z}_3 = 8\ \Omega\ \angle 90° \parallel 6\ \Omega\ \angle -90° = 24\ \Omega\ \angle -90°$

$$\mathbf{I} = \frac{\mathbf{E}_1}{\mathbf{Z}_1 + \mathbf{Z}_2 \parallel \mathbf{Z}_3} = \frac{30\text{ V}\ \angle 30°}{3\ \Omega - j24\ \Omega} = 1.24\text{ A}\ \angle 112.875°$$

$$\mathbf{I}' = \frac{\mathbf{Z}_3\mathbf{I}}{\mathbf{Z}_2 + \mathbf{Z}_3} = \frac{(6\ \Omega\ \angle -90°)(1.24\text{ A}\ \angle 112.875°)}{2\ \Omega\ \angle 90°} = 3.72\text{ A}\ \angle -67.125°$$

$\mathbf{Z}_1 \parallel \mathbf{Z}_2 = 3\ \Omega\ \angle 0° \parallel 8\ \Omega\ \angle 90° = 2.809\ \Omega\ \angle 20.556°$

$$\mathbf{I} = \frac{\mathbf{E}_2}{\mathbf{Z}_3 + \mathbf{Z}_1 \parallel \mathbf{Z}_2} = \frac{60\text{ V}\ \angle 10°}{-j6\ \Omega + 2.630\ \Omega + j0.986\ \Omega}$$

$= 10.597\text{ A}\ \angle 72.322°$

$$\mathbf{I}'' = \frac{\mathbf{Z}_1\mathbf{I}}{\mathbf{Z}_1 + \mathbf{Z}_2} = \frac{(3\ \Omega\ \angle 0°)(10.597\text{ A}\ \angle 72.322°)}{3\ \Omega + j8\ \Omega} = 3.721\text{ A}\ \angle 2.878°$$

$\mathbf{I}_{Z_1} = \mathbf{I}' + \mathbf{I}'' = 3.72\text{ A}\ \angle -67.125° + 3.721\text{ A}\ \angle 2.878°$

$= 1.446\text{ A} - j3.427\text{ A} + 3.716\text{ A} + j0.187\text{ A}$

$= 5.162\text{ A} - j3.24\text{ A}$

$= \mathbf{6.09\ A\ \angle -32.12°}$

b.

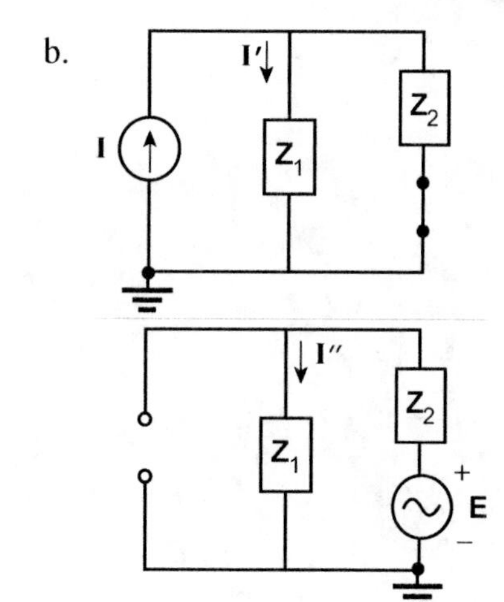

$\mathbf{Z}_1 = 8\ \Omega\ \angle 90°,\ \mathbf{Z}_2 = 5\ \Omega\ \angle -90°$

$\mathbf{I} = 0.3\text{ A}\ \angle 60°,\ \mathbf{E} = 10\text{ V}\ \angle 0°$

$$\mathbf{I}' = \frac{\mathbf{Z}_2\mathbf{I}}{\mathbf{Z}_2 + \mathbf{Z}_1} = \frac{(5\ \Omega\ \angle -90°)(0.3\text{ A}\ \angle 60°)}{+j8\ \Omega - j5\ \Omega}$$

$= 0.5\text{A}\ \angle -120°$

$$\mathbf{I}'' = \frac{\mathbf{E}}{\mathbf{Z}_1 + \mathbf{Z}_2} = \frac{10\text{ V}\ \angle 0°}{3\ \Omega\ \angle 90°} = 3.33\text{ A}\ \angle -90°$$

$\mathbf{I}_{Z_1} = \mathbf{I}_{Z_1} = \mathbf{I}' + \mathbf{I}''$

$= 0.5\text{ A}\ \angle -120° + 3.33\text{ A}\ \angle -90°$

$= -0.25\text{ A} - j0.433\text{ A} - j3.33\text{ A}$

$= -0.25\text{ A} - j3.763\text{ A}$

$= \mathbf{3.77\ A\ \angle -93.8°}$

2. a. $\mathbf{E}_1$:

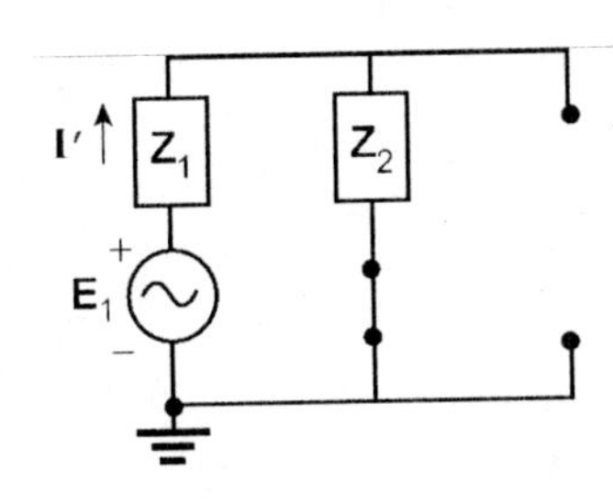

$\mathbf{E}_1 = 20\text{ V}\angle 0°$, $\quad \mathbf{Z}_1 = 4\ \Omega + j3\ \Omega = 5\ \Omega\angle 36.87°$

$\mathbf{Z}_2 = 1\ \Omega\angle 0°$

$$\mathbf{I}' = \frac{\mathbf{E}_1}{\mathbf{Z}_1 + \mathbf{Z}_2} = \frac{20\text{ V}\angle 0°}{4\ \Omega + j3\ \Omega + 1\ \Omega}$$

$$= 3.43\text{ A}\angle -30.96°$$

$\mathbf{E}_2$:

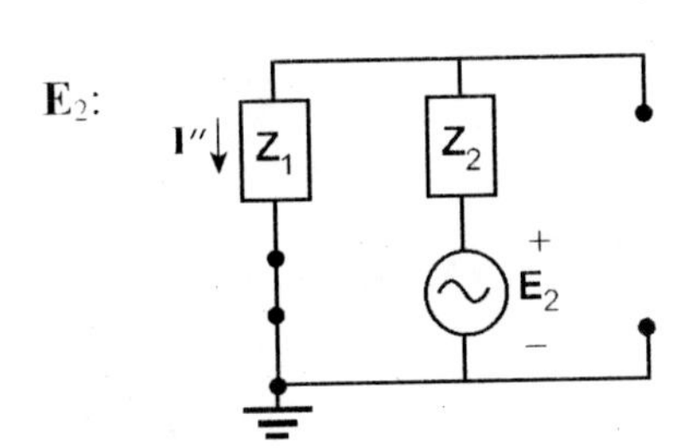

$$\mathbf{I}'' = \frac{\mathbf{E}_2}{\mathbf{Z}_1 + \mathbf{Z}_2} = \frac{120\text{ V}\angle 0°}{5.83\ \Omega\angle 30.96°}$$

$$= 20.58\text{ A}\angle -30.96°$$

$\mathbf{I}$:

$$\mathbf{I}''' = \frac{\mathbf{Z}_2\mathbf{I}}{\mathbf{Z}_2 + \mathbf{Z}_1} = \frac{(1\ \Omega\angle 0°)(0.5\text{ A}\angle 60°)}{5.83\ \Omega\angle 30.96°}$$

$$= 0.0858\text{ A}\angle 29.04°$$

$$\uparrow\mathbf{I}_L = \mathbf{I}' - \mathbf{I}'' - \mathbf{I}'''$$

$$= (3.43\text{ A}\angle -30.96°) - (20.58\text{ A}\angle -30.96°) - (0.0858\text{ A}\angle 29.04°)$$

$$= \mathbf{17.20\ A\angle 149.30°} \text{ or } \mathbf{17.20\ A\angle -30.70°}\downarrow$$

b. $\mathbf{E}$:

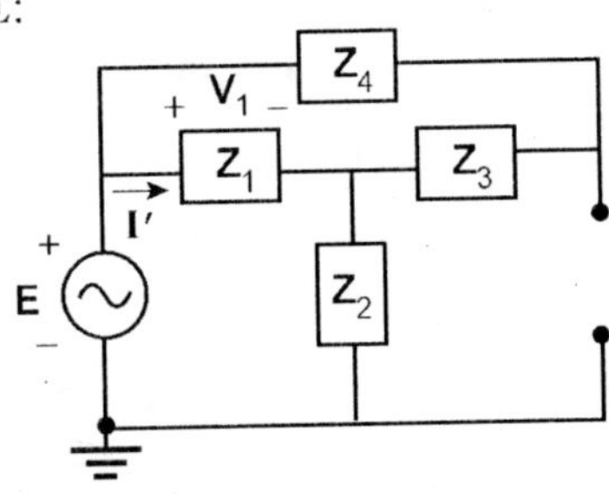

$\mathbf{Z}_1 = 3\ \Omega\angle 90°$, $\mathbf{Z}_2 = 7\ \Omega\angle -90°$

$\mathbf{E} = 10\text{ V}\angle 90°$

$\mathbf{Z}_3 = 6\ \Omega\angle -90°$, $\mathbf{Z}_4 = 4\ \Omega\angle 0°$

$\mathbf{Z}' = \mathbf{Z}_1 \| (\mathbf{Z}_3 + \mathbf{Z}_4)$

$= 3\ \Omega\angle 90° \| (4\ \Omega - j6\ \Omega)$

$= 3\ \Omega\angle 90° \| 7.21\ \Omega\angle -56.31°$

$= 4.33\ \Omega\angle 70.56°$

$$\mathbf{V}_1 = \frac{\mathbf{Z}'\mathbf{E}}{\mathbf{Z}' + \mathbf{Z}_2}$$

$$= \frac{(4.33\ \Omega\angle 70.56°)(10\text{ V}\angle 90°)}{(1.44\ \Omega + j4.08\ \Omega) - j7\Omega}$$

$$= \frac{43.3\text{ V}\angle 160.56°}{3.26\angle -63.75°} = 13.28\text{ V}\angle 224.31°$$

$$\mathbf{I}' = \frac{\mathbf{V}_1}{\mathbf{Z}_1} = \frac{13.28\text{ V}\angle 224.31°}{3\ \Omega\angle 90°}$$

$$= 4.43\text{ A}\angle 134.31°$$

I:

$$\mathbf{Z}'' = \mathbf{Z}_3 + \mathbf{Z}_1 \| \mathbf{Z}_2$$
$$= -j6\ \Omega + 3\ \Omega\ \angle 90^\circ \parallel 7\ \Omega\ \angle -90^\circ$$
$$= -j6\ \Omega + 5.25\ \Omega\ \angle 90^\circ$$
$$= -j6\ \Omega + j5.25\ \Omega$$
$$= -j0.75\ \Omega = 0.75\ \Omega \angle -90^\circ$$

CDR: $$\mathbf{I}_3 = \frac{\mathbf{Z}_4 \mathbf{I}}{\mathbf{Z}_4 + \mathbf{Z}''} = \frac{(4\ \Omega \angle 0^\circ)(0.6\ \text{A} \angle 120^\circ)}{4\ \Omega - j0.75\ \Omega} = \frac{2.4\ \text{A} \angle 120^\circ}{4.07 \angle -10.62^\circ}$$
$$= 0.59\ \text{A} \angle 130.62^\circ$$
$$\mathbf{I}'' = \frac{\mathbf{Z}_2 \mathbf{I}_3}{\mathbf{Z}_2 + \mathbf{Z}_1} = \frac{(7\ \Omega \angle -90^\circ)(0.59\ \text{A} \angle 130.62^\circ)}{-j7\ \Omega + j3\ \Omega} = \frac{4.13\ \text{A} \angle 40.62^\circ}{4 \angle -90^\circ}$$
$$= 1.03\ \text{A} \angle 130.62^\circ$$

$\mathbf{I}_L = \mathbf{I}' - \mathbf{I}''$ (direction of $\mathbf{I}'$)
$$= 4.43\ \text{A} \angle 134.31^\circ - 1.03\ \text{A} \angle 130.62^\circ$$
$$= (-3.09\ \text{A} + j3.17\ \text{A}) - (-0.67\ \text{A} + j0.78\ \text{A}) = -2.42\ \text{A} + j2.39\ \text{A}$$
$$= \mathbf{3.40\ A \angle 135.36^\circ}$$

3. DC:

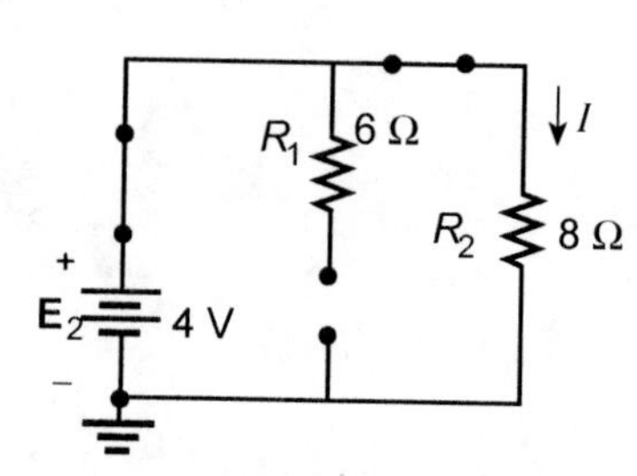

$$I_{DC} = \frac{4\ \text{V}}{8\ \Omega} = 0.5\ \text{A}$$

AC:

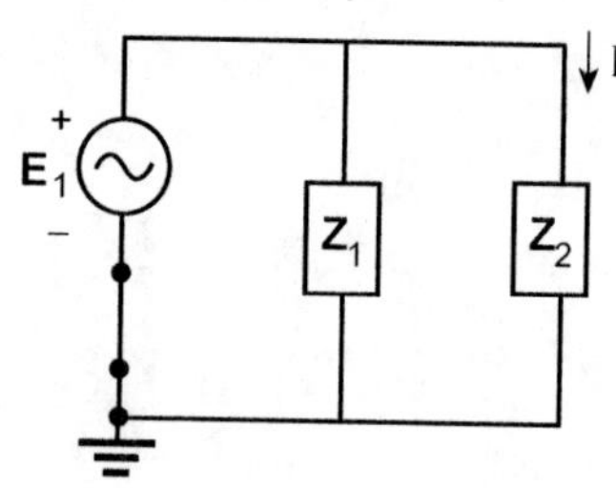

$$\mathbf{Z}_2 = R_2 + jX_L = 8\ \Omega + j4\ \Omega$$
$$= 8.944\ \Omega \angle 26.565^\circ$$
$$\mathbf{I} = \frac{\mathbf{E}_1}{\mathbf{Z}_2} = \frac{10\ \text{V} \angle 0^\circ}{8.944\ \Omega \angle 26.565^\circ}$$
$$= 1.118\ \text{A} \angle -26.565^\circ$$

$$\mathbf{I = 0.5\ A + 1.118\ A \angle -26.57^\circ}$$
$$i = \mathbf{0.5\ A + 1.58\ sin(\omega t - 26.57^\circ)}$$

4. DC:

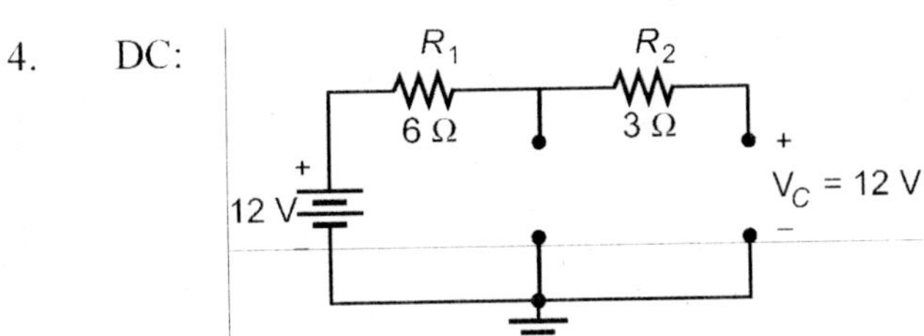

AC:

R_1 R_2 I_C
6 Ω 3 Ω
+
I X_C 1 Ω V_C
–

$$\mathbf{I}_C = \frac{(6\,\Omega\,\angle 0^\circ)(\mathbf{I})}{6\,\Omega + 3\,\Omega - j1\,\Omega}$$
$$= \frac{(6\,\Omega\,\angle 0^\circ)(4\text{ A}\,\angle 0^\circ)}{9\,\Omega - j1\,\Omega}$$
$$= \frac{24\text{ A}\,\angle 0^\circ}{9.055\angle -6.34^\circ}$$
$$= 2.65\text{ A}\,\angle 6.34^\circ$$

$\mathbf{V}_C = \mathbf{I}_C\mathbf{X}_C = (2.65\text{ A}\,\angle 6.34^\circ)(1\,\Omega\,\angle -90^\circ) = 2.65\text{ V}\,\angle -83.66^\circ$

$= \mathbf{12\text{ V} + 2.65\text{ V}\,\angle -83.66^\circ}$

$\upsilon_C = \mathbf{12\text{ V} + 3.75\sin(\omega t - 83.66^\circ)}$

5.

I Z_1 Z_2 Z_3 I′

$\mathbf{E} = 20\text{ V}\,\angle 0^\circ$
$\mathbf{Z}_1 = 10\text{ k}\Omega\,\angle 0^\circ$
$\mathbf{Z}_2 = 5\text{ k}\Omega - j5\text{ k}\Omega$
$= 7.071\text{ k}\Omega\,\angle -45^\circ$
$\mathbf{Z}_3 = 5\text{ k}\Omega\,\angle 90^\circ$
$\mathbf{I} = 5\text{ mA}\,\angle 0^\circ$

$\mathbf{Z}' = \mathbf{Z}_1 \parallel \mathbf{Z}_2 = 10\text{ k}\Omega\,\angle 0^\circ \parallel 7.071\text{ k}\Omega\,\angle -45^\circ = 4.472\text{ k}\Omega\,\angle -26.57^\circ$

(CDR) $$\mathbf{I}' = \frac{\mathbf{Z}'\mathbf{I}}{\mathbf{Z}' + \mathbf{Z}_3} = \frac{(4.472\text{ k}\Omega\,\angle -26.57^\circ)(5\text{ mA}\,\angle 0^\circ)}{4\text{ k}\Omega - j2\text{ k}\Omega + j5\text{ k}\Omega} = \frac{22.36\text{ mA}\,\angle -26.57^\circ}{5\,\angle 36.87^\circ}$$
$$= 4.472\text{ mA}\,\angle -63.44^\circ$$

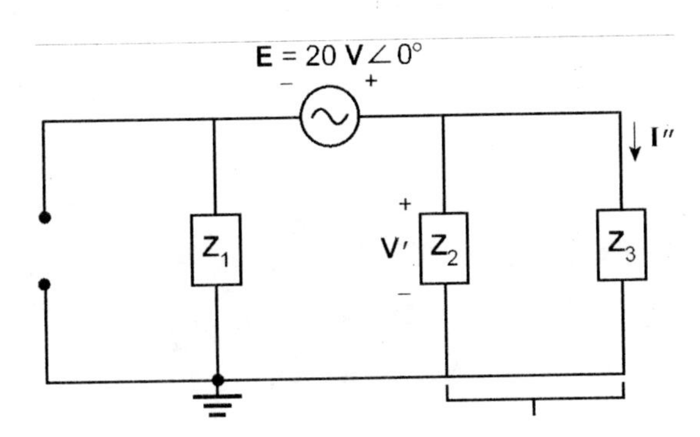

$\mathbf{Z}'' = \mathbf{Z}_2 \parallel \mathbf{Z}_3$
$= 7.071\text{ k}\Omega\,\angle -45^\circ \parallel 5\text{ k}\Omega\,\angle 90^\circ$
$= 7.071\text{ k}\Omega\,\angle 45^\circ$

(VDR) $\mathbf{V}' = \dfrac{\mathbf{Z}''\mathbf{E}}{\mathbf{Z}''+\mathbf{Z}_1} = \dfrac{(7.071\text{ k}\Omega\angle 45°)(20\text{ V}\angle 0°)}{(5\text{ k}\Omega + j5\text{ k}\Omega)+(10\text{ k}\Omega)} = \dfrac{141.42\text{ V}\angle 45°}{15.81\angle 18.435°}$

$= 8.945\text{ V}\angle 26.565°$

$\mathbf{I}'' = \dfrac{\mathbf{V}'}{\mathbf{Z}_3} = \dfrac{8.945\text{ V}\angle 26.565°}{5\text{ k}\Omega\angle 90°} = 1.789\text{ mA}\angle -63.435° = 0.8\text{ mA} - j1.6\text{ mA}$

$\mathbf{I} = \mathbf{I}' + \mathbf{I}'' = (2\text{ mA} - j4\text{ mA}) + (0.8\text{ mA} - j1.6\text{ mA}) = 2.8\text{ mA} - j5.6\text{ mA}$

$= \mathbf{6.26\text{ mA}\angle -63.43°}$

6.

$\mathbf{Z}_1 = 20\text{ k}\Omega\angle 0°$
$\mathbf{Z}_2 = 10\text{ k}\Omega\angle 90°$
$\mathbf{I} = 2\text{ mA}\angle 0°$
$\mathbf{E} = 10\text{ V}\angle 0°$

$$\mathbf{I}' = \frac{\mathbf{Z}_1(h\mathbf{I})}{\mathbf{Z}_1+\mathbf{Z}_2} = \frac{(20\text{ k}\Omega\angle 0°)(100)(2\text{ mA}\angle 0°)}{20\text{ k}\Omega + j10\text{ k}\Omega} = 0.179\text{ A}\angle -26.57°$$

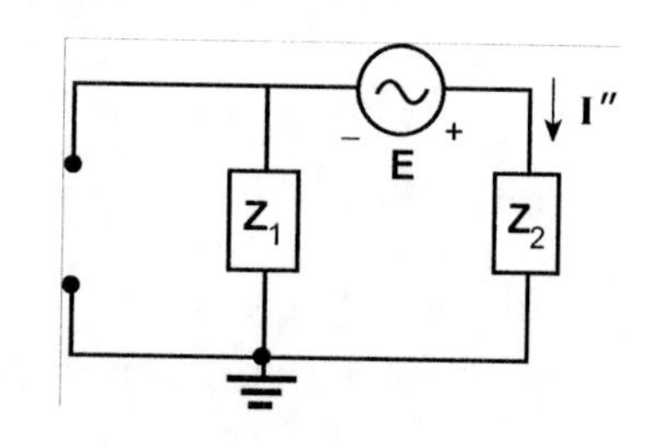

$\mathbf{I}'' = \dfrac{\mathbf{E}}{\mathbf{Z}_1+\mathbf{Z}_2} = \dfrac{10\text{ V}\angle 0°}{22.36\text{ k}\Omega\angle 26.57°}$

$= 0.447\text{ mA}\angle -26.57°$

$\mathbf{I}_L = \mathbf{I}' - \mathbf{I}''$ (direction of $\mathbf{I}'$)

$= 179\text{ mA}\angle -26.57° - 0.447\text{ mA}\angle -26.57°$

$= \mathbf{178.55\text{ mA}\angle -26.57°}$

7. $\mu\mathbf{V}$:

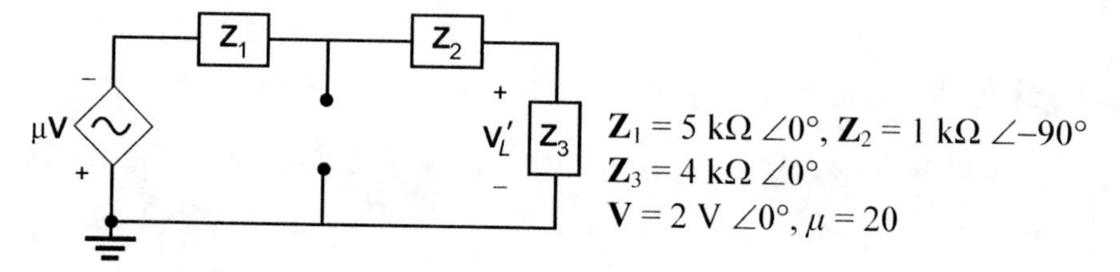

$\mathbf{Z}_1 = 5\text{ k}\Omega\angle 0°$, $\mathbf{Z}_2 = 1\text{ k}\Omega\angle -90°$
$\mathbf{Z}_3 = 4\text{ k}\Omega\angle 0°$
$\mathbf{V} = 2\text{ V}\angle 0°$, $\mu = 20$

$$\mathbf{V}'_L = \frac{-\mathbf{Z}_3(\mu\mathbf{V})}{\mathbf{Z}_1+\mathbf{Z}_2+\mathbf{Z}_3} = \frac{-(4\text{ k}\Omega\angle 0°)(20)(2\text{ V}\angle 0°)}{5\text{ k}\Omega - j1\text{ k}\Omega + 4\text{ k}\Omega} = -17.67\text{ V}\angle 6.34°$$

I:

CDR: $\mathbf{I}' = \dfrac{\mathbf{Z}_1\mathbf{I}}{\mathbf{Z}_1+\mathbf{Z}_2+\mathbf{Z}_3}$

$= \dfrac{(5\text{ k}\Omega\angle 0°)(2\text{ mA}\angle 0°)}{9.056\text{ k}\Omega\angle -6.34°}$

$= 1.104\text{ mA}\angle 6.34°$

$\mathbf{V}''_L = -\mathbf{I}'\mathbf{Z}_3 = -(1.104\text{ mA}\angle 6.34°)(4\text{ k}\Omega\angle 0°) = -4.416\text{ V}\angle 6.34°$

$\mathbf{V}_L = \mathbf{V}'_L + \mathbf{V}''_L = -17.67\text{ V}\angle 6.34° - 4.416\text{ V}\angle 6.34° = \mathbf{-22.09\text{ V}\angle 6.34°}$

8.

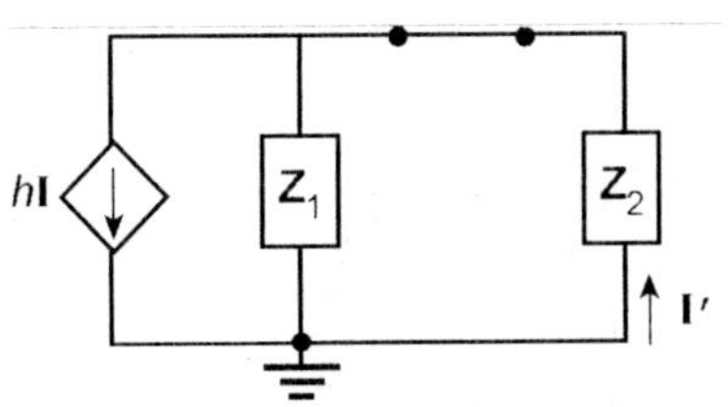

$\mathbf{Z}_1 = 20\text{ k}\Omega \angle 0°$
$\mathbf{Z}_2 = 5\text{ k}\Omega + j5\text{ k}\Omega$

$$\mathbf{I}' = \frac{\mathbf{Z}_1(h\mathbf{I})}{\mathbf{Z}_1 + \mathbf{Z}_2} = \frac{(20\text{ k}\Omega \angle 0°)(100)(1\text{ mA} \angle 0°)}{20\text{ k}\Omega + 5\text{ k}\Omega + j5\text{ k}\Omega} = 78.45\text{ mA} \angle -11.31°$$

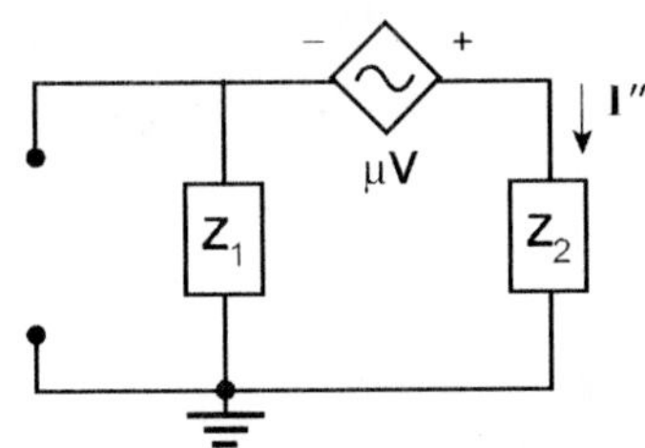

$$\mathbf{I}'' = \frac{\mu\mathbf{V}}{\mathbf{Z}_1 + \mathbf{Z}_2} = \frac{(20)(10\text{ V} \angle 0°)}{25.495\text{ k}\Omega \angle 11.31°}$$
$$= 7.845\text{ mA} \angle -11.31°$$

$\mathbf{I}_L = \mathbf{I}' - \mathbf{I}''$ (direction of $\mathbf{I}'$)
$= 78.45\text{ mA} \angle -11.31° - 7.845\text{ mA} \angle -11.31°$
$= \mathbf{70.61\text{ mA} \angle -11.31°}$

9.

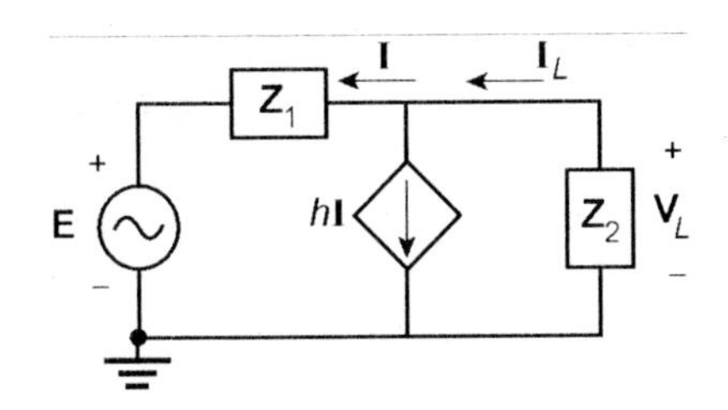

$\mathbf{Z}_1 = 2\text{ k}\Omega \angle 0°$, $\mathbf{Z}_2 = 2\text{ k}\Omega \angle 0°$
$\mathbf{V}_L = -\mathbf{I}_L\mathbf{Z}_2$
$\mathbf{I}_L = h\mathbf{I} + \mathbf{I} = (h + 1)\mathbf{I}$
$\mathbf{V}_L = -(h + 1)\mathbf{I}\mathbf{Z}_2$
and by KVL: $\mathbf{V}_L = \mathbf{I}\mathbf{Z}_1 + \mathbf{E}$
so that $\mathbf{I} = \dfrac{\mathbf{V}_L - \mathbf{E}}{\mathbf{Z}_1}$

$$\mathbf{V}_L = -(h + 1)\mathbf{I}\mathbf{Z}_2 = -(h + 1)\left[\frac{\mathbf{V}_L - \mathbf{E}}{\mathbf{Z}_1}\right]\mathbf{Z}_2$$

Subt. for $\mathbf{Z}_1$, $\mathbf{Z}_2$

$$\mathbf{V}_L = -(h + 1)(\mathbf{V}_L - \mathbf{E})$$
$$\mathbf{V}_L(2 + h) = \mathbf{E}(h + 1)$$
$$\mathbf{V}_L = \frac{(h + 1)}{(h + 2)}\mathbf{E} = \frac{51}{52}(20\text{ V} \angle 53°) = \mathbf{19.62\text{ V} \angle 53°}$$

10. $\mathbf{I}_1$:

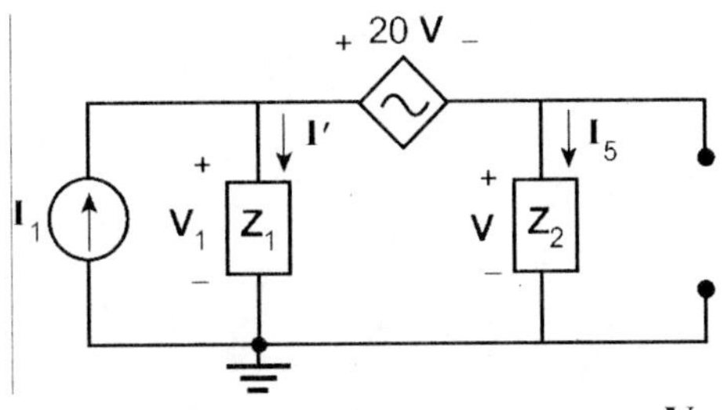

$\mathbf{I}_1 = 1\text{ mA} \angle 0°$
$\mathbf{Z}_1 = 2\text{ k}\Omega \angle 0°$
$\mathbf{Z}_2 = 5\text{ k}\Omega \angle 0°$

KVL: $\mathbf{V}_1 - 20\mathbf{V} - \mathbf{V} = 0$

$\mathbf{V}_1 = 21\mathbf{V}$

$\mathbf{I}' = \dfrac{\mathbf{V}_1}{\mathbf{Z}_1}$ $\therefore$ $\mathbf{I}' = \dfrac{21\mathbf{V}}{\mathbf{Z}_1}$ or $\mathbf{V} = \dfrac{\mathbf{Z}_1}{21}\mathbf{I}'$

$$\mathbf{V} = \mathbf{I}_5\mathbf{Z}_2 = [\mathbf{I}_1 - \mathbf{I}']\mathbf{Z}_2$$

$$\frac{\mathbf{Z}_1}{21}\mathbf{I}' = \mathbf{I}_1\mathbf{Z}_2 - \mathbf{I}'\mathbf{Z}_2$$

$$\mathbf{I}'\left[\frac{\mathbf{Z}_1}{21} + \mathbf{Z}_2\right] = \mathbf{I}_1\mathbf{Z}_2$$

and $\mathbf{I}' = \dfrac{\mathbf{Z}_2}{\dfrac{\mathbf{Z}_1}{21} + \mathbf{Z}_2}[\mathbf{I}_1] = \dfrac{(5\text{ k}\Omega\angle 0°)(1\text{ mA}\angle 0°)}{\left(\dfrac{2\text{ k}\Omega\angle 0°}{21}\right) + 5\text{ k}\Omega\angle 0°} = 0.981\text{ mA}\angle 0°$

$\mathbf{I}_2$:

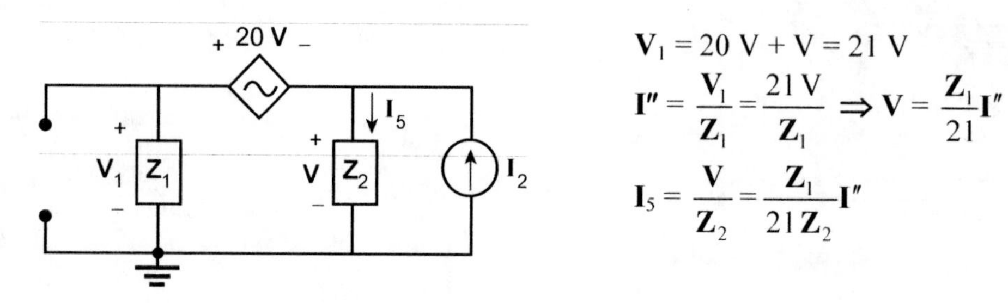

$$\mathbf{V}_1 = 20\text{ V} + \mathbf{V} = 21\text{ V}$$

$$\mathbf{I}'' = \frac{\mathbf{V}_1}{\mathbf{Z}_1} = \frac{21\text{ V}}{\mathbf{Z}_1} \Rightarrow \mathbf{V} = \frac{\mathbf{Z}_1}{21}\mathbf{I}''$$

$$\mathbf{I}_5 = \frac{\mathbf{V}}{\mathbf{Z}_2} = \frac{\mathbf{Z}_1}{21\mathbf{Z}_2}\mathbf{I}''$$

$$\mathbf{I}'' = \mathbf{I}_2 - \mathbf{I}_5 = \mathbf{I}_2 - \frac{\mathbf{Z}_1}{21\mathbf{Z}_2}\mathbf{I}''$$

$$\mathbf{I}''\left[1 + \frac{\mathbf{Z}_1}{21\mathbf{Z}_2}\right] = \mathbf{I}_2$$

$$\mathbf{I}'' = \frac{\mathbf{I}_2}{1 + \dfrac{\mathbf{Z}_1}{21\mathbf{Z}_2}} = \frac{2\text{ mA}\angle 0°}{1 + \dfrac{2\text{ k}\Omega}{21(5\text{ k}\Omega)}} = 1.963\text{ mA}\angle 0°$$

$$\mathbf{I} = \mathbf{I}' + \mathbf{I}'' = 0.981\text{ mA}\angle 0° + 1.963\text{ mA}\angle 0°$$
$$= \mathbf{2.94\text{ mA}\angle 0°}$$

11. $\mathbf{E}_1$:

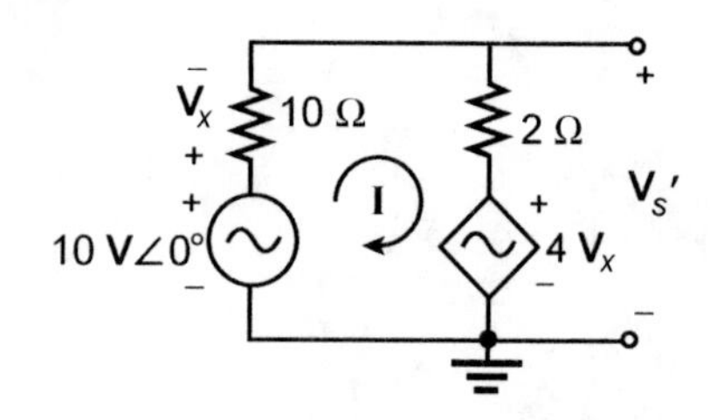

$$10\text{ V}\angle 0° - \mathbf{I}\,10\,\Omega - \mathbf{I}\,2\,\Omega - 4\,\mathbf{V}_x = 0$$
with $\mathbf{V}_x = \mathbf{I}\,10\,\Omega$

Solving for **I**:

$$\mathbf{I} = \frac{10\text{ V}\angle 0°}{52\,\Omega} = 192.31\text{ mA}\angle 0°$$

$$\mathbf{V}_s' = 10\text{ V}\angle 0° - \mathbf{I}(10\,\Omega) = 10\text{ V} - (192.31\text{ mA}\angle 0°)(10\,\Omega\angle 0°) = 8.08\text{ V}\angle 0°$$

I:

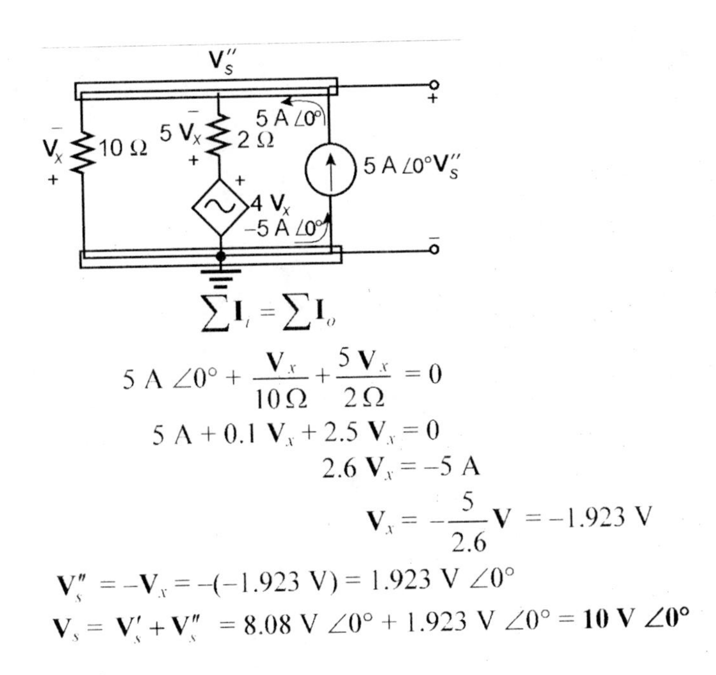

$$\sum \mathbf{I}_i = \sum \mathbf{I}_o$$

$$5 \text{ A } \angle 0° + \frac{\mathbf{V}_x}{10\,\Omega} + \frac{5\,\mathbf{V}_x}{2\,\Omega} = 0$$

$$5 \text{ A} + 0.1\,\mathbf{V}_x + 2.5\,\mathbf{V}_x = 0$$

$$2.6\,\mathbf{V}_x = -5 \text{ A}$$

$$\mathbf{V}_x = -\frac{5}{2.6}\mathbf{V} = -1.923 \text{ V}$$

$$\mathbf{V}_s'' = -\mathbf{V}_x = -(-1.923 \text{ V}) = 1.923 \text{ V } \angle 0°$$

$$\mathbf{V}_s = \mathbf{V}_s' + \mathbf{V}_s'' = 8.08 \text{ V } \angle 0° + 1.923 \text{ V } \angle 0° = \mathbf{10 \text{ V } \angle 0°}$$

12. a. $\mathbf{Z}_{Th}$:

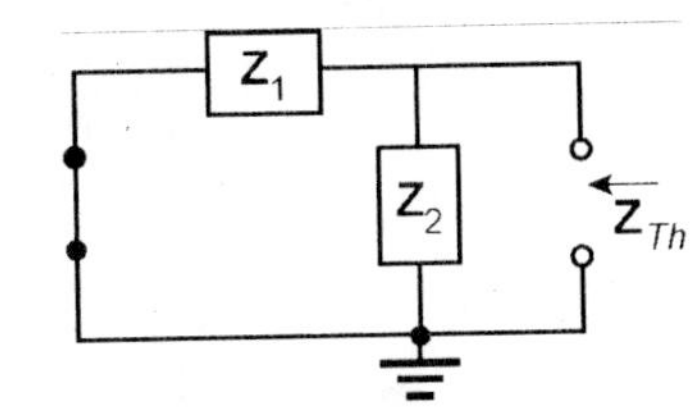

$\mathbf{Z}_1 = 3\ \Omega\ \angle 0°$, $\mathbf{Z}_2 = 4\ \Omega\ \angle 90°$

$\mathbf{E} = 100 \text{ V } \angle 0°$

$$\mathbf{Z}_{Th} = \mathbf{Z}_1 \parallel \mathbf{Z}_2 = (3\ \Omega\ \angle 0° \parallel 4\ \Omega\ \angle 90°)$$

$$= \mathbf{2.4\ \Omega\ \angle 36.87° = 1.92\ \Omega + \mathit{j}1.44\ \Omega}$$

$\mathbf{E}_{Th}$:

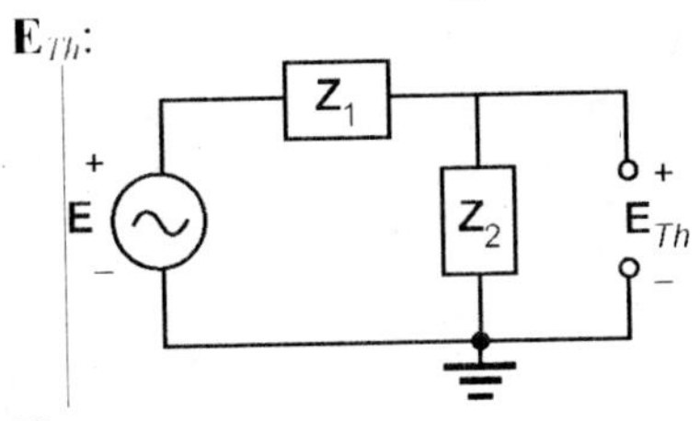

$$\mathbf{E}_{Th} = \frac{\mathbf{Z}_2\mathbf{E}}{\mathbf{Z}_2 + \mathbf{Z}_1} = \frac{(4\ \Omega\ \angle 90°)(100 \text{ V } \angle 0°)}{5\ \Omega\ \angle 53.13°}$$

$$= \mathbf{80 \text{ V } \angle 36.87°}$$

b. $\mathbf{Z}_{Th}$:

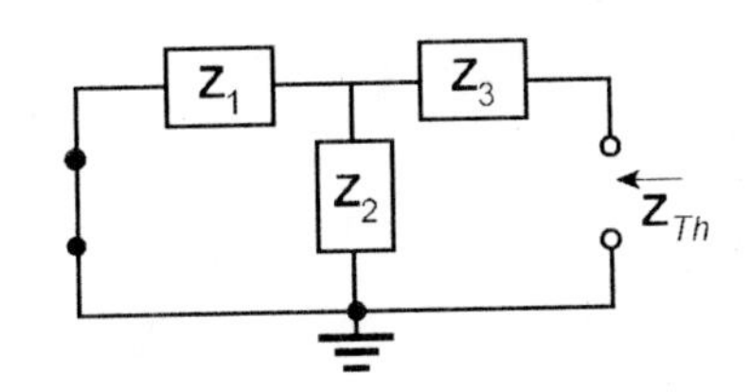

$$\mathbf{Z}_{Th} = \mathbf{Z}_3 + \mathbf{Z}_1 \parallel \mathbf{Z}_2$$

$$= +j6 \text{ k}\Omega + (2 \text{ k}\Omega\ \angle 0° \parallel 3 \text{ k}\Omega\ \angle -90°)$$

$$= +j6 \text{ k}\Omega + 1.664 \text{ k}\Omega\ \angle -33.69°$$

$$= +j6 \text{ k}\Omega + 1.385 \text{ k}\Omega - j0.923 \text{ k}\Omega$$

$$= 1.385 \text{ k}\Omega + j5.077 \text{ k}\Omega$$

$$= \mathbf{5.26 \text{ k}\Omega\ \angle 74.74°}$$

$\mathbf{E}_{Th}$:

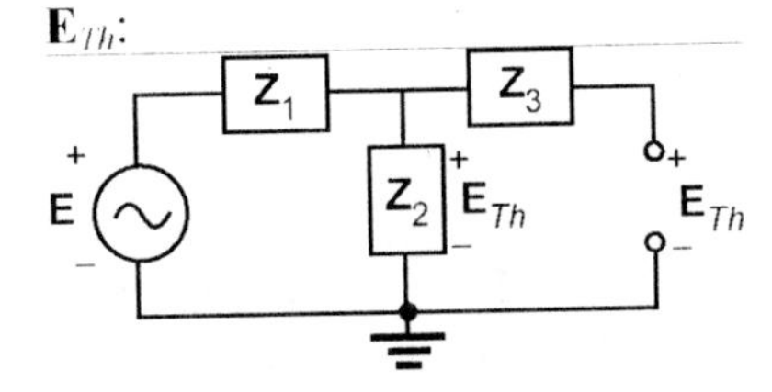

$$\mathbf{E}_{Th} = \frac{\mathbf{Z}_2\mathbf{E}}{\mathbf{Z}_2 + \mathbf{Z}_1} = \frac{(3 \text{ k}\Omega\ \angle -90°)(20 \text{ V } \angle 0°)}{2 \text{ k}\Omega - j3 \text{ k}\Omega}$$

$$= \frac{60 \text{ V } \angle -90°}{3.606\ \angle -56.31°} = \mathbf{16.64 \text{ V } \angle -33.69°}$$

13. a. From #27. $\mathbf{Z}_{Th} = \mathbf{Z}_1 \parallel \mathbf{Z}_2$

$\mathbf{Z}_{Th} = \mathbf{Z}_N = \mathbf{21.31\ \Omega\ \angle 32.2°}$

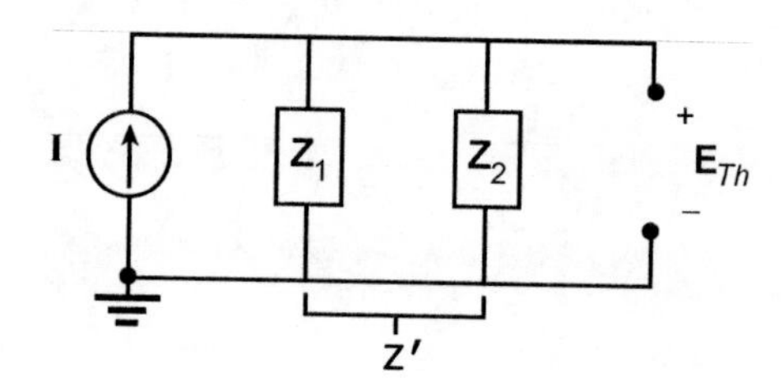

$$\mathbf{E}_{Th} = \mathbf{IZ}' = \mathbf{IZ}_{Th}$$
$$= (0.1\text{ A}\ \angle 0°)(21.31\ \Omega\ \angle 32.12°)$$
$$= \mathbf{2.13\ V\ \angle 32.2°}$$

b. From #27. $\mathbf{Z}_{Th} = \mathbf{Z}_N = \mathbf{6.81\ \Omega\ \angle{-54.23°}} = \mathbf{3.98\ \Omega - \mathit{j}5.53\ \Omega}$

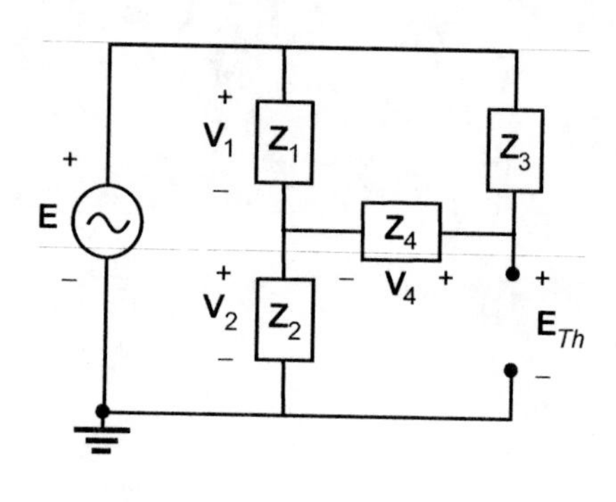

$\mathbf{Z}_1 = 2\ \Omega\ \angle 0°$, $\mathbf{Z}_3 = 8\ \Omega\ \angle{-90°}$

$\mathbf{Z}_2 = 4\ \Omega\ \angle 90°$, $\mathbf{Z}_4 = 10\ \Omega\ \angle 0°$

$\mathbf{E} = 50\text{ V}\ \angle 0°$

$\mathbf{E}_{Th} = \mathbf{V}_2 + \mathbf{V}_4$

$$\mathbf{V}_2 = \frac{\mathbf{Z}_2\mathbf{E}}{\mathbf{Z}_2 + \mathbf{Z}_1 \parallel (\mathbf{Z}_3 + \mathbf{Z}_4)}$$
$$= \frac{(4\ \Omega\ \angle 90°)(50\text{ V}\ \angle 0°)}{+j4\ \Omega + 2\ \Omega\ \angle 0° \parallel (10\ \Omega - j8\ \Omega)}$$
$$= 47.248\text{ V}\ \angle 24.7°$$

$$\mathbf{V}_1 = \mathbf{E} - \mathbf{V}_2 = 50\text{ V}\ \angle 0° - 47.248\text{ V}\ \angle 24.7° = 20.972\text{ V}\ \angle{-70.285°}$$
$$\mathbf{V}_4 = \frac{\mathbf{Z}_4\mathbf{V}_1}{\mathbf{Z}_4 + \mathbf{Z}_3} = \frac{(10\ \Omega\ \angle 0°)(20.972\text{ V}\ \angle{-70.285°})}{10\ \Omega - j8\ \Omega} = 16.377\text{ V}\ \angle{-31.625°}$$
$$\mathbf{E}_{Th} = \mathbf{V}_2 + \mathbf{V}_4 = 47.248\text{ V}\ \angle 24.7° + 16.377\text{ V}\ \angle{-31.625°}$$
$$= (42.925\text{ V} + j19.743\text{ V}) + (13.945\text{ V} - j8.587\text{ V})$$
$$= 56.870\text{ V} + j11.156\text{ V} = \mathbf{57.95\ V\ \angle 11.10°}$$

14. a. $\mathbf{Z}_{Th}$:

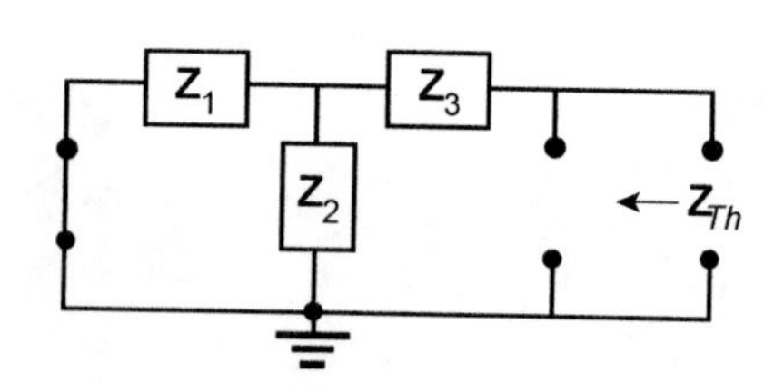

$\mathbf{Z}_1 = 10\ \Omega\ \angle 0°$, $\mathbf{Z}_2 = 8\ \Omega\ \angle 90°$

$\mathbf{Z}_3 = 8\ \Omega\ \angle{-90°}$

$$\mathbf{Z}_{Th} = \mathbf{Z}_3 + \mathbf{Z}_1 \parallel \mathbf{Z}_2$$
$$= -j8\ \Omega + 10\ \Omega\ \angle 0° \angle \parallel 8\ \Omega\ \angle 90°$$
$$= -j8\ \Omega + 6.247\ \Omega\ \angle 51.34°$$
$$= -j8\ \Omega + 3.902\ \Omega + j4.878\ \Omega$$
$$= 3.902\ \Omega - j3.122\ \Omega$$
$$= \mathbf{5.00\ \Omega\ \angle{-38.66°}}$$

$\mathbf{E}_{Th}$: Superposition:

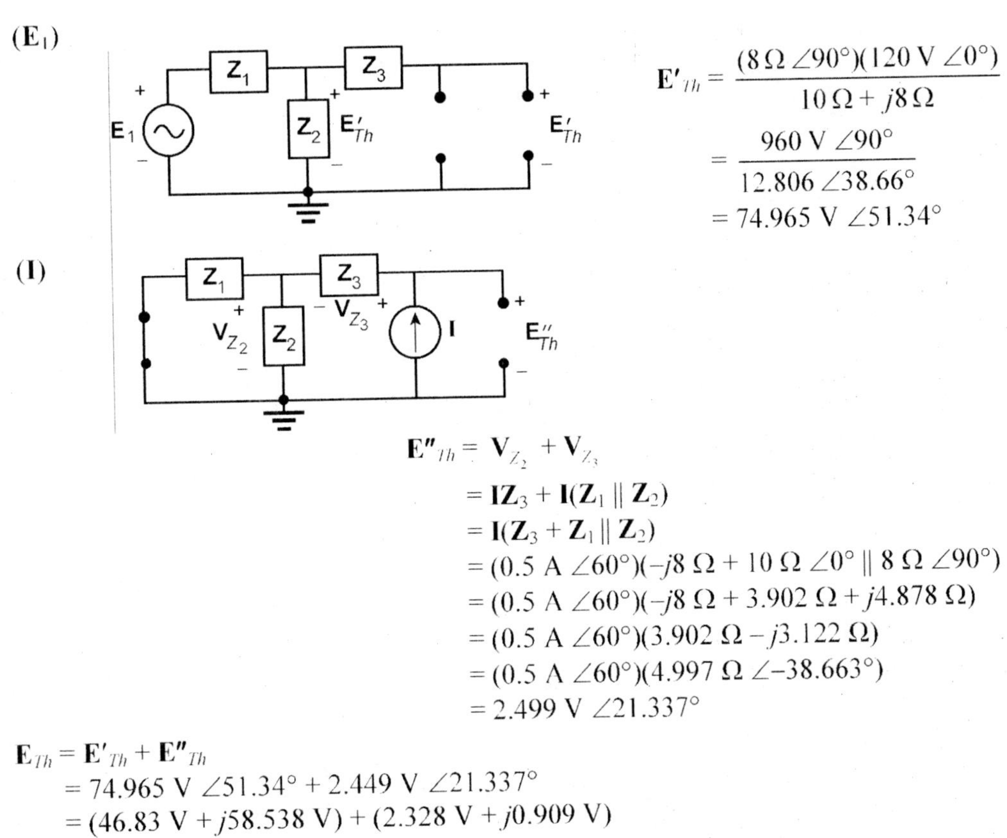

$$\mathbf{E}'_{Th} = \frac{(8\,\Omega\,\angle 90°)(120\text{ V}\,\angle 0°)}{10\,\Omega + j8\,\Omega} = \frac{960\text{ V}\,\angle 90°}{12.806\,\angle 38.66°} = 74.965\text{ V}\,\angle 51.34°$$

$$\begin{aligned}
\mathbf{E}''_{Th} &= \mathbf{V}_{Z_2} + \mathbf{V}_{Z_3}\\
&= \mathbf{I}\mathbf{Z}_3 + \mathbf{I}(\mathbf{Z}_1 \parallel \mathbf{Z}_2)\\
&= \mathbf{I}(\mathbf{Z}_3 + \mathbf{Z}_1 \parallel \mathbf{Z}_2)\\
&= (0.5\text{ A}\,\angle 60°)(-j8\,\Omega + 10\,\Omega\,\angle 0° \parallel 8\,\Omega\,\angle 90°)\\
&= (0.5\text{ A}\,\angle 60°)(-j8\,\Omega + 3.902\,\Omega + j4.878\,\Omega)\\
&= (0.5\text{ A}\,\angle 60°)(3.902\,\Omega - j3.122\,\Omega)\\
&= (0.5\text{ A}\,\angle 60°)(4.997\,\Omega\,\angle -38.663°)\\
&= 2.499\text{ V}\,\angle 21.337°
\end{aligned}$$

$$\begin{aligned}
\mathbf{E}_{Th} &= \mathbf{E}'_{Th} + \mathbf{E}''_{Th}\\
&= 74.965\text{ V}\,\angle 51.34° + 2.449\text{ V}\,\angle 21.337°\\
&= (46.83\text{ V} + j58.538\text{ V}) + (2.328\text{ V} + j0.909\text{ V})\\
&= 49.158\text{ V} + j59.447\text{ V} = \mathbf{77.14\text{ V}\,\angle 50.41°}
\end{aligned}$$

b. $\mathbf{Z}_{Th}$:

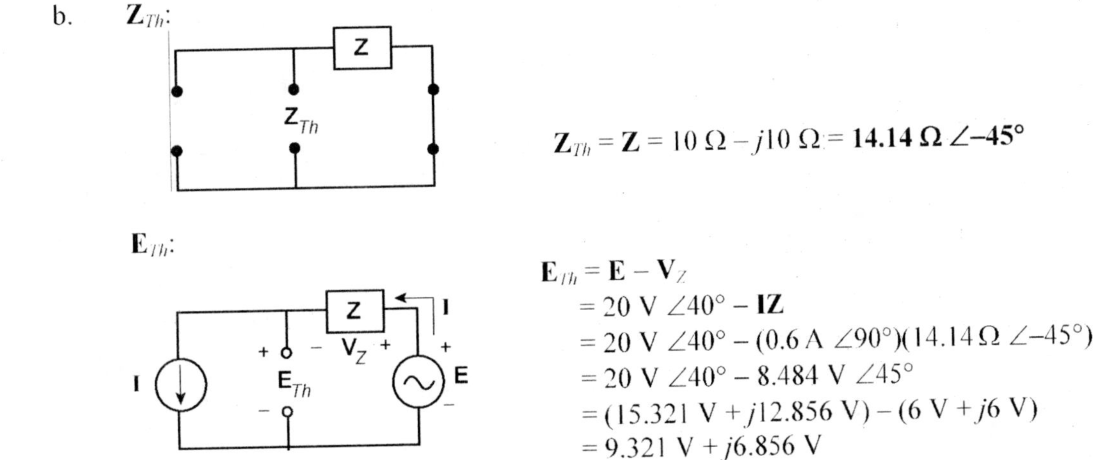

$$\mathbf{Z}_{Th} = \mathbf{Z} = 10\,\Omega - j10\,\Omega = \mathbf{14.14\,\Omega\,\angle -45°}$$

$\mathbf{E}_{Th}$:

$$\begin{aligned}
\mathbf{E}_{Th} &= \mathbf{E} - \mathbf{V}_Z\\
&= 20\text{ V}\,\angle 40° - \mathbf{IZ}\\
&= 20\text{ V}\,\angle 40° - (0.6\text{ A}\,\angle 90°)(14.14\,\Omega\,\angle -45°)\\
&= 20\text{ V}\,\angle 40° - 8.484\text{ V}\,\angle 45°\\
&= (15.321\text{ V} + j12.856\text{ V}) - (6\text{ V} + j6\text{ V})\\
&= 9.321\text{ V} + j6.856\text{ V}\\
&= \mathbf{11.57\text{ V}\,\angle 36.34°}
\end{aligned}$$

15. a.

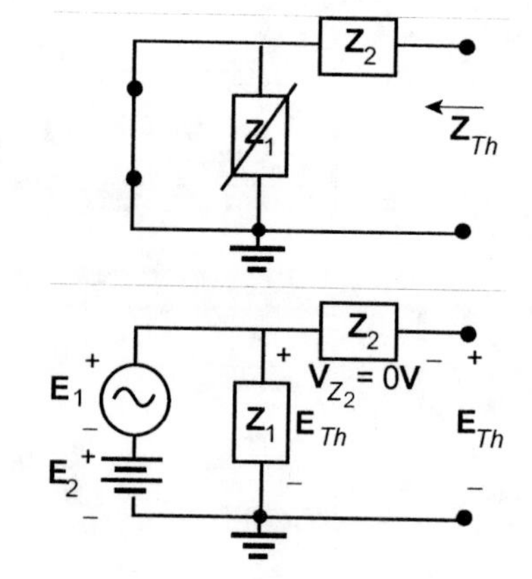

$\mathbf{Z}_1 = 6\ \Omega - j2\ \Omega = 6.325\ \Omega \angle -18.435°$
$\mathbf{Z}_2 = 4\ \Omega \angle 90°$
$\mathbf{Z}_{Th} = \mathbf{Z}_2 = \mathbf{4\ \Omega \angle 90°}$

By inspection:

$\mathbf{E}_{Th} = \mathbf{E}_2 + \mathbf{E}_1$
$= \mathbf{4\ V + 10\ V \angle 0°}$
DC AC

b.

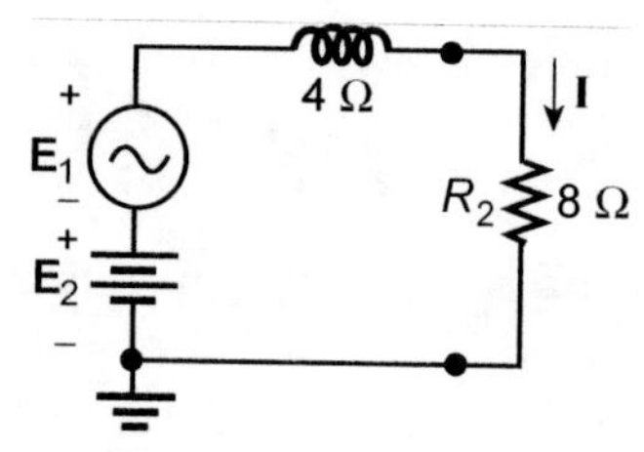

$$\mathbf{I} = \frac{E_2}{R_2} + \frac{\mathbf{E}_1}{R_2 + jX_L}$$
$$= \frac{4\ \text{V}}{8\ \Omega} + \frac{10\ \text{V} \angle 0°}{8\ \Omega + j4\ \Omega}$$
$$= 0.5\ \text{A} + \frac{10\ \text{V} \angle 0°}{8.944\ \Omega \angle 26.565°}$$
$$= 0.5\ \text{A} + 1.118\ \text{A} \angle -26.565°$$
(dc) (ac)

$\boldsymbol{i = 0.5 + 1.58 \sin(\omega t - 26.57°)}$

16. a. $\mathbf{Z}_{Th}$:

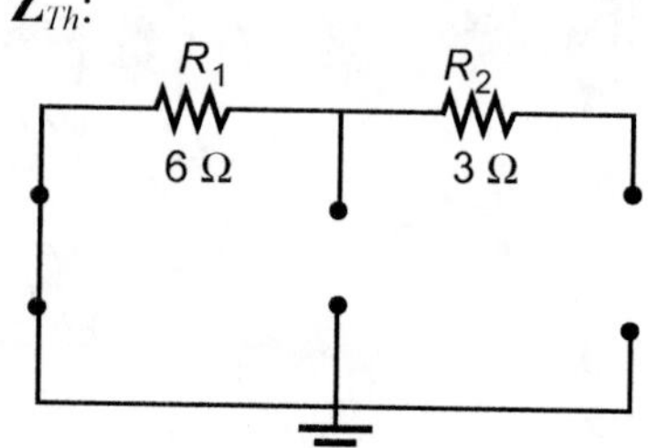

$\leftarrow \mathbf{Z}_{Th} = \mathbf{Z}_{R_1} + \mathbf{Z}_{R_2} = 6\ \Omega + 3\ \Omega = \mathbf{9\ \Omega}$

DC:

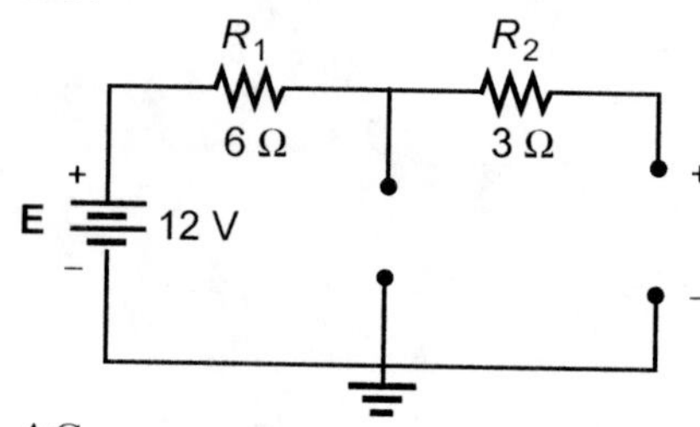

$\mathbf{E}'_{Th} = 12\ \text{V}$

AC:

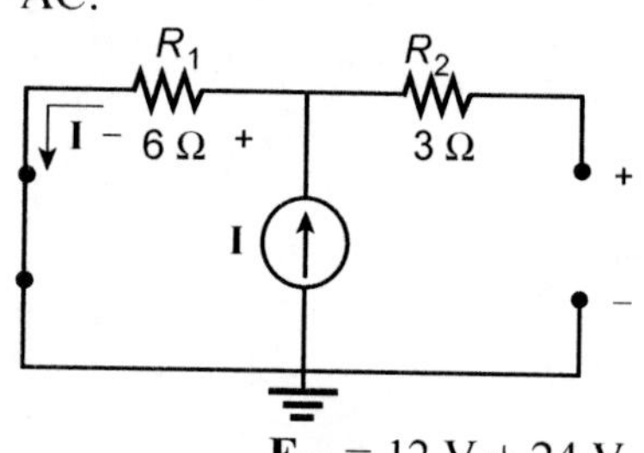

$\leftarrow \mathbf{E}''_{Th} = \mathbf{I}\mathbf{Z}_{R_1} = (4\ \text{A} \angle 0°)(6\ \Omega \angle 0°) = 24\ \text{V} \angle 0°$

$\mathbf{E}_{Th} = 12\ \text{V} + 24\ \text{V} \angle 0°$
(DC) (AC)

b.

DC: $\mathbf{V}_C = 12\text{ V}$

AC: $\mathbf{V}_C = \dfrac{\mathbf{Z}_C\mathbf{E}}{\mathbf{Z}_C + \mathbf{Z}_{R_{Th}}}$

$$= \frac{(1\,\Omega\angle-90°)(24\text{ V}\angle0°)}{-j1\,\Omega+9\,\Omega}$$

$$= \frac{24\text{ V}\angle-90°}{9.055\angle-6.34°}$$

$\mathbf{V}_C = 2.65\text{ V}\angle-83.66°$

$\upsilon_C = 12\text{ V} + 2.65\text{ V}\angle-83.66°$
$\quad = \mathbf{12\text{ V} + 3.75\sin(\omega t - 83.66°)}$

17. a. $\mathbf{Z}_{Th}$:

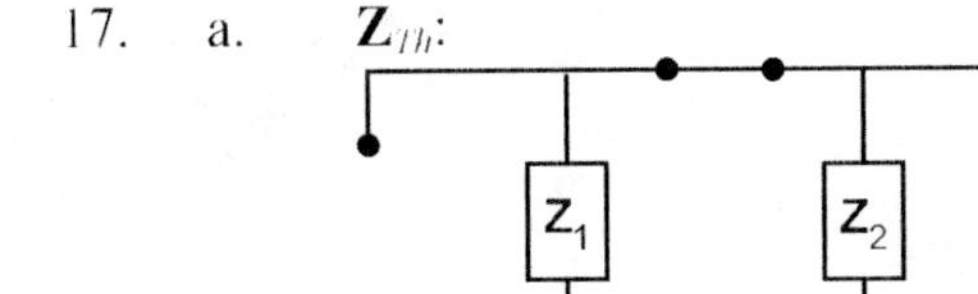

$\mathbf{Z}_1 = 10\text{ k}\Omega\angle0°$
$\mathbf{Z}_2 = 5\text{ k}\Omega - j5\text{ k}\Omega$
$\quad = 7.071\text{ k}\Omega\angle-45°$

$\mathbf{Z}_{Th} = \mathbf{Z}_1 \,\|\, \mathbf{Z}_2 = (10\text{ k}\Omega\angle0°)\,\|\,(7.071\text{ k}\Omega\angle-45°) = \mathbf{4.47\text{ k}\Omega\angle-26.57°}$

Source conversion:
$\mathbf{E}_1 = (I\angle0)(R_1\angle0°) = (5\text{ mA}\angle0°)(10\text{ k}\Omega\angle0°) = 50\text{ V}\angle0°$

$$\mathbf{E}_{Th} = \frac{\mathbf{Z}_2(\mathbf{E}+\mathbf{E}_1)}{\mathbf{Z}_2+\mathbf{Z}_1}$$

$$= \frac{(7.071\text{ k}\Omega\angle-45°)(20\text{ V}\angle0° + 50\text{ V}\angle0°)}{(5\text{ k}\Omega - j5\text{ k}\Omega)+(10\text{ k}\Omega)}$$

$$= \frac{(7.071\text{ k}\Omega\angle-45°)(70\text{ V}\angle0°)}{(15\text{ k}\Omega - j5\text{ k}\Omega)}$$

$$= \frac{494.97\text{ V}\angle-45°}{15.811\angle-18.435°}$$

$= \mathbf{31.31\text{ V}\angle-26.57°}$

b. $$\mathbf{I} = \frac{\mathbf{E}_{Th}}{\mathbf{Z}_{Th}+\mathbf{Z}_L} = \frac{31.31\text{ V}\angle-26.565°}{4.472\text{ k}\Omega\angle-26.565° + 5\text{ k}\Omega\angle90°}$$

$$= \frac{31.31\text{ V}\angle-26.565°}{4\text{ k}\Omega - j2\text{ k}\Omega + j5\text{ k}\Omega} = \frac{31.31\text{ V}\angle-26.565°}{4\text{ k}\Omega + j3\text{ k}\Omega}$$

$$= \frac{31.31\text{ V}\angle-26.565°}{5\text{ k}\Omega\angle36.87°} = \mathbf{6.26\text{ mA}\angle63.44°}$$

18.

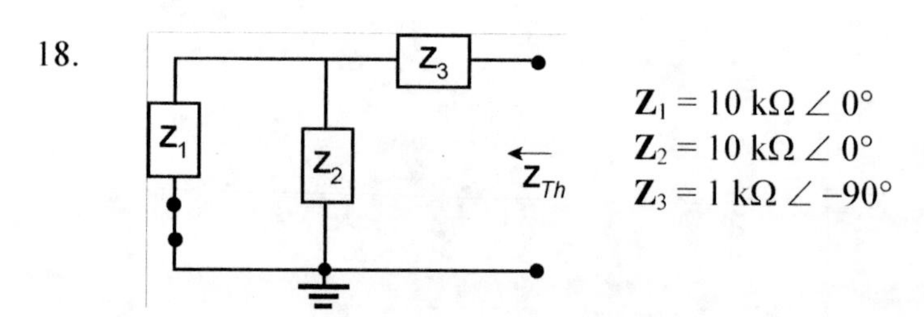

$\mathbf{Z}_1 = 10\text{ k}\Omega \angle 0°$
$\mathbf{Z}_2 = 10\text{ k}\Omega \angle 0°$
$\mathbf{Z}_3 = 1\text{ k}\Omega \angle -90°$

$$\mathbf{Z}_{Th} = \mathbf{Z}_3 + \mathbf{Z}_1 \parallel \mathbf{Z}_2 = 5\text{ k}\Omega - j1\text{ k}\Omega \cong \mathbf{5.1\text{ k}\Omega \angle{-11.31°}}$$

$\mathbf{E}_{Th}$: (VDR) $$\mathbf{E}_{Th} = \frac{\mathbf{Z}_2(20\text{ V})}{\mathbf{Z}_2 + \mathbf{Z}_1} = \frac{(10\text{ k}\Omega \angle 0°)(20\text{ V})}{10\text{ k}\Omega + 10\text{ k}\Omega} = \mathbf{10\text{ V}}$$

19. $\mathbf{Z}_{Th}$:

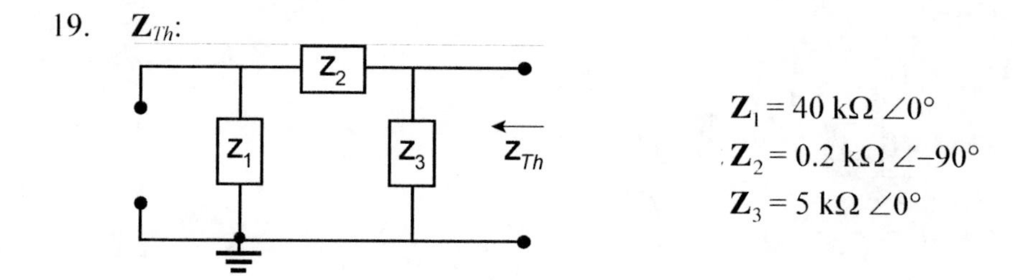

$\mathbf{Z}_1 = 40\text{ k}\Omega \angle 0°$
$\mathbf{Z}_2 = 0.2\text{ k}\Omega \angle{-90°}$
$\mathbf{Z}_3 = 5\text{ k}\Omega \angle 0°$

$$\mathbf{Z}_{Th} = \mathbf{Z}_3 \parallel (\mathbf{Z}_1 + \mathbf{Z}_2) = 5\text{ k}\Omega \angle 0° \parallel (40\text{ k}\Omega - j0.2\text{ k}\Omega) = \mathbf{4.44\text{ k}\Omega \angle{-0.03°}}$$

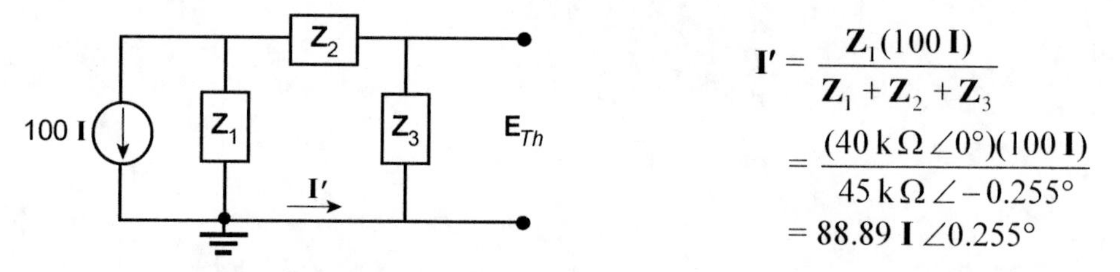

$$\mathbf{I}' = \frac{\mathbf{Z}_1(100\,\mathbf{I})}{\mathbf{Z}_1 + \mathbf{Z}_2 + \mathbf{Z}_3} = \frac{(40\text{ k}\Omega \angle 0°)(100\,\mathbf{I})}{45\text{ k}\Omega \angle{-0.255°}} = 88.89\,\mathbf{I} \angle 0.255°$$

$$\mathbf{E}_{Th} = -\mathbf{I}'\mathbf{Z}_3 = -(88.89\,\mathbf{I} \angle 0.255°)(5\text{ k}\Omega \angle 0°) = \mathbf{-444.45 \times 10^3\,I \angle 0.26°}$$

20. $\mathbf{Z}_{Th}$:

$\leftarrow \mathbf{Z}_{Th} = \mathbf{Z}_1 = \mathbf{20\text{ k}\Omega \angle 0°}$

$\mathbf{E}_{Th}$:

$h\mathbf{I}$:

$$\mathbf{E}'_{Th} = -(h\mathbf{I})(\mathbf{Z}_1) = -(100)(2\text{ mA} \angle 0°)(20\text{ k}\Omega \angle 0°) = -4\text{ kV} \angle 0°$$

E:

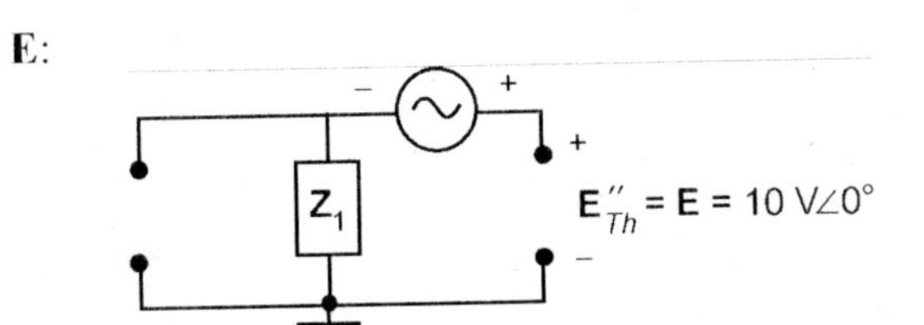

$$\mathbf{E}_{Th} = \mathbf{E}'_{Th} + \mathbf{E}''_{Th}$$
$$= -4\text{ kV }\angle 0° + 10\text{ V }\angle 0°$$
$$= \mathbf{-3990\ V\ \angle 0°}$$

21. $\mathbf{Z}_{Th}$:

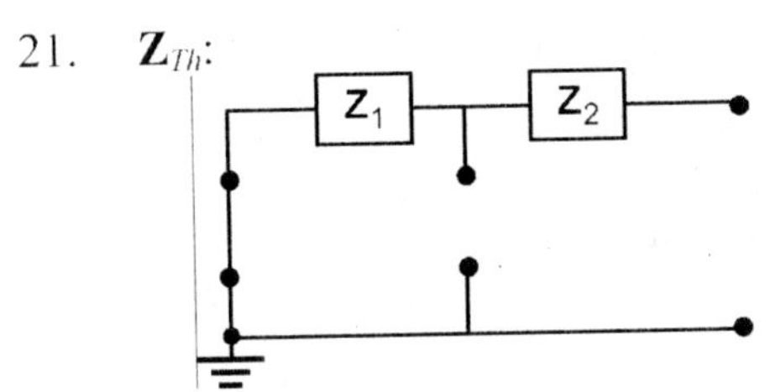

$\mathbf{Z}_1 = 5\text{ k}\Omega\angle 0°$ $\mathbf{Z}_2 = -j1$

$\leftarrow \mathbf{Z}_{Th} = \mathbf{Z}_1 + \mathbf{Z}_2 = 5\text{ k}\Omega - j1\text{ k}\Omega$
$= \mathbf{5.10\ k\Omega\ \angle -11.31°}$

$\mathbf{E}_{Th}$:

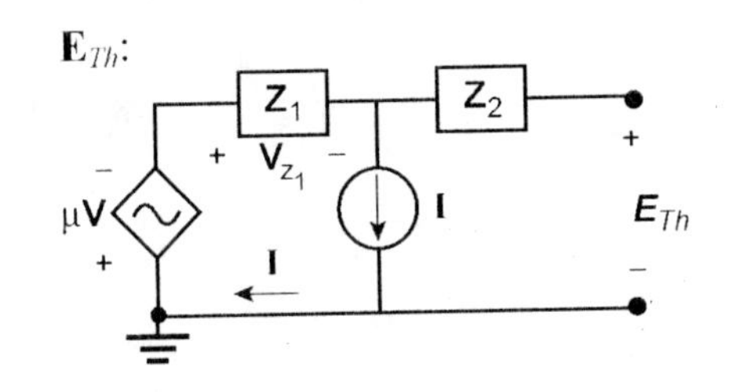

$$\mathbf{E}_{Th} = -\left[\mu\mathbf{V} + \mathbf{V}_{Z_1}\right]$$
$$= -\mu\mathbf{V} - \mathbf{IZ}_1$$
$$= -(20)(2\text{ V }\angle 0°) - (2\text{ mA }\angle 0°)(5\text{ k}\Omega\ \angle 0°)$$
$$= \mathbf{-50\ V\ \angle 0°}$$

22. $\mathbf{Z}_{Th}$:

$\mathbf{Z}_1 = 20\text{ k}\Omega\ \angle\ 0°$
$\mathbf{Z}_2 = 5\text{ k}\Omega\ \angle\ 0°$

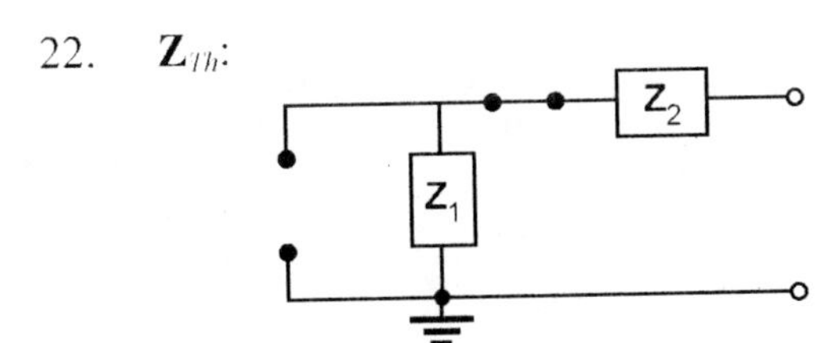

$\leftarrow \mathbf{Z}_{Th} = \mathbf{Z}_1 + \mathbf{Z}_2 = \mathbf{25\ k\Omega\ \angle\ 0°}$

$\mathbf{E}_{Th}$:

$$\text{E}_{Th} = \mu\mathbf{V} - (h\mathbf{I})(\mathbf{Z}_1)$$
$$= (20)(10\text{ V }\angle\ 0°) - (100)(1\text{ mA }\angle 0°)(20\text{ k}\Omega\ \angle\ 0°)$$
$$= \mathbf{-1800\ V\ \angle 0°}$$

23. $\mathbf{E}_{Th}$: $(\mathbf{E}_{oc})$

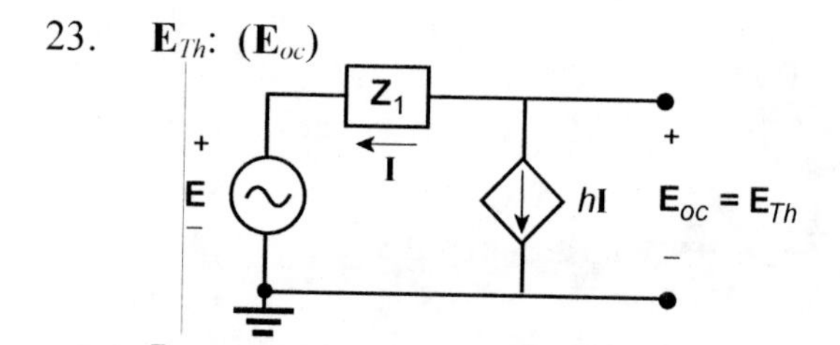

$h\mathbf{I} = -\mathbf{I}$ $\quad$ $\mathbf{Z}_1 = 2\text{ k}\Omega\ \angle 0°$

$\therefore \mathbf{I} = 0$

and $h\mathbf{I} = 0$

with $\mathbf{E}_{oc} = \mathbf{E}_{Th} = \mathbf{E} = \mathbf{20\ V\ \angle 53°}$

$\mathbf{I}_{sc}$:

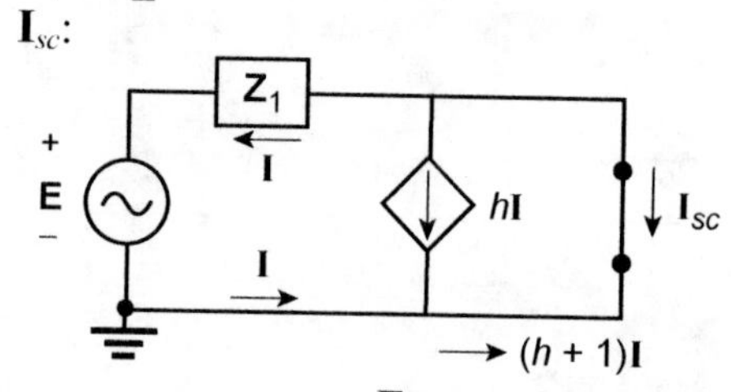

$\mathbf{I}_{sc} = -(h+1)\mathbf{I}$
$= -(h+1)(10\text{ mA}\ \angle 53°)$
$= -510\text{ mA}\ \angle 53°$

$$\mathbf{Z}_{Th} = \frac{\mathbf{E}_{oc}}{\mathbf{I}_{sc}} = \frac{20\text{ V}\ \angle 53°}{-510\text{ mA}\ \angle 53°} = \mathbf{-39.22\ \Omega\ \angle 0°}$$

24. $\mathbf{E}_{Th}$:

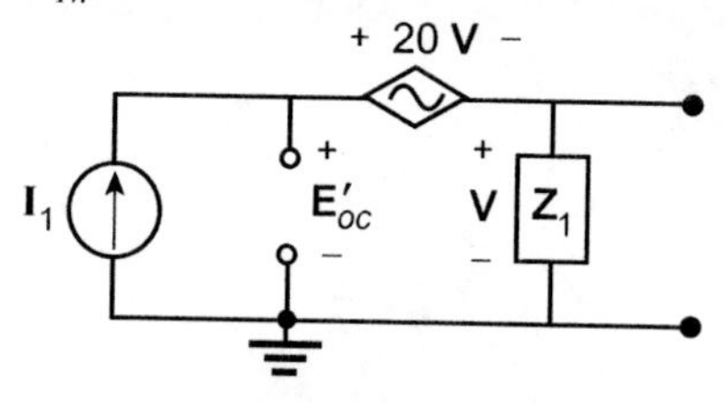

$\mathbf{E}'_{oc} = 21\text{ V}$ $\quad$ $\mathbf{Z}_1 = 5\text{ k}\Omega\ \angle 0°$

$\mathbf{V} = \mathbf{I}_1\mathbf{Z}_1 = (1\text{ mA}\ \angle 0°)(5\text{ k}\Omega\ \angle 0°)$
$= 5\text{ V}\ \angle 0°$

$\mathbf{E}'_{oc} = \mathbf{E}'_{Th} = 21(5\text{ V}\ \angle 0°)$
$= 105\text{ V}\ \angle 0°$

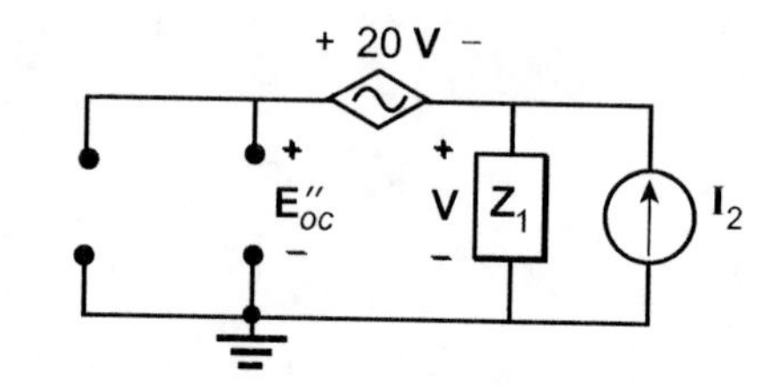

$\mathbf{V} = \mathbf{I}_2\mathbf{Z}_1$
$= (2\text{ mA}\ \angle 0°)(5\text{ k}\Omega\ \angle 0°)$
$= 10\text{ V}\ \angle 0°$

$\mathbf{E}''_{oc} = \mathbf{E}''_{Th} = \mathbf{V} + 20\ \mathbf{V} = 21\ \mathbf{V} = 210\text{ V}\ \angle 0°$

$\mathbf{I}_{sc}$:

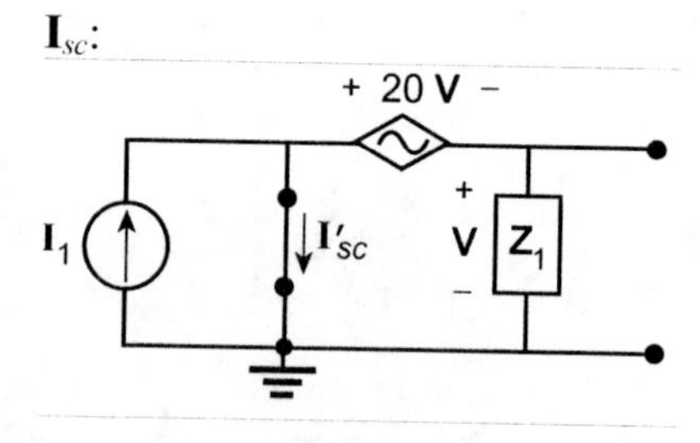

$\mathbf{I}'_{sc} = \mathbf{I}_1$

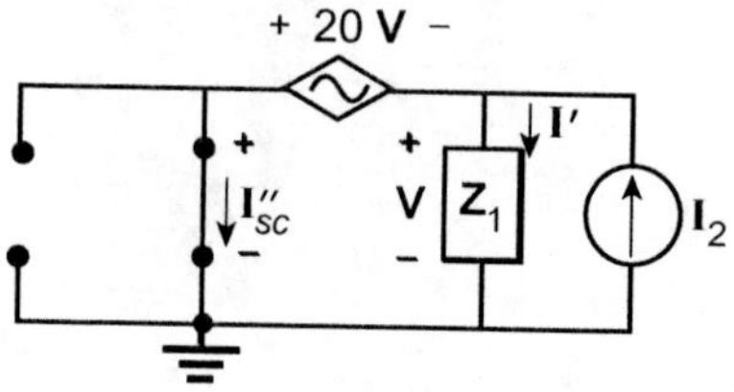

+ 20 V –

20 V = $\mathbf{V}$ $\therefore$ $\mathbf{V} = 0$ V

and $\mathbf{I}' = 0$ A

$\therefore$ $\mathbf{I}''_{sc} = \mathbf{I}_2$

$\mathbf{I}_{sc} = \mathbf{I}'_{sc} + \mathbf{I}''_{sc} = 3\text{ mA}\ \angle 0°$

$\mathbf{E}_{oc} = \mathbf{E}'_{oc} + \mathbf{E}''_{oc} = 315\text{ V}\ \angle 0° = \mathbf{E}_{Th}$

$$\mathbf{Z}_{Th} = \frac{\mathbf{E}_{oc}}{\mathbf{I}_{sc}} = \frac{315\text{ V}\ \angle 0°}{3\text{ mA}\ \angle 0°} = \mathbf{105\ k\Omega\ \angle 0°}$$

25. $\mathbf{E}_{oc}$:
($\mathbf{E}_{Th}$)

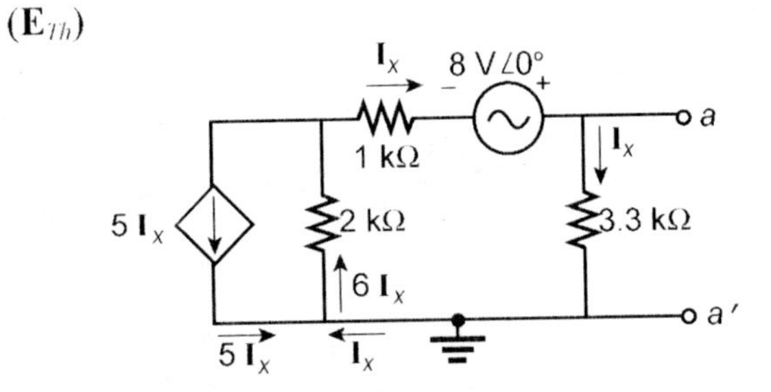

KVL: $-6\,\mathbf{I}_x(2\text{ k}\Omega) - \mathbf{I}_x(1\text{ k}\Omega) + 8\text{ V}\angle 0° - \mathbf{I}_x(3.3\text{ k}\Omega) = 0$

$$\mathbf{I}_x = \frac{8\text{ V}\angle 0°}{16.3\text{ k}\Omega} = 0.491\text{ mA}\angle 0°$$

$\mathbf{E}_{oc} = \mathbf{E}_{Th} = \mathbf{I}_x(3.3\text{ k}\Omega) = \mathbf{1.62\ V\ \angle 0°}$

$\mathbf{I}_{sc}$:

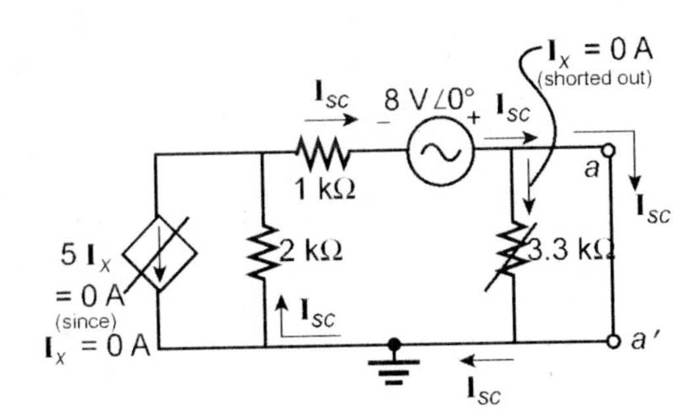

$$\mathbf{I}_{sc} = \frac{8\text{ V}}{3\text{ k}\Omega} = 2.667\text{ mA}\angle 0°$$

$$\mathbf{Z}_{Th} = \frac{\mathbf{E}_{oc}}{\mathbf{I}_{sc}} = \frac{1.62\text{ V}\angle 0°}{2.667\text{ mA}\angle 0°} = \mathbf{607.42\ \Omega\ \angle 0°}$$

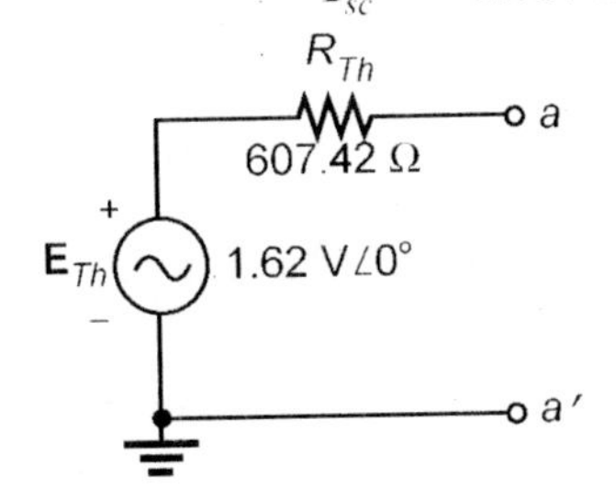

26. a. From Problem 12(a): $\mathbf{Z}_N = \mathbf{Z}_{Th} = 1.92\ \Omega + j1.44\ \Omega = \mathbf{2.4\ \Omega\ \angle 36.87°}$

$\mathbf{I}_N$:

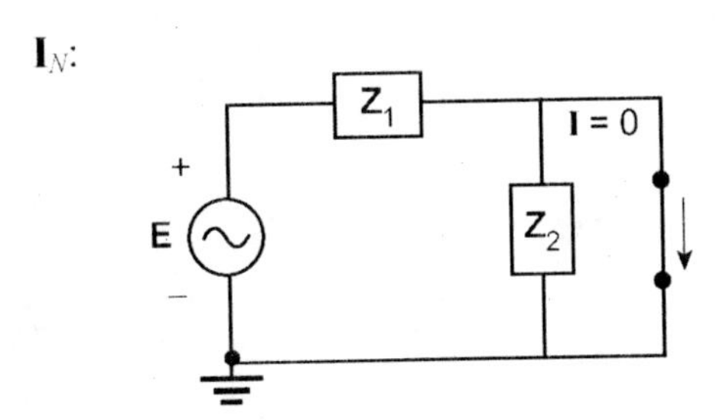

$\mathbf{Z}_1 = 3\ \Omega\angle 0°$, $\mathbf{Z}_2 = 4\ \Omega\angle 90°$

$$\mathbf{I}_{sc} = \mathbf{I}_N = \frac{\mathbf{E}}{\mathbf{Z}_1} = \frac{100\text{ V}\angle 0°}{3\ \Omega\angle 0°}$$

$= \mathbf{33.33\ A\ \angle 0°}$

b. From Problem 12(b): $\mathbf{Z}_N = \mathbf{Z}_{Th} = 5.263\text{ k}\Omega \angle 74.74° =$ **1.39 kΩ + *j*5.08 kΩ**

$\mathbf{I}_N$:

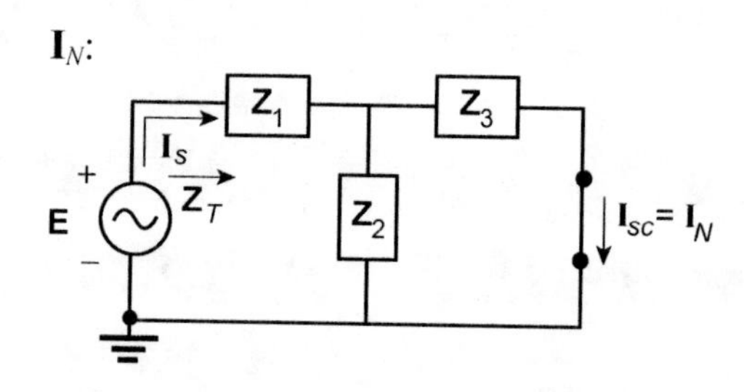

$\mathbf{Z}_1 = 2\text{ k}\Omega \angle 0°$, $\mathbf{Z}_2 = 3\text{ k}\Omega \angle -90°$
$\mathbf{Z}_3 = 6\text{ k}\Omega \angle 90°$

$$\begin{aligned}\mathbf{Z}_T &= \mathbf{Z}_1 + \mathbf{Z}_2 \parallel \mathbf{Z}_3\\ &= 2\text{ k}\Omega + 3\text{ k}\Omega \angle -90° \parallel 6\text{ k}\Omega \angle 90°\\ &= 2\text{ k}\Omega + 6\text{ k}\Omega \angle -90°\\ &= 2\text{ k}\Omega - j6\text{ k}\Omega\\ &= 6.325\text{ k}\Omega \angle -71.565°\end{aligned}$$

$$\mathbf{I}_s = \frac{\mathbf{E}}{\mathbf{Z}_T} = \frac{20\text{ V} \angle 0°}{6.325\text{ k}\Omega \angle -71.565°}$$
$$= 3.162\text{ mA} \angle 71.565°$$
$$\mathbf{I}_{sc} = \mathbf{I}_N = \frac{\mathbf{Z}_2\mathbf{I}_s}{\mathbf{Z}_2 + \mathbf{Z}_3} = \frac{(3\text{ k}\Omega \angle -90°)(3.162\text{ mA} \angle 71.565°)}{-j3\text{ k}\Omega + j6\text{ k}\Omega}$$
$$= \frac{9.486\text{ mA} \angle -18.435°}{3 \angle 90°} = \mathbf{3.16\text{ mA} \angle -108.44°}$$

27. a.

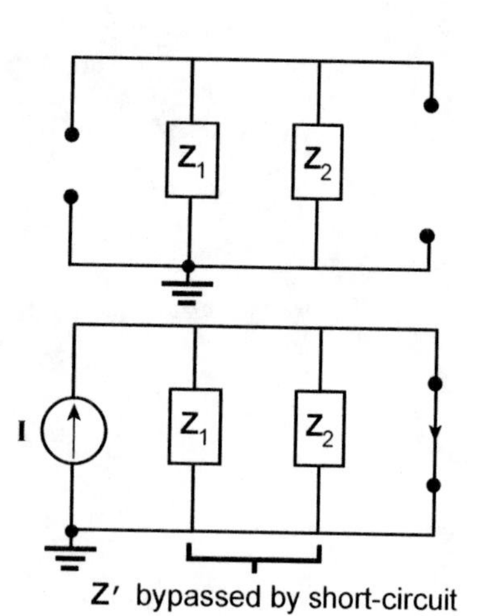

$\mathbf{Z}_1 = 20\ \Omega + j20\ \Omega = 28.284\ \Omega \angle 45°$
$\mathbf{Z}_2 = 68\ \Omega \angle 0°$

$\leftarrow \mathbf{Z}_N = \mathbf{Z}_1 \parallel \mathbf{Z}_2$
$= (28.284\ \Omega \angle 45°) \parallel (68\ \Omega \angle 0°)$
$= \mathbf{21.31\ \Omega \angle 32.2°}$

$\leftarrow \mathbf{I}_{sc} = \mathbf{I} = \mathbf{I}_N = 0.1\text{ A} \angle 0°$

b.

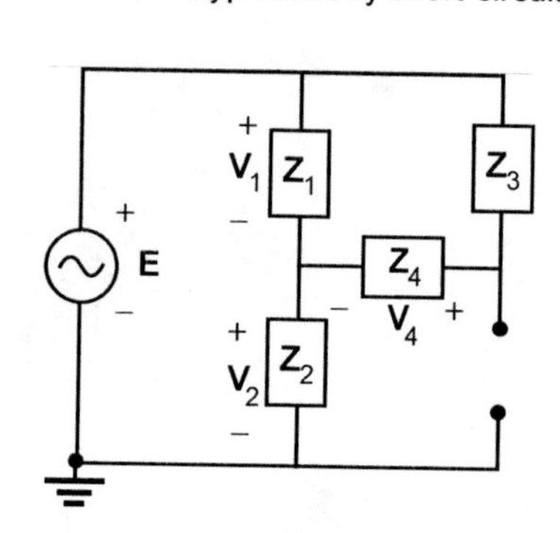

$\mathbf{Z}_1 = 2\ \Omega \angle 0°$, $\mathbf{Z}_2 = 4\ \Omega \angle 90°$
$\mathbf{Z}_3 = 8\ \Omega \angle -90°$, $\mathbf{Z}_4 = 10\ \Omega \angle 0°$
$\mathbf{E} = 50\text{ V} \angle 0°$

$\mathbf{Z}_N$:

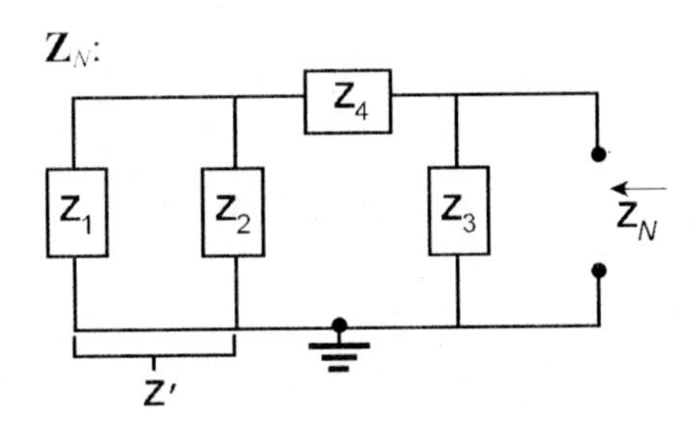

$$\mathbf{Z}' = \mathbf{Z}_1 \parallel \mathbf{Z}_2 = 2\ \Omega\ \angle 0° \parallel 4\ \Omega\ \angle 90°$$
$$= 1.789\ \Omega\ \angle 26.565° = 1.6\ \Omega + j0.8\ \Omega$$
$$\mathbf{Z}' + \mathbf{Z}_4 = 1.6\ \Omega + j0.8\ \Omega + 10\ \Omega = 11.6\ \Omega + j0.8\ \Omega = 11.628\ \Omega\ \angle 3.945°$$
$$\mathbf{Z}_N = \mathbf{Z}_3 \parallel (\mathbf{Z}' + \mathbf{Z}_4) = (8\ \Omega\ \angle -90°) \parallel (11.628\ \Omega\ \angle 3.945°) = \mathbf{6.81\ \Omega\ \angle -54.23°}$$
$$= \mathbf{3.98\ \Omega - j5.53\ \Omega}$$

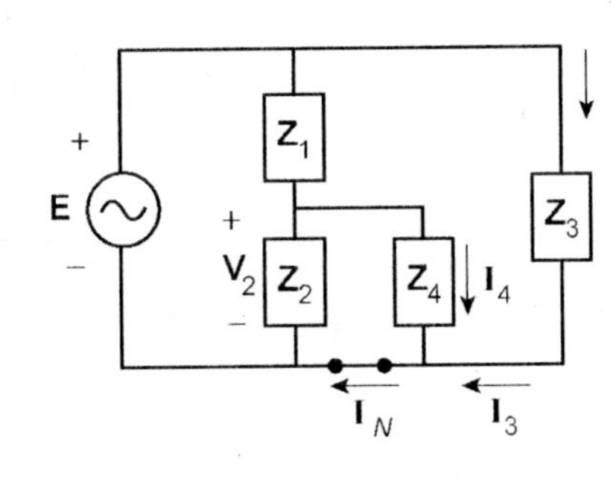

$$\mathbf{I}_3 = \frac{\mathbf{E}}{\mathbf{Z}_3} = \frac{50\ \text{V}\ \angle 0°}{8\ \Omega\ \angle -90°} = 6.250\ \text{A}\ \angle 90°$$
$$\mathbf{Z}' = \mathbf{Z}_2 \parallel \mathbf{Z}_4 = 4\ \Omega\ \angle 90° \parallel 10\ \Omega\ \angle 0°$$
$$= 3.714\ \Omega\ \angle 68.2°$$
$$\mathbf{V}_2 = \frac{\mathbf{Z}'\mathbf{E}}{\mathbf{Z}' + \mathbf{Z}_1} = \frac{(3.714\ \Omega\ \angle 68.2°)(50\ \text{V}\ \angle 0°)}{1.378\ \Omega + j3.448\ \Omega + 2\ \Omega}$$
$$= \frac{185.7\ \text{V}\ \angle 68.2°}{4.827\ \angle 45.588°} = 38.471\ \text{V}\ \angle 22.612°$$

$$\mathbf{I}_4 = \frac{\mathbf{V}_2}{\mathbf{Z}_4} = \frac{38.471\ \text{V}\ \angle 22.612°}{10\ \Omega\ \angle 0°} = 3.847\ \text{A}\ \angle 22.612°$$
$$\mathbf{I}_N = \mathbf{I}_3 + \mathbf{I}_4 = 6.250\ \text{A}\ \angle 90° + 3.847\ \text{A}\ \angle 22.612°$$
$$= +j6.25\ \text{A} + 3.551\ \text{A} + j1.479\ \text{A} = 3.551\ \text{A} + j7.729\ \text{A}$$
$$= \mathbf{8.51\ A\ \angle 65.32°}$$

28. a. From Problem 14(a): $\mathbf{Z}_N = \mathbf{Z}_{Th} = \mathbf{5.00\ \Omega\ \angle -38.66°}$

$\mathbf{I}_N$: Superposition:

$$\mathbf{Z}_T = \mathbf{Z}_1 + \mathbf{Z}_2 \parallel \mathbf{Z}_3$$
$$= 10\ \Omega + 8\ \Omega\ \angle 90° \parallel 8\ \Omega\ \angle -90°$$
$$= 10\ \Omega + \frac{64\ \Omega\ \angle 0°}{0}$$
$$= \text{very large impedance}$$
$$\mathbf{I}_s = \frac{\mathbf{E}}{\mathbf{Z}_T} = 0\ \text{A}$$
and $\mathbf{V}_{Z_1} = 0\ \text{V}$

with $\mathbf{V}_{Z_2} = \mathbf{V}_{Z_3} = \mathbf{E}_1 = 120\ \text{V}\ \angle 0°$

so that $\mathbf{I}'_{sc} = \dfrac{\mathbf{E}_1}{\mathbf{Z}_3} = \dfrac{120\ \text{V}\ \angle 0°}{8\ \Omega\ \angle -90°}$
$$= 15\ \text{A}\ \angle 90°$$

(I)

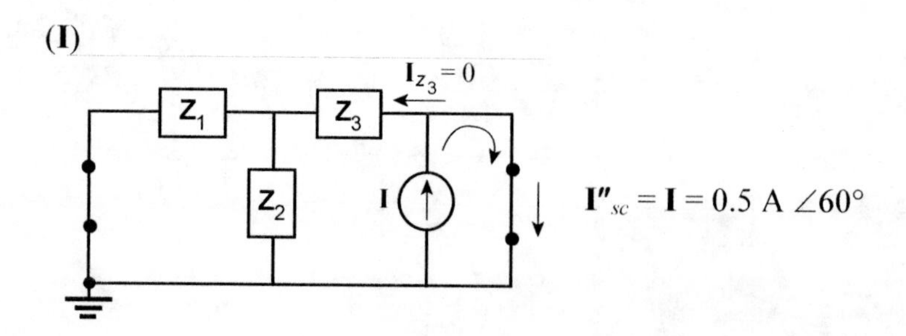

$\mathbf{I}''_{sc} = \mathbf{I} = 0.5 \text{ A } \angle 60°$

$$\mathbf{I}_N = \mathbf{I}'_{sc} + \mathbf{I}''_{sc} = +j15 \text{ A} + 0.5 \text{ A } \angle 60° = +j15 \text{ A} + 0.25 \text{ A} + j0.433 \text{ A}$$
$$= 0.25 \text{ A} + j15.433 \text{ A} = \mathbf{15.44 \text{ A } \angle 89.07°}$$

b. From Problem 14(b): $\mathbf{Z}_N = \mathbf{Z}_{Th} = 10\ \Omega - j10\ \Omega = \mathbf{14.14\ \Omega \angle{-45°}}$

$\mathbf{I}_N$:

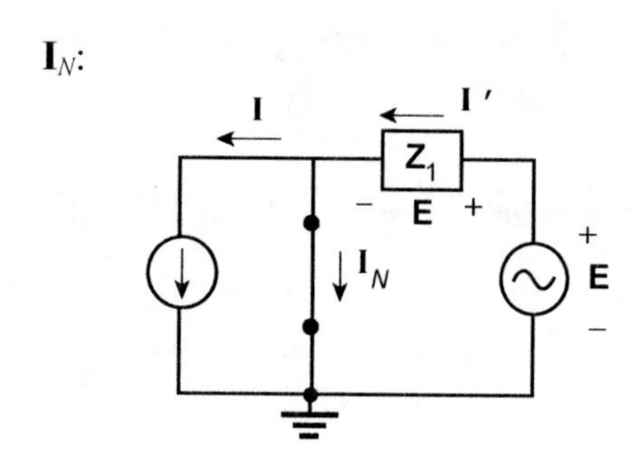

$$\mathbf{I}_N = \mathbf{I}' - \mathbf{I}$$
$$= \frac{\mathbf{E}}{\mathbf{Z}} - \mathbf{I}$$
$$= \frac{20 \text{ V } \angle 40°}{14.142\ \Omega \angle -45°} - 0.6 \text{ A } \angle 90°$$
$$= 1.414 \text{ A } \angle 85° - j0.6 \text{ A}$$
$$= 0.123 \text{ A} + j1.409 \text{ A} - j0.6 \text{ A}$$
$$= 0.123 \text{ A} + j0.809 \text{ A}$$
$$= \mathbf{0.82 \text{ A } \angle 81.35°}$$

29. a. $\mathbf{Z}_N$:

$\mathbf{E} = 20 \text{ V } \angle 0°,\ \mathbf{I}_2 = 0.4 \text{ A } \angle 20°$
$\mathbf{Z}_1 = 6\ \Omega + j8\ \Omega = 10\ \Omega \angle 53.13°$
$\mathbf{Z}_2 = \Omega - j12\ \Omega = 15\ \Omega \angle -53.13°$
$\mathbf{Z}_N = \mathbf{Z}_1 \parallel \mathbf{Z}_2 = (10\ \Omega \angle 53.13°) \parallel (15\ \Omega \angle -53.13°)$
$= \mathbf{9.66\ \Omega \angle 14.93°}$

$\mathbf{I}_N$:

(E) **($\mathbf{I}_2$)**

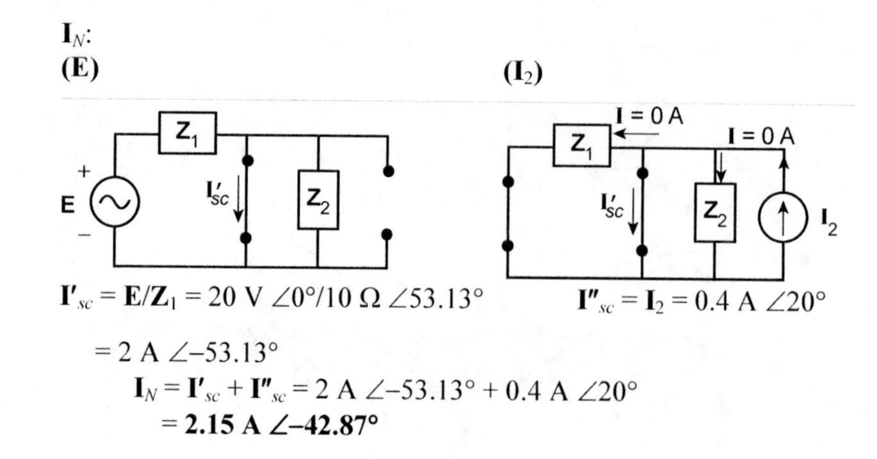

$\mathbf{I}'_{sc} = \mathbf{E}/\mathbf{Z}_1 = 20 \text{ V } \angle 0° / 10\ \Omega \angle 53.13°$ $\mathbf{I}''_{sc} = \mathbf{I}_2 = 0.4 \text{ A } \angle 20°$

$= 2 \text{ A } \angle -53.13°$

$$\mathbf{I}_N = \mathbf{I}'_{sc} + \mathbf{I}''_{sc} = 2 \text{ A } \angle -53.13° + 0.4 \text{ A } \angle 20°$$
$$= \mathbf{2.15 \text{ A } \angle -42.87°}$$

b. $\mathbf{Z}_N$:

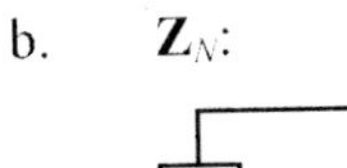

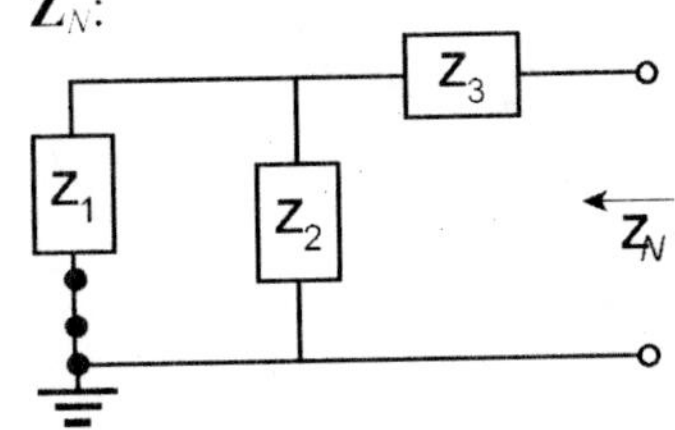

$\mathbf{E}_1 = 120\text{ V}\angle 30°,\ \mathbf{Z}_1 = 3\ \Omega\angle 0°$
$\mathbf{Z}_2 = 8\ \Omega - j8\ \Omega,\ \mathbf{Z}_3 = 4\ \Omega\angle 90°$

$$\begin{aligned}\mathbf{Z}_N &= \mathbf{Z}_3 + \mathbf{Z}_1 \parallel \mathbf{Z}_2\\ &= 4\ \Omega\angle 90° + (3\ \Omega\angle 0°) \parallel (8\ \Omega - j8\ \Omega)\\ &= \mathbf{4.37\ \Omega\angle 55.67° = 2.47\ \Omega + j3.61\ \Omega}\end{aligned}$$

$\mathbf{I}_N$:

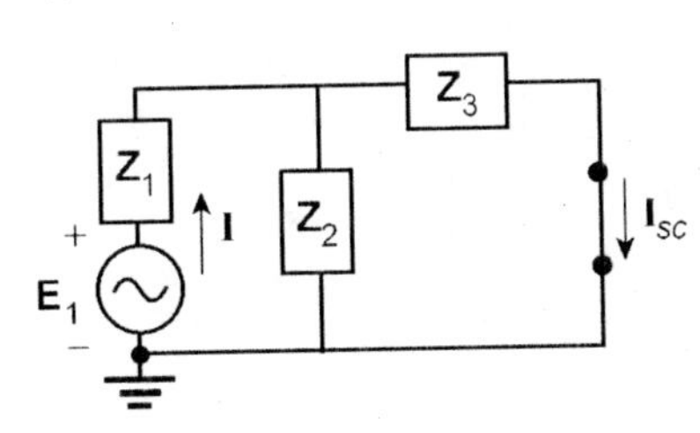

$$\begin{aligned}\mathbf{I} = \frac{\mathbf{E}_1}{\mathbf{Z}_T} &= \frac{120\text{ V}\angle 30°}{\mathbf{Z}_1 + \mathbf{Z}_2 \parallel \mathbf{Z}_3}\\ &= \frac{120\text{ V}\angle 30°}{3\ \Omega + (8\ \Omega - j8\ \Omega) \parallel 4\ \Omega\angle 90°}\\ &= \frac{120\text{ V}\angle 30°}{6.65\ \Omega\angle 46.22°}\\ &= 18.05\text{ A}\angle -16.22°\end{aligned}$$

$$\mathbf{I}_{sc} = \mathbf{I}_N = \frac{\mathbf{Z}_2(\mathbf{I})}{\mathbf{Z}_2 + \mathbf{Z}_3} = \frac{(8\ \Omega - j8\ \Omega)(18.05\text{ A}\angle -16.22°)}{8\ \Omega - j8\ \Omega + j4\ \Omega} = \mathbf{22.83\text{ A}\angle -34.65°}$$

30. a. $\mathbf{Z}_N = 8\ \Omega\angle \mathbf{0°}$

$\mathbf{I}_N$:

DC

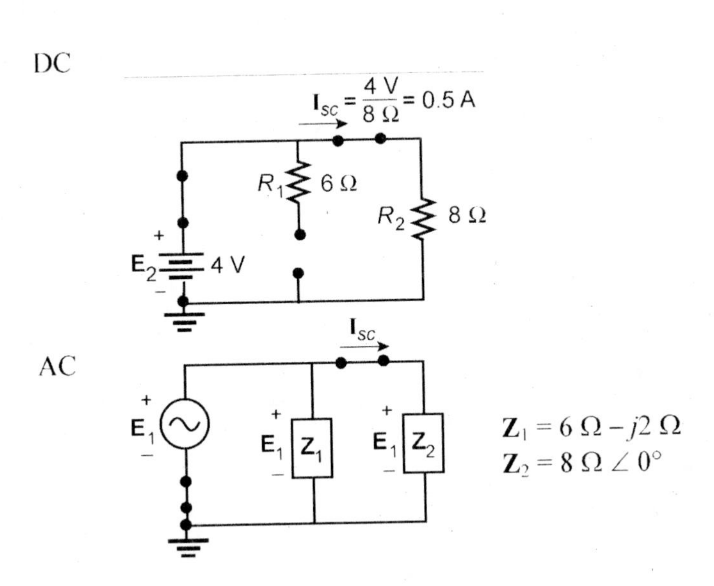

$\mathbf{Z}_1 = 6\ \Omega - j2\ \Omega$
$\mathbf{Z}_2 = 8\ \Omega\angle 0°$

$$\mathbf{I}_{sc} = \frac{\mathbf{E}_1}{\mathbf{Z}_2} = \frac{10\text{ V}\angle 0°}{8\ \Omega\angle 0°} = 1.25\text{ A}\angle 0°$$

$\mathbf{I}_N = 0.5\text{ A} + 1.25\text{ A}\angle 0°$

b.

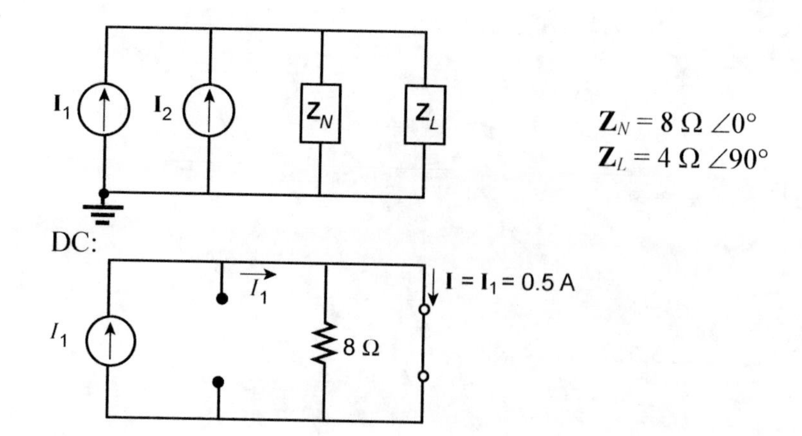

$\mathbf{Z}_N = 8\ \Omega\ \angle 0°$
$\mathbf{Z}_L = 4\ \Omega\ \angle 90°$

AC:

$$\mathbf{I} = \frac{\mathbf{Z}_N(\mathbf{I}_2)}{\mathbf{Z}_N + \mathbf{Z}_L} = \frac{(8\ \Omega\ \angle 0°)(1.25\ \text{A}\ \angle 0°)}{8\ \Omega + j4\ \Omega} = \mathbf{1.118\ A\ \angle{-26.57°}}$$

$$I_{8\Omega} = \underset{\text{(dc)}}{0.5\ \text{A}} + \underset{\text{(ac)}}{1.118\ \text{A}\ \angle{-26.57°}}$$

$$i = \mathbf{0.5 + 1.58\ sin(\omega t - 26.57°)}$$

31. a. From #16 $\mathbf{Z}_N = \mathbf{Z}_{Th} = \mathbf{9\ \Omega\ \angle 0°}$

DC:

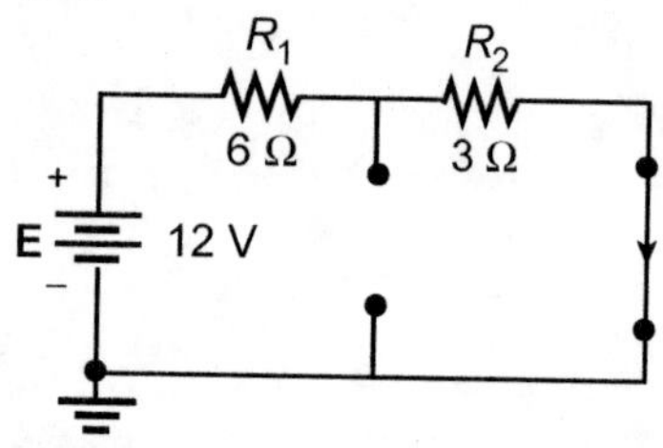

$$\mathbf{I'}_N = \frac{E}{R_T} = \frac{12\ \text{V}}{9\ \Omega} = 1.33\ \text{A}$$

AC:

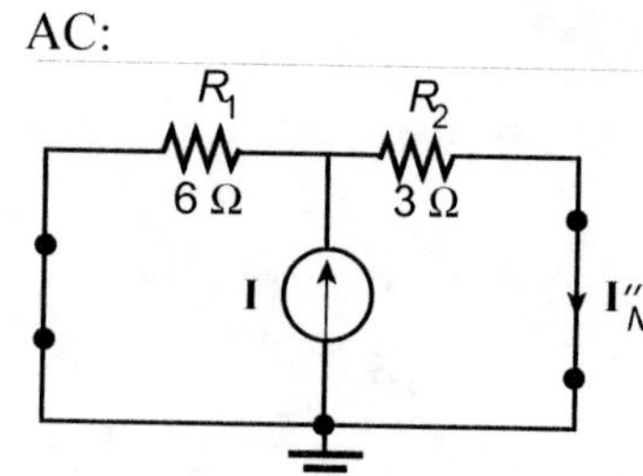

$$\mathbf{I''}_N = \frac{R_1 \mathbf{I}}{R_1 + R_2} = \frac{(6\ \Omega\ \angle 0°)(4\ \text{A}\ \angle 0°)}{9\ \Omega\ \angle 0°}$$

$$= \frac{24\ \text{V}\ \angle 0°}{9\ \Omega\ \angle 0°} = 2.67\ \text{A}\ \angle 0°$$

$\mathbf{I}_N = \mathbf{1.33\ A + 2.67\ A\ \angle 0°}$

b.

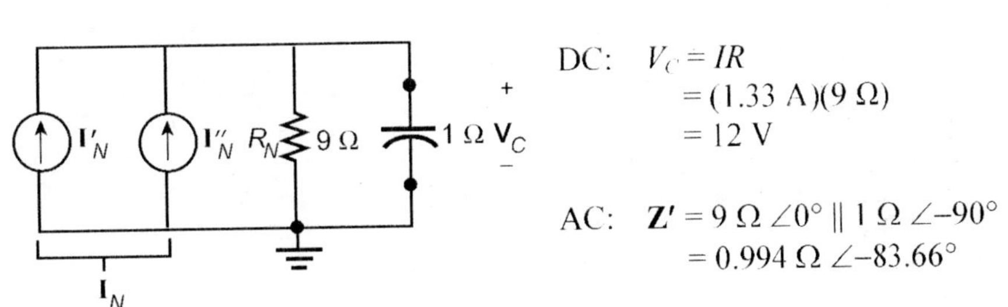

DC: $V_C = IR$
$= (1.33\text{ A})(9\ \Omega)$
$= 12\text{ V}$

AC: $\mathbf{Z}' = 9\ \Omega\ \angle 0° \parallel 1\ \Omega\ \angle -90°$
$= 0.994\ \Omega\ \angle -83.66°$

$$\mathbf{V}_C = \mathbf{I}\mathbf{Z}' = (2.667\text{ A}\ \angle 0°)(0.994\ \Omega\ \angle -83.66°)$$
$$= 2.65\text{ V}\ \angle -83.66°$$
$$V_C = \mathbf{12\ V + 2.65\ V\ \angle -83.66°}$$

32. a. Note Problem 17(a): $\mathbf{Z}_N = \mathbf{Z}_{Th} = \mathbf{4.47\ k\Omega\ \angle -26.57°}$

Using the same source conversion: $\mathbf{E}_1 = 50\text{ V}\ \angle 0°$

Defining $\mathbf{E}_T = \mathbf{E}_1 + \mathbf{E} = 50\text{ V}\ \angle 0° + 20\text{ V}\ \angle 0° = 70\text{ V}\ \angle 0°$

$\mathbf{Z}_1 = 10\text{ k}\Omega\ \angle 0°$
$\mathbf{Z}_2 = 5\text{ k}\Omega - j5\text{ k}\Omega = 7.071\text{ k}\Omega\ \angle -45°$

$$\mathbf{I}_{sc} = \frac{\mathbf{E}_T}{\mathbf{Z}_1} = \frac{70\text{ V}\ \angle 0°}{10\text{ k}\Omega\ \angle 0°} = 7\text{ mA}\ \angle 0°$$

$$\mathbf{I}_N = \mathbf{I}_{sc} = \mathbf{7\ mA\ \angle 0°}$$

b.
$$\mathbf{I} = \frac{\mathbf{Z}_N(\mathbf{I}_N)}{\mathbf{Z}_N + \mathbf{Z}_L} = \frac{(4.472\text{ k}\Omega\ \angle -26.565°)(7\text{ mA}\ \angle 0°)}{4.472\text{ k}\Omega\ \angle -26.565° + 5\text{ k}\Omega\ \angle 90°}$$
$$= \frac{31.30\text{ mA}\ \angle -26.565°}{4 - j2 + j5} = \frac{31.30\text{ mA}\ \angle -26.565°}{4 + j3}$$
$$= \frac{31.30\text{ mA}\ \angle -26.565°}{5\ \angle 36.87°} = \mathbf{6.26\ mA\ \angle 63.44°}\text{ as obtained in Problem 17.}$$

33.

$\mathbf{Z}_N$:

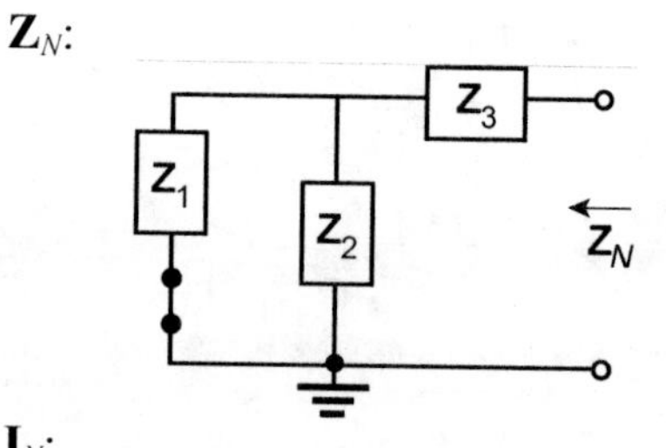

$\mathbf{Z}_1 = 10\text{ k}\Omega\ \angle 0°$, $\mathbf{Z}_2 = 10\text{ k}\Omega\ \angle 0$

$\mathbf{Z}_3 = -j1\text{ k}\Omega$

$\mathbf{Z}_N = \mathbf{Z}_3 + \mathbf{Z}_1 \parallel \mathbf{Z}_2 = 5\text{ k}\Omega - j1\text{ k}\Omega$

$= \mathbf{5.1\ k\Omega\ \angle{-11.31°}}$

$\mathbf{I}_N$:

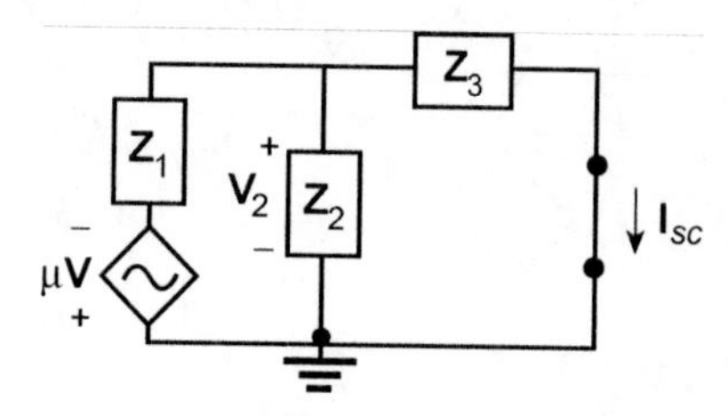

$$\mathbf{V}_2 = \frac{-(\mathbf{Z}_2 \parallel \mathbf{Z}_3)20\text{ V}}{(\mathbf{Z}_2 \parallel \mathbf{Z}_3) + \mathbf{Z}_1}$$

$$= \frac{-(0.995\text{ k}\Omega\ \angle -84.29°)(20\text{ V})}{0.1\text{ k}\Omega - j0.99\text{ k}\Omega + 10\text{ k}\Omega}$$

$V_2 = -1.961\text{ V}\ \angle{-78.69°}$

$$\mathbf{I}_N = \mathbf{I}_{sc} = \frac{\mathbf{V}_2}{\mathbf{Z}_3} = \frac{-1.961\text{ V}\ \angle -78.69°}{1\text{ k}\Omega\ \angle -90°} = \mathbf{-1.96 \times 10^{-3}\ V\ \angle 11.31°}$$

34. $\mathbf{Z}_N$:

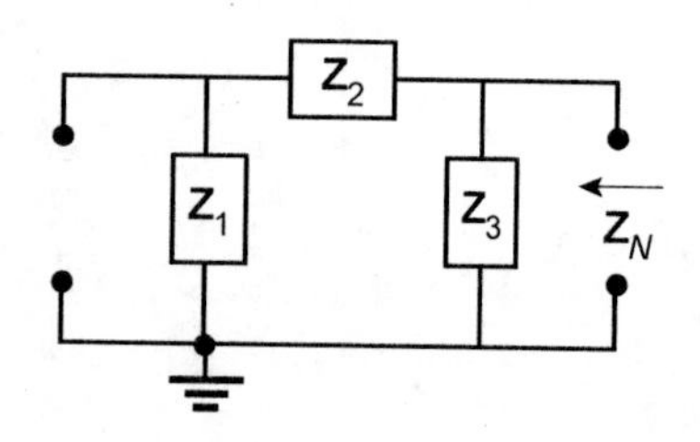

$\mathbf{Z}_1 = 40\text{ k}\Omega\ \angle 0°$, $\mathbf{Z}_2 = 0.2\text{ k}\Omega\ \angle{-90°}$

$\mathbf{Z}_3 = 5\text{ k}\Omega\ \angle 0°$

$\mathbf{Z}_N = \mathbf{Z}_3 \parallel (\mathbf{Z}_1 + \mathbf{Z}_2)$

$= 5\text{ k}\Omega\ \angle 0° \parallel (40\text{ k}\Omega - j0.2\text{ k}\Omega)$

$= \mathbf{4.44\ k\Omega\ \angle{-0.03°}}$

$\mathbf{I}_N$:

Z2 · 100 I · Z1 · Z3 · Isc · I3 = 0

$$\mathbf{I}_N = \mathbf{I}_{sc} = \frac{\mathbf{Z}_1(100\,\mathbf{I})}{\mathbf{Z}_1 + \mathbf{Z}_2}$$

$$= \frac{(40\text{ k}\Omega\ \angle 0°)(100\,\mathbf{I})}{40\text{ k}\Omega\ \angle -0.286°}$$

$= \mathbf{100\ I\ \angle 0.29°}$

35. $\mathbf{Z}_N$:

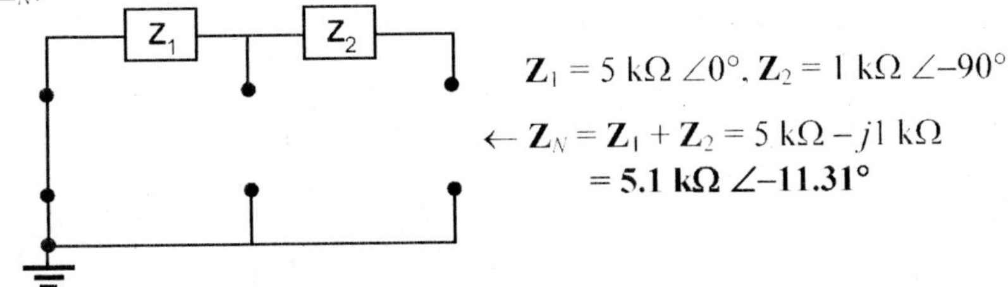

$\mathbf{Z}_1 = 5\text{ k}\Omega\ \angle 0°,\ \mathbf{Z}_2 = 1\text{ k}\Omega\ \angle{-90°}$

$\leftarrow \mathbf{Z}_N = \mathbf{Z}_1 + \mathbf{Z}_2 = 5\text{ k}\Omega - j1\text{ k}\Omega$
$= \mathbf{5.1\ k\Omega\ \angle{-11.31°}}$

$\mathbf{I}_N$:

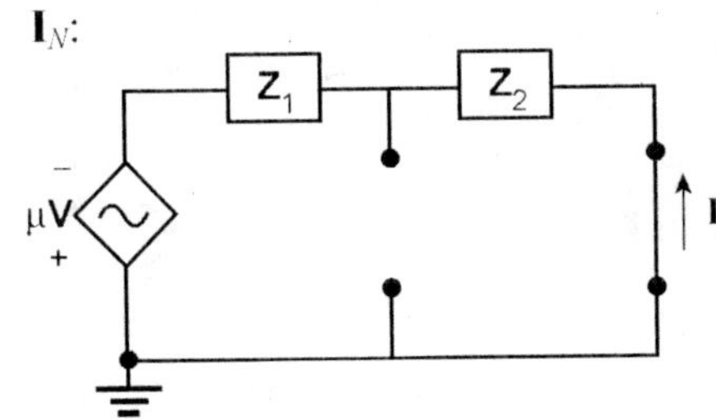

$$\mathbf{I}'_{sc} = \frac{\mu\mathbf{V}}{\mathbf{Z}_1 + \mathbf{Z}_2} = \frac{(20)(2\text{ V }\angle 0°)}{5.1\text{ k}\Omega\ \angle{-11.31°}}$$
$$= 7.843\text{ mA }\angle 11.31°$$

(**I**):

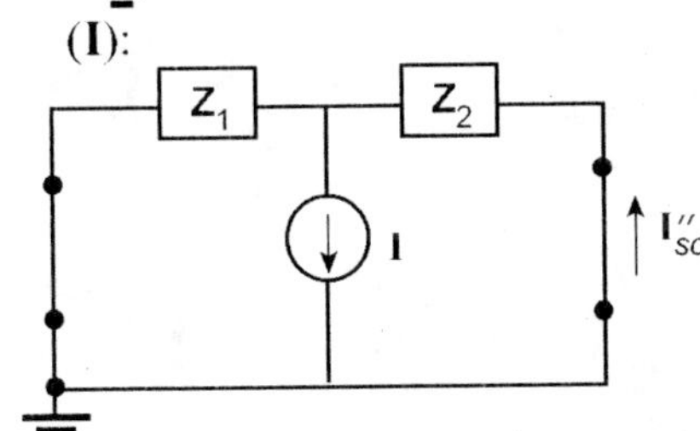

$$\mathbf{I}''_{sc} = \frac{\mathbf{Z}_1(\mathbf{I})}{\mathbf{Z}_1 + \mathbf{Z}_2}$$
$$= \frac{(5\text{ k}\Omega\ \angle 0°)(2\text{ mA }\angle 0°)}{5.1\text{ k}\Omega\ \angle{-11.31°}}$$
$$= 1.96\text{ mA }\angle 11.31°$$

$\mathbf{I}_N = \mathbf{I}'_{sc} + \mathbf{I}''_{sc} = 7.843\text{ mA }\angle 11.31° + 1.96\text{ mA }\angle 11.31°$
$= \mathbf{9.81\ mA\ \angle 11.31°}$

36. $\mathbf{Z}_N$:

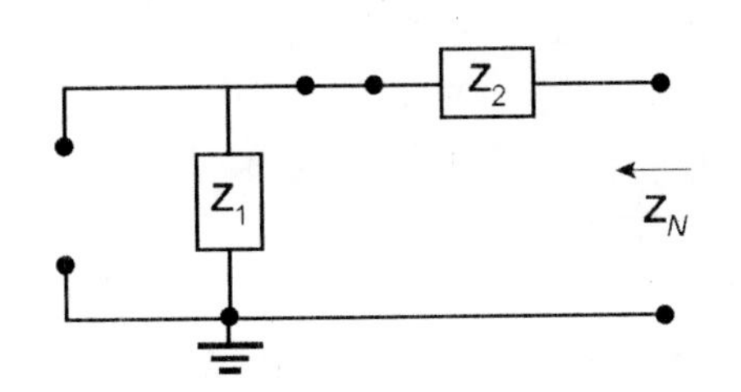

$\mathbf{Z}_1 = 20\text{ k}\Omega\ \angle 0°,\ \mathbf{Z}_2 = 5\text{ k}\Omega\ \angle 0°$
$\mathbf{V} = 10\text{ V }\angle 0°,\ \mu = 20,\ h = 100$
$\mathbf{I} = 1\text{ mA }\angle 0°$

$\mathbf{Z}_N = \mathbf{Z}_1 + \mathbf{Z}_2 = \mathbf{25\ k\Omega\ \angle 0°}$

$\mathbf{I}_N$: ($h\mathbf{I}$)

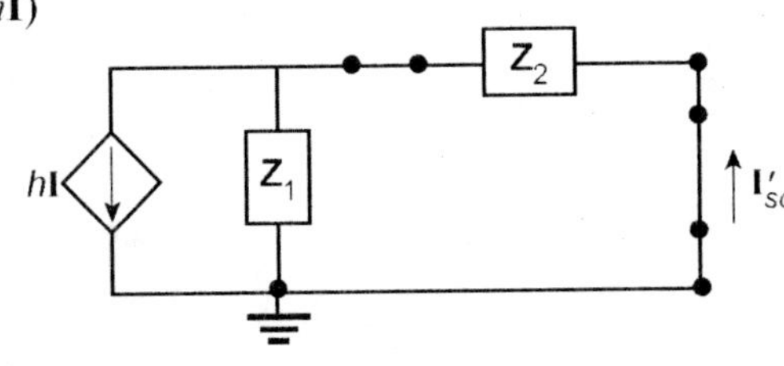

$$\mathbf{I}'_{sc} = \frac{\mathbf{Z}_1(h\mathbf{I})}{\mathbf{Z}_1 + \mathbf{Z}_2}$$
$$= \frac{(20\text{ k}\Omega\ \angle 0°)(h\mathbf{I})}{20\text{ k}\Omega\ \angle 0° + 5\text{ k}\Omega \angle 0°}$$
$$= 80\text{ mA }\angle 0°$$

($\mu\mathbf{V}$)

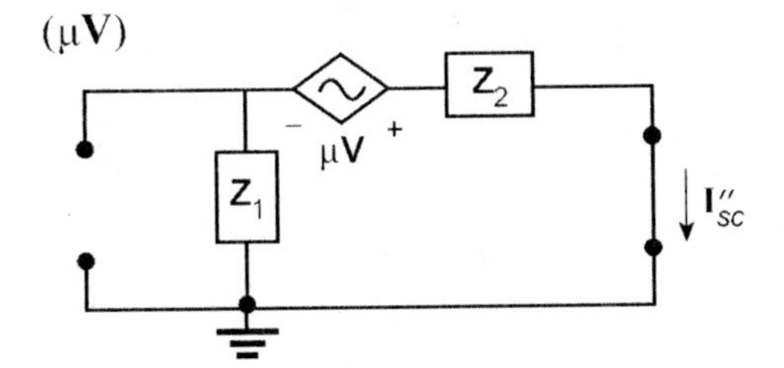

$$\mathbf{I}''_{sc} = \frac{\mu\mathbf{V}}{\mathbf{Z}_1 + \mathbf{Z}_2} = \frac{(20)(10\text{ V }\angle 0°)}{25\text{ k}\Omega}$$
$$= 8\text{ mA }\angle 0°$$

$\mathbf{I}_N$ (direction of $\mathbf{I}'_{sc}$) $= \mathbf{I}'_{sc} - \mathbf{I}''_{sc} = 80\text{ mA }\angle 0° - 8\text{ mA }\angle 0° = \mathbf{72\ mA\ \angle 0°}$

37.

$$\mathbf{Z}_1 = 1\text{ k}\Omega \angle 0°$$
$$\mathbf{Z}_2 = 3\text{ k}\Omega \angle 0°$$
$$\mathbf{Z}_3 = 4\text{ k}\Omega \angle 0°$$

$$\mathbf{V}_2 = 21\ \mathbf{V} = \mathbf{E}_{oc} \Rightarrow \mathbf{V} = \frac{\mathbf{E}_{oc}}{21}$$

$$\mathbf{I} = \mathbf{I}_1 + \mathbf{I}_2,\ \mathbf{I}_1 = \frac{\mathbf{V}}{\mathbf{Z}_1} = \frac{\mathbf{E}_{oc}}{21\mathbf{Z}_1}$$

$$\mathbf{I}_2 = \frac{\mathbf{E}_{oc}}{\mathbf{Z}_2},\ \mathbf{I} = \mathbf{I}_1 + \mathbf{I}_2 = \frac{\mathbf{E}_{oc}}{21\mathbf{Z}_1} + \frac{\mathbf{E}_{oc}}{\mathbf{Z}_2} = \mathbf{E}_{oc}\left[\frac{1}{21\mathbf{Z}_1} + \frac{1}{\mathbf{Z}_2}\right]$$

$$\mathbf{I} = \mathbf{E}_{oc}\left[\frac{\mathbf{Z}_2 + 21\ \mathbf{Z}_1}{21\ \mathbf{Z}_1\mathbf{Z}_2}\right]$$

and $\mathbf{E}_{oc} = \dfrac{21\mathbf{Z}_1\mathbf{Z}_2\mathbf{I}}{\mathbf{Z}_2 + 21\mathbf{Z}_1} = \dfrac{(21)(1\text{ k}\Omega \angle 0°)(3\text{ k}\Omega \angle 0°)(2\text{ mA} \angle 0°)}{3\text{ k}\Omega + 21(1\text{ k}\Omega \angle 0°)}$

$\mathbf{E}_{Th} = \mathbf{E}_{oc} = 5.25\text{ V} \angle 0°$

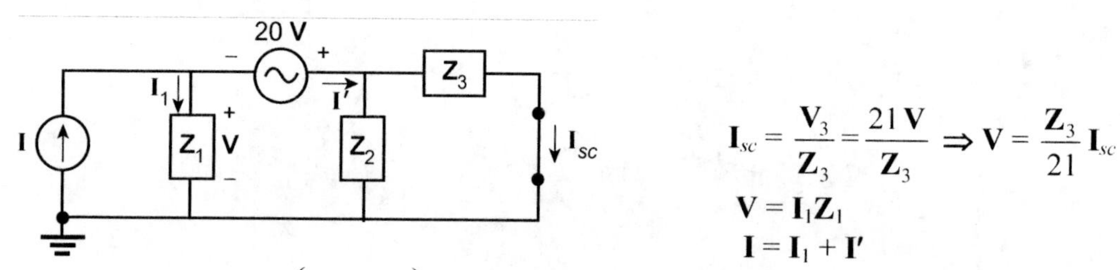

$$\mathbf{I}_{sc} = \frac{\mathbf{V}_3}{\mathbf{Z}_3} = \frac{21\mathbf{V}}{\mathbf{Z}_3} \Rightarrow \mathbf{V} = \frac{\mathbf{Z}_3}{21}\mathbf{I}_{sc}$$
$$\mathbf{V} = \mathbf{I}_1\mathbf{Z}_1$$
$$\mathbf{I} = \mathbf{I}_1 + \mathbf{I}'$$

$$\mathbf{I}_{sc} = \frac{\mathbf{Z}_2\mathbf{I}'}{\mathbf{Z}_2 + \mathbf{Z}_3} \Rightarrow \mathbf{I}' = \left(\frac{\mathbf{Z}_2 + \mathbf{Z}_3}{\mathbf{Z}_2}\right)\mathbf{I}_{sc}$$

$$\mathbf{I} = \mathbf{I}_1 + \mathbf{I}' = \frac{\mathbf{V}}{\mathbf{Z}_1} + \left(\frac{\mathbf{Z}_2 + \mathbf{Z}_3}{\mathbf{Z}_2}\right)\mathbf{I}_{sc} = \left[\frac{\mathbf{Z}_3}{21\ \mathbf{Z}_1} + \frac{\mathbf{Z}_2 + \mathbf{Z}_3}{\mathbf{Z}_2}\right]\mathbf{I}_{sc}$$

$$\mathbf{I}_{sc} = \frac{\mathbf{I}}{\dfrac{\mathbf{Z}_3}{21\ \mathbf{Z}_1} + \dfrac{\mathbf{Z}_3 + \mathbf{Z}_2}{\mathbf{Z}_2}} = \frac{2\text{ mA} \angle 0°}{\dfrac{4\text{ k}\Omega}{21\text{ k}\Omega} + \dfrac{7\text{ k}\Omega}{3\text{ k}\Omega}} = 0.79\text{ mA} \angle 0°$$

∴ $\mathbf{I}_N = \mathbf{0.79\ mA \angle 0°}$

$$\mathbf{Z}_N = \frac{\mathbf{E}_{oc}}{\mathbf{I}_{sc}} = \frac{5.25\text{ V} \angle 0°}{0.79\text{ mA} \angle 0°} = \mathbf{6.65\ k\Omega \angle 0°}$$

38.

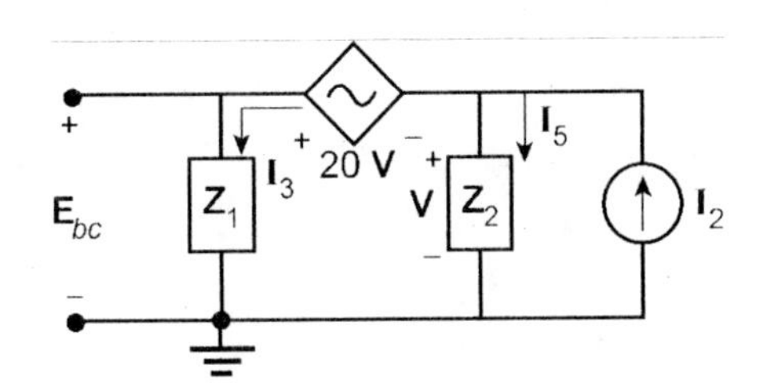

$\mathbf{Z}_1 = 2\text{ k}\Omega \angle 0°$
$\mathbf{Z}_2 = 5\text{ k}\Omega \angle 0°$

$$\mathbf{I}_2 = \mathbf{I}_3 + \mathbf{I}_5$$
$$\mathbf{V} = \mathbf{I}_5\mathbf{Z}_2 = (\mathbf{I}_2 - \mathbf{I}_3)\mathbf{Z}_2$$
$$\mathbf{E}_{oc} = \mathbf{E}_{Th} = 21\ \mathbf{V} = 21(\mathbf{I}_2 - \mathbf{I}_3)\mathbf{Z}_2$$
$$= 21\left(\mathbf{I}_2 - \frac{\mathbf{E}_{oc}}{\mathbf{Z}_1}\right)\mathbf{Z}_2$$

$$\mathbf{E}_{oc}\left[1 + 21\frac{\mathbf{Z}_2}{\mathbf{Z}_1}\right] = 21\ \mathbf{Z}_2\mathbf{I}_2$$

$$\mathbf{E}_{oc} = \frac{21\,\mathbf{Z}_2\mathbf{I}_2}{1 + 21\dfrac{\mathbf{Z}_2}{\mathbf{Z}_1}} = \frac{21(5\text{ k}\Omega \angle 0°)(2\text{ mA} \angle 0°)}{1 + 21\left(\dfrac{5\text{ k}\Omega \angle 0°}{2\text{ k}\Omega \angle 0°}\right)}$$

$$\mathbf{E}_{Th} = \mathbf{E}_{oc} = 3.925\text{ V} \angle 0°$$

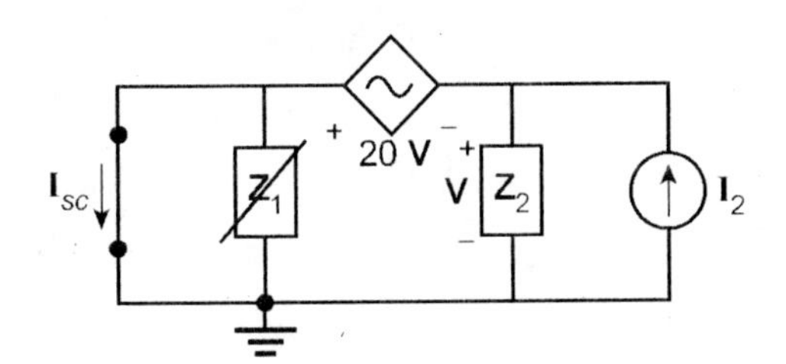

$20\ \mathbf{V} \neq -\mathbf{V}\ \therefore\ \mathbf{V} = 0$
and $\mathbf{I}_N = \mathbf{I}_{sc} = \mathbf{I}_2 =$ **$2\text{ mA} \angle 0°$**

$$\mathbf{Z}_N = \frac{\mathbf{E}_{oc}}{\mathbf{I}_{sc}} = \frac{3.925\text{ V} \angle 0°}{2\text{ mA} \angle 0°} = \mathbf{1.96\ k\Omega}$$

39. a.

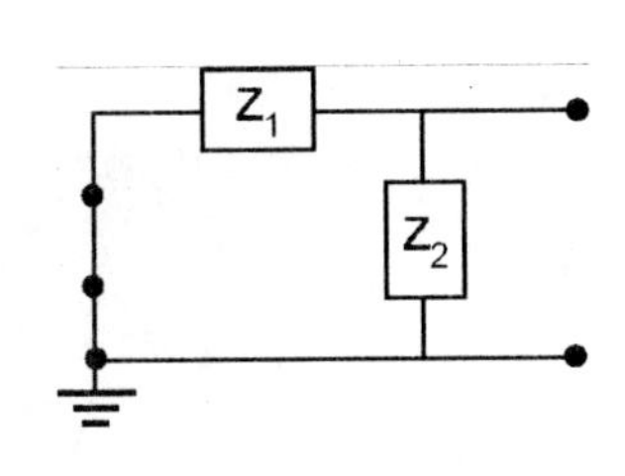

$\mathbf{Z}_1 = 3\ \Omega + j4\ \Omega,\ \mathbf{Z}_2 = -j6\ \Omega$
$\leftarrow \mathbf{Z}_{Th} = \mathbf{Z}_1 \parallel \mathbf{Z}_2$
$= 5\ \Omega \angle 53.13° \parallel 6\ \Omega \angle -90°$
$= 8.32\ \Omega \angle -3.18°$
$\mathbf{Z}_L = \mathbf{8.32\ \Omega \angle 3.18° = 8.31\ \Omega - j0.46\ \Omega}$

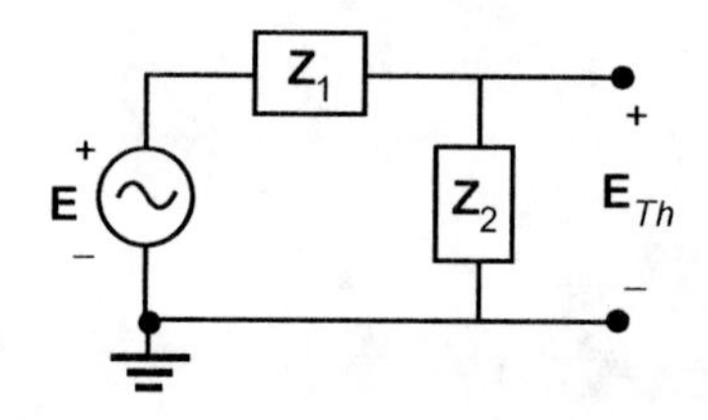

$$\mathbf{E}_{Th} = \frac{\mathbf{Z}_2\mathbf{E}}{\mathbf{Z}_2 + \mathbf{Z}_1}$$
$$= \frac{(6\,\Omega\,\angle-90°)(120\text{ V }\angle0°)}{3.61\,\Omega\,\angle-33.69°}$$
$$= \mathbf{199.45\text{ V }\angle{-56.31°}}$$
$$P_{max} = \frac{E_{Th}^2}{4R_{Th}} = \frac{(3.124\text{ V})^2}{4(8.31\,\Omega)} = \mathbf{1198.2\text{ W}}$$

b.

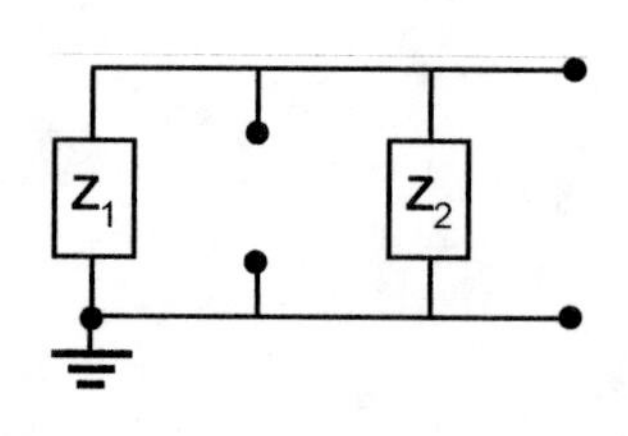

$$\mathbf{Z}_1 = 3\,\Omega + j4\,\Omega = 5\,\Omega\,\angle53.13°$$
$$\mathbf{Z}_2 = 2\,\Omega\,\angle0°$$
$$\leftarrow \mathbf{Z}_N = \mathbf{Z}_{Th} = \mathbf{Z}_1 \parallel \mathbf{Z}_2$$
$$= 5\,\Omega\,\angle53.13° \parallel 2\,\Omega\,\angle0°$$
$$= \frac{10\,\Omega\,\angle53.13°}{2 + 3 + j4}$$
$$= \frac{10\,\Omega\,\angle53.13°}{5 + j4}$$
$$= \frac{10\,\Omega\,\angle53.13°}{6.403\,\angle38.66°}$$
$$= \mathbf{1.56\,\Omega\,\angle14.47°}$$
$$\mathbf{Z}_{Th} = 1.56\,\Omega\,\angle14.47°$$
$$= 1.51\,\Omega + j0.39\,\Omega$$
$$\mathbf{Z}_L = \mathbf{1.51\,\Omega - j0.39\,\Omega}$$

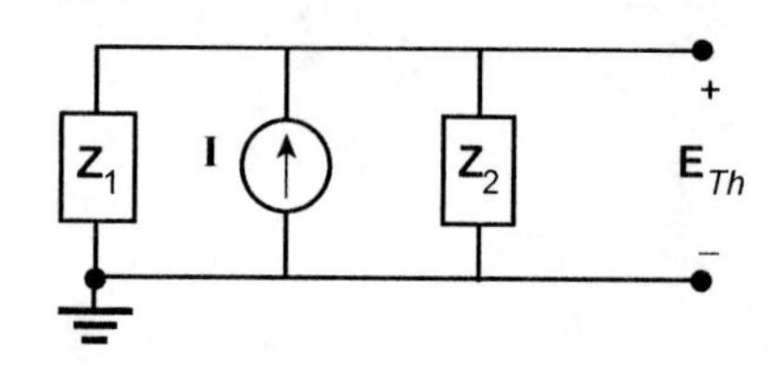

$$\mathbf{E}_{Th} = \mathbf{I}(\mathbf{Z}_1 \parallel \mathbf{Z}_2)$$
$$= (2\text{ A }\angle30°)(1.562\,\Omega\,\angle14.47°)$$
$$= \mathbf{3.12\text{ V }\angle44.47°}$$
$$P_{max} = \frac{E_{Th}^2}{4R_{Th}} = \frac{(3.12\text{ V})^2}{4(1.51\,\Omega)} = \mathbf{1.61\text{ W}}$$

40. a. $\mathbf{Z}_{Th}$:

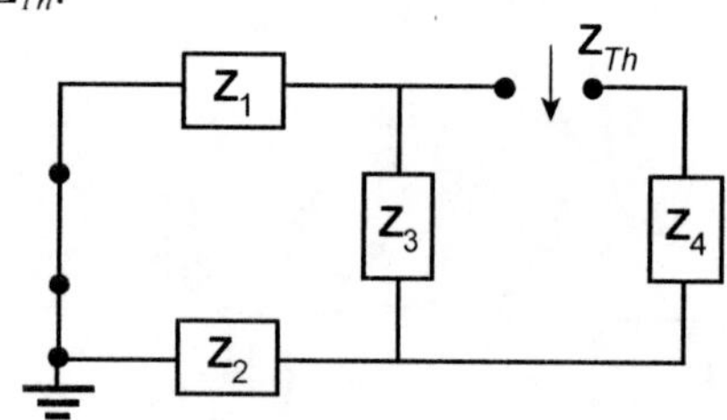

$\mathbf{Z}_1 = 4\,\Omega\,\angle90°$, $\mathbf{Z}_2 = 10\,\Omega\,\angle0°$
$\mathbf{Z}_3 = 5\,\Omega\,\angle-90°$, $\mathbf{Z}_4 = 6\,\Omega\,\angle-90°$
$\mathbf{E} = 60\text{ V }\angle60°$

$$\mathbf{Z}_{Th} = \mathbf{Z}_4 + \mathbf{Z}_3 \parallel (\mathbf{Z}_1 + \mathbf{Z}_2) = -j6\,\Omega + (5\,\Omega\,\angle-90°) \parallel (10\,\Omega + j4\,\Omega)$$
$$= 2.475\,\Omega - j4.754\,\Omega$$
$$= 11.04\,\Omega\,\angle-77.03°$$
$$\mathbf{Z}_L = \mathbf{11.04\,\Omega\,\angle77.03°}$$

$\mathbf{E}_{Th}$:

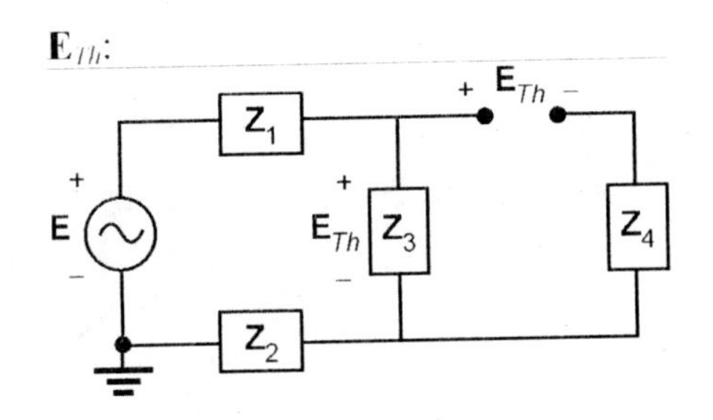

$$\mathbf{E}_{Th} = \frac{\mathbf{Z}_3(\mathbf{E})}{\mathbf{Z}_3 + \mathbf{Z}_1 + \mathbf{Z}_2} = \frac{(5\ \Omega\ \angle -90°)(60\ \text{V}\ \angle 60°)}{-j5\ \Omega + j4\ \Omega + 10\ \Omega} = \mathbf{29.85\ V\ \angle{-24.29°}}$$

$P_{\max} = E_{Th}^2/4R_{Th} = (29.85\ \text{V})^2/4(2.475\ \Omega) = \mathbf{90\ W}$

b.

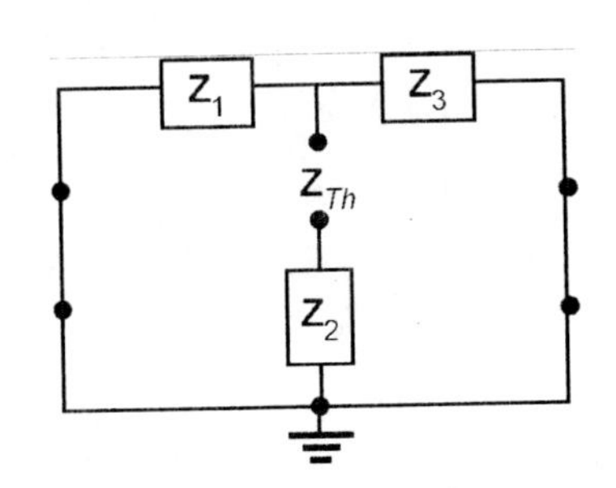

$\mathbf{Z}_1 = 3\ \Omega + j4\ \Omega = 5\ \Omega\ \angle 53.13°$
$\mathbf{Z}_2 = -j8\ \Omega$
$\mathbf{Z}_3 = 12\ \Omega + j9\ \Omega$

$\mathbf{Z}_{Th} = \mathbf{Z}_2 + \mathbf{Z}_1 \parallel \mathbf{Z}_3 = -j8\ \Omega + (5\ \Omega\ \angle 53.13°) \parallel (15\ \Omega\ \angle 36.87°)$
$= 5.71\ \Omega\ \angle{-64.30°} = 2.475\ \Omega - j5.143\ \Omega$
$\mathbf{Z}_L = \mathbf{5.71\ \Omega\ \angle 64.30° = 2.48\ \Omega + \mathit{j}5.15\ \Omega}$

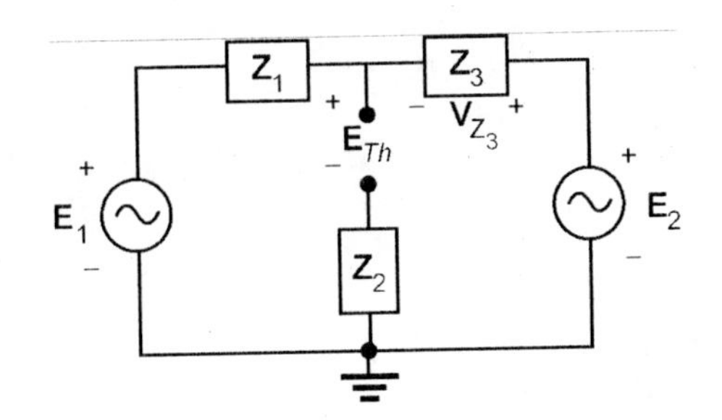

$\mathbf{E}_{Th} + \mathbf{V}_{Z_3} - \mathbf{E}_2 = 0$
$\mathbf{E}_{Th} = \mathbf{E}_2 - \mathbf{V}_{Z_3}$

$$\mathbf{V}_{Z_3} = \frac{\mathbf{Z}_3(\mathbf{E}_2 - \mathbf{E}_1)}{\mathbf{Z}_3 + \mathbf{Z}_1} = 168.97\ \text{V}\ \angle 112.53°$$

$\mathbf{E}_{Th} = \mathbf{E}_2 - \mathbf{V}_{Z_3} = 200\ \text{V}\ \angle 90° - 168.97\ \text{V}\ \angle 112.53° = \mathbf{78.24\ V\ \angle 34.16°}$

$P_{\max} = E_{Th}^2/4R_{Th} = (78.24\ \text{V})^2/4(2.475\ \Omega) = \mathbf{618.33\ W}$

41. $\mathbf{I} = \dfrac{E\angle 0°}{R_1\angle 0°} = \dfrac{1\ \text{V}\ \angle 0°}{1\ \text{k}\Omega\ \angle 0°} = 1\ \text{mA}\ \angle 0°$

$\mathbf{Z}_{Th} = 40\ \text{k}\Omega\ \angle 0°$
$\mathbf{E}_{Th} = (50\ \mathbf{I})(40\ \text{k}\Omega\ \angle 0°) = (50)(1\ \text{mA}\ \angle 0°)(40\ \text{k}\Omega\ \angle 0°) = 2000\ \text{V}\ \angle 0°$

$$P_{\max} = \frac{E_{Th}^2}{4R_{Th}} = \frac{(2\ \text{kV})^2}{4(40\ \text{k}\Omega)} = \mathbf{25\ W}$$

42. a. $\mathbf{Z}_{Th} = \mathbf{Z}_N = 8\ \Omega\ \angle 0°$ (Problem 30(b))

$\mathbf{Z}_L = \mathbf{8\ \Omega\ \angle 0°}$

$\mathbf{E}_{Th} = \mathbf{I}_N \cdot \mathbf{Z}_N$: DC: $\mathbf{E}_{Th} = \mathbf{I}'_N \cdot \mathbf{Z}_N = (0.5\text{ A})(8\ \Omega) = 4\text{ V}$

AC: $\mathbf{E}_{Th} = \mathbf{I}'_N \cdot \mathbf{Z}_N = (1.25\text{ A}\ \angle 0°)(8\ \Omega\ \angle 0°) = 10\text{ V}$

b. $$P_{max} = \frac{E_{Th}^2}{4R_{Th}} = \frac{(4\text{ V})^2}{4(8\ \Omega)} + \frac{(10\text{ V})^2}{4(8\ \Omega)} = 0.5\text{ W} + 3.13\text{ W} = \mathbf{3.63\ W}$$

43. From #16, $\mathbf{Z}_{Th} = 9\ \Omega$, $\mathbf{E}_{Th} = 12\text{ V} + 24\text{ V}\ \angle 0°$

a. $\therefore \mathbf{Z}_L = 9\ \Omega$

b. $$P_{max} = \frac{E_{Th}^2}{4R_{Th}} = \frac{(12\text{ V})^2}{4(9\ \Omega)} + \frac{(24\text{ V})^2}{4(9\ \Omega)} = 4\text{ W} + 16\text{ W} = \mathbf{20\ W}$$

or $E_{Th} = \sqrt{V_0^2 + V_{1_{\text{eff}}}^2} = 26.833\text{ V}$

and $$P_{max} = \frac{E_{Th}^2}{4R_{Th}} = \frac{(26.833\text{ V})^2}{4(9\ \Omega)} = \mathbf{20\ W}$$

44. a. Problem 17(a):

$\mathbf{Z}_{Th} = 4.47\text{ k}\Omega\ \angle -26.57° = 4\text{ k}\Omega - j2\text{ k}\Omega$

$\mathbf{Z}_L = \mathbf{4\ k\Omega + \mathit{j}2\ k\Omega}$

$\mathbf{E}_{Th} = \mathbf{31.31\ V\ \angle -26.57°}$

b. $P_{max} = E_{Th}^2/4R_{Th} = (31.31\text{ V})^2/4(4\text{ k}\Omega) = \mathbf{61.27\ mW}$

45. a. $\mathbf{Z}_{Th} = 2\text{ k}\Omega\ \angle 0° \parallel 2\text{ k}\Omega\ \angle -90° = 1\text{ k}\Omega - j1\text{ k}\Omega$

$$R_L = \sqrt{R_{Th}^2 + (X_{Th} + X_{\text{Load}})^2}$$
$$= \sqrt{(1\text{ k}\Omega)^2 + (-1\text{ k}\Omega + 2\text{ k}\Omega)^2}$$
$$= \sqrt{(1\text{ k}\Omega)^2 + (1\text{ k}\Omega)^2}$$
$$= \mathbf{1.41\ k\Omega}$$

b. $R_{av} = (R_{Th} + R_{\text{Load}})/2 = (1\text{ k}\Omega + 1.41\text{ k}\Omega)/2 = 1.21\text{ k}\Omega$

$$P_{max} = \frac{E_{Th}^2}{4R_{av}} = \frac{(50\text{ V})^2}{4(1.21\text{ k}\Omega)} = \mathbf{516.53\ mW}$$

46. **a.** $\mathbf{Z}_{Th}$:

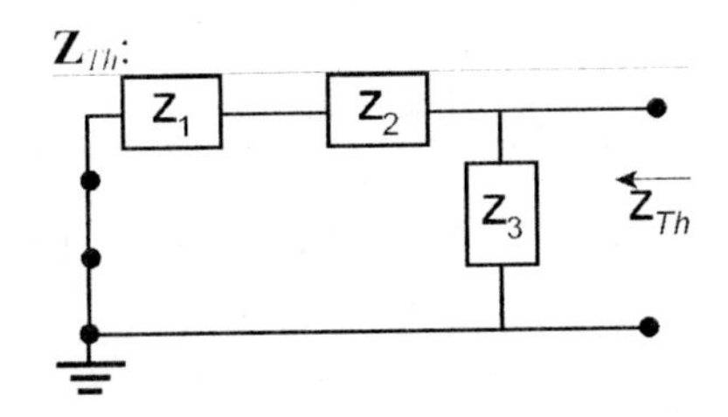

$$X_C = \frac{1}{2\pi fC} = \frac{1}{2\pi(10\text{ kHz})(4\text{ nF})} \cong 3978.87\ \Omega$$

$$X_L = 2\pi fL = 2\pi(10\text{ kHz})(30\text{ mH}) \cong 1884.96\ \Omega$$

$\mathbf{Z}_1 = 1\text{ k}\Omega\ \angle 0°$, $\mathbf{Z}_2 = 1884.96\ \Omega\ \angle 90°$

$\mathbf{Z}_3 = 3978.87\ \Omega\ \angle{-90°}$

$$\mathbf{Z}_{Th} = (\mathbf{Z}_1 + \mathbf{Z}_2) \parallel \mathbf{Z}_3 = (1\text{ k}\Omega + j1884.96\ \Omega) \parallel 3978.87\ \Omega\ \angle{-90°})$$
$$= 2133.79\ \Omega\ \angle 62.05° \parallel 3978.87\ \Omega\ \angle{-90°})$$
$$= 3658.65\ \Omega\ \angle 36.52°$$

$$\therefore\ \mathbf{Z}_L = \mathbf{3658.65\ \Omega\ \angle{-36.52°} = 2940.27\ \Omega - j2177.27\ \Omega}$$

$$C = \frac{1}{2\pi fX_C} = \frac{1}{2\pi(10\text{ kHz})(2177.27\ \Omega)} = \mathbf{7.31\ nF}$$

b. $R_L = R_{Th} = \mathbf{2940.27\ \Omega}$

c. $$\mathbf{E}_{Th} = \frac{\mathbf{Z}_3(\mathbf{E})}{\mathbf{Z}_3 + \mathbf{Z}_1 + \mathbf{Z}_2} = \frac{(3978.87\ \Omega\ \angle{-90°})(2\text{ V}\angle 0°)}{1\text{ k}\Omega + j1884.96\ \Omega - j3978.87\Omega} = 3.43\text{ V}\angle{-25.53°})$$

$$P_{max} = E_{Th}^2/4R_{Th} = (3.43\text{ V})^2/4(2940.27\ \Omega) = \mathbf{1\ mW}$$

47. $$\mathbf{I}_{ab} = \frac{(4\text{ k}\Omega\ \angle 0°)(4\text{ mA}\ \angle 0°)}{4\text{ k}\Omega + 8\text{ k}\Omega} = \mathbf{1.33\ mA\ \angle 0°}$$

$$\mathbf{V}_{ab} = (\mathbf{I}_{ab})(8\text{ k}\Omega\ \angle 0°) = \mathbf{10.67\ V\ \angle 0°}$$

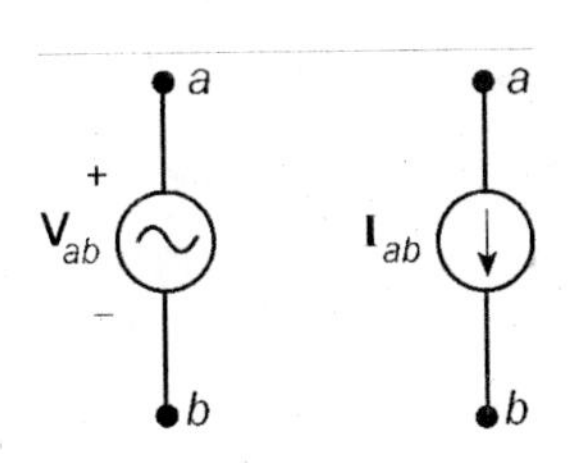

48. a.

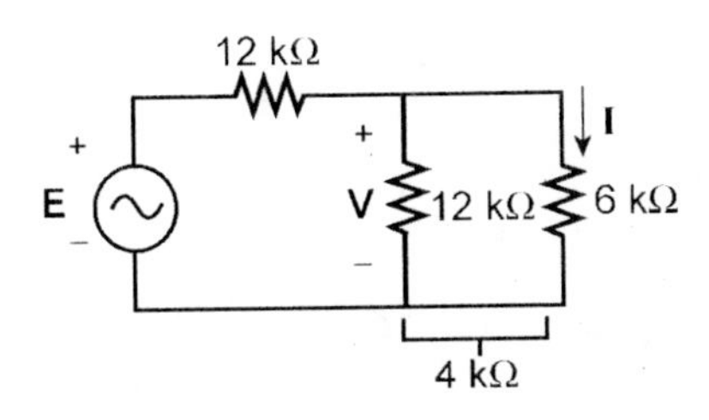

$$\mathbf{V} = \frac{4\text{ k}\Omega(\mathbf{E})}{4\text{ k}\Omega + 12\text{ k}\Omega} = \frac{1}{4}(20\text{ V}\ \angle 0°) = 5\text{ V}\ \angle 0°$$

$$\mathbf{I} = \frac{5\text{ V}\ \angle 0°}{6\text{ k}\Omega} = \mathbf{0.83\ mA\ \angle 0°}$$

b.

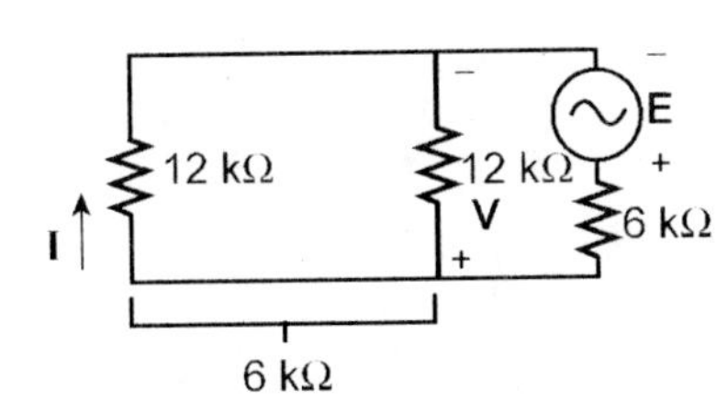

$$\mathbf{V} = \frac{6\text{ k}\Omega(\mathbf{E})}{6\text{ k}\Omega + 6\text{ k}\Omega} = \frac{1}{2}(20\text{ V}\ \angle 0°) = 10\text{ V}\ \angle 0°$$

$$\mathbf{I} = \frac{10\text{ V}\ \angle 0°}{12\text{ k}\Omega} = \mathbf{0.83\ mA\ \angle 0°}$$

49.

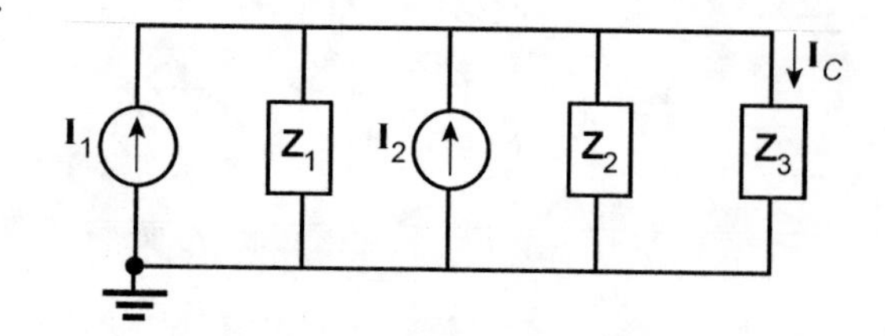

$$\mathbf{I}_1 = \frac{100\text{ V}\angle 0°}{2\text{ k}\Omega\angle 0°} = 50\text{ mA}\angle 0°$$

$$\mathbf{I}_2 = \frac{50\text{ V}\angle 0°}{4\text{ k}\Omega\angle 90°}$$

$$= 12.5\text{ mA}\angle -90°$$

$\mathbf{Z}_1 = 2\text{ k}\Omega\angle 0°$

$\mathbf{Z}_2 = 4\text{ k}\Omega\angle 90°$

$\mathbf{Z}_3 = 4\text{ k}\Omega\angle -90°$

$\mathbf{I}_T = \mathbf{I}_1 - \mathbf{I}_2 = (50\text{ mA}\angle 0° - 12.5\text{ mA}\angle -90°) = 50\text{ mA} + j12.5\text{ mA}$

$= 51.54\text{ mA}\angle 14.04°$

$\mathbf{Z}' = \mathbf{Z}_1 \parallel \mathbf{Z}_2 = (2\text{ k}\Omega\angle 0°) \parallel (4\text{ k}\Omega\angle 90°) = 1.79\text{ k}\Omega\angle 26.57°$

$$\mathbf{I}_C = \frac{\mathbf{Z}'\mathbf{I}_T}{\mathbf{Z}' + \mathbf{Z}_3} = \frac{(1.79\text{ k}\Omega\angle 26.57°)(51.54\text{ mA}\angle 14.04°)}{1.6\text{ k}\Omega + j0.8\text{ k}\Omega - j4\text{ k}\Omega}$$

$= \mathbf{25.77\text{ mA}\angle 104.04°}$

Chapter 19

1. a. $P_T = 60\text{ W} + 20\text{ W} + 40\text{ W} = \mathbf{120\text{ W}}$

   b. $Q_T = \mathbf{0\text{ VARS}}$, $S_T = P_T = \mathbf{120\text{ VA}}$

   c. $S_T = EI_s$, $I_s = \dfrac{S_T}{E} = \dfrac{120\text{ VA}}{240\text{ V}} = \mathbf{0.5\text{ A}}$

   d. $P = I_s^2 R$, $R = \dfrac{P}{I_s^2} = \dfrac{60\text{ W}}{(0.5\text{ A})^2} = 240\ \Omega$

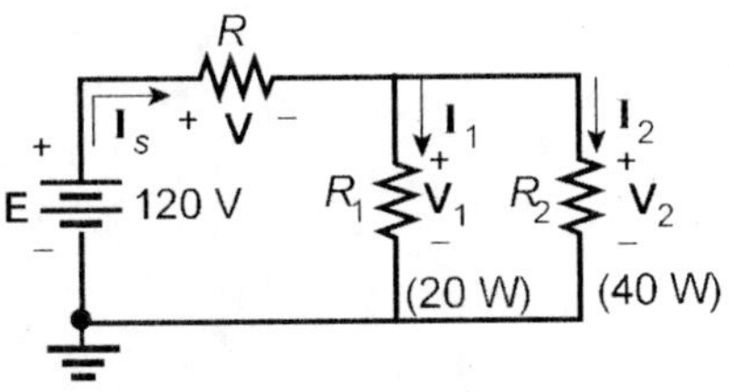

   $V = I_s R = (0.5\text{ A})(240\ \Omega) = 120\text{ V}$

   $V_1 = V_2 = E - V = 240\text{ V} - 120\text{ V} = 120\text{ V}$

   $P_1 = \dfrac{V_1^2}{R_1}$, $R_1 = \dfrac{V_1^2}{P_1} = \dfrac{(120\text{ V})^2}{20\text{ W}} = \mathbf{720\ \Omega}$

   $P_2 = \dfrac{V_2^2}{R_2}$, $R_2 = \dfrac{V_2^2}{P_2} = \dfrac{(120\text{ V})^2}{40\text{ W}} = \mathbf{360\ \Omega}$

   e. $I_1 = \dfrac{V_1}{R_1} = \dfrac{120\text{ V}}{720\ \Omega} = \mathbf{0.17\text{ A}}$, $I_2 = \dfrac{V_2}{R_2} = \dfrac{120\text{ V}}{360\ \Omega} = \mathbf{0.33\text{ A}}$

2. a. $\mathbf{Z}_T = 3\ \Omega - j5\ \Omega + j9\ \Omega = 3\ \Omega + j4\ \Omega = 5\ \Omega\ \angle 53.13^\circ$

   $\mathbf{I} = \dfrac{\mathbf{E}}{\mathbf{Z}_T} = \dfrac{50\text{ V}\ \angle 0^\circ}{5\ \Omega\ \angle 53.13^\circ} = 10\text{ A}\ \angle -53.13^\circ$

   R: $P = I^2R = (10\text{ A})^2\ 3\ \Omega = \mathbf{300\text{ W}}$
   L: $P = \mathbf{0\text{ W}}$
   C: $P = \mathbf{0\text{ W}}$

   b. R: $Q = \mathbf{0\text{ VAR}}$
   C: $Q_C = I^2X_C = (10\text{ A})^2\ 5\ \Omega = \mathbf{500\text{ VAR}}$
   L: $Q_L = I^2X_L = (10\text{ A})^2\ 9\ \Omega = \mathbf{900\text{ VAR}}$

   c. R: $S = \mathbf{300\text{ VA}}$
   C: $S = \mathbf{500\text{ VA}}$
   L: $S = \mathbf{900\text{ VA}}$

   d. $P_T = 300\text{ W}$
   $Q_T = Q_L - Q_C = \mathbf{400\text{ VAR}(L)}$
   $S_T = \sqrt{P_T^2 + Q_T^2} = EI = (50\text{ V})(10\text{ A}) = \mathbf{500\text{ VA}}$
   $F_p = \dfrac{P_T}{S_T} = \dfrac{300\text{ W}}{500\text{ VA}} = \mathbf{0.6\text{ lagging}}$

   e. –

f. $W_R = \frac{VI}{f_1}$: $W_R = 2\left[\frac{VI}{f_2}\right] = 2\left[\frac{VI}{2f_1}\right] = \frac{VI}{f_1}$

$V = IR = (10\text{ A})(3\ \Omega) = 30\text{ V}$

$$W_R = \frac{(30\text{ V})(10\text{ A})}{60\text{ Hz}} = \mathbf{5\ J}$$

g. $V_C = IX_C = (10\text{ A})(5\ \Omega) = 50\text{ V}$

$$W_C = \frac{VI}{\omega_1} = \frac{(50\text{ V})(10\text{ A})}{(2\pi)(60\text{ Hz})} = \mathbf{1.33\ J}$$

$V_L = IX_L = (10\text{ A})(9\ \Omega) = 90\text{ V}$

$$W_L = \frac{VI}{\omega_1} = \frac{(90\text{ V})(10\text{ A})}{376.8} = \mathbf{2.39\ J}$$

3. a. $P_T = 0 + 100\text{ W} + 300\text{ W} = \mathbf{400\ W}$

$Q_T = 200\text{ VAR}(L) - 600\text{ VAR}(C) + 0 = \mathbf{-400\ VAR(\mathit{C})}$

$S_T = \sqrt{P_T^2 + Q_T^2} = \mathbf{565.69\ VA}$

$$F_p = \frac{P_T}{S_T} = \frac{400\text{ W}}{565.69\text{ VA}} = \mathbf{0.707\ (leading)}$$

b. –

c. $P_T = EI_s \cos\theta_T$

$400\text{ W} = (100\text{ V})I_s(0.7071)$

$$I_s = \frac{400\text{ W}}{70.71\text{ V}} = 5.66\text{ A}$$

$\mathbf{I}_s = 5.66\text{ A} \angle 135°$

4. a. $P_T = 600\text{ W} + 500\text{ W} + 100\text{ W} = \mathbf{1200\ W}$

$Q_T = 1200\text{ VAR}(L) + 600\text{ VAR}(L) - 600\text{ VAR}(C) = \mathbf{1200\ VAR(\mathit{L})}$

$S_T = \sqrt{P_T^2 + Q_T^2} = \sqrt{(1200\text{ W})^2 + (1200\text{ VAR})^2} = \mathbf{1697\ VA}$

b. $F_p = \frac{P_T}{S_T} = \frac{1200\text{ W}}{1697\text{ VA}} = \mathbf{0.7071\ (lagging)}$

c. –

d. $I_s = \frac{S_T}{E} = \frac{1697\text{ VA}}{200\text{ V}} = 8.485\text{ A},\ 0.7071 \Rightarrow 45°\text{ (lagging)}$

$\mathbf{I_s = 8.49\ A \angle{-45°}}$

5. a. $P_T = 200\text{ W} + 200\text{ W} + 0 + 100\text{ W} = \mathbf{500\ W}$

$Q_T = 100\text{ VAR}(L) + 100\text{ VAR}(L) - 200\text{ VAR}(C) - 200\text{ VAR}(C) = \mathbf{-200\ VAR(\mathit{C})}$

$S_T = \sqrt{P_T^2 + Q_T^2} = \mathbf{538.52\ VA}$

b. $F_p = \frac{P_T}{S_T} = \frac{500 \text{ W}}{538.52 \text{ VA}} = \mathbf{0.928 \text{ (leading)}}$

c. –

d. $P_T = EI_s \cos \theta_T$

$500 \text{ W} = (50 \text{ V})I_s(0.928)$

$I_s = \frac{500 \text{ W}}{46.4 \text{ V}} = 10.776 \text{ A}$

$\mathbf{I}_s = \mathbf{10.78 \text{ A} \angle 21.88°}$

6. a. $\mathbf{I}_R = \frac{60 \text{ V} \angle 30°}{20 \,\Omega \angle 0°} = 3 \text{ A} \angle 30°$

$P = I^2R = (3 \text{ A})^2\, 20\,\Omega = \mathbf{180 \text{ W}}$

$Q_R = \mathbf{0 \text{ VAR}}$

$S = P = \mathbf{180 \text{ VA}}$

b. $\mathbf{I}_L = \frac{60 \text{ V} \angle 30°}{10\,\Omega \angle 90°} = 6 \text{ A} \angle -60°$

$P_L = \mathbf{0 \text{ W}}$

$Q_L = I^2X_L = (6 \text{ A})^2\, 10\,\Omega = \mathbf{360 \text{ VAR}(L)}$

$S = Q = \mathbf{360 \text{ VA}}$

c. $P_T = 180 \text{ W} + 400 \text{ W} = \mathbf{580 \text{ W}}$

$Q_T = 600 \text{ VAR}(L) + 360 \text{ VAR}(L) = \mathbf{960 \text{ VAR}(L)}$

$S_T = \sqrt{(580 \text{ W})^2 + (960 \text{ VAR})^2} = \mathbf{1121.61 \text{ VA}}$

$F_p = \frac{P_T}{S_T} = \frac{580 \text{ W}}{1121.61 \text{ VA}} = \mathbf{0.517 \text{ (lagging)}}$ $\theta = 58.87°$

d. $S_T = EI_s$

$I_s = \frac{S_T}{E} = \frac{1121.61 \text{ VA}}{60 \text{ V}} = 18.69 \text{ A}$

$\theta_{I_s} = 30° - 58.87° = -28.87°$

$\mathbf{I}_s = \mathbf{18.69 \text{ A} \angle -28.87°}$

7. a. R: $P = \frac{E^2}{R} = \frac{(20 \text{ V})^2}{2\,\Omega} = \mathbf{200 \text{ W}}$

$P_{L,C} = \mathbf{0 \text{ W}}$

b. R: $Q = \mathbf{0 \text{ VAR}}$

C: $Q_C = \frac{E^2}{X_C} = \frac{(20 \text{ V})^2}{5\,\Omega} = \mathbf{80 \text{ VAR}(C)}$

L: $Q_L = \frac{E^2}{X_L} = \frac{(20 \text{ V})^2}{4\,\Omega} = \mathbf{100 \text{ VAR}(L)}$

c. R: $S = \mathbf{200\ VA}$
C: $S = \mathbf{80\ VA}$
L: $S = \mathbf{100\ VA}$

d. $P_T = 200\ \text{W} + 0 + 0 = \mathbf{200\ W}$
$Q_T = 0 + 80\ \text{VAR}(C) + 100\ \text{VAR}(L) = \mathbf{20\ VAR(}\boldsymbol{L}\mathbf{)}$
$S_T = \sqrt{(200\ \text{W})^2 + (20\ \text{VAR})^2} = \mathbf{200\ VA}$
$F_p = \dfrac{P_T}{S_T} = \dfrac{200\ \text{W}}{200.998\ \text{VA}} = \mathbf{0.995\ (lagging)} \Rightarrow 5.73°$

e. –

f. $I_s = \dfrac{S_T}{E} = \dfrac{200.998\ \text{VA}}{20\ \text{V}} = 10.05\ \text{A}$
$\mathbf{I}_s = 10.05\ \text{A}\angle{-5.73°}$

8. a. $R - L$: $\mathbf{I} = \dfrac{50\ \text{V}\ \angle 60°}{5\ \Omega\ \angle 53.13°} = 10\ \text{A}\ \angle 6.87°$
$P_R = I^2R = (10\ \text{A})^2\ 3\ \Omega = \mathbf{300\ W}$
$P_L = \mathbf{0\ W}$
$P_C = \mathbf{0\ W}$

b. $Q_R = \mathbf{0\ VAR}$
$Q_L = I^2X_L = (10\ \text{A})^2\ 4\ \Omega = \mathbf{400\ VAR}$
$\mathbf{I}_C = \dfrac{50\ \text{V}\ \angle 60°}{10\ \Omega\ \angle{-90°}} = 5\ \text{A}\ \angle 150°$
$Q_C = I^2X_C = (5\ \text{A})^2\ 10\ \Omega = \mathbf{250\ VAR}$

c. $S_R = P = \mathbf{300\ VA}$
$S_L = Q_L = \mathbf{400\ VA}$
$S_C = Q_C = \mathbf{250\ VA}$

d. $P_T = P_R = \mathbf{300\ W}$
$Q_T = 400\ \text{VAR}(L) - 250\ \text{VAR}(C) = \mathbf{150\ VAR(}\boldsymbol{L}\mathbf{)}$
$S_T = \sqrt{(300\ \text{W})^2 + (150\ \text{VAR})^2} = \mathbf{335.41\ VA}$
$F_p = \dfrac{P_T}{S_T} = \dfrac{300\ \text{W}}{335.41\ \text{VA}} = \mathbf{0.894\ (lagging)}$

e. –

f. $I_s = \dfrac{S_T}{E} = \dfrac{335.41\ \text{VA}}{50\ \text{V}} = 6.71\ \text{A}$
$0.894 \Rightarrow 26.62°$ lagging
$\theta = 60° - 26.62° = 33.38°$
$\mathbf{I}_s = \mathbf{6.71\ A\ \angle 33.38°}$

9. a–c.

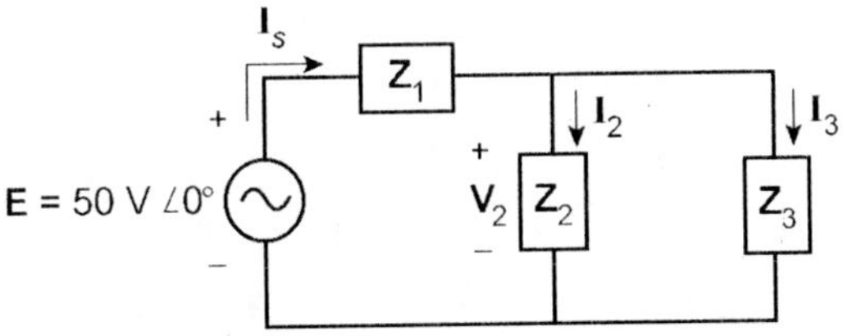

$E = 50\text{ V} \angle 0°$, $\mathbf{I}_s$, $\mathbf{Z}_1$, $\mathbf{I}_2$, $\mathbf{I}_3$, V_2, Z_2, Z_3

$X_L = \omega L = (400\text{ rad/s})(0.1\text{ H}) = 40\ \Omega$

$X_C = \dfrac{1}{\omega C} = \dfrac{1}{(400\text{ rad/s})(100\ \mu\text{F})}$

$= 25\ \Omega$

$\mathbf{Z}_1 = 40\ \Omega \angle 90°$, $\mathbf{Z}_2 = 25\ \Omega \angle -90°$

$\mathbf{Z}_3 = 30\ \Omega \angle 0°$

$$\begin{aligned}\mathbf{Z}_T = \mathbf{Z}_1 + \mathbf{Z}_2 \parallel \mathbf{Z}_3 &= +j40\ \Omega + (25\ \Omega \angle -90°) \parallel (30\ \Omega \angle 0°)\\ &= +j40\ \Omega + 19.21\ \Omega \angle -50.19°\\ &= +j40\ \Omega + 12.3\ \Omega - j14.76\ \Omega\\ &= 12.3\ \Omega + j25.24\ \Omega\\ &= 28.08\ \Omega \angle 64.02°\end{aligned}$$

$$\mathbf{I}_s = \frac{\mathbf{E}}{\mathbf{Z}_T} = \frac{50\text{ V} \angle 0°}{28.08\ \Omega \angle 64.02°} = 1.78\text{ A} \angle -64.02°$$

$$\begin{aligned}\mathbf{V}_2 = \mathbf{I}_s(\mathbf{Z}_2 \parallel \mathbf{Z}_3) &= (1.78\text{ A} \angle -64.02°)(19.21\ \Omega \angle -50.19°)\\ &= 34.19\text{ V} \angle -114.21°\end{aligned}$$

$$\mathbf{I}_2 = \frac{\mathbf{V}_2}{\mathbf{Z}_2} = \frac{34.19\text{ V} \angle -114.21°}{25\ \Omega \angle -90°} = 1.37\text{ A} \angle -24.21°$$

$$\mathbf{I}_3 = \frac{\mathbf{V}_2}{\mathbf{Z}_3} = \frac{34.19\text{ V} \angle -114.21°}{30\ \Omega \angle 0°} = 1.14\text{ A} \angle -114.21°$$

$\mathbf{Z}_1$: $P = \mathbf{0\ W}$, $Q_L = I_s^2 X_L = (1.78\text{ A})^2\, 40\ \Omega = \mathbf{126.74\ VAR(}\boldsymbol{L}\mathbf{)}$, $S = \mathbf{126.74\ VA}$

$\mathbf{Z}_2$: $P = \mathbf{0\ W}$, $Q_C = I_2^2 X_C = (1.37\text{ A})^2\, 25\ \Omega = \mathbf{46.92\ VAR(}\boldsymbol{C}\mathbf{)}$, $S = \mathbf{46.92\ VA}$

$\mathbf{Z}_3$: $P = I_3^2 R = (1.14\text{ A})^2\, 30\ \Omega = \mathbf{38.99\ W}$, $Q_R = \mathbf{0\ VAR}$, $S = \mathbf{38.99\ VA}$

d. $P_T = 0 + 0 + 38.99\text{ W} = \mathbf{38.99\ W}$

$Q_T = +126.74\text{ VAR}(L) - 46.92\text{ VAR}(C) + 0 = \mathbf{79.82\ VAR(}\boldsymbol{L}\mathbf{)}$

$S_T = \sqrt{P_T^2 + Q_T^2} = \mathbf{88.83\ VA}$

$F_p = \dfrac{P_T}{S_T} = \dfrac{38.99\text{ W}}{88.83\text{ VA}} = \mathbf{0.439\ (lagging)}$

e. –

f. $W_R = \dfrac{V_R I_R}{2f_1} = \dfrac{V_2 I_3}{2f_1} = \dfrac{(34.19\text{ V})(1.14\text{ A})}{2(63.69\text{ Hz})} = \mathbf{0.31\ J}$

$f_1 = \dfrac{\omega_1}{2\pi} = \dfrac{400\text{ rad/s}}{6.28} = 63.69\text{ Hz}$

g. $W_L = \dfrac{V_L I_L}{\omega_1} = \dfrac{(I_s X_L) I_s}{\omega_1} = \dfrac{I_s^2 X_L}{\omega_1} = \dfrac{(1.78\text{ A})^2\, 40\ \Omega}{400\text{ rad/s}} = \mathbf{0.32\ J}$

$W_C = \dfrac{V_C I_C}{\omega_1} = \dfrac{V_2 I_2}{\omega_1} = \dfrac{(34.19\text{ V})(1.37\text{ A})}{400\text{ rad/s}} = \mathbf{0.12\ J}$

10. a. $I_s = \dfrac{S_T}{E} = \dfrac{10{,}000\text{ VA}}{200\text{ V}} = 50\text{ A}$

$0.5 \Rightarrow 60°$ leading

$\therefore$ $\mathbf{I}_s$ leads $\mathbf{E}$ by 60°

$$\mathbf{Z}_T = \frac{\mathbf{E}}{\mathbf{I}_s} = \frac{200\text{ V}\angle 0°}{50\text{ A}\angle 60°} = 4\ \Omega\angle{-60°} = 2\ \Omega - j3.464\ \Omega = R - jX_C$$

b. $F_p = \dfrac{P_T}{S_T} \Rightarrow P_T = F_pS_T = (0.5)(10{,}000\text{ VA}) = \mathbf{5000\ W}$

11. a. $I = \dfrac{S_T}{E} = \dfrac{5000\text{ VA}}{120\text{ V}} = 41.67\text{ A}$

$F_p = 0.8 \Rightarrow 36.87°$ (lagging)

$\mathbf{E} = 120\text{ V}\angle 0°$, $\mathbf{I} = 41.67\text{ A}\angle{-36.87°}$

$$\mathbf{Z} = \frac{\mathbf{E}}{\mathbf{I}} = \frac{120\text{ V}\angle 0°}{41.67\text{ A}\angle{-36.87°}} = 2.88\ \Omega\angle 36.87° = \mathbf{2.30\ \Omega + \mathit{j}1.73\ \Omega} = R + jX_L$$

b. $P = S\cos\theta = (5000\text{ VA})(0.8) = \mathbf{4000\ W}$

12. a. $P_T = 0 + 300\text{ W} = \mathbf{300\ W}$

$Q_T = 600\text{ VAR}(C) + 200(L) = \mathbf{400\ VAR(\mathit{C})}$

$S_T = \sqrt{P_T^2 + Q_T^2} = \mathbf{500\ VA}$

$F_p = \dfrac{P_T}{S_T} = \dfrac{300\text{ W}}{500\text{ VA}} = \mathbf{0.6\ (leading)}$

b. $I_s = \dfrac{S_T}{E} = \dfrac{500\text{ VA}}{30\text{ V}} = 16.67\text{ A}$

$F_p = 0.6 \Rightarrow 53.13°$

$\mathbf{I_s = 16.67\ A\angle 53.13°}$

c. –

d. Load: 600 VAR(C), 0 W

$$R = 0,\ L = 0,\ Q_C = I^2X_C \Rightarrow X_C = \frac{Q_C}{I^2} = \frac{600\text{ VAR}}{(16.67\text{ A})^2} = \mathbf{2.159\ \Omega}$$

Load: 200 VAR(L), 300 W

$C = 0$, $R = P/I^2 = 300\text{ W}/(16.67\text{ A})^2 = \mathbf{1.079\ \Omega}$

$X_L = \dfrac{Q_L}{I^2} = \dfrac{200\text{ VAR}}{(16.67\text{ A})^2} = \mathbf{0.7197\ \Omega}$

$\mathbf{Z}_T = !j2.159\ \Omega + 1.0796\ \Omega + j0.7197\ \Omega$

$= \mathbf{1.08\ \Omega - \mathit{j}1.44\ \Omega}$

13. a. $P_T = 0 + 300 \text{ W} + 600 \text{ W} = \mathbf{900 \text{ W}}$
$Q_T = 500 \text{ VAR}(C) + 0 + 500 \text{ VAR}(L) = \mathbf{0 \text{ VAR}}$
$S_T = P_T = \mathbf{900 \text{ VA}}$

$$F_p = \frac{P_T}{S_T} = \mathbf{1}$$

b. $$I_s = \frac{S_T}{E} = \frac{900 \text{ VA}}{100 \text{ V}} = 9 \text{ A}, \mathbf{I}_s = \mathbf{9 \text{ A} \angle 0^\circ}$$

c. –

d.

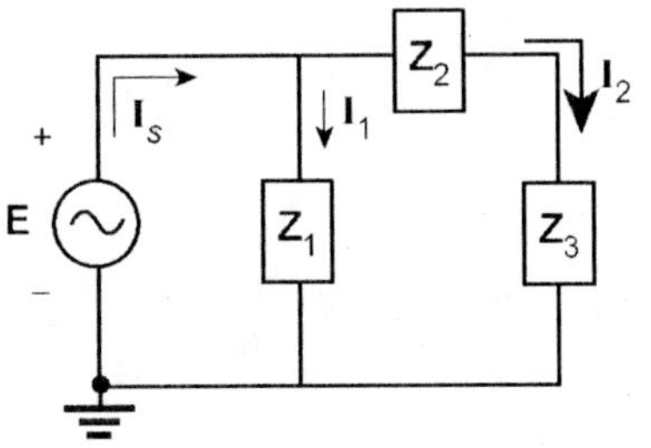

$$\mathbf{Z}_1\text{:} \quad Q_C = \frac{V^2}{X_C} \Rightarrow X_C = \frac{V^2}{Q_C} = \frac{10^4}{500} = \mathbf{20 \ \Omega}$$

$$\mathbf{I}_1 = \frac{\mathbf{E}}{\mathbf{Z}_1} = \frac{100 \text{ V} \angle 0^\circ}{20 \ \Omega \angle -90^\circ} = 5\text{A} \angle 90^\circ$$

$$\mathbf{I}_2 = \mathbf{I}_s - \mathbf{I}_1 = 9 \text{ A} - j5 \text{ A} = 10.296 \text{ A} \angle -29.05^\circ$$

$$\mathbf{Z}_2\text{:} \quad R = \frac{P}{I^2} = \frac{300 \text{ W}}{(10.296 \text{ A})^2} = \frac{300}{106} = \mathbf{2.83 \ \Omega}$$

$$X_{L,C} = \mathbf{0 \ \Omega}$$

$$\mathbf{Z}_3\text{:} \quad R = \frac{P}{I_2^2} = \frac{600 \text{ W}}{(10.296 \text{ A})^2} = \mathbf{5.66 \ \Omega}$$

$$X_L = \frac{Q}{I_2^2} = \frac{500}{(10.296 \text{ A})^2} = \mathbf{4.72 \ \Omega}, X_C = \mathbf{0 \ \Omega}$$

14. a. $P_T = 200 \text{ W} + 30 \text{ W} + 0 = \mathbf{230 \text{ W}}$
$Q_T = 0 + 40 \text{ VAR}(L) + 100 \text{ VAR}(L) = \mathbf{140 \text{ VAR}(L)}$

$$S_T = \sqrt{P_T^2 + Q_T^2} = \mathbf{269.26 \text{ VA}}$$

$$F_p = \frac{P_T}{S_T} = \frac{230 \text{ W}}{269.26 \text{ VA}} = \mathbf{0.854 \text{ (lagging)}} \Rightarrow 31.35^\circ$$

b. $$I_s = \frac{S_T}{E} = \frac{269.26 \text{ VA}}{100 \text{ V}} = 2.6926 \text{ A}$$

$\mathbf{I}_s = \mathbf{2.69 \text{ A} \angle -31.35^\circ}$

c.

$\mathbf{Z}_1$: $R = \dfrac{V^2}{P} = \dfrac{10^4}{200} = 50\ \Omega$

$X_L, X_C = 0\ \Omega$

$\mathbf{I}_1 = \dfrac{100\text{ V}\angle 0°}{50\ \Omega\angle 0°} = 2\text{ A}\angle 0°$

$$\begin{aligned}\mathbf{I}_2 &= \mathbf{I}_s - \mathbf{I}_1\\ &= 2.6926\text{ A}\angle{-31.35°} - 2\text{ A}\angle 0°\\ &= 2.299\text{ A} - j1.40\text{ A} - 2.0\text{ A}\\ &= 0.299\text{ A} - j1.40\text{ A}\\ &= 1.432\text{ A}\angle{-77.94°}\end{aligned}$$

$\mathbf{Z}_2$: $R = \dfrac{P}{I_2^2} = \dfrac{30\text{ W}}{(1.432\text{ A})^2} = \mathbf{14.63\ \Omega}$, $X_L = \dfrac{Q}{I_2^2} = \dfrac{40\text{ VAR}}{(1.432\text{ A})^2} = \mathbf{19.50\ \Omega}$

$X_C = \mathbf{0\ \Omega}$

$\mathbf{Z}_3$: $X_L = \dfrac{Q}{I_2^2} = \dfrac{100\text{ VAR}}{(1.432\text{ A})^2} = \mathbf{48.76\ \Omega}$, $R = \mathbf{0\ \Omega}$, $X_C = \mathbf{0\ \Omega}$

15. a. $P_T = 100\text{ W} + 1000\text{ W} = \mathbf{1100\text{ W}}$

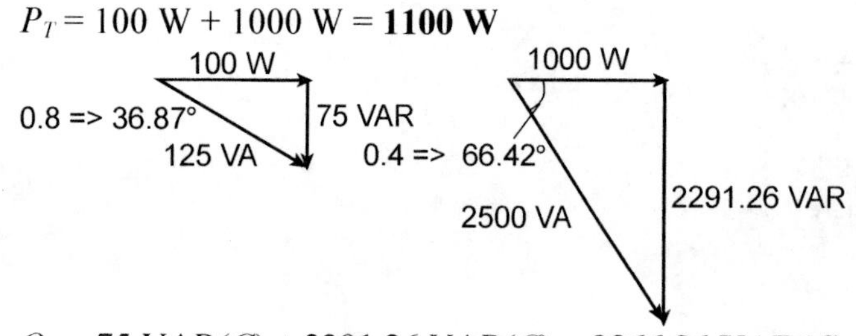

$Q_T = 75\text{ VAR}(C) + 2291.26\text{ VAR}(C) = \mathbf{2366.26\text{ VAR}(C)}$

$S_T = \sqrt{P_T^2 + Q_T^2} = \mathbf{2609.44\text{ VA}}$

$F_p = \dfrac{P_T}{S_T} = \dfrac{1100\text{ W}}{2609.44\text{ VA}} = \mathbf{0.422\ (leading)} \Rightarrow 65.04°$

b. $S_T = EI \Rightarrow E = \dfrac{S_T}{I} = \dfrac{2609.44\text{ VA}}{5\text{ A}} = 521.89\text{ V}$

$\mathbf{E = 521.89\text{ V}\angle{-65.07°}}$

c.

$I_{Z_1} = \dfrac{S}{V_1} = \dfrac{S}{E} = \dfrac{125\text{ VA}}{521.89\text{ V}} = 0.2395\text{ A}$

$I_{Z_2} = \dfrac{S}{V_2} = \dfrac{S}{E} = \dfrac{2500\text{ VA}}{521.89\text{ V}} = 4.79\text{ A}$

$\mathbf{Z}_1$: $R = \dfrac{P}{I_{Z_1}^2} = \dfrac{100\text{ W}}{(0.2395)^2} = \mathbf{1743.38\ \Omega}$

$$Q = I_{Z_1}^2 X_C \Rightarrow X_C = \frac{Q}{I_{Z_1}^2} = \frac{75\text{ VAR}}{(0.2395\text{ A})^2} = \mathbf{1307.53\ \Omega}$$

$\mathbf{Z}_2$: $R = \dfrac{P}{I_{Z_1}^2 X_C} = \dfrac{1000\text{ W}}{(4.790\text{ A})^2} = \mathbf{43.59\ \Omega}$

$$X_C = \frac{Q}{I_{Z_1}^2 X_C} = \frac{2291.26\text{ VAR}}{(4.790\text{ A})^2} = \mathbf{99.88\ \Omega}$$

16. a. $0.7 \Rightarrow 45.573°$
$P = S\cos\theta = (10\text{ kVA})(0.7) = 7\text{ kW}$
$Q = S\sin\theta = (10\text{ kVA})(0.714) = 7.14\text{ kVAR}(L)$

10 kVa
7.14 kVAR
45.573°
7 kW

b. $Q_C = 7.14\text{ kVAR} = \dfrac{V^2}{X_C}$

$$X_C = \frac{V^2}{Q_C} = \frac{(208\text{ V})^2}{7.14\text{ kVAR}} = 6.059\ \Omega$$

$$X_C = \frac{1}{2\pi fC} \Rightarrow C = \frac{1}{2\pi fX_C} = \frac{1}{(2\pi)(60\text{ Hz})(6.059\ \Omega)} = \mathbf{438\ \mu F}$$

c. Uncompensated:

$$I_s = \frac{S_T}{E} = \frac{10{,}000\text{ VA}}{208\text{ V}} = \mathbf{48.08\ A}$$

Compensated:

$$I_s = \frac{S_T}{E} = \frac{P_T}{E} = \frac{7{,}000\text{ W}}{208\text{ V}} = \mathbf{33.65\ A}$$

d.

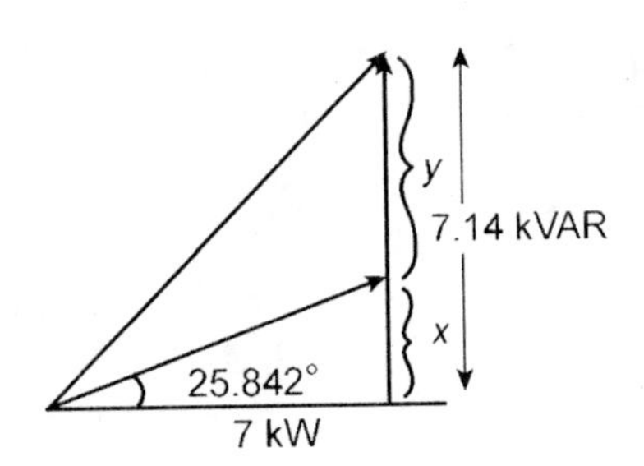

$\cos\theta = 0.9$
$\theta = \cos^{-1}0.9 = 25.842°$

$\tan\theta = \dfrac{x}{7\text{ kW}}$
$x = (7\text{ kW})(\tan 25.842°)$
$= (7\text{ kW})(0.484)$
$= 3.39\text{ kVAR}$
$y = (7.14 - 3.39)\text{ kVAR}$
$= 3.75\text{ kVAR}$

$$Q_C = 3.75 \text{ kVAR} = \frac{V^2}{X_C}$$

$$X_C = \frac{V^2}{Q_C} = \frac{(208 \text{ V})^2}{3.75 \text{ kVAR}} = 11.537 \ \Omega$$

$$C = \frac{1}{2\pi f X_C} = \frac{1}{(2\pi)(60 \text{ Hz})(11.537 \ \Omega)} = \mathbf{230 \ \mu F}$$

Uncompensated:

$I_s = \mathbf{48.08 \ A}$

Compensated:

$$S_T = \sqrt{(7 \text{ kW})^2 + (3.39 \text{ kVAR})^2} = 7.778 \text{ kVA}$$

$$I_s = \frac{S_T}{E} = \frac{7.778 \text{ kVA}}{208 \text{ V}} = \mathbf{37.39 \ A}$$

17. a. $P_T = 5 \text{ kW}, Q_T = 6 \text{ kVAR}(L)$

$$S_T = \sqrt{P_T^2 + Q_T^2} = \mathbf{7.81 \ kVA}$$

b. $$F_p = \frac{P_T}{S_T} = \frac{5 \text{ kW}}{7.81 \text{ kVA}} = \mathbf{0.640 \ (lagging)}$$

c. $$I_s = \frac{S_T}{E} = \frac{7{,}810 \text{ VA}}{120 \text{ V}} = \mathbf{65.08 \ A}$$

d. $$X_C = \frac{1}{2\pi f C}, \ Q_C = I^2 X_C = \frac{E^2}{X_C} = \frac{(120 \text{ V})^2}{X_C}$$

and $$X_C = \frac{(120 \text{ V})^2}{Q_C} = \frac{14{,}400}{6000} = 2.4 \ \Omega$$

$$C = \frac{1}{2\pi f X_C} = \frac{1}{(2\pi)(60 \text{ Hz})(2.4 \ \Omega)} = \mathbf{1105 \ \mu F}$$

e. $S_T = EI_s = P_T$

$$\therefore I_s = \frac{P_T}{E} = \frac{5000 \text{ W}}{120 \text{ V}} = \mathbf{41.67 \ A}$$

18. a. Load 1: $P = 20{,}000$ W, $Q = 0$ VAR
Load 2: $\theta = \cos^{-1}0.7 = 45.573°$

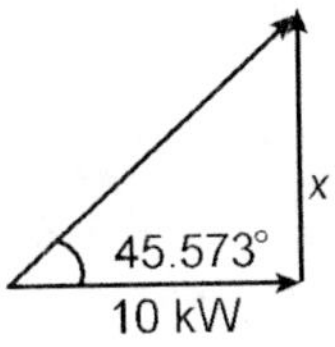

45.573°
x
10 kW

$$\tan\theta = \frac{x}{10\text{ kW}}$$
$x = (10\text{ kW})\tan 45.573°$
$= (10\text{ kW})(1.02)$
$=$ **10,202 VAR(L)**

Load 3: $\theta = \cos^{-1}0.85 = 31.788°$

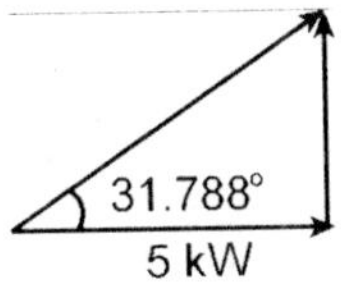

31.788°
5 kW

$$\tan\theta = \frac{x}{5\text{ kW}}$$
$x = (5\text{ kW})\tan 31.788°$
$= (5\text{ kW})(0.62)$
$= 3098.7$ VAR(L)

$P_T = 20{,}000\text{ W} + 10{,}000\text{ W} + 5{,}000\text{ W} =$ **35 kW**
$Q_T = 0 + 10{,}202\text{ VAR} + 3098.7\text{ VAR} =$ **13,300.7 VAR(L)**
$S_T = \sqrt{P_T^2 + Q_T^2} =$ **37,442 VA** $=$ **37.442 kVA**

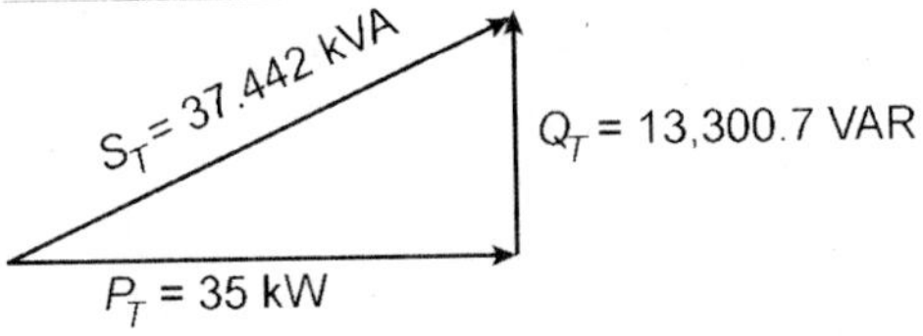

$S_T = 37.442$ kVA
$Q_T = 13{,}300.7$ VAR
$P_T = 35$ kW

b. $Q_C = Q_L = 13{,}300.7$ VAR
$$X_C = \frac{E^2}{Q_C} = \frac{(10^3\text{ V})^2}{13{,}300.7\text{ VAR}} = 75.184\ \Omega$$
$$C = \frac{1}{2\pi f X_C} = \frac{1}{(2\pi)(60\text{ Hz})(75.184\ \Omega)} = \mathbf{35.28\ \mu F}$$

c. Uncompensated:
$$I_s = \frac{S_T}{E} = \frac{37.442\text{ kVA}}{1\text{ kV}} = \mathbf{37.44\ A}$$

Compensated:
$S_T = P_T = 35$ kW
$$I_s = \frac{S_T}{E} = \frac{35\text{ kW}}{1\text{ kV}} = \mathbf{35\ A}$$

19. a. $\mathbf{Z}_T = R_1 + R_2 + R_3 + jX_L - jX_C$
$= 2\ \Omega + 3\ \Omega + 1\ \Omega + j3\ \Omega - j12\ \Omega = 6\ \Omega - j9\ \Omega = 10.82\ \Omega\ \angle -56.31°$
$$\mathbf{I} = \frac{\mathbf{E}}{\mathbf{Z}_T} = \frac{50\text{ V}\ \angle 0°}{10.82\ \Omega\ \angle -56.31°} = 4.62\text{ A}\ \angle 56.31°$$
$P = VI\cos\theta = (50\text{ V})(4.62\text{ A})\cos 56.31° =$ **128.14 W**

b. a-b: $P = I^2R = (4.62\text{ A})^2\ 2\ \Omega = \mathbf{42.69\ W}$
b-c: $P = I^2R = (4.62\text{ A})^2\ 3\ \Omega = \mathbf{64.03\ W}$
a-c: $42.69\text{ W} + 64.03\text{ W} = \mathbf{106.72\ W}$
a-d: **106.72 W**
c-d: **0 W**
d-e: **0 W**
f-e: $P = I^2R = (4.62\text{ A})^2\ 1\ \Omega = \mathbf{21.34\ W}$

20. a. $S_T = 660\text{ VA} = EI_s$

$$I_s = \frac{660\text{ VA}}{120\text{ V}} = 5.5\text{ A}$$

$\theta = \cos^{-1}0.6 = 53.13°$
$\therefore \mathbf{E} = 120\text{ V}\angle 0°,\ \mathbf{I}_s = 5.5\text{ A}\angle -53.13°$
$P = EI\cos\theta = (120\text{ V})(5.5\text{ A})(0.6) = \mathbf{396\ W}$
Wattmeter = **396 W**, Ammeter = **5.5 A**, Voltmeter = **120 V**

b. $$\mathbf{Z}_T = \frac{\mathbf{E}}{\mathbf{I}} = \frac{120\text{ V}\angle 0°}{5.5\text{ A}\angle -53.13°} = \mathbf{21.82\ \Omega\angle 53.13° = 13.09\ \Omega + \mathit{j}17.46\ \Omega} = R + jX_L$$

21. a. $$R = \frac{P}{I^2} = \frac{80\text{ W}}{(4\text{ A})^2} = \mathbf{5\ \Omega},\ \mathbf{Z}_T = \frac{E}{I} = \frac{200\text{ V}}{4\text{ A}} = 50\ \Omega$$

$$X_L = \sqrt{Z_T^2 - R^2} = \sqrt{(50\ \Omega)^2 - (5\ \Omega)^2} = 49.75\ \Omega$$

$$L = \frac{X_L}{2\pi f} = \frac{49.75\ \Omega}{(2\pi)(60\text{ Hz})} = \mathbf{132.03\ mH}$$

b. $$R = \frac{P}{I^2} = \frac{90\text{ W}}{(3\text{ A})^2} = \mathbf{10\ \Omega}$$

c. $$R = \frac{P}{I^2} = \frac{60\text{ W}}{(2\text{ A})^2} = \mathbf{15\ \Omega},\ Z_T = \frac{E}{I} = \frac{200\text{ V}}{2\text{ A}} = 100\ \Omega$$

$$X_L = \sqrt{Z_T^2 - R^2} = \sqrt{(100\ \Omega)^2 - (15\ \Omega)^2} = 98.87\ \Omega$$

$$L = \frac{X_L}{2\pi f} = \frac{98.87\ \Omega}{376.8} = \mathbf{262.39\ mH}$$

22. a. $X_L = 2\pi fL = (6.28)(50\text{ Hz})(0.08\text{ H}) = 25.12\ \Omega$

$$Z_T = \sqrt{R^2 + X_L^2} = \sqrt{(4\ \Omega)^2 + (25.12\ \Omega)^2} = 25.44\ \Omega$$

$$I = \frac{E}{Z_T} = \frac{60\text{ V}}{25.44\ \Omega} = 2.358\text{ A}$$

$P = I^2R = (2.358\text{ A})^2\ 4\ \Omega = \mathbf{22.24\ W}$

b. $I = \sqrt{\frac{P}{R}} = \sqrt{\frac{30\text{ W}}{7\ \Omega}} = \mathbf{2.07\ A}$

$$Z_T = \frac{E}{I} = \frac{60\text{ V}}{2.07\text{ A}} = 28.99\ \Omega$$

$$X_L = \sqrt{(28.99\ \Omega)^2 - (7\ \Omega)^2} = 28.13\ \Omega$$

$$L = \frac{X_L}{2\pi f} = \frac{28.13\ \Omega}{(2\pi)(50\text{ Hz})} = \mathbf{89.54\ mH}$$

c. $P = I^2R = (1.7\text{ A})^2\ 10\ \Omega = \mathbf{28.9\ W}$

$$Z_T = \frac{E}{I} = \frac{60\text{ V}}{1.7\text{ A}} = 35.29\ \Omega$$

$$X_L = \sqrt{(35.29\ \Omega)^2 - (10\ \Omega)^2} = 33.84\ \Omega$$

$$L = \frac{X_L}{2\pi f} = \frac{38.84\ \Omega}{314} = \mathbf{107.77\ mH}$$

Chapter 20

1. a. $\omega_s = \dfrac{1}{\sqrt{LC}} = \dfrac{1}{\sqrt{1\text{ H})(16\,\mu\text{F})}} = \mathbf{250\ rad/s}$

$f_s = \dfrac{\omega_s}{2\pi} = \dfrac{250\text{ rad/s}}{2\pi} = \mathbf{39.79\ Hz}$

b. $\omega_s = \dfrac{1}{\sqrt{(0.5\text{ H})(0.16\,\mu\text{F})}} = \mathbf{3535.53\ rad/s}$

$f_s = \dfrac{\omega_s}{2\pi} = \dfrac{3535.53\text{ rad/s}}{2\pi} = \mathbf{562.7\ Hz}$

c. $\omega_s = \dfrac{1}{\sqrt{(0.28\text{ mH})(7.46\,\mu\text{F})}} = \mathbf{21{,}880\ rad/s}$

$f_s = \dfrac{\omega_s}{2\pi} = \dfrac{21{,}880\text{ rad/s}}{2\pi} = \mathbf{3482.31\ Hz}$

2. a. $X_C = \mathbf{30\ \Omega}$ b. $Z_{T_s} = \mathbf{10\ \Omega}$ c. $I = \dfrac{E}{Z_{T_s}} = \dfrac{50\text{ mV}}{10\,\Omega} = \mathbf{5\ mA}$

d. $V_R = IR = (5\text{ mA})(10\ \Omega) = \mathbf{50\ mV} = E$

$V_L = IX_L = (5\text{ mA})(30\ \Omega) = \mathbf{150\ mV}$

$V_C = IX_C = (5\text{ mA})(30\ \Omega) = \mathbf{150\ mV}$

$V_L = V_C$

e. $Q_s = \dfrac{X_L}{R} = \dfrac{30\,\Omega}{10\,\Omega} = \mathbf{3}$ (low Q) f. $P = I^2R = (5\text{ mA})^2\ 10\ \Omega = \mathbf{0.25\ mW}$

3. a. $X_L = \mathbf{40\ \Omega}$

b. $I = \dfrac{E}{Z_{T_s}} = \dfrac{20\text{ mV}}{2\,\Omega} = \mathbf{10\ mA}$

c. $V_R = IR = (10\text{ mA})(2\ \Omega) = \mathbf{20\ mV} = E$

$V_L = IX_L = (10\text{ mA})(40\ \Omega) = \mathbf{400\ mV}$

$V_C = IX_C = (10\text{ mA})(40\ \Omega) = \mathbf{400\ mV}$

$V_L = V_C = 20\ V_R$

d. $Q_s = \dfrac{X_L}{R} = \dfrac{40\,\Omega}{2\,\Omega} = \mathbf{20}$ (high Q)

e. $X_L = 2\pi fL,\ L = \dfrac{X_L}{2\pi f} = \dfrac{40\,\Omega}{2\pi(5\text{ kHz})} = \mathbf{1.27\ mH}$

$X_C = \dfrac{1}{2\pi fC},\ C = \dfrac{1}{2\pi fX_C} = \dfrac{1}{2\pi(5\text{ kHz})(40\,\Omega)} = \mathbf{795.77\ nF}$

f. $BW = \dfrac{f_s}{Q_s} = \dfrac{5\text{ kHz}}{20} = \mathbf{250\text{ Hz}}$

g. $f_2 = f_s + \dfrac{BW}{2} = 5\text{ kHz} + \dfrac{0.25\text{ kHz}}{2} = \mathbf{5.13\text{ kHz}}$

$f_1 = f_s - \dfrac{BW}{2} = 5\text{ kHz} - \dfrac{0.25\text{ kHz}}{2} = \mathbf{4.88\text{ kHz}}$

4. a. $f_s = \dfrac{1}{2\pi\sqrt{LC}} \Rightarrow L = \dfrac{1}{(2\pi f_s)^2 C} = \dfrac{1}{(2\pi\ 1.8\text{ kHz})^2\ 2\ \mu\text{F}} = \mathbf{3.91\text{ mH}}$

b. $X_L = 2\pi fL = 2\pi(1.8\text{ kHz})(3.91\text{ mH}) = \mathbf{44.2\ \Omega}$

$X_C = \dfrac{1}{2\pi fC} = \dfrac{1}{2\pi(1.8\text{ kHz})(2\ \mu\text{F})} = \mathbf{44.2\ \Omega}$

$X_L = X_C$

c. $E_{\text{rms}} = (0.707)(20\text{ mV}) = 14.14\text{ mV}$

$I_{\text{rms}} = \dfrac{E_{\text{rms}}}{R} = \dfrac{14.14\text{ mV}}{4.7\ \Omega} = \mathbf{3.01\text{ mA}}$

d. $P = I^2R = (3.01\text{ mA})^2\ 4.7\ \Omega = \mathbf{42.58\ \mu W}$

e. $S_T = P_T = \mathbf{42.58\ \mu VA}$

f. $F_p = \mathbf{1}$

g. $Q_s = \dfrac{X_L}{R} = \dfrac{44.2\ \Omega}{4.7\ \Omega} = \mathbf{9.4}$

$BW = \dfrac{f_s}{Q_s} = \dfrac{1.8\text{ kHz}}{9.4} = \mathbf{191.49\text{ Hz}}$

h. $f_2 = \dfrac{1}{2\pi}\left[\dfrac{R}{2L} + \dfrac{1}{2}\sqrt{\left(\dfrac{R}{L}\right)^2 + \dfrac{4}{LC}}\right]$

$= \dfrac{1}{2\pi}\left[\dfrac{4.7\ \Omega}{2(3.91\text{ mH})} + \dfrac{1}{2}\sqrt{\left(\dfrac{4.7\ \Omega}{3.91\text{ mH}}\right)^2 + \dfrac{4}{(3.91\text{ mH})(2\ \mu\text{F})}}\right]$

$= \dfrac{1}{2\pi}\left[601.02 + 11.324\times10^3\right]$

$= \mathbf{1897.93\text{ Hz}}$

$f_1 = \dfrac{1}{2\pi}\left[-\dfrac{R}{2L} + \dfrac{1}{2}\sqrt{\left(\dfrac{R}{L}\right)^2 + \dfrac{4}{LC}}\right]$

$= \dfrac{1}{2\pi}\left[-601.02 + 11.324\times10^3\right]$

$= \mathbf{1.71\text{ kHz}}$

$P_{\text{HPF}} = \dfrac{1}{2}P_{\max} = \dfrac{1}{2}(42.58\ \mu\text{W}) = \mathbf{21.29\ \mu W}$

5. a. $BW = f_s/Q_s = 6000\text{ Hz}/15 = \mathbf{400\ Hz}$

b. $f_2 = f_s + \dfrac{BW}{2} = 6000\text{ Hz} + 200\text{ Hz} = \mathbf{6200\ Hz}$

$f_1 = f_s - \dfrac{BW}{2} = 6000\text{ Hz} - 200\text{ Hz} = \mathbf{5800\ Hz}$

c. $Q_s = \dfrac{X_L}{R} \Rightarrow X_L = Q_s R = (15)(3\ \Omega) = \mathbf{45\ \Omega} = X_C$

d. $P_{\text{HPF}} = \dfrac{1}{2} P_{\max} = \dfrac{1}{2}(I^2 R) = \dfrac{1}{2}(0.5\text{ A})^2\, 3\Omega = \mathbf{375\ mW}$

6. a. $L = \dfrac{X_L}{2\pi f} = \dfrac{200\ \Omega}{2\pi(10^4\text{ Hz})} = 3.185\text{ mH}$

$BW = \dfrac{R}{2\pi L} = \dfrac{5\ \Omega}{2\pi(3.185\text{ mH})} \cong \mathbf{250\ Hz}$

or $Q_s = \dfrac{X_L}{R} = \dfrac{X_C}{R} = \dfrac{200\ \Omega}{5\ \Omega} = 40,\ BW = \dfrac{f_s}{Q_s} = \dfrac{10{,}000\text{ Hz}}{40} = \mathbf{250\ Hz}$

b. $f_2 = f_s + BW/2 = 10{,}000\text{ Hz} + 250\text{ Hz}/2 = \mathbf{10{,}125\ Hz}$
$f_1 = f_s - BW/2 = 10{,}000\text{ Hz} - 125\text{ Hz} = \mathbf{9{,}875\ Hz}$

c. $Q_s = \dfrac{X_L}{R} = \dfrac{200\ \Omega}{5\ \Omega} = \mathbf{40}$

d. $\mathbf{I} = \dfrac{E\angle 0^\circ}{R\angle 0^\circ} = \dfrac{30\text{ V}\angle 0^\circ}{5\ \Omega\angle 0^\circ} = 6\text{ A}\angle 0^\circ,\ \mathbf{V}_L = (I\angle 0^\circ)(X_L\angle 90^\circ)$

$= (6\text{ A}\angle 0^\circ)(200\ \Omega\angle 90^\circ)$
$= \mathbf{1200\ V\ \angle 90^\circ}$

$\mathbf{V}_C = (I\angle 0^\circ)(X_C\angle -90^\circ) = \mathbf{1200\ V\ \angle -90^\circ}$

e. $P = I^2 R = (6\text{ A})^2\, 5\ \Omega = \mathbf{180\ W}$

7. a. $BW = \dfrac{f_s}{Q_s} \Rightarrow Q_s = f_s/BW = 2000\text{ Hz}/200\text{ Hz} = \mathbf{10}$

b. $Q_s = \dfrac{X_L}{R} \Rightarrow X_L = Q_s R = (10)(2\ \Omega) = \mathbf{20\ \Omega}$

c. $L = \dfrac{X_L}{2\pi f} = \dfrac{20\ \Omega}{(6.28)(2\text{ kHz})} = \mathbf{1.59\ mH}$

$C = \dfrac{1}{2\pi f X_C} = \dfrac{1}{(6.28)(2\text{ kHz})(20\ \Omega)} = \mathbf{3.98\ \mu F}$

d. $f_2 = f_s + BW/2 = 2000\text{ Hz} + 100\text{ Hz} = \mathbf{2100\text{ Hz}}$
$f_1 = f_s - BW/2 = 2000\text{ Hz} - 100\text{ Hz} = \mathbf{1900\text{ Hz}}$

8. a. $BW = 6000\text{ Hz} - 5400\text{ Hz} = \mathbf{600\text{ Hz}}$

b. $BW = f_s/Q_s \Rightarrow f_s = Q_s BW = (9.5)(600\text{ Hz}) = \mathbf{5700\text{ Hz}}$

c. $Q_s = \dfrac{X_L}{R} \Rightarrow X_L = X_C = Q_s R = (9.5)(2\ \Omega) = \mathbf{19\ \Omega}$

d. $L = \dfrac{X_L}{2\pi f} = \dfrac{19\ \Omega}{2\pi(5700\text{ Hz})} = \mathbf{0.53\text{ mH}}$

$C = \dfrac{1}{2\pi f X_C} = \dfrac{1}{2\pi(5.7\text{ kHz})(19\ \Omega)} = \mathbf{1.47\ \mu F}$

9. $I_M = \dfrac{E}{R} \Rightarrow R = \dfrac{E}{I_M} = \dfrac{5\text{ V}}{500\text{ mA}} = \mathbf{10\ \Omega}$

$BW = f_s/Q_s \Rightarrow Q_s = f_s/BW = 8400\text{ Hz}/120\text{ Hz} = 70$

$Q_s = \dfrac{X_L}{R} \Rightarrow X_L = Q_s R = (70)(10\ \Omega) = \mathbf{700\ \Omega}$

$X_C = X_L = \mathbf{700\ \Omega}$

$L = \dfrac{X_L}{2\pi f} = \dfrac{700\ \Omega}{(2\pi)(8.4\text{ kHz})} = \mathbf{13.26\text{ mH}}$

$C = \dfrac{1}{2\pi f X_C} = \dfrac{1}{(2\pi)(8.4\text{ kHz})(0.7\text{ k}\Omega)} = \mathbf{27.07\text{ nF}}$

$f_2 = f_s + BW/2 = 8400\text{ Hz} + 120\text{ Hz}/2 = \mathbf{8460\text{ Hz}}$
$f_1 = f_s - BW/2 = 8400\text{ Hz} - 60\text{ Hz} = \mathbf{8340\text{ Hz}}$

10. $Q_s = \dfrac{X_L}{R} \Rightarrow X_L = Q_s R = 20(2\ \Omega) = \mathbf{40\ \Omega} = X_C$

$BW = \dfrac{f_s}{Q_s} \Rightarrow f_s = Q_s BW = (20)(400\text{ Hz}) = \mathbf{8\text{ kHz}}$

$L = \dfrac{X_L}{2\pi f} = \dfrac{40\ \Omega}{2\pi(8\text{ kHz})} = \mathbf{795.77\ \mu H}$

$C = \dfrac{1}{2\pi f X_C} = \dfrac{1}{2\pi(8\text{ kHz})(40\ \Omega)} = \mathbf{497.36\text{ nF}}$

$f_2 = f_s + BW/2 = 8000\text{ Hz} + 400\text{ Hz}/2 = \mathbf{8200\text{ Hz}}$
$f_1 = f_s - BW/2 = 8000\text{ Hz} - 200\text{ Hz} = \mathbf{7800\text{ Hz}}$

11. a. $f_s = \dfrac{\omega_s}{2\pi} = \dfrac{2\pi \times 10^6\text{ rad/s}}{2\pi} = \mathbf{1\text{ MHz}}$

b. $\dfrac{f_2 - f_1}{f_s} = 0.16 \Rightarrow BW = f_2 - f_1 = 0.16 f_s = 0.16(1\text{ MHz}) = \mathbf{160\text{ kHz}}$

c. $P = \dfrac{V_R^2}{R} \Rightarrow R = \dfrac{V_R^2}{P} = \dfrac{(120\text{ V})^2}{20\text{ W}} = \mathbf{720\ \Omega}$

$BW = \dfrac{R}{2\pi L} \Rightarrow L = \dfrac{R}{2\pi BW} = \dfrac{720\ \Omega}{(6.28)(160\text{ kHz})} = \mathbf{0.716\ mH}$

$f_s = \dfrac{1}{2\pi\sqrt{LC}} \Rightarrow C = \dfrac{1}{4\pi^2 f_s^2 L} = \dfrac{1}{4\pi^2(10^6\text{ Hz})^2(0.716\text{ mH})} = \mathbf{35.38\ pF}$

d. $Q_\ell = \dfrac{X_L}{R_\ell} = 80 \Rightarrow R_P = \dfrac{X_L}{80} = \dfrac{2\pi f_s L}{80} = \dfrac{2\pi(10^6\text{ Hz})(0.716\text{ mH})}{80} = \mathbf{56.23\ \Omega}$

12. a. $Q_\ell = \dfrac{X_L}{R_\ell}$

$R_\ell = \dfrac{X_L}{Q_\ell} = \dfrac{2\pi fL}{Q_\ell} = \dfrac{2\pi(1\text{ MHz})(100\ \mu\text{H})}{12.5} = 50.27\ \Omega$

$\dfrac{f_2 - f_1}{f_s} = \dfrac{1}{Q_s} = 0.2$

$Q_s = \dfrac{1}{0.2} = 5 = \dfrac{X_L}{R} = \dfrac{2\pi fL}{R} = \dfrac{2\pi(1\text{ MHz})(100\ \mu\text{H})}{R} = \dfrac{628.32\ \Omega}{R}$

$R = \dfrac{628.32\ \Omega}{5} = 125.66$

$R = R_d + R_\ell$

$125.66\ \Omega = R_d + 50.27\ \Omega$

and $R_d = 125.66\ \Omega - 50.27\ \Omega = \mathbf{75.39\ \Omega}$

c. $X_C = \dfrac{1}{2\pi fC} = X_L$

$C = \dfrac{1}{2\pi f X_C} = \dfrac{1}{2\pi(1\text{ MHz})(628.32\ \Omega)} = \mathbf{253.3\ pF}$

13. a. $f_p = \dfrac{1}{2\pi\sqrt{LC}} = \dfrac{2}{2\pi\sqrt{(0.1\text{ mH})(10\text{ nF})}} = \mathbf{159.16\ kHz}$

b.

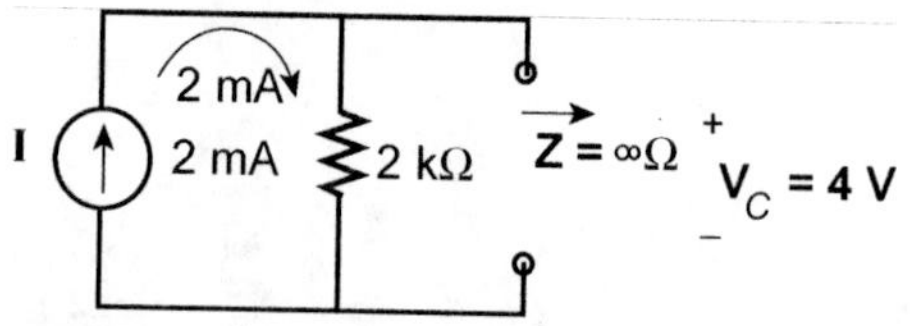

c. $I_L = \dfrac{V_L}{X_L} = \dfrac{4\text{ V}}{2\pi f_p L} = \dfrac{4\text{ V}}{100\ \Omega} = \mathbf{40\ mA}$

$I_C = \dfrac{V_L}{X_C} = \dfrac{4\text{ V}}{1/2\pi f_p C} = \dfrac{4\text{ V}}{100\ \Omega} = \mathbf{40\ mA}$

d. $Q_p = \dfrac{R_s}{X_{L_p}} = \dfrac{2\text{ k}\Omega}{2\pi f_p L} = \dfrac{2\text{ k}\Omega}{100\,\Omega} = \mathbf{20}$

14. a. $f_s = \dfrac{1}{2\pi\sqrt{LC}} = \dfrac{1}{2\pi\sqrt{(0.5\text{ mH})(30\text{ nF})}} = \mathbf{41.09\text{ kHz}}$

b. $Q_\ell = \dfrac{X_L}{R_\ell} = \dfrac{2\pi fL}{R_\ell} = \dfrac{2\pi(41.09\text{ kHz})(0.5\text{ mH})}{8\,\Omega} = \mathbf{16.14} \geq 10$ (yes)

c. Since $Q_\ell \geq 10$, $f_p \cong f_s = \mathbf{41.09\text{ kHz}}$

d. $X_L = 2\pi f_p L = 2\pi(41.09\text{ kHz})(0.5\text{ mH}) = \mathbf{129.1\,\Omega}$

$X_C = \dfrac{2}{2\pi f_p C} = \dfrac{2}{2\pi(41.09\text{ kHz})(30\text{ nF})} = \mathbf{129.1\,\Omega}$

$X_L = X_C$

e. $Z_{T_p} = Q_\ell^2 R_\ell = (16.14)^2\, 8\,\Omega = \mathbf{2.084\text{ k}\Omega}$

f. $V_C = IZ_{T_p} = (10\text{ mA})(2.084\text{ k}\Omega) = \mathbf{20.84\text{ V}}$

g. $Q_\ell \geq 10,\ Q_p = Q_\ell = \mathbf{16.14}$

$BW = \dfrac{f_p}{Q_p} = \dfrac{41.09\text{ kHz}}{16.14} = \mathbf{2545.85\text{ Hz}}$

h. $I_L = I_C = Q_\ell I_T = (16.14)(10\text{ mA}) = \mathbf{161.4\text{ mA}}$

15. a. $f_s = \dfrac{1}{2\pi\sqrt{LC}} = \dfrac{1}{2\pi\sqrt{(0.1\text{ mH})(2\,\mu\text{F})}} = \mathbf{11{,}253.95\text{ Hz}}$

b. $Q_\ell = \dfrac{X_L}{R_\ell} = \dfrac{2\pi f_s L}{R_\ell} = \dfrac{2\pi(11{,}253.95\text{ Hz})(0.1\text{ mH})}{4\,\Omega} = \mathbf{1.77}$ (low Q_ℓ)

c. $f_p = f_s\sqrt{1 - \dfrac{R_\ell^2 C}{L}} = 11{,}253.95\text{ Hz}\sqrt{1 - \dfrac{(4\,\Omega)^2\, 2\,\mu\text{F}}{0.1\text{ mH}}} = 11{,}253.95\text{ Hz}(0.825)$

$= \mathbf{9{,}280.24\text{ Hz}}$

$f_m = f_s\sqrt{1 - \dfrac{1}{4}\left[\dfrac{R_\ell^2 C}{L}\right]} = 11{,}253.95\text{ Hz}\sqrt{1 - \dfrac{1}{4}\left[\dfrac{(4\,\Omega)^2\, 2\,\mu\text{F}}{0.1\text{ mH}}\right]}$

$= 11{,}253.95\text{ Hz}(0.996) = \mathbf{10{,}794.41\text{ Hz}}$

d. $X_L = 2\pi f_p L = 2\pi(9{,}280.24 \text{ Hz})(0.1 \text{ mH}) = \mathbf{5.83\ \Omega}$

$$X_C = \frac{1}{2\pi f_p C} = \frac{1}{2\pi(9{,}280.24 \text{ Hz})(2\ \mu\text{F})} = \mathbf{8.57\ \Omega}$$

$X_L \neq X_C$, $X_C > X_L$

e. $$Z_{T_p} = R_s \parallel R_p = R_s \parallel \left(\frac{R_\ell^2 + X_L^2}{R_\ell}\right) = \frac{R_\ell^2 + X_L^2}{R_\ell} = \frac{(4\ \Omega)^2 + (5.83\ \Omega)^2}{4\ \Omega} = \mathbf{12.5\ \Omega}$$

f. $V_C = IZ_{T_p} = (2 \text{ mA})(12.5\ \Omega) = \mathbf{25\ mV}$

g. Since $R_s = \infty\ \Omega$ $$Q_p = Q_\ell = \frac{X_L}{R_\ell} = \frac{2\pi f_p L}{R_\ell} = \frac{2\pi(9{,}280.24 \text{ Hz})(0.1 \text{ mH})}{4\ \Omega} = \mathbf{1.46}$$

$$BW = \frac{f_p}{Q_p} = \frac{9{,}280.24 \text{ Hz}}{1.46} = \mathbf{6.36\ kHz}$$

h. $$I_C = \frac{V_C}{X_C} = \frac{25 \text{ mV}}{8.57\ \Omega} = \mathbf{2.92\ mA}$$

$$I_L = \frac{V_L}{Z_{R-L}} = \frac{V_C}{R_\ell + jX_L} = \frac{25 \text{ mV}}{4\ \Omega + j5.83\ \Omega} = \frac{25 \text{ mV}}{7.07\ \Omega} = \mathbf{3.54\ mA}$$

16. a. $$Q_\ell = \frac{X_L}{R_L} = \frac{100\ \Omega}{20\ \Omega} = 5 \leq 10$$

$$\therefore \frac{X_L}{R_\ell^2 + X_L^2} = \frac{1}{X_C} \Rightarrow X_C = \frac{R_\ell^2 + X_\ell^2}{X_L} = \frac{(20\ \Omega)^2 + (100\ \Omega)^2}{100\ \Omega} = \mathbf{104\ \Omega}$$

b. $$Z_T = R_s \parallel R_p = R_s \parallel \frac{R_\ell^2 + X_L^2}{R_\ell} = 1000\ \Omega \parallel \frac{10{,}400\ \Omega}{20} = \mathbf{342.11\ \Omega}$$

c. $\mathbf{E} = \mathbf{IZ}_{T_p} = (5 \text{ mA} \angle 0°)(342.11\ \Omega \angle 0°) = 1.711 \text{ V} \angle 0°$

$$\mathbf{I}_C = \frac{\mathbf{E}}{X_C \angle -90°} = \frac{1.711 \text{ V} \angle 0°}{104\ \Omega \angle -90°} = \mathbf{16.45\ mA \angle 90°}$$

$\mathbf{Z}_L = 20\ \Omega + j100\ \Omega = 101.98\ \Omega \angle 78.69°$

$$\mathbf{I}_L = \frac{\mathbf{E}}{\mathbf{Z}_L} = \frac{1.711 \text{ V} \angle 0°}{101.98\ \Omega \angle 78.69°} = \mathbf{16.78\ mA \angle -78.69°}$$

d. $$L = \frac{X_L}{2\pi f} = \frac{100\ \Omega}{2\pi(20 \text{ kHz})} = \mathbf{795.77\ \mu H}$$

$$C = \frac{1}{2\pi f X_C} = \frac{1}{2\pi(20 \text{ kHz})(104\ \Omega)} = \mathbf{76.52\ nF}$$

e. $Q_p = \dfrac{R}{X_C} = \dfrac{342.11\,\Omega}{104\,\Omega} = \mathbf{3.29}$

$BW = f_p/Q_p = 20{,}000\text{ Hz}/3.29 = \mathbf{6079.03\ Hz}$

17. a. $Q_\ell = \dfrac{X_L}{R_\ell} = \dfrac{30\,\Omega}{2\,\Omega} = 15$ (use approximate approach): $X_C = X_L = \mathbf{30\ \Omega}$

b. $Z_{T_p} = R_s \,\|\, Q_\ell^2 R_\ell = 450\,\Omega \,\|\, (15)^2\, 2\,\Omega = 450\,\Omega \,\|\, 450\,\Omega = \mathbf{225\ \Omega}$

c. $\mathbf{E} = \mathbf{I}\mathbf{Z}_{T_p} = (80\text{ mA}\,\angle 0°)(225\,\Omega\,\angle 0°) = \mathbf{18\ V\ \angle 0°}$

$\mathbf{I}_C = \dfrac{\mathbf{E}}{X_C\angle -90°} = \dfrac{18\text{ V}\,\angle 0°}{30\,\Omega\,\angle -90°} = \mathbf{0.6\ A\ \angle 90°}$

$\mathbf{I}_L = \dfrac{\mathbf{E}}{\mathbf{Z}_{R\text{-}L}} = \dfrac{18\text{ V}\,\angle 0°}{2\,\Omega + j30\,\Omega} = \dfrac{18\text{ V}\,\angle 0°}{30.07\,\Omega\,\angle 86.19°} \cong \mathbf{0.6\ A\ \angle -86.19°}$

d. $X_L = 2\pi f_p L,\ L = \dfrac{X_L}{2\pi f_p} = \dfrac{30\,\Omega}{2\pi(20\times 10^3\text{ Hz})} = \mathbf{0.239\ mH}$

$X_C = \dfrac{1}{2\pi f_p C},\ C = \dfrac{1}{2\pi f_p X_C} = \dfrac{1}{2\pi(20\times 10^3\text{ Hz})(30\,\Omega)} = \mathbf{265.26\ nF}$

e. $Q_p = \dfrac{Z_{T_p}}{X_L} = \dfrac{225\,\Omega}{30\,\Omega} = \mathbf{7.5},\ BW = \dfrac{f_p}{Q_p} = \dfrac{20{,}000\text{ Hz}}{7.5} = \mathbf{2.67\ kHz}$

18. a. $f_s = \dfrac{1}{2\pi\sqrt{LC}} = \dfrac{1}{2\pi\sqrt{(80\,\mu\text{H})(0.03\,\mu\text{F})}} = \mathbf{102.73\ kHz}$

$f_p = f_s\sqrt{1 - \dfrac{R_\ell^2 C}{L}} = 102.73\text{ kHz}\sqrt{1 - \dfrac{(1.5\,\Omega)^2\, 0.03\,\mu\text{F}}{80\,\mu\text{H}}} = 102.73\text{ kHz}(.99958)$

$= \mathbf{102.69\ kHz}$

$f_m = f_s\sqrt{1 - \dfrac{1}{4}\left[\dfrac{R_\ell^2 C}{L}\right]} = 102.73\text{ kHz}(0.99989) = \mathbf{102.72\ kHz}$

Since $f_s \cong f_p \cong f_m \Rightarrow$ high Q_p

b. $X_L = 2\pi f_p L = 2\pi(102.69\text{ kHz})(80\,\mu\text{H}) = \mathbf{51.62\ \Omega}$

$X_C = \dfrac{1}{2\pi f_p C} = \dfrac{1}{2\pi(102.69\text{ kHz})(0.03\,\mu\text{F})} = \mathbf{51.66\ \Omega}$

$X_L \cong X_C$

c. $Z_{T_p} = R_s \parallel Q_\ell^2 R_\ell$

$$Q_\ell = \frac{X_L}{R_\ell} = \frac{51.62\,\Omega}{1.5\,\Omega} = 34.41$$

$$Z_{T_p} = 10\text{ k}\Omega \parallel (34.41)^2 1.5\,\Omega = 10\text{ k}\Omega \parallel 1.776\text{ k}\Omega = \mathbf{1.51\ k\Omega}$$

d. $$Q_p = \frac{R_s \parallel Q_\ell^2 R_\ell}{X_L} = \frac{Z_{T_p}}{X_L} = \frac{1.51\text{ k}\Omega}{51.62\,\Omega} = \mathbf{29.25}$$

$$BW = \frac{f_p}{Q_p} = \frac{102.69\text{ kHz}}{29.25} = \mathbf{3.51\ kHz}$$

e. $$I_T = \frac{R_s I_s}{R_s + Q_\ell^2 R_\ell} = \frac{10\text{ k}\Omega(10\text{ mA})}{10\text{ k}\Omega + 1.78\text{ k}\Omega} = 8.49\text{ mA}$$

$$I_C = I_L \cong Q_\ell I_T = (34.41)(8.49\text{ mA}) = \mathbf{292.14\ mA}$$

f. $V_C = IZ_{T_p} = (10\text{ mA})(1.51\text{ k}\Omega) = \mathbf{15.1\ V}$

19. a. $$f_s = \frac{1}{2\pi\sqrt{LC}} = \frac{1}{2\pi\sqrt{(0.5\text{ mH})(1\,\mu\text{F})}} = \mathbf{7.12\ kHz}$$

$$f_p = f_s\sqrt{1 - \frac{R_\ell^2 C}{L}} = 7.12\text{ kHz}\sqrt{1 - \frac{(8\,\Omega)^2(1\,\mu\text{F})}{0.5\text{ mH}}} = 7.12\text{ kHz}(0.9338) = \mathbf{6.65\ kHz}$$

$$f_m = f_s\sqrt{1 - \frac{1}{4}\left[\frac{R_\ell^2 C}{L}\right]} = 7.12\text{ kHz}\sqrt{1 - \frac{1}{4}\left[\frac{(8\,\Omega)^2(1\,\mu\text{F})}{0.5\text{ mH}}\right]} = 7.12\text{ kHz }(0.9839)$$

$$= \mathbf{7.01\ kHz}$$

Low Q_p

b. $X_L = 2\pi f_p L = 2\pi(6.647\text{ kHz})(0.5\text{ mH}) = 20.88\,\Omega$

$$X_C = \frac{1}{2\pi fC} = \frac{1}{2\pi(6.647\text{ kHz})(1\,\mu\text{F})} = 23.94\,\Omega$$

$X_C > X_L$ (low Q)

c. $$Z_{T_p} = R_s \parallel R_p = R_s \parallel \frac{R_\ell^2 + X_L^2}{R_\ell} = 500\,\Omega \parallel \frac{(8\,\Omega)^2 + (20.88\,\Omega)^2}{8\,\Omega} = 500\,\Omega \parallel 62.5\,\Omega$$

$$= \mathbf{55.56\ \Omega}$$

d. $$Q_p = \frac{Z_{T_p}}{X_{L_p}} = \frac{55.56\,\Omega}{23.94\,\Omega} = \mathbf{2.32}$$

$$BW = \frac{f_p}{Q_p} = \frac{6.647\text{ kHz}}{2.32} = \mathbf{2.87\ kHz}$$

e. One method: $V_C = IZ_{T_p} = (40 \text{ mA})(55.56\ \Omega) = 2.22 \text{ V}$

$$I_C = \frac{V_C}{X_C} = \frac{2.22 \text{ V}}{23.94\ \Omega} = \mathbf{92.73\ mA}$$

$$I_L = \frac{|V_C|}{|R_l + jX_L|} = \frac{2.22 \text{ V}}{|8 + j20.88|} = \frac{2.22 \text{ V}}{22.36\ \Omega} = \mathbf{99.28\ mA}$$

f. $V_C = \mathbf{2.22\ V}$

20. a. $Z_{T_p} = \dfrac{R_l^2 + X_L^2}{R_l} = 50 \text{ k}\Omega$

$$(50\ \Omega)^2 + X_L^2 = (50 \text{ k}\Omega)(50\ \Omega)$$

$$X_L = \sqrt{250 \times 10^4 - 2.5 \times 10^3} = \mathbf{1580.3\ \Omega}$$

b. $Q = \dfrac{X_L}{R_l} = \dfrac{1580.3}{50} = 31.61 \geq 10$

$\therefore X_C = X_L = \mathbf{1580.3\ \Omega}$

c. $X_L = 2\pi f_p L \Rightarrow f_p = \dfrac{X_L}{2\pi L} = \dfrac{1580.3\ \Omega}{2\pi(16 \text{ mH})} = \mathbf{15.72\ kHz}$

d. $X_C = \dfrac{1}{2\pi f_p C} \Rightarrow C = \dfrac{1}{2\pi f_s X_C} = \dfrac{1}{2\pi(15.72 \text{ kHz})(1580.3\ \Omega)} = \mathbf{6.4\ nF}$

21. a. $Q_l = 20 > 10 \therefore f_p = f_s = \dfrac{1}{2\pi\sqrt{LC}} = \dfrac{1}{2\pi\sqrt{(200 \text{ mH})(10 \text{ nF})}} = \mathbf{3558.81\ Hz}$

b. $Q_l = \dfrac{X_L}{R_l} = \dfrac{2\pi fL}{R_l} \Rightarrow R_l = \dfrac{2\pi fL}{Q_l} = \dfrac{2\pi(3558.81 \text{ Hz})(0.2 \text{ H})}{20} = 223.61\ \Omega$

$$Z_{T_p} = R_s \parallel R_p = R_s \parallel Q_l^2 R_l = 40 \text{ k}\Omega \parallel (20)^2\, 223.61\ \Omega$$

$$Z_{T_p} = 27.64 \text{ k}\Omega$$

$$V_C = IZ_{T_p} = (5 \text{ mA})(27.64 \text{ k}\Omega) = \mathbf{138.2\ V}$$

c. $P = I^2R = (5 \text{ mA})^2 27.64 \text{ k}\Omega = \mathbf{691\ mW}$

d. $Q_p = \dfrac{R}{X_L} = \dfrac{R_s \parallel R_p}{X_L} = \dfrac{27.64 \text{ k}\Omega}{2\pi(3558.81 \text{ Hz})(0.2 \text{ H})} = \mathbf{6.18}$

$$BW = \frac{f_p}{Q_p} = \frac{3558.81 \text{ Hz}}{6.18} = \mathbf{575.86\ Hz}$$

22. a. Ratio of X_C to R_ℓ suggests high Q system.

$\therefore X_L = \mathbf{400\ \Omega} = X_C$

b. $$Q_\ell = \frac{X_L}{R_\ell} = \frac{400\ \Omega}{8\ \Omega} = \mathbf{50}$$

c. $$Q_p = \frac{R}{X_L} = \frac{R_s \parallel R_p}{X_L} = \frac{R_s \parallel Q_\ell^2 R_\ell}{X_L} = \frac{20\ \text{k}\Omega \parallel (50)^2\ 8\ \Omega}{400\ \Omega} = \frac{10\ \text{k}\Omega}{400\ \Omega} = \mathbf{25}$$

$$BW = \frac{f_p}{Q_p} \Rightarrow f_p = Q_p BW = (25)(1000\ \text{Hz}) = \mathbf{25\ kHz}$$

d. $$V_{C_{\max}} = IZ_{T_p} = (0.1\ \text{mA})(10\ \text{k}\Omega) = \mathbf{1\ V}$$

e. $$f_2 = f_p + BW/2 = 25\ \text{kHz} + \frac{1\ \text{kHz}}{2} = \mathbf{25.5\ kHz}$$

$$f_1 = f_p - BW/2 = 25\ \text{kHz} - \frac{1\ \text{kHz}}{2} = \mathbf{24.5\ kHz}$$

23. a. $$X_C = \frac{R_\ell^2 + X_L^2}{X_L} \Rightarrow X_L^2 - X_L X_C + R_\ell^2 = 0$$

$$X_L^2 - 100\ X_L + 144 = 0$$

$$X_L = \frac{-(-100) \pm \sqrt{(100)^2 - 4(1)(144)}}{2}$$

$$= 50\ \Omega \pm \frac{\sqrt{10^4 - 576}}{2} = 50\ \Omega \pm 48.54\ \Omega$$

$$X_L = \mathbf{98.54\ \Omega} \text{ or } 1.46\ \Omega$$

b. $$Q_\ell = \frac{X_L}{R_\ell} = \frac{98.54\ \Omega}{12\ \Omega} = \mathbf{8.21}$$

c. $$Q_p = \frac{R_s \parallel R_p}{X_{L_p}} = \frac{40\ \text{k}\Omega \parallel \dfrac{R_\ell^2 + X_L^2}{R_\ell}}{X_C} = \frac{40\ \text{k}\Omega \parallel \dfrac{(12\ \Omega)^2 + (98.54\ \Omega)^2}{12\ \Omega}}{100\ \Omega}$$

$$= \frac{40\ \text{k}\Omega \parallel 821.18\ \Omega}{100\ \Omega} = \frac{804.66\ \Omega}{100\ \Omega} = \mathbf{8.05}$$

$$BW = f_p/Q_p \Rightarrow f_p = Q_p BW = (8.05)(1\ \text{kHz}) = \mathbf{8.05\ kHz}$$

d. $$V_{C_{\max}} = IZ_{T_p} = (6\ \text{mA})(804.66\ \Omega) = \mathbf{4.83\ V}$$

e. $$f_2 = f_p + BW/2 = 8.05\ \text{kHz} + \frac{1\ \text{kHz}}{2} = \mathbf{8.55\ kHz}$$

$$f_1 = f_p - BW/2 = 8.05\ \text{kHz} - \frac{1\ \text{kHz}}{2} = \mathbf{7.55\ kHz}$$

24. a. $f_s = \dfrac{1}{2\pi\sqrt{LC}} = \dfrac{1}{2\pi\sqrt{(0.5\text{ mH})(30\text{ nF})}} = \mathbf{41.09\text{ kHz}}$

$$f_p = f_s\sqrt{1 - \frac{R_l^2 C}{L}} = 41.09\text{ kHz}\sqrt{1 - \frac{(6\,\Omega)^2\,30\text{ nF}}{0.5\text{ mH}}} = 41.09\text{ kHz}(0.9978) = \mathbf{41\text{ kHz}}$$

$$f_m = f_s\sqrt{1 - \frac{1}{4}\left[\frac{R_l^2 C}{L}\right]} = 41.09\text{ kHz}\sqrt{1 - \frac{1}{4}\left[\frac{(6\,\Omega)^2(30\text{ nF})}{0.5\text{ mH}}\right]} = 41.09\text{ kHz}(0.0995)$$

$$= \mathbf{41.07\text{ kHz}}$$

High Q_p

b. $\mathbf{I} = \dfrac{80\text{ V}\angle 0°}{20\text{ k}\Omega\angle 0°} = 4\text{ mA}\angle 0°,\ R_s = 20\text{ k}\Omega$

$$Q_l = \frac{X_L}{R_l} = \frac{2\pi fL}{R_l} = \frac{2\pi(41\text{ kHz})(0.5\text{ mH})}{6\,\Omega} = \mathbf{21.47}\text{ (high } Q \text{ coil)}$$

$$Q_p = \frac{R_s \parallel R_p}{X_{L_p}} = \frac{R_s \parallel \dfrac{R_l^2 + X_L^2}{R_l}}{\dfrac{R_l^2 + X_L^2}{X_L}} = \frac{20\text{ k}\Omega \parallel \dfrac{(6\,\Omega)^2 + (128.81\,\Omega)^2}{6\,\Omega}}{\dfrac{(6\,\Omega)^2 + (128.81\,\Omega)^2}{128.81\,\Omega}}$$

$$= \frac{20\text{ k}\Omega \parallel 2.771\text{ k}\Omega}{129.09\,\Omega} = \frac{2.434\text{ k}\Omega}{129.09\,\Omega} = \mathbf{18.86}\text{ (high } Q_p\text{)}$$

c. $Z_{T_p} = R_s \parallel R_p = 20\text{ k}\Omega \parallel 2.771\text{ k}\Omega = \mathbf{2.43\text{ k}\Omega}$

d. $V_C = IZ_{T_p} = (4\text{ mA})(2.43\text{ k}\Omega) = \mathbf{9.74\text{ V}}$

e. $BW = \dfrac{f_p}{Q_p} = \dfrac{41\text{ kHz}}{18.86} = \mathbf{2.17\text{ kHz}}$

f. $X_C = \dfrac{1}{2\pi fC} = \dfrac{1}{2\pi(41\text{ kHz})(30\text{ nF})} = \mathbf{129.39\,\Omega}$

$$I_C = \frac{V_C}{X_C} = \frac{9.736\text{ V}}{129.39\,\Omega} = \mathbf{75.25\text{ mA}}$$

$$I_L = \frac{V_C}{|R + jX_L|} = \frac{9.736\text{ V}}{6\,\Omega + j128.81\,\Omega} = \frac{9.736\text{ V}}{128.95\,\Omega} = \mathbf{75.50\text{ mA}}$$

25. $Q_l = \dfrac{X_L}{R_l} = \dfrac{2\pi f_p L}{R_l} \Rightarrow R_l = \dfrac{2\pi f_p L}{Q_l} = \dfrac{2\pi(20\text{ kHz})(2\text{ mH})}{80} = \mathbf{3.14\,\Omega}$

$BW = f_p/Q_p \Rightarrow Q_p = f_p/BW = 20\text{ kHz}/1.8\text{ kHz} = \mathbf{11.11}$

High Q ∴ $f_p \cong f_s = \dfrac{1}{2\pi\sqrt{LC}} \Rightarrow C = \dfrac{1}{4\pi^2 f_p^2 L} = \dfrac{1}{4\pi^2(20\text{ kHz})^2\,2\text{ mH}} = \mathbf{31.66\text{ nF}}$

$$Q_p = \frac{R}{X_C} \Rightarrow R = Q_p X_C = \frac{Q_p}{2\pi f_p C} = \frac{11.11}{2\pi(20\text{ kHz})(31.66\text{ nF})} = \mathbf{2.79\text{ k}\Omega}$$

$R_p = Q_\ell^2 R_\ell = (80)^2\, 3.14\ \Omega = 20.1\ \text{k}\Omega$

$R = R_s \parallel R_p = \dfrac{R_s R_p}{R_s + R_p} \Rightarrow R_s = \dfrac{R_p R}{R_p - R} = \dfrac{(20.1\ \text{k}\Omega)(2.793\ \text{k}\Omega)}{20.1\ \text{k}\Omega - 2.793\ \text{k}\Omega} = \mathbf{3.24\ k\Omega}$

26. $V_{C_{max}} = IZ_{T_p} \Rightarrow Z_{T_p} = \dfrac{V_{C_{max}}}{I} = \dfrac{1.8\ \text{V}}{0.2\ \text{mA}} = 9\ \text{k}\Omega$

$Q_p = \dfrac{R}{X_L} = \dfrac{R_s \parallel R_p}{X_L} = \dfrac{R_p}{X_L} \Rightarrow X_L = \dfrac{R_p}{Q_p} = \dfrac{9\ \text{k}\Omega}{30} = \mathbf{300\ \Omega} = X_C$

$BW = \dfrac{f_p}{Q_p} \Rightarrow f_p = Q_p BW = (30)(500\ \text{Hz}) = \mathbf{15\ kHz}$

$L = \dfrac{X_L}{2\pi f} = \dfrac{300\ \Omega}{2\pi(15\ \text{kHz})} = \mathbf{3.18\ mH}$

$C = \dfrac{1}{2\pi f X_C} = \dfrac{1}{2\pi(15\ \text{kHz})(300\ \Omega)} = \mathbf{35.37\ nF}$

$Q_p = Q_\ell\,(R_s = \infty\ \Omega) = \dfrac{X_L}{R_\ell} \Rightarrow R_\ell = \dfrac{X_L}{Q_p} = \dfrac{300\ \Omega}{30} = \mathbf{10\ \Omega}$

27. a. $f_s = \dfrac{1}{2\pi\sqrt{LC}} = \dfrac{1}{2\pi\sqrt{(200\ \mu\text{H})(2\ \text{nF})}} = 251.65\ \text{kHz}$

$Q_\ell = \dfrac{X_L}{R_\ell} = \dfrac{2\pi(251.65\ \text{kHz})(200\ \mu\text{H})}{20\ \Omega} = 15.81 \geq 10$

$\therefore f_p = f_s = \mathbf{251.65\ kHz}$

b. $Z_{T_p} = R_s \parallel Q_\ell^2 R_\ell = 40\ \text{k}\Omega \parallel (15.81)^2\, 20\ \Omega = \mathbf{4.44\ k\Omega}$

c. $Q_p = \dfrac{R_s \parallel Q_\ell^2 R_\ell}{X_L} = \dfrac{4.444\ \text{k}\Omega}{316.23\ \Omega} = \mathbf{14.05}$

d. $BW = \dfrac{f_p}{Q_p} = \dfrac{251.65\ \text{kHz}}{14.05} = \mathbf{17.91\ kHz}$

e. **20 μH, 20 nF**

f_s the same since product LC the same

$f_s = 251.65\ \text{kHz}$

$Q_\ell = \dfrac{X_L}{R_\ell} = \dfrac{2\pi(251.65\ \text{kHz})(20\ \mu\text{H})}{20\ \Omega} = 1.581$

Low Q_ℓ:

$f_p = f_s\sqrt{1 - \dfrac{R_\ell^2 C}{L}} = (251.65\ \text{kHz})\sqrt{1 - \dfrac{(20\ \Omega)^2(20\ \text{nF})}{20\ \mu\text{H}}}$

$= (251.65\ \text{kHz})(0.775) = \mathbf{194.93\ kHz}$

$X_L = 2\pi f_p L = 2\pi(194.93 \text{ kHz})(20 \ \mu\text{H}) = 24.496 \ \Omega$

$$R_p = \frac{R_l^2 + X_L^2}{R_l} = \frac{(20 \ \Omega)^2 + (24.496 \ \Omega)^2}{20 \ \Omega} = 50 \ \Omega$$

$Z_{T_p} = R_s \parallel R_p = 40 \text{ k}\Omega \parallel 50 \ \Omega = \mathbf{49.94 \ \Omega}$

$$Q_p = \frac{R}{X_L} = \frac{49.94 \ \Omega}{24.496 \ \Omega} = \mathbf{2.04}$$

$$BW = \frac{f_p}{Q_p} = \frac{194.93 \text{ kHz}}{2.04} = \mathbf{95.55 \text{ kHz}}$$

f. **0.4 mH, 1 nF**

$f_s = 251.65$ kHz since LC product the same

$$Q_l = \frac{X_L}{R_l} = \frac{2\pi(251.65 \text{ kHz})(0.4 \text{ mH})}{20 \ \Omega} = 31.62 \geq 10$$

$\therefore f_p = f_s = \mathbf{251.65 \text{ kHz}}$

$Z_{T_p} = R_s \parallel Q_l^2 R_l = 40 \text{ k}\Omega \parallel (31.62)^2 \, 20 \ \Omega = 40 \text{ k}\Omega \parallel (\cong 20 \text{ k}\Omega) \cong \mathbf{13.33 \text{ k}\Omega}$

$$Q_p = \frac{R_s \parallel Q_l^2 R_l}{X_L} = \frac{13.33 \text{ k}\Omega}{632.47 \ \Omega} = \mathbf{21.08}$$

$$BW = \frac{f_p}{Q_p} = \frac{251.65 \text{ kHz}}{21.08} = \mathbf{11.94 \text{ kHz}}$$

g. Network $\dfrac{L}{C} = \dfrac{200 \ \mu\text{H}}{2 \text{ nF}} = \mathbf{100 \times 10^3}$

part (e) $\dfrac{L}{C} = \dfrac{20 \ \mu\text{H}}{20 \text{ nF}} = \mathbf{1 \times 10^3}$

part (f) $\dfrac{L}{C} = \dfrac{0.4 \text{ mH}}{1 \text{ nF}} = \mathbf{400 \times 10^3}$

h. Yes, as $\dfrac{L}{C}$ ratio increased BW decreased.

Also, $V_p = IZ_{T_p}$ and for a fixed I, Z_{T_p} and therefore V_p will increase with increase in the L/C ratio.

Chapter 21

1. a. left: $d_1 = \frac{3}{16}'' = 0.1875''$, $d_2 = 1''$

$$\text{Value} = 10^3 \times 10^{0.1875''/1''}$$
$$= 10^3 \times 1.54$$
$$= \mathbf{1.54\ kHz}$$

right: $d_1 = \frac{3}{4}'' = 0.75''$, $d_2 = 1''$

$$\text{Value} = 10^3 \times 10^{0.75''/1''}$$
$$= 10^3 \times 5.623$$
$$= \mathbf{5.62\ kHz}$$

b. bottom: $d_1 = \frac{5}{16}'' = 0.3125''$, $d_2 = \frac{15}{16}'' = 0.9375''$

$$\text{Value} = 10^{-1} \times 10^{0.3125''/0.9375''} = 10^{-1} \times 10^{0.333}$$
$$= 10^{-1} \times 2.153$$
$$= \mathbf{0.22\ V}$$

top: $d_1 = \frac{11}{16}'' = 0.6875''$, $d_2 = 0.9375''$

$$\text{Value} = 10^{-1} \times 10^{0.6875''/0.9375''} = 10^{-1} \times 10^{0.720}$$
$$= 10^{-1} \times 5.248$$
$$= \mathbf{0.52\ V}$$

2. a. **5** b. **–4** c. **8** d. **–6**

e. **1.30** f. **3.94** g. **4.75** h. **–0.498**

3. a. **1000** b. $\mathbf{10^{12}}$ c. **1.59** d. **1.1**

e. $\mathbf{10^{10}}$ f. **1513.56** g. **10.02** h. **1,258,925.41**

4. a. **11.51** b. **–9.21** c. **2.996** d. **9.07**

5. $\log_{10} 48 = \mathbf{1.68}$
$\log_{10} 8 + \log_{10} 6 = 0.903 + 0.778 = \mathbf{1.68}$

6. $\log_{10} 0.2 = \mathbf{-0.699}$
$\log_{10} 18 - \log_{10} 90 = 1.255 - 1.954 = \mathbf{-0.699}$

7. $\log_{10} 0.5 = \mathbf{-0.30}$
$-\log_{10} 2 = -(0.301) = \mathbf{-0.30}$

8. $\log_{10} 27 = \mathbf{1.43}$
$3 \log_{10} 3 = 3(0.4771) = \mathbf{1.43}$

9. a. $\text{bels} = \log_{10} \frac{P_2}{P_1} = \log_{10} \frac{280 \text{ mW}}{4 \text{ mW}} = \log_{10} 70 = \mathbf{1.85}$

b. $\text{dB} = 10 \log_{10} \frac{P_2}{P_1} = 10(\log_{10} 70) = 10(1.845) = \mathbf{18.45}$

10. $\text{dB} = 10 \log_{10} \frac{P_2}{P_1}$

$6 \text{ dB} = 10 \log_{10} \frac{100 \text{ W}}{P_1}$

$0.6 = \log_{10} x$

$x = 3.981 = \frac{100 \text{ W}}{P_1}$

$P_1 = \frac{100 \text{ W}}{3.981} = \mathbf{25.12 \text{ W}}$

11. $\text{dB} = 10 \log_{10} \frac{P_2}{P_1} = 10 \log_{10} \frac{40 \text{ W}}{2 \text{ W}} = 10 \log_{10} 20 = \mathbf{13.01}$

12. $\text{dB}_m = 10 \log_{10} \frac{P}{1 \text{ mW}}$

$\text{dB}_m = 10 \log_{10} \frac{120 \text{ mW}}{1 \text{ mW}} = 10 \log_{10} 120 = \mathbf{20.79}$

13. $\text{dB}_v = 20 \log_{10} \frac{V_2}{V_1} = 20 \log_{10} \frac{8.4 \text{ V}}{0.1 \text{ V}} = 20 \log_{10} 84 = \mathbf{38.49}$

14. $\text{dB}_v = 20 \log_{10} \frac{V_2}{V_1}$

$22 = 20 \log_{10} \frac{V_o}{20 \text{ mV}}$

$1.1 = \log_{10} x$

$x = 12.589 = \frac{V_o}{20 \text{ mV}}$

$V_o = \mathbf{251.79 \text{ mV}}$

15. $\text{dB}_s = 20 \log_{10} \frac{P}{0.0002 \ \mu\text{bar}}$

$\text{dB}_s = 20 \log_{10} \frac{0.001 \ \mu\text{bar}}{0.0002 \ \mu\text{bar}} = \mathbf{13.98}$

$\text{dB}_s = 20 \log_{10} \frac{0.016 \ \mu\text{bar}}{0.0002 \ \mu\text{bar}} = \mathbf{38.06}$

Increase = **24.08 dB$_s$**

16. $60 \text{ dB}_s \Rightarrow 90 \text{ dB}_s$
quiet loud

$$60 \text{ dB}_s = 20 \log_{10} \frac{P_1}{0.002\ \mu\text{bar}} = 20 \log_{10} x$$

$$3 = \log_{10} x$$
$$x = \mathbf{1000}$$

$$90 \text{ dB}_s = 20 \log_{10} \frac{P_2}{0.002\ \mu\text{bar}} = 20 \log_{10} y$$

$$4.5 = \log_{10} y$$
$$y = \mathbf{31.623 \times 10^3}$$

$$\frac{x}{y} = \frac{\dfrac{P_1}{0.002\ \mu\text{bar}}}{\dfrac{P_2}{0.002\ \mu\text{bar}}} = \frac{P_1}{P_2} = \frac{10^3}{31.623 \times 10^3}$$

and $P_2 = \mathbf{31.62}\ \boldsymbol{P_1}$

18. a.

$$8 \text{ dB} = 20 \log_{10} \frac{V_2}{0.775 \text{ V}}$$

$$0.4 = \log_{10} \frac{V_2}{0.775 \text{ V}}$$

$$\frac{V_2}{0.775 \text{ V}} = 2.512$$

$$V_2 = (2.512)(0.775 \text{ V}) = 1.947 \text{ V}$$

$$P = \frac{V^2}{R} = \frac{(1.947 \text{ V})^2}{600\ \Omega} = \mathbf{6.32\ mW}$$

b.

$$-5 \text{ dB} = 20 \log_{10} \frac{V_2}{0.775 \text{ V}}$$

$$-0.25 = \log_{10} \frac{V_2}{0.775 \text{ V}}$$

$$\frac{V_2}{0.775 \text{ V}} = 0.562$$

$$V_2 = (0.562)(0.775 \text{ V}) = 0.436 \text{ V}$$

$$P = \frac{V^2}{R} = \frac{(0.436 \text{ V})^2}{600\ \Omega} = \mathbf{0.32\ mW}$$

19. a.

$$A_v = \frac{\mathbf{V}_o}{\mathbf{V}_i} = \frac{X_C}{\sqrt{R^2 + X_C^2}} \angle -90° + \tan^{-1} X_C/R = \frac{1}{\sqrt{\left(\dfrac{R}{X_C}\right)^2 + 1}} \angle -\tan^{-1} R/X_C$$

$$f_c = \frac{1}{2\pi RC} = \frac{1}{2\pi(2.2\text{ k}\Omega)(0.02\ \mu\text{F})} = \mathbf{3617.16\ Hz}$$

$f = f_c$: $\quad A_v = \dfrac{V_o}{V_i} = \mathbf{0.707}$

$f = 0.1 f_c$: $\quad$ At f_c, $X_C = R = 2.2\text{ k}\Omega$

$$X_C = \frac{1}{2\pi fC} = \frac{1}{2\pi 0.1 f_c C} = \frac{1}{0.1}\left[\frac{1}{2\pi f_c C}\right] = 10[2.2\text{ k}\Omega] = 22\text{ k}\Omega$$

$$A_v = \frac{1}{\sqrt{\left(\frac{R}{X_C}\right)^2 + 1}} = \frac{1}{\sqrt{\left(\frac{2.2\text{ k}\Omega}{22\text{ k}\Omega}\right)^2 + 1}} = \frac{1}{\sqrt{(.1)^2 + 1}} = \mathbf{0.995}$$

$f = 0.5f_c = \frac{1}{2}f_c$:

$$X_C = \frac{1}{2\pi fC} = \frac{1}{2\pi\left(\frac{f_c}{2}\right)C} = 2\left[\frac{1}{2\pi f_c C}\right] = 2[2.2\text{ k}\Omega] = 4.4\text{ k}\Omega$$

$$A_v = \frac{1}{\sqrt{\left(\frac{2.2\text{ k}\Omega}{4.4\text{ k}\Omega}\right)^2 + 1}} = \frac{1}{\sqrt{(0.5)^2 + 1}} = \mathbf{0.894}$$

$f = 2f_c$:

$$X_C = \frac{1}{2\pi(2f_c)C} = \frac{1}{2}\left[\frac{1}{2\pi f_c C}\right] = \frac{1}{2}[2.2\text{ k}\Omega] = 1.1\text{ k}\Omega$$

$$A_v = \frac{1}{\sqrt{\left(\frac{2.2\text{ k}\Omega}{1.1\text{ k}\Omega}\right)^2 + 1}} = \frac{1}{\sqrt{(2)^2 + 1}} = \mathbf{0.447}$$

$f = 10f_c$:

$$X_C = \frac{1}{2\pi(10f_c)C} = \frac{1}{10}\left[\frac{1}{2\pi f_c C}\right] = \frac{1}{10}[2.2\text{ k}\Omega] = 0.22\text{ k}\Omega$$

$$A_v = \frac{1}{\sqrt{\left(\frac{2.2\text{ k}\Omega}{0.22\text{ k}\Omega}\right)^2 + 1}} = \frac{1}{\sqrt{(10)^2 + 1}} = \mathbf{0.0995}$$

b. $\theta = -\tan^{-1} R/X_C$

$f = f_c$: $\theta = -\tan^{-1} = \mathbf{-45°}$

$f = 0.1f_c$: $\theta = -\tan^{-1} 2.2\text{ k}\Omega/22\text{ k}\Omega = -\tan^{-1}\frac{1}{10} = \mathbf{-5.71°}$

$f = 0.5f_c$: $\theta = -\tan^{-1} 2.2\text{ k}\Omega/4.4\text{ k}\Omega = -\tan^{-1}\frac{1}{2} = \mathbf{-26.57°}$

$f = 2f_c$: $\theta = -\tan^{-1} 2.2\text{ k}\Omega/1.1\text{ k}\Omega = -\tan^{-1} 2 = \mathbf{-63.43°}$

$f = 10f_c$: $\theta = -\tan^{-1} 2.2\text{ k}\Omega/0.22\text{ k}\Omega = -\tan^{-1} 10 = \mathbf{-84.29°}$

20. a. $f_c = \frac{1}{2\pi RC} = \frac{1}{2\pi(1\text{ k}\Omega)(0.01\,\mu\text{F})} = 15.915\text{ kHz}$

$f = 2f_c = 31.83\text{ kHz}$

$$X_C = \frac{1}{2\pi fC} = \frac{1}{2\pi(31.83\text{ kHz})(0.01\,\mu\text{F})} = 500\ \Omega$$

$$A_v = \frac{V_o}{V_i} = \frac{X_C}{\sqrt{R^2 + X_C^2}} = \frac{500\ \Omega}{\sqrt{(1\text{ k}\Omega)^2 + (0.5\text{ k}\Omega)^2}} = 0.4472$$

$V_o = 0.4472V_i = 0.4472(10\text{ mV}) = \mathbf{4.47\text{ mV}}$

b. $f = \frac{1}{10} f_c = \frac{1}{10}(15{,}915 \text{ kHz}) = 1.5915 \text{ kHz}$

$$X_C = \frac{1}{2\pi fC} = \frac{1}{2\pi(1.5915 \text{ kHz})(0.01\,\mu\text{F})} = 10 \text{ k}\Omega$$

$$A_v = \frac{V_o}{V_i} = \frac{X_C}{\sqrt{R^2 + X_C^2}} = \frac{10 \text{ k}\Omega}{\sqrt{(1 \text{ k}\Omega)^2 + (10 \text{ k}\Omega)^2}} = 0.995$$

$V_o = 0.995V_i = 0.995(10 \text{ mV}) = \mathbf{9.95 \text{ mV}}$

c. Yes, at $f = f_c$, $V_o = 7.07$ mV

at $f = \frac{1}{10} f_c$, $V_o = 9.95$ mV (much higher)

at $f = 2f_c$, $V_o = 4.47$ mV (much lower)

21. $f_c = 500 \text{ Hz} = \frac{1}{2\pi RC} = \frac{1}{2\pi(1.2 \text{ k}\Omega)C}$

$$C = \frac{1}{2\pi Rf_c} = \frac{1}{2\pi(1.2 \text{ k}\Omega)(500 \text{ Hz})} = \mathbf{0.265\ \mu F}$$

$$A_v = \frac{V_o}{V_i} = \frac{1}{\sqrt{\left(\frac{R}{X_C}\right)^2 + 1}}$$

At $f = 250$ Hz, $X_C = 2402.33\ \Omega$ and $A_v = 0.895$
At $f = 1000$ Hz, $X_C = 600.58\ \Omega$ and $A_v = 0.4475$
$\theta = -\tan^{-1} R/X_C$

At $f = 250 \text{ Hz} = \frac{1}{2} f_c$, $\theta = -26.54°$

At $f = 1 \text{ kHz} = 2f_c$, $\theta = -63.41°$

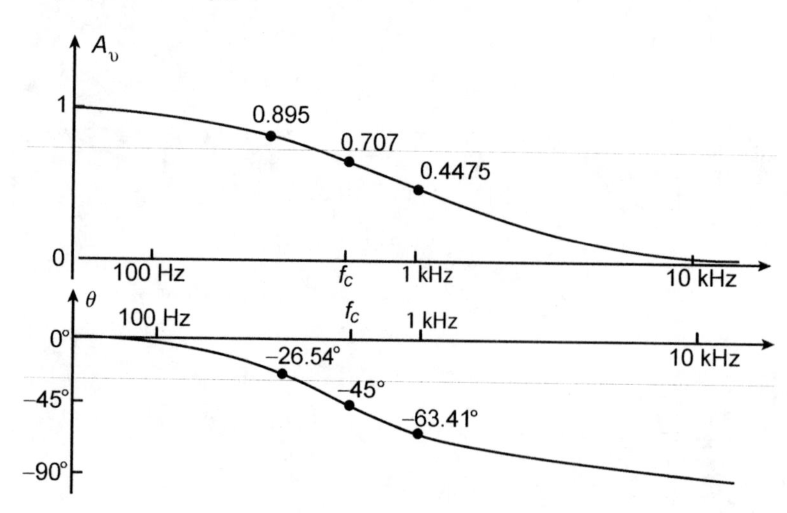

22. a. $f_c = \dfrac{1}{2\pi RC} = \dfrac{1}{2\pi(4.7\text{ k}\Omega)(500\text{ pF})} = \mathbf{67.73\text{ kHz}}$

b. $f = 0.1 f_c = 0.1(67.726\text{ kHz}) \cong 6.773\text{ kHz}$

$$X_C = \frac{1}{2\pi fC} = \frac{1}{2\pi(6.773\text{ kHz})(500\text{ pF})} = 46.997\text{ k}\Omega$$

$$A_\upsilon = \frac{V_o}{V_i} = \frac{X_C}{\sqrt{R^2 + X_C^2}} = \frac{46.997\text{ k}\Omega}{\sqrt{(4.7\text{ k}\Omega)^2 + (46.997\text{ k}\Omega)^2}} = \mathbf{0.995} \cong 1$$

c. $f = 10 f_c = 677.26\text{ kHz}$

$$X_C = \frac{1}{2\pi fC} = \frac{1}{2\pi(677.26\text{ kHz})(500\text{ pF})} \cong 470\ \Omega$$

$$A_\upsilon = \frac{V_o}{V_i} = \frac{X_C}{\sqrt{R^2 + X_C^2}} = \frac{470\ \Omega}{\sqrt{(4.7\text{ k}\Omega)^2 + (470\ \Omega)^2}} = \mathbf{0.0995} \cong 0.1$$

d. $A_\upsilon = \dfrac{V_o}{V_i} = 0.01 = \dfrac{X_C}{\sqrt{R^2 + X_C^2}}$

$$\sqrt{R^2 + X_C^2} = \frac{X_C}{0.01} = 100\,X_C$$

$$R^2 + X_C^2 = 10^4\,X_C^2$$

$$R^2 = 10^4\,X_C^2 - X_C^2 = 9{,}999\,X_C^2$$

$$X_C = \frac{R}{\sqrt{9{,}999}} = \frac{4.7\text{ k}\Omega}{99.995} \cong 47\ \Omega$$

$$X_C = \frac{1}{2\pi fC} \Rightarrow f = \frac{1}{2\pi X_C C} = \frac{1}{2\pi(47\ \Omega)(500\text{ pF})} = \mathbf{6.77\text{ MHz}}$$

23. a. $A_\upsilon = \dfrac{\mathbf{V}_o}{\mathbf{V}_i} = \dfrac{R}{\sqrt{R^2 + X_C^2}}\angle\tan^{-1} X_C/R = \dfrac{1}{\sqrt{1 + \left(\dfrac{X_C}{R}\right)^2}}\angle\tan^{-1} X_C/R$

$$f_c = \frac{1}{2\pi RC} = \frac{1}{2\pi(2.2\text{ k}\Omega)(20\text{ nF})} = \mathbf{3.62\text{ kHz}}$$

$f = f_c$: $A_\upsilon = \dfrac{V_o}{V_i} = \mathbf{0.707}$

$f = 2f_c$: At f_c, $X_C = R = 2.2\text{ k}\Omega$

$$X_C = \frac{1}{2\pi fC} = \frac{1}{2\pi(2f_c)C} = \frac{1}{2}\left[\frac{1}{2\pi f_c C}\right] = \frac{1}{2}[2.2\text{ k}\Omega] = 1.1\text{ k}\Omega$$

$$A_\upsilon = \frac{1}{\sqrt{1 + \left(\dfrac{1.1\text{ k}\Omega}{2.2\text{ k}\Omega}\right)^2}} = \mathbf{0.894}$$

$f = \frac{1}{2}f_c$: $\quad X_C = \frac{1}{2\pi\left(\frac{f_c}{2}\right)C} = 2\left[\frac{1}{2\pi f_c C}\right] = 2[2.2\text{ k}\Omega] = 4.4\text{ k}\Omega$

$$A_\upsilon = \frac{1}{\sqrt{1+\left(\frac{4.4\text{ k}\Omega}{2.2\text{ k}\Omega}\right)^2}} = \mathbf{0.447}$$

$f = 10f_c$: $\quad X_C = \frac{1}{2\pi(10f_c)C} = \frac{1}{10}\left[\frac{1}{2\pi f_c C}\right] = \frac{2.2\text{ k}\Omega}{10} = 0.22\text{ k}\Omega$

$$A_\upsilon = \frac{1}{\sqrt{1+\left(\frac{0.22\text{ k}\Omega}{2.2\text{ k}\Omega}\right)^2}} = \mathbf{0.995}$$

$f = \frac{1}{10}f_c$: $\quad X_C = \frac{1}{2\pi\left(\frac{f_c}{10}\right)C} = 10\left[\frac{1}{2\pi f_c C}\right] = 10[2.2\text{ k}\Omega] = 22\text{ k}\Omega$

$$A_\upsilon = \frac{1}{\sqrt{1+\left(\frac{22\text{ k}\Omega}{2.2\text{ k}\Omega}\right)^2}} = \mathbf{0.0995}$$

b. $f = f_c$, $\quad \theta = \mathbf{45°}$

$f = 2f_c$, $\quad \theta = \tan^{-1}(X_C/R) = \tan^{-1} 1.1\text{ k}\Omega/2.2\text{ k}\Omega = \tan^{-1}\frac{1}{2} = \mathbf{26.57°}$

$f = \frac{1}{2}f_c$, $\quad \theta = \tan^{-1}\frac{4.4\text{ k}\Omega}{2.2\text{ k}\Omega} = \tan^{-1} 2 = \mathbf{63.43°}$

$f = 10f_c$, $\quad \theta = \tan^{-1}\frac{0.22\text{ k}\Omega}{2.2\text{ k}\Omega} = \mathbf{5.71°}$

$f = \frac{1}{10}f_c$, $\quad \theta = \tan^{-1}\frac{22\text{ k}\Omega}{2.2\text{ k}\Omega} = \mathbf{84.29°}$

24. a. $f = f_c$: $A_\upsilon = \frac{V_o}{V_i} = \mathbf{0.707}$

b. $f_c = \frac{1}{2\pi RC} = \frac{1}{2\pi(10\text{ k}\Omega)(1000\text{ pF})} = 15.915\text{ kHz}$

$f = 4f_c = 4(15.915\text{ kHz}) = 63.66\text{ kHz}$

$X_C = \frac{1}{2\pi fC} = \frac{1}{2\pi(63.66\text{ kHz})(1000\text{ pF})} = 2.5\text{ k}\Omega$

$A_\upsilon = \frac{V_o}{V_i} = \frac{R}{\sqrt{R^2 + X_C^2}} = \frac{10\text{ k}\Omega}{\sqrt{(10\text{ k}\Omega)^2 + (2.5\text{ k}\Omega)^2}} = \mathbf{0.970}$ (significant rise)

c. $f = 100f_c = 100(15.915\text{ kHz}) = 1591.5\text{ kHz} \cong 1.592\text{ MHz}$

$$X_C = \frac{1}{2\pi fC} = \frac{1}{2\pi(1.592\text{ MHz})(1000\text{ pF})} = 99.972\ \Omega$$

$$A_v = \frac{R}{\sqrt{R^2 + X_C^2}} = \frac{10\text{ k}\Omega}{\sqrt{(10\text{ k}\Omega)^2 + (99.972\ \Omega)^2}} = 0.99995 \cong 1$$

d. At $f = f_c$, $V_o = 0.707V_i = 0.707(10\text{ mV}) = 7.07\text{ mV}$

$$P_o = \frac{V_o^2}{R} = \frac{(7.07\text{ mV})^2}{10\text{ k}\Omega} \cong \mathbf{5\ nW}$$

25. $$\mathbf{A}_v = \frac{\mathbf{V}_o}{\mathbf{V}_i} = \frac{1}{\sqrt{1 + \left(\frac{X_C}{R}\right)^2}} \angle \tan^{-1} X_C/R$$

$$f_c = \frac{1}{2\pi RC} \Rightarrow R = \frac{1}{2\pi f_c C} = \frac{1}{2\pi(2\text{ kHz})(0.1\ \mu\text{F})} = 795.77\ \Omega$$

$$R = 795.77\ \Omega \Rightarrow \underbrace{750\ \Omega + 47\ \Omega}_{\text{nominal values}} = 797\ \Omega$$

$$\therefore f_c = \frac{1}{2\pi(797\ \Omega)(0.1\ \mu\text{F})} = \mathbf{1996.93\ Hz}\text{ using nominal values}$$

At $f = 1\text{ kHz}$, $A_v = 0.458$
$f = 4\text{ kHz}$, $A_v \cong 0.9$

$$\theta = \tan^{-1}\frac{X_C}{R}$$

$f = 1\text{ kHz}$, $\theta = 63.4°$
$f = 4\text{ kHz}$, $\theta = 26.53°$

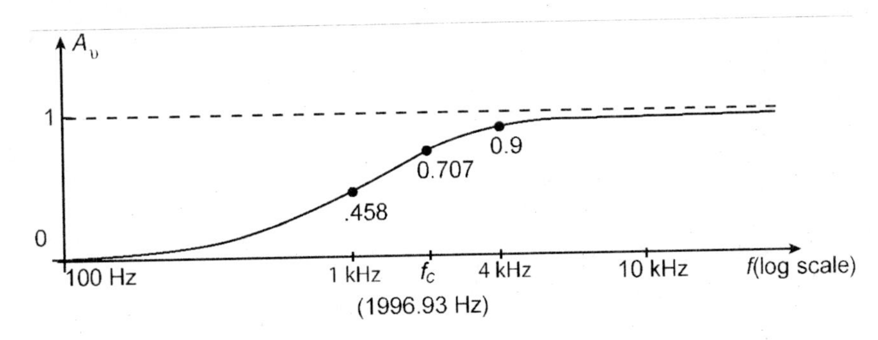

26. a. $f_c = \dfrac{1}{2\pi RC} = \dfrac{1}{2\pi(100\text{ k}\Omega)(20\text{ pF})} = \mathbf{79.58\text{ kHz}}$

b. $f = 0.01f_c = 0.01(79.577\text{ kHz}) = 0.7958\text{ kHz} \cong 796\text{ Hz}$

$$X_C = \frac{1}{2\pi fC} = \frac{1}{2\pi(796\text{ Hz})(20\text{ pF})} = 9.997\text{ M}\Omega$$

$$A_v = \frac{V_o}{V_i} = \frac{R}{\sqrt{R^2 + X_C^2}} = \frac{100\text{ k}\Omega}{\sqrt{(100\text{ k}\Omega)^2 + (9.997\text{ M}\Omega)^2}} = \mathbf{0.01} \cong 0$$

c. $f = 100f_c = 100(79.577\text{ kHz}) \cong 7.96\text{ MHz}$

$$X_C = \frac{1}{2\pi fC} = \frac{1}{2\pi(7.96\text{ MHz})(20\text{ pF})} = 999.72\ \Omega$$

$$A_v = \frac{V_o}{V_i} = \frac{R}{\sqrt{R^2 + X_C^2}} = \frac{100\text{ k}\Omega}{\sqrt{(100\text{ k}\Omega)^2 + (999.72\ \Omega)^2}} = \mathbf{0.99995} \cong 1$$

d. $A_v = \dfrac{V_o}{V_i} = 0.5 = \dfrac{R}{\sqrt{R^2 + X_C^2}}$

$$\sqrt{R^2 + X_C^2} = 2R$$

$$R^2 + X_C^2 = 4R^2$$

$$X_C^2 = 4R^2 - R^2 = 3R^2$$

$$X_C = \sqrt{3R^2} = \sqrt{3}R = \sqrt{3}\,(100\text{ k}\Omega) = 173.2\text{ k}\Omega$$

$$X_C = \frac{1}{2\pi fC} \Rightarrow f = \frac{1}{2\pi X_C C} = \frac{1}{2\pi(173.2\text{ k}\Omega)(20\text{ pF})}$$

$$f = \mathbf{45.95\text{ kHz}}$$

27. a. low-pass section: $f_{c_1} = \dfrac{1}{2\pi RC} = \dfrac{1}{2\pi(0.1\text{ k}\Omega)(2\ \mu\text{F})} = \mathbf{795.77\text{ Hz}}$

high-pass section: $f_{c_2} = \dfrac{1}{2\pi RC} = \dfrac{1}{2\pi(10\text{ k}\Omega)(8\text{ nF})} = \mathbf{1989.44\text{ Hz}}$

For the analysis to follow, it is assumed $(R_2 + jX_{C_2}) \parallel R_1 \cong R_1$ for all frequencies of interest.

At $f_{c_1} = 795.77$ Hz:

$$V_{R_1} = 0.707\ V_i$$

$$X_{C_2} = \frac{1}{2\pi fC_2} = 25\text{ k}\Omega$$

$$|V_o| = \frac{25\text{ k}\Omega(V_{R_1})}{\sqrt{(10\text{ k}\Omega)^2 + (25\text{ k}\Omega)^2}} = 0.9285\ V_{R_1}$$

$$V_o = (0.9285)(0.707\ V_i) = \mathbf{0.66\ V_i}$$

At $f_{C_2} = 1989.44$ Hz:

$$V_o = 0.707\ V_{R_1}$$

$$X_{C_1} = \frac{1}{2\pi f C_1} = 40\ \Omega$$

$$|V_{R_1}| = \frac{R_1 V_i}{\sqrt{R_1^2 + X_{C_1}^2}} = \frac{100\ \Omega(V_i)}{\sqrt{(100\ \Omega)^2 + (40\ \Omega)^2}} = 0.928\ V_i$$

$$|V_o| = (0.707)(0.928\ V_i) = \mathbf{0.66\ V_i}$$

$$\text{At } f = 795.77\text{ Hz} + \frac{(1989.44\text{ Hz} - 795.77\text{ Hz})}{2} = 1392.60\text{ Hz}$$

$X_{C_1} = 57.14\ \Omega$, $X_{C_2} = 14.29\ \text{k}\Omega$

$$|V_{R_1}| = \frac{100\ \Omega(V_i)}{\sqrt{(100\ \Omega)^2 + (57.14\ \Omega)^2}} = 0.868\ V_i$$

$$|V_o| = \frac{14.29\ \text{k}\Omega(V_{R_1})}{\sqrt{(10\ \text{k}\Omega)^2 + (14.29\ \text{k}\Omega)^2}} = 0.8193\ V_{R_1}$$

$$V_o = 0.8193(0.868\ V_i) = \mathbf{0.71 V_i}$$

$$\text{and } A_v = \frac{V_o}{V_i} = \mathbf{0.71}\ (\cong \text{maximum value})$$

After plotting the points it was determined that the gain should also be determined at $f = 500$ Hz and 4 kHz:

$f = 500$ Hz: $X_{C_1} = 159.15\ \Omega$, $X_{C_2} = 39.8\ \text{k}\Omega$,
$V_{R_1} = 0.532\ V_i$, $V_o = 0.97\ V_{R_1}$
$V_o = \mathbf{0.52\ V_i}$

$f = 4$ kHz: $X_{C_1} = 19.89\ \Omega$, $X_{C_2} = 4.97\ \text{k}\Omega$,
$V_{R_1} = 0.981\ V_i$, $V_o = 0.445\ V_{R_1}$
$V_o = \mathbf{0.44\ V_i}$

b. Using $0.707(.711) = 0.5026 \cong 0.5$ to define the bandwidth

$BW = 3.4\text{ kHz} - 0.49\text{ kHz} = 2.91\text{ kHz}$

and $BW \cong \mathbf{2.9\ kHz}$

$$\text{with } f_{\text{center}} = 490\text{ Hz} + \left(\frac{2.9\text{ kHz}}{2}\right) = \mathbf{1940\ Hz}$$

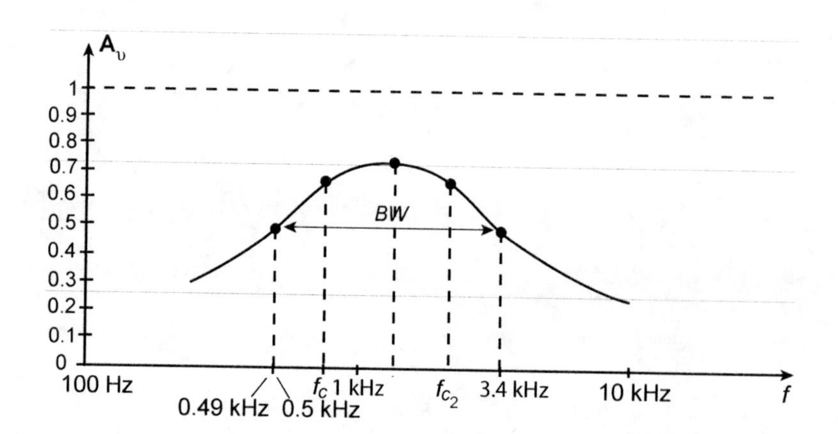

28. $f_1 = \dfrac{1}{2\pi R_1 C_1} = 4\text{ kHz}$

Choose $R_1 = 1\text{ k}\Omega$

$$C_1 = \frac{1}{2\pi f_1 R_1} = \frac{1}{2\pi(4\text{ kHz})(1\text{ k}\Omega)} = 39.8\text{ nF} \therefore \text{Use } \mathbf{39\text{ nF}}$$

$f_2 = \dfrac{1}{2\pi R_2 C_2} = 80\text{ kHz}$

Choose $R_2 = 20\text{ k}\Omega$

$$C_2 = \frac{1}{2\pi f_2 R_2} = \frac{1}{2\pi(80\text{ kHz})(20\text{ k}\Omega)} = 99.47\text{ pF} \therefore \text{Use } 100\text{ pF}$$

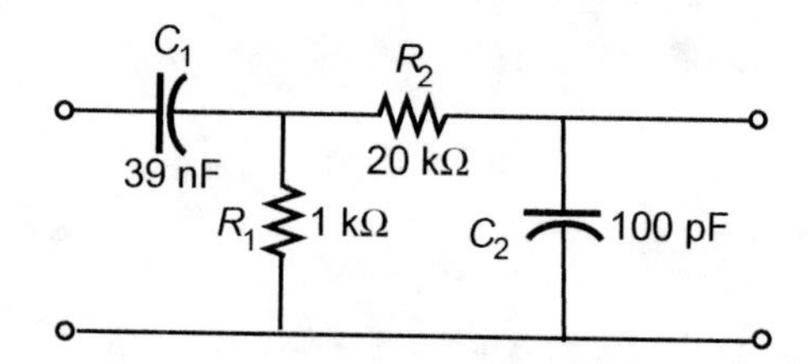

$$\text{Center frequency} = 4\text{ kHz} + \frac{80\text{ kHz} - 4\text{ kHz}}{2} = 42\text{ kHz}$$

At $f = 42$ kHz, $X_{C_1} = 97.16\ \Omega$, $X_{C_2} = 37.89\text{ k}\Omega$

Assuming $\boldsymbol{Z_2} \gg \boldsymbol{Z_1}$

$$|V_{R_1}| = \frac{R_1(V_i)}{\sqrt{R_1^2 + X_{C_1}^2}} = 0.995 V_i$$

$$|V_o| = \frac{X_{C_2}(V_{R_1})}{\sqrt{R_2^2 + X_{C_1}^2}} = 0.884 V_i$$

$V_o = 0.884\, V_{R_1} = 0.884(0.995 V_i) = \mathbf{0.88}\ \boldsymbol{V_i}$

as $f = f_1$: $V_{R_1} = 0.707 V_i$, $X_{C_2} = 221.05\text{ k}\Omega$

and $V_o = 0.996\, V_{R_1}$

so that $V_o = 0.996\, V_{R_1} = 0.996(0.707 V_i) = 0.704 V_i$

Although $A_\upsilon = 0.88$ is less than the desired level of 1, f_1 and f_2 do define a band of frequencies for which $A_\upsilon \geq 0.7$ and the power to the load is significant.

29. a. $f_s = \frac{1}{2\pi\sqrt{LC}} = \frac{1}{2\pi\sqrt{(5\text{ mH})(500\text{ pF})}} = \mathbf{100.66\ kHz}$

b. $Q_s = \frac{X_L}{R+R_l} = \frac{2\pi(100.658\text{ kHz})(5\text{ mH})}{160\,\Omega + 12\,\Omega} = \mathbf{18.39}$

$BW = \frac{f_s}{Q_s} = \frac{100.658\text{ kHz}}{18.39} = \mathbf{5{,}473.52\ Hz}$

c. At $f = f_s$: $V_{o_{max}} = \frac{R}{R+R_l}V_i = \frac{160\,\Omega(1\text{ V})}{172\,\Omega} = 0.93\text{ V}$ and $A_v = \frac{V_o}{V_i} = \mathbf{0.93}$

Since $Q_s \geq 10$, $f_1 = f_s - \frac{BW}{2} = 100.658\text{ kHz} - \frac{5{,}473.52\text{ Hz}}{2} = 97{,}921.24\text{ Hz}$

$f_2 = f_s + \frac{BW}{2} = 103{,}394.76\text{ Hz}$

At $f = 95$ kHz: $X_L = 2\pi fL = 2\pi(95 \times 10^3\text{ Hz})(5\text{ mH}) = 2.98\text{ k}\Omega$

$X_C = \frac{1}{2\pi fC} = \frac{1}{2\pi(95\times10^3\text{ Hz})(500\text{ pF})} = 3.35\text{ k}\Omega$

$\mathbf{V}_o = \frac{160\,\Omega(1\text{ V}\angle 0^\circ)}{172 + j2.98\text{ k}\Omega - j3.35\text{ k}\Omega} = \frac{160\text{ V}\angle 0^\circ}{172 - j370}$

$= \frac{160\text{ V}\angle 0^\circ}{480\angle -65.07^\circ} = \mathbf{0.39\ V\angle 65.07^\circ}$

At $f = 105$ kHz: $X_L = 2\pi fL = 2\pi(105\text{ kHz})(5\text{ mH}) = 3.3\text{ k}\Omega$

$X_C = \frac{1}{2\pi fC} = \frac{1}{2\pi(105\text{ kHz})(500\text{ pF})} = 3.03\text{ k}\Omega$

$\mathbf{V}_o = \frac{160(1\text{ V}\angle 0^\circ)}{172 + j3.3\text{ k}\Omega - j3.03\text{ k}\Omega} = \frac{160\text{ V}\angle 0^\circ}{172 + j270}$

$= \frac{160\text{ V}\angle 0^\circ}{320\angle 57.50^\circ} = \mathbf{0.5\angle -57.50^\circ}$

d. $f = f_s$: $V_{o_{max}} = \mathbf{0.93\ V}$

$f = f_1 = 97{,}921.24$ Hz, $V_o = 0.707(0.93\text{ V}) = \mathbf{0.66\ V}$

$f = f_2 = 103{,}394.76$ Hz, $V_o = 0.707(0.93\text{ V}) = \mathbf{0.66\ V}$

30. a. $f_p = \frac{1}{2\pi\sqrt{LC}}\sqrt{1 - \frac{R_l^2 C}{L}} \cong \mathbf{159.15\ kHz}$

$Q_l = \frac{X_L}{R_l} = \frac{2\pi f_p L}{R_l} = \frac{2\pi(159.15\text{ kHz})(1\text{ mH})}{16\,\Omega} = 62.5 \gg 10$

$Z_{T_p} = Q_l^2 R_l = (62.5)^2\ 16\,\Omega = 62.5\text{ k}\Omega \gg 4\text{ k}\Omega$

and $V_o \cong V_i$ at resonance.

However, $R = 4\ \text{k}\Omega$ affects the shape of the resonance curve and $BW = f_p/Q_\ell$ cannot be applied.

For $A_\upsilon = \dfrac{V_o}{V_i} = 0.707$, $|X| = R$ for the following configuration

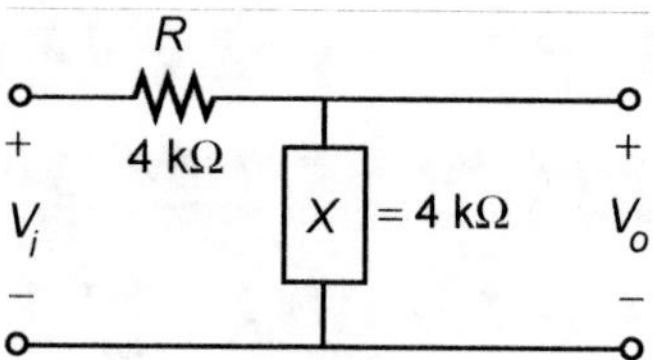

For frequencies near f_p, $X_L \gg R_\ell$ and $\mathbf{Z}_L = R_\ell + jX_L \cong X_L$ and $X = X_L \parallel X_C$.

For frequencies near f_p but less than f_p

$$X = \frac{X_C X_L}{X_C - X_L}$$

and for $A_\upsilon = 0.707$

$$\frac{X_C X_L}{X_C - X_L} = R$$

Substituting $X_C = \dfrac{1}{2\pi f_1 C}$ and $X_L = 2\pi f_1 L$

the following equation can be derived:

$$f_1^2 + \frac{1}{2\pi RC} f_1 - \frac{1}{4\pi^2 LC} = 0$$

For this situation:

$$\frac{1}{2\pi RC} = \frac{1}{2\pi(4\ \text{k}\Omega)(0.001\ \mu\text{F})} = 39.79 \times 10^3$$

$$\frac{1}{4\pi^2 LC} = \frac{1}{4\pi^2(1\ \text{mH})(0.001\ \mu\text{F})} = 2.53 \times 10^{10}$$

and solving the quadratic equation, $f_1 = 140.4$ kHz

and $\dfrac{BW}{2} = 159.15\ \text{kHz} - 140.4\ \text{kHz} = 18.75\ \text{kHz}$

with $BW = 2(18.75\ \text{kHz}) = \mathbf{37.5\ kHz}$

b. $Q_p = \dfrac{f_p}{BW} = \dfrac{159.15\ \text{kHz}}{37.5\ \text{kHz}} = \mathbf{4.24}$

31. a. $Q_s = \frac{X_L}{R + R_l} = \frac{5000\,\Omega}{400\,\Omega + 10\,\Omega} = \frac{5000\,\Omega}{410\,\Omega} = \mathbf{12.2}$

b. $BW = \frac{f_s}{Q_s} = \frac{5000\text{ Hz}}{12.2} = \mathbf{409.84\text{ Hz}}$

$f_1 = 5000\text{ Hz} - \frac{409.84\text{ Hz}}{2} = \mathbf{4.80\text{ kHz}}$

$f_2 = 5000\text{ Hz} + \frac{410\text{ Hz}}{2} = \mathbf{5.20\text{ kHz}}$

c.

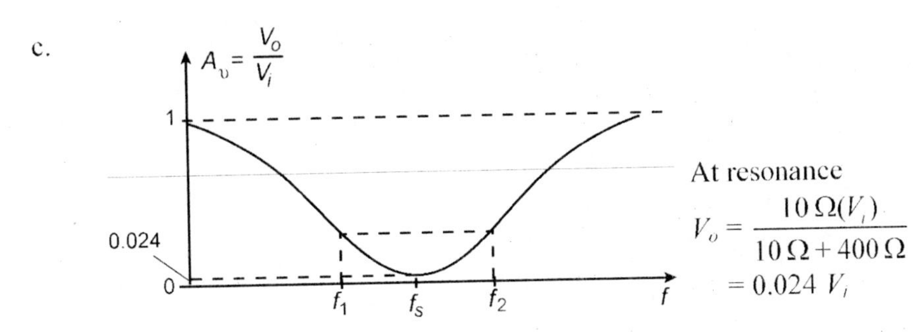

At resonance
$V_o = \frac{10\,\Omega(V_i)}{10\,\Omega + 400\,\Omega}$
$= 0.024\ V_i$

d. At resonance, $10\,\Omega \parallel 2\text{ k}\Omega = 9.95\,\Omega$

$V_o = \frac{9.95\,\Omega(V_i)}{9.95\,\Omega + 400\,\Omega} \cong 0.024\ V_i$ as above!

32. a. $Q_l = \frac{X_L}{R_l} = \frac{400\,\Omega}{10\,\Omega} = 40$

$Z_{T_p} = Q_l^2 R_l = (40)^2\ 20\,\Omega = 32\text{ k}\Omega \gg 1\text{ k}\Omega$

At resonance, $V_o = \frac{32\text{ k}\Omega V_i}{32\text{ k}\Omega + 1\text{ k}\Omega} = 0.97V_i$

and $A_v = \frac{V_o}{V_i} = 0.97$

For the low cutoff frequency note solution to Problem 30:

$$f_1^2 + \frac{1}{2\pi RC} f_1 - \frac{1}{4\pi^2 LC} = 0$$

$$C = \frac{1}{2\pi f X_C} = \frac{1}{2\pi(20\text{ kHz})(400\,\Omega)} = 19.9\text{ nF}$$

$$L = \frac{X_L}{2\pi f} = \frac{400\,\Omega}{2\pi(20\text{ kHz})} = 3.18\text{ mH}$$

Substituting into the above equation and solving
$f_1 = 16.4\text{ kHz}$

with $\frac{BW}{2} = 20\text{ kHz} - 16.4\text{ kHz} = 3.6\text{ kHz}$

and $BW = 2(3.6\text{ kHz}) = \mathbf{7.2\text{ kHz}}$

$Q_p = \frac{f_p}{BW} = \frac{20\text{ kHz}}{7.2\text{ kHz}} = \mathbf{2.78}$

b. –

c. At resonance

$$Z_{T_p} = 32\text{ k}\Omega \parallel 100\text{ k}\Omega = 24.24\text{ k}\Omega$$

$$\text{with } V_o = \frac{24.24\text{ k}\Omega\, V_i}{24.24\text{ k}\Omega + 1\text{ k}\Omega} = 0.96V_i$$

$$\text{and } A_v = \frac{V_o}{V_i} = 0.96 \text{ vs } 0.97 \text{ above}$$

At frequencies to the right and left of f_p, the impedance Z_{T_p} will decrease and be affected less and less by the parallel 100 kΩ load. The characteristics, therefore, are only slightly affected by the 100 kΩ load.

d. At resonance

$$Z_{T_p} = 32\text{ k}\Omega \parallel 20\text{ k}\Omega = 12.31\text{ k}\Omega$$

$$\text{with } V_o = \frac{12.31\text{ k}\Omega\, V_i}{12.31\text{ k}\Omega + 1\text{ k}\Omega} = 0.925V_i \text{ vs } 0.97\ V_i \text{ above}$$

At frequencies to the right and left of f_p, the impedance of each frequency will actually be less due to the parallel 20 kΩ load. The effect will be to narrow the resonance curve and decrease the bandwidth with an increase in Q_p.

33. a. $f_p = \dfrac{1}{2\pi\sqrt{LC}} = \dfrac{1}{2\pi\sqrt{(400\ \mu\text{H})(120\text{ pF})}} =$ **726.44 kHz** (band-stop)

$$X_{L_s}\angle 90° + \left(X_{L_p}\angle 90° \parallel X_C\angle -90°\right) = 0$$

$$jX_{L_s} + \frac{\left(X_{L_p}\angle 90°\right)\left(X_C\angle -90°\right)}{jX_{L_p} - jX_C} = 0$$

$$jX_{L_s} + \frac{X_{L_p}X_C}{j\left(X_{L_p} - X_C\right)} = 0$$

$$jX_{L_s} - j\frac{X_{L_p}X_C}{\left(X_{L_p} - X_C\right)} = 0$$

$$X_{L_s} - \frac{X_{L_p}X_C}{X_{L_p} - X_C} = 0$$

$$X_{L_s}X_C - X_{L_s}X_{L_p} + X_{L_p}X_C = 0$$

$$\frac{\omega L_s}{\omega C} - \omega L_s + \frac{\omega L_p}{\omega C} = 0$$

$$L_sL_p\omega^2 - \frac{1}{C}\left[L_s + L_p\right] = 0$$

$$\omega = \sqrt{\frac{L_s + L_p}{CL_sL_p}}$$

$$f = \frac{1}{2\pi}\sqrt{\frac{L_s + L_p}{CL_sL_p}} = \frac{1}{2\pi}\sqrt{\frac{460 \times 10^{-6}}{28.8 \times 10^{-19}}} = \mathbf{2.01\ MHz}\ \text{(pass-band)}$$

34. a. $f_s = \dfrac{1}{2\pi\sqrt{LC}} \Rightarrow L_s = \dfrac{1}{4\pi^2 f_s^2 C} = \dfrac{1}{4\pi^2(100\ \text{kHz})^2(200\ \text{pF})} = 12.68\ \text{mH}$

$X_L = 2\pi fL = 2\pi(30\ \text{kHz})(12.68\ \text{mH}) = 2388.91\ \Omega$

$X_C = \dfrac{1}{2\pi fC} = \dfrac{1}{2\pi(30\ \text{kHz})(200\ \text{pF})} = 26.54\ \text{k}\Omega$

$X_C - X_L = 26.54\ \text{k}\Omega - 2388.91\ \Omega = 24.15\ \text{k}\Omega(C)$

$X_{L_p} = X_{C_{(\text{net})}} = 24.15\ \text{k}\Omega$

$L_p = \dfrac{X_L}{2\pi f} = \dfrac{24.15\ \text{k}\Omega}{2\pi(30\ \text{kHz})} = \mathbf{128.19\ mH}$

35. a, b. $f_c = \dfrac{1}{2\pi RC} = \dfrac{1}{2\pi(0.47\ \text{k}\Omega)(0.05\ \mu\text{F})} = \mathbf{772.55\ Hz}$

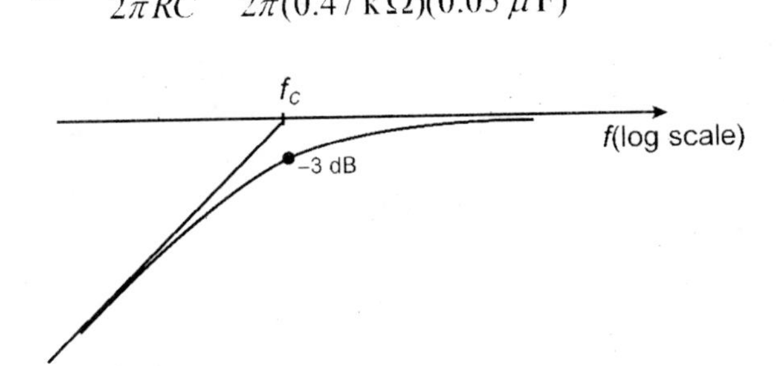

c. $f = \dfrac{1}{2}f_c$: $A_{v_{dB}} = 20\log_{10}\dfrac{1}{\sqrt{1+(f_c/f)^2}} = 20\log_{10}\dfrac{1}{\sqrt{1+(2)^2}} = \mathbf{-7\ dB}$

$f = 2f_c$: $A_{v_{dB}} = 20\log_{10}\dfrac{1}{\sqrt{1+(0.5)^2}} = \mathbf{-0.969\ dB}$

$f = \dfrac{1}{10}f_c$: $A_{v_{dB}} = 20\log_{10}\dfrac{1}{\sqrt{1+(10)^2}} = \mathbf{-20.04\ dB}$

$f = 10f_c$: $A_{v_{dB}} = 20\log_{10}\dfrac{1}{\sqrt{1+(0.1)^2}} = \mathbf{-0.043\ dB}$

d. $f = \dfrac{1}{2}f_c$: $A_v = \dfrac{1}{\sqrt{1+(f_c/f)^2}} = \dfrac{1}{\sqrt{1+(2)^2}} = \mathbf{0.447}$

$f = 2f_c$: $A_v = \dfrac{1}{\sqrt{1+(0.5)^2}} = \mathbf{0.894}$

e.

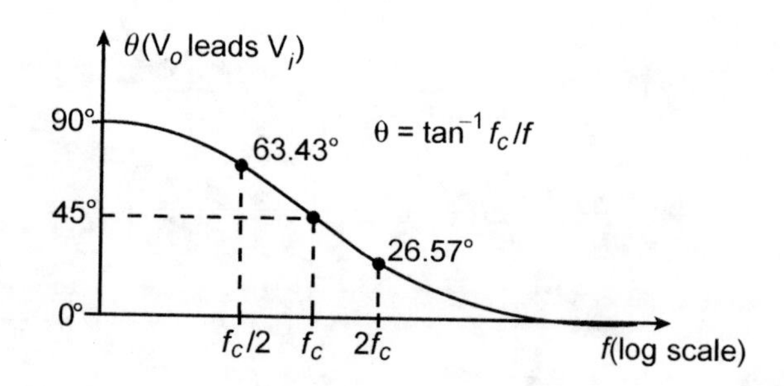

36. a. $f_c = \dfrac{1}{2\pi RC} = \dfrac{1}{2\pi(6\text{ k}\Omega \,\|\, 12\text{ k}\Omega)0.01\,\mu\text{F}} = \dfrac{1}{2\pi(4\text{ k}\Omega)(0.01\,\mu\text{F})} = \mathbf{1989.44\ Hz}$

$$\frac{V_o}{V_i} = \frac{1}{\sqrt{1+(f_c/f)^2}}$$

and $V_o = \left(\dfrac{1}{\sqrt{1+(f_c/f)^2}}\right)V_i$

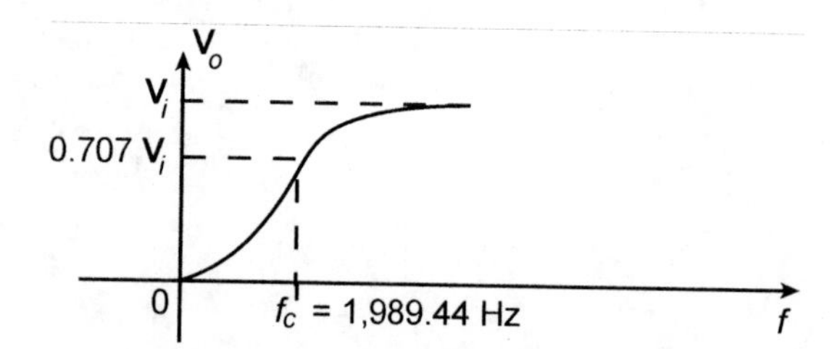

b.

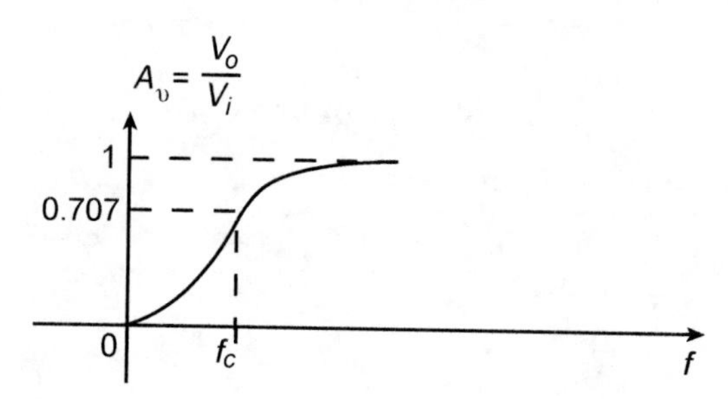

c. & d.

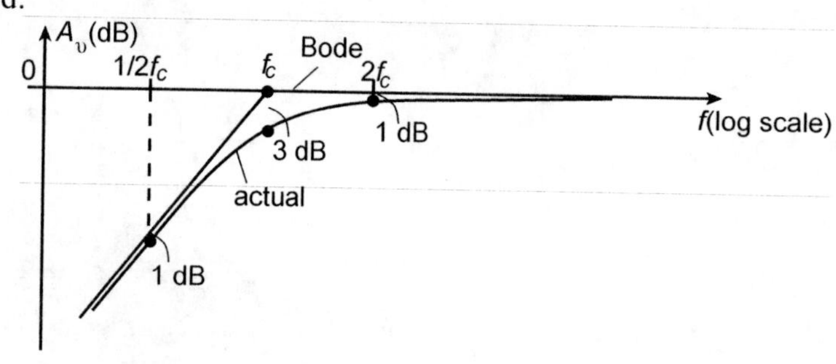

e. Remember the log scale! $1.5f_c$ is not midway between f_c and $2f_c$

$$A_{v_{dB}} = 20 \log_{10} A_v$$
$$-1.5 = 20 \log_{10} A_v$$
$$-0.075 = \log_{10} A_v$$
$$A_v = \frac{V_o}{V_i} = \mathbf{0.84}$$

f. $\theta = \tan^{-1} f_c/f$

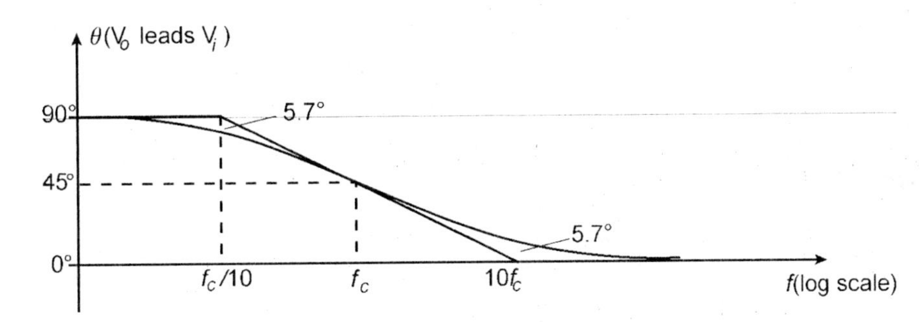

37. a, b. $\mathbf{A}_v = \frac{\mathbf{V}_o}{\mathbf{V}_i} = A_v \angle\theta = \frac{1}{\sqrt{1 + (f/f_c)^2}} \angle -\tan^{-1} f/f_c$

$$f_c = \frac{1}{2\pi RC} = \frac{1}{2\pi(12\,\text{k}\Omega)(1\,\text{nF})} = \mathbf{13.26\ kHz}$$

c. $f = f_c/2 = 6.63$ kHz

$$A_{v_{dB}} = 20 \log_{10} \frac{1}{\sqrt{1 + (0.5)^2}} = \mathbf{-0.97\ dB}$$

$f = 2f_c = 26.52$ kHz

$$A_{v_{dB}} = 20 \log_{10} \frac{1}{\sqrt{1 + (2)^2}} = \mathbf{-6.99\ dB}$$

$f = f_c/10 = 1.326$ kHz

$$A_{v_{dB}} = 20 \log_{10} \frac{1}{\sqrt{1 + (0.1)^2}} = \mathbf{-0.04\ dB}$$

$f = 10f_c = 132.6$ kHz

$$A_{v_{dB}} = 20 \log_{10} \frac{1}{\sqrt{1 + (10)^2}} = \mathbf{-20.04\ dB}$$

d. $f = f_c/2$: $\quad A_v = \frac{1}{\sqrt{1 + (0.5)^2}} = \mathbf{0.894}$

$f = 2f_c$: $\quad A_v = \frac{1}{\sqrt{1 + (2)^2}} = \mathbf{0.447}$

e. $\theta = \tan^{-1} f/f_c$

$f = f_c/2$: $\theta = -\tan^{-1} 0.5 = -26.57°$

$f = f_c$: $\theta = -\tan^{-1} 1 = -45°$

$f = 2f_c$: $\theta = -\tan^{-1} 2 = -63.43°$

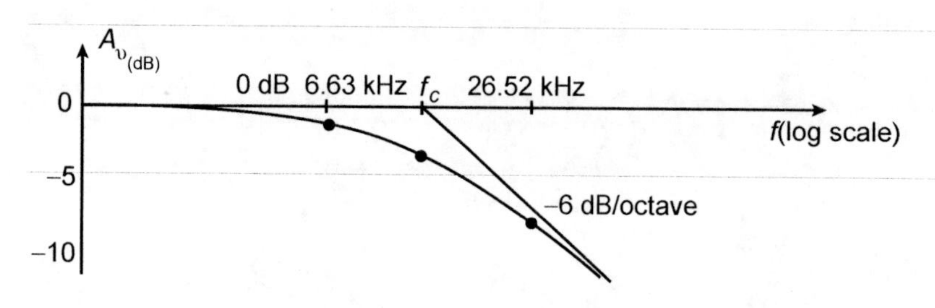

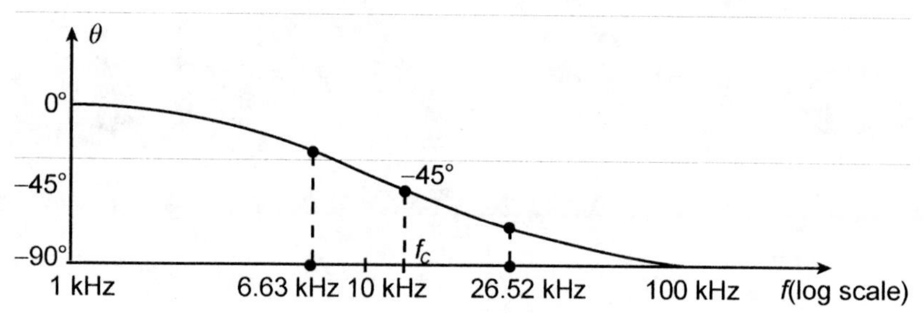

38. a. $R_2 \parallel X_C = \dfrac{(R_2)(-jX_C)}{R_2 - jX_C} = -j\dfrac{R_2X_C}{R_2 - jX_C}$

$$\mathbf{V}_o = \frac{\left(\dfrac{-jR_2X_C}{R_2 - jX_C}\right)\mathbf{V}_i}{R_1 - j\dfrac{R_2X_C}{R_2 - jX_C}} = -j\frac{R_2X_C\mathbf{V}_i}{R_1(R_2 - jX_C) - jR_2X_C}$$

$$= \frac{-jR_2X_C\mathbf{V}_i}{R_1R_2 - jR_1X_C - jR_2X_C} = \frac{-jR_2X_C\mathbf{V}_i}{R_1R_2 - j(R_1 + R_2)X_C}$$

$$= \frac{R_2X_C\mathbf{V}_i}{jR_1R_2 + (R_1 + R_2)X_C} = \frac{R_2\mathbf{V}_i}{j\dfrac{R_1R_2}{X_C} + (R_1 + R_2)}$$

$$= \frac{R_2\mathbf{V}_i}{R_1 + R_2 + j\dfrac{R_1R_2}{X_C}} = \frac{\left(\dfrac{R_2}{R_1 + R_2}\right)\mathbf{V}_i}{1 + j\left(\dfrac{R_1R_2}{R_1 + R_2}\right)\dfrac{1}{X_C}}$$

and $\mathbf{A}_\upsilon = \dfrac{\mathbf{V}_o}{\mathbf{V}_i} = \dfrac{\dfrac{R_2}{R_1 + R_2}}{1 + j\omega\left(\dfrac{R_1R_2}{R_1 + R_2}\right)C}$

or $\mathbf{A}_\upsilon = \dfrac{R_2}{R_1 + R_2}\left[\dfrac{1}{1 + j2\pi f(R_1 \parallel R_2)C}\right]$

defining $f_c = \dfrac{1}{2\pi(R_1 \| R_2)C}$

$$\mathbf{A}_\upsilon = \frac{R_2}{R_1 + R_2}\left[\frac{1}{1 + j\,f/f_c}\right]$$

and $\mathbf{A}_\upsilon = \dfrac{R_2}{R_1 + R_2}\left[\dfrac{1}{\sqrt{1 + (f/f_c)^2}} \angle -\tan^{-1} f/f_c\right]$

with $|V_o| = \dfrac{R_2}{R_1 + R_2}\left[\dfrac{1}{\sqrt{1 + (f/f_c)^2}}\right]|V_i|$

for $f \ll f_c$, $V_o = \dfrac{R_2}{R_1 + R_2}V_i = \dfrac{27\text{ k}\Omega}{4.7\text{ k}\Omega + 27\text{ k}\Omega}V_i = 0.852V_i$

at $f = f_c$: $V_o = 0.852[0.707]V_i = 0.602V_i$

$f_c = \dfrac{1}{2\pi(R_1 \| R_2)C} =$ **994.72 Hz**

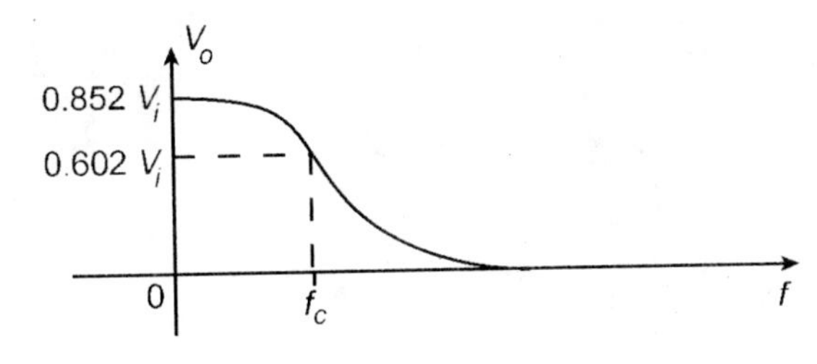

b.

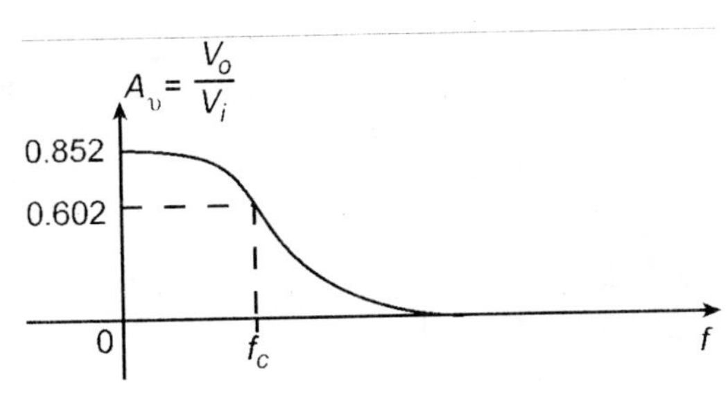

c. & d.

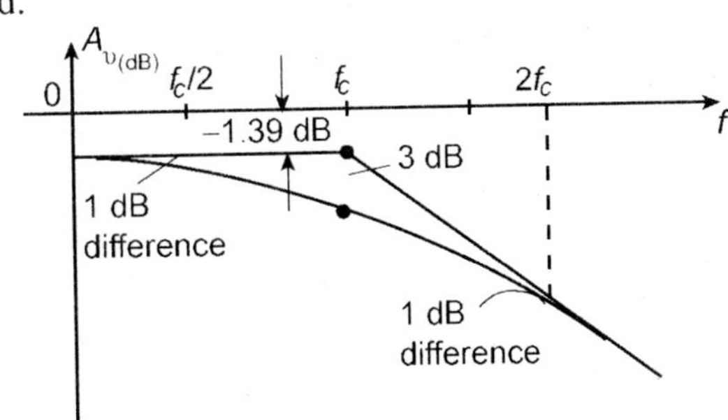

$$-20\log_{10}\frac{R_1 + R_2}{R_2} = -20\log_{10}\frac{4.7\text{ k}\Omega + 27\text{ k}\Omega}{27\text{ k}\Omega}$$

$$= -20\log_{10} 1.174 = -1.39\text{ dB}$$

e. $A_{v_{dB}} \cong -1.39 \text{ dB} - 0.5 \text{ dB} = -1.89 \text{ dB}$

$$A_{v_{dB}} = 20 \log_{10} A_v$$
$$-1.89 = 20 \log_{10} A_v$$
$$0.0945 = \log_{10} A_v$$
$$A_v = \frac{V_o}{V_i} = \mathbf{0.80}$$

f. $\theta = -\tan^{-1} f/f_c$

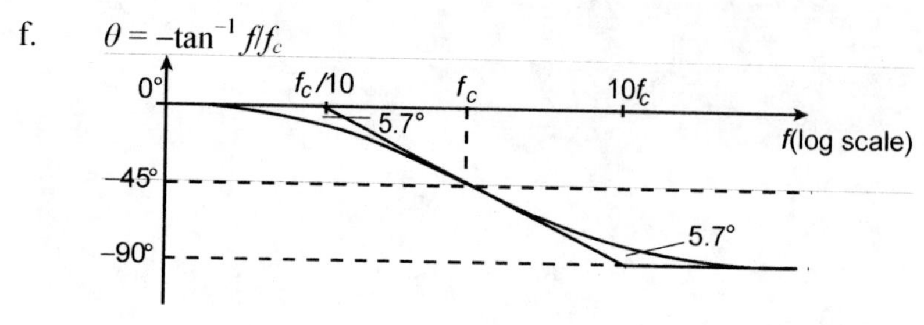

39.

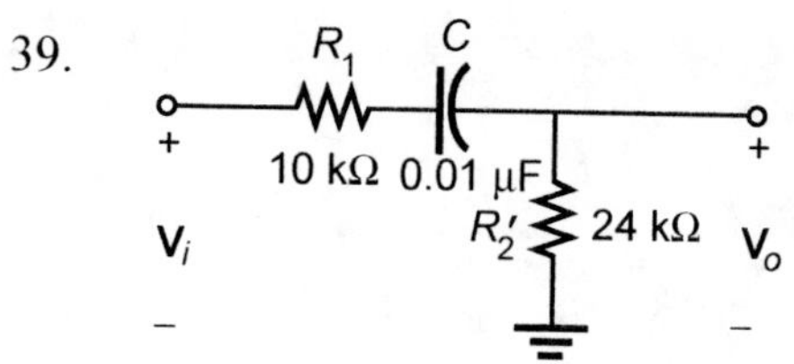

a. From Section 21.11,

$$\mathbf{A}_v = \frac{\mathbf{V}_o}{\mathbf{V}_i} = \frac{j f/f_1}{1 + jf/f_c}$$

$$f_1 = \frac{1}{2\pi R_2' C} = \frac{1}{2\pi(24 \text{ k}\Omega)(0.01 \,\mu\text{F})} = 663.15 \text{ Hz}$$

$$f_c = \frac{1}{2\pi(R_1 + R_2')C} = \frac{1}{2\pi(10 \text{ k}\Omega + 24 \text{ k}\Omega)(0.01 \,\mu\text{F})} = 468.1 \text{ Hz}$$

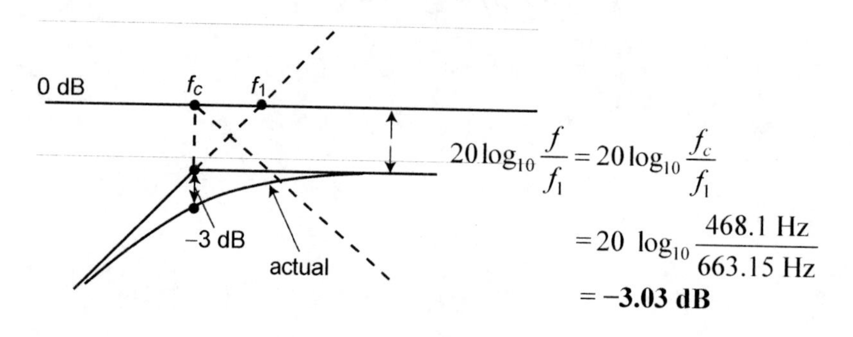

$$20 \log_{10} \frac{f}{f_1} = 20 \log_{10} \frac{f_c}{f_1}$$
$$= 20 \log_{10} \frac{468.1 \text{ Hz}}{663.15 \text{ Hz}}$$
$$= \mathbf{-3.03 \text{ dB}}$$

b. $\theta = 90° - \tan^{-1}\dfrac{f}{f_1} = +\tan^{-1}\dfrac{f_1}{f}$

$f = f_1$: $\theta = 45°$

$f = f_c$: $\theta = 54.78°$

$f = \dfrac{1}{2}f_1 = 331.58$ Hz, $\theta = 63.43°$

$f = \dfrac{1}{10}f_1 = 66.31$ Hz, $\theta = 84.29°$

$f = 2f_1 = 1{,}326.3$ Hz, $\theta = 26.57°$

$f = 10f_1 = 6{,}631.5$ Hz, $\theta = 5.71°$

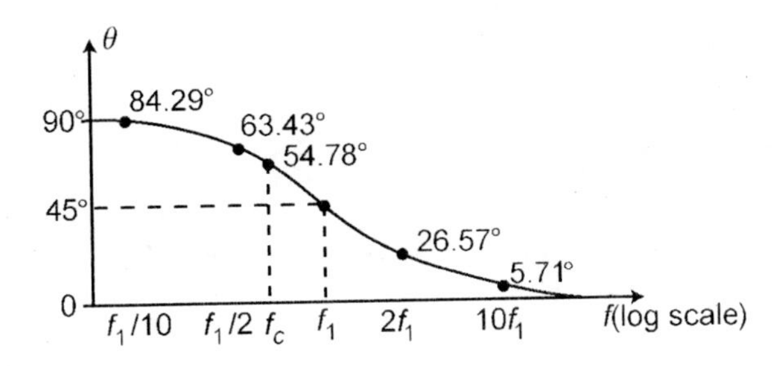

40. a.

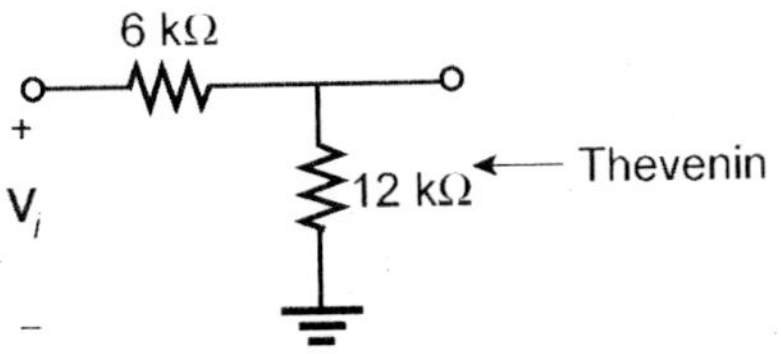

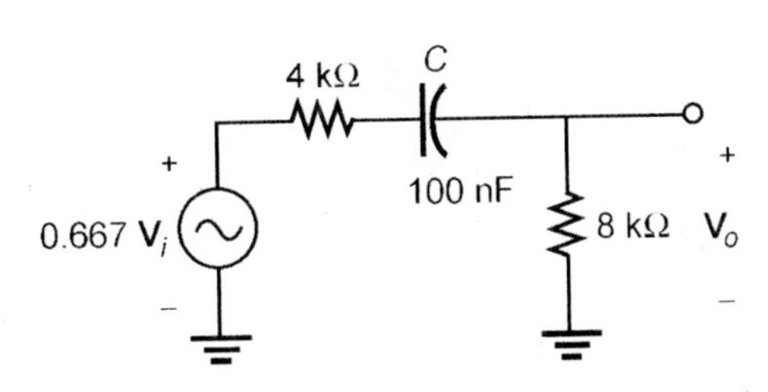

$$\mathbf{V}_{Th} = \frac{12\text{ k}\Omega\,\mathbf{V}_i}{12\text{ k}\Omega + 6\text{ k}\Omega} = 0.667\,\mathbf{V}_i$$

$R_{Th} = 6\text{ k}\Omega \parallel 12\text{ k}\Omega = 4\text{ k}\Omega$

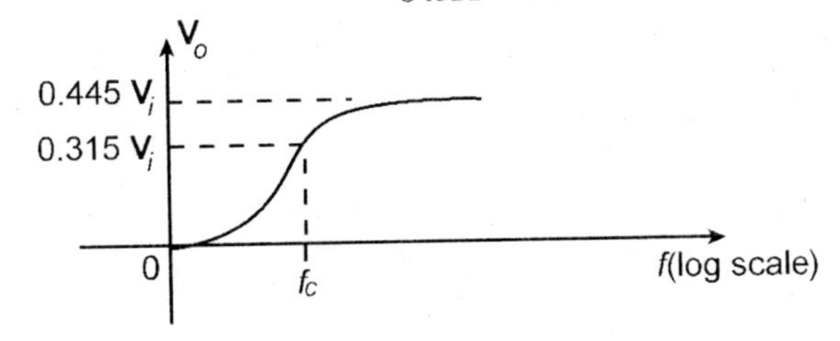

$f = \infty$ Hz: ($C \Rightarrow$ short circuit)

$$\mathbf{V}_o = \frac{8\text{ k}\Omega\,(0.667\,\mathbf{V}_i)}{8\text{ k}\Omega + 4\text{ k}\Omega} = 0.445\,\mathbf{V}_i$$

Vo
0.445 Vi
0.315 Vi
0
fc
f(log scale)

voltage-divider rule: $\mathbf{V}_o = \dfrac{R_2(0.667\,\mathbf{V}_i)}{R_1 + R_2 - jX_C} = \dfrac{0.667\,R_2\mathbf{V}_i}{R_1 + R_2 - jX_C}$

and $\mathbf{A}_v = \dfrac{\mathbf{V}_o}{\mathbf{V}_i} = \dfrac{0.667R_2}{R_1 + R_2 - jX_C} = \dfrac{j2\pi f(0.667R_2)C}{1 + j2\pi f(R_1 + R_2)C}$

so that $\mathbf{A}_v = \dfrac{j\,f/f_1}{1 + j\,f/f_c}$ with $f_1 = \dfrac{1}{2\pi 0.667R_2C} = \dfrac{1}{2\pi 0.667(8\,\text{k}\Omega)(100\,\text{nF})}$

$= 298.27\text{ Hz}$

and $f_c = \dfrac{1}{2\pi(R_1 + R_2)C} = \dfrac{1}{2\pi(4\,\text{k}\Omega + 8\,\text{k}\Omega)(100\,\text{nF})}$

$= 132.63\text{ Hz}$

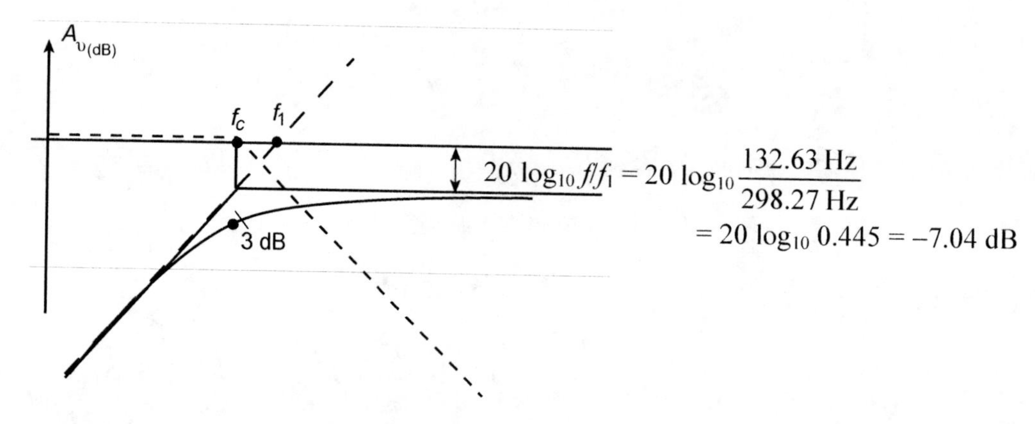

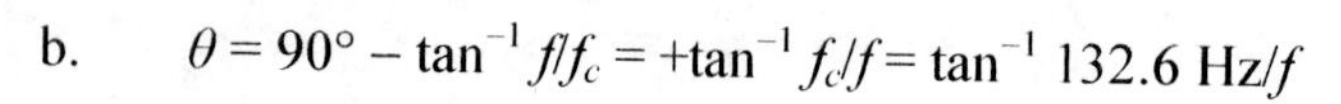

b. $\theta = 90° - \tan^{-1} f/f_c = +\tan^{-1} f_c/f = \tan^{-1} 132.6\text{ Hz}/f$

or

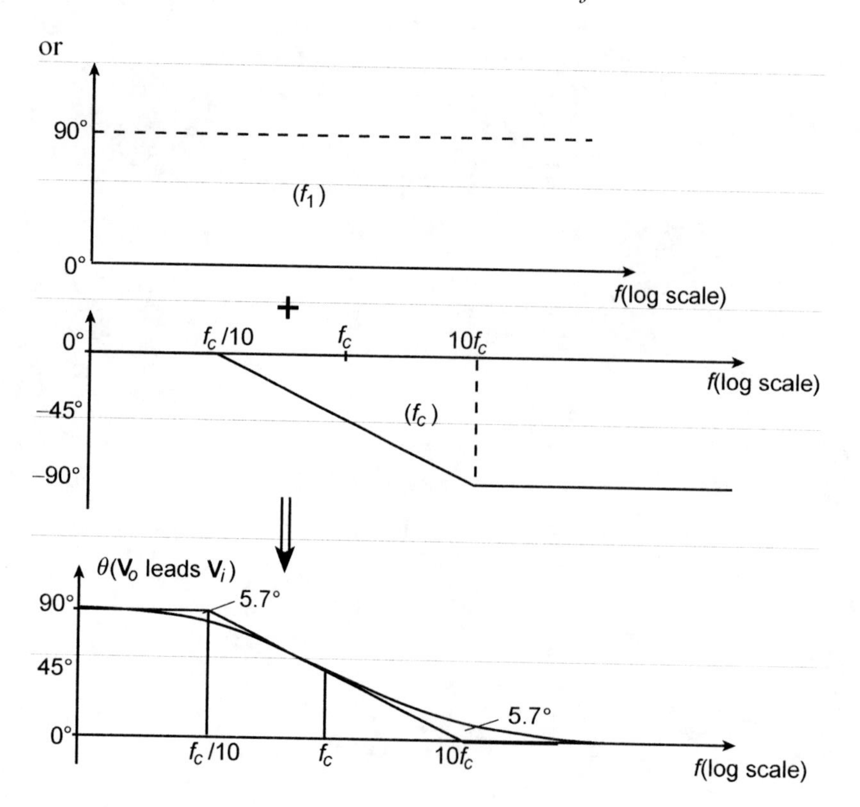

41. a. $\mathbf{A}_v = \dfrac{1 + j\dfrac{f}{f_1}}{1 + j\dfrac{f}{f_c}}$

$$f_1 = \frac{1}{2\pi R_2 C} = \frac{1}{2\pi(10\text{ k}\Omega)(800\text{ pF})} = 19{,}894.37\text{ Hz}$$

$$f_c = \frac{1}{2\pi(R_1 + R_2)C} = \frac{1}{2\pi(10\text{ k}\Omega + 90\text{ k}\Omega)(800\text{ pF})}$$
$$= 1{,}989.44\text{ Hz}$$

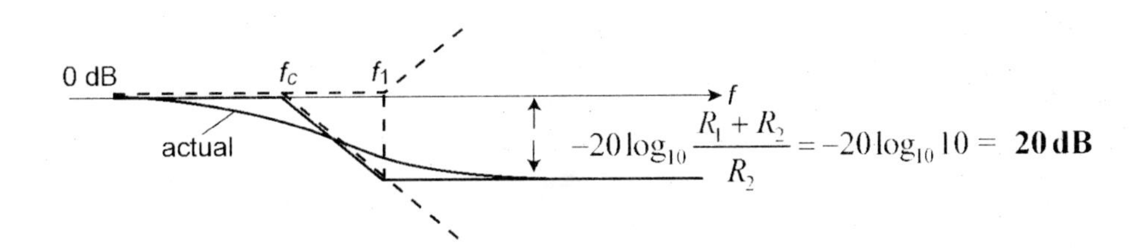

b. 0° f_C 10 kHz f_1 f
−45° −39.29° −39.29°
−52.06°

$$\theta = \tan^{-1} f/f_1 - \tan^{-1} f/f_c$$

$f = 10$ kHz

$$\theta = \tan^{-1}\frac{10\text{ kHz}}{19.89\text{ kHz}} - \tan^{-1}\frac{10\text{ kHz}}{1.989\text{ kHz}} = 26.69° - 78.75° = \mathbf{-52.06°}$$

$f = f_c$: ($f_1 = 10 f_c$)

$$\theta = \tan^{-1}\frac{f_c}{10 f_c} - \tan^{-1}\frac{f_c}{f_c} = \tan^{-1}0.1 - \tan^{-1}1 = 5.71° - 45° = \mathbf{-39.29°}$$

42. a. R_1 no effect!
Note Section 21.12.

$$\mathbf{A}_v = \frac{\mathbf{V}_o}{\mathbf{V}_i} = \frac{1 + j(f/f_1)}{1 + j(f/f_c)}$$

$$f_1 = \frac{1}{2\pi(6\text{ k}\Omega)(0.01\ \mu\text{F})} = 2652.58\text{ Hz}$$

$$f_c = \frac{1}{2\pi(12\text{ k}\Omega + 6\text{ k}\Omega)(0.01\ \mu\text{F})} = 884.19\text{ Hz}$$

Note Fig. 21.65.

Asymptote at 0 dB from $0 \to f_c$
−6 dB/octave from f_c to f_1
−9.54 dB from f_1 on $\left(-20\log\dfrac{12\text{ k}\Omega + 6\text{ k}\Omega}{6\text{ k}\Omega} = -9.54\text{ dB}\right)$

(b) Note Fig. 21.67.

From 0° to –26.50° at f_c and f_1
$\theta = \tan^{-1} f/f_1 - \tan^{-1} f/f_c$
At f = 1500 Hz (between f_c and f_1)
$\theta = \tan^{-1}$ 1500 Hz/2652.58 Hz – $\tan^{-1}$ 1500 Hz/884.19 Hz
= 29.49° – 59.48° = –30°

43. a. $\mathbf{A}_\upsilon = \dfrac{\mathbf{V}_o}{\mathbf{V}_i} = \dfrac{1 - jf_1/f}{1 - jf_c/f}$

$$f_1 = \frac{1}{2\pi R_1 C} = \frac{1}{2\pi(3.3\text{ k}\Omega)(0.05\ \mu\text{F})} = 964.58\text{ Hz}$$

$$f_c = \frac{1}{2\pi(R_1 \,||\, R_2)C} = \frac{1}{2\pi\underbrace{(3.3\text{ k}\Omega \,||\, 0.5\text{ k}\Omega)}_{0.434\text{ k}\Omega}(0.05\ \mu\text{F})} = \mathbf{7{,}334.33\ Hz}$$

$$-20\log_{10}\frac{R_1 + R_2}{R_2} = -20\log_{10}\frac{3.3\text{ k}\Omega + 0.5\text{ k}\Omega}{0.5\text{ k}\Omega} = -20\log_{10} 7.6 = -17.62\text{ dB}$$

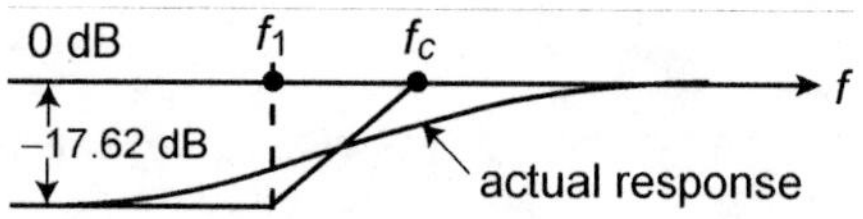

0 dB
f_1
f_c
f
–17.62 dB
actual response

b.

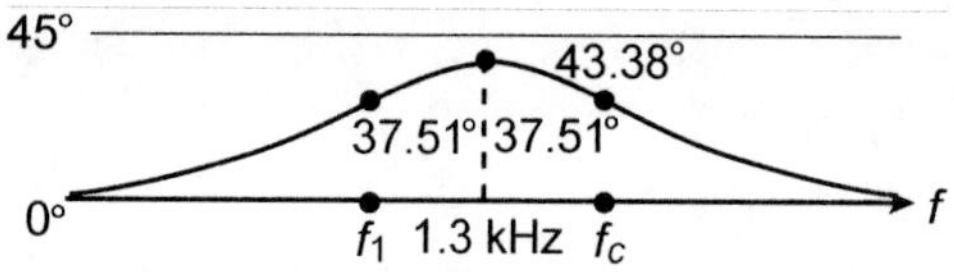

45°
43.38°
37.51°
37.51°
0°
f
f_1 1.3 kHz f_c

$$\theta = -\tan^{-1}\frac{f_1}{f} + \tan^{-1}\frac{f_c}{f}$$

f = 1.3 kHz: $\quad \theta = -\tan^{-1}\dfrac{964.58\text{ kHz}}{1.3\text{ kHz}} + \tan^{-1}\dfrac{7334.33\text{ Hz}}{1.3\text{ kHz}}$
= –36.57° + 79.95° = 43.38°

44. a. Note Section 21.13.

$$\mathbf{A}_\upsilon = \frac{1 - j(f_1/f)}{1 - j(f_c/f)}$$

$$f_1 = \frac{1}{2\pi R_1 C} = \frac{1}{2\pi(3.3\text{ k}\Omega)(0.05\ \mu\text{F})} = \mathbf{964.58\ Hz}$$

$$f_c = \frac{1}{2\pi(R_1 \,||\, R_2)C} = \frac{1}{2\pi\underbrace{(3.3\text{ k}\Omega \,||\, 0.5\text{ k}\Omega)}_{0.434\text{ k}\Omega}0.05\ \mu\text{F}} = \mathbf{7334.33\ Hz}$$

Note Fig. 21.72.

$$-20 \log_{10} \frac{R_1 + R_2}{R_2} = -20 \log_{10} \frac{3.3\,\text{k}\Omega + 0.5\,\text{k}\Omega}{0.5\,\text{k}\Omega} = -17.62 \text{ dB}$$

Asymptote at -17.62 dB from $0 \to f_1$
+6 dB/octave from f_1 to f_c
0 dB from f_c on

b. $\theta = -\tan^{-1} f_1/f + \tan^{-1} f_c/f$
Test at 3 kHz
$\theta = -\tan^{-1} 964.58 \text{ Hz}/3.0 \text{ kHz} + \tan^{-1} 7334.33 \text{ Hz}/3.0 \text{ kHz}$
$= -17.82° + 67.75° = 49.93° \cong 50°$

Therefore rising above 45° at and near the peak

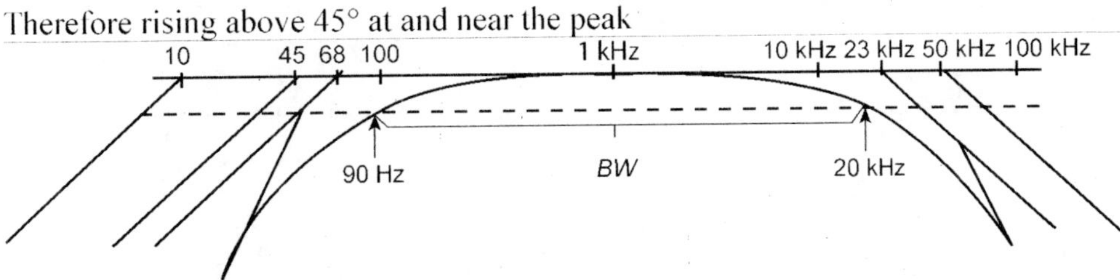

50 kHz vs 23 kHz $\rightarrow$ drop about 1 dB at 23 kHz due to 50 kHz break.
Ignore effect of break frequency at 10 Hz.
Assume -2 dB drop at 68 Hz due to break frequency at 45 Hz.
Rough sketch suggests low cut-off frequency of 90 Hz.
Checking: Ignoring upper terms

$$A'_{v\text{dB}} = -20 \log_{10} \sqrt{1 + \left(\frac{10 \text{ Hz}}{f}\right)^2} - 20 \log_{10}\sqrt{1 + \left(\frac{45 \text{ Hz}}{f}\right)^2} - 20 \log_{10}\sqrt{1 + \left(\frac{68 \text{ Hz}}{f}\right)^2}$$

$= -0.0532 \text{ dB} - 0.969 \text{ dB} - 1.96 \text{ dB}$
$= -2.98$ dB (excellent)

High frequency cutoff: Try 20 kHz

$$A'_{v\text{dB}} = -20\log_{10}\sqrt{1 + \left(\frac{f}{23 \text{ kHz}}\right)^2} - 20 \log_{10}\sqrt{1 + \left(\frac{f}{50 \text{ kHz}}\right)^2}$$

$= -2.445 \text{ dB} - 0.6445 \text{ dB}$
$= -3.09$ dB (excellent

$\therefore$ $BW = 20 \text{ kHz} - 90 \text{ Hz} =$ **19,910 Hz** $\cong$ 20 kHz
$f_1 =$ **90 Hz**, $f_2 =$ **20 kHz**

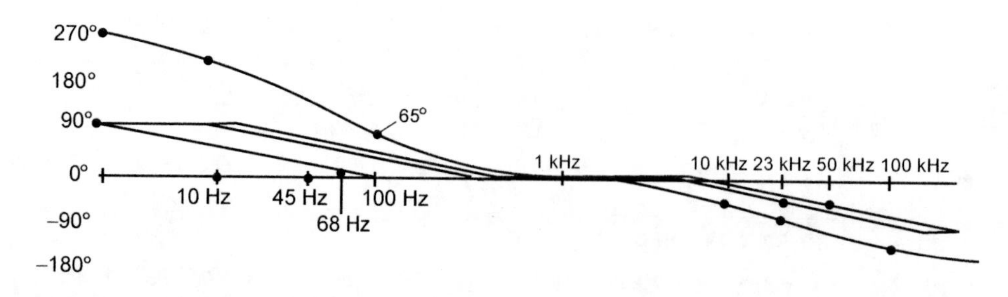

Testing: $f = 100$ Hz

$$\theta = \tan^{-1}\frac{10\text{ Hz}}{f} + \tan^{-1}\frac{45\text{ Hz}}{f} + \tan^{-1}\frac{68\text{ Hz}}{f} - \tan^{-1}\frac{f}{23\text{ kHz}} - \tan^{-1}\frac{f}{50\text{ kHz}}$$

$$= \tan^{-1} 0.1 + \tan^{-1} 0.45 + \tan^{-1} 0.68 - \tan^{-1} 0.00435 - \tan^{-1} .002$$

$$= 5.71° + 24.23° + 34.22° - 0.249° - 0.115°$$

$= \mathbf{63.8°}$ vs about 65° on the plot

45. a. $$\frac{A_v}{A_{v_{\max}}} = \frac{1}{\left(1 - j\dfrac{100\text{ Hz}}{f}\right)\left(1 - j\dfrac{130\text{ Hz}}{f}\right)\left(1 + j\dfrac{f}{20\text{ kHz}}\right)\left(1 + j\dfrac{f}{50\text{ kHz}}\right)}$$

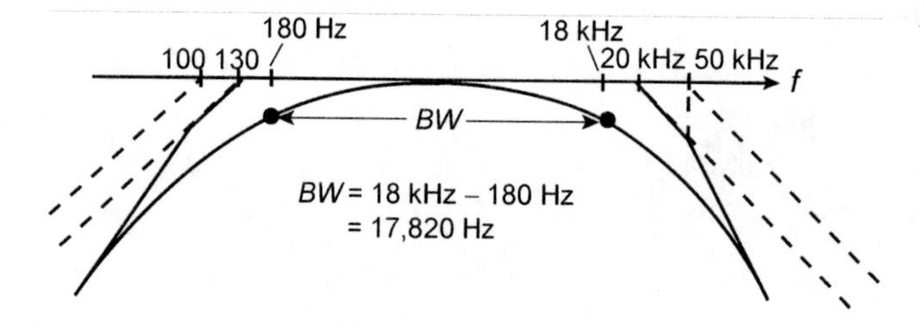

Proximity of 100 Hz to 130 Hz will raise lower cutoff frequency above 130 Hz:

Testing: $f = 180$ Hz: (with lower terms only)

$$A_{v_{\text{dB}}} = -20\log_{10}\sqrt{1 + \left(\frac{100}{f}\right)^2} - 20\log_{10}\sqrt{1 + \left(\frac{130}{f}\right)^2}$$

$$= -20\log_{10}\sqrt{1 + \left(\frac{100}{180}\right)^2} - 20\log_{10}\sqrt{1 + \left(\frac{130}{180}\right)^2}$$

$$= 1.17\text{ dB} - 1.82\text{ dB} = \mathbf{-2.99\text{ dB}} \cong -3\text{ dB}$$

Proximity of 50 kHz to 20 kHz will lower high cutoff frequency below 20 kHz:

Testing: $f = 18$ kHz: (with upper terms only)

$$A_{v_{\text{dB}}} = -20\log_{10}\sqrt{1 + \left(\frac{f}{20\text{ kHz}}\right)^2} - 20\log_{10}\sqrt{1 + \left(\frac{f}{50\text{ kHz}}\right)^2}$$

$$= -20\log_{10}\sqrt{1 + \left(\frac{18\text{ kHz}}{20\text{ kHz}}\right)^2} - 20\log_{10}\sqrt{1 + \left(\frac{13\text{ kHz}}{20\text{ kHz}}\right)^2}$$

$$= -2.576\text{ dB} - 0.529\text{ dB} = \mathbf{-3.105\text{ dB}}$$

b.

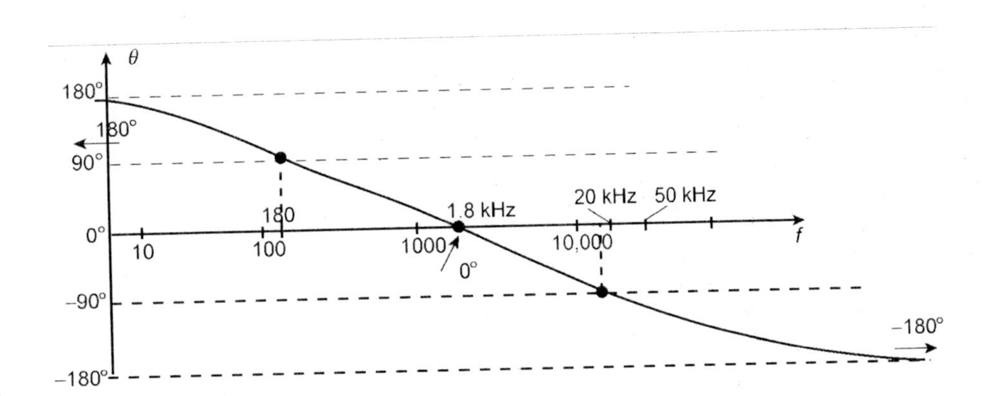

Testing: $f = 1.8$ kHz:

$$\theta = \tan^{-1}\frac{100}{1.8\text{ kHz}} + \tan^{-1}\frac{130}{1.8\text{ kHz}} - \tan^{-1}\frac{1.8\text{ kHz}}{20\text{ kHz}} - \tan^{-1}\frac{1.8\text{ kHz}}{50\text{ kHz}}$$

$$= 3.18° + 4.14° - 5.14° - 2.06°$$

$$= \mathbf{0.12°} \cong \mathbf{0°}$$

47. $f_{\text{low}} = f_{\text{high}} - BW = 36\text{ kHz} - 35.8\text{ kHz} = 0.2\text{ kHz} = 200\text{ Hz}$

$$A_v = \frac{-120}{\left(1 - j\dfrac{50}{f}\right)\left(1 - j\dfrac{200}{f}\right)\left(1 + j\dfrac{f}{36\text{ kHz}}\right)}$$

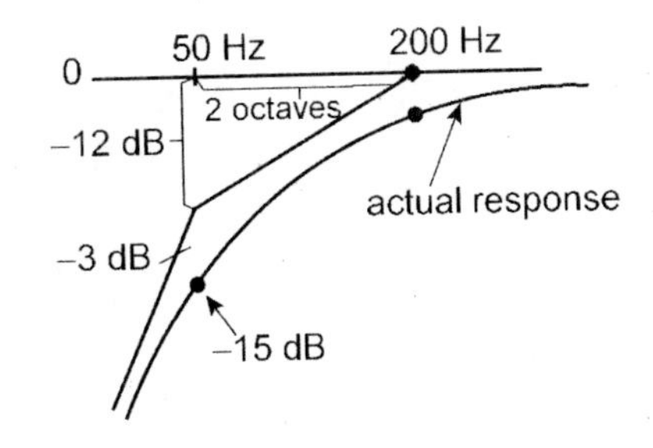

48. $$\mathbf{A}_v = \frac{0.05}{0.05 - j\dfrac{100}{f}} = \frac{1}{1 - j\dfrac{100}{0.05f}} = \frac{1}{1 - j\dfrac{2000}{f}} = \frac{+jf}{+jf + 2000}$$

$$= \frac{+j\dfrac{f}{2000}}{1 + j\dfrac{f}{2000}} \text{ and } f_1 = 2000\text{ Hz}$$

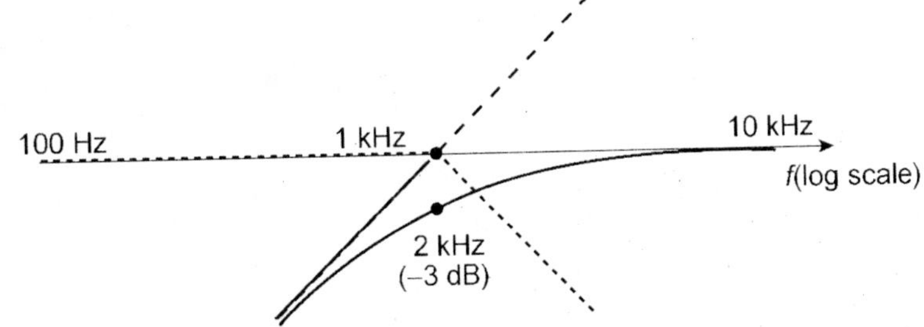

49. $\mathbf{A}_{\upsilon} = \dfrac{200}{200 + j0.1f} = \dfrac{1}{1 + j\dfrac{0.1f}{200}} = \dfrac{1}{1 + j\dfrac{f}{2000}}$

$A_{\upsilon_{\text{dB}}} = 20\ \log_{20} \dfrac{1}{\sqrt{1 + \left(\dfrac{f}{2000}\right)^2}}$, $\dfrac{f}{2000} = 1$ and $f = \mathbf{2\ kHz}$

50. $\mathbf{A}_{\upsilon} = \dfrac{jf/1000}{(1 + jf/1000)(1 + jf/10{,}000)}$

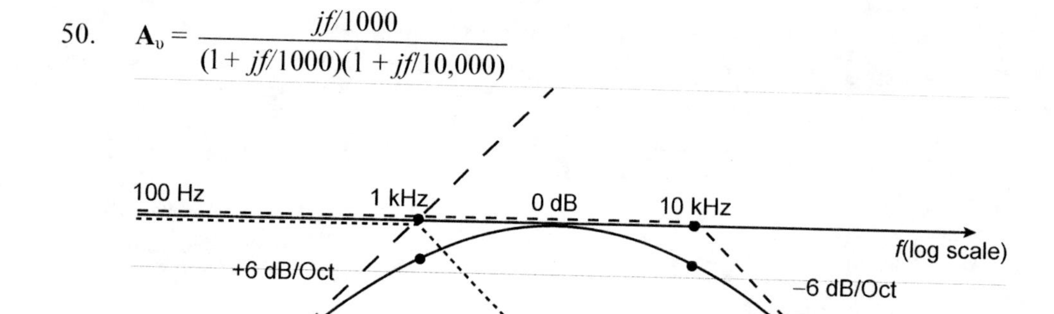

51. $\mathbf{A}_{\upsilon} = \dfrac{\left(1 + j\dfrac{f}{1000}\right)\left(1 + j\dfrac{f}{2000}\right)}{\left(1 + j\dfrac{f}{3000}\right)^2}$

$\mathbf{A}_{\upsilon_{\text{dB}}} = 20\ \log_{10}\sqrt{1 + \left(\dfrac{f_1}{1000}\right)^2} + 20\ \log_{10}\sqrt{1 + \left(\dfrac{f_2}{2000}\right)^2} + 40\ \log_{10}\dfrac{1}{\sqrt{1 + \left(\dfrac{f_3}{3000}\right)^2}}$

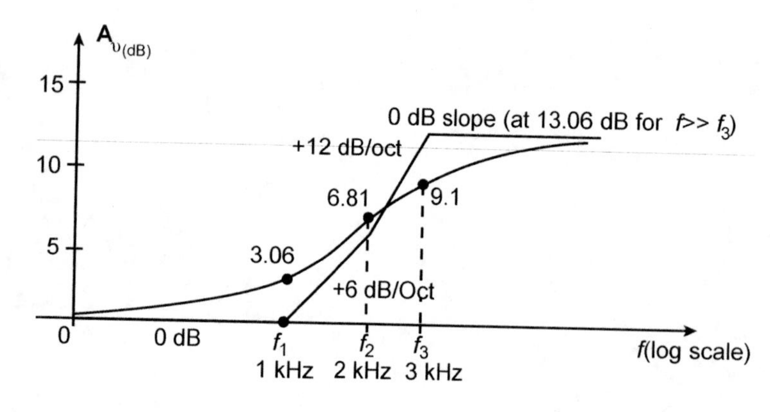

52. $\dfrac{j\omega}{1000} = j\dfrac{2\pi f}{1000} = j\dfrac{f}{\dfrac{1000}{2\pi}} = j\dfrac{f}{159.16\text{ Hz}}, \quad \dfrac{j\omega}{5000} = j\dfrac{f}{795.78\text{ Hz}}$

$$A_\upsilon = \frac{40(1 + jf/159.16)}{(jf/159.16)(1 + jf/795.78)}$$

+32 dB

+6 dB/octave
159.16 Hz

159.16 Hz
−6 dB/octave

795.78 Hz
−6 dB/octave

$A_{\upsilon(\text{dB})}$
60
50
40
32
30
20
10
0
795.78 Hz
159.16 Hz
Actual
response
100 Hz
1 kHz
f(log scale)

53. a. Woofer – 400 Hz:

$X_L = 2\pi fL = 2\pi(400\text{ Hz})(4.7\text{ mH}) = 11.81\ \Omega$

$$X_C = \frac{1}{2\pi fC} = \frac{1}{2\pi(400\text{ Hz})(39\ \mu\text{F})} = 10.20\ \Omega$$

$R \parallel X_C = 8\ \Omega \angle 0° \parallel 10.20 \angle{-90°} = 6.3\ \Omega \angle{-38.11°}$

$$\mathbf{V}_o = \frac{(R \parallel X_C)(\mathbf{V}_i)}{(R \parallel X_C) + jX_L} = \frac{(6.3\ \Omega \angle -38.11°)(\mathbf{V}_i)}{(6.3\ \Omega \angle -38.11°) + j\,11.81\ \Omega}$$

$\mathbf{V}_o = 0.673 \angle{-96.11°}\ \mathbf{V}_i$

and $A_\upsilon = \dfrac{V_o}{V_i} = \mathbf{0.673}$ vs desired 0.707 (off by less than 5%)

Tweeter – 5 kHz:

$X_L = 2\pi fL = 2\pi(5\text{ kHz})(0.39\text{ mH}) = 12.25\ \Omega$

$$X_C = \frac{1}{2\pi fC} = \frac{1}{2\pi(5\text{ kHz})(2.7\ \mu\text{F})} = 11.79\ \Omega$$

$R \parallel X_L = 8\ \Omega \angle 0° \parallel 12.25\ \Omega \angle 90° = 6.7\ \Omega \angle 33.15°$

$$\mathbf{V}_o = \frac{(6.7\ \Omega \angle 33.15°)(\mathbf{V}_i)}{(6.7\ \Omega \angle 33.15°) - j\,11.79\ \Omega}$$

$\mathbf{V}_o = 0.678 \angle 88.54°\ \mathbf{V}_i$

and $A_v = \dfrac{V_o}{V_i}$ = **0.678** vs 0.707 (off by less than 5%)

b. Woofer – 3 kHz:

$$X_L = 2\pi fL = 2\pi(3\text{ kHz})(4.7\text{ mH}) = 88.59\ \Omega$$

$$X_C = \frac{1}{2\pi fC} = \frac{1}{2\pi(3\text{ kHz})(39\ \mu\text{F})} = 1.36\ \Omega$$

$$R \parallel X_C = 8\ \Omega \angle 0° \parallel 1.36\ \Omega \angle{-90°} = 1.341\ \Omega \angle{-80.35°}$$

$$\mathbf{V}_o = \frac{(R \parallel X_C)(\mathbf{V}_i)}{(R \parallel X_C) + jX_L} = \frac{(1.341\ \Omega \angle -80.35°)(\mathbf{V}_i)}{(1.341\ \Omega \angle -80.35°) + j\,88.59\ \Omega}$$

$$\mathbf{V}_o = 0.015 \angle{-170.2°}\ \mathbf{V}_i$$

and $A_v = \dfrac{V_o}{V_i}$ = **0.015** vs desired 0 (excellent)

Tweeter – 3 kHz:

$$X_L = 2\pi fL = 2\pi(3\text{ kHz})(0.39\text{ mH}) = 7.35\ \Omega$$

$$X_C = \frac{1}{2\pi fC} = \frac{1}{2\pi(3\text{ kHz})(2.7\ \mu\text{F})} = 19.65\ \Omega$$

$$R \parallel X_L = 8\ \Omega \angle 0° \parallel 7.35\ \Omega \angle 90° = 5.42\ \Omega \angle 47.42°$$

$$\mathbf{V}_o = \frac{(R \parallel X_L)(\mathbf{V}_i)}{(R \parallel X_L) + jX_C} = \frac{(5.42\ \Omega \angle 47.42°)(\mathbf{V}_i)}{(5.42\ \Omega \angle 47.42°) - j\,19.65\ \Omega}$$

$$\mathbf{V}_o = 0.337 \angle 124.24°\ \mathbf{V}_i$$

and $A_v = \dfrac{V_o}{V_i}$ = **0.337** (acceptable since relatively close to cut frequency for tweeter)

c. Mid-range speaker – 3 kHz:

1.36 Ω 7.35 Ω
+ + +
V_i V_1 88.59 Ω 19.65 Ω 8 Ω V_o
Z‴ Z″ Z′
– – –

$$\underbrace{\mathbf{Z}' = 7.41\ \Omega \angle -22.15°}$$

$$\underbrace{\mathbf{Z}'' = 8.24\ \Omega \angle 33.58°}$$

$$\underbrace{\mathbf{Z}''' = 7.816\ \Omega \angle 37.79°}$$

$$\mathbf{V}_1 = \frac{\mathbf{Z}'''\mathbf{V}_i}{\mathbf{Z}''' - jX_C} = \frac{(7.816\ \Omega \angle 37.79°)\mathbf{V}_i}{7.816\ \Omega \angle 37.79° - j1.36\ \Omega} = 1.11 \angle 8.83°\ \mathbf{V}_i$$

$$\mathbf{V}_o = \frac{\mathbf{Z}'\mathbf{V}_1}{\mathbf{Z}' + jX_L} = \frac{(7.41\ \Omega \angle -22.15°)\mathbf{V}_i}{7.41\ \Omega \angle -22.15° + j7.35\ \Omega} = 0.998 \angle{-46.9°}\ \mathbf{V}_i$$

and $A_v = \dfrac{V_o}{V_i}$ = **0.998** (excellent)

Chapter 22

1. a. $M = k\sqrt{L_pL_s} \Rightarrow L_s = \dfrac{M^2}{L_pk^2} = \dfrac{(80 \text{ mH})^2}{(50 \text{ mH})(0.8)^2} = \mathbf{0.2\ H}$

   b. $e_p = N_p\dfrac{d\phi_p}{dt} = (20)(0.08 \text{ Wb/s}) = \mathbf{1.6\ V}$

   $e_s = kN_s\dfrac{d\phi_p}{dt} = (0.8)(80 \text{ t})(0.08 \text{ Wb/s}) = \mathbf{5.12\ V}$

   c. $e_p = L_p\dfrac{di_p}{dt} = (50 \text{ mH})(0.03 \times 10^3 \text{ A/s}) = \mathbf{15\ V}$

   $e_s = M\dfrac{di_p}{dt} = (80 \text{ mH})(0.03 \times 10^3 \text{ A/s}) = \mathbf{24\ V}$

2. a. $k = 1$

   (a) $L_s = \dfrac{M^2}{L_pk^2} = \dfrac{(80 \text{ mH})^2}{(50 \text{ mH})(1)^2} = \mathbf{128\ mH}$

   (b) $e_p = \mathbf{1.6\ V}$, $e_s = kN_s\dfrac{d\phi_p}{dt} = (1)(80 \text{ t})(0.08 \text{ Wb/s}) = \mathbf{6.4\ V}$

   (c) $e_p = \mathbf{15\ V}$, $e_s = \mathbf{24\ V}$

   b. $k = 0.2$

   (a) $L_s = \dfrac{M^2}{L_pk^2} = \dfrac{(80 \text{ mH})^2}{(50 \text{ mH})(0.2)^2} = \mathbf{3.2\ H}$

   (b) $e_p = \mathbf{1.6\ V}$, $e_s = kN_s\dfrac{d\phi_p}{dt} = (0.2)(80 \text{ t})(0.08 \text{ Wb/s}) = \mathbf{1.28\ V}$

   (c) $e_p = \mathbf{15\ V}$, $e_s = \mathbf{24\ V}$

3. a. $L_s = \dfrac{M^2}{L_pk^2} = \dfrac{(80 \text{ mH})^2}{(50 \text{ mH})(0.9)^2} = \mathbf{158.02\ mH}$

   b. $e_p = N_p\dfrac{d\phi_p}{dt} = (300 \text{ t})(0.08 \text{ Wb/s}) = \mathbf{24\ V}$

   $e_s = kN_s\dfrac{d\phi_p}{dt} = (0.9)(25 \text{ t})(0.08 \text{ Wb/s}) = \mathbf{1.8\ V}$

   c. e_p and e_s the same as problem 1: $e_p = \mathbf{15\ V}$, $e_s = \mathbf{24\ V}$

4. a. $E_s = \dfrac{N_s}{N_p} E_p = \dfrac{64\text{ t}}{8\text{ t}}(25\text{ V}) = \mathbf{200\text{ V}}$

b. $\Phi_{\max} = \dfrac{E_p}{4.4 fN_p} = \dfrac{25\text{ V}}{4.44(60\text{ Hz})(8\text{ t})} = \mathbf{11.73\text{ mWb}}$

5. a. $E_s = \dfrac{N_s}{N_p} E_p = \dfrac{30\text{ t}}{240\text{ t}}(25\text{ V}) = \mathbf{3.13\text{ V}}$

b. $\Phi_{m(\max)} = \dfrac{E_p}{4.44\, fN_p} = \dfrac{25\text{ V}}{(4.44)(60\text{ Hz})(240\text{ t})} = \mathbf{391.02\ \mu Wb}$

6. $E_p = \dfrac{N_p}{N_s} E_s = \dfrac{60\text{ t}}{720\text{ t}}(240\text{ V}) = \mathbf{20\text{ V}}$

7. $f = \dfrac{E_p}{(4.44)N_p\Phi_{m(\max)}} = \dfrac{25\text{ V}}{(4.44)(8\text{ t})(12.5\text{ mWb})} = \mathbf{56.31\text{ Hz}}$

8. a. $I_L = aI_p = \left(\dfrac{1}{5}\right)(2\text{ A}) = \mathbf{0.4\text{ A}}$

$V_L = I_L Z_L = \left(\dfrac{2}{5}\text{ A}\right)(2\ \Omega) = \mathbf{0.8\text{ V}}$

b. $Z_{\text{in}} = a^2 Z_L = \left(\dfrac{1}{5}\right)^2 2\ \Omega = \mathbf{0.08\ \Omega}$

9. $Z_p = \dfrac{V_g}{I_p} = \dfrac{1600\text{ V}}{4\text{ A}} = \mathbf{400\ \Omega}$

10. $V_g = aV_L = \left(\dfrac{1}{4}\right)(1200\text{ V}) = \mathbf{300\text{ V}}$

$I_p = \dfrac{V_g}{Z_i} = \dfrac{300\text{ V}}{4\ \Omega} = \mathbf{75\text{ A}}$

11. $I_L = I_s = \dfrac{V_L}{Z_L} = \dfrac{240\text{ V}}{20\ \Omega} = 12\text{ A}$

$\dfrac{I_s}{I_p} = a = \dfrac{N_p}{N_s} \Rightarrow \dfrac{12\text{ A}}{0.05\text{ A}} = \dfrac{N_p}{50}$

$N_p = \dfrac{50(12)}{0.05} = \mathbf{12{,}000\text{ turns}}$

12. a. $a = \dfrac{N_p}{N_s} = \dfrac{400\text{ t}}{1200\text{ t}} = \dfrac{1}{3}$

$Z_i = a^2 Z_L = \left(\dfrac{1}{3}\right)^2 [9\ \Omega + j12\ \Omega] = 1\ \Omega + j1.333\ \Omega = 1.667\ \Omega\ \angle 53.13°$

$I_p = V_g/Z_i = 100\text{ V}/1.667\ \Omega = \mathbf{60\ A}$

b. $I_L = aI_p = \dfrac{1}{3}(60\text{ A}) = \mathbf{20\ A},\ V_L = I_L Z_L = (20\text{ A})(15\ \Omega) = \mathbf{300\ V}$

13. a. $Z_p = a^2 Z_L \Rightarrow a = \sqrt{\dfrac{Z_p}{Z_L}}$

$Z_p = \dfrac{V_p}{I_p} = \dfrac{10\text{ V}}{20\text{ V}/72\ \Omega} = 36\ \Omega$

$a = \sqrt{\dfrac{36\ \Omega}{4\ \Omega}} = \mathbf{3}$

b. $\dfrac{V_s}{V_p} = \dfrac{N_s}{N_p} = \dfrac{1}{3} \Rightarrow V_s = \dfrac{1}{3}V_p = \dfrac{1}{3}(10\text{ V}) = \mathbf{3\frac{1}{3}\ V}$

$P = \dfrac{V_s^2}{Z_s} = \dfrac{(3.33\text{ V})^2}{4\ \Omega} = \mathbf{2.78\ W}$

14. a. $R_e = R_p + a^2 R_s = 4\ \Omega + (4)^2\ 1\ \Omega = \mathbf{20\ \Omega}$

b. $X_e = X_p + a^2 X_s = 8\ \Omega + (4)^2\ 2\ \Omega = \mathbf{40\ \Omega}$

c.

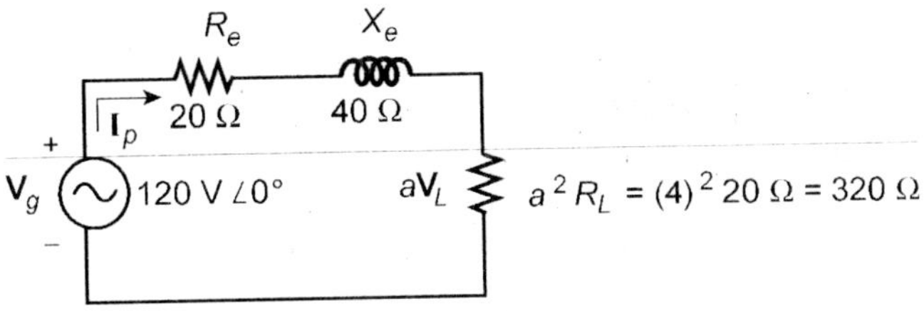

R_e X_e
20 Ω 40 Ω
$\mathbf{I}_p$
V_g 120 V ∠0°
aV_L $a^2R_L = (4)^2\ 20\ \Omega = 320\ \Omega$

d. $\mathbf{I}_p = \dfrac{\mathbf{V}_g}{\mathbf{Z}_p} = \dfrac{120\text{ V}\ \angle 0°}{20\ \Omega + 320\ \Omega + j40\ \Omega} = \dfrac{120\text{ V}\ \angle 0°}{340\ \Omega + j40\ \Omega} = \mathbf{0.351\ A\ \angle{-6.71°}}$

e. $a\mathbf{V}_L = \dfrac{a^2 R_L \mathbf{V}_g}{(R_e + a^2 R_L) + jX_e} = \mathbf{I}_p a^2 R_L$

or $\mathbf{V}_L = a\mathbf{I}_p R_L \angle 0° = (4)(0.351\text{ A}\ \angle{-6.71°})(20\ \Omega\ \angle 0°) = \mathbf{28.1\ V\ \angle{-6.71°}}$

f. –

g. $V_L = \dfrac{N_s}{N_p}V_g = \dfrac{1}{4}(120\text{ V}) = \mathbf{30\ V}$

15. a. $a = \dfrac{N_p}{N_s} = \dfrac{4\text{ t}}{1\text{ t}} = 4$

$R_e = R_p + a^2R_s = 4\ \Omega + (4)^2\ 1\ \Omega = 20\ \Omega$

$X_e = X_p + a^2X_s = 8\ \Omega + (4)^2\ 2\ \Omega = 40\ \Omega$

$\mathbf{Z}_p = \mathbf{Z}_{R_e} + \mathbf{Z}_{X_e} + a^2\mathbf{Z}_{X_L} = 20\ \Omega + j40\ \Omega + j(4)^2\ 20\ \Omega$

$= 20\ \Omega + j40\ \Omega + j320\ \Omega = 20\ \Omega + j360\ \Omega = \mathbf{360.56\ \Omega\ \angle 86.82^\circ}$

b. $\mathbf{I}_p = \dfrac{\mathbf{V}_g}{\mathbf{Z}_p} = \dfrac{120\text{ V}\ \angle 0^\circ}{360.56\ \Omega\ \angle 86.82^\circ} = 332.82\text{ mA}\ \angle -86.82^\circ$

c. $\mathbf{V}_{R_e} = (I\angle\theta)(R_e\angle 0^\circ) = (332.82\text{ mA}\ \angle -86.82^\circ)(20\ \Omega\ \angle 0^\circ)$

$= \mathbf{6.66\ V\ \angle -86.82^\circ}$

$\mathbf{V}_{X_e} = (I\angle\theta)(X_e\angle 90^\circ) = (332.82\text{ mA}\ \angle -86.32^\circ)(40\ \Omega\ \angle 90^\circ)$

$= \mathbf{13.31\ V\ \angle 3.18^\circ}$

$\mathbf{V}_{X_L} = \mathbf{I}(a^2 Z_{X_L}) = (332.82\text{ mA}\ \angle -86.82^\circ)(320\ \Omega\ \angle 90^\circ)$

$= \mathbf{106.50\ V\ \angle 3.18^\circ}$

16. a. $a = N_p/N_s = 4\text{ t}/1\text{ t} = 4$, $R_e = R_p + a^2R_s = 4\ \Omega + (4)^2\ 1\ \Omega = 20\ \Omega$

$X_e = X_p + a^2X_s = 8\ \Omega + (4)^2\ 2\ \Omega = 40\ \Omega$

$\mathbf{Z}_p = R_e + jX_e - ja^2X_C = 20\ \Omega + j40\ \Omega - j(4)^2\ 20\ \Omega$

$= 20\ \Omega - j280\ \Omega = \mathbf{280.71\ \Omega\ \angle -85.91^\circ}$

b. $\mathbf{I}_p = \dfrac{\mathbf{V}_g}{\mathbf{Z}_p} = \dfrac{120\text{ V}\ \angle 0^\circ}{280.71\ \Omega\ \angle -85.91^\circ} = \mathbf{0.43\ A\ \angle 85.91^\circ}$

c. $\mathbf{V}_{R_e} = (I_p\angle\theta)(R_e\angle 0^\circ) = (0.427\text{ A}\ \angle 85.91^\circ)(20\ \Omega\ \angle 0^\circ) = \mathbf{8.54\ V\ \angle 85.91^\circ}$

$\mathbf{V}_{X_e} = (I_p\angle\theta)(X_e\angle 90^\circ) = (0.427\text{ A}\ \angle 85.91^\circ)(40\ \Omega\ \angle 90^\circ) = \mathbf{17.08\ V\ \angle 175.91^\circ}$

$\mathbf{V}_{X_C} = (I_p\angle\theta)(a^2X_C\angle -90^\circ) = (0.427\text{ A}\ \angle 85.91^\circ)(320\ \Omega\ \angle -90^\circ) = \mathbf{136.64\ V\ \angle -4.09^\circ}$

17. –

18. Coil 1: $L_1 - M_{12}$

Coil 2: $L_2 - M_{12}$

$L_T = L_1 + L_2 - 2M_{12} = 4\text{ H} + 7\text{ H} - 2(1\text{ H}) = \mathbf{9\ H}$

19. $L_{T(+)} = L_1 + L_2 + 2M_{12}$

$M_{12} = k\sqrt{L_1L_2} = (0.8)\sqrt{(200\text{ mH})(600\text{ mH})} = \mathbf{277\ mH}$

$L_{T(+)} = 200\text{ mH} + 600\text{ mH} + 2(277\text{ mH}) = \mathbf{1.35\ H}$

20. $M_{23} = k\sqrt{L_2L_3} = 1\sqrt{(1\text{ H})(4\text{ H})} = 2\text{ H}$

Coil 1: $L_1 + M_{12} - M_{13} = 2\text{ H} + 0.2\text{ H} - 0.1\text{ H} = 2.1\text{ H}$

Coil 2: $L_2 + M_{12} - M_{23} = 1\text{ H} + 0.2\text{ H} - 2\text{ H} = -0.8\text{ H}$

Coil 3: $L_3 - M_{23} - M_{13} = 4\text{ H} - 2\text{ H} - 0.1\text{ H} = 1.9\text{ H}$

$L_T = 2.1\text{ H} - 0.8\text{ H} + 1.9\text{ H} = \mathbf{3.2\text{ H}}$

21. $\mathbf{E}_1 - \mathbf{I}_1[\mathbf{Z}_{R_1} + \mathbf{Z}_{L_1}] - \mathbf{I}_2[\mathbf{Z}_m] = 0$

$\mathbf{I}_2[\mathbf{Z}_{L_2} + \mathbf{Z}_{R_L}] + \mathbf{I}_1[\mathbf{Z}_m] = 0$

$\mathbf{I}_1(\mathbf{Z}_{R_1} + \mathbf{Z}_{L_1}) + \mathbf{I}_2(\mathbf{Z}_m) = \mathbf{E}_1$

$\mathbf{I}_1(\mathbf{Z}_m) + \mathbf{I}_2(\mathbf{Z}_{L_2} + \mathbf{Z}_{R_L}) = 0$ $\qquad X_m = -\omega M \angle 90^\circ$

---

22. $$\mathbf{Z}_i = \mathbf{Z}_p + \frac{(\omega M)^2}{\mathbf{Z}_s + \mathbf{Z}_L} = R_p + jX_{L_p} + \frac{(\omega M)^2}{R_s + jX_{L_s} + R_L}$$

$R_p = 2\ \Omega,\ X_{L_p} = \omega L_p = (10^3\text{ rad/s})(8\text{ H}) = 8\text{ k}\Omega$

$R_s = 1\ \Omega,\ X_{L_s} = \omega L_s = (10^3\text{ rad/s})(2\text{ H}) = 2\text{ k}\Omega$

$M = k\sqrt{L_pL_s} = 0.05\sqrt{(8\text{ H})(2\text{ H})} = 0.2\text{ H}$

$$\mathbf{Z}_i = 2\ \Omega + j8\text{ k}\Omega + \frac{(10^3\text{ rad/s}\cdot 0.2\text{ H})^2}{1\ \Omega + j2\text{ k}\Omega + 20\ \Omega}$$

$$= 2\ \Omega + j8\text{ k}\Omega + \frac{4\times 10^4\ \Omega}{21 + j2\times 10^3}$$

$= 2\ \Omega + j8\text{ k}\Omega + 0.21\ \Omega - j19.99\ \Omega = 2.21\ \Omega + j7980\ \Omega$

$\mathbf{Z}_i = \mathbf{7980\ \Omega \angle 89.98^\circ}$

23. a. $$a = \frac{N_p}{N_s} = \frac{V_p}{V_s} = \frac{2400\text{ V}}{120\text{ V}} = \mathbf{20}$$

b. $$10{,}000\text{ VA} = V_sI_s \Rightarrow I_s = \frac{10{,}000\text{ VA}}{V_s} = \frac{10{,}000\text{ VA}}{120\text{ V}} = \mathbf{83.33\text{ A}}$$

c. $$I_p = \frac{10{,}000\text{ VA}}{V_p} = \frac{10{,}000\text{ VA}}{2400\text{ V}} = \mathbf{4.17\text{ A}}$$

d. $$a = \frac{V_p}{V_s} = \frac{120\text{ V}}{2400\text{ V}} = 0.05 = \frac{1}{20}$$

$$I_s = \frac{10{,}000\text{ VA}}{2400\text{ V}} = \mathbf{4.17\text{ A}},\ I_p = \mathbf{83.33\text{ A}}$$

24. $I_s = I_1 = \mathbf{2\ A}$, $E_p = V_L = \mathbf{40\ V}$

$E_s = V_s - V_L = 200\text{ V} - 40\text{ V} = \mathbf{160\ V}$

$V_g I_1 = V_L I_L \Rightarrow I_L = V_g/V_L \cdot I_1 = \dfrac{200\text{ V}}{40\text{ V}}(2\text{ A}) = \mathbf{10\ A}$

$I_p + I_1 = I_L \Rightarrow I_p = I_L - I_1 = 10\text{ A} - 2\text{A} = \mathbf{8\ A}$

25. a. $\mathbf{E}_s = \dfrac{N_s}{N_p}\mathbf{E}_p$

$= \dfrac{25\text{ t}}{100\text{ t}}(100\text{ V}\angle 0°) = \mathbf{25\ V\angle 0°} = \mathbf{V}_L$

$\mathbf{I}_s = \dfrac{\mathbf{E}_s}{\mathbf{Z}_L} = \dfrac{25\text{ V}\angle 0°}{5\,\Omega\angle 0°} = \mathbf{5\ A\angle 0°} = \mathbf{I}_L$

b. $\mathbf{Z}_i = a^2\mathbf{Z}_L = \left(\dfrac{N_p}{N_s}\right)^2\mathbf{Z}_L = \left(\dfrac{100\text{ t}}{25\text{ t}}\right)^2 5\,\Omega\angle 0° = (4)^2\,5\,\Omega\angle 0° = \mathbf{80\,\Omega\angle 0°}$

c. $\mathbf{Z}_{1/2} = \dfrac{1}{4}\mathbf{Z}_i = \dfrac{1}{4}(80\,\Omega\angle 0°) = \mathbf{20\,\Omega\angle 0°}$

26. a. $\mathbf{E}_2 = \dfrac{N_2}{N_1}\mathbf{E}_1 = \dfrac{15\text{ t}}{90\text{ t}}(60\text{ V}\angle 0°) = \mathbf{10\ V\angle 0°}$

$\mathbf{E}_3 = \dfrac{N_3}{N_1}\mathbf{E}_1 = \dfrac{45\text{ t}}{90\text{ t}}(60\text{ V}\angle 0°) = \mathbf{30\ V\angle 0°}$

$\mathbf{I}_2 = \dfrac{\mathbf{E}_2}{\mathbf{Z}_2} = \dfrac{10\text{ V}\angle 0°}{8\,\Omega\angle 0°} = \mathbf{1.25\ A\angle 0°}$

$\mathbf{I}_3 = \dfrac{\mathbf{E}_3}{\mathbf{Z}_3} = \dfrac{30\text{ V}\angle 0°}{5\,\Omega\angle 0°} = \mathbf{6\ A\angle 0°}$

b. $\dfrac{1}{R_1} = \dfrac{1}{(N_1/N_2)^2R_2} + \dfrac{1}{(N_1/N_3)^2R_3}$

$= \dfrac{1}{(90\text{ t}/15\text{ t})^2\,8\,\Omega} + \dfrac{1}{(90\text{ t}/45\text{ t})^2\,5\,\Omega}$

$\dfrac{1}{R_1} = \dfrac{1}{288\,\Omega} + \dfrac{1}{20\,\Omega} = 0.05347\text{ S}$

$R_1 = \mathbf{18.70\,\Omega}$

27. a. $\mathbf{E}_2 = \dfrac{N_2}{N_1}\mathbf{E}_1 = \left(\dfrac{40\text{ t}}{120\text{ t}}\right)(120\text{ V}\angle 60°) = \mathbf{40\ V\angle 60°}$

$\mathbf{I}_2 = \dfrac{\mathbf{E}_2}{\mathbf{Z}_2} = \dfrac{40\text{ V}\angle 60°}{12\,\Omega\angle 0°} = \mathbf{3.33\ A\angle 60°}$

$\mathbf{E}_3 = \dfrac{N_3}{N_1}\mathbf{E}_1 = \left(\dfrac{30\text{ t}}{120\text{ t}}\right)(120\text{ V}\angle 60°) = \mathbf{30\ V\angle 60°}$

$\mathbf{I}_3 = \dfrac{\mathbf{E}_3}{\mathbf{Z}_3} = \dfrac{30\text{ V}\angle 60°}{10\,\Omega\angle 0°} = \mathbf{3\ A\angle 60°}$

b. $$\frac{1}{R_1} = \frac{1}{(N_1/N_2)^2 R_2} + \frac{1}{(N_1/N_3)^2 R_3}$$

$$= \frac{1}{(120\,\text{t}/40\,\text{t})^2 12\,\Omega} + \frac{1}{(120\,\text{t}/30\,\text{t})^2 10\,\Omega}$$

$$\frac{1}{R_1} = \frac{1}{108\,\Omega} + \frac{1}{160\,\Omega} = 0.0155\text{ S}$$

$$R_1 = \frac{1}{0.0155\text{ S}} = \mathbf{64.52\ \Omega}$$

28. $\mathbf{Z}_M = \mathbf{Z}_{M_{12}} = \omega M_{12} \angle 90°$

$$\mathbf{E} - \mathbf{I}_1\mathbf{Z}_1 - \mathbf{I}_1\mathbf{Z}_{L_1} - \mathbf{I}_1(-\mathbf{Z}_m) - \mathbf{I}_2(+\mathbf{Z}_m) - \mathbf{I}_1\mathbf{Z}_{L_2} + \mathbf{I}_2\mathbf{Z}_{L_2} - \mathbf{I}_1(-\mathbf{Z}_m) = 0$$

$$\mathbf{E} - \mathbf{I}_1(\mathbf{Z}_1 + \mathbf{Z}_{L_1} - \mathbf{Z}_m + \mathbf{Z}_{L_2} - \mathbf{Z}_m) - \mathbf{I}_2(\mathbf{Z}_m - \mathbf{Z}_{L_2}) = 0$$

or $$\mathbf{I}_1(\mathbf{Z}_1 + \mathbf{Z}_{L_1} + \mathbf{Z}_{L_2} - 2\,\mathbf{Z}_m) + \mathbf{I}_2(\mathbf{Z}_m - \mathbf{Z}_{L_2}) = \mathbf{E}$$

$$-\mathbf{I}_2\mathbf{Z}_2 - \mathbf{Z}_{L_2}(\mathbf{I}_2 - \mathbf{I}_1) - \mathbf{I}_1(+\mathbf{Z}_m) = 0$$

or $$\mathbf{I}_1(\mathbf{Z}_m - \mathbf{Z}_{L_2}) + \mathbf{I}_2(\mathbf{Z}_2 + \mathbf{Z}_{L_2}) = 0$$

---

29. $$\mathbf{E}_1 - \mathbf{I}_1\mathbf{Z}_1 - \mathbf{I}_1\mathbf{Z}_{L_1} - \mathbf{I}_2(-\mathbf{Z}_{M_{12}}) - \mathbf{I}_3(+\mathbf{Z}_{M_{13}}) = 0$$

or $$\mathbf{E}_1 - \mathbf{I}_1[\mathbf{Z}_1 + \mathbf{Z}_{L_1}] + \mathbf{I}_2\mathbf{Z}_{M_{12}} - \mathbf{I}_3\mathbf{Z}_{M_{13}} = 0$$

$$-\mathbf{I}_2(\mathbf{Z}_2 + \mathbf{Z}_3 + \mathbf{Z}_{L_2}) + \mathbf{I}_3\mathbf{Z}_2 - \mathbf{I}_1(-\mathbf{Z}_{M_{12}}) = 0$$

or $$-\mathbf{I}_2(\mathbf{Z}_2 + \mathbf{Z}_3 + \mathbf{Z}_{L_2}) + \mathbf{I}_3\mathbf{Z}_2 + \mathbf{I}_1\mathbf{Z}_{M_{12}} = 0$$

$$-\mathbf{I}_3(\mathbf{Z}_2 + \mathbf{Z}_4 + \mathbf{Z}_{L_3}) + \mathbf{I}_2\mathbf{Z}_2 - \mathbf{I}_1(+\mathbf{Z}_{M_{13}}) = 0$$

or $$-\mathbf{I}_3(\mathbf{Z}_2 + \mathbf{Z}_4 + \mathbf{Z}_{L_3}) + \mathbf{I}_2\mathbf{Z}_2 - \mathbf{I}_1\mathbf{Z}_{M_{13}} = 0$$

$$\therefore \quad \begin{aligned}
&[\mathbf{Z}_1 + \mathbf{Z}_{L_1}]\mathbf{I}_1 - \mathbf{Z}_{M_{12}}\mathbf{I}_2 + \mathbf{Z}_{M_{13}}\mathbf{I}_3 = \mathbf{E}_1\\
&\mathbf{Z}_{M_{12}}\mathbf{I}_1 - [\mathbf{Z}_2 + \mathbf{Z}_3 + \mathbf{Z}_{L_2}]\mathbf{I}_2 + \mathbf{Z}_2\mathbf{I}_3 = 0\\
&\mathbf{Z}_{M_{13}}\mathbf{I}_1 \quad \mathbf{Z}_2\mathbf{I}_2 + [\mathbf{Z}_2 + \mathbf{Z}_4 + \mathbf{Z}_{L_3}]\mathbf{I}_3 = 0
\end{aligned}$$

Chapter 23

1. a. $E_\phi = E_l/\sqrt{3} = 208\text{ V}/1.732 = \mathbf{120.1\text{ V}}$ b. $V_\phi = E_\phi = \mathbf{120.1\text{ V}}$

 c. $I_\phi = \dfrac{V_\phi}{R_\phi} = \dfrac{120.1\text{ V}}{10\,\Omega} = \mathbf{12.01\text{ A}}$ d. $I_L = I_\phi = \mathbf{12.01\text{ A}}$

2. a. $E_\phi = E_l/\sqrt{3} = 208\text{ V}/1.732 = \mathbf{120.1\text{ V}}$ b. $V_\phi = E_\phi = \mathbf{120.1\text{ V}}$

 c. $\mathbf{Z}_\phi = 12\,\Omega - j16\,\Omega = 20\,\Omega\,\angle{-53.13°}$ d. $I_L = I_\phi = \mathbf{6\text{ A}}$

 $I_\phi = \dfrac{V_\phi}{Z_\phi} = \dfrac{120.1\text{ V}}{20\,\Omega} \cong \mathbf{6\text{ A}}$

3. a. $E_\phi = \mathbf{120.1\text{ V}}$ b. $V_\phi = \mathbf{120.1\text{ V}}$

 c. $\mathbf{Z}_\phi = (10\,\Omega\,\angle 0° \parallel (10\,\Omega\,\angle{-90°}) = 7.071\,\Omega\,\angle{-45°}$

 $I_\phi = \dfrac{V_\phi}{Z_\phi} = \dfrac{120.1\text{ V}}{7.071\,\Omega} = \mathbf{16.98\text{ A}}$

 d. $I_L = \mathbf{16.98\text{ A}}$

4. a. $\theta_2 = \mathbf{-120°}$, $\theta_3 = \mathbf{120°}$

 b. $\mathbf{V}_{an} = \mathbf{120\text{ V}\,\angle 0°}$, $\mathbf{V}_{bn} = \mathbf{120\text{ V}\,\angle{-120°}}$, $\mathbf{V}_{cn} = \mathbf{120\text{ V}\,\angle 120°}$

 c. $\mathbf{I}_{\text{an}} = \dfrac{\mathbf{V}_{an}}{\mathbf{Z}_{an}} = \dfrac{120\text{ V}\,\angle 0°}{20\,\Omega\,\angle 0°} = \mathbf{6\text{ A}\,\angle 0°}$

 $\mathbf{I}_{\text{bn}} = \dfrac{\mathbf{V}_{bn}}{\mathbf{Z}_{bn}} = \dfrac{120\text{ V}\,\angle{-120°}}{20\,\Omega\,\angle 0°} = \mathbf{6\text{ A}\,\angle{-120°}}$

 $\mathbf{I}_{\text{cn}} = \dfrac{\mathbf{V}_{cn}}{\mathbf{Z}_{cn}} = \dfrac{120\text{ V}\,\angle 120°}{20\,\Omega\,\angle 0°} = \mathbf{6\text{ A}\,\angle 120°}$

 d. $I_L = I_\phi = \mathbf{6A}$ e. $V_L = \sqrt{3}\,V_\phi = \sqrt{3}\,(120\text{ V}) = \mathbf{207.8\text{ V}}$

5. a. $\theta_2 = \mathbf{-120°}$, $\theta_3 = \mathbf{+120°}$

 b. $\mathbf{V}_{an} = \mathbf{120\text{ V}\,\angle 0°}$, $\mathbf{V}_{bn} = \mathbf{120\text{ V}\,\angle{-120°}}$, $\mathbf{V}_{cn} = \mathbf{120\text{ V}\,\angle 120°}$

 c. $\mathbf{Z}_\phi = 9\,\Omega + j12\,\Omega = 15\,\Omega\,\angle 53.13°$

 $\mathbf{I}_{an} = \dfrac{120\text{ V}\,\angle 0°}{15\,\Omega\,\angle 53.13°} = \mathbf{8\text{ A}\,\angle{-53.13°}}$, $\mathbf{I}_{bn} = \dfrac{120\text{ V}\,\angle{-120°}}{15\,\Omega\,\angle 53.13°} = \mathbf{8\text{ A}\,\angle{-173.13°}}$

 $\mathbf{I}_{cn} = \dfrac{120\text{ V}\,\angle 120°}{15\,\Omega\,\angle 53.13°} = \mathbf{8\text{ A}\,\angle 66.87°}$

e. $I_l = I_\phi = \mathbf{8\ A}$

f. $E_L = \sqrt{3}\ E_\phi = (1.732)(120\text{ V}) = \mathbf{207.85\ V}$

6. a, b. The same as problem 4.

c. $\mathbf{Z}_\phi = 6\ \Omega\ \angle 0° \parallel 8\ \Omega\ \angle -90° = 4.8\ \Omega\ \angle -36.87°$

$$\mathbf{I}_{an} = \frac{\mathbf{V}_{an}}{\mathbf{Z}_{an}} = \frac{120\text{ V}\ \angle 0°}{4.8\ \Omega\ \angle -36.87°} = \mathbf{25\ A\ \angle 36.87°}$$

$$\mathbf{I}_{bn} = \frac{\mathbf{V}_{bn}}{\mathbf{Z}_{bn}} = \frac{120\text{ V}\ \angle -120°}{4.8\ \Omega\ \angle -36.87°} = \mathbf{25\ A\ \angle -83.13°}$$

$$\mathbf{I}_{cn} = \frac{\mathbf{V}_{cn}}{\mathbf{Z}_{cn}} = \frac{120\text{ V}\ \angle 120°}{4.8\ \Omega\ \angle -36.87°} = \mathbf{25\ A\ \angle 156.87°}$$

d. $I_l = I_\phi = \mathbf{25\ A}$

e. $V_L = \sqrt{3}\ V_\phi = \sqrt{3}\ (120\text{ V}) = \mathbf{207.84\ V}$

7. $$V_\phi = V_{an} = V_{bn} = V_{cn} = \frac{V_L}{\sqrt{3}} = \frac{220\text{ V}}{1.732} = \mathbf{127.0\ V}$$

$\mathbf{Z}_\phi = 10\ \Omega - j10\ \Omega = 14.42\ \Omega\ \angle -45°$

$$I_\phi = I_{an} = I_{bn} = I_{cn} = \frac{V_\phi}{Z_\phi} = \frac{127\text{ V}}{14.142\ \Omega} = \mathbf{8.98\ A}$$

$I_L = I_{Aa} = I_{Bb} = I_{Cc} = I_\phi = \mathbf{8.98\ A}$

8. $\mathbf{Z}_\phi = 12\ \Omega + j16\ \Omega = 20\ \Omega \angle 53.13°$

$$I_\phi = \frac{V_\phi}{Z_\phi} = \frac{50\text{ V}}{20\ \Omega} = \mathbf{2.5\ A}$$

$Z_{T_\phi} = 13\ \Omega + j16\ \Omega = 20.62\ \Omega\ \angle 50.91°$

$V_\phi = I_\phi Z_{T_\phi} = (2.5\text{ A})(20.62\ \Omega) = 51.55\text{ V}$

$V_L = \sqrt{3}\ V_\phi = \left(\sqrt{3}\right)(51.55\text{ V}) = \mathbf{89.29\ V}$

9. a. $$\mathbf{E}_{AN} = \frac{22\text{ kV}}{\sqrt{3}} \angle -30° = \mathbf{12.7\ kV\ \angle -30°}$$

$$\mathbf{E}_{BN} = \frac{22\text{ kV}}{\sqrt{3}} \angle -150° = \mathbf{12.7\ kV\ \angle -150°}$$

$$\mathbf{E}_{CN} = \frac{22\text{ kV}}{\sqrt{3}} \angle 90° = \mathbf{12.7\ kV\ \angle 90°}$$

b, c. $\mathbf{I}_{Aa} = \mathbf{I}_{an} = \dfrac{\mathbf{E}_{AN}}{\mathbf{Z}_{AN}} = \dfrac{12.7\text{ kV}\angle -30°}{(30\,\Omega + j40\,\Omega) + (0.4\text{ k}\Omega + j1\text{ k}\Omega)}$

$= \dfrac{12.7\text{ kV}\angle -30°}{430\,\Omega + j1040\,\Omega} = \dfrac{12.7\text{ kV}\angle -30°}{1125.39\,\Omega\angle 67.54°}$

$= \mathbf{11.29\text{ A}\angle{-97.54°}}$

$\mathbf{I}_{Bb} = \mathbf{I}_{bn} = \dfrac{\mathbf{E}_{BN}}{\mathbf{Z}_{BN}} = \dfrac{12.7\text{ kV}\angle -150°}{1125.39\,\Omega\angle 67.54°} = \mathbf{11.29\text{ A}\angle{-217.54°}}$

$\mathbf{I}_{Cc} = \mathbf{I}_{cn} = \dfrac{\mathbf{E}_{CN}}{\mathbf{Z}_{CN}} = \dfrac{12.7\text{ kV}\angle 90°}{1125.39\,\Omega\angle 67.54°} = \mathbf{11.29\text{ A}\angle 22.46°}$

d. $\mathbf{V}_{an} = \mathbf{I}_{an}\mathbf{Z}_{an} = (11.29\text{ A}\angle{-97.54°})(400 + j1000)$

$= (11.29\text{ A}\angle{-97.54°})(1077.03\,\Omega\angle 68.2°)$

$= \mathbf{12.16\text{ kV}\angle{-29.34°}}$

$\mathbf{V}_{bn} = \mathbf{I}_{bn}\mathbf{Z}_{bn} = (11.29\text{ A}\angle{-217.54°})(1077.03\angle 68.2°)$

$= \mathbf{12.16\text{ kV}\angle{-149.34°}}$

$\mathbf{V}_{cn} = \mathbf{I}_{cn}\mathbf{Z}_{cn} = (11.29\text{ A}\angle 22.46°)(1077.03\angle 68.2°)$

$= \mathbf{12.16\text{ kV}\angle 90.66°}$

10. a. $E_\phi = E_L/\sqrt{3} = 208\text{ V}/1.732 = \mathbf{120.1\text{ V}}$

b. $V_\phi = E_L = \mathbf{208\text{ V}}$

c. $I_\phi = \dfrac{V_\phi}{Z_\phi} = \dfrac{208\text{ V}}{20\,\Omega} = \mathbf{10.4\text{ A}}$

d. $I_L = \sqrt{3}\,I_\phi = (1.732)(10.4\text{ A}) = \mathbf{18\text{ A}}$

11. a. $E_\phi = E_L/\sqrt{3} = 208\text{ V}/1.732 = \mathbf{120.1\text{ V}}$

b. $V_\phi = E_L = \mathbf{208\text{ V}}$

c. $\mathbf{Z}_\phi = 6.8\,\Omega + j14\,\Omega = 15.564\,\Omega\angle 64.09°$

$I_\phi = \dfrac{V_\phi}{Z_\phi} = \dfrac{208\text{ V}}{15.564\,\Omega} = \mathbf{13.36\text{ A}}$

d. $I_L = \sqrt{3}\,I_\phi = (1.732)(13.36\text{ A}) = \mathbf{23.14\text{ A}}$

12. $\mathbf{Z}_\phi = 18\,\Omega\angle 0° \parallel 18\,\Omega\angle{-90°} = 12.728\,\Omega\angle{-45°}$

a. $E_\phi = V_L/\sqrt{3} = 208\text{ V}/\sqrt{3} = \mathbf{120.09\text{ V}}$

b. $V_\phi = \mathbf{208\text{ V}}$

c. $I_\phi = \dfrac{V_\phi}{Z_\phi} = \dfrac{208\text{ V}}{12.728\,\Omega} = \mathbf{16.34\text{ A}}$

d. $I_L = \sqrt{3}\,I_\phi = (1.732)(16.34\text{ A}) = \mathbf{28.30\text{ A}}$

13. a. $\theta_2 = \mathbf{-120°}$, $\theta_3 = \mathbf{+120°}$

b. $\mathbf{V}_{ab} = \mathbf{208\text{ V}\angle 0°}$, $\mathbf{V}_{bc} = \mathbf{208\text{ V}\angle{-120°}}$, $\mathbf{V}_{ca} = \mathbf{208\text{ V}\angle 120°}$

c. –

d. $\mathbf{I}_{ab} = \dfrac{\mathbf{V}_{ab}}{\mathbf{Z}_{ab}} = \dfrac{208\text{ V }\angle 0^\circ}{22\,\Omega\angle 0^\circ} = \mathbf{9.46\text{ A }\angle 0^\circ}$

$\mathbf{I}_{bc} = \dfrac{\mathbf{V}_{bc}}{\mathbf{Z}_{bc}} = \dfrac{208\text{ V }\angle 120^\circ}{22\,\Omega\angle 0^\circ} = \mathbf{9.46\text{ A }\angle{-120^\circ}}$

$\mathbf{I}_{ca} = \dfrac{\mathbf{V}_{ca}}{\mathbf{Z}_{ca}} = \dfrac{208\text{ V }\angle 120^\circ}{22\,\Omega\angle 0^\circ} = \mathbf{9.46\text{ A }\angle 120^\circ}$

e. $I_L = \sqrt{3}\ I_\phi = (1.732)(9.46\text{ A}) = \mathbf{16.38\text{ A}}$

f. $E_\phi = E_L/\sqrt{3} = 208\text{ V}/1.732 = \mathbf{120.1\text{ V}}$

14. a. $\theta_2 = \mathbf{-120^\circ}$, $\theta_3 = \mathbf{+120^\circ}$

b. $\mathbf{V}_{ab} = \mathbf{208\text{ V }\angle 0^\circ}$, $\mathbf{V}_{bc} = \mathbf{208\text{ V }\angle{-120^\circ}}$, $\mathbf{V}_{ca} = \mathbf{208\text{ V }\angle 120^\circ}$

c. –

d. $\mathbf{Z}_\phi = 100\,\Omega - j100\,\Omega = 141.42\,\Omega\angle{-45^\circ}$

$\mathbf{I}_{ab} = \dfrac{\mathbf{V}_{ab}}{\mathbf{Z}_{ab}} = \dfrac{208\text{ V }\angle 0^\circ}{141.42\,\Omega\angle{-45^\circ}} = \mathbf{1.47\text{ A }\angle 45^\circ}$

$\mathbf{I}_{bc} = \dfrac{\mathbf{V}_{bc}}{\mathbf{Z}_{bc}} = \dfrac{208\text{ V }\angle{-120^\circ}}{141.42\,\Omega\angle{-45^\circ}} = \mathbf{1.47\text{ A }\angle{-75^\circ}}$

$\mathbf{I}_{ca} = \dfrac{\mathbf{V}_{ca}}{\mathbf{Z}_{ca}} = \dfrac{208\text{ V }\angle 120^\circ}{141.42\,\Omega\angle{-45^\circ}} = \mathbf{1.47\text{ A }\angle 165^\circ}$

e. $I_l = \sqrt{3}\ I_\phi = (1.732)(1.471\text{ A}) = \mathbf{2.55\text{ A}}$

f. $E_\phi = E_L/\sqrt{3} = 208\text{ V}/1.732 = \mathbf{120.1\text{ V}}$

15. a, b. The same as problem 13.

c. –

d. $\mathbf{Z}_\phi = 3\,\Omega\angle 0^\circ \parallel 4\,\Omega\angle 90^\circ = 2.4\,\Omega\angle 36.87^\circ$

$\mathbf{I}_{ab} = \dfrac{\mathbf{V}_{ab}}{\mathbf{Z}_{ab}} = \dfrac{208\text{ V }\angle 0^\circ}{2.4\,\Omega\angle 36.87^\circ} = \mathbf{86.67\text{ A }\angle{-36.87^\circ}}$

$\mathbf{I}_{bc} = \dfrac{\mathbf{V}_{bc}}{\mathbf{Z}_{bc}} = \dfrac{208\text{ V }\angle{-120^\circ}}{2.4\,\Omega\angle 36.87^\circ} = \mathbf{86.67\text{ A }\angle{-156.87^\circ}}$

$\mathbf{I}_{ca} = \dfrac{\mathbf{V}_{ca}}{\mathbf{Z}_{ca}} = \dfrac{208\text{ V }\angle 120^\circ}{2.4\,\Omega\angle 36.87^\circ} = \mathbf{86.67\text{ A }\angle 83.13^\circ}$

e. $I_L = \sqrt{3}\, I_\phi = (1.732)(86.67\text{ A}) = \mathbf{150.11\text{ A}}$

f. $E_\phi = \mathbf{120.1\text{ V}}$

16. $V_{ab} = V_{bc} = V_{ca} = \mathbf{220\text{ V}}$

$\mathbf{Z}_\phi = 10\ \Omega + j10\ \Omega = 14.142\ \Omega\angle 45°$

$$I_{ab} = I_{bc} = I_{ca} = \frac{V_\phi}{Z_\phi} = \frac{220\text{ V}}{14.142\ \Omega} = \mathbf{15.56\text{ A}}$$

17. a. $$\mathbf{I}_{ab} = \frac{\mathbf{V}_{ab}}{\mathbf{Z}_{ab}} = \frac{16\text{ kV}\angle 0°}{300\ \Omega + j1000\ \Omega} = \frac{16\text{ kV}\angle 0°}{1044.03\ \Omega\angle 73.30°}$$

$\mathbf{I}_{ab} = \mathbf{15.33\text{ A}\angle{-73.30°}}$

$$\mathbf{I}_{bc} = \frac{\mathbf{V}_{bc}}{\mathbf{Z}_{bc}} = \frac{16\text{ kV}\angle -120°}{1044.03\ \Omega\angle 73.30°} = \mathbf{15.33\text{ A}\angle{-193.30°}}$$

$$\mathbf{I}_{ca} = \frac{\mathbf{V}_{ca}}{\mathbf{Z}_{ca}} = \frac{16\text{ kV}\angle 120°}{1044.03\ \Omega\angle 73.30°} = \mathbf{15.33\text{ A}\angle 46.7°}$$

b. $\mathbf{I}_{Aa} - \mathbf{I}_{ab} + \mathbf{I}_{ca} = 0$

$\mathbf{I}_{Aa} = \mathbf{I}_{ab} - \mathbf{I}_{ca} = 15.33\text{ A}\angle{-73.30°} - 15.33\text{ A}\angle 46.7°$

$= (4.41\text{ A} - j14.68\text{ A}) - (10.51\text{ A} + j11.16\text{ A})$

$= 4.41\text{ A} - 10.51\text{ A} - j(14.68\text{ A} + 11.16\text{ A})$

$= -6.11\text{ A} - j25.84\text{ A} = \mathbf{26.55\text{ A}\angle{-103.30°}}$

$\mathbf{I}_{Bb} + \mathbf{I}_{ab} = \mathbf{I}_{bc}$

$\mathbf{I}_{Bb} = \mathbf{I}_{bc} - \mathbf{I}_{ab} = 15.33\text{ A}\angle{-193.30°} - 15.33\text{ A}\angle{-73.30°}$

$= \mathbf{26.55\text{ A}\angle 136.70°}$

$\mathbf{I}_{Cc} + \mathbf{I}_{bc} = \mathbf{I}_{ca}$

$\mathbf{I}_{Cc} = \mathbf{I}_{ca} - \mathbf{I}_{bc} = 15.33\text{ A}\angle 46.7° - 15.33\text{ A}\angle{-193.30°}$

$= \mathbf{26.55\text{ A}\angle 16.70°}$

c. $\mathbf{E}_{AB} = \mathbf{I}_{Aa}(10\ \Omega + j20\ \Omega) + \mathbf{V}_{ab} - \mathbf{I}_{Bb}(22.361\ \Omega\angle 63.43°)$

$= (26.55\text{ A}\angle{-103.30°})(22.361\ \Omega\angle 63.43°) + 16\text{ kV}\angle 0°$

$- (26.55\text{ A}\angle 136.70°)(22.361\ \Omega\angle 63.43°)$

$= (455.65\text{ V} - j380.58\text{ V}) + 16{,}000\text{ V} - (-557.42\text{ V} - j204.32\text{ V})$

$= 17.01\text{ kV} - j176.26\text{ V}$

$= \mathbf{17.01\text{ kV}\angle{-0.59°}}$

$\mathbf{E}_{BC} = \mathbf{I}_{Bb}(22.361\ \Omega\angle 63.43°) + \mathbf{V}_{bc} - \mathbf{I}_{Cc}(22.361\ \Omega\angle 63.53°)$

$= (26.55\text{ A}\angle 136.70°)(22.361\ \Omega\angle 63.53°) + 16\text{ kV}\angle{-120°}$

$- (26.55\text{ A}\angle 16.70°)(22.361\ \Omega\angle 63.53°)$

$= \mathbf{17.01\text{ kV}\angle{-120.59°}}$

$\mathbf{E}_{CA} = \mathbf{I}_{Cc}(22.361\ \Omega\angle 63.43°) + \mathbf{V}_{ca} - \mathbf{I}_{Aa}(22.361\ \Omega\angle 63.43°)$

$= \mathbf{17.01\text{ kV}\angle 119.41°}$

18. a. $E_\phi = E_L = \mathbf{208\ V}$

b. $V_\phi = \dfrac{E_L}{\sqrt{3}} = \dfrac{208\text{ V}}{1.732} = \mathbf{120.1\ V}$

c. $I_\phi = \dfrac{V_\phi}{Z_\phi} = \dfrac{120.1\text{ V}}{30\ \Omega} = \mathbf{4.00\ A}$

d. $I_L = I_\phi \cong \mathbf{4\ A}$

19. a. $E_\phi = E_L = \mathbf{208\ V}$

b. $V_\phi = E_L\ \sqrt{3} = \mathbf{120.09\ V}$

c. $I_\phi = \dfrac{V_\phi}{Z_\phi} = \dfrac{120.09\text{ V}}{16.971\ \Omega} = \mathbf{7.08\ A}$

d. $I_L = I_\phi = \mathbf{7.08\ A}$

20. a, b. The same as problem 18.

c. $\mathbf{Z}_\phi = 15\ \Omega\ \angle 0° \parallel 20\ \Omega\ \angle{-90°} = 12\ \Omega\ \angle{-36.87°}$

$$I_\phi = \frac{V_\phi}{Z_\phi} = \frac{120.1\text{ V}}{12\ \Omega} \cong \mathbf{10\ A}$$

d. $I_l = I_\phi \cong \mathbf{10\ A}$

21. $V_{an} = V_{bn} = V_{cn} = \dfrac{120\text{ V}}{\sqrt{3}} = \dfrac{120\text{ V}}{1.732} = \mathbf{69.28\ V}$

$$I_{an} = I_{bn} = I_{cn} = \frac{69.28\text{ V}}{24\ \Omega} = \mathbf{2.89\ A}$$

$I_{Aa} = I_{Bb} = I_{Cc} = \mathbf{2.89\ A}$

22. $V_{an} = V_{bn} = V_{cn} = \dfrac{120\text{ V}}{\sqrt{3}} = \mathbf{69.28\ V}$

$\mathbf{Z}_\phi = 10\ \Omega + j20\ \Omega = 22.36\ \Omega\angle 63.43°$

$$I_{an} = I_{bn} = I_{cn} = \frac{\mathbf{V}_\phi}{\mathbf{Z}_\phi} = \frac{69.28\text{ V}}{22.36\ \Omega} = \mathbf{3.10\ A}$$

$I_{Aa} = I_{Bb} = I_{Cc} = I_\phi = \mathbf{3.10\ A}$

23. $V_{an} = V_{bn} = V_{cn} = \mathbf{69.28\ V}$

$\mathbf{Z}_\phi = 20\ \Omega\ \angle 0° \parallel 15\ \Omega\ \angle{-90°} = 12\ \Omega\ \angle{-53.13°}$

$$I_{an} = I_{bn} = I_{cn} = \frac{69.28\text{ V}}{12\ \Omega} = \mathbf{5.77\ A}$$

$I_{Aa} = I_{Bb} = I_{Cc} = \mathbf{5.77\ A}$

24. a. $E_\phi = E_L = \mathbf{440\ V}$

b. $V_\phi = E_L = E_\phi = \mathbf{440\ V}$

c. $I_\phi = \dfrac{V_\phi}{Z_\phi} = \dfrac{440\text{ V}}{220\ \Omega} = \mathbf{2\ A}$

d. $I_L = \sqrt{3}\ I_\phi = (1.732)(2\text{ A}) = \mathbf{3.46\ A}$

25. a. $E_\phi = E_L = \mathbf{440\ V}$ b. $V_\phi = E_L = \mathbf{440\ V}$

c. $\mathbf{Z}_\phi = 12\ \Omega - j9\ \Omega = 15\ \Omega\ \angle -36.87°$

$$I_\phi = \frac{V_\phi}{Z_\phi} = \frac{440\text{ V}}{15\,\Omega} = \mathbf{29.33\ A}$$

d. $I_L = \sqrt{3}\ I_\phi = (1.732)(29.33\text{ A}) = \mathbf{50.8\ A}$

26. a, b. The same as problem 24.

c. $\mathbf{Z}_\phi = 22\ \Omega\ \angle 0° \parallel 22\ \Omega\ \angle 90° = 15.56\ \Omega\ \angle 45°$

$$I_\phi = \frac{V_\phi}{Z_\phi} = \frac{440\text{ V}}{15.56\,\Omega} = \mathbf{28.28\ A}$$

d. $I_L = \sqrt{3}\ I_\phi = (1.732)(28.28\text{ A}) = \mathbf{48.98\ A}$

27. a. $\theta_2 = \mathbf{-120°}$, $\theta_3 = \mathbf{+120°}$

b. $\mathbf{V}_{ab} = \mathbf{100\ V\ \angle 0°}$, $\mathbf{V}_{bc} = \mathbf{100\ V\ \angle -120°}$, $\mathbf{V}_{ca} = \mathbf{100\ V\ \angle 120°}$

c. –

d. $$\mathbf{I}_{ab} = \frac{\mathbf{V}_{ab}}{\mathbf{Z}_{ab}} = \frac{100\text{ V}\ \angle 0°}{20\,\Omega\ \angle 0°} = \mathbf{5\ A\ \angle 0°}$$

$$\mathbf{I}_{bc} = \frac{\mathbf{V}_{bc}}{\mathbf{Z}_{bc}} = \frac{100\text{ V}\ \angle -120°}{20\,\Omega\ \angle 0°} = \mathbf{5\ A\ \angle -120°}$$

$$\mathbf{I}_{ca} = \frac{\mathbf{V}_{ca}}{\mathbf{Z}_{ca}} = \frac{100\text{ V}\ \angle 120°}{20\,\Omega\ \angle 0°} = \mathbf{5\ A\ \angle 120°}$$

e. $I_{Aa} = I_{Bb} = I_{Cc} = \sqrt{3}\ (5\text{ A}) = \mathbf{8.66\ A}$

28. a. $\theta_2 = \mathbf{-120°}$, $\theta_3 = \mathbf{+120°}$

b. $\mathbf{V}_{ab} = \mathbf{100\ V\ \angle 0°}$, $\mathbf{V}_{bc} = \mathbf{100\ V\ \angle -120°}$, $\mathbf{V}_{ca} = \mathbf{100\ V\ \angle 120°}$

c. –

d. $\mathbf{Z}_\phi = 12\ \Omega + j16\ \Omega = 20\ \Omega\ \angle 53.13°$

$$\mathbf{I}_{ab} = \frac{\mathbf{V}_{ab}}{\mathbf{Z}_{ab}} = \frac{100\text{ V}\ \angle 0°}{20\,\Omega\ \angle 53.13°} = \mathbf{5\ A\ \angle -53.13°}$$

$$\mathbf{I}_{bc} = \frac{\mathbf{V}_{bc}}{\mathbf{Z}_{bc}} = \frac{100\text{ V}\ \angle -120°}{20\,\Omega\ \angle 53.13°} = \mathbf{5\ A\ \angle -173.13°}$$

$$\mathbf{I}_{ca} = \frac{\mathbf{V}_{ca}}{\mathbf{Z}_{ca}} = \frac{100 \text{ V} \angle 120°}{20 \ \Omega \angle 53.13°} = \mathbf{5 \ A \angle 66.87°}$$

e. $I_{Aa} = I_{Bb} = I_{Cc} = \sqrt{3} \ I_{\phi} = (1.732)(5 \text{ A}) = \mathbf{8.66 \ A}$

29. a. $\theta_2 = \mathbf{-120°}$, $\theta_3 = \mathbf{120°}$

b. $\mathbf{V}_{ab} = \mathbf{100 \ V \angle 0°}$, $\mathbf{V}_{bc} = \mathbf{100 \ V \angle -120°}$, $\mathbf{V}_{ca} = \mathbf{100 \ V \angle 120°}$

c. –

d. $\mathbf{Z}_{\phi} = 20 \ \Omega \angle 0° \parallel 20 \ \Omega \angle -90° = 14.14 \ \Omega \angle -45°$

$$\mathbf{I}_{ab} = \frac{100 \text{ V} \angle 0°}{14.14 \ \Omega \angle -45°} = \mathbf{7.07 \ A \angle 45°}$$

$$\mathbf{I}_{bc} = \frac{100 \text{ V} \angle -120°}{14.14 \ \Omega \angle -45°} = \mathbf{7.07 \ A \angle -75°}$$

$$\mathbf{I}_{ca} = \frac{100 \text{ V} \angle 120°}{14.14 \ \Omega \angle -45°} = \mathbf{7.07 \ A \angle 165°}$$

e. $I_{Aa} = I_{Bb} = I_{Cc} = \left(\sqrt{3}\right)(7.07 \text{ A}) = \mathbf{12.25 \ A}$

30. $P_T = 3I_{\phi}^2 R_{\phi} = 3(6 \text{ A})^2 \ 12 \ \Omega = \mathbf{1296 \ W}$

$Q_T = 3I_{\phi}^2 X_{\phi} = 3(6 \text{ A})^2 \ 16 \ \Omega = \mathbf{1728 \ VAR(\mathit{C})}$

$S_T = \sqrt{P_T^2 + Q_T^2} = \mathbf{2160 \ VA}$

$$F_p = \frac{P_T}{S_T} = \frac{1296 \text{ W}}{2160 \text{ VA}} = \mathbf{0.6 \ (leading)}$$

31. $V_{\phi} = 120 \text{ V}$, $I_{\phi} = 120 \text{ V}/20 \ \Omega = 6 \text{ A}$

$P_T = 3I_{\phi}^2 R_{\phi} = 3(6 \text{ A})^2 \ 20 \ \Omega = \mathbf{2160 \ W}$

$Q_T = \mathbf{0 \ VAR}$

$S_T = P_T = \mathbf{2160 \ VA}$

$$F_p = \frac{P_T}{S_T} = \frac{2160 \text{ W}}{2160 \text{ VA}} = \mathbf{1}$$

32. $P_T = 3I_{\phi}^2 R_{\phi} = 3(8.98 \text{ A})^2 \ 10 \ \Omega = \mathbf{2419.21 \ W}$

$Q_T = 3I_{\phi}^2 X_{\phi} = 3(8.98 \text{ A})^2 \ 10 \ \Omega = \mathbf{2419.21 \ VAR(\mathit{C})}$

$S_T = \sqrt{P_T^2 + Q_T^2} = \mathbf{3421.28 \ VA}$

$$F_p = \frac{P_T}{S_T} = \frac{2419.21 \text{ W}}{3421.28 \text{ VA}} = \mathbf{0.7071 \ (leading)}$$

33. $V_\phi = 208\text{ V}$

$$P_T = 3\left(\frac{V_\phi^2}{R_\phi}\right) = 3 \cdot \frac{(208\text{ V})^2}{18\,\Omega} = \mathbf{7210.67\ W}$$

$$Q_T = 3\left(\frac{V_\phi^2}{X_\phi}\right) = 3 \cdot \frac{(208\text{ V})^2}{18\,\Omega} = \mathbf{7210.67\ VAR(\mathit{C})}$$

$$S_T = \sqrt{P_T^2 + Q_T^2} = \mathbf{10{,}197.42\ VA}$$

$$F_p = \frac{P_T}{S_T} = \frac{7210.67\text{ W}}{10{,}197.42\text{ VA}} = \mathbf{0.707\ (leading)}$$

34. $P_T = 3I_\phi^2 R_\phi = 3(1.471\text{ A})^2\, 100\,\Omega = \mathbf{649.15\ W}$

$$Q_T = 3I_\phi^2 X_\phi = 3(1.471\text{ A})^2\, 100\,\Omega = \mathbf{649.15\ VAR(\mathit{C})}$$

$$S_T = \sqrt{P_T^2 + Q_T^2} = \mathbf{918.04\ VA}$$

$$F_p = \frac{P_T}{S_T} = \frac{649.15\text{ W}}{918.04\text{ VA}} = \mathbf{0.7071\ (leading)}$$

35. $P_T = 3I_\phi^2 R_\phi = 3(15.56\text{ A})^2\, 10\,\Omega = \mathbf{7.26\ kW}$

$$Q_T = 3I_\phi^2 X_\phi = 3(15.56\text{ A})^2\, 10\,\Omega = \mathbf{7.26\ kVAR}$$

$$S_T = \sqrt{P_T^2 + Q_T^2} = \mathbf{10.27\ kVA}$$

$$F_p = \frac{P_T}{S_T} = \frac{7.263\text{ kW}}{10.272\text{ kVA}} = \mathbf{0.7071\ (lagging)}$$

36. $P_T = 3\dfrac{V_\phi^2}{R_\phi} = \dfrac{3(120.1\text{ V})^2}{15\,\Omega} = \mathbf{2884.80\ W}$

$$Q_T = 3\frac{V_\phi^2}{X_\phi} = \frac{3(120.1\text{ V})^2}{20\,\Omega} = \mathbf{2163.60\ VAR(\mathit{C})}$$

$$S_T = \sqrt{P_T^2 + Q_T^2} = \mathbf{3605.97\ VA}$$

$$F_p = \frac{P_T}{S_T} = \frac{2884.80\text{ W}}{3605.97\text{ VA}} = \mathbf{0.8\ (leading)}$$

37. $\mathbf{Z}_\phi = 10\,\Omega + j20\,\Omega = 22.36\,\Omega\,\angle 63.43°$

$$V_\phi = \frac{V_L}{\sqrt{3}} = \frac{120\text{ V}}{1.732} = 69.28\text{ V}$$

$$I_\phi = \frac{V_\phi}{Z_\phi} = \frac{69.28\text{ V}}{22.36\,\Omega} = 3.098\text{ A}$$

$$P_T = 3I_\phi^2 R_\phi = 3(3.098\text{ A})^2\, 10\,\Omega = \mathbf{287.93\ W}$$

$Q_T = 3I_\phi^2 X_\phi = 3(3.098\ \text{A})^2\ 20\ \Omega = \mathbf{575.86\ VAR}$

$S_T = \sqrt{P_T^2 + Q_T^2} = \mathbf{643.83\ VA}$

$F_p = \dfrac{P_T}{S_T} = \dfrac{287.93\ \text{W}}{643.83\ \text{VA}} = \mathbf{0.447\ (lagging)}$

38. $P_T = 3\dfrac{V_\phi^2}{R_\phi} = \dfrac{3(440\ \text{V})^2}{22\ \Omega} = \mathbf{26.4\ kW}$

$Q_T = P_T = \mathbf{26.4\ kVAR(}\boldsymbol{L}\mathbf{)}$

$S_T = \sqrt{P_T^2 + Q_T^2} = \mathbf{37.34\ kVA}$

$F_p = \dfrac{P_T}{S_T} = \dfrac{26.4\ \text{kW}}{37.34\ \text{kVA}} = \mathbf{0.707\ (lagging)}$

39. $\mathbf{Z}_\phi = 12\ \Omega + j16\ \Omega = 20\ \Omega\ \angle 53.13^\circ$

$I_\phi = \dfrac{V_\phi}{Z_\phi} = \dfrac{100\ \text{V}}{20\ \Omega} = 5\ \text{A}$

$P_T = 3I_\phi^2 R_\phi = 3(5\ \text{A})^2\ 12\ \Omega = \mathbf{900\ W}$

$Q_T = 3I_\phi^2 X_\phi = 3(5\ \text{A})^2\ 16\ \Omega = \mathbf{1200\ VAR(}\boldsymbol{L}\mathbf{)}$

$S_T = \sqrt{P_T^2 + Q_T^2} = \mathbf{1500\ VA}$

$F_p = \dfrac{P_T}{S_T} = \dfrac{900\ \text{W}}{1500\ \text{VA}} = \mathbf{0.6\ (lagging)}$

40. $P_T = \sqrt{3}\, E_L I_L \cos\theta$

$4800\ \text{W} = (1.732)(200\ \text{V})I_L\,(0.8)$

$I_L = 17.32\ \text{A}$

$I_\phi = \dfrac{I_L}{\sqrt{3}} = \dfrac{17.32\ \text{A}}{1.732} = 10\ \text{A}$

$\theta = \cos^{-1} 0.8 = 36.87^\circ$

$\mathbf{Z}_\phi = \dfrac{\mathbf{V}_\phi}{\mathbf{I}_\phi} = \dfrac{200\ \text{V}\ \angle 0^\circ}{10\ \text{A}\ \angle -36.87^\circ} = 20\ \Omega\ \angle 36.87^\circ = \mathbf{16\ \Omega + \boldsymbol{j}12\ \Omega}$

41. $P_T = \sqrt{3}\, E_L I_L \cos\theta$

$1200\ \text{W} = \sqrt{3}\,(208\ \text{V})I_L(0.6) \Rightarrow I_L = 5.55\ \text{A}$

$V_\phi = \dfrac{V_L}{\sqrt{3}} = \dfrac{208\ \text{V}}{1.732} = 120.1\ \text{V}$

$\theta = \cos^{-1} 0.6 = 53.13^\circ$ (leading)

$\mathbf{Z}_\phi = \dfrac{\mathbf{V}_\phi}{\mathbf{I}_\phi} = \dfrac{120.1\ \text{V}\ \angle 0^\circ}{5.55\ \text{A}\ \angle 53.13^\circ} = 21.64\ \Omega\ \angle -53.13^\circ = \underbrace{12.98\ \Omega}_{R} - j\underbrace{17.31\ \Omega}_{X_C}$

42. Δ: $\mathbf{Z}_\phi = 15\ \Omega + j20\ \Omega = 25\ \Omega\angle 53.13°$

$$I_\phi = \frac{V_\phi}{Z_\phi} = \frac{125\ \text{V}}{25\ \Omega} = 5\ \text{A}$$

$$P_T = 3I_\phi^2 R_\phi = 3(5\ \text{A})^2\ 15\ \Omega = \mathbf{1125\ W}$$

$$Q_T = 3I_\phi^2 X_\phi = 3(5\ \text{A})^2\ 20\ \Omega = \mathbf{1500\ VAR}(\boldsymbol{L})$$

Y: $V_\phi = V_L/\sqrt{3} = 125\ \text{V}/1.732 = \mathbf{72.17\ V}$

$\mathbf{Z}_\phi = 3\ \Omega - j4\ \Omega = 5\ \Omega\angle -53.13°$

$$I_\phi = \frac{V_\phi}{Z_\phi} = \frac{72.17\ \text{V}}{5\ \Omega} = \mathbf{14.43\ A}$$

$$P_T = 3I_\phi^2 R_\phi = 3(14.43\ \text{A})^2\ 3\ \Omega = \mathbf{1874.02\ W}$$

$$Q_T = 3I_\phi^2 X_\phi = 3(14.43\ \text{A})^2\ 4\ \Omega = \mathbf{2498.7\ VAR}$$

$P_T = 1125\ \text{W} + 1874.02\ \text{W} = \mathbf{2999.02\ W}$

$Q_T = 1500\ \text{VAR}(L) - 2498.7\ \text{VAR}(C) = \mathbf{998.7\ VAR}(\boldsymbol{C})$

$S_T = \sqrt{P_T^2 + Q_T^2} = \mathbf{3161\ VA}$

$$F_p = \frac{P_T}{S_T} = \frac{2999.02\ \text{W}}{3161\ \text{VA}} = \mathbf{0.949\ (leading)}$$

43. a. $E_\phi = \dfrac{16\ \text{kV}}{\sqrt{3}} = \mathbf{9{,}237.6\ V}$

b. $I_L = I_\phi = \mathbf{80\ A}$

c. $P_{\phi_L} = \dfrac{1200\ \text{kW}}{3} = 400\ \text{kW}$

$P_{4\Omega} = (80\ \text{A})^2 4\ \Omega = 25.6\ \text{kW}$

$P_T = 3P_\phi = 3(25.6\ \text{kW} + 400\ \text{kW}) = \mathbf{1276.8\ kW}$

d. $F_p = \dfrac{P_T}{S_T}$, $S_T = \sqrt{3}\ V_L I_L = \sqrt{3}\,(16\ \text{kV})(80\ \text{A}) = 2{,}217.025\ \text{kVA}$

$$F_p = \frac{1{,}276.8\ \text{kW}}{2{,}217.025\ \text{kVA}} = \mathbf{0.576\ lagging}$$

e. $\theta_L = \cos^{-1} 0.576 = 54.83°$ (lagging)

$$\mathbf{I}_{Aa} = \frac{\mathbf{E}_{AN}\angle 0°}{\underbrace{Z_T\angle 54.83°}_{\text{for entire load}}} \Rightarrow \underbrace{\mathbf{80A}}_{\text{given}}\ \angle \mathbf{-54.83°}$$

f. $\mathbf{V}_{an} = \mathbf{E}_{AN} - \mathbf{I}_{Aa}(4\ \Omega + j20\ \Omega)$

$= 9237.6\text{ V}\angle 0° - (80\text{ A}\angle -54.83°)(20.396\ \Omega\angle 78.69°)$

$= 9237.6\text{ V}\angle 0° - 1631.68\text{ V}\angle 23.86°$

$= 9237.6\text{ V} - (1492.22\text{ V} + j660\text{ V})$

$= 7745.38\text{ V} - j660\text{ V}$

$= \mathbf{7773.45\ V\ \angle{-4.87°}}$

g. $$\mathbf{Z}_\phi = \frac{\mathbf{V}_{an}}{\mathbf{I}_{Aa}} = \frac{7773.45\text{ V}\angle -4.87°}{80\text{ A}\angle -54.83°} = 97.168\ \Omega\angle 49.95°$$

$$= \underbrace{62.52\ \Omega}_{R} + j\underbrace{74.38\ \Omega}_{X_C}$$

h. F_p(entire system) = **0.576 (lagging)**
F_p(load) = **0.643 (lagging)**

i. $$\eta = \frac{P_o}{P_i} = \frac{P_i - P_{\text{lost}}}{P_i} = \frac{1276.8\text{ kW} - 3(25.6\text{ kW})}{1276.8\text{ kW}} = 0.9398 \Rightarrow \mathbf{93.98\%}$$

44. a. –

b. $$V_\phi = \frac{220\text{ V}}{\sqrt{3}} = 127.02\text{ V},\ \mathbf{Z}_\phi = 10\ \Omega - j10\ \Omega = 14.14\ \Omega\angle -45°$$

$$I_\phi = \frac{V_\phi}{Z_\phi} = \frac{127.02\text{ V}}{14.14\ \Omega} = 8.98\text{ A}$$

$$P_T = 3I_\phi^2 R_\phi = 3(8.98\text{ A})^2\ 10\ \Omega = \mathbf{2419.2\ W}$$

Each wattmeter: $$\frac{2419.2\text{ W}}{3} = \mathbf{806.4\ W}$$

45. b. $P_T = \mathbf{5899.64\ W}$, $P_{\text{meter}} = \mathbf{1966.55\ W}$

46. a. –

b. $P_T = P_\ell + P_h = 85\text{ W} + 200\text{ W} = \mathbf{285\ W}$

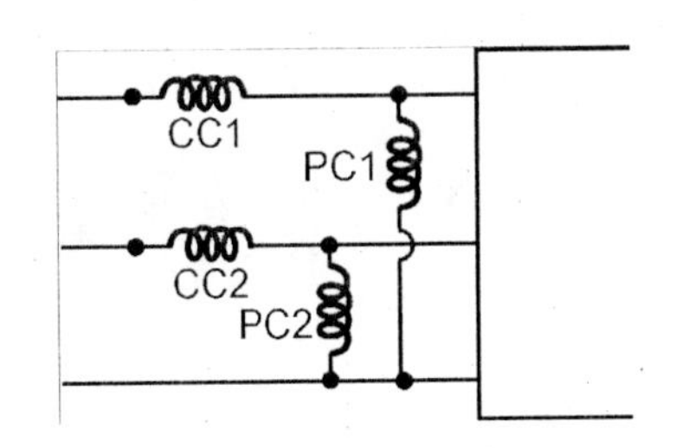

c. $$0.2 \Rightarrow \frac{P_\ell}{P_h} = 0.5$$

$$P_h = \frac{P_\ell}{0.5} = \frac{100\text{ W}}{0.5} = \mathbf{200\ W}$$

$P_T = P_h - P_\ell = 200\text{ W} - 100\text{ W} = \mathbf{100\ W}$

48. a. $\mathbf{I}_{ab} = \dfrac{\mathbf{E}_{AB}}{R\angle 0°} = \dfrac{208\text{ V}\angle 0°}{10\,\Omega\angle 0°} = \mathbf{20.8\text{ A}\angle 0°}$

$\mathbf{I}_{bc} = \dfrac{\mathbf{E}_{BC}}{R\angle 0°} = \dfrac{208\text{ V}\angle -120°}{10\,\Omega\angle 0°} = \mathbf{20.8\text{ A}\angle -120°}$

$\mathbf{I}_{ca} = \dfrac{\mathbf{E}_{CA}}{R\angle 0°} = \dfrac{208\text{ V}\angle 120°}{10\,\Omega\angle 0°} = \mathbf{20.8\text{ A}\angle 120°}$

b. $\mathbf{I}_{Aa} + \mathbf{I}_{ca} - \mathbf{I}_{ab} = 0$

$\mathbf{I}_{Aa} = \mathbf{I}_{ab} - \mathbf{I}_{ca}$
$= 20.8\text{ A}\angle 0° - 20.8\text{ A}\angle 120°$
$= 20.8\text{ A} - (-10.4\text{ A} + j18.01\text{ A})$
$= 31.2\text{ A} - j18.01\text{ A}$
$= \mathbf{36.02\text{ A}\angle -30°}$

$\mathbf{I}_{Bb} + \mathbf{I}_{ab} - \mathbf{I}_{bc} = 0$

$\mathbf{I}_{Bb} = \mathbf{I}_{bc} - \mathbf{I}_{ab}$
$= 20.8\text{ A}\angle -120° - 20.8\text{ A}\angle 0°$
$= (-10.4\text{ A} - j18.01\text{ A}) - 20.8\text{ A}$
$= -31.2\text{ A} - j18.01\text{ A}$
$= \mathbf{36.02\text{ A}\angle -150°}$

$\mathbf{I}_{Cc} + \mathbf{I}_{bc} - \mathbf{I}_{ca} = 0$

$\mathbf{I}_{Cc} = \mathbf{I}_{ca} - \mathbf{I}_{bc}$
$= 20.8\text{ A}\angle 120° - 20.8\text{ A}\angle -120°$
$= (-10.4\text{ A} + j18.01\text{ A}) - (-10.4\text{ A} - j18.01\text{ A})$
$= -10.4\text{ A} + 10.4\text{ A} + j18.01\text{ A} + j18.01\text{ A}$
$= \mathbf{32.02\text{ A}\angle 90°}$

c. $P_1 = V_{ac}I_{Aa}\cos_{\mathbf{I}_{Aa}}^{\mathbf{V}_{ca}}$, $\mathbf{V}_{ac} = V_{ca}\angle\theta - 180° = 208\text{ V}\angle 120° - 180°$
$= 208\text{ V}\angle -60°$
$\mathbf{I}_{Aa} = 36.02\text{ A}\angle -30°$
$= (208\text{ V})(36.02\text{ A})\cos 30°$
$= \mathbf{6488.4\text{ W}}$

$P_2 = V_{bc}I_{Bb}\cos_{\mathbf{I}_{Bb}}^{\mathbf{V}_{bc}}$, $\mathbf{V}_{bc} = 208\text{ V}\angle -120°$, $\mathbf{I}_{Bb} = 36.02\text{ A}\angle -150°$
$= (208\text{ V})(36.02\text{ A})\cos 30°$
$= \mathbf{6488.4\text{ W}}$

d. $P_T = P_1 + P_2 = 6488.4\text{ W} + 6488.4\text{ W}$
$= \mathbf{12{,}976.8\text{ W}}$

49. a. $V_\phi = E_\phi = \dfrac{E_L}{\sqrt{3}} = \mathbf{120.09\ V}$

b. $I_{an} = \dfrac{V_{an}}{Z_{an}} = \dfrac{120.09\text{ V}}{14.142\,\Omega} = \mathbf{8.49\ A}$

$I_{bn} = \dfrac{V_{bn}}{Z_{bn}} = \dfrac{120.09\text{ V}}{16.971\,\Omega} = \mathbf{7.08\ A}$

$I_{cn} = \dfrac{V_{cn}}{Z_{cn}} = \dfrac{120.09\text{ V}}{2.828\,\Omega} = \mathbf{42.47\ A}$

c. $P_T = I_{an}^2\,10\,\Omega + I_{bn}^2\,12\,\Omega + I_{cn}^2\,2\,\Omega$

$= (8.49\text{ A})^2\,10\,\Omega + (7.08\text{ A})^2\,12\,\Omega + (42.47\text{ A})^2\,2\,\Omega$

$= 720.80\text{ W} + 601.52\text{ W} + 3.61\text{ kW}$

$= \mathbf{4.93\ kW}$

$Q_T = P_T = \mathbf{4.93\ kVAR}(\boldsymbol{L})$

$S_T = \sqrt{P_T^2 + Q_T^2} = \mathbf{6.97\ kVA}$

$F_p = \dfrac{P_T}{S_T} = \mathbf{0.707\ (lagging)}$

d. $\mathbf{E}_{an} = 120.09\text{ V}\angle{-30^\circ}$, $\mathbf{E}_{bn} = 120.09\text{ V}\angle{-150^\circ}$, $\mathbf{E}_{cn} = 120.09\text{ V}\angle 90^\circ$

$\mathbf{I}_{an} = \dfrac{\mathbf{E}_{an}}{\mathbf{Z}_{an}} = \dfrac{120.09\text{ V}\angle{-30^\circ}}{10\,\Omega + j10\,\Omega} = \dfrac{120.09\text{ V}\angle{-30^\circ}}{14.142\,\Omega\angle 45^\circ} = \mathbf{8.49\ A\ \angle{-75^\circ}}$

$\mathbf{I}_{bn} = \dfrac{\mathbf{E}_{bn}}{\mathbf{Z}_{bn}} = \dfrac{120.09\text{ V}\angle{-150^\circ}}{12\,\Omega + j12\,\Omega} = \dfrac{120.09\text{ V}\angle{-150^\circ}}{16.971\,\Omega\angle 45^\circ} = \mathbf{7.08\ A\ \angle{-195^\circ}}$

$\mathbf{I}_{cn} = \dfrac{\mathbf{E}_{cn}}{\mathbf{Z}_{cn}} = \dfrac{120.09\text{ V}\angle 90^\circ}{2\,\Omega + j2\,\Omega} = \dfrac{120.09\text{ V}\angle 90^\circ}{2.828\,\Omega\angle 45^\circ} = \mathbf{42.47\ A\ \angle 45^\circ}$

e. $\mathbf{I}_N = \mathbf{I}_{an} + \mathbf{I}_{bn} + \mathbf{I}_{cn}$

$= 8.49\text{ A}\angle{-75^\circ} + 7.08\text{ A}\angle{-195^\circ} + 42.47\text{ A}\angle 45^\circ$

$= (2.02\text{ A} - j8.20\text{ A}) + (-6.84\text{ A} + j1.83\text{ A}) + (30.30\text{ A} + j30.30\text{ A})$

$= 25.66\text{ A} - j23.93\text{ A}$

$= \mathbf{35.09\ A\ \angle{-43.00^\circ}}$

50. $\mathbf{Z}_1 = 12\,\Omega - j16\,\Omega = 20\,\Omega\angle{-53.13^\circ}$, $\mathbf{Z}_2 = 3\,\Omega + j4\,\Omega = 5\,\Omega\angle 53.13^\circ$
$\mathbf{Z}_3 = 20\,\Omega\angle 0^\circ$

$\mathbf{E}_{AB} = 200\text{ V}\angle 0^\circ$, $\mathbf{E}_{BC} = 200\text{ V}\angle{-120^\circ}$, $\mathbf{E}_{CA} = 200\text{ V}\angle 120^\circ$

$\mathbf{Z}_\Delta = \mathbf{Z}_1\mathbf{Z}_2 + \mathbf{Z}_1\mathbf{Z}_3 + \mathbf{Z}_2\mathbf{Z}_3$

$= (20\,\Omega\angle{-53.13^\circ})(5\,\Omega\angle 53.13^\circ) + (20\,\Omega\angle{-53.13^\circ})(20\,\Omega\angle 0^\circ)$
$+ (5\,\Omega\angle 53.13^\circ)(20\,\Omega\angle 0^\circ)$

$= 100\,\Omega\angle 0^\circ + 400\,\Omega\angle{-53.13^\circ} + 100\,\Omega\angle 53.13^\circ$

$= 100\,\Omega + (240\,\Omega - j320\,\Omega) + (60\,\Omega + j80\,\Omega)$

$= 400\,\Omega - j240\,\Omega$

$= 466.48\,\Omega\angle{-30.96^\circ}$

$$\mathbf{I}_{an} = \frac{\mathbf{E}_{AB}\mathbf{Z}_3 - \mathbf{E}_{CA}\mathbf{Z}_2}{\mathbf{Z}_\Delta} = \frac{(200\text{ V}\angle 0°)(20\ \Omega\angle 0°) - (200\text{ V}\angle 120°)(5\ \Omega\angle 53.13°)}{\mathbf{Z}_\Delta}$$

$$= \frac{4000\text{ A}\angle 0° - 1000\text{ A}\angle 173.13°}{466.48\angle -30.96°} = \mathbf{10.71\ A\ \angle 29.59°}$$

$$\mathbf{I}_{bn} = \frac{\mathbf{E}_{BC}\mathbf{Z}_1 - \mathbf{E}_{AB}\mathbf{Z}_3}{\mathbf{Z}_\Delta} = \frac{(200\text{ V}\angle -120°)(20\ \Omega\angle -53.13°) - (200\text{ V}\angle 0°)(20\ \Omega\angle 0°)}{\mathbf{Z}_\Delta}$$

$$= \frac{4000\text{ A}\angle -173.13° - 4000\text{ A}\angle 0°}{466.48\angle -30.96°} = \mathbf{17.12\ A\ \angle -145.61°}$$

$$\mathbf{I}_{cn} = \frac{\mathbf{E}_{CA}\mathbf{Z}_2 - \mathbf{E}_{BC}\mathbf{Z}_1}{\mathbf{Z}_\Delta} = \frac{(200\text{ V}\angle 120°)(5\ \Omega\angle 53.13°) - (200\text{ V}\angle -120°)(20\ \Omega\angle -53.13°)}{\mathbf{Z}_\Delta}$$

$$= \frac{1000\text{ A}\angle 173.13° - 4000\text{ A}\angle -173.13°}{466.48\angle -30.96°} = \mathbf{6.51\ A\ \angle 42.32°}$$

$$P_T = I_{an}^2\, 12\ \Omega + I_{bn}^2\, 4\ \Omega + I_{cn}^2\, 20\ \Omega$$

$$= 1376.45\text{ W} + 1172.38\text{ W} + 847.60\text{ W} = \mathbf{3396.43\ W}$$

$$Q_T = I_{an}^2\, 16\ \Omega + I_{bn}^2\, 3\ \Omega = 1835.27\text{ VAR}(C) + 879.28\text{ VAR}(L) = \mathbf{955.99\ VAR(\mathit{C})}$$

$$S_T = \sqrt{P_T^2 + Q_T^2} = \mathbf{3508.40\ VA}$$

$$F_p = \frac{P_T}{S_T} = \frac{3396.43\text{ W}}{3508.40\text{ VA}} = \mathbf{0.968\ (leading)}$$

Chapter 24

1. a. **positive-going** b. $V_b = 2$ **V** c. $t_p =$ **0.2 ms**

   d. Amplitude = 8 V − 2 V = **6 V**

   e. $\% \text{ tilt} = \dfrac{V_1 - V_2}{V} \times 100\%$

   $$V = \frac{8\text{ V} + 7.5\text{ V}}{2} = 7.75\text{ V}$$

   $$\% \text{ tilt} = \frac{8\text{ V} - 7.5\text{ V}}{7.75\text{ V}} \times 100\% = \mathbf{6.5\%}$$

2. a. **negative-going** b. **+7 mV** c. **3 μs**

   d. **−8 mV** (from base line level)

   e. $V = \dfrac{-8\text{ mV} - 7\text{ mV}}{2} = \dfrac{-15\text{ mV}}{2} = -7.5\text{ mV}$

   $$\% \text{ Tilt} = \frac{V_1 - V_2}{V} \times 100\% = \frac{-8\text{ mV} - (-7\text{ mV})}{-7.5\text{ mV}} \times 100\%$$

   $$= \frac{-1\text{ mV}}{-7.5\text{ mV}} \times 100\% = \mathbf{13.3\%}$$

   f. $T = 15\ \mu\text{s} - 7\ \mu\text{s} = 8\ \mu\text{s}$

   $$\text{prf} = \frac{1}{T} = \frac{1}{8\ \mu\text{s}} = \mathbf{125\ kHz}$$

   g. $\text{Duty cycle} = \dfrac{t_p}{T} \times 100\% = \dfrac{3\ \mu\text{s}}{8\ \mu\text{s}} \times 100\% = \mathbf{37.5\%}$

3. a. **positive-going** b. $V_b =$ **10 mV** c. $t_p = \left(\dfrac{8}{10}\right) 4\text{ ms} = \mathbf{3.2\ ms}$

   d. Amplitude = (30 − 10)mV = **20 mV**

   e. $\% \text{ tilt} = \dfrac{V_1 - V_2}{V} \times 100\%$

   $$V = \frac{30\text{ mV} + 28\text{ mV}}{2} = 29\text{ mV}$$

   $$\% \text{ tilt} = \frac{30\text{ mV} - 28\text{ mV}}{29\text{ mV}} \times 100\% \cong \mathbf{6.9\%}$$

4. $t_r \cong$ (0.2 div.)(2 ms/div.) = **0.4 ms**
$t_f \cong$ (0.4 div.)(2 ms/div.) = **0.8 ms**

5. $\text{tilt} = \dfrac{V_1 - V_2}{V} = 0.1$ with $V = \dfrac{V_1 + V_2}{2}$

Substituting V into top equation,

$$\frac{V_1 - V_2}{\dfrac{V_1 + V_2}{2}} = 0.1 \text{ leading to } V_2 = \frac{0.95\,V_1}{1.05} \text{ or } V_2 = 0.905(15\text{ mV}) = 13.58\text{ mV}$$

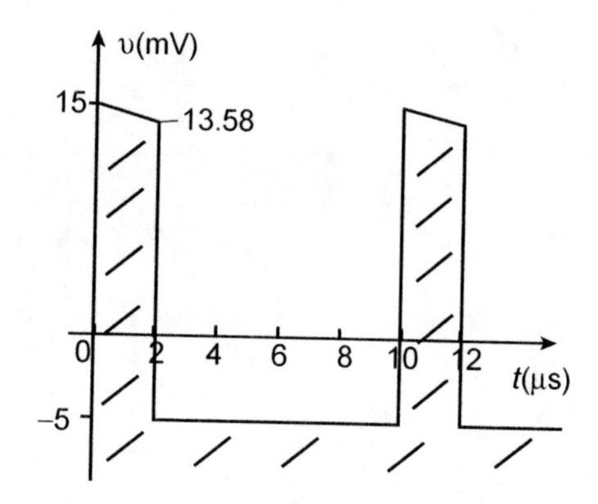

6. a. t_r = 80% of straight line segment
= 0.8(2 μs) = **1.6 μs**

b. t_f = 80% of 4 μs interval
= 0.8(4 μs) = **3.2 μs**

c. At 50% level (10 mV)
t_p = (8 – 1)μs = **7 μs**

d. $\text{prf} = \dfrac{1}{T} = \dfrac{1}{20\,\mu\text{s}}$ = **50 kHz**

7. a. T = (4.8 – 2.4)div.[50 μs/div.] = **120 μs**

b. $f = \dfrac{1}{T} = \dfrac{1}{120\,\mu\text{s}}$ = 8.33 kHz

c. Maximum Amplitude: (2.2 div.)(0.2 V/div.) = 0.44 V = **440 mV**
Minimum Amplitude: (0.4 div.)(0.2 V/div.) = 0.08 V = **80 mV**

8. T = (3.6 – 2.0)ms = 1.6 ms

$\text{prf} = \dfrac{1}{T} = \dfrac{1}{1.6\text{ ms}}$ = **625 Hz**

$\text{Duty cycle} = \dfrac{t_p}{T} \times 100\% = \dfrac{0.2\text{ ms}}{1.6\text{ ms}} \times 100\%$ = **12.5%**

9. $T = (15 - 7)\mu s = 8\ \mu s$

$$\text{prf} = \frac{1}{T} = \frac{1}{8\ \mu s} = \mathbf{125\ kHz}$$

$$\text{Duty cycle} = \frac{t_p}{T} \times 100\% = \frac{(20 - 15)\mu s}{8\ \mu s} \times 100\% = \frac{5}{8} \times 100\% = \mathbf{62.5\%}$$

10. $T = (3.6\ \text{div.})(2\ \text{ms/div.}) = 7.2\ \text{ms}$

$$\text{prf} = \frac{1}{T} = \frac{1}{7.2\ \text{ms}} = \mathbf{138.89\ Hz}$$

$$\text{Duty cycle} = \frac{t_p}{T} \times 100\% = \frac{1.6\ \text{div.}}{3.6\ \text{div.}} \times 100\% = \mathbf{44.4\%}$$

11. a. $T = (9 - 1)\mu s = \mathbf{8\ \mu s}$ b. $t_p = (3 - 1)\mu s = \mathbf{2\ \mu s}$

c. $$\text{prf} = \frac{1}{T} = \frac{1}{8\ \mu s} = \mathbf{125\ kHz}$$

d. $V_{av} = (\text{Duty cycle})(\text{Peak value}) + (1 - \text{Duty cycle})(V_b)$

$$\text{Duty cycle} = \frac{t_p}{T} \times 100\% = \frac{2\ \mu s}{8\ \mu s} \times 100\% = 25\%$$

$$V_{av} = (0.25)(6\ \text{mV}) + (1 - 0.25)(-2\ \text{mV})$$
$$= 1.5\ \text{mV} - 1.5\ \text{mV} = \mathbf{0\ V}$$

or

$$V_{av} = \frac{(2\ \mu s)(6\ \text{mV}) - (2\ \mu s)(6\ \text{mV})}{8\ \mu s} = \mathbf{0\ V}$$

e. $$V_{eff} = \sqrt{\frac{(36 \times 10^{-6})(2\ \mu s) + (4 \times 10^{-6})(6\ \mu s)}{8\ \mu s}} = \mathbf{3.46\ mV}$$

12. Eq. 24.5 cannot be applied due to tilt in the waveform.
(Method of Section 13.6)
Between 2 and 3.6 ms

$$V_{av} = \frac{(3.4\ \text{ms} - 2\ \text{ms})(2\ \text{V}) + (3.6\ \text{ms} - 3.4\ \text{ms})(7.5\ \text{V}) + \frac{1}{2}(3.6\ \text{ms} - 3.4\ \text{ms})(0.5\ \text{V})}{3.6\ \text{ms} - 2\ \text{ms}}$$

$$= \frac{(1.4\ \text{ms})(2\ \text{V}) + (0.2\ \text{ms})(7.5\ \text{V}) + \frac{1}{2}(0.2\ \text{ms})(0.5\ \text{V})}{1.6\ \text{ms}}$$

$$= \frac{2.8\ \text{V} + 1.5\ \text{V} + 0.05\ \text{V}}{1.6} = \mathbf{2.719\ V}$$

13. Ignoring tilt and using 20 mV level to define t_p

t_p = (2.8 div. – 1.2 div.)(2 ms/div.) = 3.2 ms

T = (at 10 mV level) = (4.6 div. – 1 div.)(2 ms/div.) = 7.2 ms

$$\text{Duty cycle} = \frac{t_p}{T} \times 100\% = \frac{3.2\text{ ms}}{7.2\text{ ms}} \times 100\% = 44.4\%$$

V_{av} = (Duty cycle)(peak value) + (1 – Duty cycle)(V_b)
= (0.444)(30 mV) + (1 – 0.444)(10 mV)
= 13.320 mV + 5.560 mV
= **18.88 mV**

14. V_{av} = (Duty cycle)(Peak value) + (1 – Duty cycle)(V_b)

$$\text{Duty cycle} = \frac{t_p}{T} \text{ (decimal form)}$$

$$= \frac{(8-1)\mu\text{s}}{20\ \mu\text{s}} = 0.35$$

V_{av} = (0.35)(20 mV) + (1 – 0.35)(0)
= 7 mV + 0
= **7 mV**

15. Using methods of Section 13.8:

$A_1 = b_1h_1$ = [(0.2 div.)(50 μs/div.)][(2 div.)(0.2 V/div.)] = 4 μsV
$A_2 = b_2h_2$ = [(0.2 div.)(50 μs/div.)][(2.2 div.)(0.2 V/div.)] = 4.4 μsV
$A_3 = b_3h_3$ = [(0.2 div.)(50 μs/div.)][(1.4 div.)(0.2 V/div.)] = 2.8 μsV
$A_4 = b_4h_4$ = [(0.2 div.)(50 μs/div.)][(1 div.)(0.2 V/div.)] = 2.0 μsV
$A_5 = b_5h_5$ = [(0.2 div.)(50 μs/div.)][(0.4 div.)(0.2 V/div.)] = 0.8 μsV

$$V_{av} = \frac{(4 + 4.4 + 2.8 + 2.0 + 0.8)\mu\text{sV}}{120\ \mu\text{s}} = \mathbf{117\ mV}$$

16. Using the defined polarity of Fig. 24.57 for υ_C, V_i = –5 V, V_f = +20 V and $\tau = RC$ = (10 kΩ)(0.02 μF) = 0.2 ms

a. $\upsilon_C = V_i + (V_f - V_i)(1 - e^{-t/\tau})$
$= -5 + (20 - (-5))(1 - e^{-t/0.2\text{ ms}})$
$= -5 + 25(1 - e^{-t/0.2\text{ ms}})$
$= -5 + 25 - 25e^{-t/0.2\text{ ms}}$
υ_C = **20 V – 25 V$e^{-t/0.2\text{ ms}}$**

b.

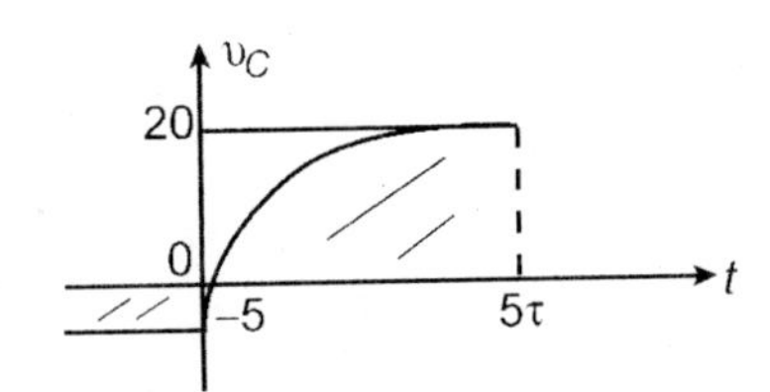

c. $I_i = 0$

$$i_C = \frac{E - \upsilon_C}{R} = \frac{20\text{ V} - \left[20\text{ V} - 25\text{ V}e^{-t/0.2\text{ ms}}\right]}{10\text{ k}\Omega} = \mathbf{2.5\text{ mA}e^{-t/0.2\text{ ms}}}$$

d.

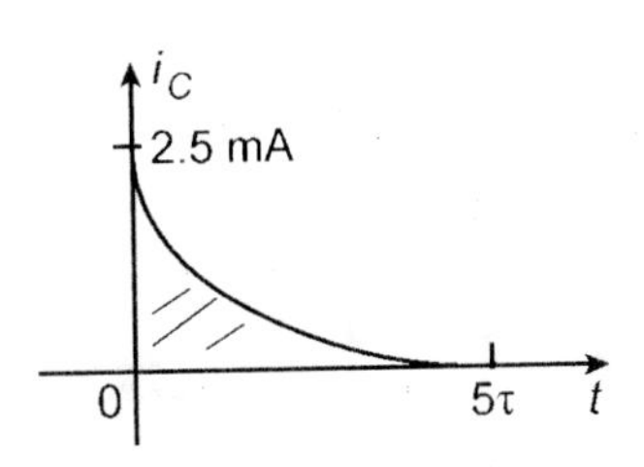

17. $\upsilon_C = V_i + (V_f - V_i)(1 - e^{-t/RC})$
$= 8 + (4 - 8)(1 - e^{-t/20\text{ ms}})$
$= 8 - 4(1 - e^{-t/20\text{ ms}})$
$= 8 - 4 + 4e^{-t/20\text{ ms}}$
$= 4 + 4e^{-t/20\text{ ms}}$
$\upsilon_C = \mathbf{4\text{ V}(1 + e^{-t/20\text{ ms}})}$

$\tau = RC = (2\text{ k}\Omega)(10\ \mu\text{F})$
$= 20\text{ ms}$

18. $V_i = 10\text{ V},\ V_f = 2\text{ V},\ \tau = RC = (1\text{ k}\Omega)(1000\ \mu\text{F}) = 1\text{ s}$
$\upsilon_C = V_i + (V_f - V_i)(1 - e^{-t/\tau})$
$= 10\text{ V} + (2\text{ V} - 10\text{ V})(1 - e^{-t})$
$= 10 - 8(1 - e^{-t})$
$= 10 - 8 + 8e^{-t}$
$\upsilon_C = \mathbf{2\text{ V} + 8\text{ V}e^{-t}}$

19. $V_i = 10\text{ V},\ I_i = 0\text{ A}$

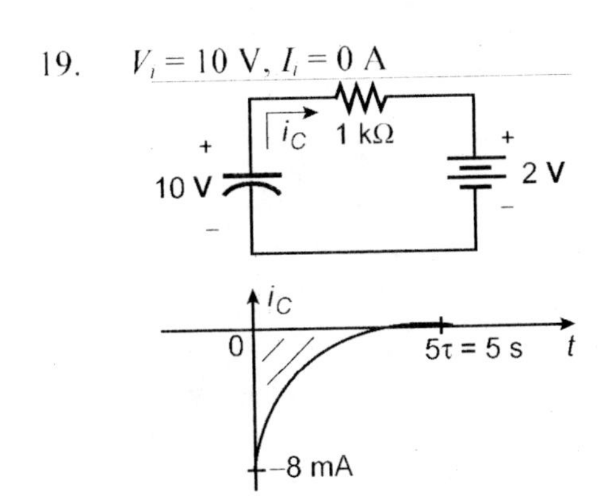

Using the defined direction of i_C

$$i_C = \frac{-(10\text{ V} - 2\text{ V})}{1\text{ k}\Omega}e^{-t/\tau}$$

$$\tau = RC = (1\text{ k}\Omega)(1000\ \mu\text{F}) = 1\text{ s}$$

$$i_C = -\frac{8\text{ V}}{1\text{ k}\Omega}e^{-t}$$

and $i_C = \mathbf{-8\text{mA}e^{-t}}$

20. $\tau = RC = (5\text{ k}\Omega)(0.04\ \mu\text{F}) = 0.2\text{ ms}$ (throughout)

$\upsilon_C = E(1 - e^{-t/\tau}) = \mathbf{20\ V(1 - e^{-t/0.2\ ms})}$

(Starting at $t = 0$ for each plot)

a. $T = \dfrac{1}{f} = \dfrac{1}{500\text{ Hz}} = 2\text{ ms}$

$\dfrac{T}{2} = 1\text{ ms}$

$5\tau = 1\text{ ms} = \dfrac{T}{2}$

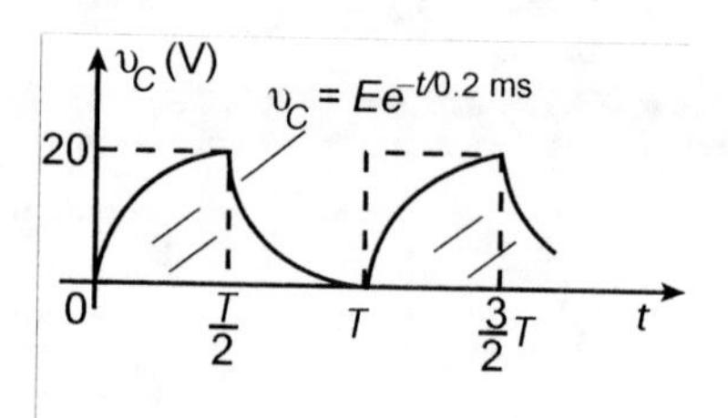

b. $T = \dfrac{1}{f} = \dfrac{1}{100\text{ Hz}} = 10\text{ ms}$

$\dfrac{T}{2} = 5\text{ ms}$

$5\tau = 1\text{ ms} = \dfrac{1}{5}\left(\dfrac{T}{2}\right)$

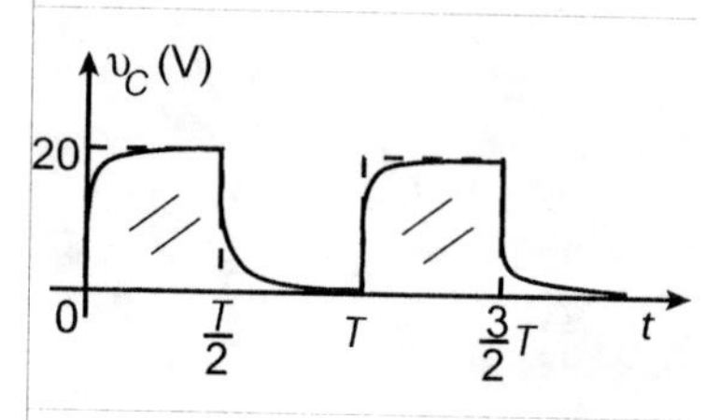

c. $T = \dfrac{1}{f} = \dfrac{1}{5\text{ Hz}} = 0.2\text{ ms}$

$\dfrac{T}{2} = 0.1\text{ ms}$

$5\tau = 1\text{ ms} = 10\left(\dfrac{T}{2}\right)$

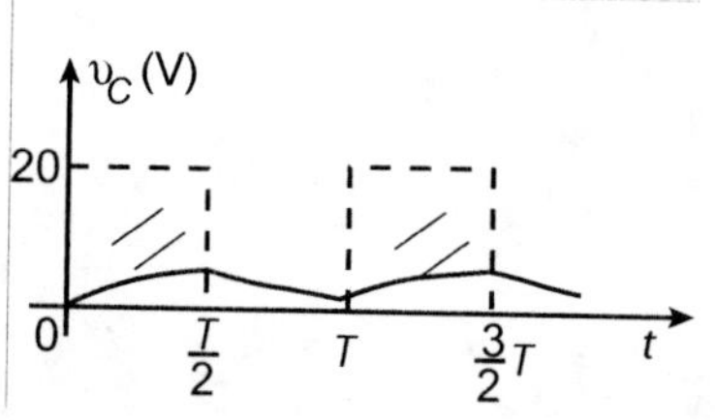

21. The mathematical expression for i_C is the same for each frequency!

$\tau = RC = (5\text{ k}\Omega)(0.04\ \mu\text{F}) = 0.2\text{ ms}$

and $i_C = \dfrac{20\text{ V}}{5\text{ k}\Omega}e^{-t/0.2\text{ ms}} = \mathbf{4\ mAe^{-t/0.2\ ms}}$

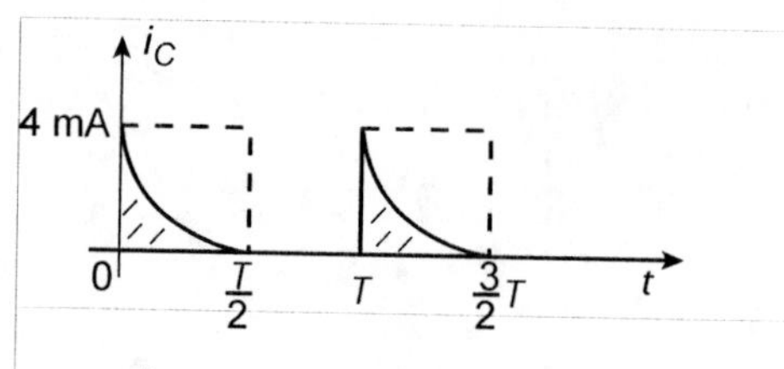

a. $T = \dfrac{1}{500\text{ Hz}} = 2\text{ ms}, \dfrac{T}{2} = 1\text{ ms}$

$5\tau = 5(0.2\text{ ms}) = 1\text{ ms} = \dfrac{T}{2}$

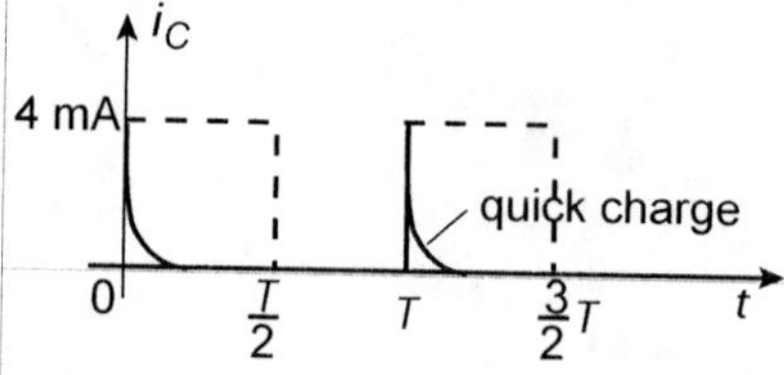

b. $T = \dfrac{1}{100\text{ Hz}} = 10\text{ ms}, \dfrac{T}{2} = 5\text{ ms}$

$5\tau = 1\text{ ms} = \dfrac{1}{5}\left(\dfrac{T}{2}\right)$

c. $T = \dfrac{1}{5000\text{ Hz}} = 0.2\text{ ms}, \dfrac{T}{2} = 0.1\text{ ms}$

$5\tau = 1\text{ ms} = 10\left(\dfrac{T}{2}\right)$

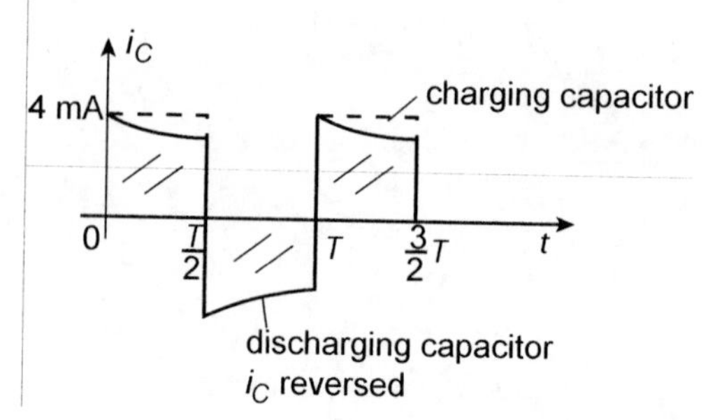

22. $\tau = 0.2$ ms as above

$$T = \frac{1}{500\text{ Hz}} = 2\text{ ms}$$

$$5\tau = 1\text{ ms} = \frac{T}{2}$$

$$0 \to \frac{T}{2}: \; \upsilon_C = 20\text{ V}(1 - e^{-t/0.2\text{ ms}})$$

$$\frac{T}{2} \to T: \; V_i = 20\text{ V}, V_f = -20\text{ V}$$

$$\begin{aligned}\upsilon_C &= V_i + (V_f - V_i)(1 - e^{-t/\tau})\\ &= 20 + (-20 - 20)(1 - e^{-t/0.2\text{ ms}})\\ &= 20 - 40(1 - e^{-t/0.2\text{ ms}})\\ &= 20 - 40 + 40e^{-t/0.2\text{ ms}}\end{aligned}$$

$$\boldsymbol{\upsilon_C = -20\text{ V} + 40\text{ V}e^{-t/0.2\text{ ms}}}$$

$$T \to \frac{3}{2}T: \; V_i = -20\text{ V}, V_f = +20\text{ V}$$

$$\begin{aligned}\upsilon_C &= V_i + (V_f - V_i)(1 - e^{-t/\tau})\\ &= -20 + (20 - (-20))(1 - e^{-t/\tau})\\ &= -20 + 40(1 - e^{-t/\tau})\\ &= -20 + 40 - 40e^{-t/\tau}\end{aligned}$$

$$\boldsymbol{\upsilon_C = 20\text{ V} - 40\text{ V}e^{-t/0.2\text{ ms}}}$$

23. $\upsilon_C = V_i + (V_f - V_i)(1 - e^{-t/RC})$

$$V_i = 20\text{ V}, V_f = 20\text{ V}$$

$$\upsilon_C = 20 + (20 - 20)(1 - e^{-t/RC})$$

$$= \mathbf{20\text{ V}} \text{ (for } 0 \to \frac{T}{2})$$

For $\frac{T}{2} \to T$, $\upsilon_i = 0$ V and $\upsilon_C = \mathbf{20\text{ V}e^{-t/\tau}}$

$\tau = RC = 0.2$ ms

with $\frac{T}{2} = 1$ ms and $5\tau = \frac{T}{2}$

For $T \to \frac{3}{2}T$, $\upsilon_i = 20$ V

$$\upsilon_C = \mathbf{20\text{ V}(1 - e^{-t/\tau})}$$

For $\frac{3}{2}T \to 2T$, $\upsilon_i = 0$ V

$$\upsilon_C = \mathbf{20\text{ V}e^{-t/\tau}}$$

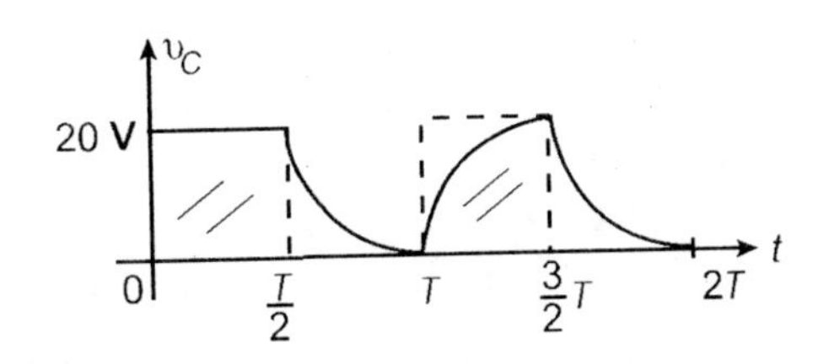

24. $\tau = RC = 0.2 \text{ ms}$

$5\tau = 1 \text{ ms} = \dfrac{T}{2}$

$V_i = -10 \text{ V},\ V_f = +20 \text{ V}$

$0 \to \dfrac{T}{2}$:

$$\upsilon_C = V_i + (V_f - V_i)(1 - e^{-t/\tau})$$
$$= -10 + (20 - (-10))(1 - e^{-t/\tau})$$
$$= -10 + 30(1 - e^{-t/\tau})$$
$$= -10 + 30 - 30e^{-t/\tau}$$
$$\upsilon_C = \mathbf{+20\ V - 30\ V}e^{-t/0.2\text{ ms}}$$

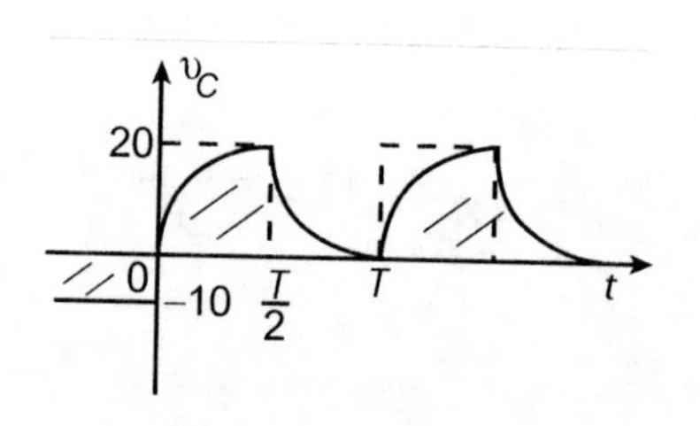

$\dfrac{T}{2} \to T$: $\quad V_i = 20 \text{ V},\ V_f = 0 \text{ V}$

$$\upsilon_C = \mathbf{20\ V}e^{-t/0.2\text{ ms}}$$

25. $\mathbf{Z}_p$: $X_C = \dfrac{1}{2\pi fC} = \dfrac{1}{2\pi(10\text{ kHz})(3\text{ pF})} = 5.31\text{ M}\Omega$

$$\mathbf{Z}_p = \frac{(9\text{ M}\Omega\angle 0°)(5.31\text{ M}\Omega\angle -90°)}{9\text{ M}\Omega - j5.31\text{ M}\Omega} = 4.573\text{ M}\Omega \angle -59.5°$$

$\mathbf{Z}_s$: $C_T = 18\text{ pF} + 9\text{ pF} = 27\text{ pF}$

$$X_C = \frac{1}{2\pi fC_T} = \frac{1}{2\pi(10\text{ kHz})(27\text{ pF})} = 0.589\text{ M}\Omega$$

$$\mathbf{Z}_s = \frac{(1\text{ M}\Omega\angle 0°)(0.589\text{ M}\Omega\angle -90°)}{1\text{ M}\Omega - j0.589\text{ M}\Omega} = 0.507\text{ M}\Omega \angle -59.5°$$

$$\mathbf{V}_{\text{scope}} = \frac{\mathbf{Z}_s\mathbf{V}_i}{\mathbf{Z}_s + \mathbf{Z}_p} = \frac{(0.507\text{ M}\Omega\angle -59.5°)(100\text{ V}\angle 0°)}{(0.257\text{ M}\Omega - j0.437\text{ M}\Omega) + (2.324\text{ M}\Omega - j3.939\text{ M}\Omega)}$$

$$= \frac{50.7\times 10^6\text{ V}\angle -59.5°}{5.07\times 10^6\angle -59.5°} = \mathbf{10\ V\ \angle 0°} = \frac{1}{10}(100\text{ V}\angle 0°)$$

$$\theta_{\mathbf{Z}_s} = \theta_{\mathbf{Z}_p} = \mathbf{-59.5°}$$

26. $\mathbf{Z}_p$: $X_C = \dfrac{1}{\omega C} = \dfrac{1}{(10^5\text{ rad/s})(3\text{ pF})} = 3.333\text{ M}\Omega$

$$\mathbf{Z}_p = \frac{(9\text{ M}\Omega\angle 0°)(3.333\text{ M}\Omega)}{9\text{ M}\Omega - j3.333\text{ M}\Omega} = 3.126\text{ M}\Omega \angle -69.68°$$

$\mathbf{Z}_s$: $X_C = \dfrac{1}{\omega C} = \dfrac{1}{(10^5\text{ rad/s})(27\text{ pF})} = 0.370\text{ M}\Omega$

$$\mathbf{Z}_s = \frac{(1\text{ M}\Omega\angle 0°)(0.370\text{ M}\Omega\angle -90°)}{1\text{ M}\Omega - j0.370\text{ M}\Omega} = 0.347\text{ M}\Omega \angle -69.68°$$

✓ $\theta_{\mathbf{Z}_p} = \theta_{\mathbf{Z}_s}$

$$\mathbf{V}_{\text{scope}} = \frac{\mathbf{Z}_s\mathbf{V}_i}{\mathbf{Z}_s + \mathbf{Z}_p} = \frac{(0.347\ \text{M}\Omega\ \angle -69.68^\circ)(100\ \text{V}\ \angle 0^\circ)}{(0.121\ \text{M}\Omega - j0.325\ \text{M}\Omega) + (1.086\ \text{M}\Omega - j2.931\ \text{M}\Omega)}$$

$$= \frac{34.70 \times 10^6\ \text{V}\ \angle -69.68^\circ}{3.470 \times 10^6\ \angle -69.68^\circ}$$

$$\cong \mathbf{10\ V\ \angle 0^\circ} = \frac{1}{10}(100\ \text{V}\ \angle 0^\circ)$$

Chapter 25

1. I: a. no b. no c. yes d. no e. yes

   II: a. yes b. yes c. yes d. yes e. no

   III: a. yes b. yes c. no d. yes e. yes

   IV: a. no b. no c. yes d. yes e. yes

2. b. $$i = \frac{2I_m}{\pi}\left(1 + \frac{2}{3}\cos(2\omega t - 90°) - \frac{2}{15}\cos(4\omega t - 90°) + \frac{2}{35}\cos(6\omega t - 90°) + \ldots\right)$$

   c. $$\frac{2I_m}{\pi} - \frac{I_m}{2} = \frac{2I_m}{\pi}\left[1 - \frac{\pi}{4}\right]$$

   $$i = \frac{2I_m}{\pi}\left[1 - \frac{\pi}{4} + \frac{2}{3}\cos(2\omega t - 90°) - \frac{2}{15}\cos(4\omega t - 90°) + \frac{2}{35}\cos(6\omega t - 90°) + \ldots\right]$$

   d.

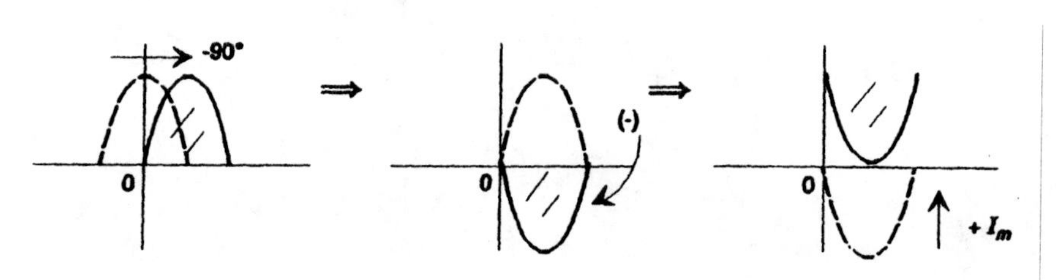

$$i = \frac{-2I_m}{\pi}\left[1 - \frac{\pi}{4} + \frac{2}{3}\cos(2\omega t - 90°) - \frac{2}{15}\cos(4\omega t - 90°) + \frac{2}{35}\cos(6\omega t - 90°) + \ldots\right]$$

3. a. $\upsilon = -4 + 2\sin\alpha$

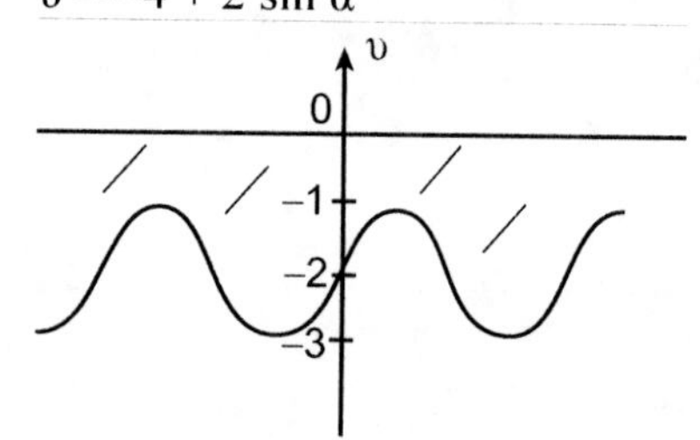

   b. $\upsilon = (\sin\alpha)^2$

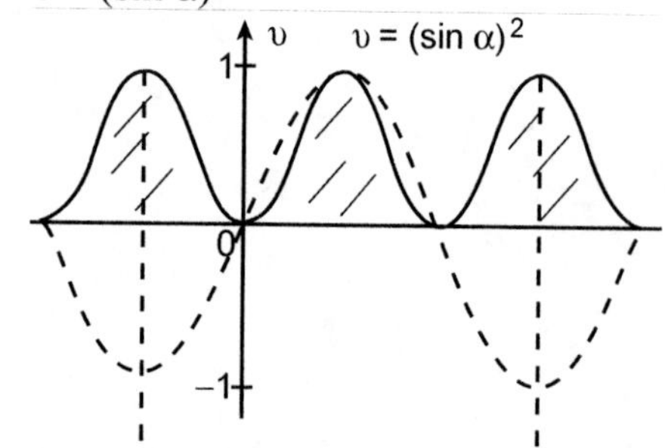

c. $i = 2 - 2\cos\alpha$

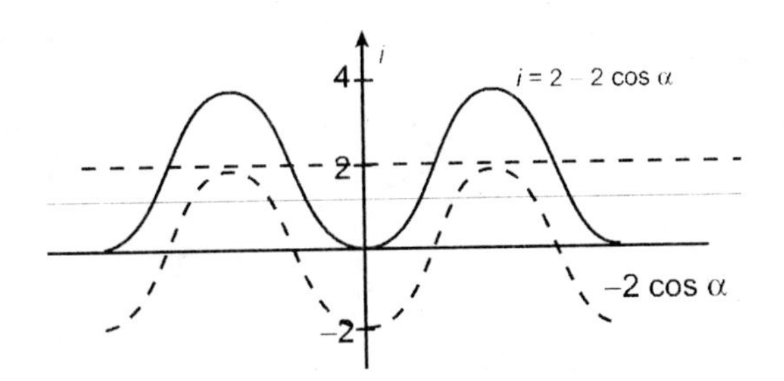

4. a.

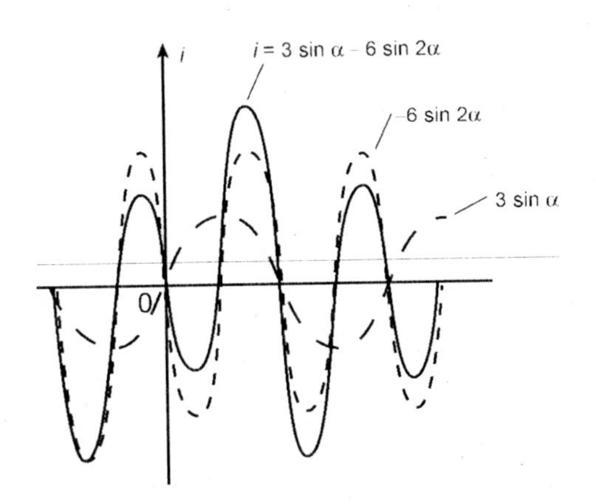

b.

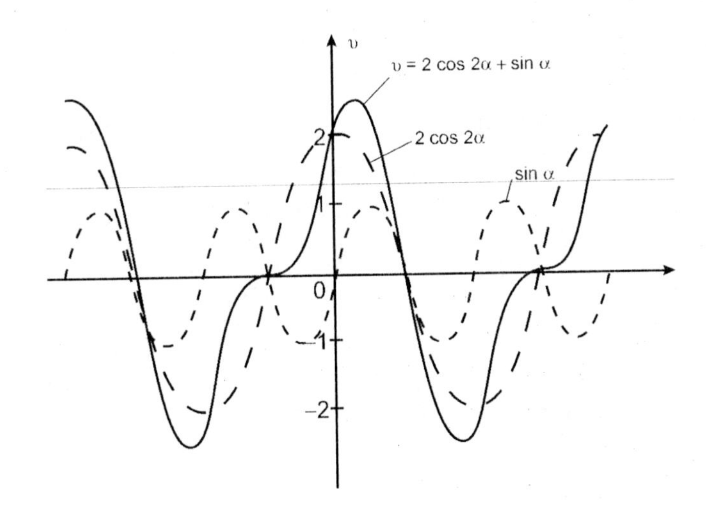

5. a.

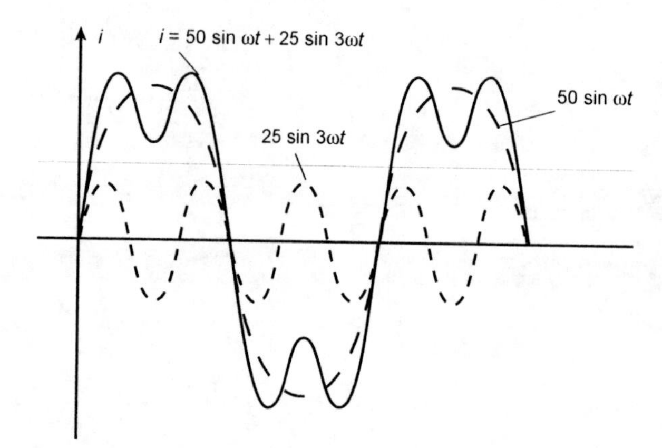

i
i = 50 sin ωt + 25 sin 3ωt
50 sin ωt
25 sin 3ωt

b.

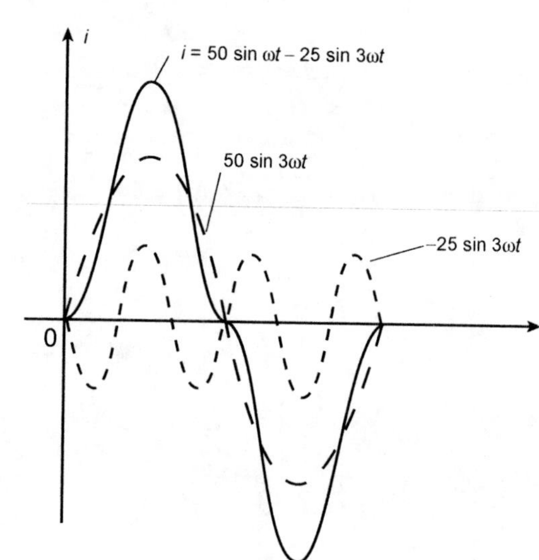

i
i = 50 sin ωt − 25 sin 3ωt
50 sin 3ωt
−25 sin 3ωt
0

c.

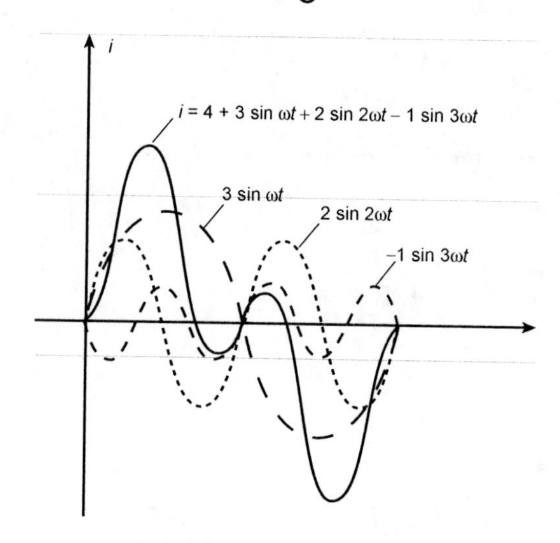

i
i = 4 + 3 sin ωt + 2 sin 2ωt − 1 sin 3ωt
3 sin ωt
2 sin 2ωt
−1 sin 3ωt

6. a. $V_{av} = \mathbf{100\ V}$

$$V_{eff} = \sqrt{(100\text{ V})^2 + \frac{(50\text{ V})^2 + (25\text{ V})^2}{2}} = \mathbf{107.53\ V}$$

b. $I_{av} = \mathbf{3\ A}$

$$I_{eff} = \sqrt{(3\text{ A})^2 + \frac{(2\text{ A})^2 + (0.8\text{ A})^2}{2}} = \mathbf{3.36\ A}$$

7. a. $$V_{eff} = \sqrt{\frac{(20\text{ V})^2 + (15\text{ V})^2 + (10\text{ V})^2}{2}} = \mathbf{19.04\ V}$$

b. $$I_{eff} = \sqrt{\frac{(6\text{ A})^2 + (2\text{ A})^2 + (1\text{ A})^2}{2}} = \mathbf{4.53\ A}$$

8. $$P_T = V_0 I_0 + V_1 I_1 \cos\theta_1 + \ldots + V_n I_n \cos\theta_n$$
$$= (100\text{ V})(3\text{ A}) + \frac{(50\text{ V})(2\text{ A})}{2}\cos 53^\circ + \frac{(25\text{ V})(0.8\text{ A})}{2}\cos 70^\circ$$
$$= 300 + (50)(0.6018) + (10)(0.3420)$$
$$= \mathbf{333.52\ W}$$

9. $$P = \frac{(20\text{ V})(6\text{ A})}{2}\cos 20^\circ + \frac{(15\text{ V})(2\text{ A})}{2}\cos 30^\circ + \frac{(10\text{ V})(1\text{ A})}{2}\cos 60^\circ$$
$$= 60(0.9397) + 15(0.866) + 5(0.5)$$
$$= \mathbf{71.87\ W}$$

10. a. DC: $E = 18\text{ V}, I_o = \frac{E}{R} = \frac{18\text{ V}}{12\ \Omega} = 1.5\text{ A}$

$\omega = 400$ rad/s: $X_L = \omega L = (400\text{ rad/s})(0.02\text{ H}) = 8\ \Omega$

$$\mathbf{Z} = 12\ \Omega + j8\ \Omega = 14.42\ \Omega\ \angle 33.69^\circ$$

$$\mathbf{I} = \frac{\mathbf{E}}{\mathbf{Z}} = \frac{30\text{ V}/\sqrt{2}\ \angle 0^\circ}{14.42\ \Omega\ \angle 33.69^\circ} = \frac{2.08\text{ A}}{\sqrt{2}}\ \angle{-33.69^\circ}$$

$$i = 1.5 + \sqrt{2}\left(\frac{2.08}{\sqrt{2}}\right)\sin(400t - 33.69^\circ)$$

$$i = \mathbf{1.5 + 2.08\sin(400t - 33.69^\circ)}$$

b. $$I_{eff} = \sqrt{(1.5\text{ A})^2 + \frac{(2.08\text{ A})^2}{2}} = \mathbf{2.10\ A}$$

c. DC: $\upsilon_R = E = 18$ V, $\mathbf{V}_R = \left(\frac{2.08\text{ A}}{\sqrt{2}}\angle -33.69°\right)(12\,\Omega\,\angle 0°)$

$$= \frac{24.96\text{ V}}{\sqrt{2}}\angle -33.69°$$

$$\upsilon_R = 18 + \sqrt{2}\left(\frac{24.96}{\sqrt{2}}\right)\sin(400t - 33.69°)$$

$$\boldsymbol{\upsilon_R = 18 + 24.96\sin(400t - 33.69°)}$$

d. $V_{R_{\text{eff}}} = \sqrt{(18\text{ V})^2 + \frac{(24.96\text{ V})^2}{2}} = \mathbf{25.21\text{ V}}$

e. DC: $V_L = 0$ V

$\omega = 400$ rad/s: $\mathbf{V}_L = \left(\frac{2.08\text{ A}}{\sqrt{2}}\angle -33.69°\right)(8\,\Omega\,\angle 90°)$

$$= \frac{16.64\text{ A}}{\sqrt{2}}\angle 56.31°$$

$$\upsilon_L = \mathbf{0 + 16.64\sin(400t + 56.31°)}$$

f. $V_{L_{\text{eff}}} = \sqrt{0^2 + \frac{(16.64\text{ V})^2}{2}} = \mathbf{11.77\text{ V}}$

g. $P = I_{\text{eff}}^2 R = (2.101\text{ A})^2\,12\,\Omega = \mathbf{52.97\text{ W}}$

11. a. DC: $I_{\text{DC}} = \frac{24\text{ V}}{12\,\Omega} = 2$ A

$\omega = 400$ rad/s:

$$\mathbf{Z} = 12\,\Omega + j(400\text{ rad/s})(0.02\text{ H}) = 12\,\Omega + j8\,\Omega = 14.422\,\Omega\,\angle 33.69°$$

$$\mathbf{I} = \frac{30\text{ V}\,\angle 0°}{14.422\,\Omega\,\angle 33.69°} = 2.08\text{ A}\,\angle -33.69°\text{ (peak values)}$$

$\omega = 800$ rad/s:

$$\mathbf{Z} = 12\,\Omega + j(800\text{ rad/s})(0.02\text{ H}) = 12\,\Omega + j16\,\Omega = 20\,\Omega\,\angle 53.13°$$

$$\mathbf{I} = \frac{10\text{ V}\,\angle 0°}{20\,\Omega\,\angle 53.13°} = 0.5\text{ A}\,\angle -53.13°\text{ (peak values)}$$

$$\boldsymbol{i = 2 + 2.08\sin(400t - 33.69°) + 0.5\sin(800t - 53.13°)}$$

b. $I_{\text{eff}} = \sqrt{(2\text{ A})^2 + \frac{(2.08\text{ A})^2 + (0.5\text{ A}^2)}{2}} = \mathbf{2.51\text{ A}}$

c. $\upsilon_R = iR = i(12\,\Omega)$

$$= \mathbf{24 + 24.96\sin(400t - 33.69°) + 6\sin(800t - 53.13°)}$$

d. $V_{\text{eff}} = \sqrt{(24\text{ V})^2 + \frac{(24.96\text{ V})^2 + (6\text{ V})^2}{2}} = \mathbf{30.09\text{ V}}$

e. DC: $V_L = 0$ V

$\omega = 400$ rad/s: $\mathbf{V}_L = (2.08\text{ A}\ \angle{-33.69°})(8\ \Omega\ \angle 90°)$
$= 16.64\text{ V}\ \angle 56.31°$

$\omega = 800$ rad/s: $\mathbf{V}_L = (0.5\text{ A}\ \angle{-53.13°})(16\ \Omega\ \angle 90°)$
$= 8\text{ V}\ \angle 36.87°$

$\upsilon_L = \mathbf{0 + 16.64\ sin(400}\boldsymbol{t}\mathbf{ + 56.31°) + 8\ sin(800}\boldsymbol{t}\mathbf{ + 36.87°)}$

f. $$V_{\text{eff}} = \sqrt{(0)^2 + \frac{(16.64\text{ V})^2 + (8\text{ V})^2}{2}} = \mathbf{13.06\ V}$$

g. $P_T = I_{\text{eff}}^2 R = (2.508\text{ A})^2\ 12\ \Omega = \mathbf{75.48\ W}$

12. a. DC: $I = -\dfrac{60\text{ V}}{12\ \Omega} = -5$ A

$\omega = 300$ rad/s: $X_L = \omega L = (300\text{ rad/s})(0.02\text{ H}) = 6\ \Omega$

$\mathbf{Z} = 12\ \Omega + j16\ \Omega = 13.42\ \Omega\ \angle 26.57°$

$\mathbf{E} = (0.707)(20\text{ V})\ \angle 0° = 14.14\text{ V}\ \angle 0°$

$$\mathbf{I} = \frac{\mathbf{E}}{\mathbf{Z}} = \frac{14.14\text{ V}\ \angle 0°}{13.42\ \Omega\ \angle 26.57°} = 1.054\text{ A}\ \angle{-26.57°}$$

$\omega = 600$ rad/s: $X_L = \omega L = (600\text{ rad/s})(0.02\text{ H}) = 12\ \Omega$

$\mathbf{Z} = 12\ \Omega + j12\ \Omega = 16.97\ \Omega\ \angle 45°$

$\mathbf{E} = -(0.707)(10\text{ V})\ \angle 0° = -7.07\text{ V}\ \angle 0°$

$$\mathbf{I} = \frac{\mathbf{E}}{\mathbf{Z}} = -\frac{7.07\text{ V}\ \angle 0°}{16.97\ \Omega\ \angle 45°} = -0.417\text{ A}\ \angle{-45°}$$

$i = -5 + (1.414)(1.054)\sin(300t - 26.57°) - (1.414)(0.417)\sin(600t - 45°)$

$i = \mathbf{-5 + 1.49\ sin(300}\boldsymbol{t}\mathbf{ - 26.57°) - 0.59\ sin(600}\boldsymbol{t}\mathbf{ - 45°)}$

b. $$I_{\text{eff}} = \sqrt{(10\text{ A})^2 + \frac{(1.49\text{ A})^2 + (0.59\text{ A})^2}{2}} = \mathbf{10.06\ A}$$

c. DC: $V = IR = (-5\text{ A})(12\ \Omega) = -60$ V

$\omega = 300$ rad/s: $\mathbf{V}_R = (1.054\text{ A}\ \angle{-26.57°})(12\ \Omega\ \angle 0°)$
$= 12.648\text{ V}\ \angle{-26.57°}$

$\omega = 600$ rad/s: $\mathbf{V}_R = (-0.417\text{ A}\ \angle{-45°})(12\ \Omega\ \angle 0°)$
$= -5\text{ V}\ \angle{-45°}$

$\upsilon_R = -60 + (1.414)(12.648)\sin(300t - 26.57°) - (1.414)(5)\sin(600t - 45°)$

$\upsilon_R = \mathbf{-60 + 17.88\ sin(300}\boldsymbol{t}\mathbf{ - 26.57°) - 7.07\ sin(600}\boldsymbol{t}\mathbf{ - 45°)}$

d. $$V_{R_{\text{eff}}} = \sqrt{(60\text{ V})^2 + \frac{(17.88\text{ V})^2 + (7.07\text{ V})^2}{2}} = \mathbf{61.52\ V}$$

e. DC: $V_L = 0$ V

$\omega = 300$ rad/s: $\mathbf{V}_L = (1.054\text{ A} \angle -26.57°)(6\ \Omega \angle 90°) = 6.324\text{ V} \angle 63.43°$

$\omega = 600$ rad/s: $\mathbf{V}_L = (-0.417\text{ A} \angle -45°)(6\ \Omega \angle 90°) = -2.502\text{ V} \angle 45°$

$\upsilon_L = 0 + (1.414)(6.324)\sin(300t + 63.43°) - (1.414)(2.502)\sin(600t + 45°)$

$\boldsymbol{\upsilon_L = 8.94 \sin(300t + 63.43°) - 3.54 \sin(600t + 45°)}$

f. $V_{L_{\text{eff}}} = \sqrt{\dfrac{(8.94\text{ V})^2 + (3.54\text{ V})^2}{2}} = \mathbf{6.8\ V}$

g. $P = I_{\text{eff}}^2 R = (10.06\text{ A})^2\ 12\ \Omega = \mathbf{1214.44\ W}$

13. a. DC: $I = \mathbf{0\ A}$

$\omega = 400$ rad/s: $X_C = \dfrac{1}{\omega C} = \dfrac{1}{(400\text{ rad/s})(125\ \mu\text{F})} = 20\ \Omega$

$\mathbf{Z} = 15\ \Omega - j20\ \Omega = 25\ \Omega \angle -53.13°$

$\mathbf{E} = (0.707)(30\text{ V}) \angle 0° = 21.21\text{ V} \angle 0°$

$\mathbf{I} = \dfrac{\mathbf{E}}{\mathbf{Z}} = \dfrac{21.21\text{ V} \angle 0°}{25\ \Omega \angle -53.13°} = 0.848\text{ A} \angle 53.13°$

$i = 0 + (1.414)(0.848)\sin(400t + 53.13°)$

$\boldsymbol{i = 1.2 \sin(400t + 53.13°)}$

b. $I_{\text{eff}} = \sqrt{\dfrac{(1.2\text{ A})^2}{2}} = \mathbf{0.85\ A}$ as above

c. DC: $V_R = 0$ V

$\omega = 400$ rad/s: $\mathbf{V}_R = (0.848\text{ A} \angle 53.13°)(15\ \Omega \angle 0°) = 12.72\text{ V} \angle 53.13°$

$\upsilon_R = 0 + (1.414)(12.72)\sin(400t + 53.13°)$

$\boldsymbol{\upsilon_R = 18 \sin(400t + 53.13°)}$

d. $V_{R_{\text{eff}}} = \sqrt{\dfrac{(18\text{ V})^2}{2}} = \mathbf{12.73\ V}$

e. DC: $V_C = 18$ V

$\omega = 400$ rad/s: $\mathbf{V}_C = (0.848\text{ A} \angle 53.13°)(20\ \Omega \angle -90°)$

$= 16.96\text{ V} \angle -36.87°$

$\upsilon_C = 18 + (1.414)(16.96)\sin(400t - 36.87°)$

$\boldsymbol{\upsilon_C = 18 + 23.98 \sin(400t - 36.87°)}$

f. $V_{C_{\text{eff}}} = \sqrt{(18\text{ V})^2 + \dfrac{(23.98\text{ V})^2}{2}} = \mathbf{24.73\ V}$

g. $P = I_{\text{eff}}^2 R = (0.848\text{ A})^2\ 15\ \Omega = \mathbf{10.79\ W}$

14. a. $e = \frac{200}{\pi} + \frac{400}{3\pi} \cos 2\omega t - \frac{400}{15\pi} \cos 4\omega t$

$= 63.69 + 42.46 \sin(2\omega t + 90°) - 8.49 \sin(4\omega t + 90°)$

$\omega = 377$ rad/s:

$e = 63.69 + 42.46 \sin(754t + 90°) - 8.49 \sin(1508t + 90°)$

DC: $X_L = 0 \therefore V_L = 0$ V

$\omega = 754$ rad/s: $X_C = \frac{1}{\omega C} = \frac{1}{(754 \text{ rad/s})(1\,\mu\text{F})} = 1330\ \Omega$

$X_L = \omega L = (754 \text{ rad/s})(0.1 \text{ H}) = 75.4\ \Omega$

$\mathbf{Z}' = (1\ \text{k}\Omega \angle 0°) \parallel 75.4\ \Omega \angle 90° = 75.19\ \Omega \angle 85.69°$

$\mathbf{E} = (0.707)(42.46 \text{ V}) \angle 90° = 30.02 \text{ V} \angle 90°$

$$\mathbf{V}_o = \frac{\mathbf{Z}'(\mathbf{E})}{\mathbf{Z}' + \mathbf{Z}_C} = \frac{(75.19\,\Omega \angle 85.69°)(30.02 \text{ V} \angle 90°)}{75.19\,\Omega \angle 85.69° + 1330\,\Omega \angle -90°} = 1.799 \text{ V} \angle -94.57°$$

$\omega = 1508$ rad/s: $X_C = \frac{1}{\omega C} = \frac{1}{(1508 \text{ rad/s})(1\,\mu\text{F})} = 6631.13\ \Omega$

$X_L = \omega L = (1508 \text{ rad/s})(0.1 \text{ H}) = 150.8\ \Omega$

$\mathbf{Z}' = (1\ \text{k}\Omega \angle 0°) \parallel 150.8\ \Omega \angle 90° = 149.12\ \Omega \angle 81.42°$

$\mathbf{E} = (0.707)(8.49 \text{ V}) \angle 90° = 6 \text{ V} \angle 90°$

$$\mathbf{V}_o = \frac{\mathbf{Z}'(\mathbf{E})}{\mathbf{Z}' + \mathbf{Z}_C} = \frac{(149.12\,\Omega \angle 81.42°)(6 \text{ V} \angle 90°)}{149.12\,\Omega \angle 81.42° + 6631.13\,\Omega \angle -90°}$$

$= 1.73 \text{ V} \angle -101.1°$

$\upsilon_o = 0 + 1.414(1.799)\sin(754t - 94.57°) - 1.414(1.73)\sin(1508t - 101.1°)$

$\upsilon_o =$ $\mathbf{2.54 \sin(754t - 94.57°) - 2.45 \sin(1508t - 101.1°)}$

b. $V_{o_{\text{eff}}} = \sqrt{\frac{(2.54 \text{ V})^2 + (2.45 \text{ V})^2}{2}} = \mathbf{2.50\ V}$

c. $P = \frac{(V_{\text{eff}})^2}{\text{R}} = \frac{(2.50 \text{ V})^2}{1\,\text{k}\Omega} = \mathbf{6.25\ mW}$

15. $i = 0.318I_m + 0.500\,I_m \sin \omega t - 0.212I_m \cos 2\omega t - 0.0424I_m \cos 4\omega t + \ldots\ (I_m = 10 \text{ mA})$

$i = 3.18 \times 10^{-3} + 5 \times 10^{-3} \sin \omega t - 2.12 \times 10^{-3} \sin(2\omega t + 90°)$
$- 0.424 \times 10^{-3} \sin(4\omega t + 90°) + \ldots$

$i \cong 3.18 \times 10^{-3} + 5 \times 10^{-3} \sin \omega t - 2.12 \times 10^{-3} \sin(2\omega t + 90°)$

DC: $I_o = 0$ A, $V_o = 0$ V

$\omega = 377$ rad/s; $X_L = \omega L = (377 \text{ rad/s})(1.2 \text{ mH}) = 0.452\ \Omega$

$X_C = \frac{1}{\omega C} = \frac{1}{(377 \text{ rad/s})(200\,\mu\text{F})} = 13.26\ \Omega$

$\mathbf{Z}' = 200\ \Omega - j13.26\ \Omega = 200.44\ \Omega \angle -3.79°$

$\mathbf{I} = (0.707)(5 \times 10^{-3})\text{A} \angle 0° = 3.54 \text{ mA} \angle 0°$

$$\mathbf{I}_o = \frac{\mathbf{Z}_L \mathbf{I}}{\mathbf{Z}_L + \mathbf{Z}'} = \frac{(0.452\,\Omega \angle 90°)(3.54 \text{ mA} \angle 0°)}{j0.452\,\Omega + 200\,\Omega - j13.26\,\Omega} = 7.98\,\mu\text{A} \angle 93.66°$$

$\mathbf{V}_o = (7.98\ \mu\text{A}\ \angle 93.66°)(200\ \Omega\ \angle 0°) = 1.596\ \text{mV}\ \angle 93.66°$

$\omega = 754$ rad/s: $X_L = \omega L = (754\ \text{rad/s})(1.2\ \text{mH}) = 0.905\ \Omega$

$$X_C = \frac{1}{\omega C} = \frac{1}{(754\ \text{rad/s})(200\ \mu\text{F})} = 6.63\ \Omega$$

$$\mathbf{Z}' = 200\ \Omega - j6.63\ \Omega = 200.11\ \Omega\ \angle -1.9°$$

$$\mathbf{I} = (0.707)(2.12\ \text{mA})\ \angle 90° = 1.5\ \text{mA}\ \angle 90°$$

$$\mathbf{I}_o = \frac{\mathbf{Z}_L\mathbf{I}}{\mathbf{Z}_L + \mathbf{Z}'} = \frac{(0.905\ \Omega\ \angle 90°)(1.5\ \text{mA}\ \angle 90°)}{j0.905\ \Omega + 200\ \Omega - j6.63\ \Omega} = 6.8\ \mu\text{A}\ \angle 181.64°$$

$\mathbf{V}_o = (6.8\ \mu\text{A}\ \angle 181.64°)(200\ \Omega\ \angle 0°) = 1.36\ \text{mA}\ \angle 181.64°$

$\upsilon_o = 0 + (1.414)(1.596 \times 10^{-3})\sin(377t + 93.66°)$

$\qquad - (1.414)(1.360 \times 10^{-3})\sin(754t + 181.64°)$

$\upsilon_o = \mathbf{2.26 \times 10^{-3} \sin(377t + 93.66°) + 1.92 \times 10^{-3} \sin(754t + 1.64°)}$

16. a. $60 + 70 \sin \omega t + 20 \sin(2\omega t + 90°) + 10 \sin(3\omega t + 60°)$

$+20 + 30 \sin \omega t - 20 \sin(2\omega t + 90°) + 5 \sin(3\omega t + 90°)$

DC: $60 + 20 = 80$

ω: $70 + 30 = 100 \Rightarrow 100 \sin \omega t$

2ω: 0

3ω: $10\ \angle 60° + 5\angle 90° = 5 + j8.66 + j5 = 5 + j13.66 = 14.55\ \angle 69.9°$

Sum = $\mathbf{80 + 100 \sin \omega t + 14.55 \sin(3\omega t + 69.9°)}$

b. $20 + 60 \sin \alpha + 10 \sin(2\alpha - 180°) + 5 \sin(3\alpha + 180°)$

$-5 + 10 \sin \alpha + \quad 0 \quad - 4 \sin(3\alpha - 30°)$

DC: $20 - 5 = 15$

α: $60 + 10 = 70 \Rightarrow 70 \sin \alpha$

2α: $10 \sin(2\alpha - 180°)$

3α: $5\ \angle 180° - 4\ \angle -30° = -5 - [3.46 - j2] = -8.46 + j2$

$= 8.69\ \angle 166.7°$

Sum = $\mathbf{15 + 70 \sin \alpha + 10 \sin(2\alpha - 180°) + 8.69 \sin(3\alpha + 166.7°)}$

17. $i_T = i_1 + i_2$

$= 10 + 30 \sin 20t \qquad - 0.5 \sin(40t + 90°)$

$+20 + 4 \sin(20t + 90°) + 0.5 \sin(40t + 30°)$

DC: $10\ \text{A} + 20\ \text{A} = 30\ \text{A}$

$\omega = 20$ rad/s: $30\ \text{A}\ \angle 0° + 4\ \text{A}\ \angle 90° = 30\ \text{A} + j4\ \text{A} = 30.27\ \text{A}\ \angle 7.59°$

$\omega = 40$ rad/s: $-0.5\ \text{A}\ \angle 90° + 0.5\ \text{A}\ \angle 30°$

$= -j0.5\ \text{A} + 0.433\ \text{A} + j0.25\ \text{A}$

$= 0.433\ \text{A} - j0.25\ \text{A} = 0.5\ \text{A}\ \angle -30°$

$i_T = \mathbf{30 + 30.27 \sin(20t + 7.59°) + 0.5 \sin(40t - 30°)}$

18. $e = \upsilon_1 + \upsilon_2$

$= \quad 20 - 200 \sin 600t + 100 \sin(1200t + 90°) + 75 \sin 1800t$

$\quad -10 + 150 \sin(600t + 30°) \quad + 0 \quad + 50 \sin(1800t + 60°)$

DC: 20 V – 10 V = 10 V

ω: 600 rad/s: $-200\text{ V} \angle 0° + 150\text{ V} \angle 30° = 102.66\text{ V} \angle 133.07°$

ω = 1200 rad/s: $100 \sin(1200t + 90°)$

ω = 1800 rad/s: $75\text{ V} \angle 0° + 50\text{ V} \angle 60° = 108.97\text{ V} \angle 23.41°$

e = **$10 + 102.66 \sin(600t + 133.07°) + 100 \sin(1200t + 90°) + 108.97 \sin(1800t + 23.41°)$**

TEST ITEM FILE

Contents

Chapter 1 Introduction

True/False

1) When a power of 10 moves from the numerator to the denominator, the sign of the exponent changes.

2) SI units of measurement have been adopted as a standard in most scientific and engineering literature.

3) The unit of mass in the SI system is the slug.

4) The prefix *milli* corresponds to 10^6 in power of 10 notation.

5) The notation μs is an abbreviation for microseconds.

6) The numerical value substituted into an equation must have the unit of measurement specified by the equation.

7) The MKS systems uses Meters, Kilograms, and Seconds as standards units.

8) The international Bureau of Weights and Standards is located in Washington, D.C.

9) The speed of light in a vacuum is approximately 299,792,458 m/s.

10) The SI prefix pico is equal to 10^{12}.

11) The precision of a reading can be determined by the number of significant digits present.

12) The relationship between magnetic and electrical effects is referred to as the Edison effect.

13) When using the power of ten, moving the decimal point to the right indicates a positive power of ten.

14) Scientific notation dictates that decimal points be placed directly after the first digit greater than one, but less than ten.

15) When using the powers of ten, 1×10^{-3} would be a larger number than 1×10^{-6}.

Multiple Choice

16) If the value 1.2×10^3 doubles, it becomes

A) 1.2×10^4 B) 1.2×10^6 C) 2.4×10^3 D) 2.4×10^6

17) One microfarad is equivalent to how many picofarads?

A) 10 B) 1,000 C) 100,000 D) 1,000,000

18) The value $(10^{16})^2$ is the same as

A) 10^8 B) 10^{18} C) 10^{32} D) 100^{32}

19) Expressed as a power of 10, the number 0.0006 is the same as

A) 6.0^{-4} B) 6.0×10^{-4} C) 6.0×10^{-3} D) 6.0×10^4

20) The value $(12 \times 10^3) + (1 \times 10^4)$ equals

A) 13×10^7 B) 22×10^3 C) 121×10^4 D) 13×10^{12}

21) The *joule* is the SI unit of measurement for

A) mass B) force C) temperature D) energy

22) The value $(10^n \div 10^m)$ is equivalent to

A) $1^n \div 1^m$ B) 10^{m+n} C) 10^{n-m} D) 10^{m-n}

23) The value $(16)^{1/2}$ is equivalent to

A) $1 \div 16^2$ B) 4 C) 8 D) 256

24) Express the number 0.00000000047 farads in picofarads.

A) 0.00047 picofarads B) 0.47 picofarads
C) 470 picofarads D) 470,000 picofarads

25) The expression $(10^n)(10^m)$ is equivalent to

A) 100^{nm} B) 10^{nm} C) 10^{n+m} D) $10^{n_2 m}$

26) The symbol Σ means

A) the sum of B) approximately equal
C) absolute magnitude D) therefore

27) What is *one minute* expressed in milliseconds?

A) 6.0×10^{-2} ms B) 6.0×10^{1} ms C) 6.0×10^{4} ms D) 6.0×10^{7} ms

28) The value 100 megawatts is equivalent to

A) 100×10^{3} watts B) 100×10^{6} watts
C) 100×10^{-3} watts D) 100×10^{-6} watts

29) The number $(8 \times 10^{3})^{1/3}$ is equivalent to

A) 26.67 B) 1.95×10^{-12} C) 20 D) 80

30) The number $(6 \times 10^{3})^{2}$ is equivalent to

A) 36×10^{6} B) 6×10^{3} C) 36×10^{5} D) 6×10^{5}

31) The computer language name BASIC is an acronym for

A) Beginning Analysis System for Integrated Circuits.
B) Beginning Analysis Systems Instruction Code.
C) Beginning Analysis System for Instruments and Control.
D) Beginning All-purpose Symbolic Instruction Code.

32) The computer program named SPICE is an acronym for

A) Simulation Program with Improved Command Efficiency.
B) Simulation Program with Integrated Circuit Emphasis.
C) Simulation Program for Instrumentation, Control, and Electronics.
D) Simulation Program Interfaced to Common Elements.

33) Calculate the following: (5/4)(8/15)(1/8) =

A) 1/12 B) 5/3 C) 3 D) 2/3

34) Calculate the following: 7.74 – 5.05 – 10.4 =

A) 7.71 B) -2.49 C) 2.39 D) 2.49

35) Evaluate the following expression: $((0.1)^{2} + (0.3)^{3})/(0.5) =$

A) 0.74 B) 7.4 C) 0.047 D) 0.074

36) Evaluate the following expression: $(15 \times 10^{-6})/(5 \times 10^{-9}) =$

A) 3×10^{-3} B) 3×10^{3} C) 0.03 D) 300

37) Express the number .0000003597 using the powers of ten.

A) 359×10^{-5} B) 3.59×10^{-7} C) 35.9×10^{-4} D) 359.7×10^{-6}

38) Express 462 na in scientific notation.

A) 4620×10^{-10} a B) 462×10^{-9} a
C) 46.2×10^{-8} a D) 4.62×10^{-7} a

39) Which of the following would express .000000000046 using engineering notation?

A) $.46 \times 10^{-3}$ B) 4.6×10^{-11} C) 46×10^{-12} D) 460×10^{-13}

40) Current flow between a filament and a positive plate in an evacuated tube is known as:

A) Voltage effect B) Edison effect C) Fleming effect D) Open lamp

41) Which of the following describes the numbering format that specifies all powers of ten must be in multiples of 3, and that the mantissa must be greater than or equal to 1, but less than 1000?

A) Composition notation B) Computer notation
C) Engineering notation D) Scientific notation

Short Answer

42) Convert 50 meters per second to feet per minute. Assume that there are 39.37 inches per meter.

43) Express the result of the following computation in scientific notation.

$$\frac{(4.0 \times 10^6)^{1/2}}{8000}$$

44) Why are powers of 10 used to express numeric values in scientific and engineering work?

45) If temperature increases at a rate of 0.01°K per second, how many *hours* must elapse to increase the temperature 100°K?

46) Express the result of the following computation in scientific notation. $\frac{(60 \times 10^4)(4 \times 10^{-7})}{20 \times 10^5}$

47) Express as a power of 10 the prefix *Giga.*

48) Convert 0.001 μF to picofarads.

49) Use the conversion factor 1 watt = 0.00134 horsepower to determine the amount of power (in watts) produced by a 10 hp riding lawn mower engine.

50) The CGS system uses what as standard units?

51) Convert 68 degrees Celsius to degrees Kelvin.

52) Convert 1.5 MHz to Kilohertz.

53) Determine the number of seconds in 6 months, assuming 30 days in each month.

Answer Key
Testname: CHAPTER 1

1) TRUE
2) TRUE
3) FALSE
4) FALSE
5) TRUE
6) TRUE
7) TRUE
8) FALSE
9) TRUE
10) FALSE
11) TRUE
12) FALSE
13) TRUE
14) TRUE
15) TRUE
16) C
17) D
18) C
19) B
20) B
21) D
22) C
23) B
24) C
25) C
26) A
27) C
28) B
29) C
30) A
31) D
32) B
33) A
34) C
35) D
36) B
37) B
38) D
39) C
40) B
41) C
42) 9,842.5 feet/minute
43) 2.5 × 10–1
44) To reduce the difficulty of writing very large or very small numbers.
45) 2.78 hours
46) 1.2×10^{-7}
47) 10^9
48) 1000 pf
49) 7463 W
50) centimeters, grams, seconds
51) 341 degrees Kelvin
52) 1500 KHz
53) 15552000 seconds

Chapter 2 Voltage and Current

True/False

1) The free proton is the positive charge carrier in a solid conductor.

2) Elements that are good conductors usually have only one electron in the valence ring.

3) One ampere of current is present when one coulomb of charge passes through a conductor in one second.

4) Copper has the highest conductivity of any metal used in electronics.

5) Current flowing from a battery is measured by placing an ammeter across the battery terminals.

6) An instrument designed to read current is called an voltmeter.

7) A dc generator is a source of AC voltage through the turning of the shaft of the device by external means.

8) A neutron is a particle having no electrical charge.

9) A terminal point between elements of a network is called a node.

10) A battery with an ampere-hour rating of 100 will theoretically provide a steady current of 100 mA for one hour and 50 mA for two hours.

11) The terminal voltage of a battery is proportional to the length of the discharge time at a particular drain current.

12) Under normal operating conditions a 1.5 volt battery is considered to be in good condition if the loaded terminal voltage drops by .2 volts.

13) A voltage source that cannot be recharged is called a primary cell.

Multiple Choice

14) What is the current (in amperes) if 10.0 coulombs of charge pass through a wire in 2.0 seconds?

A) 0.2 amperes B) 5 amperes C) 10 amperes D) 20 amperes

15) How much energy is expended in moving a 20 coulomb charge through a potential difference of 0.5 volts?

A) 0.025 joules B) 10 joules C) 20 joules D) 40 joules

16) A 9-volt battery with a 500 mAh capacity is connected to a circuit which draws 100 mA. How long will the battery be able to power this circuit?

A) 0.05 hours B) 0.2 hours C) 0.5 hours D) 5 hours

17) Which one of these statements is true?

A) The current capacity of a battery decreases with an increase in current demand.

B) The current capacity of a battery increases with an increase in current demand.

C) The current capacity of a battery increases at relatively high temperatures.

D) The current capacity of a battery increases at relatively low temperatures.

18) Which one of these statements describes an ideal voltage source?

A) It provides a proportional change in terminal voltage as the current demand changes.

B) It provides a proportional change in current as the terminal voltage changes.

C) It provides a fixed terminal voltage, even though the current demand may vary.

D) It provides a fixed current to a load, even though the terminal voltage may vary.

19) Which one of these statements is true?

A) An insulator allows no current to pass, regardless of the magnitude of the applied voltage.

B) Insulator materials typically have four electrons in the outermost valence ring.

C) An insulator has very few free electrons in the valence ring.

D) Air provides better insulation qualities than do solid materials such as glass or mica.

20) A semiconductor with a negative temperature coefficient

A) exhibits a large resistance change at temperatures below 0°C.

B) exhibits a negative resistance at temperatures below 0°C.

C) exhibits a decrease in resistance as temperature increases.

D) exhibits an increase in resistance as temperature increases.

21) Reverse connection of a voltmeter in a dc circuit will cause

A) a reading that is below scale or negative.

B) a reading equal to the reciprocal of the applied voltage.

C) the meter to display current in amperes.

D) the same reading as the normal connection, since meters are polarity insensitive.

22) If an electrical circuit can operate for 10.0 hours with a 2-Ah battery, what is the average current that the circuit demands?

A) 0.2 amperes B) 2 amperes C) 5 amperes D) 20 amperes

23) A common *primary* battery is the

A) lead-acid type. B) carbon-zinc type.

C) nickel-cadmium type. D) silicon-germanium type.

24) How many electrons are contained in the third shell of a copper atom? (Note that the copper atom contains 29 electrons.)

A) 1 B) 8 C) 18 D) 29

25) What potential (voltage) exists between two power supply terminals if 5 joules of energy are required to move 10 coulombs of charge between the two terminals?

A) 0.5 V B) 2 V C) 5 V D) 10 V

26) How long will a 50 Ah automobile battery power headlights that draw 20 amperes of current?

A) 0.4 hours B) 2.5 hours C) 50 hours D) 1000 hours

27) Germanium and silicon are examples of

A) conductors B) insulators

C) semiconductors D) battery electrolytes

28) In a neutral atom,

A) the combined mass of all electrons equals the mass of all protons.

B) electrons all reside in the first (innermost) shell.

C) the number of electrons is equal to the number of neutrons.

D) the number of electrons is equal to the number of protons.

29) Negative dc voltage sources can be created in the Windows version of PSpice by

A) double-clicking on the voltage source symbol.

B) selecting an ac (alternating current) source.

C) pressing the INVERT icon on the menu bar.

D) rotating the source using the menu Edit-Rotate selection.

30) What is the current in amperes if 0.71 coulomb of charge passes by a point every 8.9 ms?

A) 7.97 Amps B) 79.7 Amps C) 797.7 Amps D) 0.797 Amps

31) Determine the potential difference if it takes 300 mJ of energy to move a charge of 67 microcoulombs.

A) 4.47 KiloVolt B) 0.447 KiloVolt C) 44.7 KiloVolt D) 447.0 KiloVolt

32) What is the charge in coulombs if 8.5 mA of current flow through a surface every 90 ms?

A) 765 milliC B) 765 nanoC C) 765 microC D) 765 C

33) An electron that gains sufficient energy from the surrounding medium to leave its parent atom, is called a ________ electron.

A) Free B) Harmless C) Nuclear D) Shell

34) In a battery there is an accumulation of electrons on one terminal of the battery and an accumulation of positive ions on the other terminal. This will result in a(n) ________.

A) decrease in battery current B) increase in battery deterioration

C) potential difference D) weak battery

35) How must ammeters be connected in a circuit when used to measure current?

A) Directly across the component

B) Varies with the component being measured

C) Varies with circuit construction

D) In series with the component being measured

36) Four 12-volt batteries connected together by a conductor, positive terminal to negative terminal will result in which of the following voltage?

A) 3 volts B) 6 volts C) 12 volts D) 48 volts

37) If 40 joules of energy are required to move 25 coulombs of charge, what would the voltage be?

A) .6 volts B) 1.6 volts C) 16 volts D) 1000 volts

38) How many joules would be required to create a voltage of 25 volts if 80 coulombs of charge were transferred?

A) 3.2 B) 32 C) 200 D) 2000

Short Answer

39) An electrical circuit consists of a battery and a single load. Draw a sketch to show how to connect a voltmeter and an ammeter to the circuit. Show meter polarity on your diagram.

40) One coulomb is the total charge associated with 6.242×10^{18} electrons. How many electrons will pass through a conductor if 50 μA of current flows for 5 seconds?

41) Sketch the shell structure of the copper atom. (A copper atom contains 29 electrons).

42) Name five good conductors of electricity.

43) Name five good insulating materials.

44) The PSpice (Windows) program has what advantage over the DOS version of the program?

45) VOM stands for ________.

46) DMM stands for ________.

47) A Voltmeter is designed to measure ________.

48) A Proton is a particle whose polarity is ________.

Answer Key
Testname: CHAPTER 2

1) FALSE
2) TRUE
3) TRUE
4) FALSE
5) FALSE
6) FALSE
7) FALSE
8) TRUE
9) TRUE
10) FALSE
11) TRUE
12) TRUE
13) TRUE
14) B
15) B
16) D
17) A
18) C
19) C
20) C
21) A
22) A
23) B
24) C
25) A
26) B
27) C
28) D
29) D
30) B
31) A
32) C
33) A
34) C
35) D
36) D
37) B
38) D
39) Sketch should show the voltmeter across (in parallel with) battery terminals with the + voltmeter terminal connected to the + battery terminal. The ammeter should be in the current path (in series), with the + ammeter terminal nearest the + battery terminal.
40) 1.5605×10^{15} electrons
41) first ring: 2 electrons, second ring: 8, third ring: 18, fourth ring: 1
42) copper, gold, silver, aluminum, tungsten, etc.
43) air, mica, rubber, teflon, glass, etc.
44) The Windows approach allows the user to see a complete schematic for the circuit, rather than just a list of nodes.
45) Volt-Ohm-Meter
46) Digital Multimeter
47) Voltage
48) Positive

Chapter 3 Resistance

True/False

1) A circular mil is the area of a round conductor one millimeter in diameter.

2) Resistance decreases as the cross-sectional area of a conductor increases.

3) A varistor is a two-terminal device which changes in resistance as the temperature changes.

4) A photoconductive cell generates electricity when light strikes its exposed surfaces.

5) The resistance between the outside terminals of a potentiometer is fixed, regardless of the position of the wiper arm.

6) The temperature at which all molecular motion ceases is 273.15 degrees Celsius.

7) An ohmmeter is used to detect open-circuit and short-circuit situations.

8) A thermistor is a device whose resistance is temperature sensitive.

9) A photoconductive cell is a device whose resistance is determined by the intensity of the light exposed on its surface.

10) Resistance is directly proportional to the length of a conductor.

11) When selecting a conductor, malleability and ductility do not have to be considerations in the selection process.

12) Superconductors are conductors of electrical charge that for all practical purposes, have infinite resistance.

13) The value of resistance between the outside terminals of a potentiometer regardless of the position of the wiper is fixed at the full rated value.

Multiple Choice

14) What is the area in circular mils of a round conductor with a 0.1-inch diameter?

A) 0.01 CM B) 0.1 CM C) 100 CM D) 10,000 CM

15) Doubling the area of a conductor

A) doubles the resistance.

B) cuts the resistance in half.

C) increases resistance by a factor of 4.

D) decreases resistance by a factor of 4.

16) Doubling the length of a conductor

A) doubles the resistance.

B) cuts the resistance in half.

C) increases resistance by a factor of 4.

D) decreases resistance by a factor of 4.

17) Which of these color code patterns is found on a 270 Ω 5% resistor?

A) red, violet, brown, silver

B) red, violet, brown, gold

C) red, violet, black, silver

D) red, violet, brown, silver

18) A 10 kΩ resistor has a conductance of

A) 10^4 siemens

B) 10^{-4} siemens

C) 10^8 siemens

D) 10^{-8} siemens

19) The fifth color band found on some resistors denotes

A) temperature coefficient, in ohmic percentage change per °C.

B) manufacturer's resistance tolerance, which indicates the precision with which the resistor was made.

C) reliability, in percentage of failures per 1000 hours of use.

D) power rating, in tenth-watt increments.

20) Four 470 Ω ±5% resistors are measured with an ohmmeter. One of the measured resistor values is not within the ±5% tolerance. Which *one* of the following readings is out of bounds?

A) 445.0 Ω

B) 470.6 Ω

C) 476.0 Ω

D) 490.0 Ω

21) The color bands blue, gray, brown, gold describe which one of these resistors?

A) 68 Ω ±10%

B) 68 Ω ±5%

C) 680 Ω ±10%

D) 680 Ω ±5%

22) Which *one* of these statements is true of the ohmmeter?

A) It is used to measure resistance of a single resistor in a network without removing the resistor from the circuit.

B) It is used to measure resistance in a circuit only if the circuit is powered by low-voltage batteries.

C) It should be stored with the selector switch in the resistance mode.

D) It displays a resistance of zero if the leads touch each other, and an infinite reading if there is no connection at all.

23) A non-linear resistor used to suppress high-voltage transients is called a

A) thermistor
B) rheostat
C) photoconductive cell
D) varistor

24) A superconductor is

A) a conductor of electric charge that exhibits a negative resistance effect.

B) a conductor of electric charge that has sufficient cross-sectional area to make its resistance nearly zero.

C) a conductor of electric charge that exhibits zero resistance only in zero-gravity conditions.

D) a conductor of electric charge that has virtually no resistance when subjected to very low temperatures.

25) Which *one* of these materials has a *positive* temperature coefficient?

A) glass
B) rubber
C) germanium
D) copper

26) Which *one* of these statements is true?

A) As conductor length increases, conductance increases proportionally.

B) As conductor area decreases, conductance increases proportionally.

C) As conductor area increases, conductance increases proportionally.

D) As resistance increases, conductance increases proportionally.

27) The resistance between the two outside terminals of a potentiometer is 100 kΩ. If the resistance between the wiper and one outside terminal is 20 kΩ, what is the resistance between the wiper and the other outside terminal?

A) 16 kΩ
B) 20 kΩ
C) 80 kΩ
D) 100 kΩ

28) The wiper terminal and one of the two outside terminals of a 100 kΩ potentiometer are soldered together. If the wiper is set at the center position, what resistance exists between the two outside terminals?

A) 0 Ω
B) 50 kΩ
C) 80 kΩ
D) 100 kΩ

29) The resistivity ϕ has units of

A) ohms.
B) CM.
C) ohms/foot.
D) CM-ohms/foot.

30) Which letter represents resistance in electronic formula?

A) E
B) R
C) I
D) C

31) The electronic device used to measure resistance is:

A) Ammeter. B) Voltmeter. C) Ohmmeter. D) Wattmeter.

32) What is the resistance of 30 feet of silver wire with a diameter of 0.040 inches at 20 degrees Celsius?

A) 2.59 ohms B) 52.9 ohms C) 35.7 ohms D) none of above

33) What is the color code for a resistor whose value is 650 ohms?

A) Blue, Green, Brown
B) Green, Blue, Brown
C) Brown, Black, Green
D) Green, Black, Brown

34) As the temperature of most conductors increases, the resistance of the conductor will do which of the following?

A) Decrease
B) Increase
C) Rise to room temperature
D) Stay the same

35) The resistance of a conductor is inversely proportional to which of the following?

A) Length
B) The value of resistance
C) Cross-sectional area
D) Voltage

36) Semiconductors are known to have a negative temperature coefficient because an increase in temperature will result in which of the following?

A) An increase in the resistance level

B) A decrease in the resistance level

C) An increase in resistance only at room temperature

D) A decrease in resistance only at room temperature

37) Which of the following describes the measurement of how well a material will conduct electricity?

A) Temperature coefficient of ten or more

B) Dependent on the meter being on zero

C) Amount of insulation around the conductor

D) Conductance measured in siemens

Short Answer

38) What is the resistance of 1000 feet of #30 copper wire? Assume that the resistivity of copper is 10.37 (CM-Ω)/ft and the diameter of a #30 conductor is 0.01 inches.

39) The inferred absolute temperature for copper is −243.5°C. If the resistance of a copper wire is 10 Ω at 25°C, what is its resistance at 200°C?

40) Compute the resistance of a 1" × 1" square copper bar 10 feet long. The resistivity of copper is 10.37 (CM−Ω)/ft.

41) List and describe three applications of superconductors.

42) Is it possible for a 470 Ω +5% resistor and a 560 Ω +20% resistor to have identical resistance values? Explain your answer.

43) What safety precaution must be observed when using an ohmmeter?

44) What resistance reading would result across a fuse if the fuse were "blown"?

45) The "pairing" of electrons as they travel through a medium is called __________.

46) An element whose terminal resistance can be varied in a linear or nonlinear manner is called __________.

47) The unit for resistance is called __________.

48) A technique employing bands of color to indicate the resistance levels and tolerance of resistors is called __________.

Answer Key
Testname: CHAPTER 3

1) FALSE
2) TRUE
3) FALSE
4) FALSE
5) TRUE
6) FALSE
7) TRUE
8) TRUE
9) TRUE
10) TRUE
11) FALSE
12) FALSE
13) TRUE
14) D
15) B
16) A
17) B
18) B
19) C
20) A
21) D
22) D
23) D
24) D
25) D
26) C
27) C
28) B
29) D
30) B
31) C
32) D
33) A
34) B
35) C
36) B
37) D
38) 103.7 Ω
39) 16.517 Ω
40) $7.32E^{-5}$ Ω
41) Strong magnets, high-speed computer logic, high-energy particle accelerators, and power transmission.
42) Yes - the 470 Ω resistor could be as large as 493.5 Ω, and the 560 Ω resistor could be as small as 448 Ω.
43) Always turn off power to the circuit before attaching the ohmmeter.
44) Infinite resistance.
45) Cooper effect
46) Rheostat
47) Ohms
48) Color Coding

Chapter 4 Ohm's Law, Power, and Energy

True/False

1) The power dissipated by a resistor doubles if the applied voltage doubles.

2) Ohm's law shows that current is directly proportional to the applied voltage and is inversely proportional to resistance.

3) The horsepower is a measure of the electrical efficiency of a system.

4) One *watt* is the same as one joule per second.

5) A 1000 watt load that operates for one hour consumes the same amount of energy as a 100 watt load that operates for 10 hours.

6) Ohms's Law is named in honor of Georg Simon Ohm.

7) Power is an indication of how much work can be done in a specified amount of voltage.

8) 1 Horsepower is equal to 647 watts in the electrical system.

9) A fuse is a device whose sole purpose is to ensure that voltage levels do not exceed a safe level.

10) Power is directly proportional to the resistance times the current squared.

11) Power can be delivered or absorbed by the polarity of the voltage and the direction of the current divided by the resistance.

Multiple Choice

12) A 12 volt automobile taillight bulb draws 6 amperes from the battery. What is the "hot" resistance of this lamp?

A) 2 Ω B) 3 Ω C) 24 Ω D) 72 Ω

13) What voltage is developed across a 330 Ω resistor if 100 mA of current flows through it?

A) 0.3 V B) 3.3 V C) 33 V D) 3300 V

14) The current consumed by a digital wristwatch is 20 μA. What is the equivalent resistance of the watch if it is powered by a 1.5 V battery?

A) 30 μΩ B) 75 Ω C) 33.3 kΩ D) 75 kΩ

15) How much power is dissipated by a light bulb if its applied voltage is 12 V and its resistance is 12 Ω?

A) 1 watt B) 12 watts C) 144 watts D) 1728 watts

16) Efficiency is determined by

A) dividing the power input by the power output.

B) dividing power output by the power input.

C) multiplying the power input by the power output.

D) subtracting the power output from the power input.

17) A system with an input power of 50 watts and an output power of 20 watts has an efficiency of

A) 20% B) 25% C) 40% D) 50%

18) What is the total efficiency of three systems in cascade if the individual efficiencies are 40%, 30%, and 10%?

A) 1.2% B) 1.33% C) 10% D) 80%

19) One kilowatt-hour is equivalent to

A) 1.0×10^3 joules B) 6.0×10^3 joules

C) 6.0×10^4 joules D) 3.6×10^6 joules

20) How many joules of energy will a 10 watt lamp dissipate in one minute?

A) 10 joules B) 60 joules C) 600 joules D) 3600 joules

21) 50 mA of current flow through a 10 kΩ resistor. How much *power* is dissipated?

A) 0.25 μw B) 5 μw C) 25 w D) 500 w

22) An electric heater draws 12 amps from a 120 volt power source. How much power does the heater dissipate?

A) 10 watts B) 1200 watts C) 1440 watts D) 17,280 watts

23) What applied voltage will cause a 20 Ω resistor to dissipate 5 watts?

A) 4 V B) 10 V C) 100 V D) 250 V

24) A wattmeter

A) has four terminals; two for current and two for voltage.

B) is used by power companies to measure energy supplied to customers.

C) is connected across the device being measured.

D) displays electrical efficiency directly as a percentage.

25) The watt-hour is a unit of

A) energy. B) power. C) efficiency. D) torque.

26) What is the resistance of a circuit if a voltage change from 6 V to 12 V changes the current from 2 A to 4 A?

A) 2 Ω B) 3 Ω C) 6 Ω D) 12 Ω

27) The PSpice (Windows) part known as IPROBE

A) will result in a meter symbol that displays the current in the branch.

B) will inject current into the circuit branch under test.

C) must be connected to the PC's printer port to allow access to the program.

D) must precede other commands to allow an analysis to be completed.

28) The electronic instrument used to measure power is called a:

A) Ammeter B) Voltmeter C) Ohmmeter D) Wattmeter

29) According to Ohm's Law, which of the following is directly proportional to voltage if resistance is kept constant?

A) Current B) Electromotive Force

C) Frequency D) Reactance

30) Which of the following is the correct Ohm's Law relationship?

A) $E = I + R$ B) $E = I/R$ C) $E = R/I$ D) $E = IR$

31) In which of the following does the current in an electrical circuit equal the electromotive force divided by the resistance?

A) Coulomb's Law B) Kirchhoff's Law

C) Ohm's Law D) Watt's Law

32) A series circuit with a resistor has a voltage drop of 10 volts and a current of 5 mA. If the resistance and voltage are doubled, what is the value of the current through the circuit?

A) 2.5 mA B) 5 mA C) 10 mA D) 20 mA

33) How much horsepower is developed by a motor with 240 volts applied and drawing 30 amps?

A) not enough information to calculate
B) .965 hp
C) 9.65 hp
D) 96.5 hp

34) Which of the following is a word used to describe an indication of how much work can be done in a specific amount of time, or a rate of doing work?

A) efficiency B) energy C) power D) voltage

35) How much power is dissipated by a circuit with 15000 ohms of resistance and 10 mA of current?

A) .15 watts B) 1.5 watts C) 15 watts D) 7.5 watts

36) What is the purpose of fuses and circuit breakers in a system?

A) Limit the voltage across a component
B) Limit the resistance in a circuit
C) Reduce the number of fuses in a circuit
D) Limit the current in a circuit

37) A fuse that reads an infinite resistance can be considered which one of the following?

A) Should be replaced by a piece of wire
B) A defective fuse
C) A good fuse
D) A partially blown fuse

Short Answer

38) If an electric circuit requires 1 amp at 50 volts, how much current will it require if the voltage is increased to 75 volts?

39) A solar cell with an efficiency of 12% drives a small motor with an efficiency of 85%. What is the overall efficiency of the system?

40) How much current will a 120 V motor with a 5 hp output and 70% efficiency draw?

41) If electricity costs 8¢ per kWh, how much will it cost to run a 2500 watt water heater for 3 hours?

42) A power supply outputs 25 W into a load. The power supply input voltage is 115 V and the input current is 0.5 A. What is the efficiency of the power supply?

43) How is the PSpice (Windows) command Draw-Wire used?

44) Using Ohm's Law, find V when the current I = 4.2 milliamps and R = 1.5 Kilohms.

45) Using Ohm's Law, find I when the current V = 9.3 Volts and R = 1.5 Kilohms.

46) What is the power dissipated by a 1.2 Kilohm resistor if the voltage drop across the resistor is 56 volts?

47) What is the value of a resistor if 2 milliamps flows through the resistor and 3.5 watts is dissipated by the resistor?

Answer Key
Testname: CHAPTER 4

1) FALSE
2) TRUE
3) FALSE
4) TRUE
5) TRUE
6) TRUE
7) FALSE
8) FALSE
9) FALSE
10) TRUE
11) FALSE
12) A
13) C
14) D
15) B
16) B
17) C
18) A
19) D
20) C
21) C
22) C
23) B
24) A
25) A
26) B
27) A
28) D
29) A
30) D
31) C
32) B
33) C
34) C
35) B
36) D
37) B
38) 1.5 A
39) 10.2%
40) 44.4 A
41) 60¢
42) 43.5%
43) The Draw-Wire command is used as a pencil to connect components in the drawing.
44) 6.3 volts
45) 6.2 milliamps
46) 2.61 watts
47) 875 kilohms

Chapter 5 Series dc Circuits

True/False

1) When a 10 kΩ resistor, a 1 kΩ resistor, and a 100 Ω resistor are connected in series, the current through each resistor is the same, and the voltage across each resistor is the same.

2) The total resistance in a series circuit is equal to the sum of the individual resistances.

3) The sum of the voltage drops in a series circuit is always equal to the applied voltage.

4) High internal resistance corresponds with good voltage regulation in a power supply.

5) Ammeters are always placed in series with the branch in which the current is measured.

6) Voltage divider rule is a method by which current in a series circuit can be determined without first calculating the voltage in a circuit.

7) The portion of a circuit consisting of one or more elements in parallel is called a branch.

8) Polarity is defined based on the conventional current through a resistive element.

9) The current that flows through series elements of a circuit is the same in each element.

Multiple Choice

10) Kirchhoff's voltage law states that

A) the algebraic sum of the potential rises and drops around a closed loop is zero.

B) the algebraic sum of the resistances is equal to the sum of the voltages.

C) the algebraic sum of the individual currents around a closed loop is zero.

D) the voltages developed across each element in a series circuit are identical.

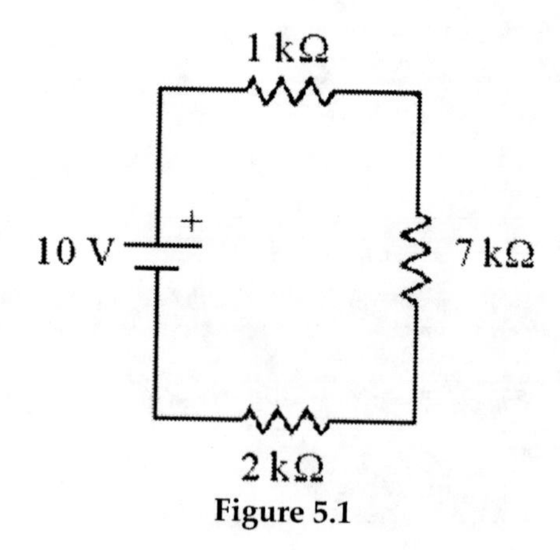

Figure 5.1

11) See Figure 5.1. The total resistance in this circuit is

A) 1 kΩ B) 2 kΩ C) 7 kΩ D) 10 kΩ

12) See Figure 5.1. The total current flowing from the battery is

A) 1 mA B) 10 mA C) 1.43 mA D) 5 mA

13) See Figure 5.1. The total power dissipated by the 7 kΩ resistor is

A) 1 mW B) 2 mW C) 7 mW D) 10 mW

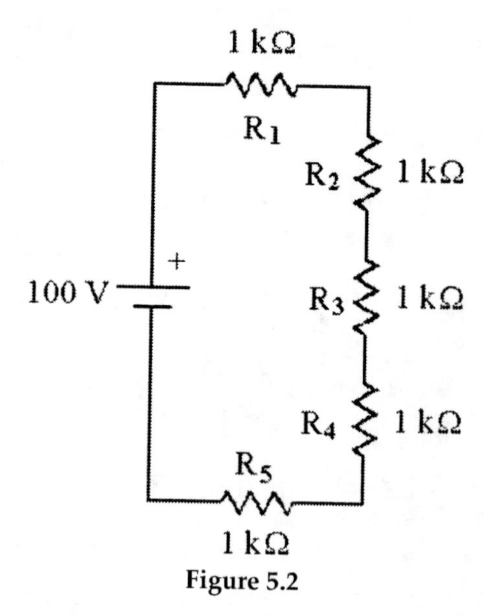

Figure 5.2

14) See Figure 5.2. How much power is dissipated by R_5?

A) 200 mW B) 400 mW C) 1 W D) 2 W

15) See Figure 5.2. If R3 is short circuited, how much power is dissipated by R5?

A) 325 mW B) 625 mW C) 1.25 W D) 2.5 W

16) In double-subscript notation, V_{ab} = +7 V denotes that

A) point a is 7 V more positive than point b.

B) point b is 7 V more positive than point a.

C) point a is +7 V with respect to ground.

D) point b is +7 V with respect to ground.

17) If point x in a series circuit measures -3 V with respect to ground, and point y measures +7 V with respect to ground, then voltage V_{xy} is

A) -4 V B) +4 V C) -10 V D) +10 V

18) Which *one* of these statements is true of Kirchhoff's voltage law (KVL)?

A) A plus sign is assigned to each potential drop.

B) A minus sign is assigned to each potential rise.

C) The KVL technique only works when all voltage sources are oriented in the same direction around the loop.

D) The KVL technique works correctly with either clockwise loop direction or counter-clockwise loop direction.

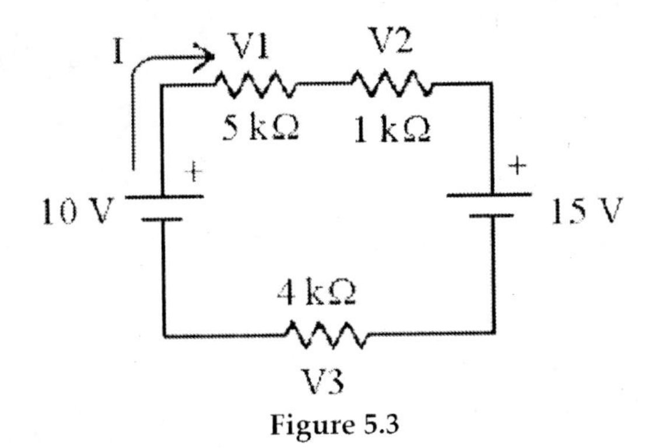

Figure 5.3

19) See Figure 5.3. Which one of the following KVL equations describes this circuit?

A) +10 V + V1 + V2 - 15 V + V3 = 0 B) +10 V - V1 - V2 - 15 V - V3 = 0

C) -10 V - V1 - V2 + 15 V - V3 = 0 D) +10 V - V1 - V2 + 15 V - V3 = 0

20) See Figure 5.3. The total current I is

A) +500 μA B) -500 μA C) +2.5 mA D) -2.5 mA

21) See Figure 5.3. Which *one* of the following statements is true if the 10 V battery is replaced by a 15 V battery?

A) Current I will increase by 50%.
B) Current I will drop to zero.
C) Polarity of current I will reverse.
D) Both batteries will be damaged.

22) In double-subscript notation, the voltage V_{ab} is the same as

A) $V_a - V_b$
B) $V_a + V_b$
C) $V_a \times V_b$
D) V_a

23) Which *one* statement is true of resistors in a series circuit?

A) Each resistor dissipates the same power, regardless of its resistance value.
B) Large-value resistors dissipate more power than small-value resistors.
C) Small-value resistors dissipate more power than large-value resistors.
D) The smallest resistor drops the largest voltage.

24) If the voltage dropped across a resistor increases by a factor of 10, the power dissipated by the resistor

A) increases by a factor of 10.
B) increases by a factor of 20.
C) increases by a factor of 100.
D) decreases.

25) Which one of the following is true of the C++ programming language?

A) It uses command statements that are easily understood English words, unlike BASIC.
B) It is much slower than BASIC.
C) It provides a lower-level access to a computer system's hardware.
D) It must be run on a large "mainframe" computer, since a PC is too slow.

26) The statement that "the algebraic sum of voltage drops around a closed electrical circuit must equal zero" is:

A) Coulomb's voltage law
B) Faraday's voltage law
C) Ohm's voltage law
D) Kirchhoff's voltage law

27) The sum of the series IR drops around a closed loop must:

A) Equal infinity
B) Equal the applied voltage
C) Equal 120 volts
D) Be the same

28) Given a series circuit containing resistors of different values, which statement is not true?

A) The current through each resistor is the same.

B) The sum of the voltage drops across each resistive element will be equal to the source voltage.

C) The total resistance is the sum of the value of the resistors.

D) The voltage drop across each resistor will be the same.

29) To measure voltage drops in a series circuit, a voltmeter should be connected in:

A) Series Only

B) Parallel Only

C) Either Series or Parallel

D) Neither Series nor Parallel

30) The total resistance in a series circuit is __________.

A) dependent on the number of current paths

B) the reciprocal of the total resistance

C) equal to the sum of the current levels

D) equal to the sum of the resistance values

31) A series circuit with a voltage source of 15 volts and a total resistance of 7500 ohms will dissipate how much power?

A) 30 mW

B) .3 W

C) 3 W

D) 30 W

32) A circuit has a source voltage of 15 volts and two resistors with a total resistance of 4000 ohms. If R_1 has a potential of 9.375 volts, what is the value of R_2?

A) 500 ohms

B) 1000 ohms

C) 1500 ohms

D) 2000 ohms

33) A series circuit dissipates a total of 56.25 mW of power with a current of 3.75 mA. If R_2 dissipates 21.09 mW of power, what is the value of R_1?

A) 1000 ohms

B) 1500 ohms

C) 2000 ohms

D) 2500 ohms

34) According to Kirchhoff's law, a series circuit with 50 volts applied, the sum of the voltage drops would be equal to __________.

A) zero

B) 25 volts

C) 50 volts

D) the sum of the voltage drops across the series elements

35) If two 9 volt batteries were connected in series (negative to positive) and a third battery was added in series connected (positive to negative terminal) the total voltage would be?

A) zero volts B) 4.5 volts C) 9 volts D) 18 volts

36) Which of the following will apply to the largest resistor in a series circuit?

A) Have the largest current going through it

B) Have the greatest voltage drop

C) Dissipate the largest amount of power

D) Have a voltage drop equal to the other resistors in the circuit

37) Which of the following expresses a double-superscript notation of $V_{ab} = -15$ v?

A) Point a has a higher potential than b B) Point a has the same potential as b

C) Point a has a lower potential than b D) Point a cannot be determined

38) When using an ammeter, which of the following describes the correct method of connecting the meter?

A) In series with the branch in which current is measured

B) Across the element to be measured

C) Between the source and ground

D) Ensure the red lead is on the negative terminal

Short Answer

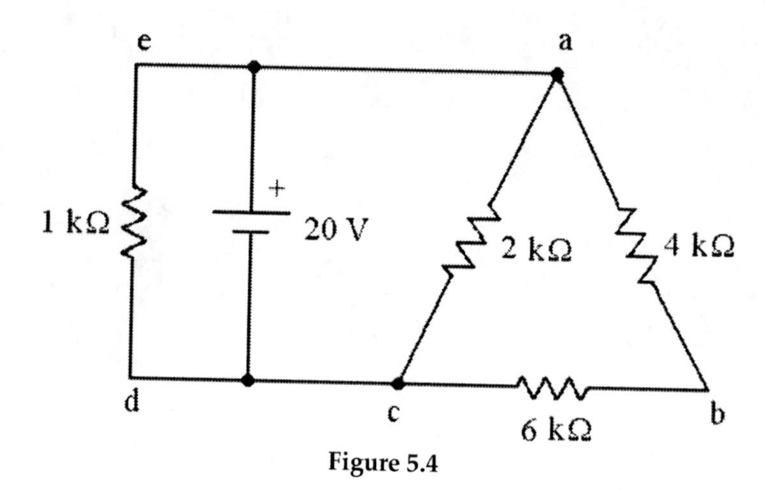

Figure 5.4

39) See Figure 5.4. Write Kirchhoff's voltage law equations to compute V_{ab}, V_{ac}, V_{bc}, and V_{de}

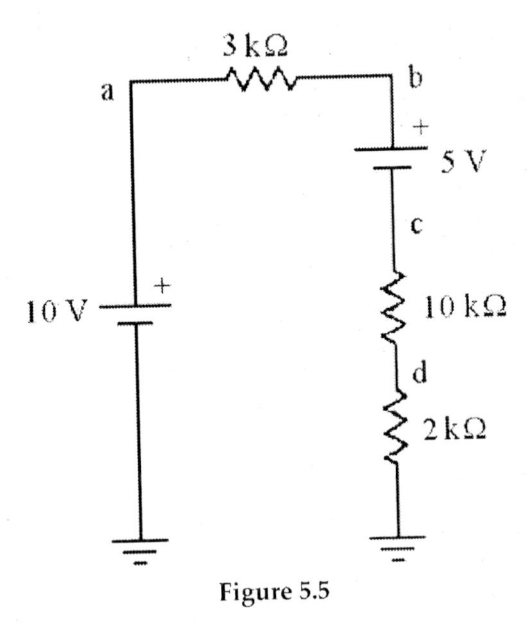

Figure 5.5

40) See Figure 5.5. Use Kirchhoff's voltage law to calculate V_{ab}, V_{cd}, and V_d.

41) What is the voltage regulation of a power supply if its no-load output (V_{NL}) is 30 V, and its full-load output (V_{FL}) is 25 V?

42) Calculate the internal resistance of a power supply if a no-load output of $V_{NL} = 50$ V, and an output voltage of 45 V when a 10 A load is connected.

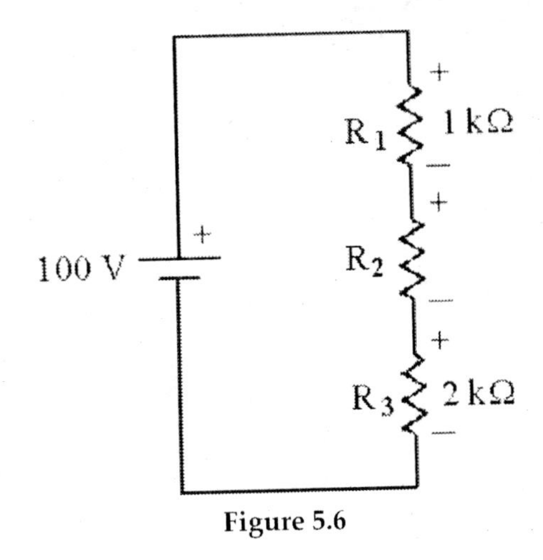

Figure 5.6

43) See Figure 5.6. Use the voltage divider rule to choose R_2 such that $V_{R1} = 30$ V

44) Write a BASIC statement that will compute and display resistance of series resistors R1, R4, and R7.

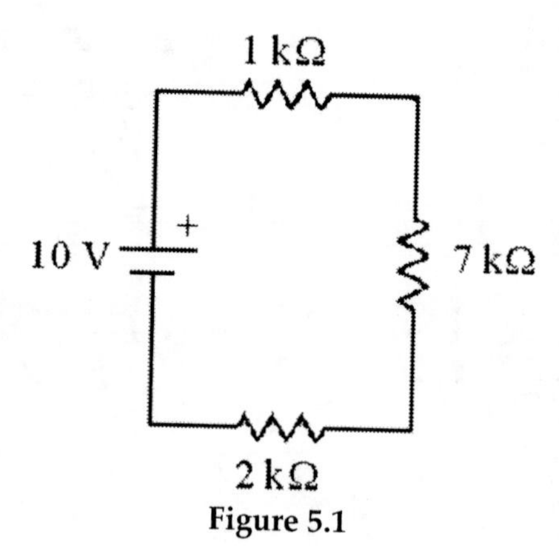

Figure 5.1

45) What is the total resistance of the circuit shown in Figure 5.1, assuming that each resistor is 20% above its nominal value?

46) The voltage measured across an open component in a series circuit is equal to ________.

47) The voltage measured across an shorted component in a series circuit is equal to ________.

48) If a circuit contains three resistors in series, what would be the total resistance if R1 = 10 ohms, R2 = 13 ohms and R3 = 5 ohms?

49) A circuit has three elements connected in series, two resistors R1 = 5 ohms R2 = 15 ohms and a 20 volt DC power supply. What current flows through the series circuit?

50) What is the total resistance of thirty 6 ohm resistors connected in series?

Answer Key
Testname: CHAPTER 5

1) FALSE
2) TRUE
3) TRUE
4) FALSE
5) TRUE
6) FALSE
7) FALSE
8) TRUE
9) TRUE
10) A
11) D
12) A
13) C
14) B
15) B
16) A
17) C
18) D
19) B
20) B
21) B
22) A
23) B
24) C
25) C
26) D
27) B
28) D
29) B
30) D
31) A
32) C
33) D
34) D
35) C
36) B
37) C
38) A
39) +8 V, +20 V, +12 V, −20 V
40) +1.0 V, +3.33 V, +0.67 V
41) 20%
42) 0.5 Ω
43) 333.3 Ω
44) PRINT R1+R4+R7
45) 12 kΩ
46) The applied voltage
47) zero
48) 28 ohms
49) 1 amp
50) 180 ohms

Chapter 6 Parallel dc Circuits

True/False

1) For parallel elements, total conductance is the sum of the individual conductances.

2) The total resistance of a parallel resistor network is always more than the value of the smallest resistor.

3) Kirchhoff's current law can be used only if three or more currents are associated with a given junction.

4) The total parallel resistance of N equal resistors, each with value R, is N × R.

5) According to the current divider rule, current divides in a parallel network such that a small resistor always draws a smaller share of the total current than does a large resistor.

6) Two elements, branches, or networks are in series if they have two points in common.

7) For parallel elements, the total conductance is the sum of the individual conductances.

8) The total resistance of parallel resistors is always greater than the value of the smallest resistor.

9) The total resistance of two parallel resistors is the product of the two divided by their sum.

10) If there are two resistors in a parallel circuit, total resistance can be calculated by the product divided by the sum.

Multiple Choice

11) The total conductance of a 4 Ω resistor and a 2 Ω resistor in parallel is

A) 0.75 S B) 1.33 S C) 6 S D) 8 S

12) What is the total resistance of one thousand 10 kΩ resistors in parallel?

A) 1 Ω B) 10 Ω C) 10 kΩ D) 10 MΩ

13) Kirchhoff's current law states that

A) the sum of the currents around a closed loop is zero.

B) the sum of the currents entering a junction must equal the sum of the currents leaving the junction.

C) the sum of the currents entering a junction must equal zero.

D) the total current entering a given junction is constant, even with changes in supply voltage.

14) A 6 Ω resistor and a 9 Ω resistor are connected in parallel across a 10 V battery. What is the total current drawn from the battery?

A) 0.36 A B) 0.67 A C) 2.78 A D) 3.33 A

15) Which one of the following statements is true?

A) For minimum measurement error, voltmeters should have low internal resistance and ammeters should have high internal resistance.

B) For minimum measurement error, voltmeters should have high internal resistance and ammeters should have low internal resistance.

C) For minimum measurement error, voltmeters should have low internal resistance and ammeters should have low internal resistance.

D) For minimum measurement error, voltmeters should have high internal resistance and ammeters should have high internal resistance.

16) A volt-ohm-milliammeter (VOM) is monitoring the output of a dc power supply. The VOM is set on the 25 V range and the meter shows 20.0 V. What is the internal resistance of the VOM if it has a 20 kΩ/V rating?

A) 20 kΩ B) 400 kΩ C) 500 kΩ D) 900 kΩ

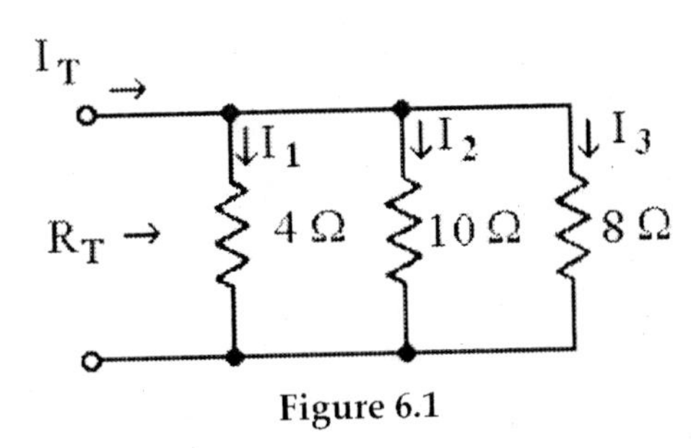

Figure 6.1

17) See Figure 6.1. What is the total resistance R_T?

A) 0.045 Ω B) 0.475 Ω C) 2.11 Ω D) 22 Ω

18) See Figure 6.1. Use Kirchhoff's current law to compute I_2, given $I_T = 100$ mA.

A) 21.1 mA
B) 26.3 mA
C) 53.7 mA
D) 100 mA

19) What is the total resistance R_T of the circuit shown in Figure 6.1 if the 8 Ω resistor is replaced by a short circuit?

A) 0 Ω
B) 2.86 Ω
C) 2.10 Ω
D) infinity

20) Two voltage sources connected in parallel

A) add algebraically.

B) violate Kirchhoff's voltage law if they have different output voltages.

C) cancel each other, producing a net voltage of zero.

D) are more economical than a single large voltage source.

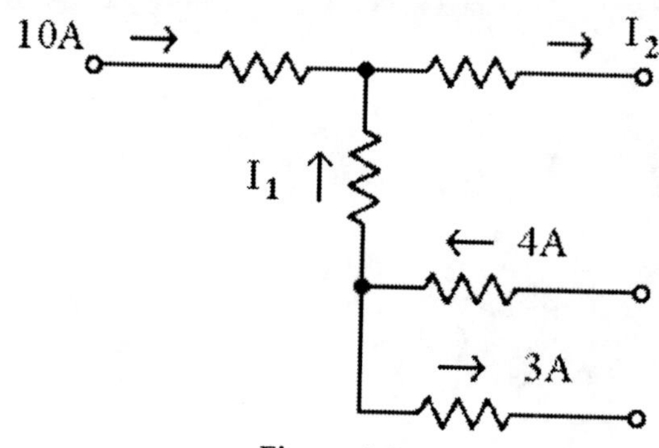

Figure 6.2

21) See Figure 6.2. What is the value of I_2? Use Kirchhoff's current law to determine the answer.

A) 7 A
B) 9 A
C) 10 A
D) 11 A

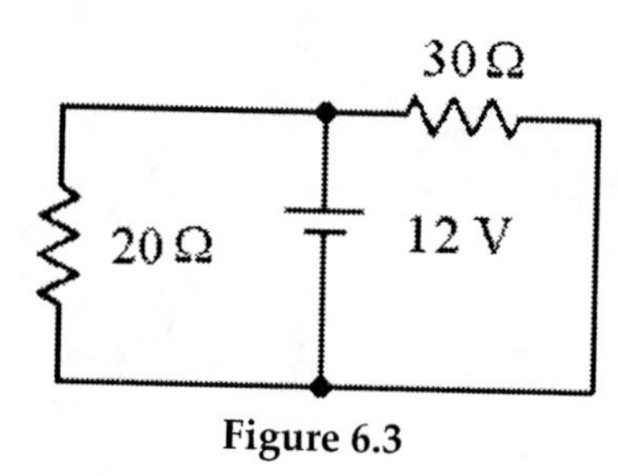

Figure 6.3

22) See Figure 6.3. What is the current drawn from the battery?

A) 0.4 A
B) 0.6 A
C) 0.8 A
D) 1.0 A

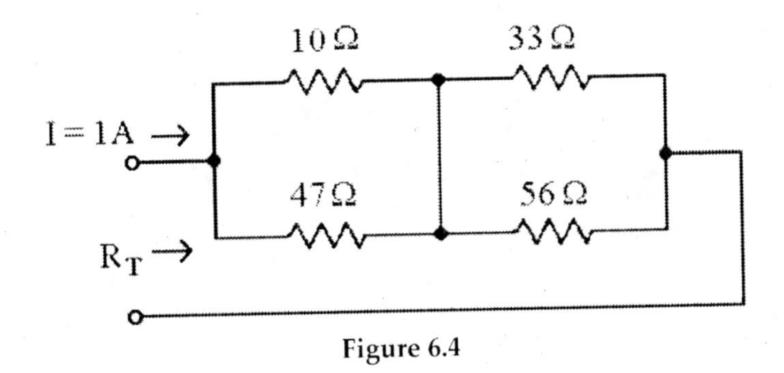

Figure 6.4

23) See Figure 6.4. Which two resistors are in parallel?

A) 10 Ω and 47 Ω

B) 10 Ω and 33 Ω

C) 10 Ω and 56 Ω

D) None are in parallel.

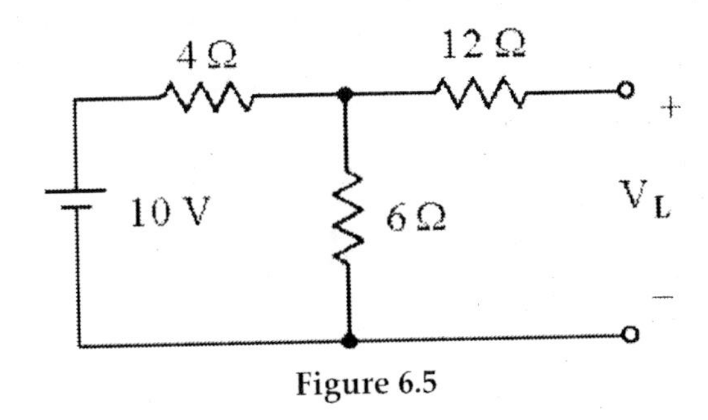

Figure 6.5

24) See Figure 6.5. What is the open circuit output voltage V_L?

A) 4 V

B) 6 V

C) 8 V

D) 10 V

25) See Figure 6.5. What is the new voltage V_L if the 4 Ω resistor is shorted?

A) 4 V

B) 6 V

C) 8 V

D) 10 V

26) See Figure 6.5. What is the new voltage V_L if the 6 Ω resistor is open?

A) 4 V

B) 6 V

C) 8 V

D) 10 V

27) A Circuit with no available path for current to flow is a/an:

A) Closed Circuit

B) Long Circuit

C) Open Circuit

D) Short Circuit

28) Which of the following describes two elements that have two points in common?

A) They are considered to be in opposition

B) They are considered to be in parallel

C) They would be connected in series

D) The would be connected in a series/parallel configuration

29) What is the total resistance of a parallel circuit consisting of $G_1 = .004$ S, $G_2 = .002$ S, $G_3 = .001$ S and $G_4 = .0005$ S?

A) 133.33 ohms B) 1,333 ohms C) 2.666 ohms D) 3,750 ohms

30) Which of the following provides the total resistance of a parallel circuit consisting of $R_2 = 10K$, $R_3 = 2K$ in parallel with each other?

A) 18K B) More than 2K C) Less than 2K D) 3.33K

31) Which of the following describes what takes place as the spread in numerical values between two parallel resistors increase?

A) Total resistance increases

B) Total resistance is unchanged

C) Total resistance will be closer in value to the smaller resistor

D) Total resistance will be closer to the larger resistance

32) What is the total resistance of a parallel circuit with three resistors with the values of 60, 120 and 180 ohms each?

A) 32.73 ohms B) 62.46 ohms C) 125.6 ohms D) 155 ohms

33) In a parallel circuit, if $R_1 = 300$ ohms and $R_2 = 4.7K$ ohms the total resistance would be 282 ohms. What will the total resistance be if the value of R_1 is doubled?

A) 141 ohms B) 282 ohms C) 532 ohms D) 654 ohms

34) As additional resistors are added to a parallel circuit, what will happen to total resistance?

A) Total resistance will increase.

B) Total resistance will decrease.

C) Total resistance will remain the same.

D) Total resistance will only be affected by resistors of equal value.

35) A circuit consists of two resistors in parallel with each other. R_1 = 60 ohms and R_2 = 120 ohms. The circuit has 10 volts applied. An ammeter, placed to read total current is reading .17 amps. What is the problem with the circuit?

A) There is no problem.

B) R_1 is open.

C) R_2 is open.

D) Applied voltage is low.

Short Answer

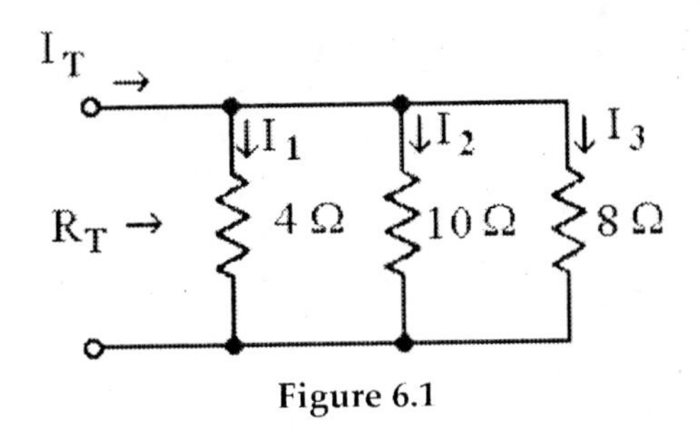

Figure 6.1

36) See Figure 6.1. What is the total conductance, G_T?

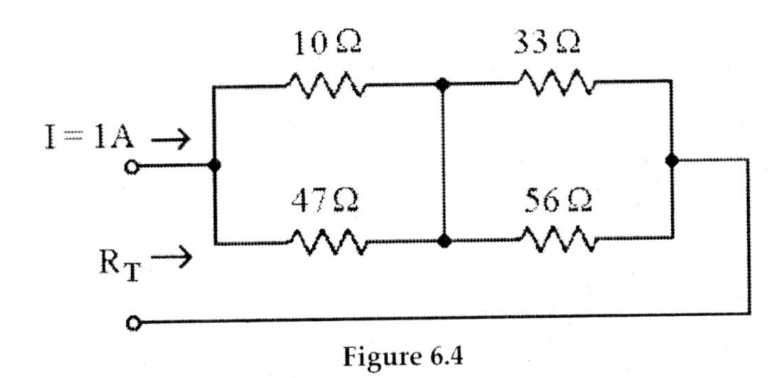

Figure 6.4

37) See Figure 6.4. What is the value of the current flowing through the 10 ohm resistor?

38) See Figure 6.4. Compute R_T and the current through the 47 Ω resistor.

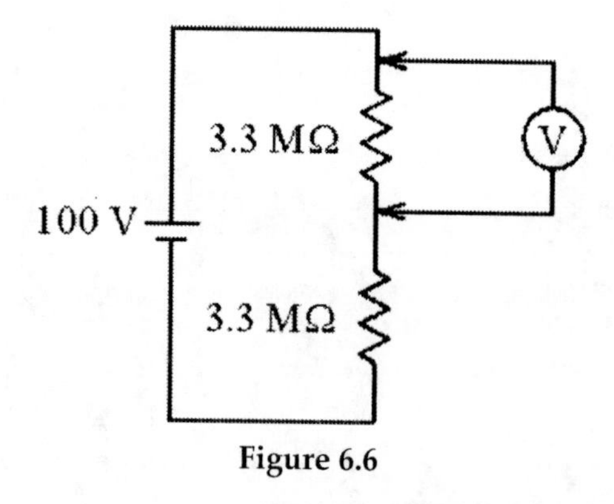

Figure 6.6

39) See Figure 6.6. Compute the voltage reading if an ideal voltmeter is used.

40) See Figure 6.6. Compute the voltage reading if a digital multimeter with 11 MΩ internal resistance is used.

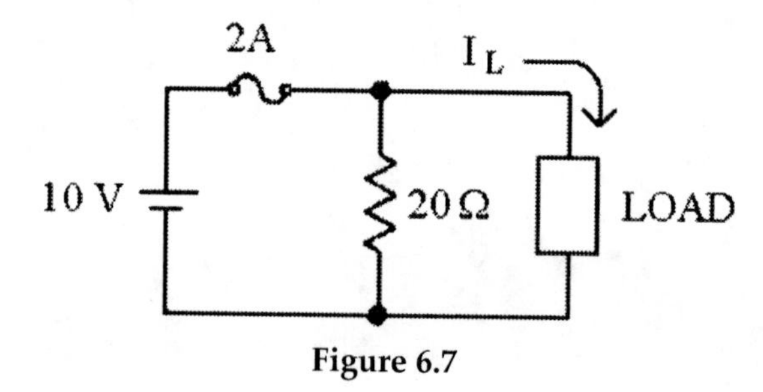

Figure 6.7

41) See Figure 6.7. Calculate the maximum current I_L that can be drawn without blowing the fuse.

42) A 330 Ω ± 10% resistor and a 470 Ω ± 5% resistor are connected in parallel. Taking into account the tolerances of the two resistors, determine the largest and the smallest parallel resistance produced by this network.

43) When a branch of a parallel resistance network is replaced by an open circuit, will the total resistance R_T increase, decrease, or stay the same?

44) What is the conductance of a short circuit? Of an open circuit?

45) The total resistance in a parallel circuit is always __________ in relation to the value of the smallest resistive branch.

46) The total power dissipated in a parallel circuit is equal to the __________ of the individual powers dissipated in the branch circuits.

47) Which law states that the algebraic sum of the currents entering and leaving a node is equal to zero?

48) The voltage across parallel elements in a resistive circuit is the __________.

Answer Key
Testname: CHAPTER 6

1) TRUE
2) FALSE
3) FALSE
4) FALSE
5) FALSE
6) FALSE
7) TRUE
8) FALSE
9) TRUE
10) TRUE
11) A
12) B
13) B
14) C
15) B
16) C
17) C
18) A
19) A
20) B
21) D
22) D
23) A
24) B
25) D
26) D
27) C
28) B
29) A
30) C
31) A
32) A
33) C
34) B
35) C
36) 0.475 siemens
37) 0.82 amps
38) 29.01 Ω, 175.4 mA
39) 50 V
40) 43.48 V
41) 1.5 A
42) largest is 209.15 Ω, smallest is 178.36 Ω.
43) Increase
44) infinite siemens, 0 siemens
45) less than
46) sum
47) Kirchhoff's current law
48) same

Chapter 7 Series–Parallel Circuits

True/False

1) A ladder network is a cascaded set of series–parallel combinations that has the appearance of a ladder.

2) A transistor is a series–parallel circuit comprised of three variable resistors.

3) The d'Arsonval movement is basically an iron–core coil mounted between permanent magnet poles.

4) An ammeter shunt is a series resistor that limits the current passing through the meter movement.

5) Typical ohmmeters contain an internal voltage source that drives current through the unknown resistance being measured.

6) Series–parallel networks are networks that contain both series and parallel circuit configurations.

7) A transistor is a three terminal semiconductor electronic device that can be used for amplification and switching purposes.

8) A Megohmmeter is an instrument for measuring very high resistance levels.

9) The voltage drops across all the elements in a parallel–series network is not equal to the source voltage.

10) Using the reduce and redraw approach to solve series–parallel networks, series and parallel elements can be simply added together.

11) When solving a series–parallel circuit, begin by starting furthest away from the source and work backward toward the source.

12) If the supply has internal resistance, the application of a load can affect the terminal voltage.

13) When a load is applied to a potentiometer, the voltage across a load connected to the wiper arm is determined solely by the potentiometer.

14) The maximum current that the d'Arsonval movement can read independently is equal to the current sensitivity of the movement.

Multiple Choice

15) To minimize potentiometer loading,

A) the load resistance must be very small compared with the potentiometer resistance.

B) the load resistance must be very large compared with the potentiometer resistance.

C) only high–resistance potentiometers should be used.

D) connect a 1 Ω resistor between the wiper and the load.

16) The series resistor in a voltmeter

A) has a large resistance for a high–voltage range and a small resistance for a low–voltage range.

B) has a small resistance for a high–voltage range and a large resistance for a low–voltage range.

C) bypasses a portion of the current around the meter movement, allowing a low–voltage meter to be used in a high–voltage circuit.

D) should be as small as possible to minimize voltmeter loading effects.

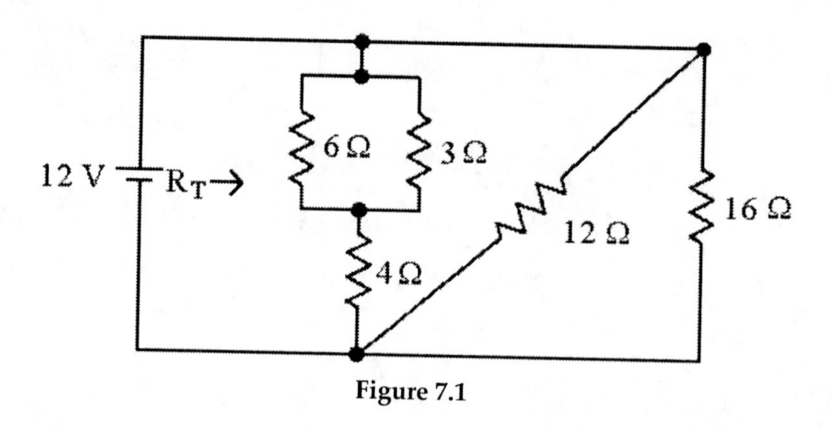

Figure 7.1

17) See Figure 7.1. What is the total resistance R_T?

A) 2.4 Ω B) 3.2 Ω C) 4.8 Ω D) 6.4 Ω

18) See Figure 7.1. What is the current through the 3Ω resistor?

A) 0.33 A B) 1.0 A C) 1.33 A D) 2.0 A

19) See Figure 7.1. What is the voltage dropped across the 12 ohm resistor?

A) 12 volts B) 1.2 volts C) 0.12 volts D) 3 volts

20) See Figure 7.1. What power is dissipated across the 16 ohm resistor?

A) 0.9 watts B) 90 watts C) 9 watts D) 12 watts

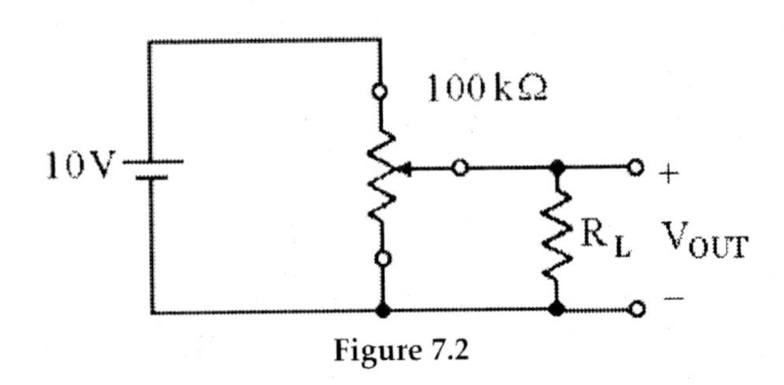

Figure 7.2

21) See Figure 7.2. What is V_{OUT} if the wiper is at the midpoint of the potentiometer and R_L = 100 kΩ?

A) 3 V B) 4 V C) 5 V D) 6 V

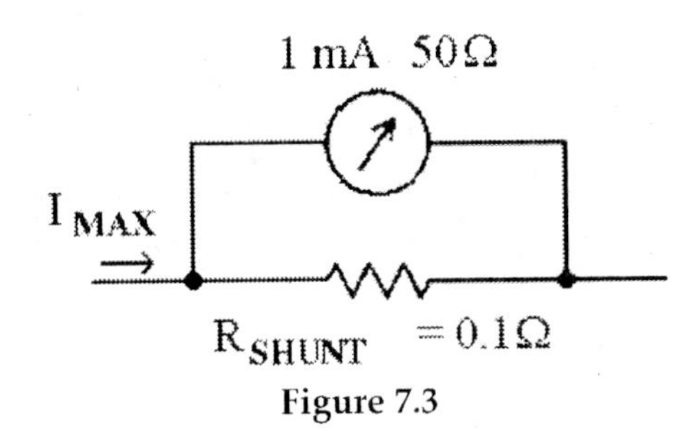

Figure 7.3

22) See Figure 7.3. What voltage V must be applied to the circuit to result in full-scale meter deflection?

A) 1 mV B) 5 mV C) 50 mV D) 500 mV

23) See Figure 7.3. What is I_{MAX}, such that the meter movement reaches full-scale deflection?

A) 1.0 mA B) 5.01 mA C) 50.1 mA D) 501 mA

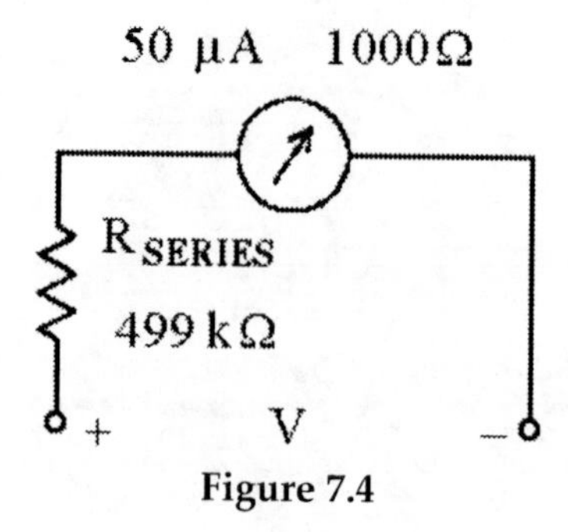

Figure 7.4

24) See Figure 7.4. What voltage V must be applied to the circuit to result in full-scale deflection?

A) 50 mV B) 5.0 V C) 24.95 V D) 25.0 V

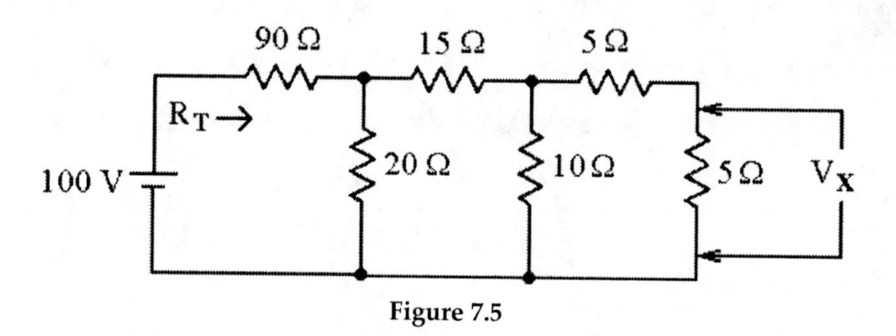

Figure 7.5

25) See Figure 7.5. What is the value of R_T?

A) 100 Ω B) 110 Ω C) 120 Ω D) 145 Ω

26) See Figure 7.5. What is the voltage dropped across the 90 Ω resistor?

A) 18.2 V B) 81.8 V C) 90.0 V D) 100.0 V

27) See Figure 7.5. What is R_T if the 10 Ω resistor is short-circuited?

A) 0 Ω B) 98.6 Ω C) 100.0 Ω D) 101.1 Ω

28) Increasing R_{SHUNT} in an ammeter will

A) increase I_{MAX}, the maximum current that can be measured.

B) decrease I_{MAX}, the maximum current that can be measured.

C) decrease the ammeter series resistance, thus reducing loading effects.

D) cause an increase in power dissipated when I_{MAX} is measured.

29) Increasing R_{SERIES} in a voltmeter circuit will

A) increase V_{MAX}, the maximum voltage that can be measured.

B) decrease V_{MAX}, the maximum voltage that can be measured.

C) decrease the overall voltmeter resistance, thus reducing its loading effects.

D) help conserve energy by reducing the power consumption when V_{MAX} is measured.

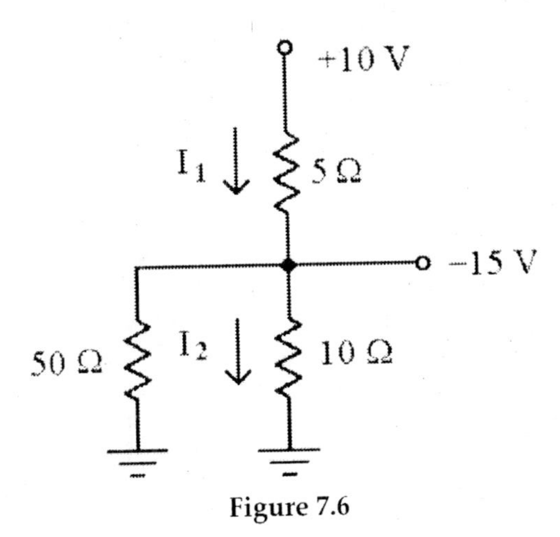

Figure 7.6

30) See Figure 7.6. What is the current I_2?

A) -1.5 A B) +1.5 A C) -0.67 A D) +0.67 A

31) See Figure 7.6. What is the current I_1?

A) +0.75 A B) +2.0 A C) -5.0 A D) +5.0 A

32) See Figure 7.6. What is the power dissipated across the 10 ohm resistor?

A) 2.25 watts B) 0.225 watts C) 225 watts D) 22.5 watts

33) Which of the following describes what an ammeter using a d'Arsonval movement will have to limit the current flow through the movement?

A) Multiplier resistor B) Potentiometer

C) Shunt resistor D) Switch

34) What is the total resistance of a circuit consisting of the following values: R_1 = 2.2K ohms in a series with a source voltage on 15V dc; R_2 = 1.5K ohms and R_3 = 2K ohms, in parallel with each other and in series with R_1; and R_4 = 1K ohm, in series with the parallel combination of R_2 and R_3?

A) 1857 ohms B) 3200 ohms C) 4057 ohms D) 6800 ohms

Short Answer

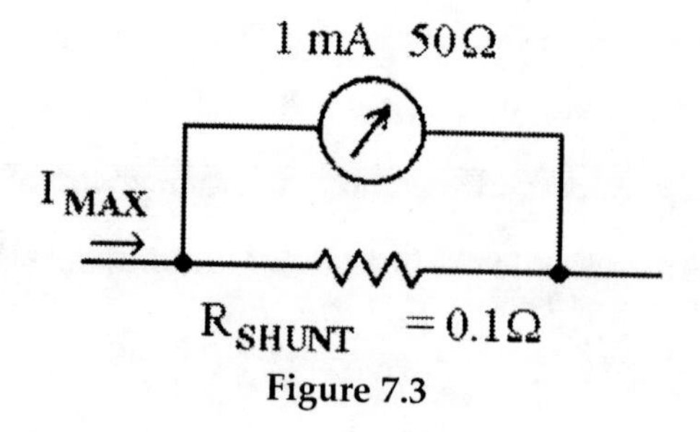

Figure 7.3

35) See Figure 7.3. Select an approximate value for R_{SHUNT} such that I_{MAX} is 10.0 A.

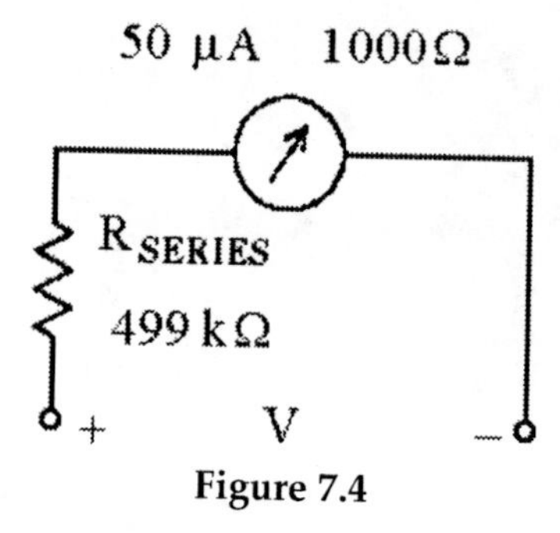

Figure 7.4

36) See Figure 7.4. Select a value for R_{SERIES} such that an input of 100 V produces a full-scale meter deflection.

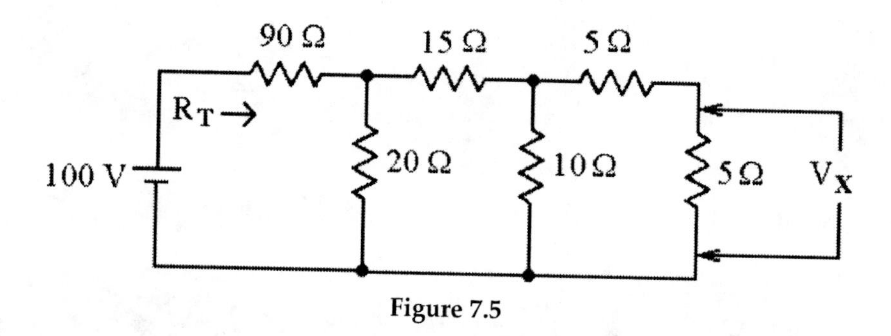

Figure 7.5

37) See Figure 7.5. Calculate V_X.

38) See Figure 7.5. Calculate the current through the 20 Ω resistor.

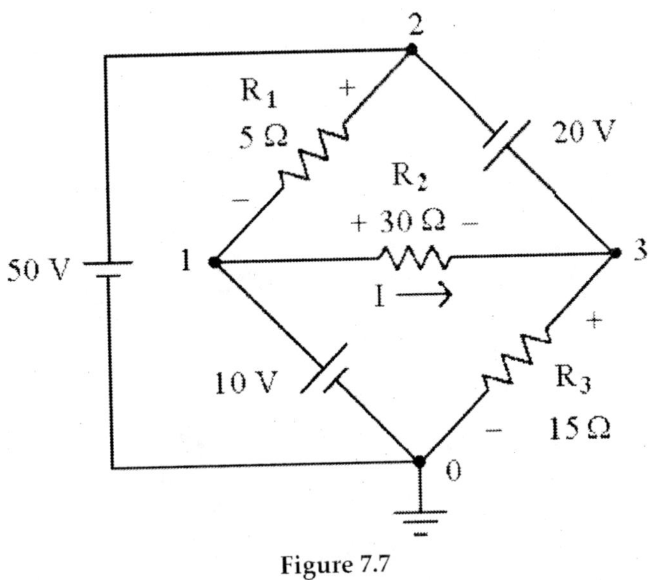

Figure 7.7

39) See Figure 7.7. Determine the current I.

40) How will increasing the resistance of the series resistor in a voltmeter circuit change the maximum voltage that can be measured? (Will maximum voltage increase, decrease, or remain the same?)

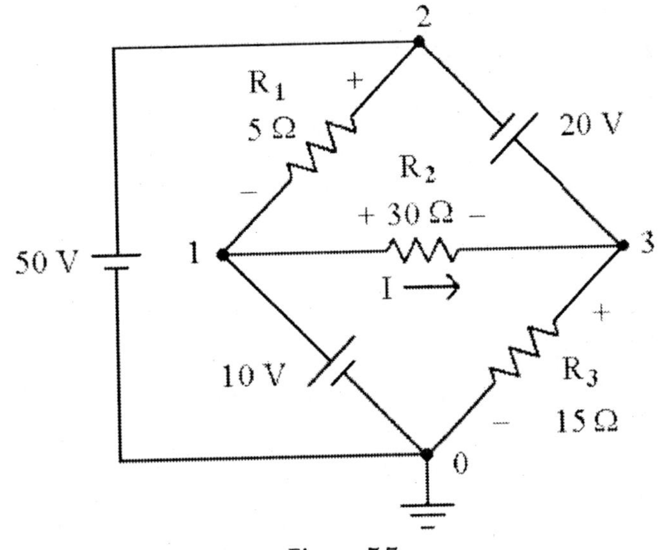

Figure 7.7

41) See Figure 7.7. Determine the voltage drop across the 30 ohm resistor.

42) See Figure 7.7. Determine the power dissipated across the 15 ohm resistor.

43) See Figure 7.7. Determine the current flowing through the 5 ohm resistor.

44) See Figure 7.7. Determine the current flowing through the 15 ohm resistor.

Answer Key
Testname: CHAPTER 7

1) TRUE
2) FALSE
3) TRUE
4) FALSE
5) TRUE
6) TRUE
7) TRUE
8) TRUE
9) FALSE
10) FALSE
11) TRUE
12) TRUE
13) FALSE
14) TRUE
15) B
16) A
17) B
18) C
19) A
20) C
21) B
22) C
23) D
24) D
25) A
26) C
27) B
28) B
29) A
30) A
31) D
32) D
33) C
34) C
35) 5 mΩ
36) 2.0 MΩ
37) 1.25 V
38) 0.5 A
39) 2.0 A
40) Maximum voltage will increase.
41) -60 volts
42) 326.7 watts
43) 8 amps
44) 4.7 amps

Chapter 8 Methods of Analysis and Selected Topics (dc)

True/False

1) An ideal current source has a 0 Ω resistance in parallel with it.

2) An ideal voltage source has an infinite resistance in series with it.

3) A node is defined as a junction of two or more branches.

4) When using mesh analysis, each loop must be drawn in the clockwise direction.

5) A current source determines the current in the branch in which it is located.

6) The magnitude and polarity of the voltage across a current source is not a function of the network to which it is attached.

7) Source conversion are equivalent only at their external terminals.

8) Current sources of different amplitudes can be connected in series.

9) An ideal current source would have ten ohms of resistance.

10) A loop current is a branch current only when it is the only loop current assigned to that branch.

11) Any node including the effect of elements tied only to other nodes is referred to as a supernode.

12) To perform a conversion from one type of source to another, a voltage source must have a resistor in parallel with it and a current source must have a resistor in series.

13) From the application of Kirchhoff's voltage law, around a closed loop the polarity of a voltage source is unaffected by the direction of the assigned loop currents.

Multiple Choice

14) Which one of these statements is true of two or more current sources in parallel?

A) They violate Kirchhoff's Current Law.

B) They may be replaced by one current source.

C) A series resistor must be included in each branch.

D) The magnitude of the combined current is always less than the smallest individual current.

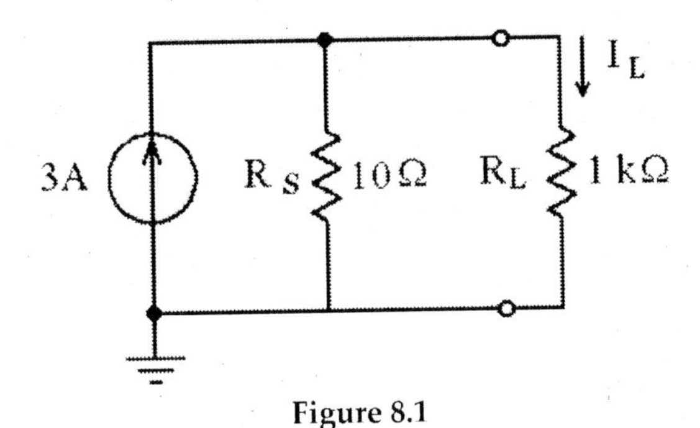

Figure 8.1

15) See Figure 8.1. When converted to a voltage source, the equivalent voltage is

A) 0.3 V B) 3.33 V C) 30 V D) 3000 V

16) See Figure 8.1. When converted to a voltage source, the equivalent series resistance is

A) 0.3 Ω B) 3.33 Ω C) 10 Ω D) 30 Ω

17) See Figure 8.1. What is I_L?

A) 2.97 mA B) 29.7 mA C) 297.0 mA D) 2.97 A

18) See Figure 8.1. When using PSpice (Windows) to determine I_L, if the sign of the answer is negative, it means that

A) the answer is correct, as I_L is negative.

B) the current source should be replaced by a voltage source before running the analysis.

C) the circuit ground symbol should be removed, allowing the circuit to "float."

D) the IPROBE component was connected backwards.

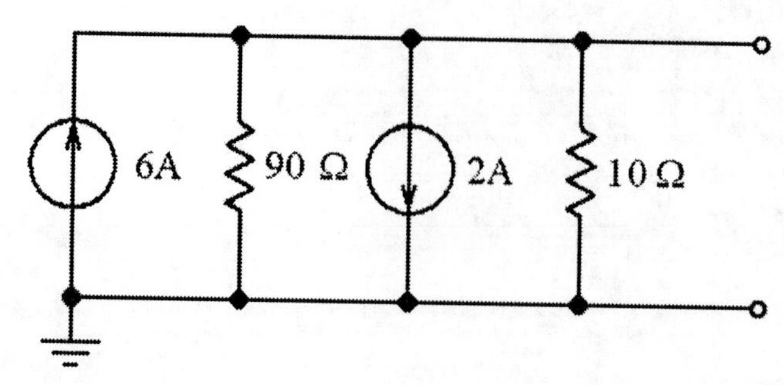

Figure 8.2

19) See Figure 8.2. The two current sources are equivalent to

A) a single 1.5 A source in parallel with a resistor.

B) a single 4 A source in parallel with a resistor.

C) a single 8 A source in parallel with a resistor.

D) a single 36 V source in parallel with a resistor.

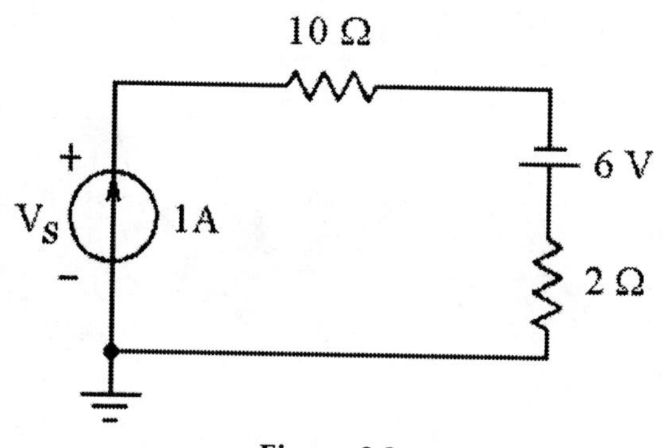

Figure 8.3

20) See Figure 8.3. What is V_S?

A) -6 V

B) +6 V

C) -4 V

D) +18 V

21) See Figure 8.3. If the 2 Ω resistor short circuits, what would happen to the voltage across the 10 Ω resistor?

A) The voltage would stay the same.

B) The voltage would drop to zero.

C) The voltage would decrease.

D) The voltage would increase.

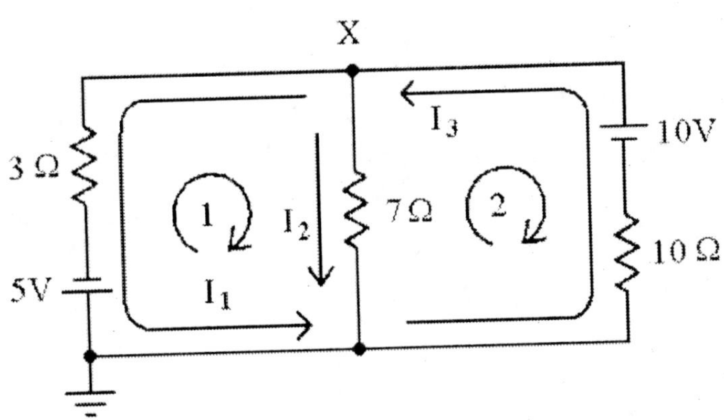

Figure 8.4

22) See Figure 8.4. Which equation describes node X?

A) $I_3 = I_2 - I_1$

B) $I_3 = I_2 + I_1$

C) $I_1 + I_2 + I_3 = 0$

D) $-I_1 - I_2 - I_3 = 0$

23) See Figure 8.4. If the branch current method is used, which equation describes loop 1?

A) $0 = +5V - (3\ \Omega)I_1 + (7\ \Omega)I_2$

B) $0 = +5V + (3\ \Omega)I_1 - (7\ \Omega)I_3$

C) $0 = -5V - (3\ \Omega)I_1 + (7\ \Omega)I_2$

D) $0 = -5V + (3\ \Omega)I_1 - (7\ \Omega)I_2$

24) See Figure 8.4. The equation for I_2 in terms of I_3 and I_1 is:

A) $I_2 = I_1 - I_3$

B) $I_2 = -I_1 - I_3$

C) $I_2 = I_1 + I_3$

D) $I_2 = I_3 - I_1$

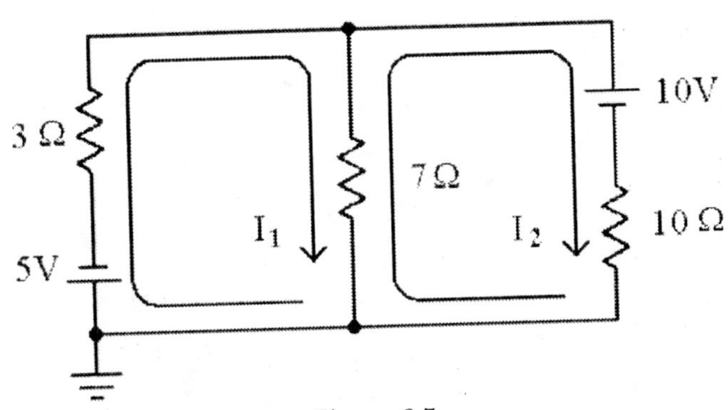

Figure 8.5

25) See Figure 8.5. Which of the following terms describes the voltage across the 7Ω resistor when using the mesh analysis (general) approach?

A) $(7\ \Omega)I_1$

B) $(7\ \Omega)I_2$

C) $(7\ \Omega)(I_1 - I_2)$

D) $(7\Omega)(I_1 + I_2)$

26) See Figure 8.5. Which statement is true if the loop current I_2 is found to be a negative number?

A) The nodal analysis approach should have been used, not the mesh analysis approach.

B) The determinant used to compute the current should have been third-order, not second-order.

C) The 10 V battery and 10 Ω resistor should have been converted to a current source.

D) The original direction assumed for I_2 is wrong.

27) See Figure 8.5. If nodal analysis were to be used to solve for unknown voltages in this circuit, how many nodes would be needed (including the reference node)?

A) 1 B) 2 C) 3 D) 4

28) See Figure 8.5. Transform the 5 volt source and the 3 ohm resistor to a current source and a resistor.

A) 5/3 amp current source in parallel with a 3 ohm resistor

B) 5/3 amp current source in series with a 3 ohm resistor

C) 3 amp current source in parallel with a 5/3 ohm resistor

D) 3 amp current source in series with a 5/3 ohm resistor

29) See Figure 8.5. The equation obtained from performing mesh analysis on mesh #1 is:

A) $5V + 3I_1 + 7(I_2 - I_1) = 0$ B) $5V + 3I_1 + 7(I_1 - I_2) = 0$

C) $5V + 3I_1 - 7(I_1 - I_2) = 0$ D) $5V - 3I_1 + 7(I_1 - I_2) = 0$

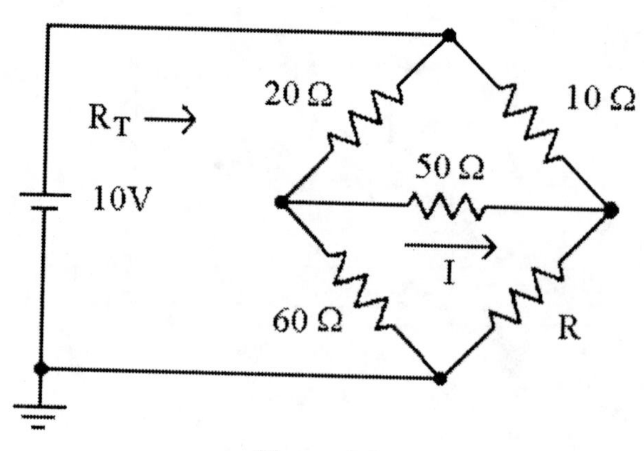

Figure 8.6

30) See Figure 8.6. What value of R will result in a balanced bridge?

A) 10 Ω B) 30 Ω C) 60 Ω D) 120 Ω

31) Which one of the following techniques would allow the calculation of R_T in the circuit of Figure 8.6?

A) Y-to-Δ conversion

B) Δ-to-Y conversion

C) voltage-to-current source conversion

D) linear bilateral analysis

32) In nodal analysis, how many equations will need to be solved if the circuit contains five nodes (including the reference node)?

A) 3

B) 4

C) 5

D) 6

33) The branch-current analysis, mesh analysis, and nodal analysis methods described in chapter 8 are applied to *linear bilateral* networks. What is the meaning of the word *bilateral* in this context?

A) Each network must contain at least two voltage and/or current sources.

B) Each node must be connected to more than two components.

C) The excitation current or voltage must periodically switch polarity.

D) A circuit element does not change in behavior if the current through that element is reversed.

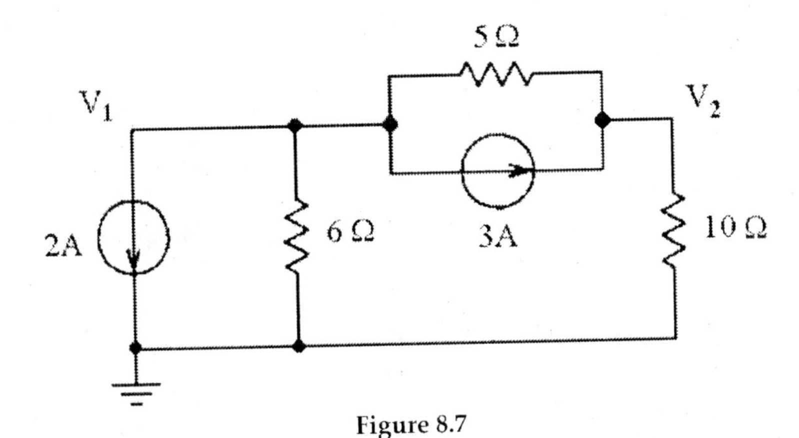

Figure 8.7

34) See Figure 8.7, transform the 2 amp current source in parallel with the 6 ohm resistor to a voltage source and a resistor.

A) 12 volt source in parallel with a 6 ohm resistor

B) 6 volt source in parallel with a 12 ohm resistor

C) 12 volt source in series with a 6 ohm resistor

D) 6 volt source in series with a 12 ohm resistor

35) Which of the following describes a junction of two or more branches, where a branch is any combination of series elements?

A) Connection

B) Loop

C) Node

D) Sub-circuit

36) The mesh–analysis approach eliminates the need to substitute the results of Kirchhoff's current law into the equations derived from the results of:

A) Calculating total current

B) Calculating total resistance

C) Finding equivalent resistance in branches

D) Kirchhoff's voltage law

37) Which of the following describes a network that is popular wherever detection of small changes in quantity is required?

A) Linear amplifier

B) Operational amplifier

C) Unbalanced bridge

D) Wheatstone bridge

38) When using the mesh analysis, which of the following describes the sign required if the current loop passes from the positive to the negative terminal?

A) Depends on the results of angle theta

B) Positive sign

C) Depends on the value of the current

D) Negative sign

Short Answer

39) Given these three equations, compute I_2 using determinants.

$5 = 2I_1 - 4I_3 + I_2$
$I_1 = I_3 - 7$
$I_3 - I_2 = I_1$

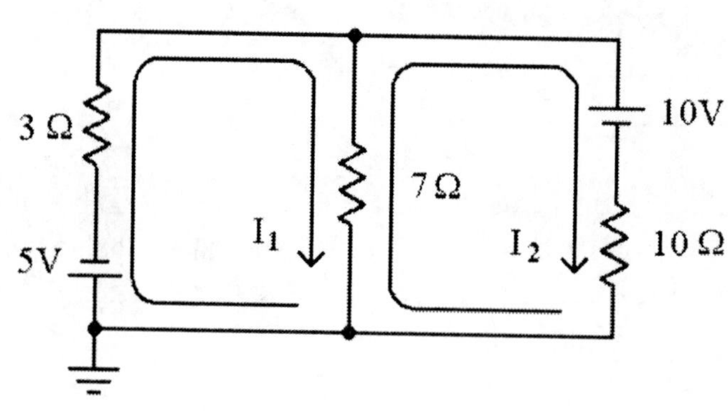

Figure 8.5

40) See Figure 8.5. Compute the voltages across the 3 Ω, 7 Ω, and 10 Ω resistors.

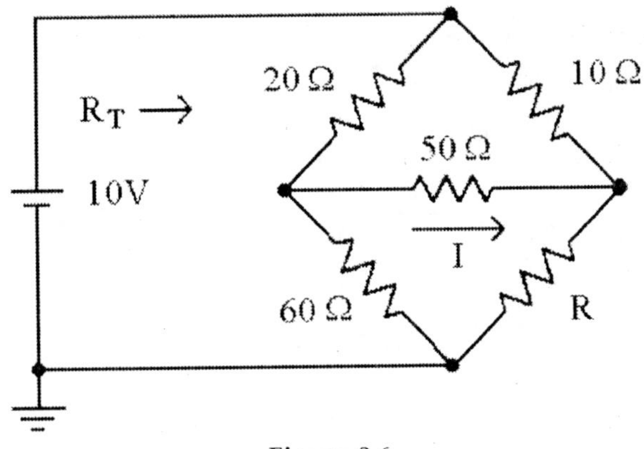

Figure 8.6

41) See Figure 8.6. If R = 100 Ω, what is R_T for this bridge network? Use the delta–wye conversion method.

42) See Figure 8.6. Using R = 100 Ω, compute the current I through the 50 Ω resistor. Use the analysis method of your choice.

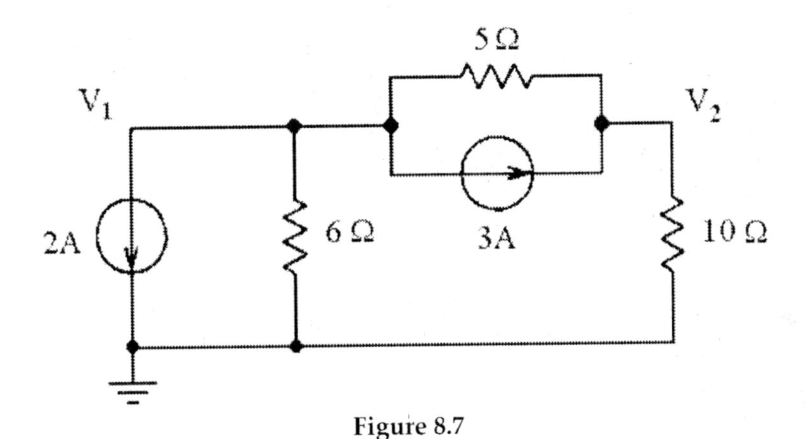

Figure 8.7

43) See Figure 8.7. Use nodal analysis to solve for voltages V_1 and V_2.

44) What PSpice (Windows) component is used as a current source?

45) Use the determinant function on the TI–85 calculator to compute I_2 in the equations below:

$3I_1 + 2I_2 = 6$

$I_1 + 4I_2 = -3$

46) What advantage does MathCAD provide in solving systems of simultaneous equations, compared with the TI–85 calculator?

47) The method of Mesh or loop analysis involves using what law?

48) The method of Nodal Analysis involves the use of what law?

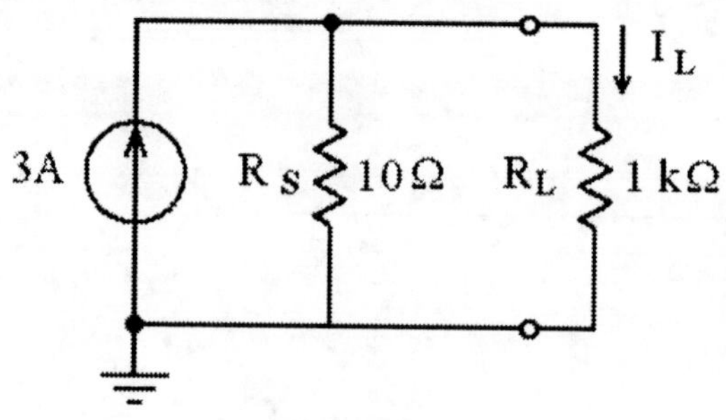

Figure 8.1

49) See Figure 8.1. How much power is produced by the current source?

50) See Figure 8.1. How much power is dissipated by the 10 ohm resistor?

51) See Figure 8.1. Which leg of the parallel circuit will carry most of the 3 amp source current?

Answer Key
Testname: CHAPTER 8

1) FALSE
2) FALSE
3) TRUE
4) FALSE
5) TRUE
6) FALSE
7) TRUE
8) FALSE
9) FALSE
10) TRUE
11) TRUE
12) FALSE
13) TRUE
14) B
15) C
16) C
17) B
18) D
19) B
20) B
21) A
22) B
23) D
24) D
25) C
26) D
27) B
28) A
29) B
30) B
31) B
32) B
33) D
34) C
35) C
36) D
37) D
38) D
39) 7 A
40) +3.84 V, -1.16 V, -11.16 V (polarity referenced from top to bottom)
41) 45.6 Ω
42) 21.47 mA (flows from right to left)
43) V1 = -12.86 V, V2 = 1.43 V
44) IDC
45) I2 = det[[3 6][1 -3]]/det[[3 2][1 4]] which produces the result -1.5 (amps)
46) MathCAD equations can be typed in directly, without converting them to the determinant format.
47) Kirchhoff's voltage law
48) Kirchhoff's Current law
49) 89.11 watts
50) 88.2 watts
51) 10 ohms

Chapter 9 Network Theorems

True/False

1) When using the superposition theorem, each ideal voltage and current source must be replaced by an open circuit.

2) Thevenin's theorem permits the reduction of any two-terminal linear dc network to one having a single voltage source and series resistance.

3) Norton's theorem permits the reduction of any two-terminal linear dc network to one having a single current source and a series resistance.

4) Under maximum power transfer conditions, the operating efficiency of a system is 100%.

5) The reciprocity theorem is applicable only to single-source networks.

6) The resistance calculated using Norton's theorem is equal to the resistance calculated using Thevenin's theorem for the same electrical network.

7) The total power delivered to a resistive element can be determined by the sum of the power levels established by each source.

8) In the superposition method, you replace a voltage source with an open circuit.

9) In the superposition method, you replace a current source with a short circuit.

10) For any physical network, the value of E_{th} can be determined experimentally by measuring the open-circuit voltage across the load terminals.

11) The primary difference between the equivalent circuit of Norton and Thevenin is that Nortons consists of voltage and a series resistor.

12) The superposition principle is applicable to power effects because the power loss in a resistor varies as the square of the current.

13) The Norton and Thevenin equivalent circuits can be found from each other by using source transformation.

14) The efficiency of a system is defined by the ratio of the power delivered to the load to all the power supplied by the source.

Multiple Choice

15) When using the superposition theorem on a two-source network, if the current produced by one source is in one direction, while that produced by the other source is in the opposite direction through the same resistor,

A) all voltage sources were not properly converted to current sources.

B) the absolute values of the two currents add algebraically, and the direction is the same as the direction of the larger current.

C) a mistake in the sign of the result occurred.

D) the resulting current is the difference of the two and has the direction of the larger current.

16) Power effects in a dc network cannot be determined using superposition because

A) open sources and shorted sources neither consume nor produce power.

B) power computations require a voltage source and a current source in each circuit.

C) power is proportional to the square of the current or voltage.

D) all voltage and current sources are ideal devices that consume no power.

17) Which one of these network theorems states that any two-terminal linear bilateral dc network can be replaced by a current source and a parallel resistor?

A) Thevenin's theorem
B) Norton's theorem
C) Millman's theorem
D) reciprocity theorem

18) Which theorem is limited to use in single-source networks?

A) superposition theorem
B) substitution theorem
C) Millman's theorem
D) reciprocity theorem

19) Under maximum power transfer conditions, which one is true?

A) The algebraic sum of all resistances in the source equals the algebraic sum of all resistances in the load.

B) The Thevenin resistance of the source equals the equivalent resistance of the load.

C) The equivalent load resistance is very large compared to the equivalent resistance of the source.

D) The equivalent load resistance is very small compared to the equivalent resistance of the source.

20) Millman's theorem states that

A) if the voltage across and the current through a branch are known, the branch can be replaced by a combination of elements that maintain the same voltage across and current through that branch.

B) any number of parallel voltage sources can be reduced to a single source.

C) any two-terminal linear bilateral source can be replaced by an equivalent circuit consisting of a current source and a parallel resistor.

D) the current in any branch of a network, due to a single voltage source elsewhere in the network, will equal the current through the branch in which the source was originally located if the source is placed in the branch in which the current was originally measured.

21) The substitution theorem states that

A) if the voltage across and the current through a branch are known, the branch can be replaced by a combination of elements that maintain the same voltage across and current through that branch.

B) any number of parallel voltage sources can be reduced to a single source.

C) any two-terminal linear bilateral source can be replaced by an equivalent circuit consisting of a current source and a parallel resistor.

D) the current in any branch of a network, due to a single voltage source elsewhere in the network, will equal the current through the branch in which the source was originally located if the source is placed in the branch in which the current was originally measured.

22) The reciprocity theorem states that

A) if the voltage across and the current through a branch are known, the branch can be replaced by a combination of elements that maintain the same voltage across and current through that branch.

B) any number of parallel voltage sources can be reduced to a single source.

C) any two-terminal linear bilateral source can be replaced by an equivalent circuit consisting of a current source and a parallel resistor.

D) the current in any branch of a network, due to a single voltage source elsewhere in the network, will equal the current through the branch in which the source was originally located if the source is placed in the branch in which the current was originally measured.

23) Which theorem states that any branch voltage can be replaced by a branch current as long as the voltage drop across the branch and current through the branch remain the same?

A) Millman's Theorem

B) Substitution Theorem

C) Superposition Theorem

D) Reciprocity Theorem

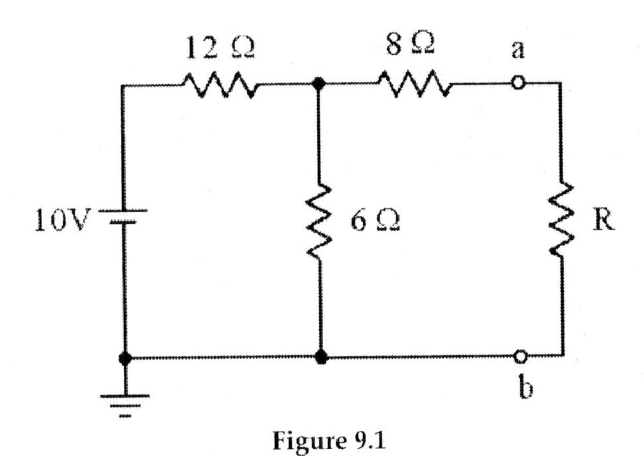

Figure 9.1

24) See Figure 9.1. What is the Thevenin resistance external to the resistor R?

A) 3.4 Ω B) 12 Ω C) 14 Ω D) 15.4 Ω

25) See Figure 9.1. What is the Thevenin voltage external to the resistor R?

A) 3.3 Ω B) 4.3 Ω C) 6.7 Ω D) 10 Ω

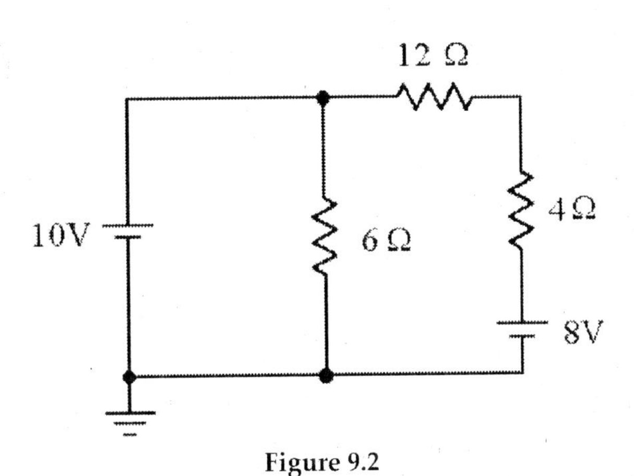

Figure 9.2

26) See Figure 9.2. Using the superposition theorem, what is the portion of the current through the 6 Ωresistor caused by the 8 V battery?

A) 0 A B) 0.36 A C) 0.5 A D) 1.67 A

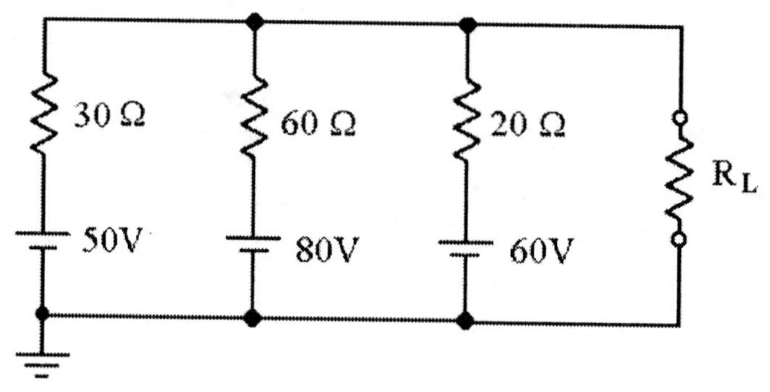

Figure 9.3

27) See Figure 9.3. Using Millman's theorem, what is R_{eq}, external to the load?

A) 5 Ω B) 10 Ω C) 60 Ω D) 110 Ω

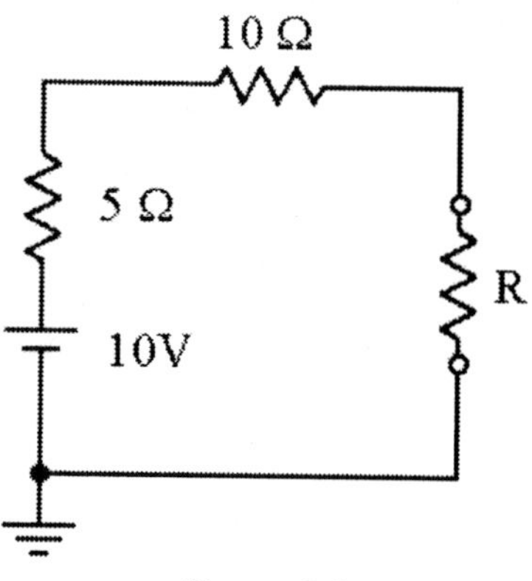

Figure 9.4

28) See Figure 9.4. What is the Norton equivalent resistance R_N external to the resistor R?

A) 3.33 Ω B) 5 Ω C) 15 Ω D) infinity

29) See Figure 9.4. What is the Norton equivalent current I_N?

A) 0.33 A B) 0.67 A C) 1.0 A D) 2.0 A

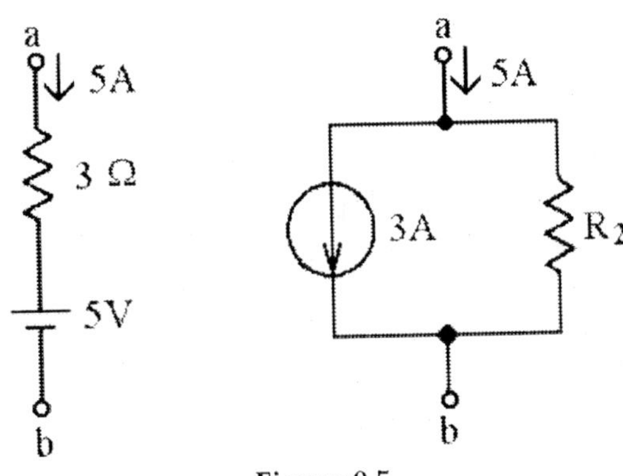

Figure 9.5

30) See Figure 9.5. What value of R makes these two circuits equivalent substitutions between terminals a and b?

A) 3 Ω B) 4 Ω C) 10 Ω D) 15 Ω

31) What PSpice (Windows) trace can be viewed with Probe to display the power dissipated by a 100 Ω resistor R4?

A) I(R4)*100

B) I(R4)*I(R4)*100

C) I(R4)*I(R4)/100

D) I(R4)/(100*100)

32) The reciprocity theorem states that

A) if the voltage across and the current through a branch are known, the branch can be replaced by a combination of elements that maintain the same voltage across and current through that branch.

B) any number of parallel voltage sources can be reduced to a single source.

C) any two-terminal linear bilateral source can be replaced by an equivalent circuit consisting of a current source and a parallel resistor.

D) the current in any branch of a network, due to a single voltage source elsewhere in the network, will equal the current through the branch in which the source was originally located if the source is placed in the branch in which the current was originally measured.

33) Thevenin's theorem states that you can replace a bilateral dc network with an equivalent circuit consisting of

A) a voltage source and a series resistor.

B) a current source and a series resistor.

C) a current source and a parallel resistor.

D) a voltage source and a parallel resistor.

34) Norton's theorem states that you can replace a bilateral dc network with an equivalent circuit consisting of

A) a voltage source and a series resistor.
B) a current source and a series resistor.
C) a current source and a parallel resistor.
D) a voltage source and a parallel resistor.

35) Leon-Charles Thevenin died in

A) 1972.
B) 1923.
C) 1927.
D) 1827.

36) Thevenin's theorem states that the Thevenin voltage is equal to

A) open circuit voltage at the network terminals.
B) short circuit voltage at the network terminals.
C) open circuit current at the network terminals.
D) short circuit current at the network terminals.

37) For a two-source network, if current produced by one source is in one direction, while the current produced by the other source is in the opposite direction through the same resistor, the resulting current is?

A) The difference between the two and has the same direction
B) The sum of the two and the direction of either
C) The average of the two and the direction of the largest
D) The product of the two and the direction of the smaller

38) Which network theorem states "The current through, or voltage across, an element in a linear bilateral network is equal to the algebraic sum of the currents or voltages produced independently by each other"?

A) Norton's maximum power transfer
B) Substitution
C) Superposition
D) Thevenin's

39) Which network theorem states "Any two-terminal, linear bilateral dc network can be replaced by an equivalent circuit consisting of a voltage source and a series resistor"?

A) Norton's maximum power transfer
B) Substitution
C) Superposition
D) Thevenin's

40) When R_{int} is equal to R_L, which of the following will occur?

A) No current will flow.
B) Resistance will be zero.
C) A load will receive maximum power.
D) A load will receive minimum power.

41) Which of the following is true of a series, open circuit?

A) A current can be read, but voltage will be zero.

B) A voltage can be read, but current will be zero.

C) Source voltage and current will be read.

D) Voltage and current will be equal.

Short Answer

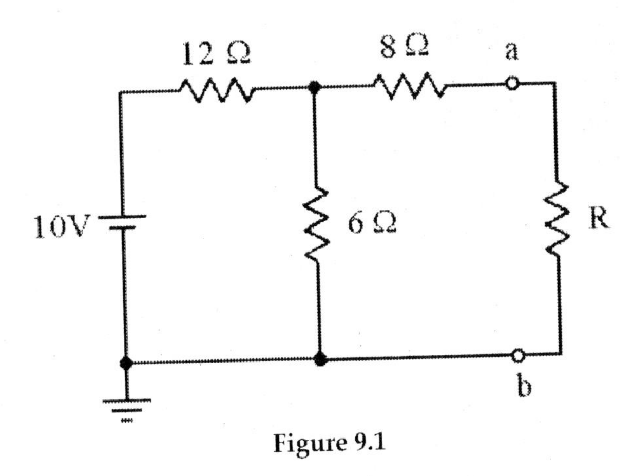

Figure 9.1

42) See Figure 9.1. Compute a value for R such that maximum power transfer occurs.

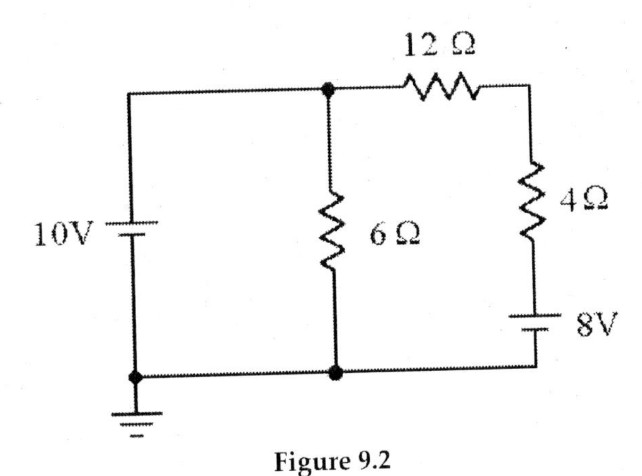

Figure 9.2

43) See Figure 9.2. Use the superposition theorem to compute the voltage across the 4 Ω resistor.

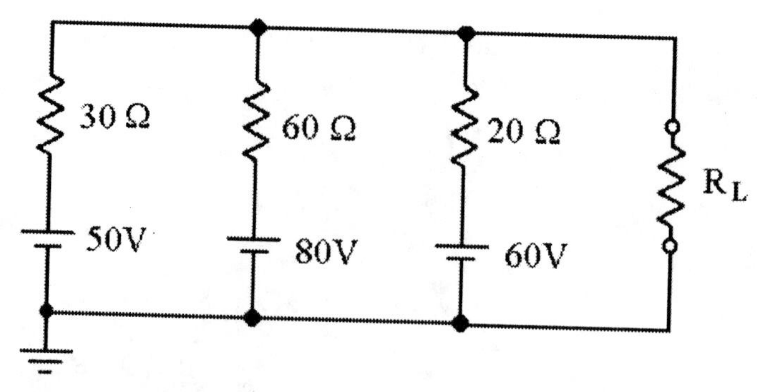

Figure 9.3

44) See Figure 9.3. Use Millman's theorem to determine the voltage across R_L. Assume that R_L has a value of 50 Ω.

45) Why are power generation stations *not* designed for maximum power transfer?

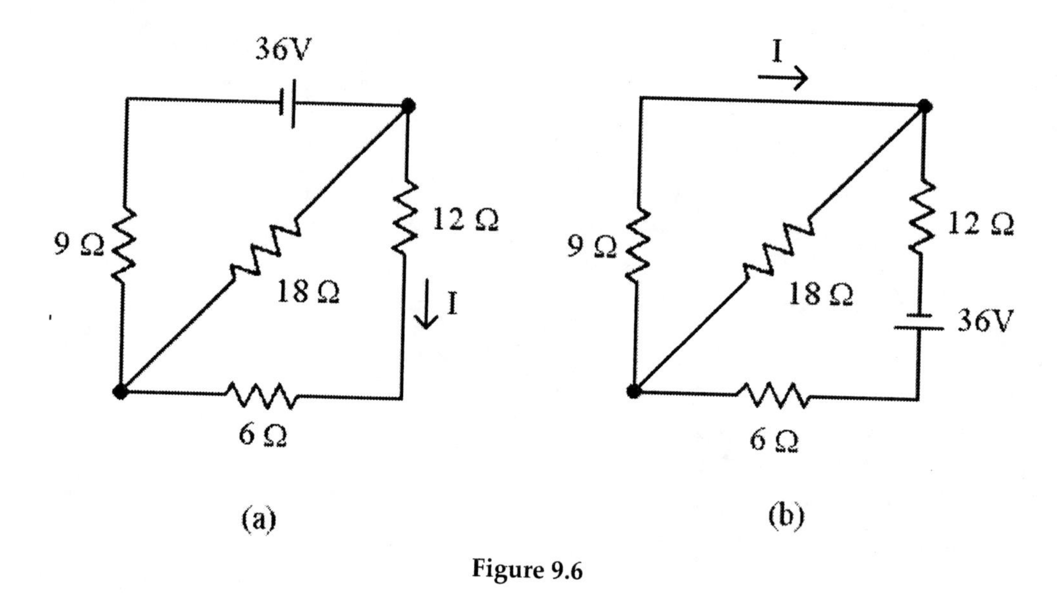

Figure 9.6

46) See Figure 9.6. Use the reciprocity theorem to prove that the current I is the same in circuits (a) and (b).

47) Write a BASIC program statement that will print the power dissipated by resistor R, given the current I flowing through it.

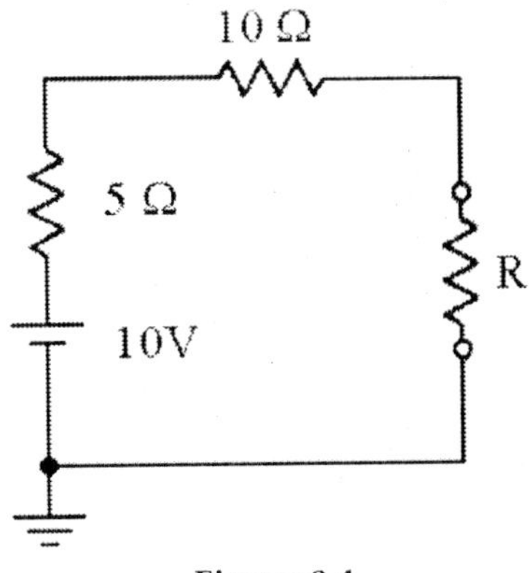

Figure 9.4

48) Write a BASIC program that will print the total power dissipated by the network in Figure 9.4, as R is swept from 0 Ω to 50 Ω.

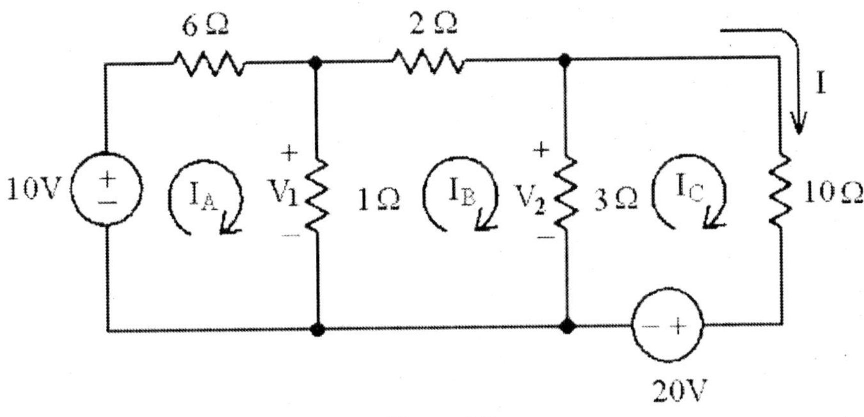

Figure 9.7

49) See Figure 9.7. Solve for the current flowing through the 10 ohms resistor by applying the superposition theorem.

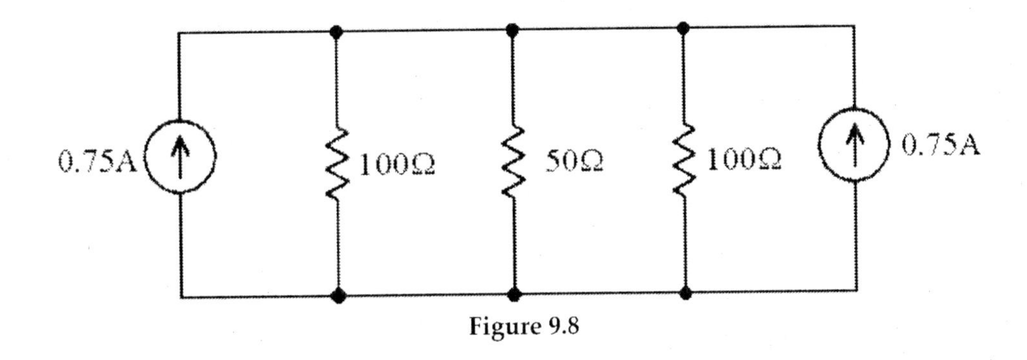

Figure 9.8

50) See Figure 9.8. Obtain the Norton current and Norton resistance circuit for the network assuming the 50 ohms resistor is the load resistor.

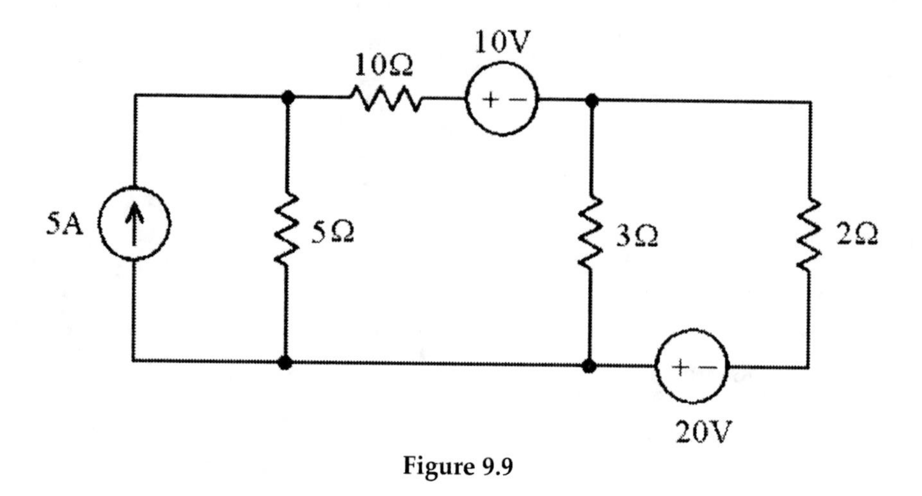

Figure 9.9

51) See Figure 9.9. Using Thevenin's Theorem determine the current in the 2 ohms resistor.

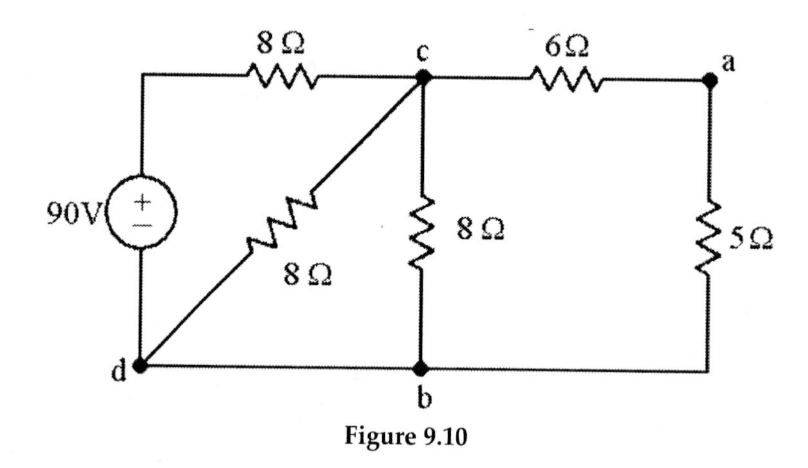

Figure 9.10

52) See Figure 9.10. Calculate the Thevenin voltage and Thevenin resistance circuit for the network at the terminals ab of the circuit.

1) FALSE
2) TRUE
3) FALSE
4) FALSE
5) TRUE
6) TRUE
7) FALSE
8) FALSE
9) FALSE
10) TRUE
11) FALSE
12) FALSE
13) TRUE
14) TRUE
15) D
16) C
17) B
18) D
19) B
20) B
21) A
22) D
23) B
24) B
25) A
26) A
27) B
28) C
29) B
30) C
31) B
32) D
33) A
34) C
35) C
36) A
37) A
38) C
39) D
40) C
41) B
42) 12 Ω
43) +0.5 V (polarity referenced from top to bottom)
44) +50 V (polarity referenced from top to bottom)
45) Because maximum power transfer occurs at 50% efficiency - much too costly for commercial power generation.
46) Both currents equal 1 A.
47) PRINT (11^2)*R
48)
```
10 V=10
20 FOR R=0 TO 50
30 PRINT (V^2)/(R+15)
40 NEXT R
```
49) I = -1.68 amps
50) IN = 1.5 amps, RN = 50 ohms
51) 5 amps
52) V_{TH} = 30V; R_{TH} = 10 ohms

Chapter 10 Capacitors

True/False

1) Ideal capacitors do not dissipate energy; they store it for use in the circuit.

2) Capacitance is directly proportional to the area of the plates and inversely proportional to the distance between the plates.

3) Electrolytic capacitors have low leakage currents and high breakdown voltages.

4) The total capacitance of several capacitors connected in series equals the sum of the individual capacitances.

5) An ideal capacitor looks like an open circuit to dc current once it has charged to its final value.

6) Electric flux lines always extend from a positively charged body to a negatively charged body.

7) A capacitor has a capacitance of 1 farad if 1 coulomb of charge is deposited on the plates by a potential difference of 1 volt across the plates.

8) The insulating material between the capacitor plates is called a conductor.

9) Permittivity is measured in farads per meter.

10) When breakdown occurs in a capacitor, the capacitor will display the same characteristics as an open circuit.

11) Similar to resistors, when you want to increase capacitance, you would connect them in series.

12) The ideal capacitor completely dissipates all energy supplied to it.

Multiple Choice

13) What is the capacitance of a capacitor if 10 μC of charge are present when 100 V are applied across its plates?

A) 0.1 μF B) 10 μF C) 1000 μF D) 10^7 μF

14) A parallel-plate capacitor has plates measuring 10 cm × 10 cm, spaced 1 mm apart. The dielectric is mica with a relative permittivity of 5.0, and the permittivity of a vacuum is 8.85 × 10−12 F/m. Which of these choices is closest to the actual capacitance value?

A) 5 pF B) 50 pF C) 500 pF D) 5000 pF

15) What is the maximum voltage that can be applied across the plates of a capacitor if the plate spacing is 0.05 inches? The dielectric is air, which has a dielectric strength of 75 V/mil.

A) 75 V B) 375 V C) 1500 V D) 3750 V

16) Which type of capacitor is used in applications requiring several thousand microfarads of capacitance?

A) mica B) electrolytic C) ceramic D) polyester

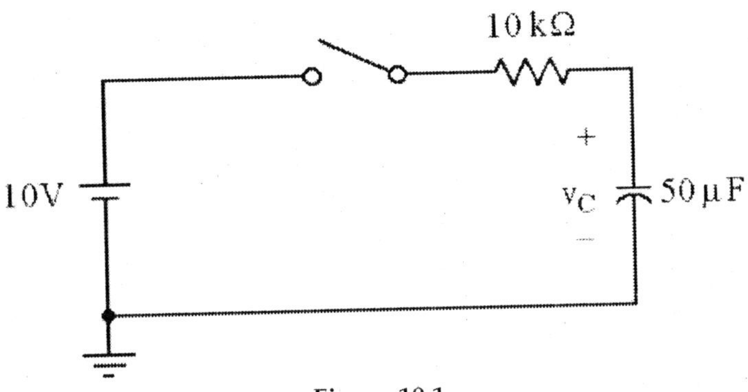

Figure 10.1

17) See Figure 10.1. What is the time constant t for this circuit?

A) 5 ms B) 50 ms C) 500 ms D) 5 s

18) See Figure 10.1. If the initial voltage of the capacitor = 0V, after the closing of the switch, when will the voltage v_C reach 5.0 V?

A) 0.35 s
B) 0.5 s
C) 1.5 s
D) It will never reach 5.0 V.

19) See Figure 10.1. If the initial voltage of the capacitor = 0V, what is the maximum instantaneous current that will flow through the capacitor after the closing of the switch?

A) 5 μA B) 1 mA C) 200 kA D) infinity

20) See Figure 10.1. The voltage v_C will reach 99% of its maximum value after how much time has elapsed?

A) 50 μs
B) 1 time constant
C) 5 time constants
D) 50 time constants

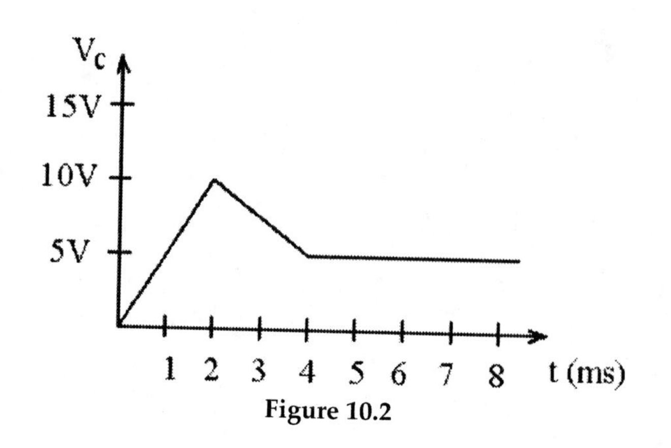

Figure 10.2

21) See Figure 10.2. The voltage across a 10 μF capacitor is changing as shown in the diagram. What is the current through the capacitor at t = 1 ms?

A) 0 A
B) 10 μA
C) 10 mA
D) 50 mA

22) See Figure 10.2. The voltage across a 10 μF capacitor is changing as shown in the diagram. What is the current through the capacitor at t = 6 ms?

A) 0 A
B) 10 μA
C) 10 mA
D) 50 mA

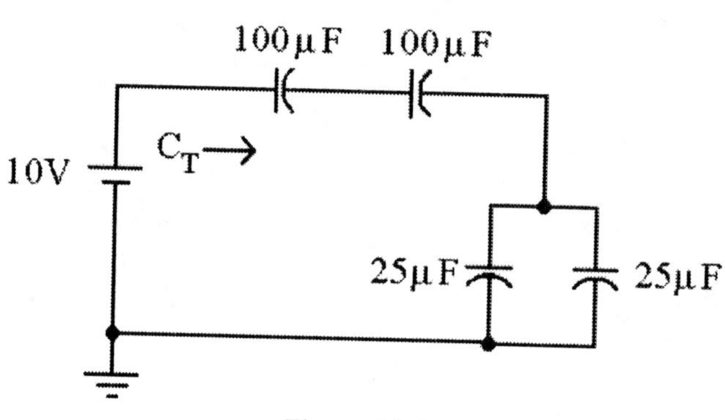

Figure 10.3

23) See Figure 10.3. What is the total capacitance C_T?

A) 12.5 μF
B) 25 μF
C) 50 μF
D) 212.5 μF

24) What must be added to Figure 10.3 in order to model the circuit with PSpice to find circuit currents and voltages?

A) A pulse source.

B) A switch to initiate the voltage connection.

C) High-resistance resistors from junctions of capacitors to ground.

D) PSpice ammeter and voltmeter components.

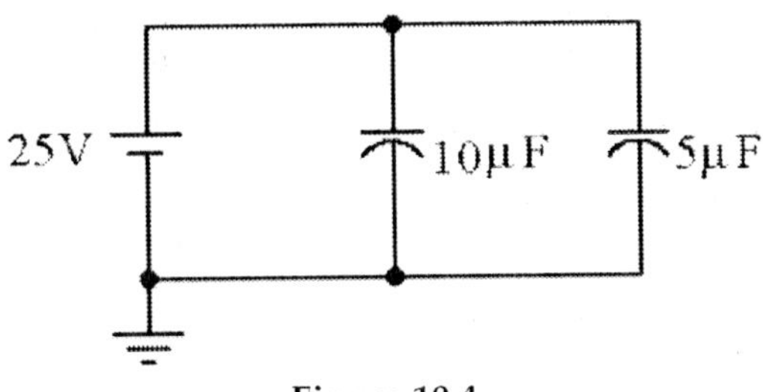

Figure 10.4

25) See Figure 10.4. Find the total charge stored on the capacitors in this circuit.

A) 0.133 μC B) 0.6 μC C) 83.3 μC D) 375 μC

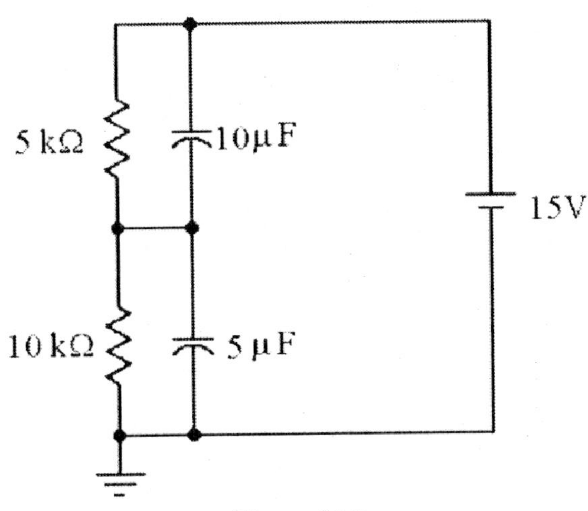

Figure 10.5

26) See Figure 10.5. What is the voltage across the 5 μF capacitor after each capacitor has charged to its final value?

A) 0 V B) 5 V C) 10 V D) 15 V

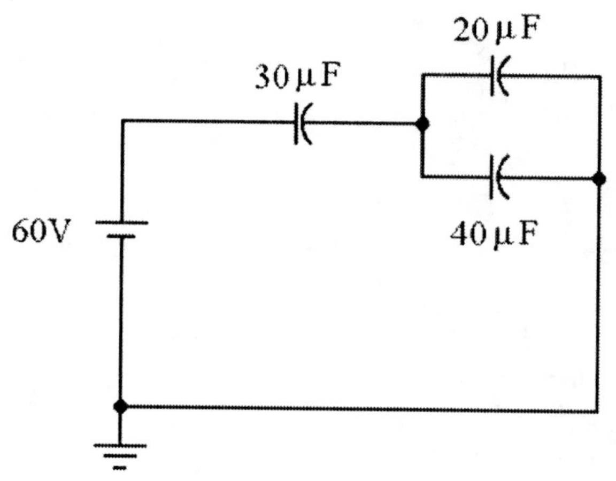

Figure 10.6

27) See Figure 10.6. What is the voltage across the 20 μF capacitor?

A) 20 V B) 30 V C) 40 V D) 60 V

28) The type of capacitance that results not by design, but because two conducting surfaces are in close proximity to each other is called

A) variable capacitance.
B) tantalum capacitance.
C) stray capacitance.
D) electrolytic capacitance.

29) Two capacitors are placed in series, what is their equivalent capacitance if the value of one capacitor is 1 microfarad and the value of the other capacitor is 3 microfarads?

A) 7.5 microfarads
B) 0.75 microfarads
C) 75 microfarads
D) 0.75 millifarads

30) The equivalent capacitance of capacitors C1 and C2 connected in series is 7.3 microfarads. If the capacitance of C1 = 9.6 microfarads, what is the capacitance of C2?

A) 2.3 microfarads
B) 30.5 microfarads
C) 35 microfarads
D) 84.5 microfarads

31) What is a dielectric?

A) A conductive plate in a capacitor
B) A measurement of capacitance
C) A charged particle
D) An insulator between two metal plates in a capacitor

32) Which of the following describes the action of a capacitor?

A) Opposes changes in the flow of current

B) Converts ac into dc

C) Creates a dc resistance

D) Stores electrical energy

33) What is the Q of a 500 pF capacitor with 50 volts applied?

A) .025 C B) .25 nC C) 2.5 nC D) 25 nC

34) What is the value of a capacitor with 250 volts applied and has 500 pC of charge?

A) 200 μF B) 2 pF C) .5 pF D) 500 μF

35) Which of the following is true of a capacitor once the charging phase in a dc network has passed?

A) Breakdown of the capacitor takes place.

B) The capacitor can be replaced by an open circuit.

C) The capacitor can be replaced by a short circuit.

D) Resistor values are no longer important.

36) How long will it take for a 2.2 μF capacitor to charge when connected in series with a 820 ohm resistor to a 25 volt source?

A) .18 ms B) 1.8 ms C) 18 ms D) 180 ms

37) What is the total capacitance of three capacitors connected in series with values of 2.2 μF, 6 μF and 3.2 μF?

A) 11.4 μF B) .92 μF C) 1.07 μF D) .107 μF

38) The voltage that can be applied across a capacitor for long periods of time without breaking down is known as:

A) Breakdown voltage B) Surge voltage

C) Initial Voltage D) Working voltage

39) What is the total capacitance of three capacitors connected in parallel with values of 2.2 μF, 6 μF and 3.2 μF?

A) 11.4 μF B) 114 μF C) 1.07 μF D) .107 μF

Short Answer

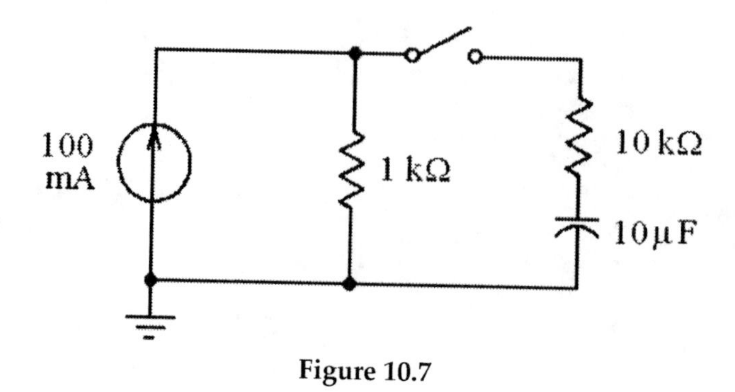

Figure 10.7

40) See Figure 10.7. Compute the time constant t for this circuit.

41) See Figure 10.7. After the switch closes, what is the final voltage reached across the 10 μF capacitor?

42) If a 0.1 μF capacitor has charged to 10 V before disconnecting it from the power source, how long will it take to discharge the capacitor to 3 V if R_{LEAK} = 100 MΩ?

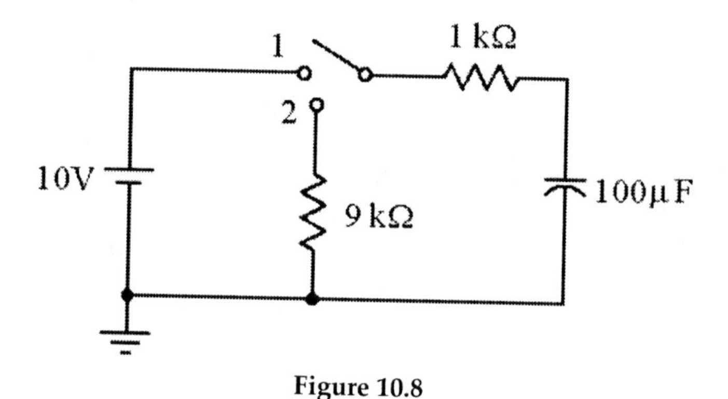

Figure 10.8

43) See Figure 10.8. Assuming the capacitor is initially discharged, what is the instantaneous current through the 1 kΩ resistor 0.2 s after throwing the switch to position 1?

44) See Figure 10.8. Assume that the capacitor has charged to v_C = 6 V. How long will it take for the capacitor to discharge to v_C = 4 V after the switch is thrown to position 2?

45) What do parameters V1 and V2 specify in a pulse source defined in PSpice (Windows)?

46) What is the time constant of a network that contains a 1 microfarad capacitor in series with a 1 Kilohm resistor?

47) What is the capacitive reactance of a 0.47 microfarads capacitor at 4300 Hz?

48) Assuming an ideal capacitor, with no leakage, what is the capacitive reactance of a 10 microfarad capacitance at dc?

49) What is the capacitive reactance of a 33 microfarad capacitor at 6500 Hz?

Answer Key
Testname: CHAPTER 10

1) TRUE
2) TRUE
3) FALSE
4) FALSE
5) TRUE
6) TRUE
7) TRUE
8) FALSE
9) TRUE
10) FALSE
11) FALSE
12) FALSE
13) A
14) C
15) D
16) B
17) C
18) A
19) B
20) C
21) D
22) A
23) B
24) C
25) D
26) C
27) A
28) C
29) B
30) B
31) D
32) D
33) D
34) B
35) B
36) C
37) C
38) D
39) A
40) 0.11 s
41) 100 V
42) 12.04 s
43) 1.35 mA
44) 0.41 s
45) V1 is the initial level; V2 is the pulsed level.
46) 1ms
47) 79 ohms
48) infinity
49) 0.74 ohms

Chapter 11 Inductors

True/False

1) Ideal inductors do not dissipate energy; they store energy in the form of a magnetic field.

2) Inductance is directly proportional to the area of the magnetic core and inversely proportional to the core length.

3) The time constant x for an inductor equals its inductance divided by its resistance.

4) The total inductance of several coils in parallel equals the sum of the individual inductances.

5) An ideal inductor looks like an open circuit to dc current once the magnetic field has reached its final value.

6) An inductance tends to oppose changes in current.

7) Lenz's law states an induced effect is always such as to oppose the cause that produced it.

8) The greater the change in current through the coil, the smaller the induced voltage.

9) Voltage across the coil is determined by the magnitude of the change in current through the coil and by the rate of change of current through the coil.

10) The larger the inductance, the more the circuit will oppose a rapid buildup in current level.

11) The steady-state level of the inductor current can be found by substituting its short-circuit equivalent and finding the resulting current through the element.

12) Because the energy of a coil is stored in the form of a magnetic field, the inductor can continue to store energy after current is removed.

13) The total inductance for inductors in series and parallel can be found the same way as resistors in series and parallel.

Multiple Choice

14) An air-core coil consists of 100 turns of wire wrapped on a 1 cm diameter coil form 4 cm long. What is the approximate inductance of this coil?

A) 5 μH B) 25 μH C) 250 μH D) 3 mH

15) If an air-core coil has an inductance of 2 μH, what will the inductance become if an iron core is inserted? Assume that the iron core has a relative permeability μ_T, of 1000.

A) 2×10^{-9} H B) 2 μH C) 63 μH D) 2000 μH

16) A toroidal inductor can be described as

A) any inductor that contains a ferromagnetic core.

B) an inductor that contains a doughnut-shaped core.

C) a permeability-tuned inductor, in which the core is adjustable within the coil to vary the inductance.

D) any inductor that contains core material exhibiting a linear BH characteristic curve.

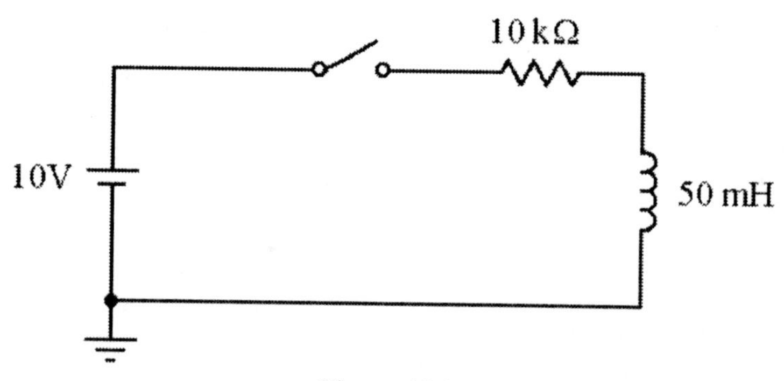

Figure 11.1

17) See Figure 11.1. What is the time constant τ in this circuit?

A) 5 μs B) 50 ms C) 500 s D) 2×10^5 s

18) See Figure 11.1. After the closing of the switch, what will the voltage across the *resistor* be after the voltage and current in the circuit reach a steady-state value? Assume that the inductor in this circuit is an ideal (lossless) device.

A) 0 V B) 2.5 V C) 5 V D) 10 V

19) See Figure 11.1. After the closing of the switch, when will the current through the inductor reach 800 μA? Assume that the inductor is an ideal (lossless) device.

A) 2.0 μs B) 5.0 μs C) 8.0 μs D) 10.0 μs

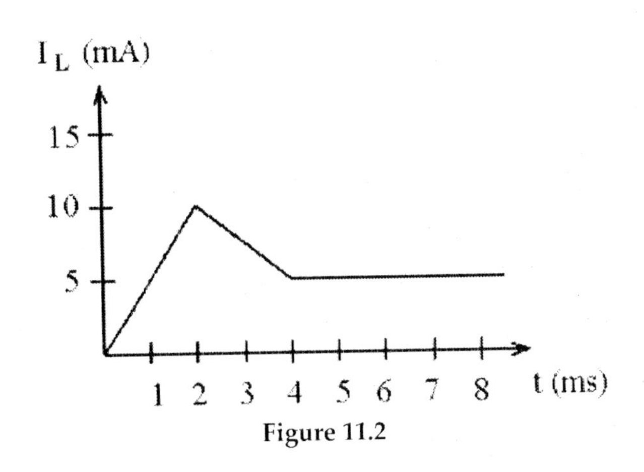

Figure 11.2

20) See Figure 11.2. The current through a 10 mH coil is changing as shown in the diagram. What is the voltage across the coil at t = 1 ms?

A) 0 V
B) 2 mV
C) 10 mV
D) 50 mV

21) See Figure 11.2. The current through a 10 mH coil is changing as shown in the diagram. What is the voltage across the coil at t = 6 ms?

A) 0 V
B) 2 mV
C) 10 mV
D) 50 mV

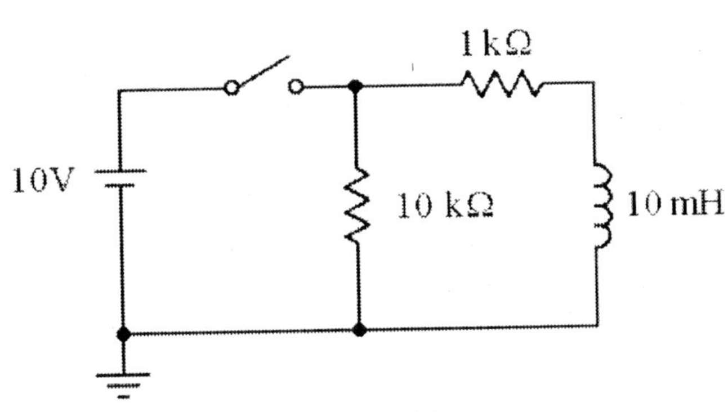

Figure 11.3

22) See Figure 11.3. After the closing of the switch, what will the current through the inductor be after the circuit voltages and currents have reached steady-state values? Assume that the inductor is an ideal (lossless) device.

A) 0 mA
B) 9.1 mA
C) 10 mA
D) 11 mA

23) See Figure 11.3. After the current has reached a steady-state value, the switch opens. What will the voltage across the inductor be the instant that the switch opens?

A) 1 V
B) 9 V
C) 10 V
D) 110 V

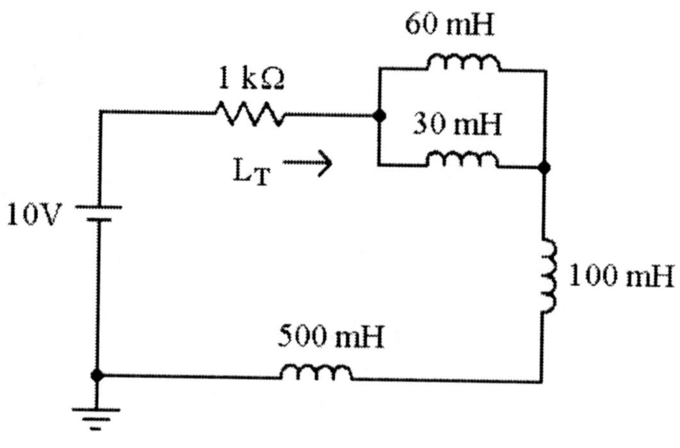

Figure 11.4

24) See Figure 11.4. What is the total inductance L_T?

A) 43 mH
B) 173 mH
C) 620 mH
D) 690 mH

25) How can PSpice (Windows) plot the voltage across the 30 mH inductor in Figure 11.4?

A) Plot V(L2:1)
B) Plot V(L2)
C) Plot–Add Plot–V(L2:1)–V(L2:2)
D) Plot V(L2:2)

26) What is the rate of change of flux if 50 V are induced in a coil consisting of 100 turns of wire?

A) 0.5 Wb/s
B) 2 Wb/s
C) 150 Wb/s
D) 5000 Wb/s

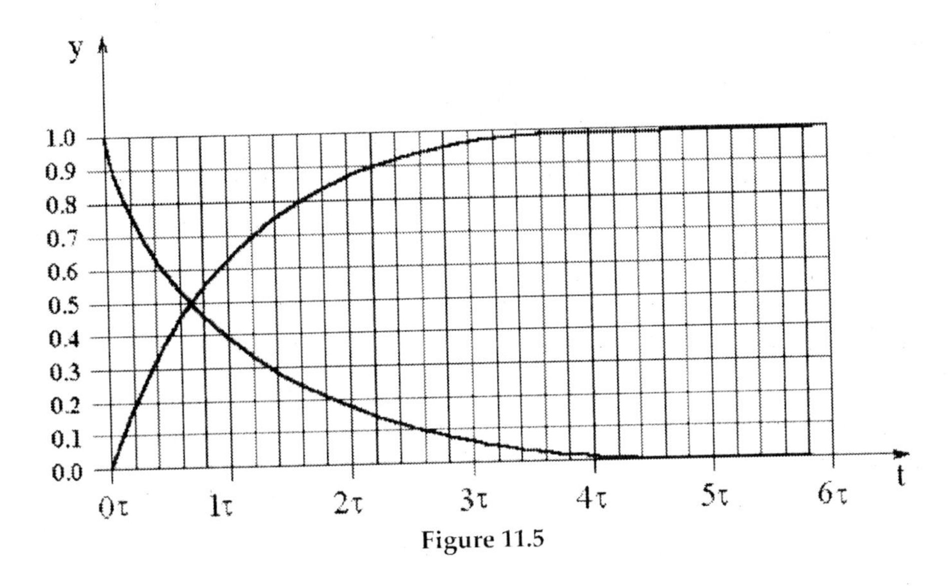

Figure 11.5

27) See Figure 11.5. These curves describe the voltage and current characteristics in an R-L circuit. In a series R-L circuit (similar to Figure 11.1), the voltage across the inductor reaches 80% of its final value

A) immediately.

B) 0.2 time constants after closing the switch.

C) 1.6 time constants after closing the switch.

D) 5.0 time constants after closing the switch.

28) See Figure 11.5. The point at which the two curves cross is the *only* point at which

A) the current through the coil is the same as the current through the resistor.

B) the voltage across the coil is the same as the voltage across the resistor.

C) the voltage across the coil has the same numeric value as the current through the coil.

D) the steady-state conditions exist.

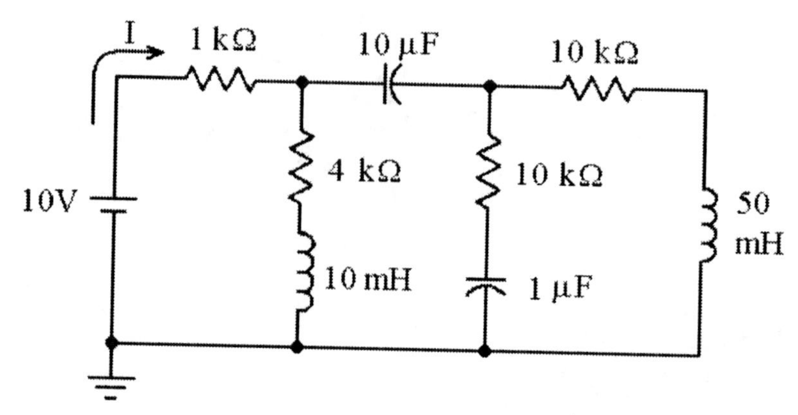

Figure 11.6

29) See Figure 11.6. What is the source current I after steady–state voltage and current conditions are reached?

A) 0 mA B) 0.9 mA C) 2 mA D) 4 mA

30) The notation $\frac{di}{dt}$ in an inductor refers to

A) the rate of change of current with respect to time.

B) the ratio of current to number of turns.

C) the magnetizing force applied per turn.

D) the coil permeability as a function of temperature.

31) The reactance of a 25 millihenry coil at 5000 hertz is which of the following?

A) 0.0013 ohms B) 785,000 ohms C) 785 ohms D) 13 ohms

32) What is the reactance of a 25 millihenry coil at 600 hertz?

A) 785 ohms B) 94 ohms C) 0.011 ohms D) 94,000 ohms

33) What is the inductance of a single–layer coil on a 0.8 inch diameter nonmagnetic core with a length of 1.25 inch and 320 turns or wire?

A) 960 millihenrys B) 3.8 millihenrys

C) 3.8 henrys D) 1200 millihenrys

34) Assume you need a 150 millihenry coil on a 0.75 inch nonmagnetic diameter, 1 inch long. How many turns of wire will be required?

A) 15,000 B) 15 C) 122.5 D) 507.5

35) If you have a coil consisting of 500 turns on a magnetic core with a cross-sectional area of 0.35 inch, and a permeability rating of 750, and the coil is 1.5 inches long, what is the inductance?

A) 6580 millihenrys
B) 6.6 millihenrys
C) 13 millihenrys
D) 100 millihenrys

36) Coils of various dimensions designed to introduce specified amounts of inductance into a circuit are called?

A) Changed coils
B) Electromagnets
C) Inductors
D) Semiconductors

37) What is the time constant for a coil of 33 mH and a resistor of 2K ohms?

A) 1.65 μS
B) 16.5 μS
C) 165 μS
D) 60.6 mS

38) What value of resistance would create a time constant of 50 μS using a 150 mH inductor?

A) 1K ohms
B) 2K ohms
C) 3K ohms
D) 4K ohms

Short Answer

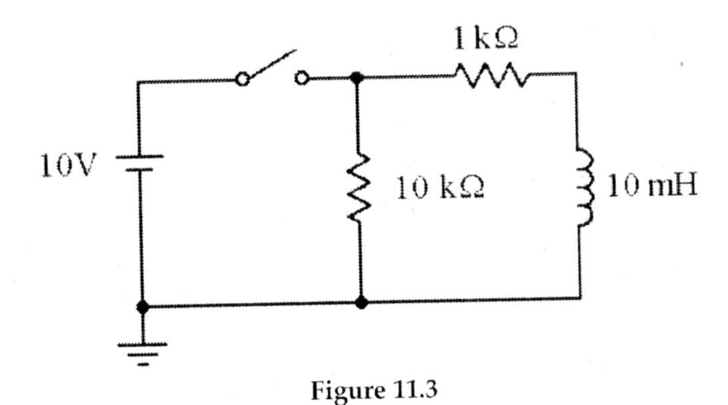

Figure 11.3

39) See Figure 11.3. What is the steady-state current through the coil after the switch closes?

40) See Figure 11.3. Assume that the 10 kΩ resistor is changed to a 10 MΩ resistor and that steady-state conditions are present before the change. What will the maximum coil voltage reach after the switch opens?

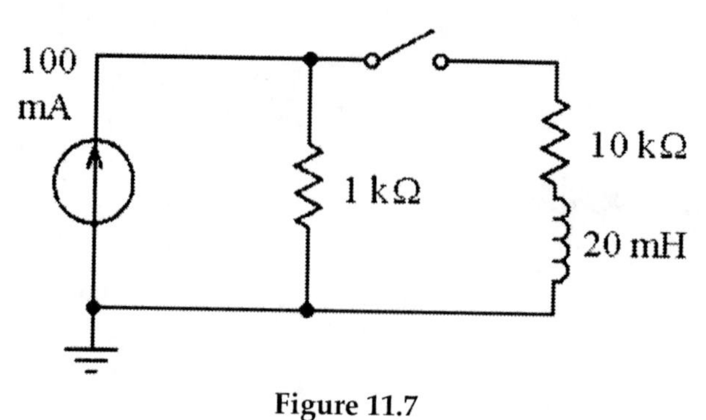

Figure 11.7

41) See Figure 11.7. What is the time constant τ for this circuit?

42) See Figure 11.7. After the closing of the switch, what is the final steady-state voltage value across the 10 kΩ resistor?

43) How much energy is stored in a 1 mH inductor if 3 A of current flow through it?

44) Write a BASIC program statement to solve the equation $i_L = I_m e^{-\frac{t}{(L/R)}}$

45) Write a BASIC program statement to compute the parallel equivalent of 2 inductors L_1 and L_2.

46) What is the time constant of a 500 millihenry coil and a 3,300 ohm resistor in series?

47) In an RL circuit, the time constant is the time required for the induced current to reach what percentage of its full value?

Answer Key
Testname: CHAPTER 11

1) TRUE
2) TRUE
3) TRUE
4) FALSE
5) FALSE
6) TRUE
7) TRUE
8) FALSE
9) TRUE
10) TRUE
11) TRUE
12) FALSE
13) TRUE
14) B
15) D
16) B
17) A
18) D
19) C
20) D
21) A
22) C
23) D
24) C
25) C
26) A
27) C
28) B
29) C
30) A
31) C
32) B
33) A
34) C
35) B
36) C
37) B
38) C
39) 10 mA
40) 100 kV
41) 1.8 μs
42) 90.9 V
43) 4.5 mJ
44) IL=IM*EXP(-T/(L/R))
45) LT=L1*L2/(L1+L2)
46) 0.015 seconds
47) 63%

Chapter 12 Magnetic Circuits

True/False

1) When using the "right–hand rule", the thumb points in the direction of conventional current flow, and the fingers point in the direction of the magnetic field.

2) Magnetizing force is independent of the type of core material.

3) Permeability is the lagging effect between flux density and the applied magnetizing force.

4) Magnetomotive force is inversely proportional to the number of turns of wire around the core.

5) The weber is the unit of magnetic flux.

6) The ends of a magnet are called poles.

7) Another name for magnetic lines of force is flux.

8) Reluctance is the magnetic equivalent of electrical current.

9) The creation of permanent magnets is made possible by residual flux density.

10) An increase in the number of turns and a decrease in the current through a wire will result in an increase for magnetomotive force.

Multiple Choice

11) Materials with very high permeabilities (hundreds or thousands of times that of free space) are called

A) diamagnetic.
B) ferromagnetic.
C) paramagnetic.
D) electromagnetic.

12) The spreading of the flux lines outside the air gap in a magnetic core is called

A) hysteresis.
B) permeability.
C) saturation.
D) fringing.

13) The magnetomotive force per unit length is called

A) the magnetizing force.
B) flux density.
C) permeability.
D) reluctance.

14) What is the approximate flux density in a round iron core if its diameter is 2 cm and flux β is 5×10^{-5} Wb?

A) 5×10^{-7} Teslas

B) 0.16 Teslas

C) 6.3 Teslas

D) 2×10^{6} Teslas

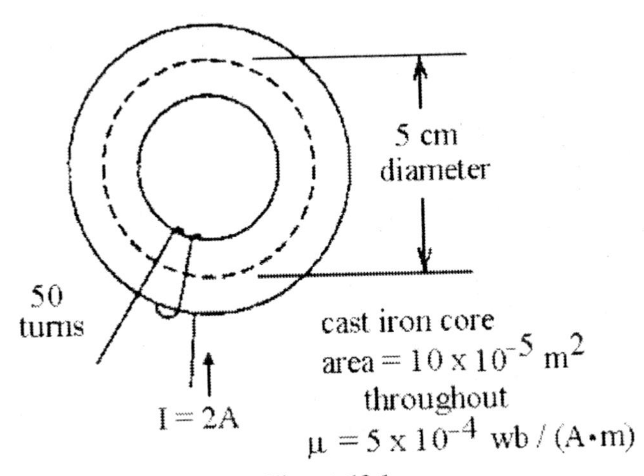

Figure 12.1

15) See Figure 12.1. What is the magnetomotive force in this magnetic circuit?

A) 100 Amp-turns

B) 0.38 Teslas

C) 0.04 turns/Amp

D) 25 Amp-turns

16) See Figure 12.1. What is the flux density in the core?

A) 0.05 Teslas

B) 0.318 Teslas

C) 1.0 Teslas

D) 20 Teslas

17) What is the reluctance in a magnetic circuit if a magnetomotive force of 500 At produces a flux of 10×10^{-5} Wb?

A) 2×10^{-7} At/Wb

B) 0.05 At/Wb

C) 20 At/Wb

D) 5×10^{6} At/Wb

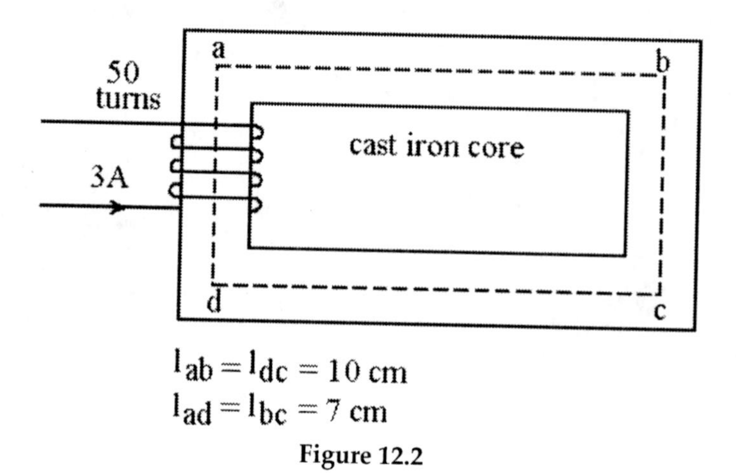

Figure 12.2

18) See Figure 12.2. How large is the source of magnetomotive force in this circuit?

A) 0.06 At
B) 3 At
C) 50 At
D) 150 At

19) See Figure 12.2. What is the magnetizing force H in this circuit?

A) 2.27×10^{-3} At/m
B) 1.96×10^{-2} At/m
C) 51.0 At/m
D) 441.2 At/m

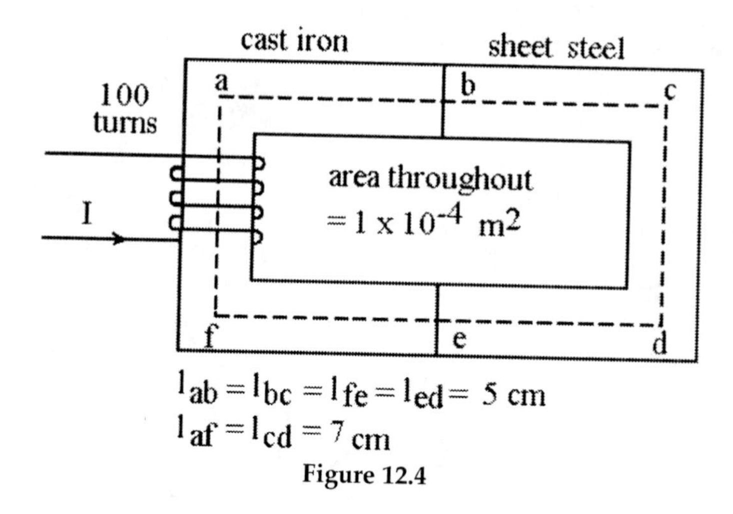

Figure 12.4

20) See Figure 12.4. If a flux of 6×10^{-5} Wb is established in the core, what is the flux density?

A) 2.25×10^{-5} T
B) 0.6 T
C) 1.67 T
D) 4.5×10^{4} T

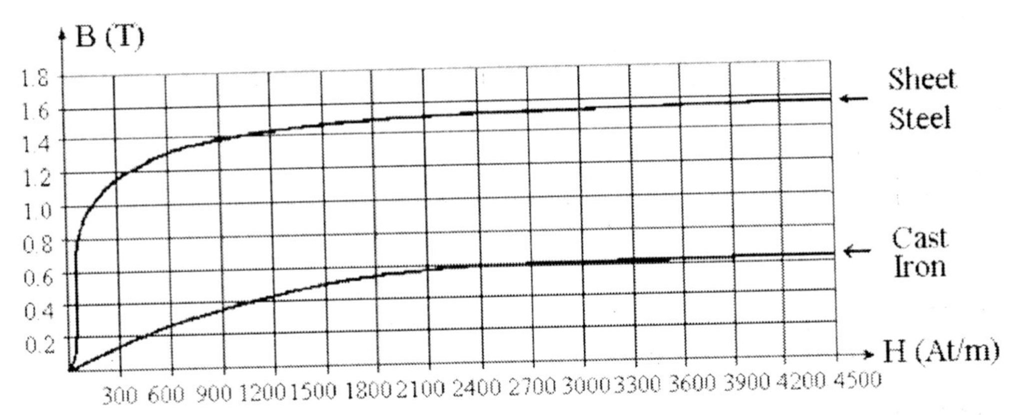

Figure 12.3

21) See the BH curves in Figure 12.3. If the flux density B in a cast iron core is 0.4 T, what is the magnetomotive force drop in the core if the core length is 10 cm and the area is 2×10^{-4} m^2?

A) 0.21 At
B) 105 At
C) 1.05×10^4 At
D) 5.25×10^6 At

22) The flux density that remains when the magnetizing force is removed is called

A) the residual flux density.
B) the coercive force.
C) the saturation potential.
D) the bubble domain region.

23) Ampere's circuital law states that

A) magnetic flux lines follow the path of least reluctance.
B) current in the magnetic core equals the magnetomotive force divided by the reluctance.
C) the algebraic sum of the rises and drops around a closed loop in a magnetic circuit is zero.
D) the sum of the fluxes entering a junction equals the sum of the fluxes leaving a junction.

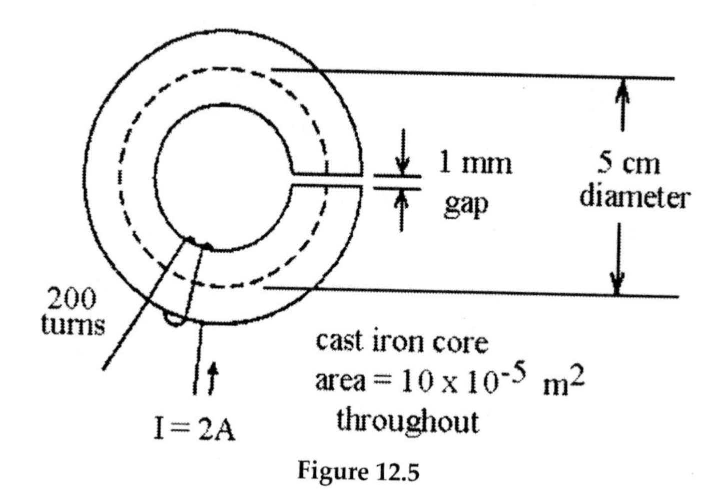

Figure 12.5

24) See Figure 12.5. If the current I is fixed, inserting a piece of cast iron into the air gap will

A) cause the magnetomotive force to increase.

B) cause the magnetomotive force to decrease.

C) cause the flux β to decrease.

D) cause the flux β to increase.

25) Which one of these statements is true of a cast iron magnetic circuit in which the core contains an air gap?

A) The air gap acts as an open circuit, thus preventing any flux lines from forming.

B) The air gap has a very low reluctance compared to the surrounding iron core.

C) The permeability of the air gap is about the same as the permeability of free space.

D) The flux density of the air gap is much greater than the flux density of the surrounding iron core.

26) A dynamic microphone changes sound into an electrical signal using

A) piezoelectric effects.

B) carbon granule movement inside of a magnetic field.

C) capacitive effects of a moving plate.

D) a moving coil inside of a magnetic field.

27) A Hall effect sensor generates an output when

A) current flows through it, perpendicular to its crystalline structure.

B) photons strike its surface.

C) it is exposed to a magnetic field.

D) it is placed in a liquid Nitrogen bath.

28) If like poles of two magnets are brought near each other, what will happen?

A) They will attract each other.
B) They will be damaged.
C) They will repel each other.
D) An electrical current will be generated.

29) What is the magnetic equivalent to electrical voltage?

A) Flux
B) Magnetomotive force
C) Reluctance
D) Magnetic field

30) What is the magnetic equivalent to electrical resistance?

A) Flux
B) Magnetomotive force
C) Reluctance
D) Magnetic field

31) How can an electrical current be induced with a coil and a magnet?

A) Placing a coil at right angles to the magnetic field.
B) Placing the coil parallel to the magnetic field.
C) Holding both the magnet and coil perfectly stationary.
D) Moving either the magnet or the coil.

32) What is the effect on flux density as area of a magnetic field is increased?

A) Increases
B) Reverses the N and S pole
C) Remains the same
D) Decreases

33) A measure of the ease with which magnetic lines can be established in the material is known as:

A) Flux density
B) Flux distribution
C) Permeability
D) Teslas

34) Which of the following do the number of turns, the current and length of the core determine?

A) Flux density
B) Magnetizing force
C) Permeability
D) Reluctance

35) Which of the following describes a point where all domains will have the orientation of the applied magnetizing force and any further increase in external field will not increase the strength of the magnetic flux through the core?

A) Choking
B) Hysteresis
C) Reluctance
D) Saturation

36) Magnetomotive force in magnetism is the equivalent to which of the following values?

A) Voltage B) Current C) Resistance D) Conductance

37) Which of the following in magnetic circuits is the equivalent of flux in electronic circuits?

A) Voltage B) Current C) Resistance D) Conductance

38) The key element in writing of information on a disk and reading information from a disk is?

A) Flux density B) Electromagnetism

C) Reluctance D) Hysteresis

39) Which of the following devices generates an output voltage when exposed to a magnetic field?

A) Resistor B) Magnetic reed switch

C) Hall effect sensor D) Capacitor

Short Answer

40) Write the equation that expresses Ohm's Law for magnetic circuits.

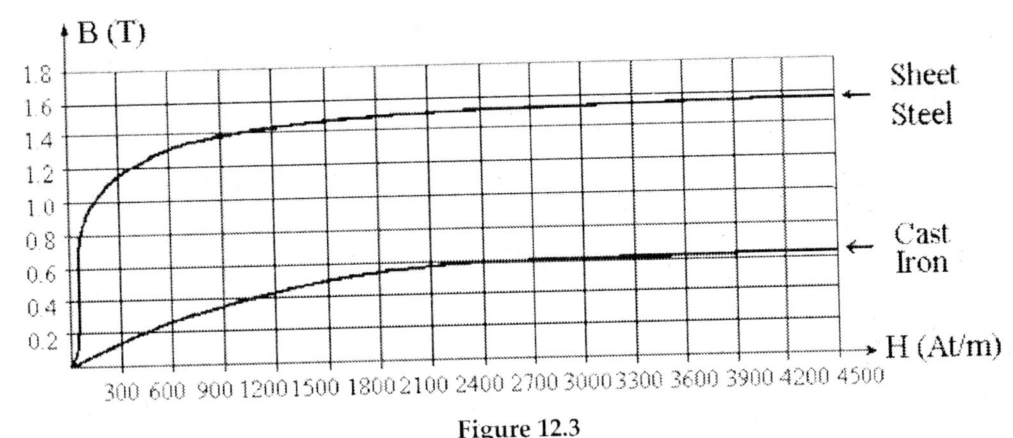

Figure 12.3

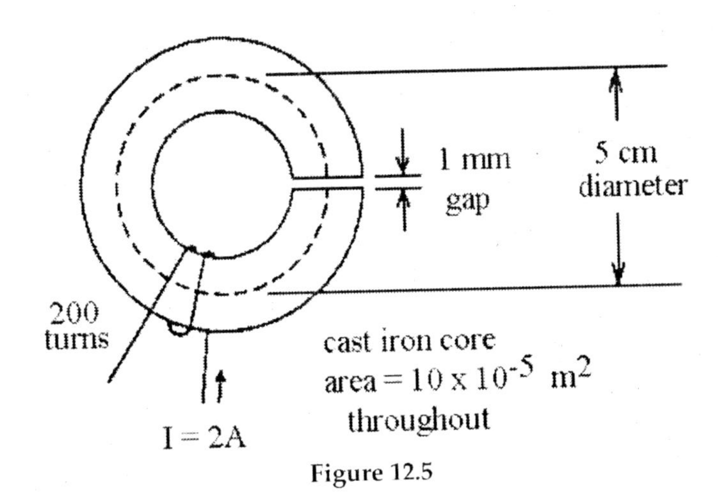

Figure 12.5

41) See Figure 12.5 and the BH curves in Figure 12.3. A flux of 5×10^{-5} Wb exists in this magnetic circuit. Determine the magnetizing force H in the iron core.

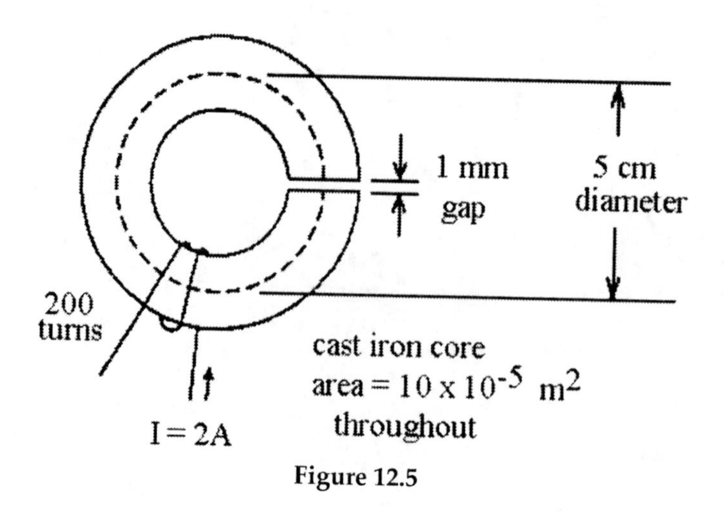

Figure 12.5

42) See Figure 12.5. A flux of 5×10^{-5} Wb exists in this magnetic circuit. If permeability of air is $4\pi \times 10^{-7}$ Wb/A-m, what is the magnetizing force of the air gap?

43) See Figure 12.5. Using results from previous problems, determine the current I.

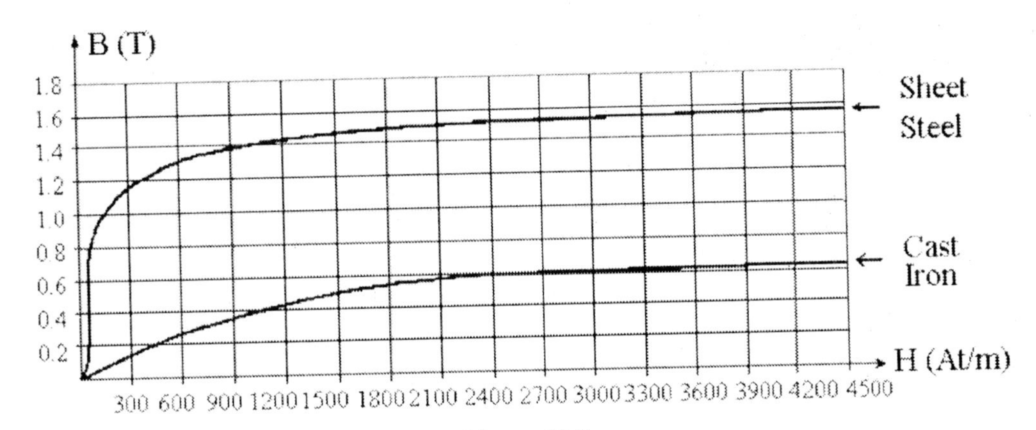

Figure 12.3

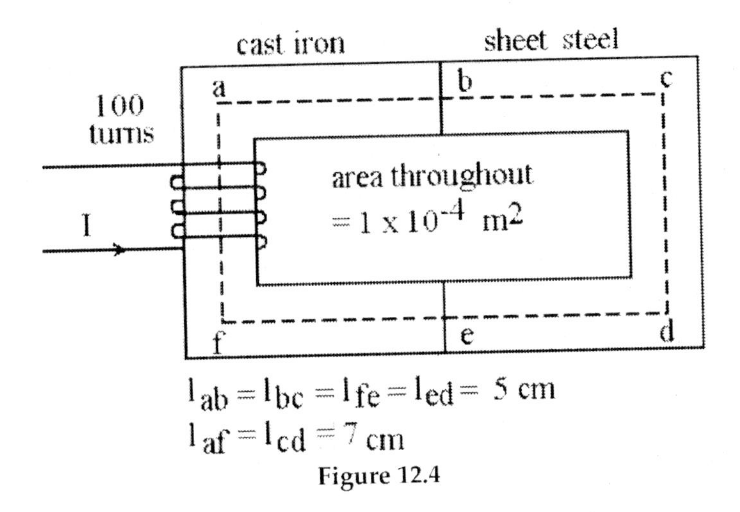

$l_{ab} = l_{bc} = l_{fe} = l_{ed} = 5$ cm

$l_{af} = l_{cd} = 7$ cm

Figure 12.4

44) See Figure 12.4 and the BH curves in Figure 12.3. Compute I such that a flux $\beta = 5 \times 10^{-5}$ Wb exists in the core.

45) Describe an application in which a magnetic reed switch is used.

46) How does the hard disk read/write head in a computer distinguish a "0" level from a "1" level?

47) Assume you have a 50 turn toroidal coil 0.15 inch high, with an outside diameter of 0.8 inch, an inside diameter of 0.3 inch and a permeability of 400. What is the inductance of this coil?

48) How many turns are required for a toroidal coil 0.15 inch high, with an outside diameter of 0.8 inch, an inside diameter of 0.3 inch and a permeability of 400 to have an inductance of 1466 millihenrys?

49) Define *saturation* as it pertains to a magnetic core material.

50) Rotating an armature in a magnetic field produces what type of electricity?

Answer Key
Testname: CHAPTER 12

1) TRUE
2) TRUE
3) FALSE
4) FALSE
5) TRUE
6) TRUE
7) TRUE
8) FALSE
9) TRUE
10) FALSE
11) B
12) D
13) A
14) B
15) A
16) B
17) D
18) D
19) D
20) B
21) B
22) A
23) C
24) D
25) C
26) D
27) C
28) C
29) B
30) C
31) D
32) D
33) C
34) B
35) D
36) A
37) B
38) B
39) C
40) flux = mmf ÷ reluctance
41) 1500 At/m
42) 3.98 × 105 At/m
43) 3.2 A
44) 2.7 A
45) A magnetic reed switch could detect a window or door being opened, in order to trigger a burglar alarm.
46) A 1 is identified as a positive-going pulse, while a 0 is identified as a negative-going pulse.
47) 727 millihenrys
48) 71 turns
49) An increasing magnetic field strength no longer increases the magnetic flux in the core.
50) ac

Chapter 13 Sinusoidal Alternating Waveforms

True/False

1) The peak voltage produced by an ac generator occurs when the coil moves in parallel with the magnetic flux lines.

2) The peak value of a waveform is the maximum instantaneous value as measured from the zero-volt level.

3) The quantity π is the ratio of the circumference of a circle to its diameter.

4) The cosine curve leads the sine curve by 180°.

5) The average value of a sine wave is zero.

6) The duration of an alternating cycle is called a period.

7) There are 57.3 degrees in one radian.

8) The SI unit of frequency is called a hertz.

9) The SI unit of radian frequency is radians per second.

10) R, L and C elements have response characteristics that affect all alternating waveforms.

11) Increasing the frequency of a waveform increases the period.

12) If a waveform crosses the horizontal axis with a positive-going slope of 90° sooner than the other waveform, it is said to lag by 90°.

13) The effective value of any current or voltage is the value indicated on a dc meter.

14) The equivalent dc value of a sinusoidal current or voltage is 70.7% of its peak value.

15) A true RMS meter will read the effective value of any waveform.

Multiple Choice

16) What is the period of a 50 kHz sine wave?

A) 5×10^4 s   B) 5 μs   C) 50 μs   D) 20 μs

17) What is the angular velocity of a 50 kHz sine wave?

A) $5\pi \times 10^4 \frac{\text{rad}}{\text{sec}}$n   B) $\pi \times 10^5$ rad/s   C) $5\pi \times 10^4$ rad/s   D) $2\pi \times 10^5$ rad/s

18) What angle in degrees is equivalent to $\pi/3$ radians?

A) 120°   B) 90°   C) 30°   D) 60°

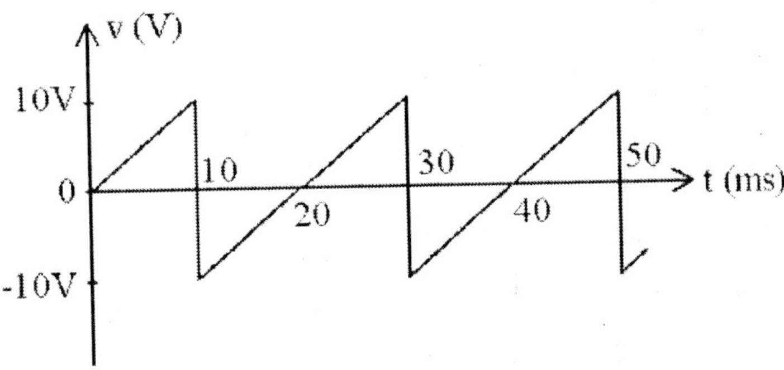

Figure 13.1

19) See Figure 13.1. What is the period of this waveform?

A) 50 ms   B) 30 ms   C) 10 ms   D) 20 ms

20) See Figure 13.1. What is the frequency of this waveform?

A) 33 Hz   B) 50 Hz   C) 20 Hz   D) 100 Hz

21) See Figure 13.1. What is the peak-to-peak voltage of this waveform?

A) +10 V   B) −10 V   C) +20 V   D) 0 V

22) See Figure 13.1. What is the *average* value of this waveform?

A) +5 V   B) +7.07 V   C) 0 V   D) +10 V

23) What angle in radians is equivalent to 270°?

A) π B) $3\pi/2$ C) $3\pi/4$ D) $\pi/2$

24) What is the amplitude in the equation v = 35 sin(5000t)?

A) 5000/π V
B) 5000 V
C) 35 V
D) 35π V

25) What is the frequency in the equation v = 35 sin(5000t)?

A) 2500/π Hz
B) 5000 Hz
C) 5000π Hz
D) 35 Hz

26) If i = 10 sin α,what is i at α = 30°?

A) -9.88 V
B) +10 V
C) +5 V
D) 0 V

27) If i = 4 sin(θt + 50°) and v = 7 sin(θt - 30°), which one of these statements is true?

A) i lags v by 80°
B) i leads v by 20°
C) i leads v by 80°
D) i lags v by 20°

28) What is the *effective* voltage if v = 10 sin(θt - 50°)?

A) 14.14 V
B) 20 V
C) 10 V
D) 7.07 V

29) If the *effective* voltage of an ac receptacle is 120V, what is the *peak-to-peak* voltage?

A) 169.7 V
B) 240 V
C) 339.4 V
D) 84.8 V

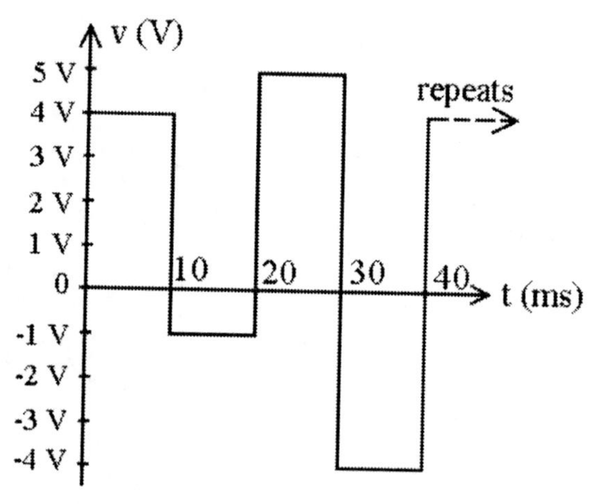

Figure 13.2

30) See Figure 13.2. What is the *average* value of this waveform?

A) +1 V
B) +4 V
C) +3 V
D) +2 V

31) Which PSpice (Windows) ac voltage source is useful for most applications?

A) VRMS
B) VAVE
C) VAC
D) VSIN

32) PSpice defines the magnitude of a source to be its

A) peak value.
B) peak-to-peak value.
C) average value.
D) rms value.

33) Find the period of a periodic wave that has a frequency of 0.2 Hz.

A) 50 seconds
B) 0.5 seconds
C) 5 seconds
D) 5 milliseconds

34) Find the frequency of a periodic wave that has a period of one hour.

A) 27.8 mHz
B) 0.278 mHz
C) 278 mHz
D) 2.78 mHz

35) Which of the following will be necessary to increase the frequency of a sinusoidal waveform?

A) Increase the time period between successive repetitions
B) Decrease the time period between successive repetitions
C) Reverse polarity
D) Increase the amplitude

36) Which of the following best describes the peak-to-peak value?

A) The difference of the positive and negative peaks
B) The product of the positive and negative peaks
C) 70.7% of the positive and negative peaks
D) The sum of the magnitude of the positive and negative peaks

37) What is the frequency of a waveform that has a period of 8 ms?

A) 1.25 Hz
B) 1.25 KHz
C) 125 Hz
D) 12.5 Hz

38) The magnitude of a waveform at any instant of time is called the?

A) Average value
B) Peak-to-peak value
C) Peak value
D) Instantaneous value

Short Answer

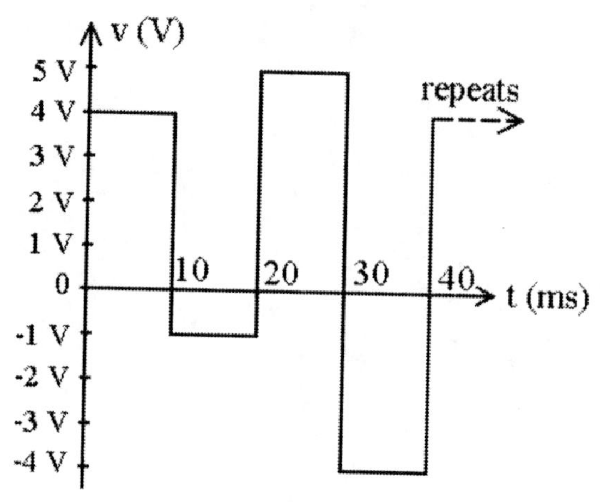

Figure 13.2

39) See Figure 13.2. Compute the *effective* voltage value of this waveform.

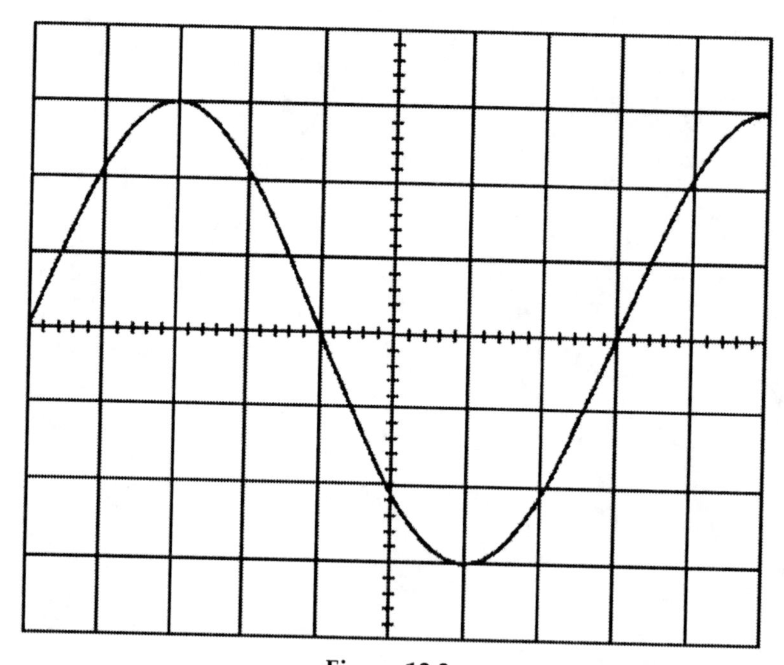

Figure 13.3

40) See Figure 13.3. An oscilloscope screen produces the waveform shown. The vertical sensitivity control is set to 20 volts per major division, and the horizontal sensitivity is set at 100 μs per major division. What is the frequency of the displayed waveform?

41) See Figure 13.3. An oscilloscope screen produces the waveform shown. The vertical sensitivity control is set to 20 volts per major division, and the horizontal sensitivity is set at 100 μs per major division. Write the general voltage equation that describes this waveform.

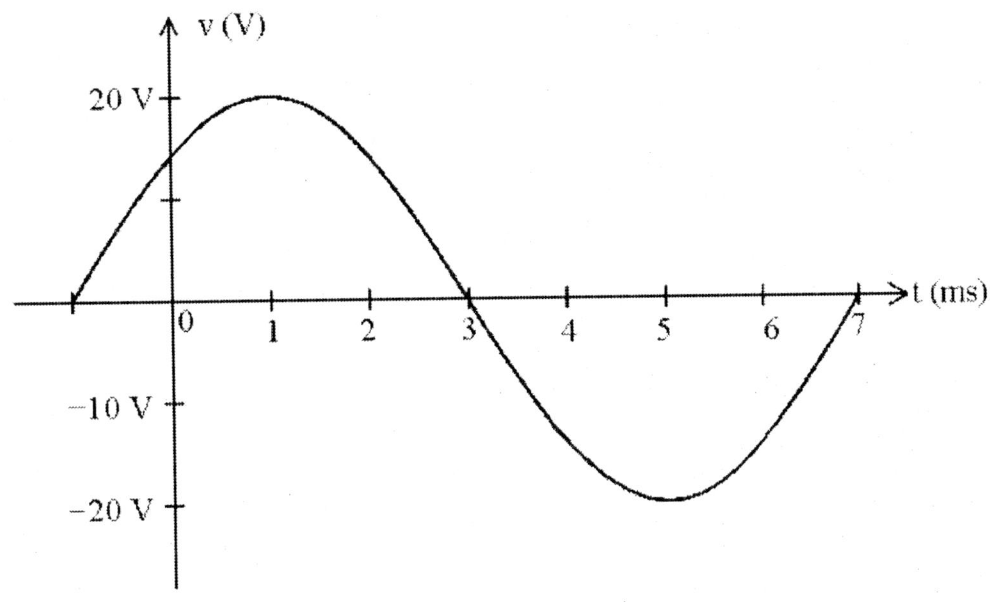

Figure 13.4

42) See Figure 13.4. Write the general voltage equation that describes this waveform.

43) What is the phase relationship between voltage v and current i if
$v = 15 \sin(\theta t + 30^\circ)$ and
$i = 20 \sin(\theta t - 10^\circ)$?

44) What C++ statement will display the message *Please enter amplitude in volts* on the screen?

45) Convert the following angle in degrees to an angle in radians: 49 degrees

46) Find the period for the periodic wave, if the frequency of the periodic wave is 83.3 KHz.

47) What are the period and frequency of a periodic wave that has 12 cycles in 46 milliseconds?

48) Find the amplitude and frequency of $42.1 \sin(377t + 30^\circ)$

Answer Key
Testname: CHAPTER 13

1) FALSE
2) TRUE
3) TRUE
4) FALSE
5) TRUE
6) TRUE
7) TRUE
8) TRUE
9) TRUE
10) FALSE
11) FALSE
12) FALSE
13) FALSE
14) TRUE
15) TRUE
16) D
17) D
18) D
19) D
20) B
21) C
22) C
23) B
24) C
25) A
26) C
27) C
28) D
29) C
30) A
31) D
32) A
33) C
34) B
35) B
36) D
37) C
38) D
39) 3.81 V
40) 1.25 kHz
41) $60 \sin(2500\pi t)$
42) $20 \sin(250\pi t + 45°)$
43) v leads i by 40°
44) cout<<"Please enter amplitude in volts";
45) 0.855 radians
46) 12 microseconds
47) 3.83 milliseconds, 261 Hz
48) 42.1, 60 Hz

Chapter 14 The Basic Elements and Phasors

True/False

1) The derivative of a sine wave is a maximum at the peak amplitude of the waveform.

2) The voltage across an inductor leads the current through it by 90°.

3) Inductive reactance increases directly in proportion to frequency.

4) The more reactive the load, the lower the power factor.

5) The complex conjugate is found by changing the sign of the real part in the rectangular form.

6) The length of a phasor is called the modulus or magnitude.

7) $v(t) = V_m\cos(wt + \theta)$ is the standard form for a phasor.

8) Phasor algebra for sinusoidal quantities is applicable only for waveforms which have different frequencies.

9) The derivative of a sine wave is a cosine wave.

10) For a purely resistive element, the voltage and the current through the element are in phase.

11) For an inductor the voltage lags the current through it by 90 degrees.

12) Inductive reactance does not dissipate electrical energy.

13) Unlike inductive reactance, capacitive reactance dissipates energy in the form of heat.

14) A power factor of 1 indicates that maximum power is being delivered.

15) Whether there is a leading or lagging of current or voltage is not a consideration with power factor.

Multiple Choice

16) Which one of the following is the derivative of 12 cos(30t - 15°)?

A) +360 sin(30t - 15°)

B) +360 cos(30t - 15°)

C) -360 sin(30t - 15°)

D) -360 cos(30t - 15°)

17) What is the inductive reactance at 800 Hz of a 1 mH inductor with an internal resistance of 20 Ω?

A) 12 Ω

B) 5.0 Ω

C) 20 Ω

D) 0.2 Ω

18) At what frequency does a 10 μF capacitor have a reactance of 100 Ω?

A) 15.9 kHz

B) 1.59 kHz

C) 159 Hz

D) 1.59 MHz

19) If the voltage v = 50 sin(500t - 75°) is impressed across a 25 Ω resistor, which equation describes the resistor current?

A) 1250 sin(500t - 75°)

B) 2 cos(500t - 75°)

C) 2 sin(500t - 75°)

D) 2 sin(20t - 3°)

20) The voltage across a 100 mH coil is v = 100 sin 50t. Which of these expressions describes the current?

A) 2000 sin(50t - 90°)

B) 20 sin(50t + 90°)

C) 20 sin 50t

D) 20 sin(50t - 90°)

21) The voltage across a capacitor is v = 100 sin(377t + 50°) and the current through it is 18.8 sin(377t + 70°). What is the value of the capacitance?

A) 199 μF

B) 377 μF

C) 1880 μF

D) 5.3 μF

22) How much power is dissipated by a resistor if the current through it is i = 10 sin(θt + 30°) and the voltage across it is v = 50 sin(θt - 30°)?

A) 250 W

B) 5 W

C) 353.5 W

D) 500 W

23) How much power is dissipated by an R-L-C network if the current through it is i = 10 sin(θt + 30°) and the voltage across it is v = 50 sin(θt - 20°)?

A) 246 W

B) 161 W

C) 500 W

D) 250 W

24) Which one of the following polar values is equivalent to 30 + j40?

A) 50 ∠53.1°

B) 50 ∠36.9°

C) 70 ∠36.9°

D) 70 ∠53.1°

25) Which one of the following rectangular values is equivalent to the polar form 20 ∠55°?

A) 16.38 – j11.47 B) 16.38 + j11.47 C) 11.17 – j16.38 D) 11.47 + j16.38

26) Which one of the following values is equivalent to (5 + j3)(4 – j6)?

A) 2 – j18 B) 2 + j18 C) 38 – j18 D) 38 + j18

27) Which one of the following phasor domain expressions is equivalent to the time domain expression 50 sin(θt + 15°)?

A) 70.7 ∠–15° B) 50 ∠15° C) 35.35 ∠15° D) 70.7 ∠15°

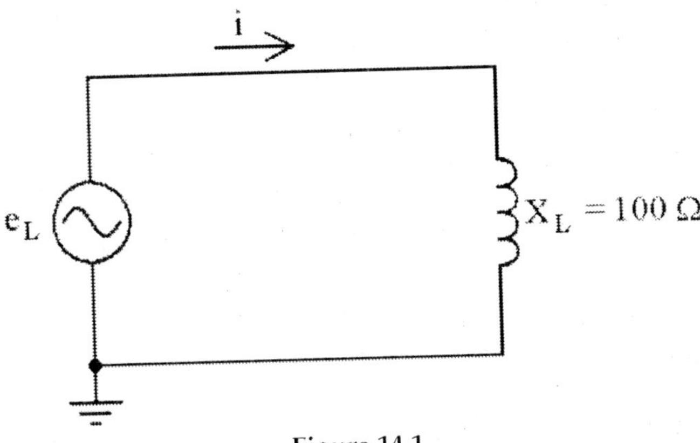

Figure 14.1

28) See Figure 14.1. What is the coil current if e_L is 500 sin(50t + 20°)?

A) 5 sin(50t + 20°)

B) 5 sin(50t – 70°)

C) 5 sin(50t + 110°)

D) 5 sin 50t

29) What is the power factor in a system if v = 120 sin(377t + 20°) and i = 60 sin(377t – 45°)?

A) 0.423 leading B) 0.906 lagging C) 0.906 leading D) 0.423 lagging

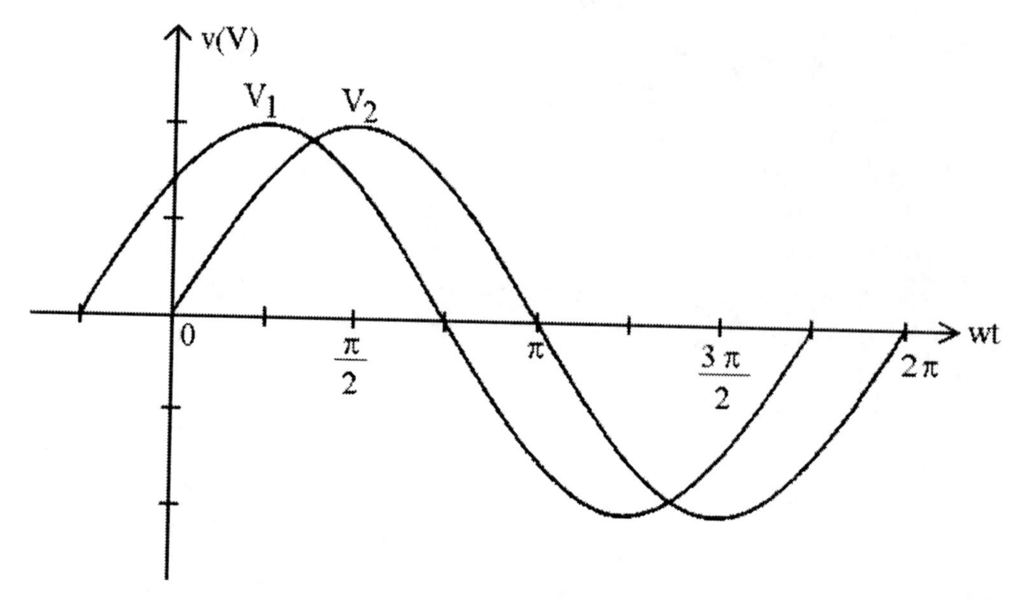

Figure 14.3

30) See Figure 14.3. What relationship exists between voltages v_1 and v_2?

A) v_1 leads v_2 by $(\pi/4)°$.

B) v_1 lags v_2 by 45°.

C) v_1 leads v_2 by 45°.

D) v_1 lags v_2 by $(\pi/4)°$.

31) Which relationship is true of *power factor*?

A) The more resistive the total impedance, the closer the power factor is to 1.

B) The power factor will be lagging in a capacitive circuit.

C) The more resistive the total impedance, the closer the power factor is to 0.

D) The power factor is the ratio of the total power in a circuit to the circuit current.

32) The inductive voltage is directly related to the frequency of which of the following?

A) Inductance of the coil

B) Resistance

C) Flux density

D) Current

33) The opposition to the flow of current which results in the continual interchange of energy between source and magnetic field is known as ________.

A) Inductive phase shift

B) Inactive causes

C) Resistor influence

D) Inductive reactance

34) A measurement of the rate at which a capacitor will store a charge on its plates is called?

A) Capacitance

B) Total voltage

C) Reactance

D) Plate separation

35) A capacitor or an inductor will change characteristics and begin to act like each other when they are exposed to ________.

A) Very low current
B) Very low frequencies
C) Very high frequencies
D) Very high voltage

36) The average power, or real power is the power delivered to and dissipated by the ________.

A) Load
B) Resistor
C) Capacitor
D) Inductor

Short Answer

37) Determine the frequency at which the reactance of a 10 μF capacitor equals that of a 0.5 H coil.

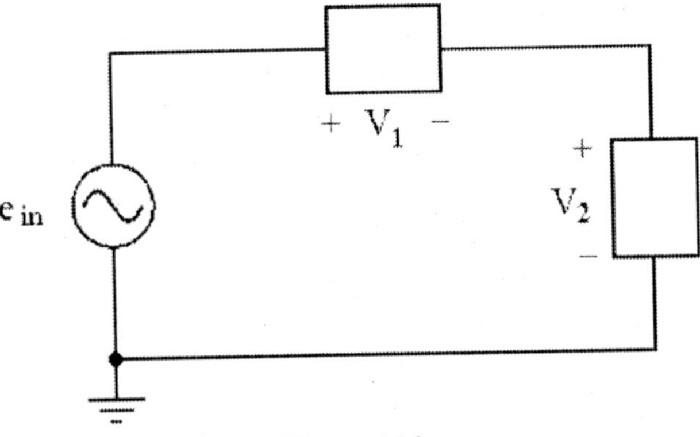

Figure 14.2

38) See Figure 14.2. Determine v_2 if e_{in} = 100 sin(377t − 15°) and v_1 = 80 sin(377t + 40°).

39) Reduce the expression 5 ∠60° + 3 ∠−20°, leaving your answer in rectangular form.

40) Express the phasor voltage V = 25 ∠30° as a sine wave if the frequency is 1000 Hz.

41) The current i = 0.5 sin 377t passes through a 10 μF capacitor. Find the sinusoidal expression for the voltage across the capacitor.

42) Write a BASIC statement that converts an angle called DEGREES to radians.

43) Convert 4 − j3 to polar form.

44) Change $45e^{j-400}$ to rectangular form.

45) Change 0 − j25 to polar form.

46) Perform the operation, $(1 + j)(1 - j2)/(3 + j)$, and express the answer in polar rectangular form.

Answer Key
Testname: CHAPTER 14

1) FALSE
2) TRUE
3) TRUE
4) TRUE
5) FALSE
6) TRUE
7) TRUE
8) FALSE
9) TRUE
10) TRUE
11) FALSE
12) TRUE
13) FALSE
14) TRUE
15) FALSE
16) C
17) B
18) C
19) C
20) D
21) A
22) A
23) B
24) A
25) D
26) C
27) C
28) B
29) D
30) C
31) A
32) A
33) D
34) A
35) C
36) A
37) 71.2 Hz
38) 85 sin(377t - 65.4°)
39) 5.32 + j3.3
40) 35.36 sin(2000πt + 30°)
41) v = 132.63 sin(377t - 90°)
42) RADIANS=DEGREES*3.14159/180
43) Amplitude = 5, Phase = -37 degrees
44) 34 - j29
45) Amplitude = 25, Phase = 90 degrees
46) 0.798 - j0.602

Chapter 15 Series and Parallel ac Circuits

True/False

1) The angle associated with the total impedance is the angle by which the applied voltage leads the source current.

2) Inductive reactance is plotted on the negative imaginary axis on an impedance diagram.

3) Admittance is the reciprocal of impedance.

4) Power factor can be determined by forming the ratio of the total circuit resistance to the magnitude of the total circuit impedance.

5) The susceptance of a given capacitor decreases as frequency increases.

6) Impedance is the combination of capacitive reactance, inductive reactance, and dc resistance.

7) Inductive elements are storage devices and, unlike resistors, do not dissipate energy.

8) The advantage of an impedance diagram is that it will reflect all impedance on the positive real axis.

9) Total impedance of a system is the reciprocal of the sum of the individual impedances.

10) The basic format for the voltage divider rule in ac circuits is unlike that for dc circuits.

11) The heavier the current flow for a given voltage, the larger the value for admittance.

12) In analysis of a parallel RLC networks, inductive reactance would predominate at low frequencies and capacitive reactance at high frequencies.

13) For parallel elements, the element with the smallest impedance will have the least impact on the total impedance at that frequency.

Multiple Choice

14) Which one of the following expressions describes the impedance of a 100 mH inductor at 1000 Hz?

A) $200\pi\ \Omega\ \angle 0°$ B) $200\pi\ \Omega\ \angle -90°$ C) $200\pi\ \Omega + j0\ \Omega$ D) $200\pi\ \Omega\ \angle +90°$

15) Express the impedance of a 10 μF capacitor at 60 Hz in rectangular form.

A) 265.3 Ω - j0 Ω

B) 0 Ω - j265.3 Ω

C) 0 Ω - j0.00377 Ω

D) 0 Ω + j265.3 Ω

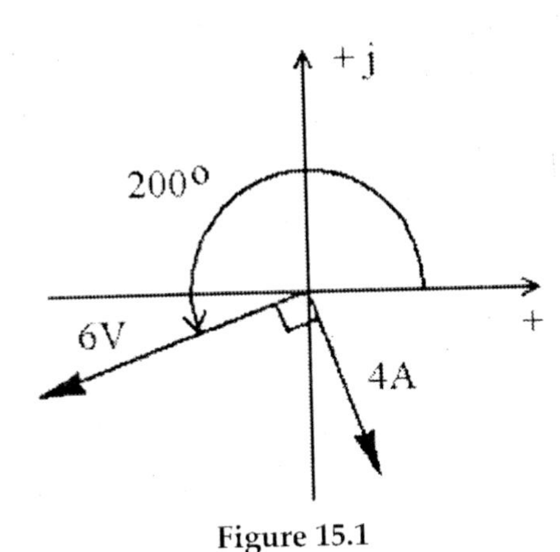

Figure 15.1

16) See Figure 15.1. Which one of these equations describes the voltage in this circuit?

A) -2.05 V - j5.64 V

B) 5.64 V - j2.05 V

C) 2.05 V - j5.64 V

D) -5.64 V - j2.05 V

17) See Figure 15.1. Which one of the following statements is true?

A) The equivalent circuit is capacitive.

B) The equivalent circuit is inductive.

C) The circuit has no reactive component, since the voltage phasor is not in a +j quadrant.

D) Voltage leads current by 90°.

18) What is the total impedance Z_T of a series network consisting of a 5 Ω resistor, an inductor having 10 Ω reactance, and a capacitor with 15 Ω reactance?

A) 5 Ω + j5 Ω

B) 5 Ω - j5 Ω

C) 5 Ω - j25 Ω

D) 5 Ω + j25 Ω

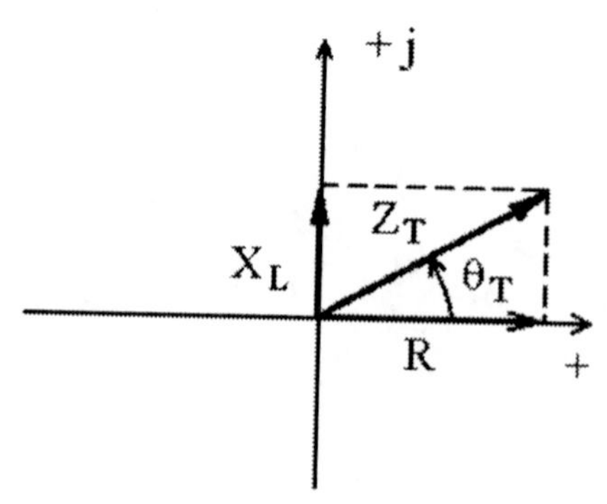

Figure 15.2

19) See Figure 15.2. If R = 50 Ω and X_L = 20 Ω, find Z_T and θ_T.

A) 53.85 Ω ∠−21.8°
B) 53.85 Ω ∠+21.8°
C) 53.85 Ω ∠−68.2°
D) 53.85 Ω ∠+68.2°

20) See Figure 15.2. Increasing R while keeping X_L constant

A) increases Z_T but not θ.
B) causes no change in power factor.
C) increases power factor.
D) decreases power factor.

21) See Figure 15.2. If R = 100 Ω and θ = 30°, what is the power factor?

A) 0.3 leading
B) 0.866 leading
C) 0.3 lagging
D) 0.866 lagging

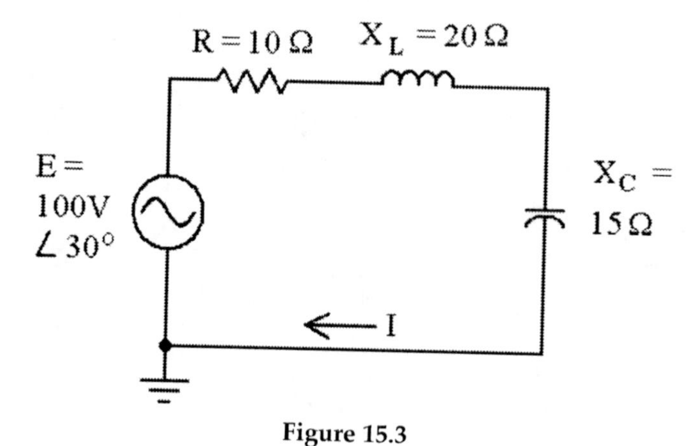

Figure 15.3

22) See Figure 15.3. What is Z_T in polar form?

A) 11.18 Ω ∠63.43°
B) 10 Ω ∠5°
C) 11.18 Ω ∠26.6°
D) 5 Ω ∠10°

23) See Figure 15.3. The total impedance of this circuit may be made purely resistive by

A) decreasing the signal frequency.

B) increasing R to 5 Ω.

C) increasing R to 35 Ω.

D) increasing the signal frequency.

24) What is the susceptance of a 100 μF capacitor at 1000 Hz?

A) 1.59 S

B) 10-4 S

C) 104 S

D) 0.63 S

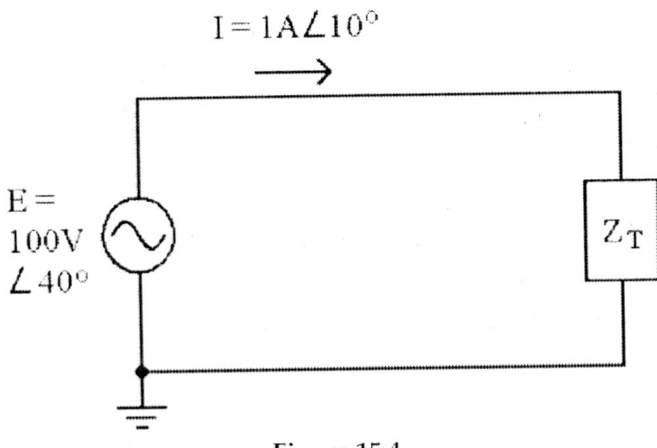

Figure 15.4

25) See Figure 15.4. Determine Z_T, expressed in rectangular form.

A) 64.3 Ω + j76.6 Ω

B) 86.6 Ω + j50 Ω

C) 100 Ω + j50 Ω

D) 100 Ω + j30 Ω

26) A circuit has a power factor of 0.8 lagging. The circuit dissipates 100 W of power with an input voltage of 500 V. What is the impedance of the circuit, expressed in rectangular form?

A) 1200 Ω + j1600 Ω

B) 1600 Ω + j1200 Ω

C) 1200 Ω - j1600 Ω

D) 1600 Ω - j1200 Ω

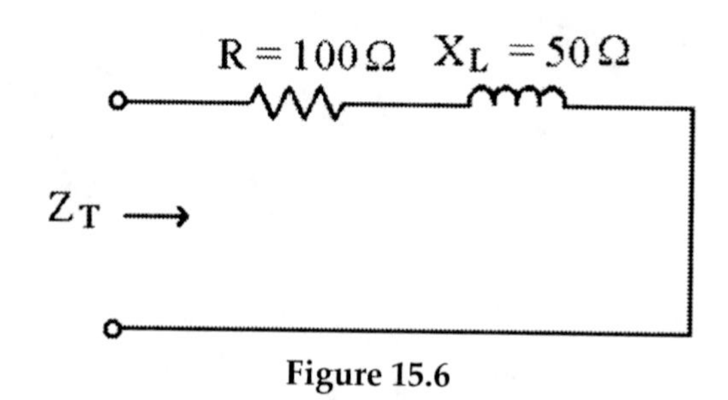

Figure 15.6

27) See Figure 15.6. Which one of the following combinations is equivalent to the given series circuit?

A) R = 125 Ω in parallel with X_L = 250 Ω.
B) R = 40 Ω in parallel with X_L = 20 Ω.
C) R = 20 Ω in parallel with X_L = 40 Ω.
D) R = 250 Ω in parallel with X_L = 125 Ω.

28) See Figure 15.6. What is the total impedance Z_T for this circuit?

A) 111.8 Ω ∠–26.6°
B) 111.8 Ω ∠63.4°
C) 111.8 Ω ∠26.6°
D) 111.8 Ω ∠–63.4°

29) Which one of the following is true of ac circuits with reactive elements?

A) The smaller the resistive element of a circuit, the closer the power factor is to unity.
B) The magnitude of the voltage across any one element can never exceed the applied voltage.
C) The impedance of any one element can never exceed the total network impedance.
D) Depending on the frequency applied, the circuit can look either inductive or capacitive.

30) Ignoring capacitive effects, what is the impedance of a 250 mH coil with an internal resistance of 55 ohms at 60 Hz?

A) 10,900 ohms
B) 94.2 ohms
C) 149.2 ohms
D) 109 ohms

31) Ignoring capacitive effects, what is the impedance of a 100 mH coil with an internal resistance of 45 ohms in parallel with a 4700 ohm resistor at a frequency of 500 Hz?

A) 237 ohms
B) 317 ohms
C) 5014 ohms
D) 314 ohms

32) Ignoring inductive effects, what is the impedance of a RC series capacitor made up of a 56 Kilohm resistor and a 0.033 microfarad capacitor at a signal frequency of 450 Hz?

A) 66,730 ohms
B) 57,019 ohms
C) 10,730 ohms
D) 45,270 ohms

33) Ignoring any effects of dc resistance, what is the total reactance of a 250 mH coil in series with a 4.7 microfarad capacitor at a signal frequency of 1000 Hz?

A) 1604 ohms
B) 1570 ohms
C) 1536 ohms
D) 35 ohms

34) Ignoring any effects of dc resistance, what is the total reactance of a 250 mH coil in series with a 4.7 microfarad capacitor at a signal frequency of 450 Hz?

A) 706 ohms B) 97 ohms C) 84 ohms D) 781 ohms

35) Ignoring any effects of dc resistance, what is the total reactance of a 250 mH coil in series with a 4.7 microfarad capacitor at a signal frequency of 60 Hz?

A) 113 ohms B) 659 ohms C) -471 ohms D) 111 ohms

36) In a series resonant LC circuit, what is the impedance at resonant frequency?

A) Determined solely by dc resistance B) Infinity

C) Zero D) The maximum impedance value

37) In a parallel resonant LC circuit, what is the impedance at the resonant frequency?

A) Infinity B) Zero

C) The maximum impedance value D) Determined solely by dc resistance

38) If you need an LC circuit to be resonant at 2500 Hz, and use a 150 mH coil, what should the capacitance value be?

A) 0.15 microfarads B) 27 microfarads

C) 0.015 microfarads D) 0.027 microfarads

39) Capacitive reactance is a measurement of how much the capacitive element will impede __________.

A) Resistance of components B) Current through the network

C) Voltage across elements D) Power dissipated by the network

40) In a series R-C circuit, at low frequencies, the total reactance of the capacitor will be high and the total impedance will be capacitive in nature, at high frequencies the circuit will become __________.

A) Purely capacitive B) Purely resistive

C) Balanced D) More inductive

41) A measure of how well an ac circuit will admit, or allow current to flow in the circuit is __________.

A) Admittance B) Inductance C) Resistance D) Capacitance

Short Answer

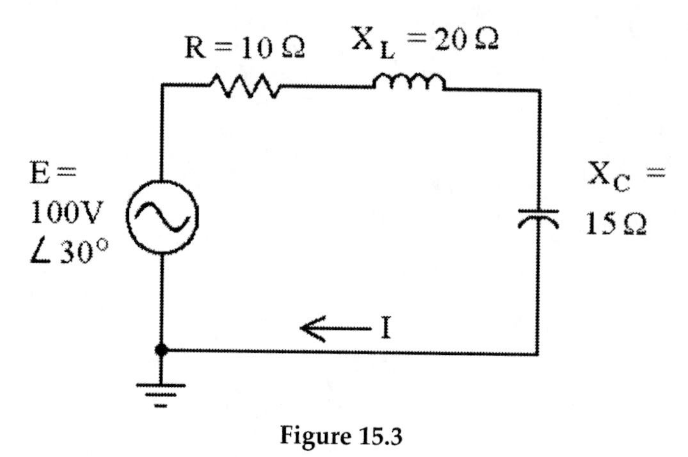

Figure 15.3

42) See Figure 15.3. Calculate the current I.

43) See Figure 15.3. Use the voltage divider rule to calculate the voltage across the coil.

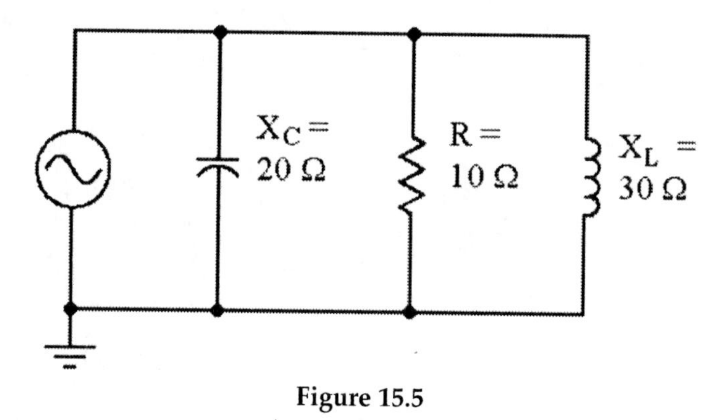

Figure 15.5

44) See Figure 15.5. Compute the total impedance Z_T.

45) See Figure 15.5. What component, when placed in parallel with the existing components, would make the total impedance Z_T purely resistive?

46) See Figure 15.5. Sketch the impedance diagram for this circuit.

47) How can PSpice be used to find the total impedance Z_T of a parallel RLC network?

48) Define *independent source*.

Answer Key
Testname: CHAPTER 15

1) TRUE
2) FALSE
3) TRUE
4) TRUE
5) FALSE
6) TRUE
7) TRUE
8) FALSE
9) FALSE
10) FALSE
11) TRUE
12) TRUE
13) FALSE
14) D
15) B
16) D
17) A
18) B
19) B
20) C
21) D
22) C
23) A
24) D
25) B
26) B
27) A
28) C
29) D
30) D
31) A
32) B
33) D
34) C
35) A
36) A
37) A
38) D
39) B
40) B
41) A
42) 8.94 A ∠3.4°
43) 178.9 V ∠93.4°
44) 9.86 ∠-9.5°
45) A capacitance with X_C = 10 Ω
46) Sketch R = 100 Ω on positive horizontal axis, XL = 50 Ω on the +j vertical axis, and ZT = 118.8 Ω at an angle of 26.6°.
47) Connect a 1 A ∠0° source, then plot or print the voltage across the network. Since ZT = V ÷ I, and I = 1 A ∠0°, the resulting plot has units of ohms.
48) The magnitude of the source is independent of any other network parameters.

Chapter 16 Series–Parallel ac Networks

True/False

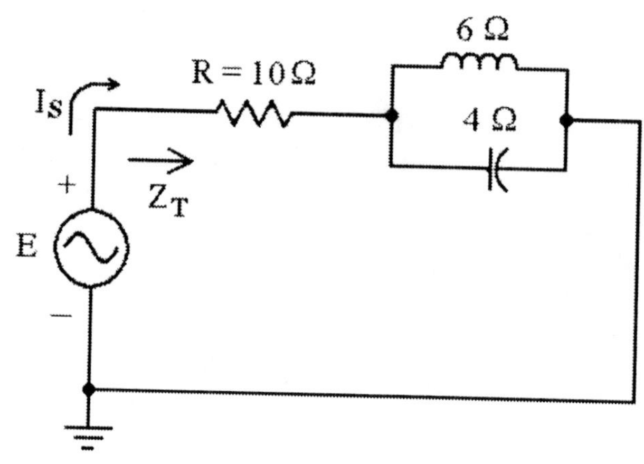

Figure 16.1

1) See Figure 16.1. The total impedance Z_T of this circuit is independent of the applied frequency.

2) See Figure 16.1. I_S may be found by dividing E by Z_T.

3) See Figure 16.1. $Z_T = R \parallel X_C \parallel X_L$.

4) See Figure 16.1. The current divider rule can be applied to determine the current through the capacitor.

5) In a series–parallel circuit, if e = 50 V ∠20° and i = 25 A ∠20°, then the total impedance Z_T is purely resistive.

6) Determining the source current is the most critical step in solving series–parallel ac networks.

7) The equivalent circuit is used in determining the source current in series–parallel ac networks.

8) The fundamental concept for solving series–parallel ac networks is different from solving series–parallel dc networks.

9) Unknown voltages in series–parallel ac networks can only be across passive elements.

10) The purpose of re–drawing a series–parallel ac network is to reduce the network to a series resistive circuit.

11) If the total impedance has a negative phase angle the network is capacitive in nature.

12) For parallel current sources, the equivalent current source is their sum or difference.

13) The effect of a capacitor for the full audio range is negligible and will allow ac to pass with little disturbance.

14) The advantage of ladder networks is that it is not necessary to know total impedance to be able to determine total current.

15) The use of a ground fault interrupter does not mean a person will not receive a shock, however it will shut off power quickly.

16) Coax cable offers reduced signal interference because of the insertion of a R-C at 300-foot intervals.

17) Combining the impedance of more than one element can be of value in determining the total voltage across a series combination.

18) The higher the frequency, the better the short-circuit approximation for X_C for ac conditions.

19) The formula to determine the total impedance of two parallel impedances is the sum of the impedances divided by the product of the impedances.

Multiple Choice

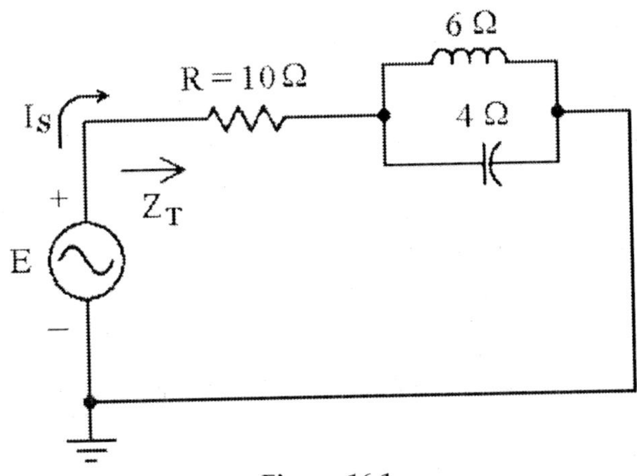

Figure 16.1

20) See Figure 16.1. What is the total impedance Z_T of this circuit?

A) 10 Ω - j2.4 Ω B) 10 Ω - j2 Ω C) 10 Ω + j12 Ω D) 10 Ω - j12 Ω

21) See Figure 16.1. If $I_S = 1\ A\ \angle 80°$, what is the current through the coil?

A) $0.5\ A\ \angle 100°$ B) $2\ A\ \angle -100°$ C) $0.5\ A\ \angle -100°$ D) $2\ A\ \angle 100°$

22) A 1 kHz signal E is applied in the circuit shown in Figure 16.1. What is the value of inductor L?

A) 1910 μH B) 1047 μH C) 955 μH D) 26.5 μH

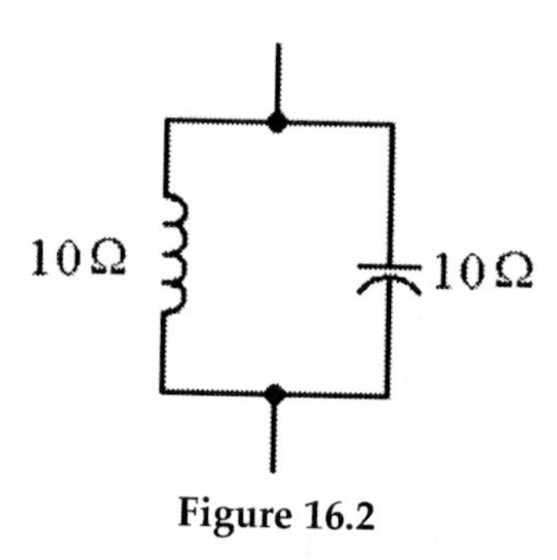

Figure 16.2

23) See Figure 16.2. What is the total impedance Z_T for this circuit?

A) $100\ \Omega\ \angle 0°$ B) $0\ \Omega\ \angle 0°$ C) $5\ \Omega\ \angle 0°$ D) infinity

24) See Figure 16.2. As the frequency increases, the total impedance Z_T of this circuit

A) becomes more resistive.

B) increases, approaching infinity.

C) becomes more capacitive.

D) becomes more inductive.

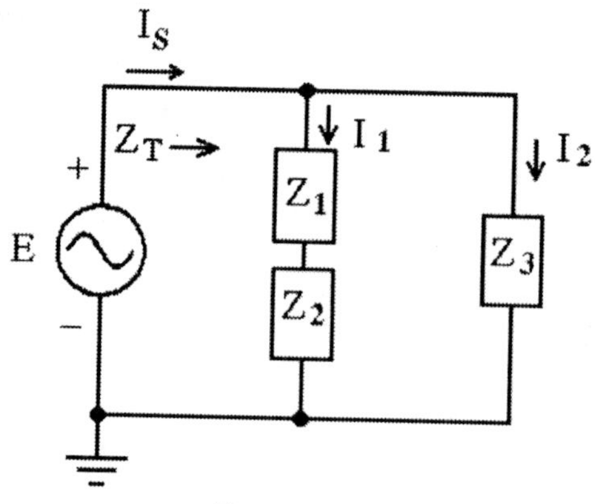

Figure 16.3

25) See Figure 16.3. Which one equation describes the total impedance Z_T for this circuit?

A) $Z_T = (Z_1 \parallel Z_2) \parallel Z_3$

B) $Z_T = Z_1 + Z_2 + Z_3$

C) $Z_T = Z_1 + Z_2 - Z_3$

D) $Z_T = (Z_1 + Z_2) \parallel Z_3$

26) See Figure 16.3. Which one equation describes current I_2?

A) $I_2 = I_1$
B) $I_2 = I_S - I_1$
C) $I_2 = I_S + I_1$
D) $I_2 = I_S$

27) See Figure 16.3. Which one equation describes source voltage E?

A) $E = I_S Z_T$
B) $E = I_S{}^2 Z_T$
C) $E = I_S \div Z_T$
D) $E = Z_T \div I_S$

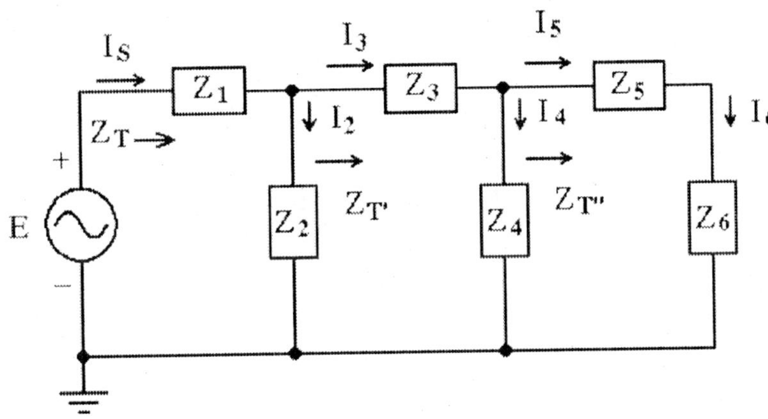

Figure 16.4

28) See Figure 16.4. Which one of these statements is true?

A) $I_S = I_3$
B) $I_3 = I_4 + I_6$
C) $I_4 = I_6$
D) $I_3 = I_2 + I_5$

29) See Figure 16.4. Which one equation describes the total impedance Z_T?

A) $Z_T = Z_1 \parallel Z_2$
B) $Z_T = Z_1 + Z_3 + Z_5 + Z_6'$
C) $Z_T = Z_1 + Z_T'$
D) $Z_T = Z_1 + (Z_2 \parallel Z_T')$

30) See Figure 16.4. If $E = 10\ V \angle 30°$ and $I_S = 5\ A \angle 10°$, what is the total impedance Z_T?

A) 32.1 Ω + j38.3 Ω
B) 38.3 Ω + j32.1 Ω
C) 0.47 Ω - j0.17 Ω
D) 1.88 Ω + j0.68 Ω

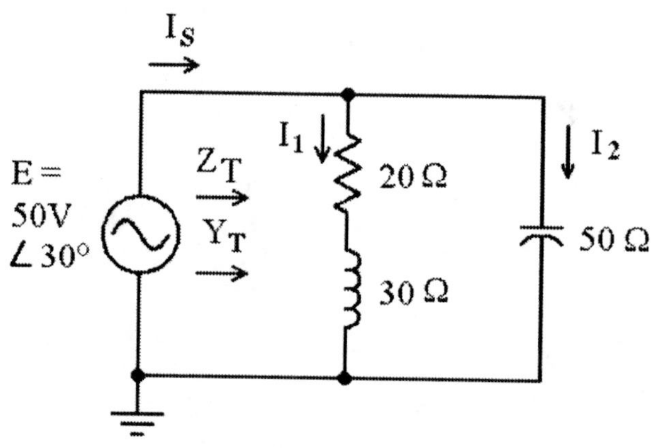

Figure 16.5

31) See Figure 16.5. What is the total admittance Y_T of this circuit?

A) 0.028 S ∠−56.31°
B) 0.02 S ∠90°
C) 0.016 S ∠−11.31°
D) 63.73 S ∠11.31°

32) See Figure 16.5. What is the value of current I_1?

A) 1.39 A ∠−26.31°
B) 1 A ∠120°
C) 1 A ∠−120°
D) 0.72 A ∠26.31°

33) See Figure 16.5. What is the value of current I_2?

A) 0.72 A ∠26.31°
B) 1.39 A ∠−26.31°
C) 1 A ∠−120°
D) 1 A ∠120°

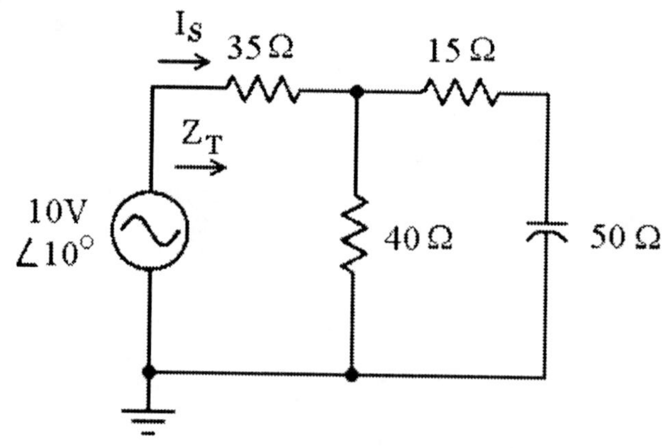

Figure 16.6

34) See Figure 16.6. What is the total impedance Z_T?

A) 50.2 Ω ∠−10.7°
B) 49.3 Ω ∠−9.4°
C) 39.2 Ω ∠−30.7°
D) 17.1 Ω ∠−33.2°

35) See Figure 16.6. What is the total current I_S?

A) 0.2 A ∠10.7° B) 502 A ∠−10.7° C) 5.0 A ∠10.7° D) 5.0 A ∠−10.7°

36) Which parameter in PSpice (Windows) specifies the magnitude of the current through resistor R1?

A) M(I(R1)) B) IMAG(R1) C) MAG(I(R1)) D) I(R1)

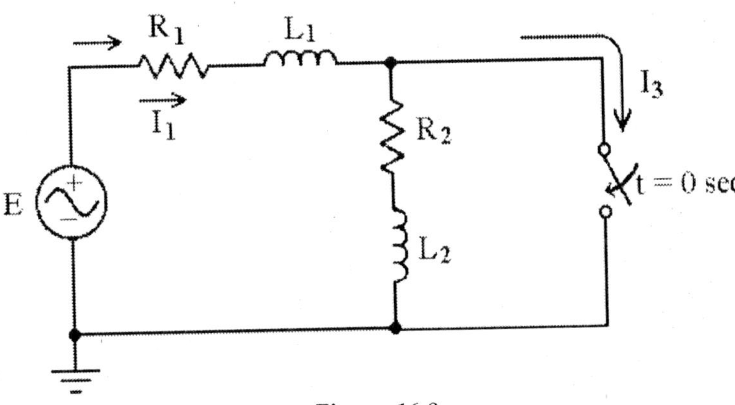

Figure 16.8

37) For the circuit shown in Figure 16.8, $I_1 = I_2$ and has been flowing for a long time before the switch is closed. If the switch is closed at time t_0, what is the behavior of I_1 at t_0?

A) I_1 is continuous and increasing.

B) I_1 is discontinuous and increasing.

C) I_1 is continuous and decreasing.

D) The system is stable and not transient.

E) I_1 is discontinuous and decreasing.

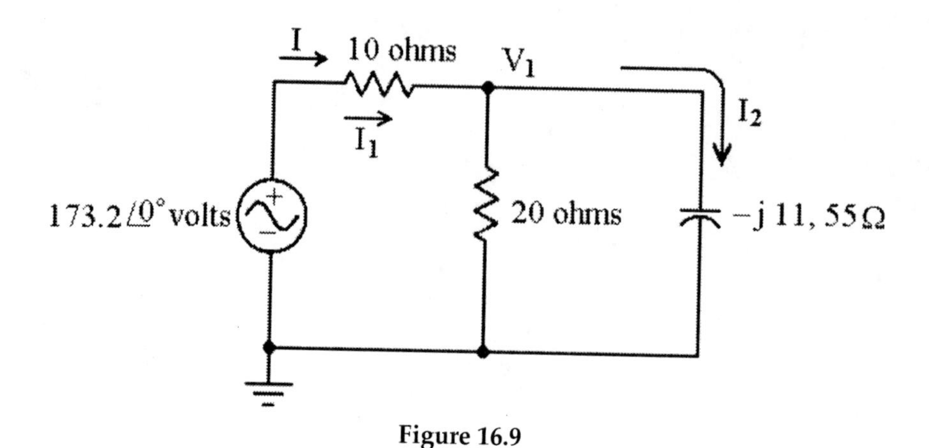

Figure 16.9

38) For the circuit shown in Figure 16.9, the current flowing through the 10 Ω resistor is

A) 10 ∠30° B) 173.2 ∠0° C) 8.66 ∠60° D) 5 ∠−30°

39) For the circuit shown in Figure 16.9, the current flowing through the 20 Ω resistor is

A) 10 ∠30° B) 5 ∠−30° C) 173.2 ∠0° D) 8.66 ∠60°

40) For the circuit shown in Figure 16.9, the current flowing through the 20 Ω capacitor is

A) 173.2 ∠0° B) 10 ∠30° C) 8.78 ∠59.2° D) 5 ∠−30°

Short Answer

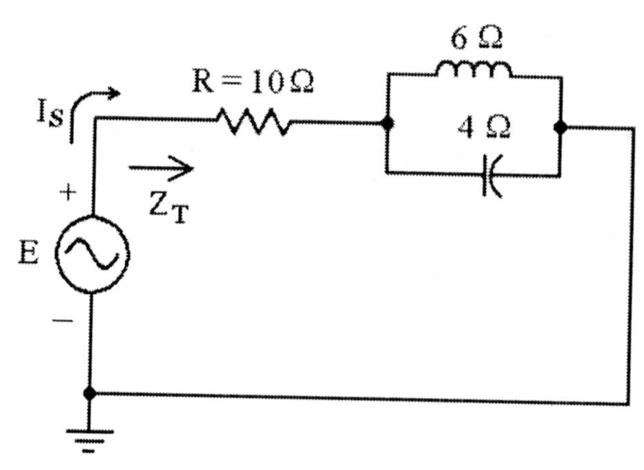

Figure 16.1

41) See Figure 16.1. If I_S = 1 A ≥80°, determine the value of the source voltage E_S.

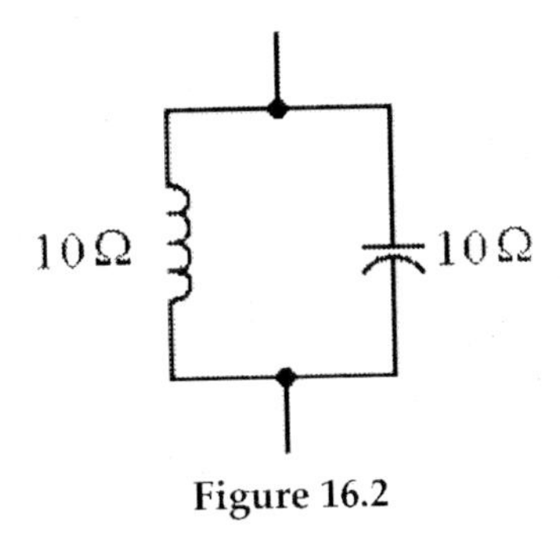

Figure 16.2

42) See Figure 16.2. If L = 10 mH, what is the applied frequency? What is the value of the capacitor?

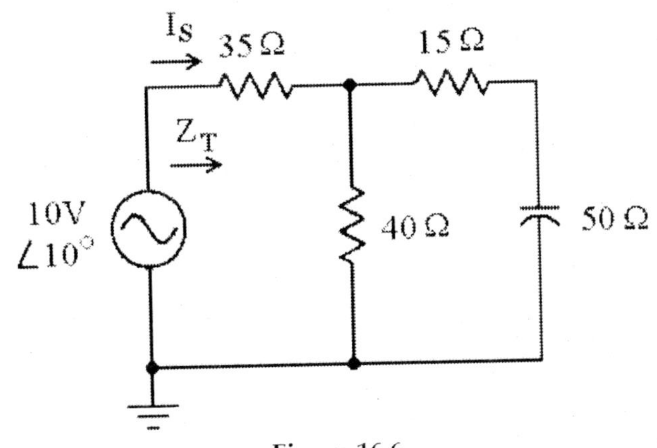

Figure 16.6

43) See Figure 16.6. Compute the current through the 40 Ω resistor.

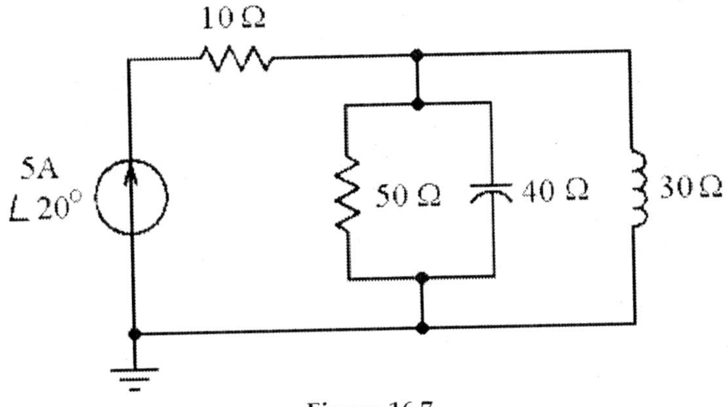

Figure 16.7

44) See Figure 16.7. Compute the total circuit impedance Z_T.

45) See Figure 16.7. Find the voltage across the coil.

46) Describe how PSpice (Windows) can be used to solve for Z_T in the circuit shown in Figure 16.7.

47) What is meant by the PSpice (Windows) Probe notation P(V(E:+))−P(I(E))?

48) What must be done before PSpice can compute cos θ, where θ is an angle in degrees?

49) For many single source, series–parallel networks, the analysis is one that works back to the source, determines the __________, and then finds its way to the desired unknown.

50) Series–parallel ac networks may contain any number of elements whose impedance is dependent on the applied __________.

51) __________ networks are a repetitive combination of series–parallel ac branches.

52) In a series–parallel circuit, if e = 100 V ∠0° and I = 25 ∠90°, then the total impedance is purely __________.

Answer Key
Testname: CHAPTER 16

1) FALSE
2) TRUE
3) FALSE
4) TRUE
5) TRUE
6) TRUE
7) TRUE
8) FALSE
9) FALSE
10) FALSE
11) TRUE
12) FALSE
13) TRUE
14) FALSE
15) TRUE
16) FALSE
17) TRUE
18) TRUE
19) FALSE
20) D
21) B
22) C
23) D
24) C
25) D
26) B
27) A
28) B
29) D
30) D
31) C
32) A
33) D
34) A
35) A
36) A
37) A
38) A
39) B
40) C
41) 15.62 V $\angle 29.8^\circ$
42) 159 Hz, 100 μF
43) 85 mA $\angle -22.4^\circ$
44) 55.5 $\angle 18.6^\circ$
45) 231 V $\angle 42.6^\circ$
46) Set I to 1 A $\angle 0^\circ$, find voltage V $\geq 0^\circ$ across current source. The answer has the same value as Z $\angle \theta^\circ$
47) The phase angle between the voltage E and the current through the source.
48) Convert θ to radians.
49) source current
50) frequency
51) Ladder
52) capacitive

Chapter 17 Methods of Analysis and Selected Topics (ac)

True/False

1) A dependent voltage source is one whose magnitude is controlled by a current or voltage elsewhere in the system.

2) The conversion of a voltage source into a current source produces a current source with magnitude $I = E \div Z$, where Z is the value of the impedance in series with the voltage source.

3) Mesh and nodal analysis techniques are not usable if the network has only one voltage or current source.

4) When applying the mesh analysis method to an ac circuit, it is good practice to represent the resistances and reactances as subscripted impedances.

5) For an ac bridge to be balanced, a galvanometer across the bridge network must sense equal voltage magnitudes, but not necessarily equal phase angles.

6) Nodal Analysis is an extension of Kirchhoff's Current Law.

7) It is possible to have more than one reference node when using Nodal Analysis.

8) A current source connected to a series resistor can be converted to a battery with a parallel resistor.

9) Mesh Analysis is a direct extension of Kirchhoff's Voltage Law.

10) For networks with two or more sources that are not in series or parallel, analysis methods such as mesh or nodal analysis should be used.

11) The format approach to mesh analysis can be applied to networks with both, dependent or independent sources.

12) The format approach to mesh analysis requires that the voltage source first be converted to a current source.

13) A bridge network is a configuration with a diamond appearance with one branch in series and one branch in parallel.

Multiple Choice

14) Which one of these bridge networks is used to determine the value of an unknown capacitor and its associated resistance?

A) Wein bridge
B) Maxwell bridge
C) Capacitance comparison bridge
D) Hay bridge

15) Which one of these bridge networks is used to determine the resistance and inductance of a coil in which the resistance is a small fraction of the reactance X_L?

A) Hay bridge
B) Wein bridge
C) Maxwell bridge
D) Capacitance comparison bridge

16) Which one of these bridge networks is used to determine the resistance and inductance of a coil in which the resistance is a large value compared with the reactance X_L?

A) Wein bridge
B) Hay bridge
C) Maxwell bridge
D) Capacitance comparison bridge

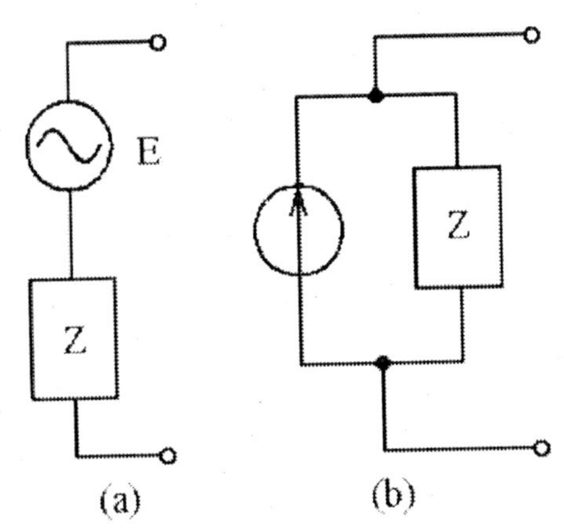

Figure 17.1

17) See Figure 17.1. The voltage source (a) consists of E = 50 V ∠20° and Z = 100 Ω ∠30°. If this voltage source is converted to a current source (b), what is the value of the parallel impedance element Z?

A) 2.0 Ω ∠10°
B) 0.01 Ω ∠−30°
C) 100 Ω ∠30°
D) 0.5 Ω ∠−10°

18) See Figure 17.1. The voltage source (a) consists of E = 50 V ∠20° and Z = 100 Ω ∠30°. If this voltage source is converted to a current source (b), what is the value of the current I?

A) 5000 A ∠50°
B) 50 A ∠20°
C) 0.5 A ∠−10°
D) 2.0 A ∠10°

19) See Figure 17.1. The current source (a) includes a current I = 10 A ∠20° and an impedance consisting of a 10 Ω resistor in series with a 20 Ω inductive reactance. If this current source is converted to a voltage source as shown in (b), what is the value of the series impedance element Z?

A) 20 Ω ∠90°
B) 22.4 Ω ∠26.6°
C) 22.4 Ω ∠63.4°
D) 10 Ω ∠0°

20) See Figure 17.1. The current source (a) includes a current I = 10 A ∠20° and an impedance consisting of a 10 Ω resistor in series with a 20 Ω inductive reactance. If this current source is converted to a voltage source as shown in (b), what is the value of the voltage source E?

A) 224 V ∠83.4°
B) 2.2 V ∠43.4°
C) 10 V ∠20°
D) 0.45 V ∠-43.4°

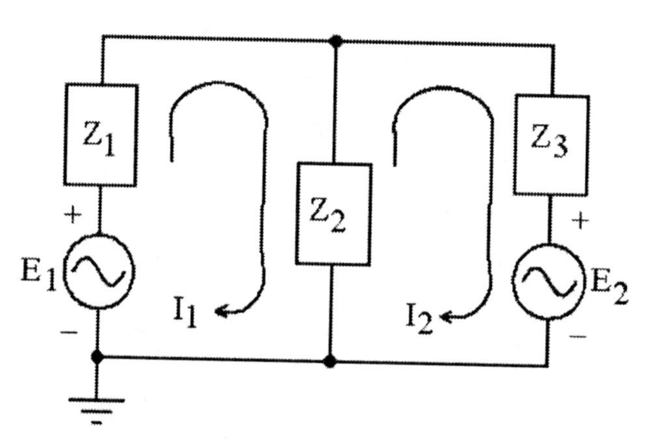

Figure 17.2

21) See Figure 17.2. Consider the mesh analysis (format approach) solution method for this circuit. Which one equation describes the loop on the left?

A) $-I_1(Z_1 + Z_2) - I_2Z_2 = E_1$
B) $I_1(Z_1 + Z_2) - I_2Z_2 = E_1$
C) $-I_1(Z_1 + Z_2) + I_2Z_2 = E_1$
D) $I_1(Z_1 + Z_2) + I_2Z_2 = E_1$

22) See Figure 17.2. Which one equation describes the current I_1? Hint: solve for I_1 using determinants.

A) $I_1 = E_1/(Z_1 + Z_2)$

B) $I_1 = ((E_1 - E_2)Z_2 + E_1Z_3)/(Z_1Z_2 + Z_1Z_3 + Z_2Z_3)$

C) $I_1 = ((Z_1 + Z_2)(Z_2 + Z_3) - (Z_2)^2/(Z_1Z_2 + Z_1Z_3 + Z_2Z_3)$

D) $I_1 = (-E_2(Z_1 + Z_2) + E_1Z_2)/(Z_1Z_2 + Z_1Z_3 + Z_2Z_3)$

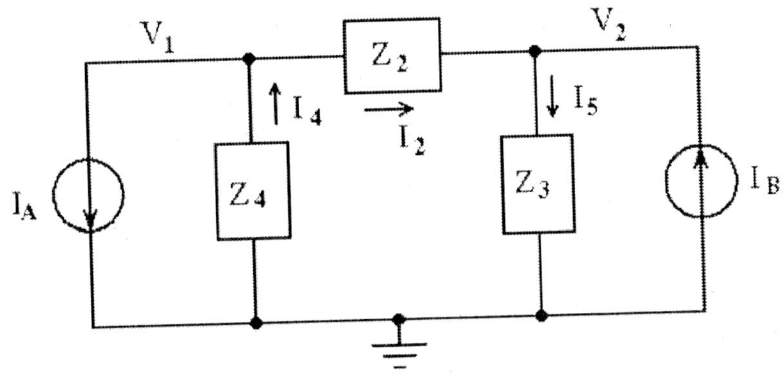

Figure 17.3

23) See Figure 17.3. When setting up this circuit for nodal analysis solution, which one equation describes node 1?

A) $I_2 = I_4 - I_3$ B) $I_4 = I_A + I_2$ C) $I_A = I_4$ D) $I_3 = I_A + I_4$

24) See Figure 17.3. Which one equation describes current I_2?

A) $I_2 = I_4 + I_A$ B) $I_2 = (V_1 + V_2)/Z_2$

C) $I_2 = (V_1 - V_2)/Z_2$ D) $I_2 = -I_A$

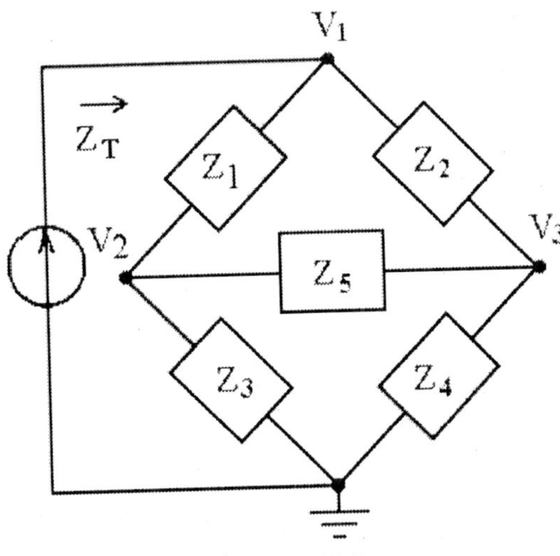

Figure 17.4

25) See Figure 17.4. In a general bridge circuit such as this, what condition will result in a balanced bridge?

A) $Z_1Z_3 = Z_2Z_4$ B) $Z_1Z_2 = Z_3Z_4$ C) $Z_1Z_4 = Z_2Z_3$ D) $Z_3 = Z_4$

26) See Figure 17.4. Assume that the bridge is balanced. If $Z_1 = 10\ \Omega\ \angle 0°$, $Z_2 = 20\ \Omega\ \angle 30°$, $Z_3 = 4\ \Omega\ \angle -10°$, what must Z_4 be?

A) $8\ \Omega\ \angle 20°$
B) $4\ \Omega\ \angle -10°$
C) $2\ \Omega\ \angle -40°$
D) $50\ \Omega\ \angle 40°$

27) When converting a Δ network to an equivalent Y network,

A) the impedance of each Y branch is equal to the sum of all possible products divided by the sum of each individual impedance.

B) the impedance of each Y branch is equal to the sum of the possible product combinations of the impedances of the Δ divided by the impedance of the Δ farthest from the impedance being determined.

C) the impedance of each Y branch is equal to the reciprocal of the sum of the reciprocals of the adjacent impedances in the Δ.

D) the impedance of each Y branch is equal to the product of the impedances in the two closest branches in the Δ, divided by the sum of the impedances in the Δ.

28) When converting a Y network to an equivalent Δ network,

A) the impedance of each Δ branch is equal to the product of the impedances in the two closest branches in the Y, divided by the sum of the impedances in the Y.

B) the impedance of each Δ branch is equal to the sum of all possible products divided by the sum of each individual impedance.

C) the impedance of each Δ branch is equal to the sum of the possible product combinations of the impedances of the Y divided by the impedance of the Y farthest from the impedance being determined.

D) the impedance of each Δ branch is equal to the reciprocal of the sum of the reciprocals of the adjacent impedances in the Y.

29) Which PSpice (Windows) part is a current-controlled current source?

A) ISIN
B) IAC
C) CCCS
D) F

30) Which type of PSpice (Windows) AC Current source allows frequency and phase angle to be specified?

A) IDC
B) ISRC
C) ISIN
D) IAC

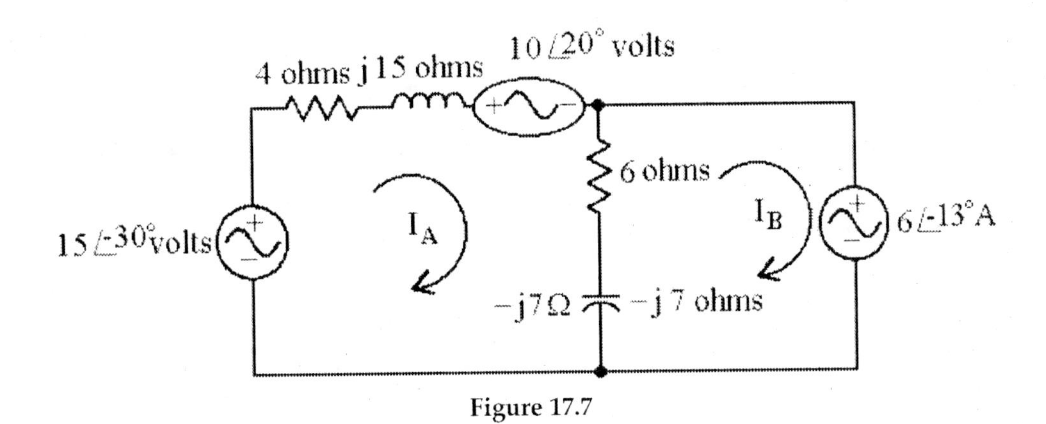

Figure 17.7

31) Use Mesh Analysis to find the mesh current I_1 for the circuit shown in Figure 17.7.

A) 3 ∠−13° B) 1.28 ∠85.5° C) 1.28 ∠−85.5° D) −3 ∠−13°

32) Referring to the circuit shown in Figure 17.7, use Mesh Analysis to find the mesh current I_2.

A) 1.28 ∠−85.5° B) 1.28 ∠85.5° C) −3 ∠−13° D) 3 ∠−13°

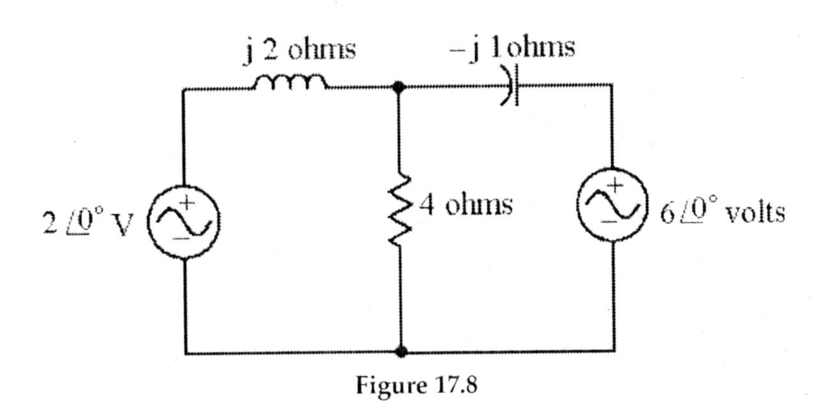

Figure 17.8

33) Referring to the circuit shown in Figure 17.8, determine the current through the 2 Ω inductor, by using Mesh Analysis.

A) 20 A ∠−143.13° B) 4.47 A ∠153.47° C) 3.6 A ∠123.7°

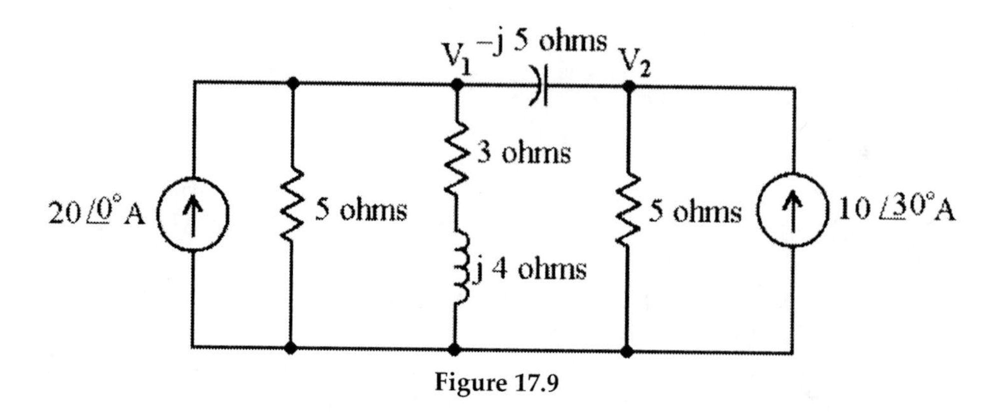

Figure 17.9

34) Convert the voltage source of the circuit shown in Figure 17.9 to a current source and find the current through the capacitor by Nodal Analysis.

A) 0.8 A ∠26.57°
B) 0.12 A ∠36.87°
C) 4.02 A ∠−63.43°
D) 5 A ∠−90°

35) A source whose magnitude is determined by a current or voltage of the system in which it appears is referred to as which kind of source?

A) Dependent
B) Uncontrolled
C) Inadequate
D) Independent

36) Which of the following is not part of the Mesh Analysis for independent voltage sources?

A) Assign a distinct current in the clockwise direction to reach independent closed loop of the network.

B) Once the equation is written, substitute the equation for the controlling quantity.

C) Apply Kirchhoff's voltage law around each closed loop in the clockwise direction.

D) Indicate the polarities within each loop for each impedance, as determined by the assumed direction of loop current for that loop.

37) A bridge configuration used for measuring the resistance and inductance of coils in those cases where the resistance is a small fraction of the reactance of the coil is known as a __________.

A) Capacitance bridge
B) Nodal bridge
C) Maxwell bridge
D) Haybridge

38) Nodal analysis is a method through which the nodal __________ of a network can be determined.

A) Resistance
B) Impedance
C) Voltages
D) Currents

39) Mesh analysis is a method through which the loop __________ of a network can be determined.

A) Impedance
B) Currents
C) Voltages
D) Resistance

40) An approach that applies to all networks with independent or dependent sources where the controlling variable is not a part of the network under investigation is called ________.

A) Mesh approach
B) Nodal approach
C) Format approach
D) Independent approach

Short Answer

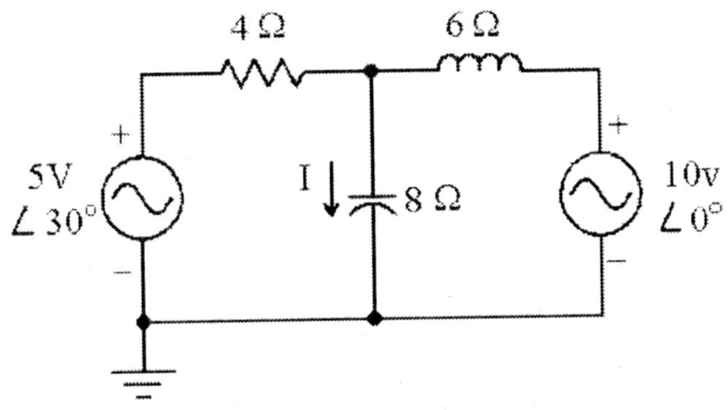

Figure 17.5

41) See Figure 17.5. Use mesh analysis to compute the current I through the capacitor.

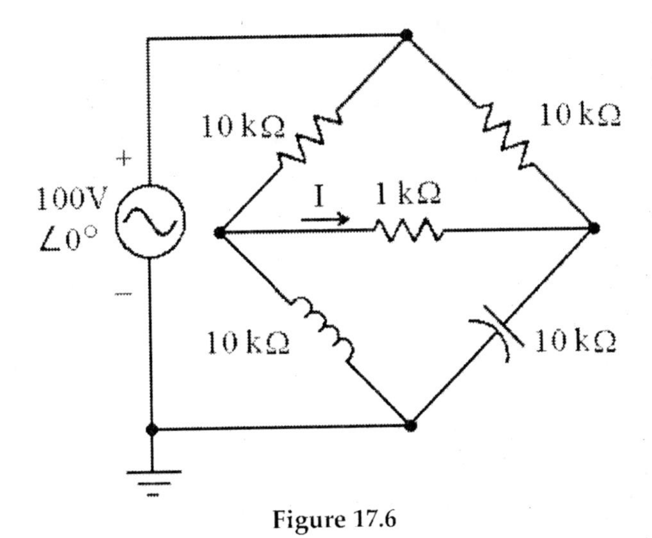

Figure 17.6

42) See Figure 17.6. Use mesh analysis to determine the current I.

43) See Figure 17.6. Determine V_A and V_B.

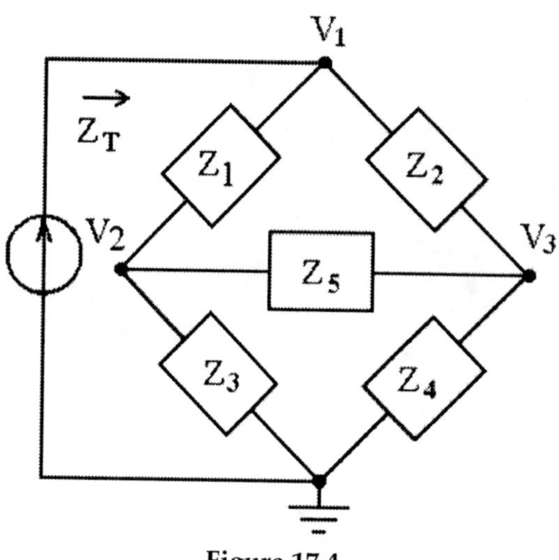

Figure 17.4

44) See Figure 17.4. Assume that $Z_1 = 10\ \Omega\ \angle 0°$, $Z_2 = 20\ \Omega\ \angle 90°$, $Z_3 = 4\ \Omega\ \angle{-90°}$, $Z_4 = 6\ \Omega\ \angle 0°$, and $Z_5 = 10\ \Omega\ \angle 90°$. Compute Z_T using Δ-Y conversion techniques.

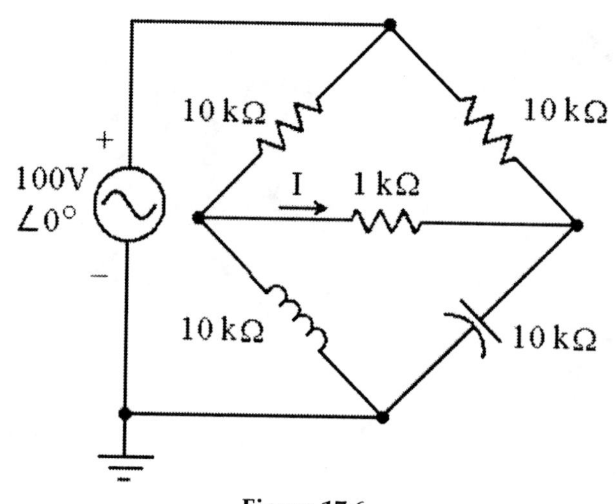

Figure 17.6

45) See Figure 17.6. Will voltages V_A and V_B increase, decrease, or remain the same as frequency increases? Why?

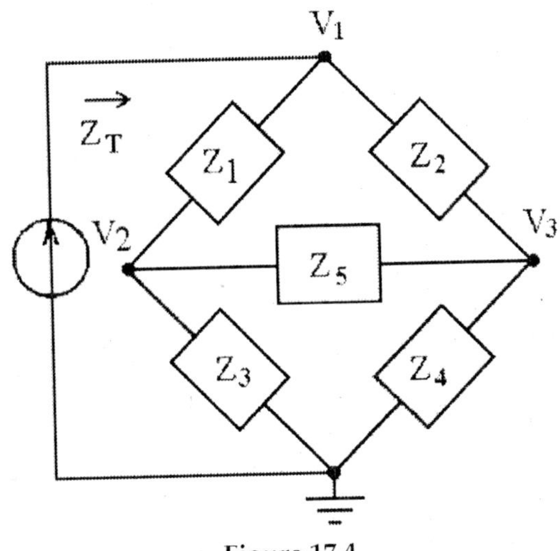

Figure 17.4

46) How can PSpice (Windows) be used to solve for Z_T in Figure 17.4?

47) What MathCAD statement can be used as a constant to convert radians to degrees?

48) Define the term *dependent source.*

49) Mesh Analysis is particularly valuable in determining unknown __________ in circuits with several loops and energy sources.

50) The primary use of Nodal Analysis is its use in finding unknown __________.

51) To be able to use Nodal Analysis, we must be able to determine the number of __________ within the networks.

52) For Mesh Analysis, the number of required equations must equal the number of chosen independent __________.

Answer Key
Testname: CHAPTER 17

1) TRUE
2) TRUE
3) FALSE
4) TRUE
5) FALSE
6) TRUE
7) FALSE
8) FALSE
9) TRUE
10) TRUE
11) TRUE
12) TRUE
13) FALSE
14) C
15) A
16) C
17) C
18) C
19) C
20) A
21) B
22) B
23) B
24) C
25) C
26) A
27) D
28) C
29) D
30) C
31) B
32) C
33) C
34) A
35) A
36) B
37) D
38) C
39) B
40) C
41) 0.74 A $\angle 55.57°$
42) 9.09 mA $\angle 90°$
43) V_A = 9.56 V $\angle 2.7°$, V_B = 9.56 V $\angle -2.7°$
44) 10 $\angle 6.73°$
45) V_A increases, V_B decreases due to increase in inductive reactance and decrease in capacitive reactance caused by the change in frequency.
46) Connect a 1A $\angle 0°$ source, then measure the voltage V1. The magnitude and phase angle are the same as for Z_T.
47) deg: $= \frac{\pi}{180}$
48) A dependent source is one whose magnitude and/or phase angle is determined by a current or voltage of the system in which it appears.
49) currents
50) voltages
51) nodes
52) closed loops

Chapter 18 Network Theorems (ac)

True/False

1) The superposition theorem is applicable to power effects in ac circuits, since it is dealing with a nonlinear relationship.

2) One of the most frequent applications of the superposition theorem is in electronic systems in which dc and ac analyses are treated separately.

3) Thevenin's theorem for ac circuits states that any 2-terminal linear ac network can be replaced by an equivalent circuit consisting of a voltage source and an impedance in series.

4) Norton's theorem allows a 2-terminal linear bilateral ac network consisting of a current source and an impedance.

5) Maximum power will be delivered to a load when the load impedance equals the Thevenin impedance of the source.

6) In order to use the Superposition Theorem, there must be at least two energy sources in the network.

7) The Thevenin's equivalent circuit consists of a voltage source in parallel with a resistor.

8) In order to remove a voltage source from a circuit, we must replace it with an open circuit.

9) An application of the superposition theorem is to electronic systems in which ac and dc analysis are equal and the total solution is the sum of the two.

10) Because the reactances of a circuit are frequently dependent, the Thevenin circuit that is found for a particular network is applicable at any frequency.

11) To apply the superposition theorem to ac networks the only variation is that the analyst will work with impedance and phasors instead of resistors and real numbers.

12) For dependent sources, the application of the superposition theorem is basically the same as for independent sources with the solution expressed in terms of the controlling variables.

Multiple Choice

13) Which one of the following statements describes a current-controlled current source?

A) A current source whose output is controlled by a current elsewhere in the system.

B) A current source whose outlet is a function of a remote voltage source.

C) A current source whose output is dependent on its internal impedance.

D) A current source whose output is independent of the load impedance.

14) When using the superposition theorem in ac network analysis, which one of the following statements is true?

A) Voltage sources are replaced by open circuits.

B) Current sources are replaced by short circuits.

C) Voltage sources are replaced by short circuits.

D) All impedances are replaced by their complex conjugates.

15) Which theorem is limited to use in single-source network?

A) superposition theorem

B) reciprocity theorem

C) substitution theorem

D) Millman's theorem

16) Millman's theorem states that

A) if the voltage across and the current through a branch are known, the branch can be replaced by a combination of elements that maintain the same voltage across and current through that branch.

B) any two-terminal linear bilateral source can be replaced by an equivalent circuit consisting of a current source and a parallel resistor.

C) the current in any branch of a network, due to a single voltage source elsewhere in the network, will equal the current through the branch in which the source was originally located if the source is placed in the branch in which the current was originally measured.

D) any number of parallel voltage sources can be reduced to a single source.

17) The substitution theorem states that

A) the current in any branch of a network, due to a single voltage source elsewhere in the network, will equal the current through the branch in which the source was originally located if the source is placed in the branch in which the current was originally measured.

B) any two-terminal linear bilateral source can be replaced by an equivalent circuit consisting of a current source and a parallel resistor.

C) if the voltage across and the current through a branch are known, the branch can be replaced by a combination of elements that maintain the same voltage across and current through that branch.

D) any number of parallel voltage sources can be reduced to a single source.

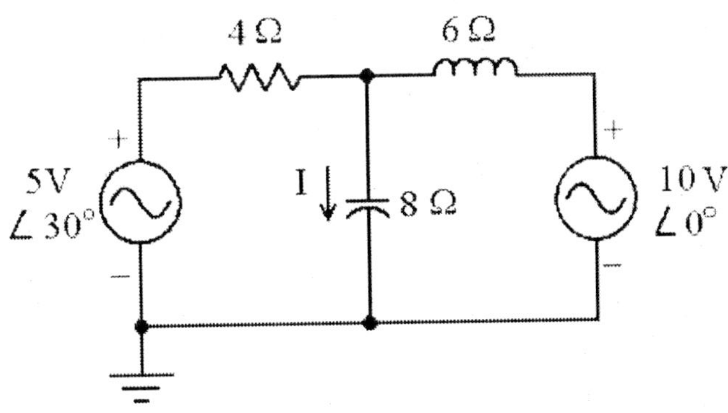

Figure 18.1

18) See Figure 18.1. Using the superposition theorem, what is the portion of the current through the capacitor caused by the 5V ∠30° voltage source?

A) 0.741 A ∠55.6°

B) 0.616 A ∠129.5°

C) 0.89 A ∠93.4°

D) 0.822 A ∠9.5°

19) See Figure 18.1. Using the superposition theorem, what is the portion of the current through the capacitor caused by the 10V ∠0° voltage source?

A) 5.0 A ∠90°

B) 0.616 A ∠129.5°

C) 0.822 A ∠9.5°

D) 0.741 A ∠55.6°

20) When using the superposition theorem on a 2-source ac network, if the current produced by one source flows through a component in one direction, while the current produced through the component by the other source is in the opposite direction,

A) all voltage sources were not properly converted to current sources.

B) a mistake in the sign of the result occurred.

C) the resulting current is the difference of the two and has the direction of the larger current.

D) the absolute values of the two currents add algebraically, and the direction is in the direction of the larger current.

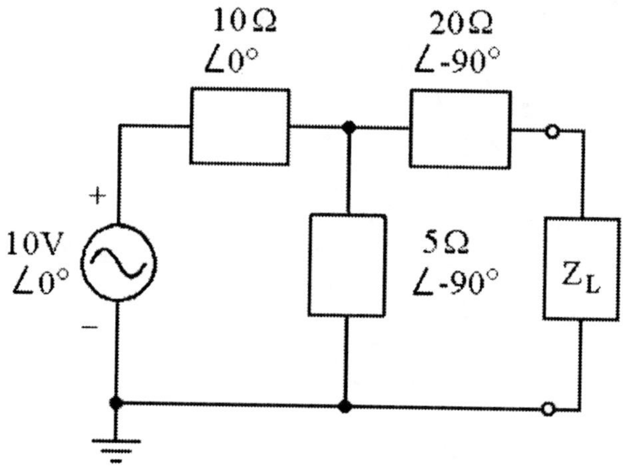

Figure 18.2

21) See Figure 18.2. What is the Thevenin impedance external to Z_L?

A) 4.47 Ω ∠-63.4°

B) 24.1 Ω ∠ -85.2°

C) 30 Ω ∠90°

D) 22.4 Ω ∠63.4°

22) See Figure 18.2. What is the Thevenin voltage external to Z_L?

A) 10 V ∠0°

B) 3.33 V ∠-26.6°

C) 4.47 V ∠-63.4°

D) 3.33 V ∠0°

23) If Z_{th} = 10 Ω - j30 Ω, what must the load impedance be for maximum power transfer to occur?

A) 10 Ω + j30 Ω

B) 10 Ω - j30 Ω

C) -10 Ω - j30 Ω

D) -10 Ω + j30 Ω

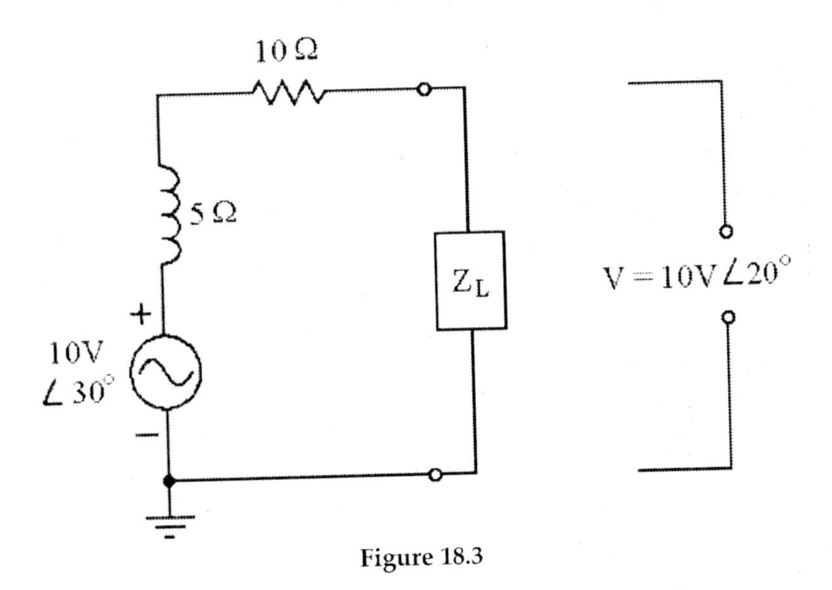

Figure 18.3

24) See Figure 18.3. What is the Norton equivalent impedance Z_N external to Z_L?

A) 5.0 Ω ∠90° B) 0.47 Ω ∠−26.6° C) 11.18 Ω ∠26.6° D) 10.0 Ω ∠0°

25) See Figure 18.3. What is the Norton equivalent current I_N external to Z_L?

A) 0 A ∠0° B) 0.67 A ∠26.6° C) 0.89 A ∠3.4° D) 0.67 A ∠30°

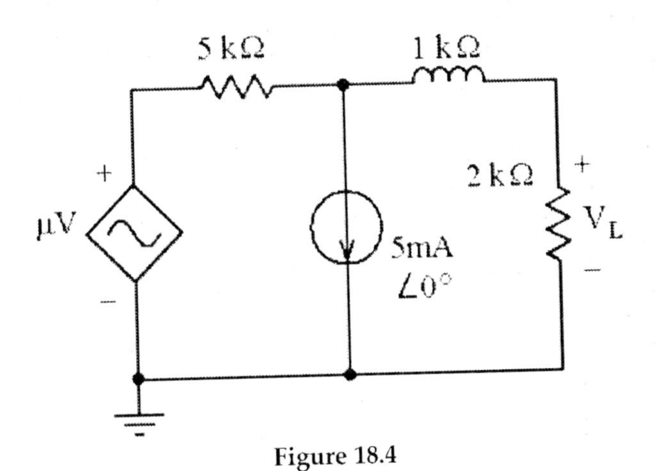

Figure 18.4

26) See Figure 18.4. What is the value of the dependent voltage source? Assume that $\mu = 3.3$.

A) 50 V ∠20° B) 5 V ∠−20° C) 500 V ∠20° D) 10 V ∠20°

27) The direction of current flow in an independent current source in PSpice is

A) toward the terminal with the lowest node number.

B) toward the top or right side of the drawing.

C) from the – to the + terminals.

D) from the + to the – terminals.

28) What mathematical relationship allows calculation of the Thevenin impedance of a circuit?

A) $E_{SC} \div I_{OC}$ B) $E_{OC} \div I_{SC}$ C) $E_{SC} \div I_{SC}$ D) $E_{OC} \div I_{OC}$

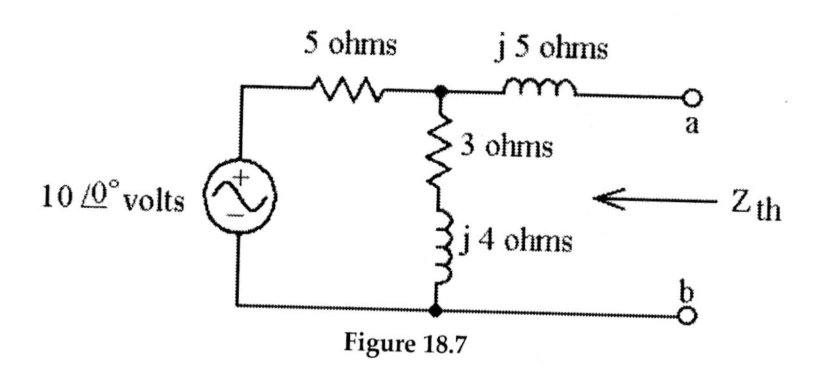

Figure 18.7

29) Using Thevenin's theorem, what should be the value of Z_{th} for the circuit shown in figure 18.7?

A) 2.5 – j6.25 B) –2.5 – j6.25 C) 2.5 + j6.25 D) –2.5 + j6.25

30) For the circuit shown in figure 18.7, what should be the value of V_{th} for the Thevenin equivalent circuit?

A) 1.298 ∠145.34° B) 2.596 ∠2.2° C) 3.226 ∠–40° D) 5.59 ∠26.56°

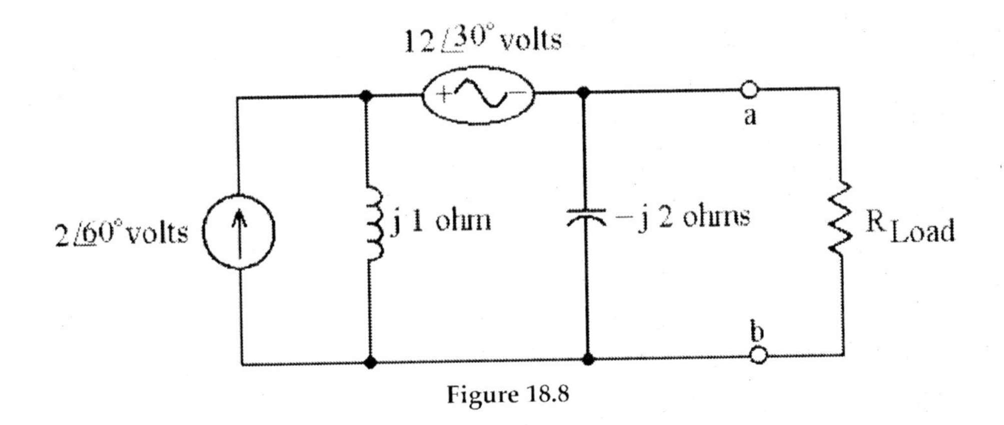

Figure 18.8

31) What should be the value of I_N and R_N of the Norton equivalent circuit for the complex network shown in figure 18.8?

A) 2 ∠60°, 2 ∠-90°
B) 2 ∠60°, 2 ∠90°
C) 13.1 ∠112.4°, 2 ∠-90°
D) 13.1 ∠112.4°, 2 ∠90°

32) Which of the following theorems eliminates the need to consider the effects of each source independently when solving linear equations?

A) Norton's
B) Substitution
C) Superposition
D) Reciprocity

33) To ensure maximum power to the load, the maximum power transfer theorem is used to determine which of the following for the load?

A) Impedance
B) Current
C) Voltage
D) Resistance

34) Which of the following describes what takes place when the load impedance is the conjugate of the Thevenin impedance across its terminals?

A) A matching impedance must be placed in parallel
B) The circuit will be capacitive
C) The circuit will appear resistive
D) Maximum power will be delivered to the load

35) Which of the following theorems states, for single-source networks, the magnitude of the current in any branch of a network, due to a single voltage source anywhere else in the network; will equal the magnitude of the current through the branch in which the source was located if the source is placed in the branch in which the current was originally measured?

A) Superposition
B) Norton
C) Reciprocity
D) Milliman

36) A voltage source whose parameters are controlled by a voltage elsewhere in the system is referred to as which of the following?

A) Voltage-controlled
B) Current-controlled
C) Remote-controlled
D) Impedance-controlled

Short Answer

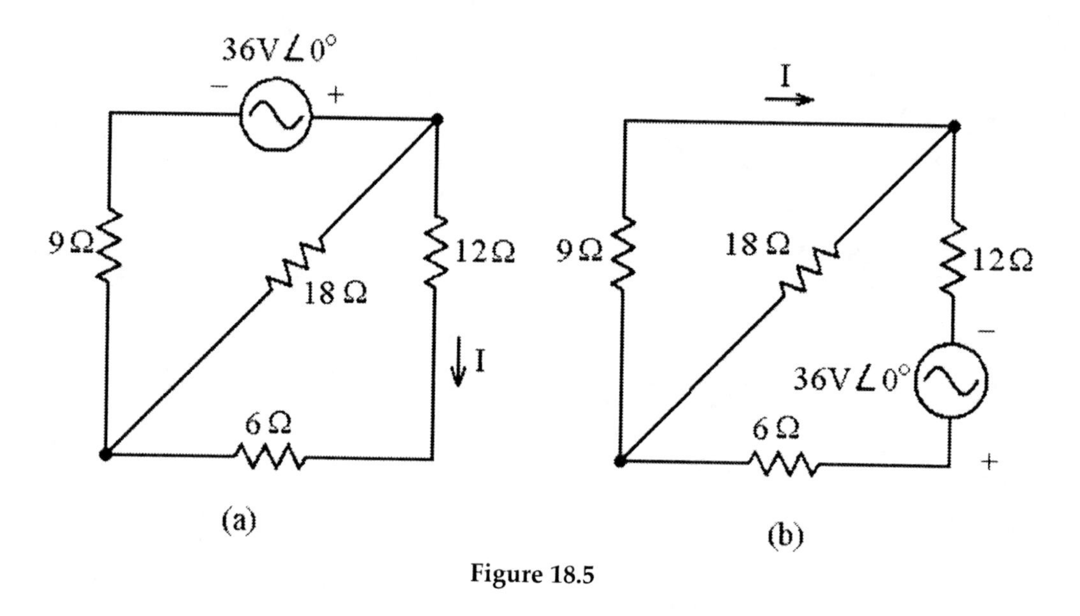

Figure 18.5

37) See Figure 18.5. Use the reciprocity theorem to prove that the current I is the same in circuits (a) and (b).

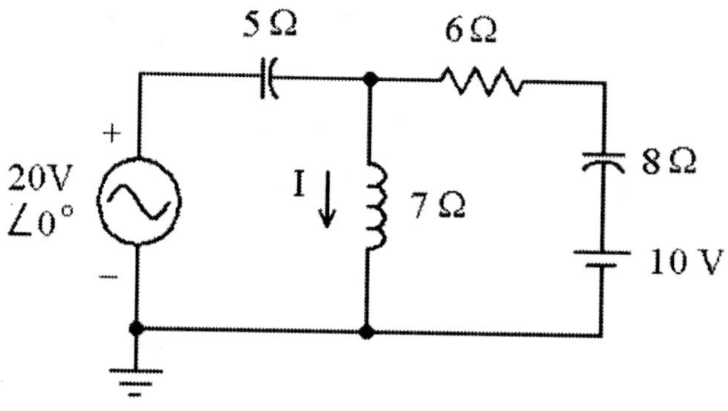

Figure 18.6

38) See Figure 18.6. Use superposition to determine the current I through the 7 Ω inductive reactance due to the 10 V battery.

39) What type of dependent source is in use in PSpice if its name is EFET?

40) After running a PSpice dc analysis of a network containing an inductor, it was discovered that voltage on both sides of the inductor was the same. Is something wrong? Explain.

41) The PSpice (Windows) Bias Point Detail option allows what type of solution (ac or dc) to be found?

42) The reciprocity theorem says that in a linear ac network the ratio of applied voltage to current measured at a point is identical to the ratio obtained if the source and meter locations are exchanged. This ratio is known as the __________ impedance.

43) Since the Thevenin and Norton equivalent impedance are the same, the Thevenin and the Norton equivalent circuit will deliver the same maximum __________.

44) In order to remove a current source from a circuit, we must replace it with an __________ circuit.

45) The only difference in applying network theorems to ac circuits rather than dc circuits is that we will be working with __________ and __________ instead of just resistors and real numbers.

Answer Key
Testname: CHAPTER 18

1) FALSE
2) TRUE
3) TRUE
4) TRUE
5) FALSE
6) TRUE
7) FALSE
8) FALSE
9) FALSE
10) FALSE
11) TRUE
12) TRUE
13) A
14) C
15) B
16) D
17) C
18) B
19) C
20) C
21) B
22) C
23) A
24) C
25) C
26) C
27) D
28) B
29) C
30) D
31) D
32) C
33) A
34) D
35) C
36) A
37) Both currents are 1 A $\angle 0°$
38) The current I is zero because the capacitor blocks all dc current.
39) Voltage Controlled Voltage Source
40) Nothing is wrong - the inductor acts like a short circuit to dc.
41) dc solution
42) transfer
43) power
44) open
45) impedances, phasors

Chapter 19 Power (ac)

True/False

1) The total power delivered to a pure inductor is dissipated in the form of heat.

2) The unit of apparent power is the volt-ampere.

3) Power factor is the ratio of the average power to the apparent power.

4) A capacitive element can be placed in parallel with an inductive element to bring the power factor closer to unity.

5) The skin effect causes the effective area of a conductor to increase, thereby reducing the resistance of the conductor.

6) The units of apparent power are watts (W).

7) The power factor is equal to one for purely reactive loads.

8) The power factor of a single-phase alternating current circuit is defined as the ratio of real power (kW) to apparent power (kVA).

9) Energy dissipation occurs only in the resistive part of a circuit since inductors and capacitors merely store and release energy.

10) The total power delivered to a resistor will be dissipated in the form of heat.

11) A watt-meter reading is an indication of watts dissipated and reflects the magnitude of the current drawn.

12) The net flow of power to the pure(ideal) capacitor is zero over a full cycle.

Multiple Choice

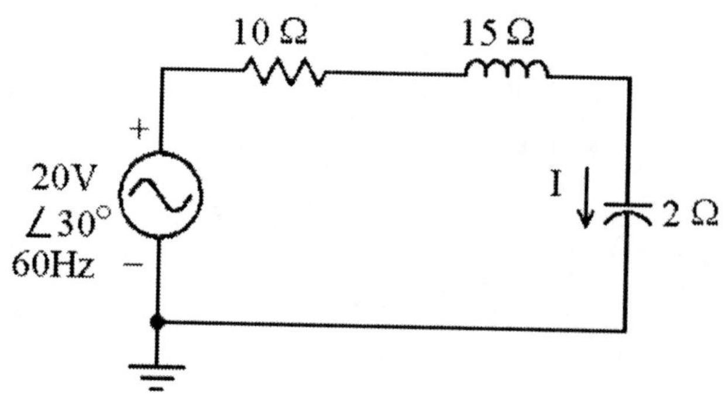

Figure 19.1

13) See Figure 19.1. What is the total real power (P_T) delivered to this circuit?

A) 24.4 W B) 14.9 W C) 20.0 W D) 0 W

14) See Figure 19.1. What is the total apparent power delivered to this circuit?

A) 24.4 VA B) 30.8 VA C) 14.9 VA D) 15.4 VA

15) See Figure 19.1. What is the total reactive power (Q_T) delivered to this circuit?

A) 24.4 VAR B) 19.3 VAR C) 0 VAR D) 14.9 VAR

16) In a certain electric circuit, if P_T = 600 W, S_T = 1000 VA, and Q_T = 800 VAR (capacitive), what is the power factor?

A) 0.6 leading B) 0.75 leading C) 0.5 leading D) 0.8 leading

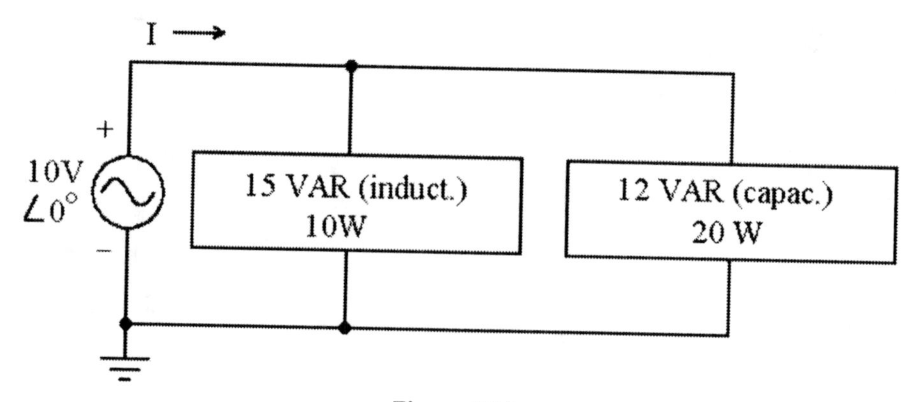

Figure 19.2

17) See Figure 19.2. How much total real power (P_T) is consumed in this network?

A) 10 W B) 6.67 W C) 30 W D) 27 W

18) See Figure 19.2. What is the total reactive power (Q_T) in this network?

A) 6.67 VAR
B) 30 VAR
C) 3 VAR
D) 27 VAR

19) See Figure 19.2. Determine the total apparent power (S_T).

A) 33 VA
B) 6.67 VA
C) 3 VA
D) 30.15 VA

20) A 10 hp motor has an efficiency of 75% and a power factor of 0.8 (lagging). How much input power is consumed?

A) 5595 W
B) 9947 W
C) 9325 W
D) 7460 W

21) A 10 hp motor has an efficiency of 75% and a power factor of 0.8 (lagging). How much apparent power is consumed?

A) 13,262 VA
B) 7460 VA
C) 5595 VA
D) 12,433 VA

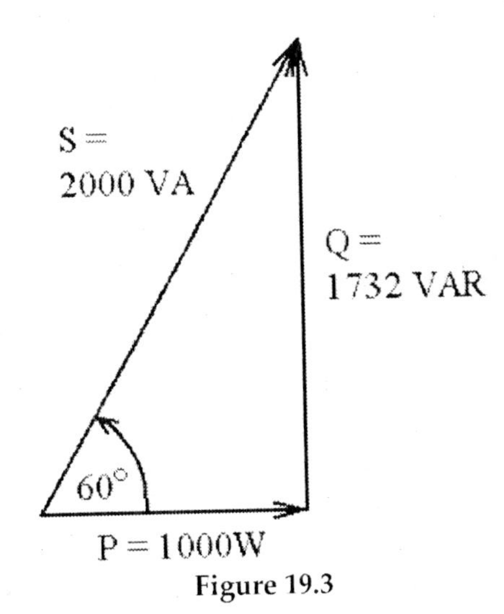

Figure 19.3

22) See Figure 19.3. The power triangle shown represents the characteristics of a 230 V 60 Hz ac motor. What is the power factor of this motor?

A) 0.866
B) 0.577
C) 1.0
D) 0.5

23) See Figure 19.3. How much current is consumed by this motor if the supply voltage is 230 V ac at 60 Hz?

A) 4.35 A
B) 0.23 A
C) 8.7 A
D) 7.53 A

24) See Figure 19.3. If the power factor in this application could be improved to unity, how much supply current would be consumed?

A) 7.53 A
B) 0 A
C) 4.35 A
D) 8.7 A

25) Which one of these statements is true of eddy currents?

A) They are currents in the core material caused by a changing magnetic flux linking the core.

B) They are of little concern except at very high frequencies.

C) They cause large losses in air core coils, and can be reduced by using an iron core.

D) They allow designers to use hollow conductors at very high frequencies.

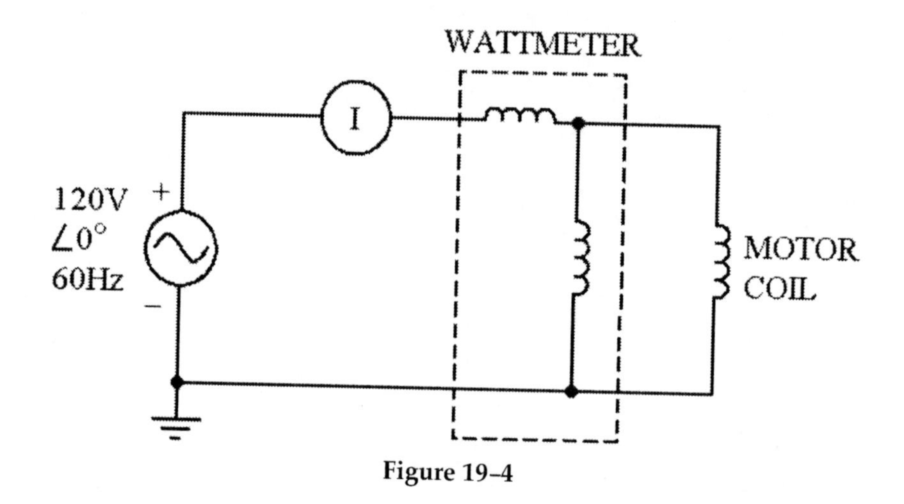

Figure 19–4

26) See Figure 19.4. The measured current I is 10 A and the measured power is 900 W. What is the resistance of the motor coil?

A) 7.94 Ω B) 90 Ω C) 9 Ω D) 12 Ω

27) See Figure 19.4. The measured current I is 10 A and the measured power is 900 W. What is the inductance of the motor coil?

A) 23.9 mH B) 31.8 mH C) 21.1 mH D) 7.9 mH

28) The power curve produced when a sinusoidal waveform is applied to a resistor

A) swings positive and negative, as do the voltage and current curves.

B) has a frequency that is the same as the source voltage frequency.

C) is a constant dc level.

D) has a frequency that is twice the source voltage frequency.

29) The average value of a power curve is

A) the power absorbed by the system.

B) the product of the peak voltage and peak current.

C) the square of the average voltage.

D) the square of the average current.

30) A sinusoidal AC voltage with an rms value of 60 V is applied to a purely resistive load. What steady voltage generates the same power as the alternating voltage?

A) 60 V
B) 120 V
C) 38.2 V
D) 42.4 V
E) 84.9 V

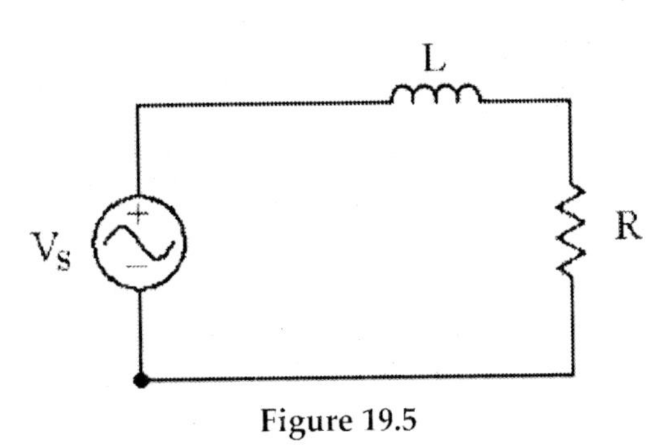

Figure 19.5

31) Determine the power factor angle for the circuit shown in Figure 19.5 if $R = 25\ \Omega$, $L = 0.2$ H, $V_S = 200$ V, and $f_S = 60$ Hz.

A) 36.4°
B) 71.6°
C) 56.4°
D) 52.4°
E) 46.4°

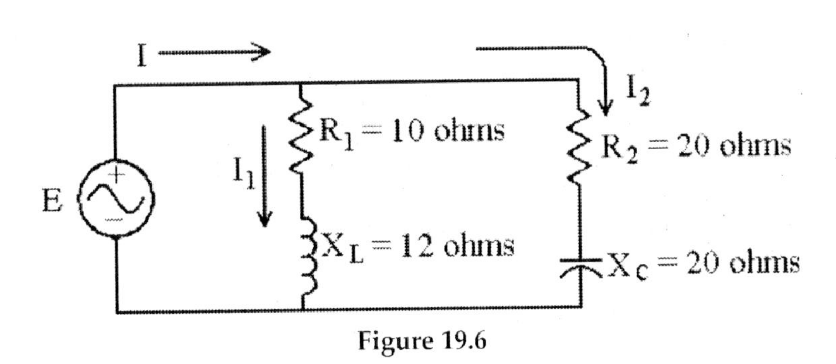

Figure 19.6

32) What is the power factor for the circuit in Figure 19.6?

A) 83.7%
B) 98.7%
C) 78.7%
D) 73.7%
E) 93.7%

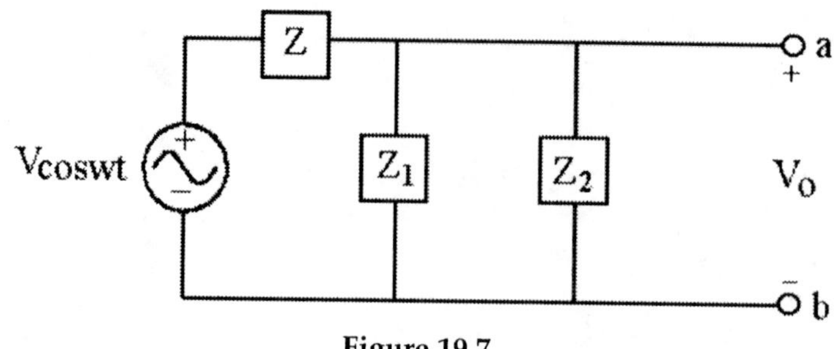

Figure 19.7

33) Referring to the circuit shown in Figure 19.7, for what condition is the average power that is transferred to the load maximized given that the load is $Z_L = Z_1 \parallel Z_2$?

A) $Z^* = Z_1 \parallel Z_2$

B) $Z^* = Z_1 + Z_2$

C) $Z = Z_1 = Z_2$

D) $Z = (Z_1 + Z_2)/2$

E) $Z \times Z^* = Z_1 \times Z_2$

34) Which of the following is power that is determined solely by the product of the terminal voltage and current of the load?

A) Inductive power
B) Average power
C) Reaction power
D) Apparent power

35) Which of the following is power associated with reactive elements that provide a measure of energy associated with magnetic and electric fields of inductive and capacitive elements?

A) Apparent power
B) Resistive power
C) Impedance power
D) Reactive power

36) Which of the following describes the power dissipated in the form of heat by a network or system?

A) Real Power
B) Resistive power
C) Effective power
D) Average power

37) What is the net flow of power to the pure (ideal) inductor over a full cycle where no energy is lost?

A) In phase with the source
B) One
C) Zero
D) Dependent on capacitance

38) If a network has both capacitive and inductive elements, the reactive component of the power triangle will be determined by the ________ between the reactive power delivered by each.

A) Difference B) Average C) RMS D) Sum

39) Total real, reactive or apparent power is ________ of whether the loads are in series, parallel or a series-parallel combination.

A) Independent
B) An indirect consideration
C) Dependent
D) Comparison

40) The process of introducing elements with the capacitive terminal characteristics in an inductive circuit has the sole purpose of improving ________.

A) Inductance
B) Phase angle
C) Power factor
D) Power dissipation

Short Answer

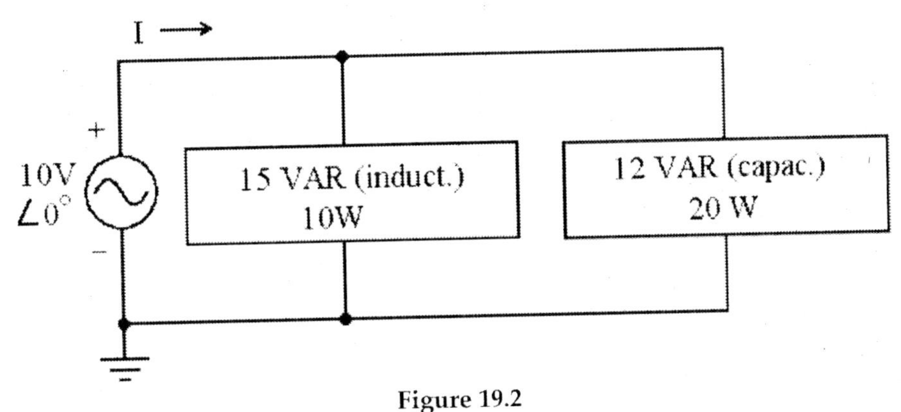

Figure 19.2

41) See Figure 19.2. Sketch the power triangle for this network.

42) See Figure 19.2. Calculate the supply current I.

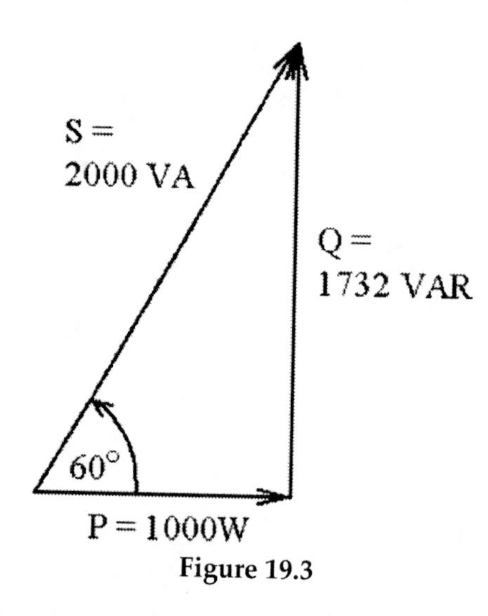

Figure 19.3

43) See Figure 19.3. Determine the capacitance value that, when placed in parallel with this load, would produce a unity power factor. Assume that the source is 230 V at 60 Hz.

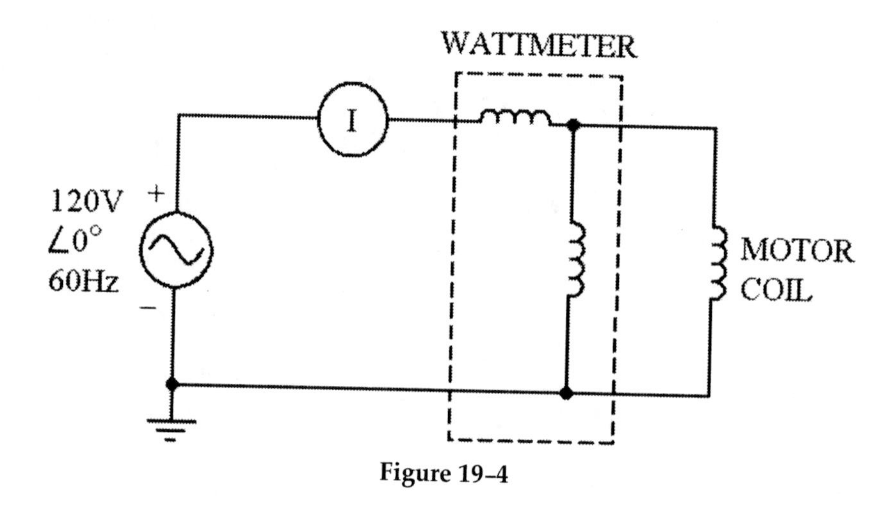

Figure 19–4

44) See Figure 19.4. If the motor coil has had its power factor corrected to unity, and the wattmeter reads 1200 W, how much current is indicated on the ammeter?

45) How can eddy current losses be reduced in a magnetic core?

46) Write a BASIC program that will print the power factor of a load, given the phase angle T in degrees, voltage V, and current I.

47) Write a BASIC program that will calculate true power, given apparent power VA, and phase angle T in degrees.

48) Which power value (true, reactive, or apparent) must be minimized in order for unity power factor to be approached?

49) Suppose that a circuit draws 5000 kVA with a power factor of 0.72. The 60-Hz line voltage is 220 V (rms). A __________ capacitor is required to increase the power factor to 0.86.

50) In as much as apparent power is paid for but only real power is dissipated, it may be possible to reduce electrical utility charges if the power angle is reduced without changing the real power. This operation, known as __________, is routinely accomplished by changing the circuit reactance in order to reduce the reactive power.

51) __________ power results from an actual draw of current in motors and charge on capacitors.

52) Apparent power is the magnitude of __________ power.

Answer Key
Testname: CHAPTER 19

1) FALSE
2) TRUE
3) TRUE
4) TRUE
5) FALSE
6) FALSE
7) FALSE
8) TRUE
9) TRUE
10) TRUE
11) FALSE
12) TRUE
13) B
14) A
15) B
16) A
17) C
18) C
19) D
20) B
21) D
22) D
23) C
24) C
25) A
26) C
27) C
28) D
29) A
30) A
31) B
32) E
33) A
34) D
35) D
36) A
37) C
38) A
39) A
40) C
41) P_T is 30 W in left to right (horizontal) direction, Q_T is 3 VAR in upward (vertical) direction, and S_T is 30.15 VA from tail of P_T to head of Q_T.
42) 3.13 A $\angle -16.57°$
43) 86.8 μF
44) 10 A
45) Reduce eddy current losses by constructing the core of thin laminated sheets of ferromagnetic material insulated from one another.
46) THETARAD=T/180*3.14159
PF=V*I*COS(THETARAD)
PRINT PF
47) THETA=T/180*3.14159
P=VA*COS(THETA)
48) Reactive power
49) 72.67 MF
50) power factor correction
51) Reactive
52) complex

Chapter 20 Resonance

True/False

1) Bandwidth is the range of frequencies between the half-power frequencies.

2) High selectivity is associated with a wide bandwidth.

3) The total impedance of a series RLC circuit at resonance is equal to the resistance of the circuit.

4) For a given reactance, the Q of a coil is higher for a coil with high resistance than for one with low resistance.

5) The average power absorbed by a resonant circuit is at a minimum at resonance.

6) Power dissipation is a maximum in a resonant parallel-RLC circuit at resonance.

7) Current and voltage are in phase in series resonant circuits.

8) Current is a minimum in a resonant series-RLC circuit.

9) At the half-power frequencies, the power dissipated in the resistor is half of the power dissipated at the resonant frequency.

10) Once an ideal system has reached a state of resonance, it requires further reactive power to sustain itself.

11) In a resonant circuit, there will be a total resistive element that is comprised of the source resistance, inductor resistance and design resistance.

12) The minimum impedance occurs at the resonant frequency and is equal to the resistance.

13) For parallel resonance with a current source driving the network, the frequency response for the driving impedance is the same as that for the output-voltage.

14) In a resonant circuit, for a particular range of frequencies the response will be near or equal to the maximum.

15) At resonance, an increase in resistance or a decrease in the ratio of inductance to capacitance will result in a decrease in the resonant impedance with a corresponding increase in the current.

Multiple Choice

16) Which one of these statements is true of a high-Q series resonant circuit?

A) The circuit has a large bandwidth.

B) The circuit has a relatively low coil resistance and a relatively high inductive reactance.

C) The circuit has a high average power compared to its reactive power.

D) The circuit has a small selectivity.

17) What is the resonant frequency of a series circuit consisting of a 100 pf capacitor, a 10 kΩ resistor, and a 1 mH inductor?

A) 503 kHz B) 3.16 MHz C) 159 Hz D) 1.58 MHz

18) What is the Q of a 1 mH coil at 1 kHz if its series resistance is 10 Ω?

A) 0.63 B) 1.0 C) 1.59 D) 0.8

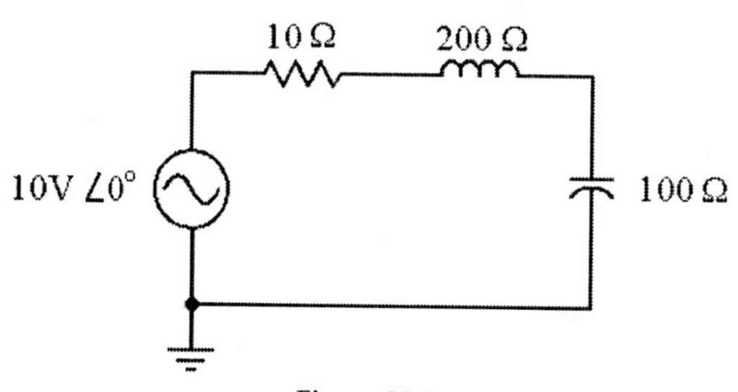

Figure 20.1

19) See Figure 20.1. Which of the following statements is true of this circuit?

A) It is operating at its resonant frequency.

B) The resonant frequency can be attained by decreasing the inductance in the circuit.

C) The resonant frequency can be attained by increasing the frequency of the source.

D) The resonant frequency can be attained by decreasing the capacitance in the circuit.

20) See Figure 20.1. What is the Q of the coil?

A) 0.05 B) 20 C) 10 D) 200

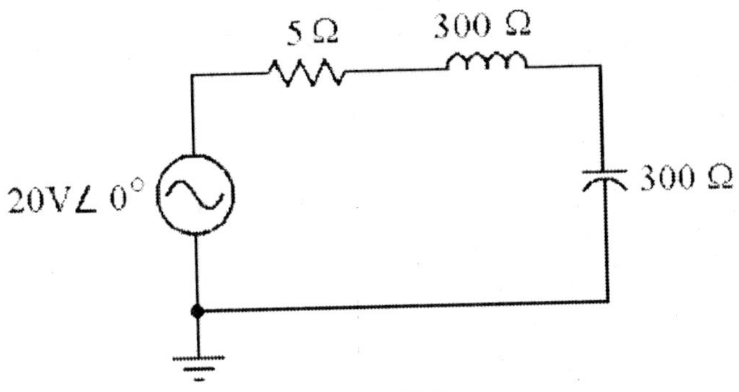

Figure 20.2

21) See Figure 20.2. What is the source current at resonance?

A) 0.25 A ∠0° B) 66.7 mA ∠-90° C) 4 A ∠0° D) 66.7 mA ∠+90°

22) See Figure 20.2. What is the voltage across the capacitor in this resonant circuit?

A) 1200 V B) 300 V C) 60 V D) 20 V

23) See Figure 20.2. What is the voltage across the resistor in this resonant circuit?

A) 20 V B) 80 V C) 1200 V D) 1180 V

24) See Figure 20.2. If the resonant frequency is 10 kHz, what is the bandwidth?

A) 333 Hz B) 7071 Hz C) 5000 Hz D) 10,000 Hz

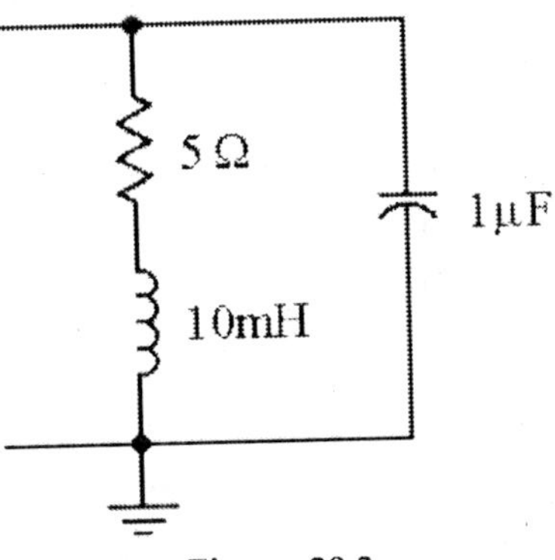

Figure 20.3

25) See Figure 20.3. What is the resonant frequency of this parallel network?

A) 15.9 MHz B) 15.9 Hz C) 159 Hz D) 1.59 kHz

26) See Figure 20.3. What is the Q of the coil at resonance?

A) 50 B) 10 C) 2 D) 20

27) See Figure 20.3. What is the total impedance of this circuit at resonance?

A) 2 kΩ
B) 25 Ω
C) 20 kΩ
D) 5 Ω

28) Doubling both the inductance and the capacitance values in Figure 20.3 will cause f_S to

A) decrease by a factor of 2.
B) decrease by a factor of 4.
C) increase by a factor of 2.
D) remain the same.

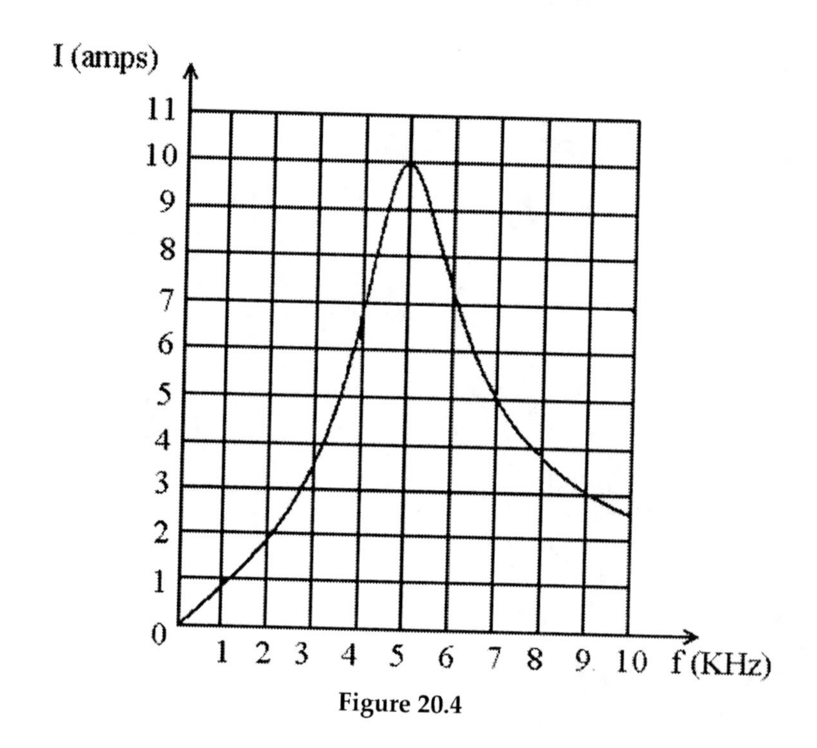

Figure 20.4

29) See Figure 20.4. This curve describes a series resonant circuit. What is the power delivered to the load if the load looks like a 5 Ω resistance at resonance?

A) 50 W
B) 1000 W
C) 500 W
D) 100 W

30) See Figure 20.4. This curve describes a series resonant circuit. What is the approximate bandwidth of this circuit?

A) 3.45 kHz
B) 1.9 kHz
C) 2.5 kHz
D) 5.0 kHz

31) See Figure 20.4. This curve describes a series resonant circuit. Which one of the following is a half-power frequency?

A) 4150 Hz
B) 5000 Hz
C) 3550 Hz
D) 7000 Hz

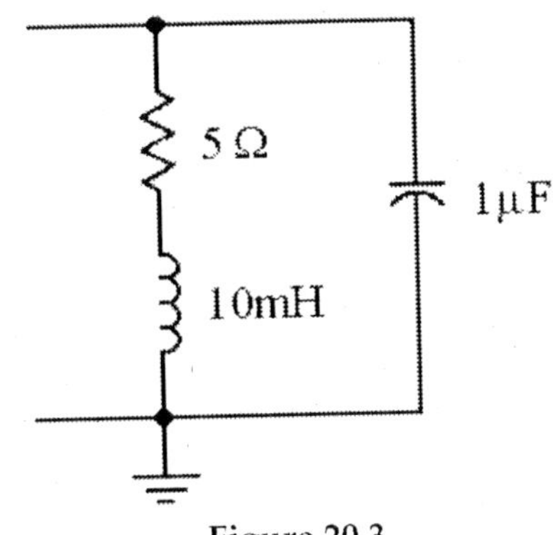

Figure 20.3

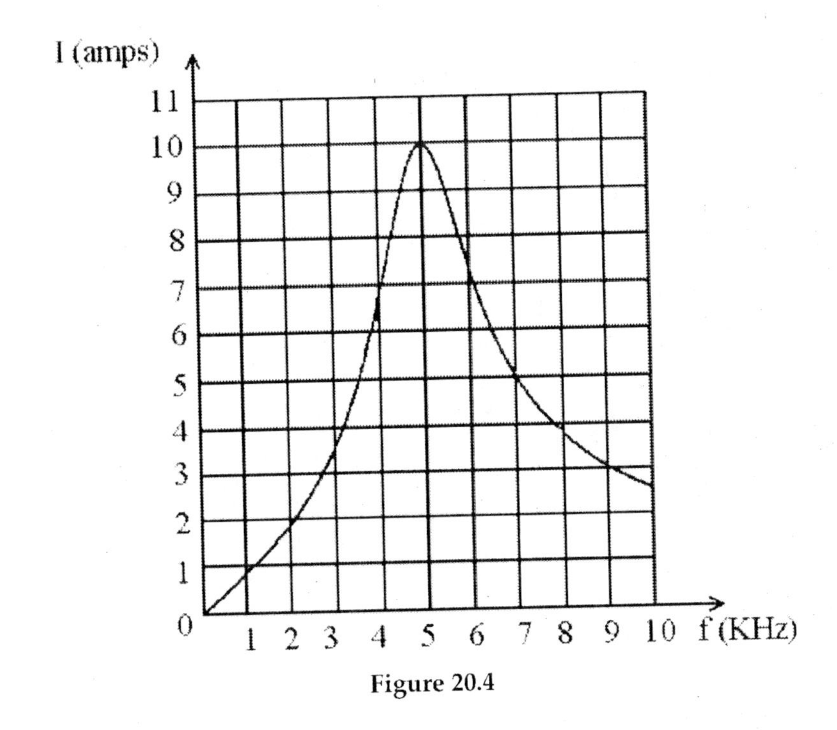

Figure 20.4

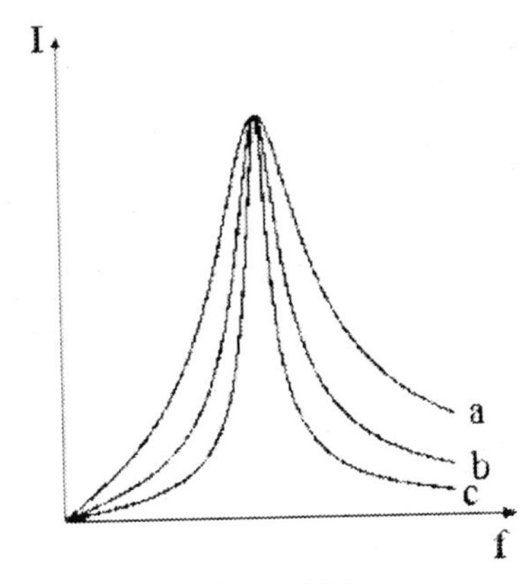

Figure 20.5

32) Reducing the resistance of the 5 Ω resistor in Figure 20.3 to 2.5 Ω will cause

A) the resonant frequency f_S to increase.
B) Q of the circuit to double.
C) Q of the circuit to be cut in half.
D) the resonant frequency f_S to decrease.

33) At 60 Hz, a series LCR circuit contains reactances X_L = 20 Ω and X_C = 14 Ω and resistance = 10 Ω. What is the impedance at resonant frequency?

A) 26.4 Ω
B) 24.4 Ω
C) 10 Ω
D) 20 Ω
E) 14 Ω

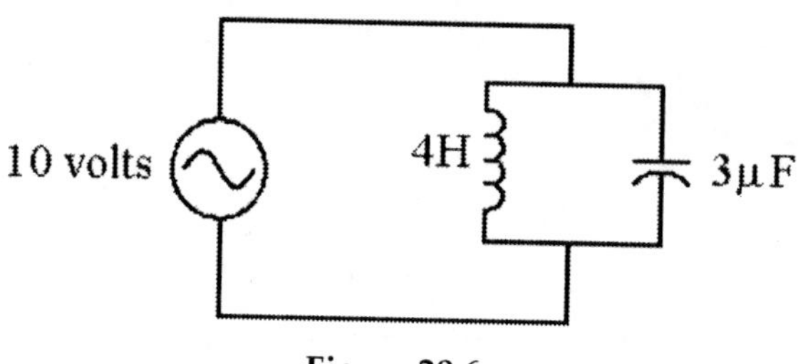

Figure 20.6

34) What is the resonant frequency of the circuit shown in Figure 20.6?

A) 1.45 Hz
B) 45.94 Hz
C) 4.59 Hz
D) 75.40 Hz
E) 1.91 Hz

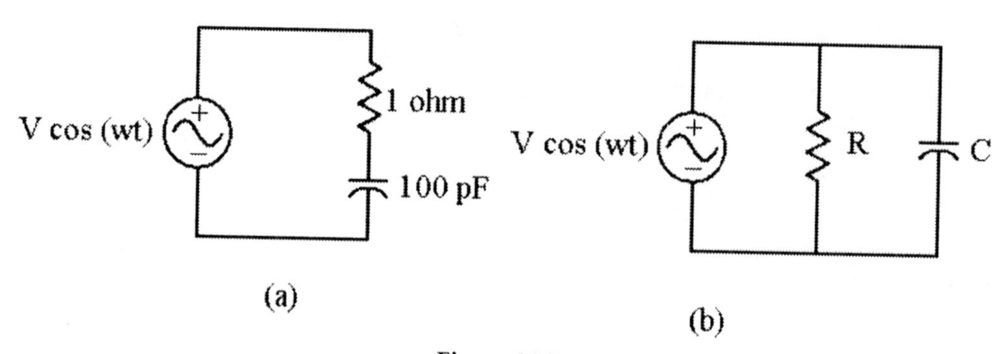

Figure 20.7

35) What should be the values of the capacitor C and the resistor R in order for the circuits shown in Figure 20.7(a) and 20.7(b) to be equivalent at the frequency of 15.9 MHz?

A) R = 10 kΩ, C = 1 pF
B) R = 10 Ω, C = 1 pF
C) impossible
D) R = 10 kΩ, C = 100 pF
E) R = 1 Ω, C = 100 pF

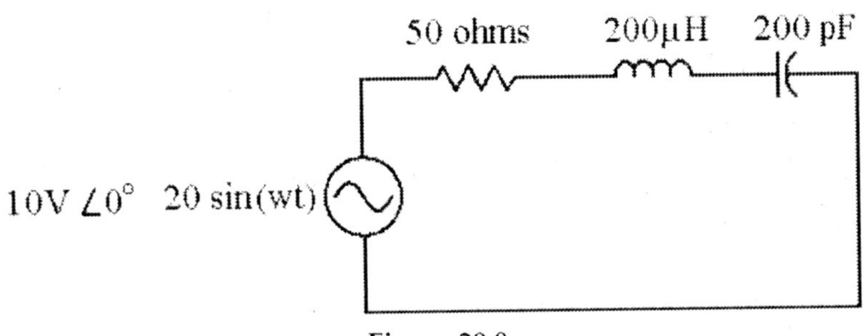

Figure 20.8

36) A series-RLC circuit, shown in Figure 20.8, is connected across a sinusoidal voltage with peak of 20 V. What is the resonant frequency (in rad/s)?

A) 4×10^{-14} rad/s

B) 70.7 rad/s

C) 2×10^{-7} rad/s

D) 5×10^{6} rad/s

E) 7.07×10^{4} rad/s

37) Which of the following describes the ratio of reactive power of the inductor or capacitor to the average power of the resistor at resonance?

A) Resistor resonance

B) Quality factor

C) Reactive energy

D) Power factor

38) In a parallel resonant circuit, impedance will be relatively __________ at resonance as compared to a series circuit.

A) High

B) Low

C) An average of resistance and inductance

D) Equivalent to inductance

39) Frequencies that define the points on the resonance curve that are 70.7% of the peak current or voltage value are known as the frequencies that determine

A) Bandwidth

B) Selected

C) Average

D) Resonant

Short Answer

40) What is the bandwidth of a series resonant circuit if its resonant frequency is 1000 Hz and Q_S = 20?

41) If the half-power frequencies are 2000 Hz and 2500 Hz, what is the resonant frequency?

42) Is a small bandwidth better than a large bandwidth for a tuned circuit that controls signal selection in a radio receiver? Why?

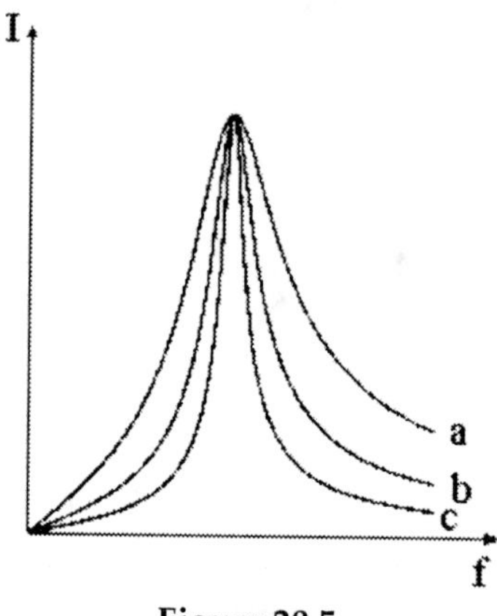

Figure 20.5

43) See Figure 20.5. These curves describe three series resonant circuits. If the resistance R is the same for all three circuits, what circuit differences would result in response curve (c) compared to response curve (a)?

44) See Figure 20.5. These curves describe three series resonant circuits. Which response curve represents the circuit with the highest Q?

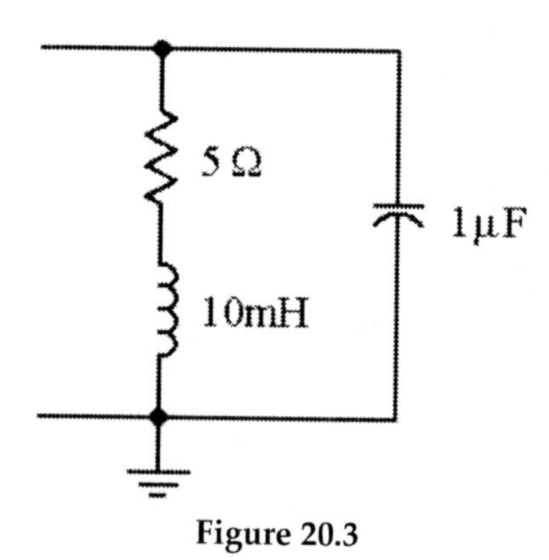

Figure 20.3

45) What PSpice (Windows) parameter can be added to the PSpice Trace display to show the voltage phase relationship across the capacitor in Figure 20.3?

46) List the steps needed to measure the bandwidth of the circuit shown in Figure 20.3. Assume that the circuit has been simulated with PSpice (Windows) and Probe has been used to display the voltage across the capacitor.

47) How many data points must be calculated by a PSpice analysis if the points are to be from 100 Hz to 1000 Hz in 10 Hz steps?

48) In a resonant network, the power factor is __________.

49) The __________ is the range of frequencies between the half-power points.

50) The frequency at which a circuit becomes purely resistive is the __________ frequency.

51) Resistance is the __________ in a series resonant circuit at resonance

Answer Key
Testname: CHAPTER 20

1) TRUE
2) FALSE
3) TRUE
4) FALSE
5) FALSE
6) FALSE
7) TRUE
8) FALSE
9) TRUE
10) FALSE
11) TRUE
12) TRUE
13) TRUE
14) TRUE
15) TRUE
16) B
17) A
18) A
19) B
20) B
21) C
22) A
23) A
24) A
25) D
26) D
27) A
28) A
29) C
30) B
31) A
32) B
33) C
34) B
35) D
36) D
37) B
38) A
39) A
40) 50 Hz
41) 2236 Hz
42) A small bandwidth (higher selectivity) is better because the individual stations can be separated more readily.
43) Increase L and decrease C by a proportional amount. (The higher L gives the tuned circuit a higher Q).
44) Curve C.
45) VP(C1:1)
46) Move the cursor to f1, where vc is one-half vc (peak). Note the frequency f1. Move cursor to f2, where vc is one-half vc (peak). Note the frequency f2. Subtract f2-f1 to get bandwidth.
47) 91
48) unity
49) bandwidth
50) resonant
51) impedance

Chapter 21 Decibels, Filters, and Bode Plots

True/False

1) The common logarithm of the number 1 is 0.

2) In order to double the sound level as perceived by the human ear, the source wattage must increase by a factor of 10.

3) A frequency ratio of 8:1 is known as an octave.

4) The output of a low-pass filter will be less than 50% of the input signal at frequencies above the cutoff frequency f_c.

5) A power gain of 3 dB is equivalent to an output power that is twice the power of the input.

6) Band-pass filters pass a range of frequencies between low and high cut-off frequencies.

7) Both high-pass and low-pass filters pass frequencies higher than some cut-off frequency.

8) Decibels are used to provide a comparison between power levels and voltage levels.

9) In the audio industry, it is a generally accepted rule that an increase in sound level is accomplished with 3-dB increments in the output level.

10) An R-C high-pass filter can be constructed from an R-C low pass filter by simply reversing the position of the capacitor and resistor.

11) The only noise that can really affect audio signals is the 60 Hz from a power source.

Multiple Choice

12) Which one of these expressions is equivalent to $\log_{10}ab$?

A) $\log_{10} a - \log_{10} b$ B) $\log_{10} a + \log_{10} b$

C) $\log_{10} a \times \log_{10} b$ D) $\log_{10} b - \log_{10} a$

13) A 20 dB power gain represents an output-to-input ratio of

A) 2:1 B) 6:1 C) 100:1 D) 10:1

14) A 10 mV input to an amplifier produces a 5 V output. What is the voltage gain in dB?

A) 27 dB
B) 76 dB
C) 500 dB
D) 54 dB

15) What power level is 3 dB above 10 W?

A) 14.1 W
B) 10 W
C) 20 W
D) 13 W

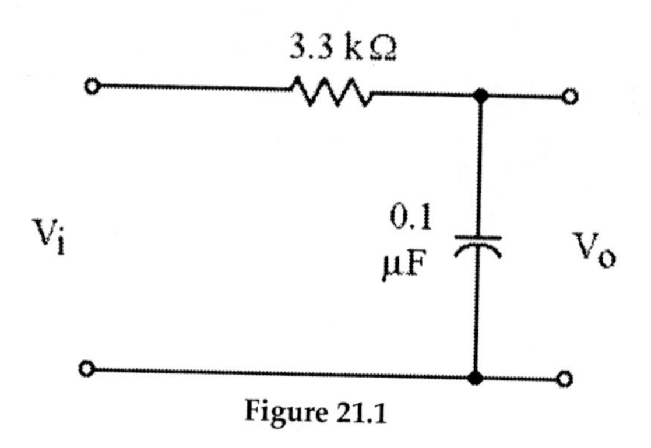

Figure 21.1

16) See Figure 21.1. What is the cutoff frequency f_c for this low-pass filter?

A) 8.8 Hz
B) 3030 Hz
C) 482 Hz
D) 1590 Hz

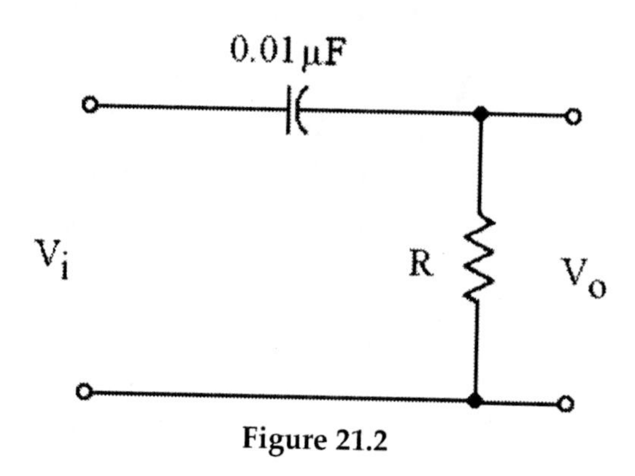

Figure 21.2

17) See Figure 21.2. Determine the resistance R that will produce a cutoff frequency of 200 Hz.

A) 141.4 Ω
B) 79.6 kΩ
C) 200 Ω
D) 500 kΩ

18) See Figure 21.2. At the cutoff frequency f_c,

A) V_o lags V_i by 90°
B) V_o leads V_i by 90°
C) V_o leads V_i by 45°
D) V_o lags V_i by 45°

19) See Figure 21.2. V_i has a peak amplitude of 10 V. What is the peak amplitude of V_o at the cutoff frequency f_c?

A) 20 V
B) 7.07 V
C) 5 V
D) 10 V

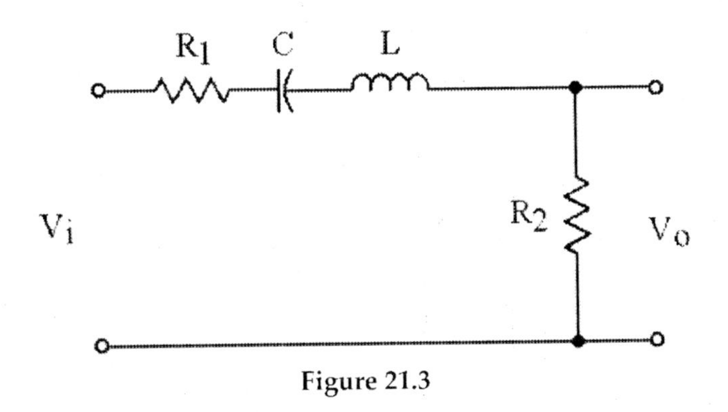

Figure 21.3

20) See Figure 21.3. This circuit is an example of what type of filter?

A) band-pass B) low-pass C) band-stop D) high-pass

21) The output signal Bode plot for a low-pass filter "rolls off" after f_c at a rate of

A) 3 dB per octave B) 3 dB per decade

C) 6 dB per decade D) 6 dB per octave

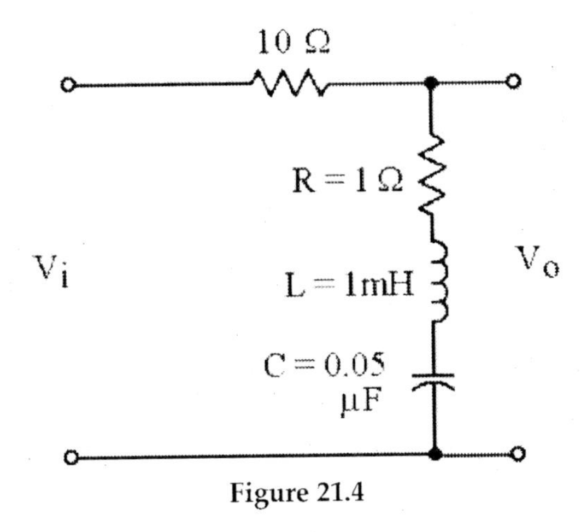

Figure 21.4

22) See Figure 21.4. This band-stop filter has a center frequency f_s. At this frequency, what is V_o if V_i is 10 V?

A) 0 V B) 1.0 V C) 0.9 V D) 10.0 V

23) See Figure 21.4. What is the band-stop center frequency f_s?

A) 1.59 kHz B) 318.0 kHz C) 22.5 kHz D) 11.25 kHz

24) See Figure 21.4. What is the bandwidth of this band-stop filter?

A) 22.5 kHz B) 11.25 kHz C) 1.9 kHz D) 12.8 kHz

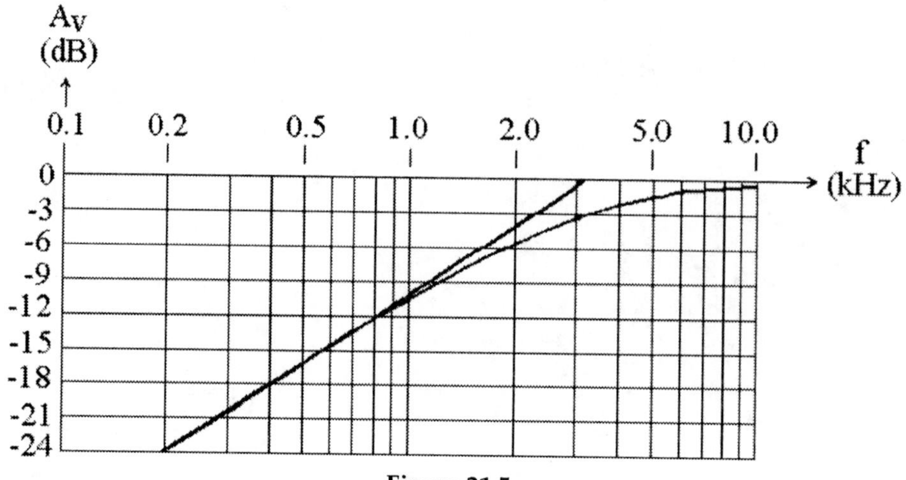

Figure 21.5

25) See Figure 21.5. This Bode plot represents a particular high-pass filter. What is the cutoff frequency f_1?

A) 2.6 kHz B) 1.8 kHz C) 4.0 kHz D) 3.2 kHz

26) See Figure 21.5. What is the A_V level (in dB) at f = 1500 Hz?

A) -7.4 dB B) -6.0 dB C) -12.1 dB D) -3.0 dB

27) The crossover network section that drives the woofer in a 3-way audio speaker system is

A) a band-stop RLC filter.
B) a low-pass RL filter.
C) a high-pass RC filter.
D) a band-pass RLC filter.

28) Which PSpice (Windows) Probe trace parameter will cause a db plot of voltage at R1 to be displayed?

A) V(R1:1) B) Vdb(R1) C) db(V(R1:1)) D) db(R1:1)

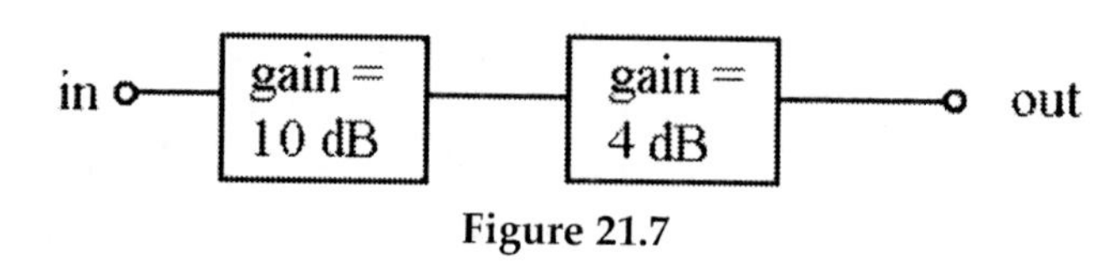

Figure 21.7

29) Referring to Figure 21.7, what is the overall gain of the cascaded system?

A) 40 dB B) 14 dB C) 1.6 dB D) 16 dB E) 11.5 dB

30) What is the bandwidth of a resonant circuit that consists of a 10 Ω resistance, a 1 mH inductor, and a 2 nF capacitor in series?

A) 1591 Hz B) 112,540 Hz C) 111,745 Hz D) 111,745 Hz

31) What are the half-power points of a resonant circuit that consists of a 10 Ω resistance, a 1 mH inductor, and a 2 nF capacitor in series?

A) 113,336 Hz, 1591 Hz
B) 112,540 Hz, 113,336 Hz
C) 111,745 Hz, 113,336 Hz
D) 111,745 Hz, 112,540 Hz

32) In a low-pass RC filter, having a cutoff frequency of 2 kHz, C = 80 nF. Determine R.

A) 27.2 kΩ
B) 98.0 Ω
C) 995 Ω
D) 44.7 Ω

33) Which of the following describes the equation: $\text{Log}_{10}\ ab = \text{Log}_{10}\ a + \text{Log}_{10}\ b$?

A) The sum of a plus b is equal to the Log10 1
B) The log of a number taken to a power is equal to the product of the log
C) The log of the product of two numbers is the sum of the logs of the numbers
D) The $\log_{10}$ times ab is equal to a plus b

34) If the sound received by the human ear is to be doubled, the acoustical sources rating must be increased by a factor of __________.

A) 20
B) 30
C) 40
D) 10

35) Filters composed of a series or parallel combinations of R, L and C elements are known as __________ filters.

A) Reactive
B) Passive
C) Active
D) Common

36) A process whereby a quantity such as voltage, current, or impedance is divided by a quantity of the same unit of measure to establish a dimensionless level of a specific value or range is __________.

A) Balancing
B) Normalization
C) Passivity
D) Actuation

37) Which of the following describes a filter designed to pass signals within a specific range?

A) Passive
B) High-pass
C) Band-pass
D) Stop-pass

38) Which of the following describes a filter consisting of transistors or operational amplifiers in combination with R, L, and C elements?

A) Band-pass
B) Active
C) High-pass
D) Passive

39) Which of the following networks are used in audio systems to ensure the proper frequencies are channeled to the appropriate speaker?

A) Balanced
B) Woffer
C) Wye
D) Crossover

40) Which of the following describes networks that display both pass-band and stop-band characteristics?

A) Double-tuned filters
B) Inductive filters
C) Balanced filters
D) Resonant-tuned filters

Short Answer

41) What is the difference between an active filter and a passive filter?

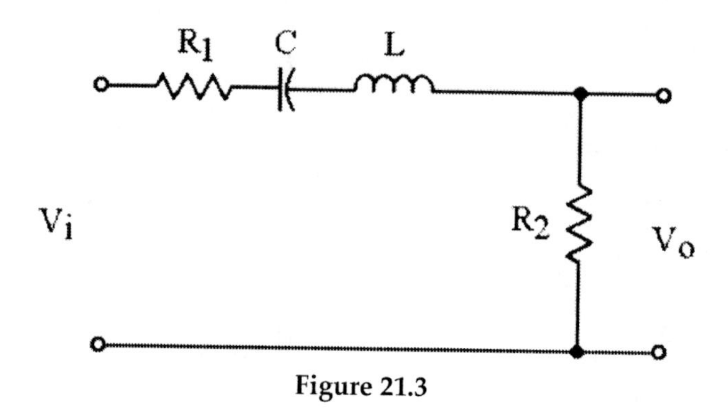

Figure 21.3

42) See Figure 21.3. The output of this pass-band filter will never quite reach the amplitude of the input. Why?

43) For a low-pass filter with a cutoff frequency of 200 Hz, at what frequency will A_v be -20 dB?

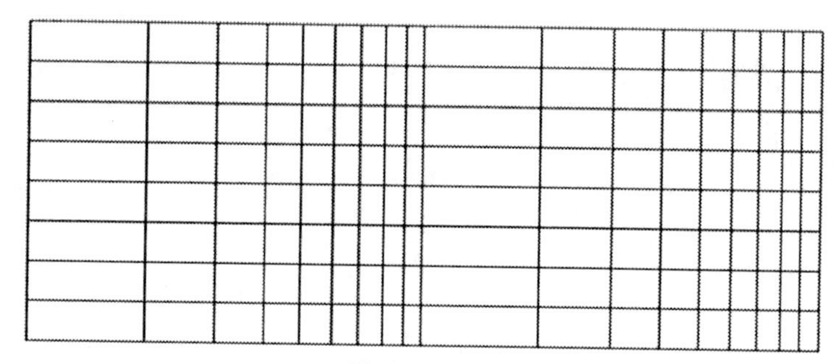

Figure 21.6

44) See Figure 21.6. Sketch the Bode plot for the low-pass filter described in the previous problem.

45) An attenuation of -20 dB is equivalent to what voltage ratio V_o:V_{in}?

46) Calculate the voltage applied to a 600 Ω load by a "1 mW" signal.

47) What type of filter would be used to reject 60 Hz powerline noise in an instrumentation system?

48) How can the crossover frequencies for a 3-way audio speaker network be determined using PSpice?

49) The parallel RLC resonant circuit is a ________ filter.

50) The series RLC resonant circuit is a ________ filter.

51) The ratio of output voltage divided by input voltage is called the ________.

52) ________ employ active devices such as transistors and operational amplifiers in combination with R, L, and C elements.

1) TRUE
2) TRUE
3) FALSE
4) FALSE
5) TRUE
6) TRUE
7) FALSE
8) TRUE
9) TRUE
10) TRUE
11) FALSE
12) B
13) C
14) D
15) C
16) C
17) B
18) C
19) B
20) A
21) D
22) C
23) C
24) C
25) D
26) A
27) B
28) C
29) B
30) A
31) C
32) C
33) C
34) D
35) B
36) B
37) C
38) B
39) D
40) A
41) An active filter uses active devices such as transistors or operational amplifiers in addition to passive R, L, and C elements. A passive filter is composed of series/parallel R, L, and C elements only.
42) Because R_1 and R_2 form a voltage divider at resonance. R_2 must be >> R_1 for the output to approach the input level.
43) -20 dB gain at a frequency of 2.0 kHz.
44) Sketch a line between 200 Hz at 0 dB and 2000 Hz at -20 dB. Draw the actual response curve through the -3 dB point at 200 Hz, approaching the two asymptotes.
45) V_o:V_i = 1:10
46) 0.775 V
47) band-stop
48) Plot each of the three response curves (low-pass, band-pass, and high-pass) and note where low-pass and band-pass curves cross. Also, note where band-pass curves and high-pass curves cross. These are the "crossover" frequency points.
49) Stop band (band reject)
50) band-pass
51) transfer function
52) Active filters

Chapter 22 Transformers

True/False

1) The coefficient of coupling between two coils can never be greater than one.

2) Two loosely coupled coils have a high coefficient of coupling.

3) A step-down transformer is one in which the primary voltage is smaller than the secondary voltage.

4) Transformation ratio is the ratio of the primary to the secondary turns in a transformer.

5) The dot convention is used to denote the polarity of the induced voltage across a mutually coupled coil.

6) An auto transformer does not have a secondary coil.

7) Copper losses are the only losses in transformers.

8) Given two coils, the greater the co-efficient of coupling or inductance of either coil, the greater the inductance.

9) The primary and secondary currents of a transformer are related by the direct ratios of their turns.

10) Loosely coupled coils have a very high co-efficient of coupling because of the space of the windings.

11) The iron core transformer will increase the co-efficient of coupling between the coils by increasing the mutual flux.

Multiple Choice

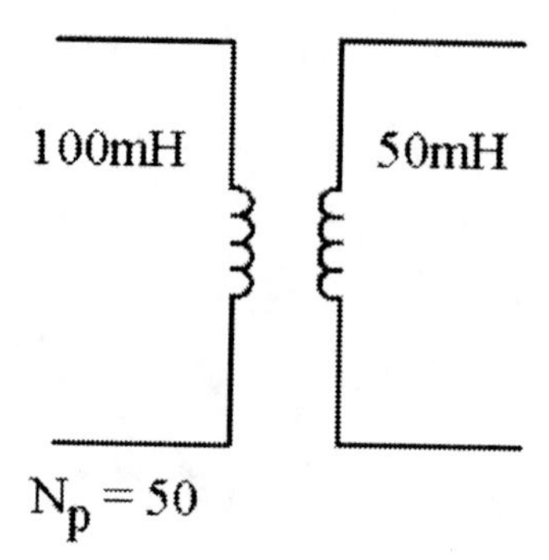

Figure 22.1

12) See Figure 22.1. What is the mutual inductance between the two coils if the coefficient of coupling is 0.7?

A) 105 mH B) 49.5 mH C) 150 mH D) 33.3 mH

13) See Figure 22.1. What is the induced voltage e_p in the primary if the primary flux changes at 300 mWb/s?

A) 15 V B) 6 V C) 3000 V D) 1.2 V

14) See Figure 22.1. What is the induced voltage e_p in the primary if the primary current changes at a 5 A/s rate?

A) 0.7 V B) 5.0 V C) 0.5 V D) 7.0 V

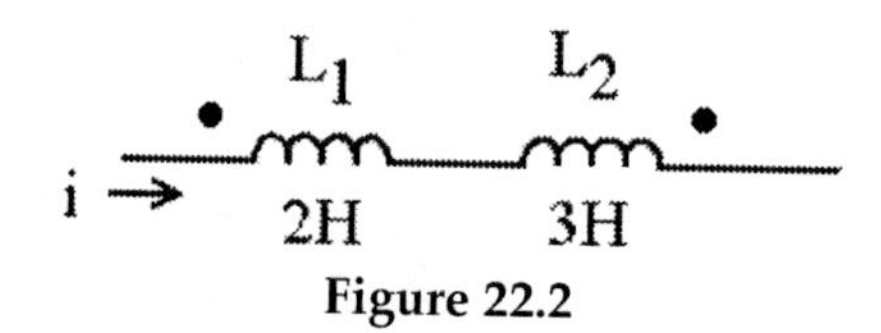

Figure 22.2

15) See Figure 22.2. If the mutual inductance $M_{12} = 1$ H, what is the total inductance L_T of this circuit?

A) 6 H B) 5 H C) 1.2 H D) 3 H

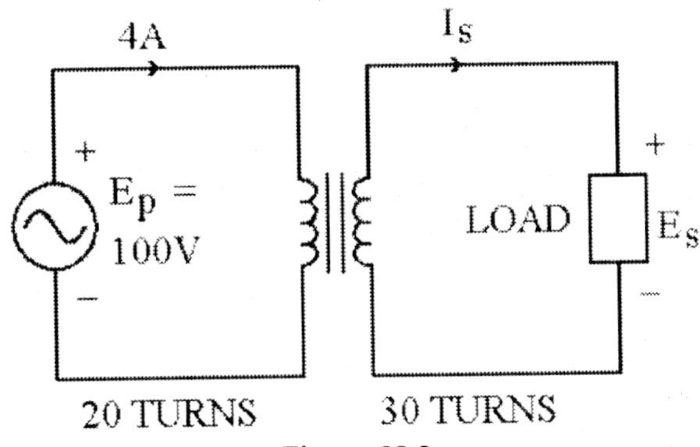

Figure 22.3

16) See Figure 22.3. What is the transformation ratio for this transformer?

A) 20 B) 30 C) 1.5 D) 0.667

17) See Figure 22.3. What is the voltage E_S across the load?

A) 150 V B) 66.7 V C) 100 V D) 120 V

18) See Figure 22.3. What is the current I_S through the load?

A) 1.5 A B) 4 A C) 2.67 A D) 6 A

19) See Figure 22.3. If this transformer is an ideal device, how much power is transferred to the load?

A) 0 W B) 400 W C) 600 W D) 266.7 W

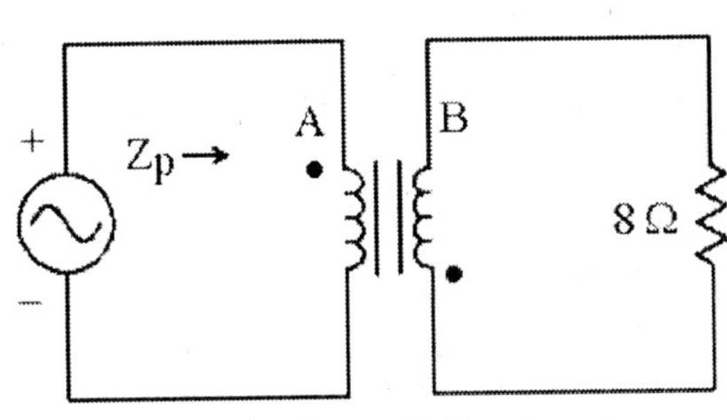

Figure 22.4

20) See Figure 22.4. An 8 Ω load is connected to the transformer secondary as shown. What is the primary impedance Z_P if the primary has 160 turns and the secondary has 10 turns?

A) 2048 Ω B) 2 Ω C) 128 Ω D) 0.5 Ω

21) See Figure 22.4. The transformer shown is connected to an 8 Ω resistive load. If the secondary contains 10 turns of wire and the required primary impedance is 5 kΩ, how many turns are used in the primary?

A) 625 turns B) 50 turns C) 250 turns D) 25 turns

22) A power transformer nameplate lists 2 kVA, 500/100 V, 60 Hz. If the applied primary voltage is 20 V, what is the maximum safe primary current?

A) 2000 A B) 25 A C) 20 A D) 100 A

23) A power transformer nameplate lists 2 kVA, 500/100 V, 60 Hz. If the 100 V number is the secondary voltage, find the current rating of the secondary.

A) 400 A B) 100 A C) 20 A D) 25 A

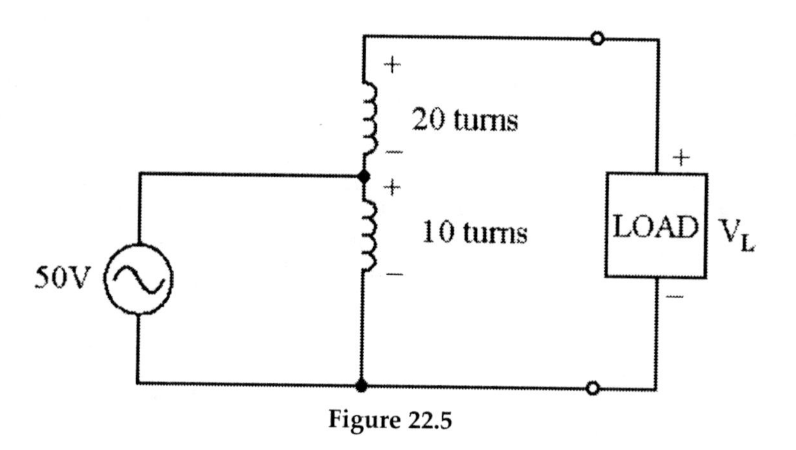

Figure 22.5

24) See Figure 22.5. In this autotransformer circuit, what is the voltage V_L across the load? Assume an ideal transformer.

A) 100 V B) 50 V C) 25 V D) 150 V

25) The disadvantage of using an autotransformer instead of a two-circuit power transformer is

A) it is difficult to obtain a high secondary voltage.

B) no isolation exists between input and output.

C) a smaller apparent power can be transformed.

D) it cannot be used in a step-down configuration.

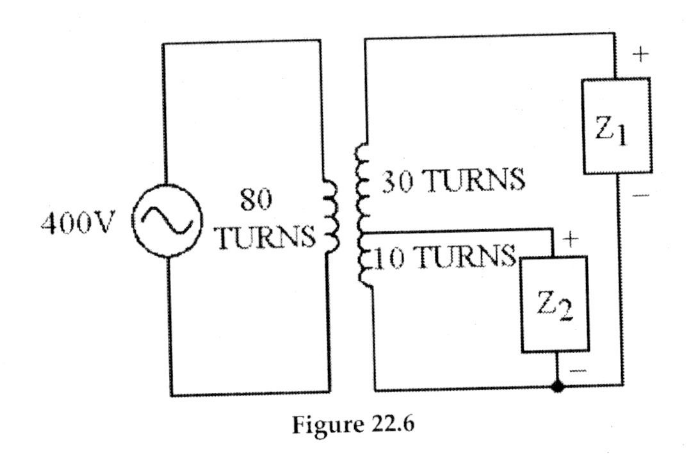

Figure 22.6

26) See Figure 22.6. Determine the voltage E_2 across Z_2.

A) 150 V B) 50 V C) 200 V D) 3200 V

27) What turns ratio must be used in an impedance matching transformer that matches a 300 Ω twin line to a 75 Ω coaxial cable?

A) 2:1 B) 4:1 C) 1:1 D) 8:1

28) The acronym LVDT stands for

A) Linear Voltage Differential Transformer.

B) Low Voltage Display Transformer.

C) Linear Variable Differential Transformer.

D) Low Voltage Distribution Transformer.

29) If 0.3 A flows in the secondary and 30 A flow in the primary of a perfectly matched, ideal transformer, what is the primary to secondary turns ratio?

A) 1:10,000 B) 1:10 C) 10:1 D) 100:1 E) 1:100

30) An ideal transformer has 200 primary turns and 20 secondary turns. What is the secondary voltage if the primary voltage is 120 V?

A) 12,000 V B) 120 V C) 12 V D) 1.2 V E) 1200 V

31) Five watts are dissipated in a primary (input) circuit that includes a perfectly matched, ideal transformer with a primary to secondary turns ratio of 15:1. If the input resistance is 2000 Ω, what is the load resistance?

A) 133 Ω B) 79 Ω C) 8.9 Ω D) 6243 Ω E) 30,000 Ω

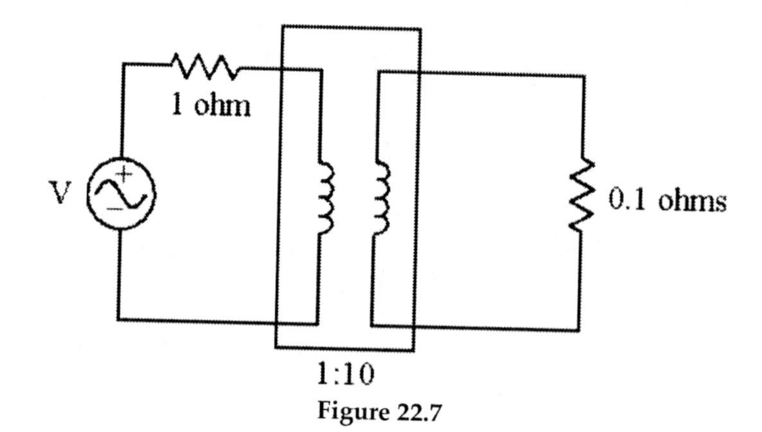

Figure 22.7

32) Referring to the circuit shown in Figure 22.7, the 0.1 Ω resistor is connected by an ideal transformer with a turns ratio of 1:10 to a 100 V AC voltage source. The current I is given by

A) 51.3 A B) 9.1 A C) 99.01 A D) 50 A E) 9.33 A

33) What is the name of the inductance that exists between magnetically coupled coils of the same or different dimensions?

A) Leakage current
B) Mutual inductance
C) Secondary current
D) Resonant inductance

34) Which of the following describes the impedance appearing at the primary of a transformer due to a load connected to the secondary?

A) Load impedance
B) Reflected impedance
C) Mutual impedance
D) Resonant impedance

35) Which of the statements below describes a measure of the magnetic coupling of two coils that range from a minimum of zero to a maximum of one?

A) Maximum winding ratio
B) Flux linkage
C) Flux density
D) Co-efficient of coupling

36) Which of the terms below describes the ratio of the number of turns of the primary to the number of turns to the secondary?

A) Transformation ratio
B) Secondary turns
C) Flux ratio
D) Primary ratio

37) Which of the following describes the flux linking the coil that does not pass through the ferromagnetic circuit?

A) Loose flux
B) Primary flux
C) Secondary flux
D) Leakage flux

38) A transformer whose secondary voltage is greater than its primary voltage is know as a __________ transformer.

A) Low impedance

B) Step-up

C) Primary

D) Step-down

Short Answer

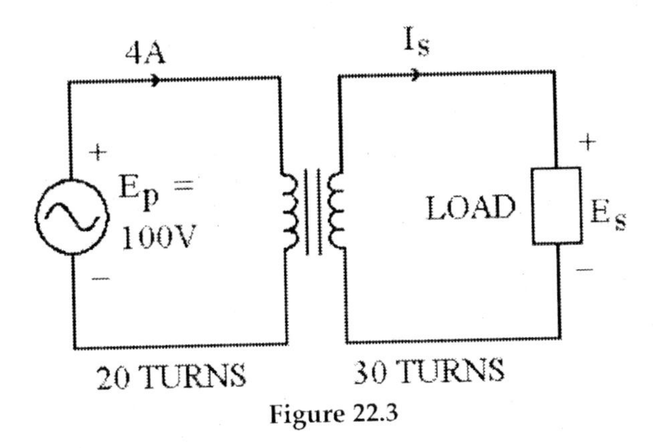

Figure 22.3

39) See Figure 22.3. What is the volt-amp rating of this transformer if the transformer is operating at its rated capacity?

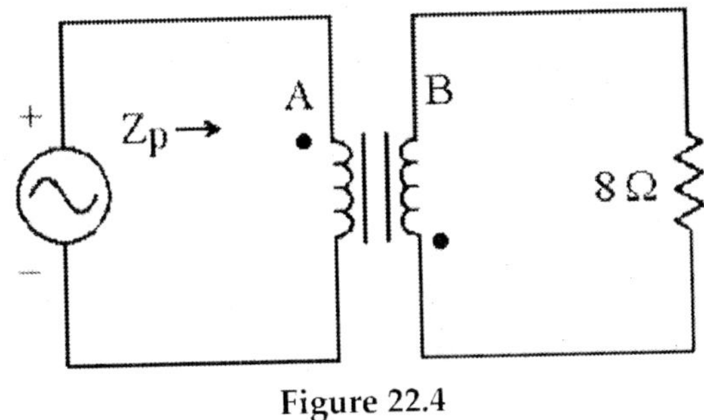

Figure 22.4

40) See Figure 22.4. Are points A and B in phase or out of phase?

41) Describe an application in which a transformer is used as an isolation device.

42) A power transformer with 5 V and 6.3 V secondary windings is connected with the two secondaries in series. The measured output across the secondaries is only 1.3 V. Why?

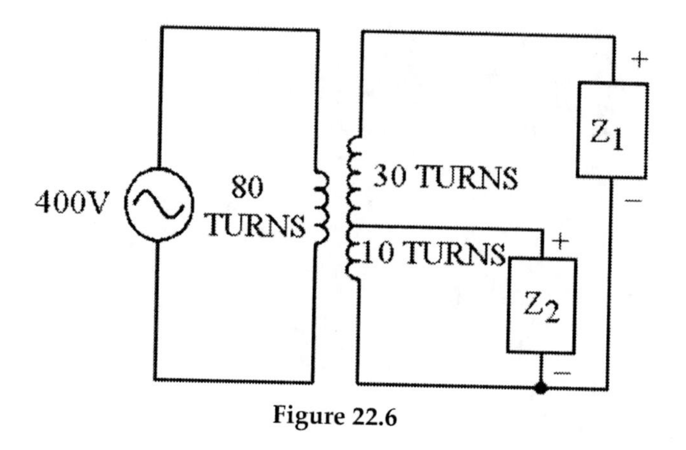

Figure 22.6

43) See Figure 22.6. Compute the voltage E_1.

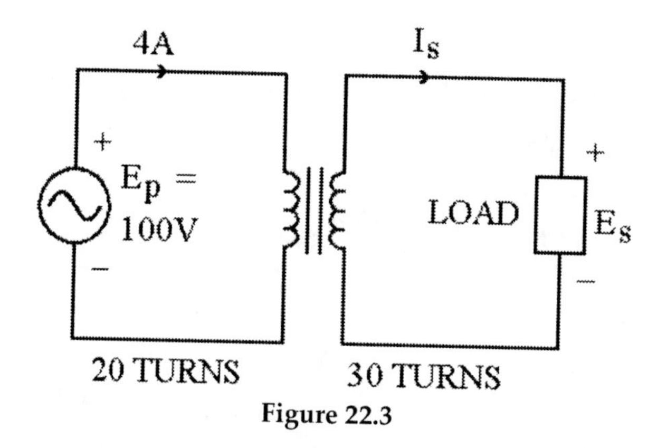

Figure 22.3

44) Compute the primary impedance Z_p in Figure 22.3.

45) What value can be modified in PSpice (Windows) to vary a transformer's "quality?"

46) What transformer turns ratio will match a 5 kΩ amplifier output impedance to an 8 Ω speaker?

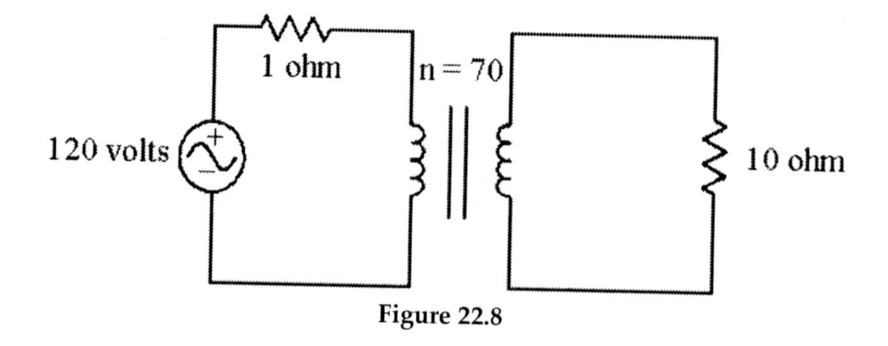

Figure 22.8

47) Referring to Figure 22.8, the average power dissipated in the circuit is __________.

48) The ratio of the numbers of primary to secondary windings is the __________.

49) The coefficient of coupling for ideal transformers is __________.

50) If the turns ratio is less than one, then the transformer increases voltage and is a __________ transformer.

1) TRUE
2) FALSE
3) FALSE
4) TRUE
5) TRUE
6) TRUE
7) FALSE
8) TRUE
9) TRUE
10) FALSE
11) TRUE
12) B
13) A
14) C
15) D
16) D
17) A
18) C
19) B
20) A
21) D
22) D
23) C
24) D
25) B
26) B
27) A
28) C
29) E
30) C
31) C
32) B
33) B
34) B
35) D
36) A
37) D
38) B
39) 400 VA
40) out of phase.
41) One application is the prevention of the ground connection of an instrument probe from shorting to ground a live point in the circuit being measured.
42) The two secondaries are out of phase and are "bucking" or canceling each other.
43) 200 V
44) 25 Ω
45) modify the coupling coefficient.
46) 25:1 step-down
47) 293 MW
48) turns ratio
49) unity
50) step-up

Chapter 23 Polyphase Systems

True/False

1) In general, the three-phase system is more economical for transmitting power at a fixed power loss than is the single-phase system.

2) A servomechanism is a common example of a two-phase system.

3) At any instant in time, the algebraic sum of the three phase voltages in a three-phase generator is equal to 86.6% of the voltage present on a single phase.

4) The frequency generated by a polyphase generator is dependent on the speed of rotation and number of poles.

5) The neutral connection between a generator and load will have zero current flowing through it under all conditions.

6) It is possible to convert a delta system to a wye system, but impossible to convert a wye system to a delta system.

7) Three-phase energy distribution systems are more efficient than multiple single-phase systems.

8) The phase currents and the line currents are equal in magnitude in the wye system.

9) There is a neutral wire in the delta system.

10) The number of phases that can be produced by a polyphase generator is limited to three.

11) With a Y-connected load and the load is balanced, the neutral connection can be removed without affecting the circuit in any manner.

12) The characteristics of an unbalanced polyphase load would be three-phase, four-wire and a y-connected load.

13) It is standard practice to describe the phase sequence in terms of the line voltages even though the line and phase voltages of a delta-connected system are the same.

Multiple Choice

14) The magnitude of the phase voltage in a Y-connected generator is 100 V. What is the magnitude of the line voltage?

A) 173.2 V B) 86.6 V C) 57.5 V D) 100 V

15) In a three-phase motor, if two phase voltages are interchanged,

A) the neutral current will increase significantly.

B) two of the phase voltages will cancel and the motor will operate as a single phase unit.

C) the direction of rotation will reverse.

D) the motor will stall, possibly burning out one or more phase windings.

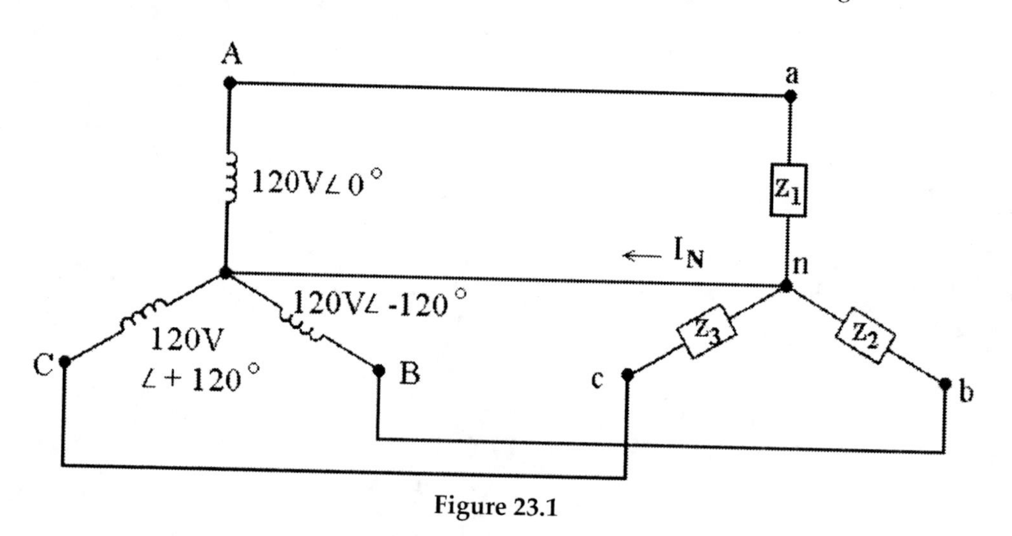

Figure 23.1

16) See Figure 23.1. What is the line voltage of the generator?

A) 69.3 V B) 208 V C) 120 V D) 240 V

17) See Figure 23.1. If Z_1, Z_2, and Z_3 are each 20 Ω resistors, what is the current I_{bn}?

A) 6 A ∠60° B) 6 A ∠−120° C) 6 A ∠0° D) 6 A ∠120°

18) See Figure 23.1. If Z_1, Z_2, and Z_3 are each 20 Ω resistors, what is the magnitude of the neutral current I_N?

A) 6 A B) 12 A C) 0 A D) 18 A

19) See Figure 23.1. If Z_1, Z_2, and Z_3 are each 20 Ω resistors, how much average power is dissipated by Z_2?

A) 720 W B) 2160 W C) 1247 W D) 416 W

20) See Figure 23.1. If Z_1 is a 4 Ω inductive reactance in series with a 3 Ω resistance, what is the current I_{an}?

A) 24 A ∠−36.80°
B) 30 A ∠−90°
C) 40 A ∠0°
D) 24 A ∠36.87°

21) If the three 20 Ω loads considered in the previous problem were connected in parallel across a 120 V single phase generator, how much current would be drawn from the generator?

A) 24 A
B) 18 A
C) 6 A
D) 12 A

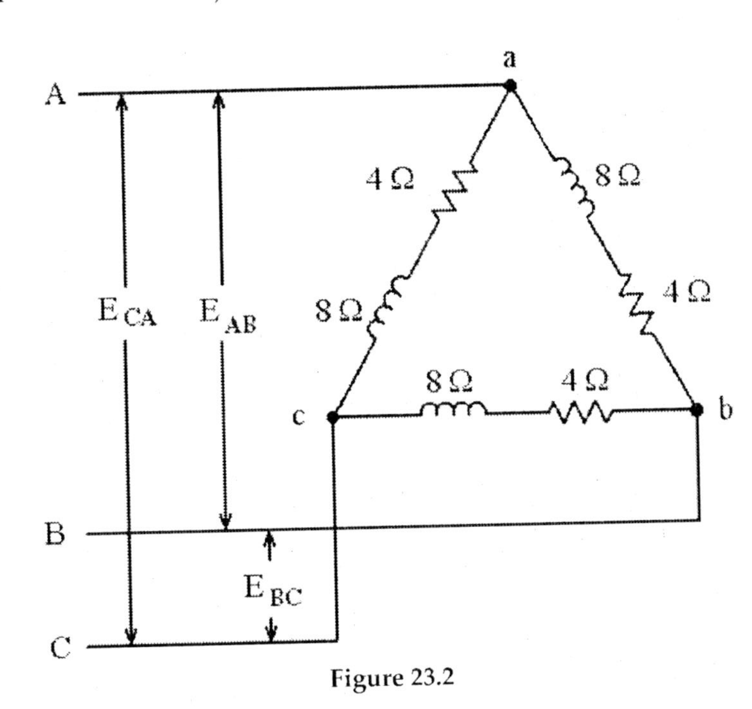

Figure 23.2

22) See Figure 23.2. If E_{CA} = 120 V ∠+120°, E_{AB} = 120 V ∠0°, and E_{BC} = 120 V ∠−120°, what is the phase current I_{bc}?

A) 13.4 A ∠−146.6°
B) 15 A ∠−210°
C) 30 A ∠−120°
D) 13.4 A ∠−183.43°

23) See Figure 23.2. If the amplitude of each phase current is 25A, what is the magnitude of each line current?

A) 43.3 A
B) 75 A
C) 25 A
D) 14.43 A

24) See Figure 23.2. If E_{CA} = 120 V ∠+120°, E_{AB} = 120 V ∠0°, and E_{BC} = 120 V ∠−120°, what is the total average power in the delta network?

A) 3600 W
B) 10,800 W
C) 720 W
D) 2160 W

25) See Figure 23.2. If E_{CA} = 120 V ∠+120°, E_{AB} = 120 V ∠0°, and E_{BC} = 120 V ∠−120°, what is the total apparent power for the delta network?

A) 1610 VA B) 1073 VA C) 4830 VA D) 3220 VA

26) See Figure 23.2. If E_{CA} = 120 V ∠+120°, E_{AB} = 120 V ∠120°, and E_{BC} = 120 V ∠−120°, what is the total reactive power for the delta network?

A) 2160 VAR B) 4320 VAR C) 2880 VAR D) 3220 VAR

27) The three-wattmeter method can determine total average power by

A) averaging the three readings.

B) multiplying the highest reading by the square root of 3.

C) taking the square root of the sum of the squares of the wattmeter readings.

D) summing the three wattmeter readings.

28) For a three-phase, four-wire, Y-connected load that is unbalanced, the neutral current is:

A) equal to the sum of the phase currents.

B) equal to the largest phase current minus the other two phase currents.

C) in phase with the smallest phase current.

D) zero.

29) Which one of the following statements pertaining to three-phase systems is correct?

A) Three-phase power poles can be lighter and further apart (compared with comparable single-phase load).

B) Thinner conductors can be used to connect a three-phase motor to the power source.

C) Larger three-phase motors do not require additional starting circuitry.

D) All of the above.

30) Industrial buildings supplied by 208 V three-phase power obtain 120 V single-phase service

A) between one line and the neutral conductor.

B) between two lines.

C) from a separate power line.

D) Single-phase and three-phase systems may not be used in the same building, according to the National Electric Code regulations.

31) In a balanced three-phase system with a power factor of unity, the line voltage, E_L, and the line current I_L, deliver the normal AC power. What is the expression for the power, P?

A) $P = \sqrt{3} E_L I_L$

B) $P = \frac{\sqrt{3}}{2} E_L I_L$

C) $P = E_L I_L$

D) $P = (1/2) \times E_L I_L$

E) $P = \frac{1}{\sqrt{2}} E_L I_L$

32) What is the relationship between the line current, I_L, and the phase current I_1, in a balanced delta system?

A) $I_L = \sqrt{3} I_1$

B) $\frac{I_1}{\sqrt{2}}$

C) $\frac{I_1}{\sqrt{3}}$

D) $I_L = \sqrt{2} I_1$

E) $I_{L1} = I_1$

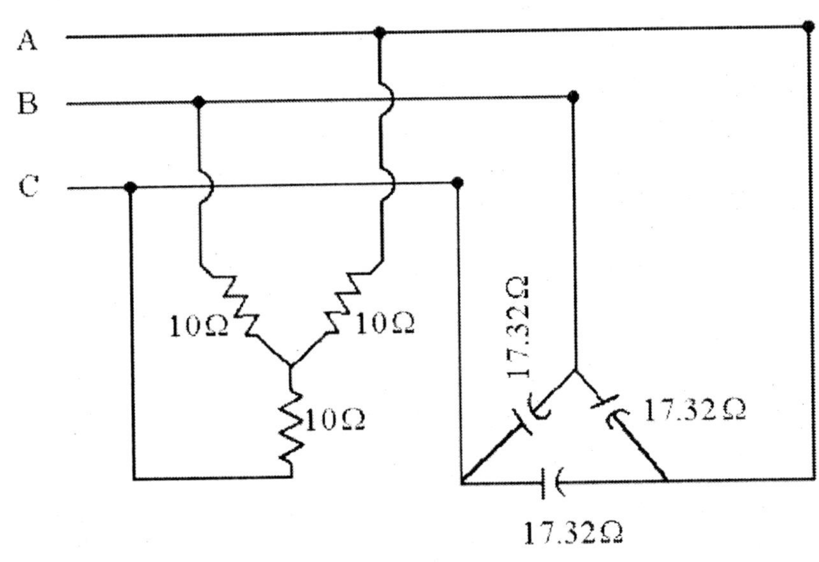

Figure 23.3

33) The circuit shown in Figure 23.3 shows a 10 Ω per phase resistive Y connected balanced load and a 17.32 Ω per phase capacitive Δ connected balanced load supplied by a 3 phase 220 V network. The current supplied by the load is?

A) 30.06 A B) 50.86 A C) 25.43 A D) 43.99 A E) 60.12 A

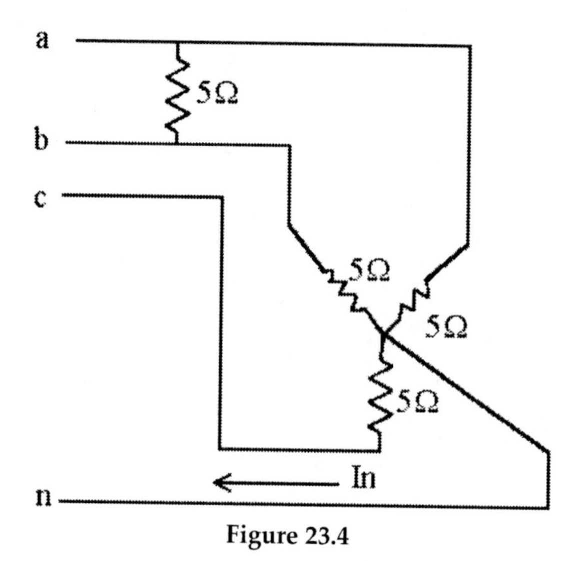

Figure 23.4

34) The circuit shown in Figure 23.4 has a balanced three phase voltage of positive sequence and value 220 V is applied to a balanced load and to a second load connected between phases a and b. The current in phase a is given by:

A) 88.0 A B) 55.7 A C) 50.8 A D) 69.9 A E) 67.2 A

35) An ac generator that develops more than one ac phase voltage per rotation of the rotor is known as a(n) __________ ac generator.

A) In-phase
B) Polyphase
C) Impedance-matched
D) Out of phase

36) The frequency of a polyphase ac generator is determined by the speed the shaft is turning and which of the following?

A) Impedance of the shaft
B) Direction the rotor is turning
C) Number of poles on the rotor
D) Diameter of the rotor

37) Which of the following describes the order in which the generated sinusoidal voltages of a polyphase generator will affect the load to which they are applied?

A) Phase sequence
B) Sinusoidal order
C) Load regulation
D) Voltage order

38) Which of the following describes the voltage that appears between the line and neutral of a y-connected generator and from line-to-line in a delta-connected generator?

A) Phase voltage
B) Line voltage
C) Lag voltage
D) Terminal voltage

39) Which of the following describes why three-phase motors have preferred running and starting characteristics compared to a single-phase system?

A) A more even flow of power to the transducer can be delivered

B) Three-phase have a sinusoidal phase relationship

C) Current leads voltage and allows the motor to start easier

D) Three-phase require no transducers or complicated rotors

40) At any instant of time, the algebraic sum of the three-phase voltages of a three-phase generator is equal to ________.

A) 120 V B) 360 V C) 240 V D) Zero volts

Short Answer

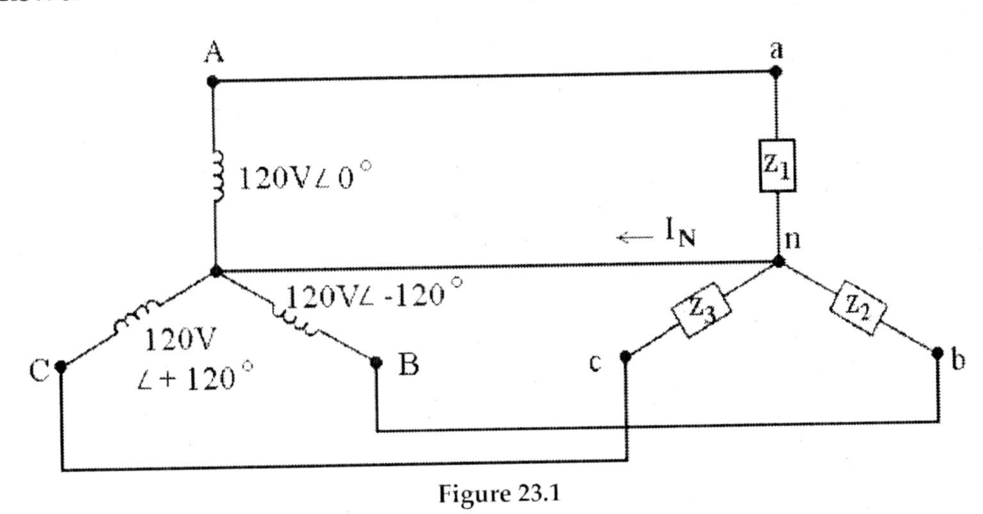

Figure 23.1

41) See Figure 23.1. If Z_2 and Z_3 are 10 Ω resistances, and Z_1 is a 4 Ω inductive reactance in series with a 3 Ω resistance what is the neutral current I_N?

42) If total apparent power S_T and total average power P_T are known, how is the power factor determined?

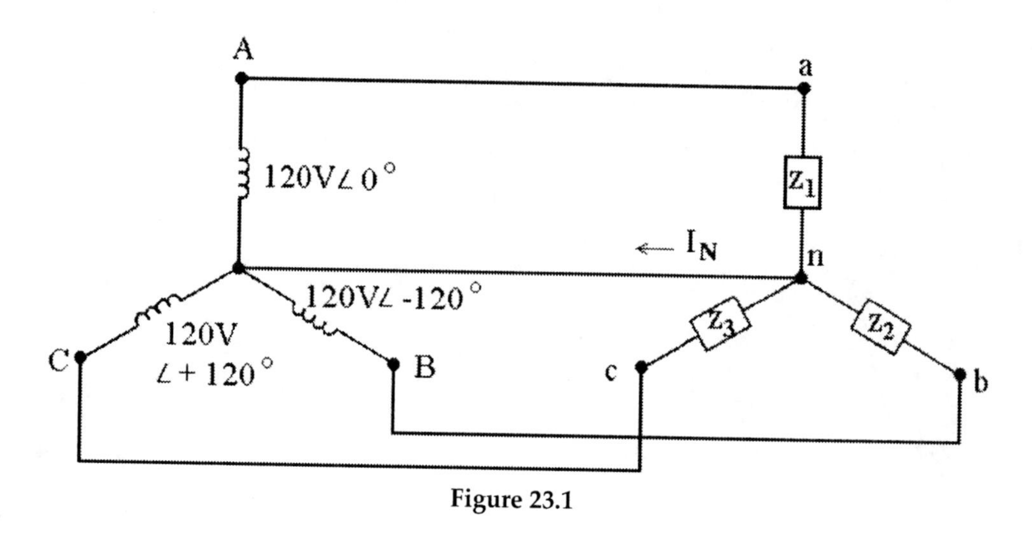

Figure 23.1

43) See Figure 23.1. When is the neutral wire unnecessary?

44) See Figure 23.1. What is the phase sequence (ABC, ACB, etc.) of the generator? (Hint: use E_{AN} as a reference).

45) What instrument is used to show the phase sequence in a polyphase circuit?

46) In a PSpice model of a three-phase balanced network, where should the reference node be placed?

47) Why was a 1 mΩ resistor placed in series with one of the three independent voltage sources in the PSpice model of a balanced three-phase load described in the textbook?

48) In a balanced three-phase system, the phase angles are out of phase by what angle?

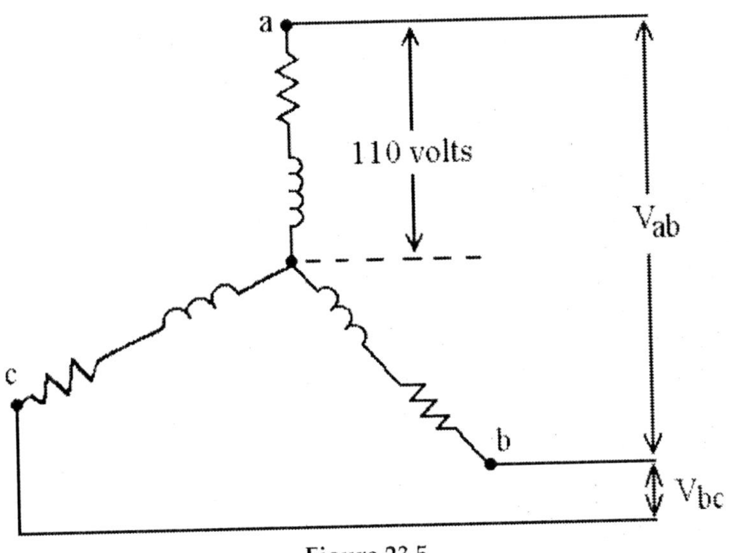

Figure 23.5

49) Referring to Figure 23.5, the line-to-line voltage, V_{ab}, of the balanced wye connection is ________.

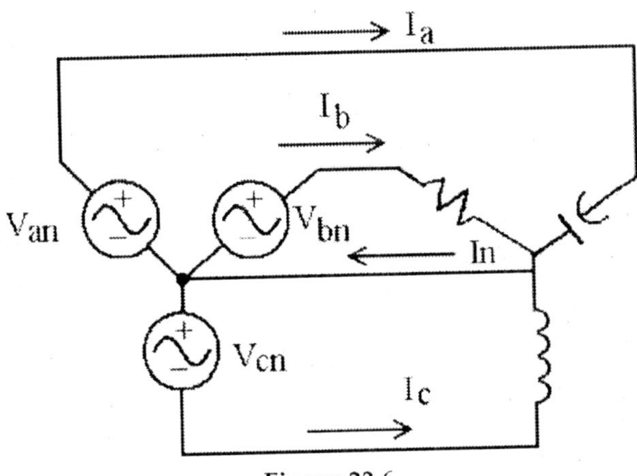

Figure 23.6

50) Referring to Figure 23.6, an unbalanced Y connected load is supplied by a 4- wire network from a three phase balanced voltage source with the phase sequence ... a b c a b ...To find the three phase currents I_a, I_b, I_c and the current in the neutral wire In, ________ loop equations must be solved.

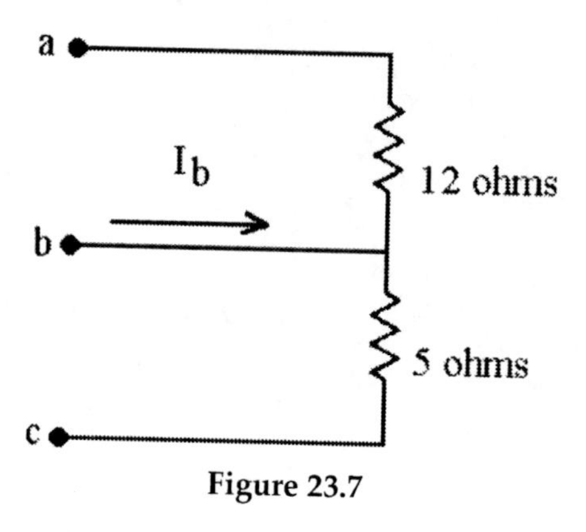

Figure 23.7

51) Referring to Figure 23.7, the three-wire, three-phase network shown here with an unbalanced load, a balanced three line 220 V voltage of positive sequence is applied. The current in line b is __________ amps.

52) The three phase loads are __________ in an unbalanced system.

Answer Key
Testname: CHAPTER 23

1) TRUE
2) TRUE
3) FALSE
4) TRUE
5) FALSE
6) FALSE
7) TRUE
8) TRUE
9) FALSE
10) FALSE
11) TRUE
12) TRUE
13) TRUE
14) A
15) C
16) B
17) B
18) C
19) A
20) A
21) B
22) D
23) A
24) D
25) C
26) B
27) D
28) A
29) D
30) A
31) A
32) A
33) C
34) E
35) B
36) C
37) A
38) A
39) A
40) D
41) 19.3 A ∠83°
42) $F_p = P_T/S_T$
43) The neutral wire is not needed only when the three impedances are identical.
44) ABC
45) a phase-sequence indicator.
46) At the center of the balanced load.
47) To avoid having a continuous loop of independent voltage sources.
48) 120°
49) 191 V
50) 3
51) 55.5
52) unequal

Chapter 24 Pulse Waveforms and the R–C Response

True/False

1) The pulse width of a non-ideal pulse is measured at an amplitude equal to 50% of the peak value.

2) The rise time of a pulse is the time required for the pulse to go from the base-line voltage to the peak voltage.

3) The rise time of an ideal pulse is zero.

4) For a fixed pulse repetition rate, the duty cycle increases as the pulse width decreases.

5) A square wave is a repetitive pulse waveform with a duty cycle of 50%.

6) Generally the amplitude of a pulse waveform is the peak-to-peak value.

7) The shape of a periodic pulse affects the determination of the pulse repetition frequency.

8) An ideal pulse is a pulse waveform characterized by having vertical sides, sharp corners and a flat peak response.

9) The duty cycle is defined by the period divided by the pulse width times 100%.

10) The duty cycles provide a percentage indication of the portion of the total period encompassed by the pulse waveform.

11) A periodic pulse train is a sequence of pulses that repeats itself after a specific period of time.

12) A compensated attenuator probe can reduce signal and its effects of resistance of a scope signal displayed.

13) The shape of the periodic pulse determines the pulse repetition frequency.

Multiple Choice

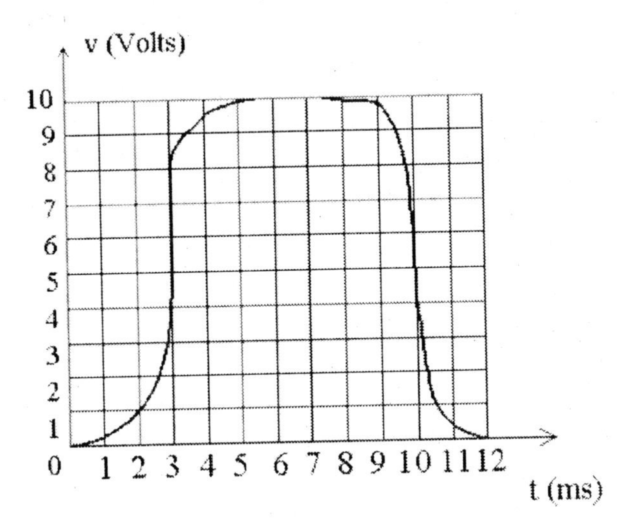

Figure 24.1

14) See Figure 24.1. What is the pulse width of this pulse?

A) 12 ms B) 6 ms C) 8.5 ms D) 7 ms

15) See Figure 24.1. What is the fall time of this pulse?

A) 2 ms B) 1 ms C) 2.5 ms D) 1.5 ms

16) See Figure 24.1. What is the rise time of this pulse?

A) 1.5 ms B) 3 ms C) 2 ms D) 1 ms

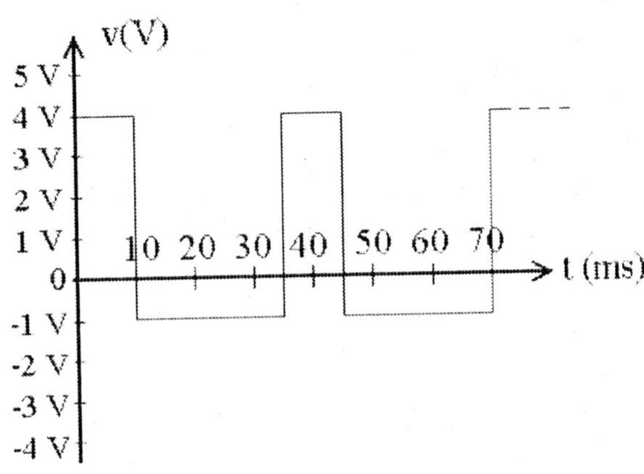

Figure 24.2

17) See Figure 24.2. What is the duty cycle of this periodic pulse waveform?

A) 71.4% B) 10.0% C) 25.0% D) 28.6%

18) See Figure 24.2. What is the pulse repetition frequency?

A) 28.6 Hz
B) 100.0 Hz
C) 22.2 Hz
D) 40.0 Hz

19) See Figure 24.2. Assume that the capacitor is initially charged to +3 V before the switch is closed. What is the mathematical expression for v_C after the switch closes?

A) $3(1 - e^{-t/RC})$
B) $3 + 7(1 - e^{-t/RC})$
C) $7(1 - e^{-t/RC})$
D) $10(1 - e^{-t/RC})$

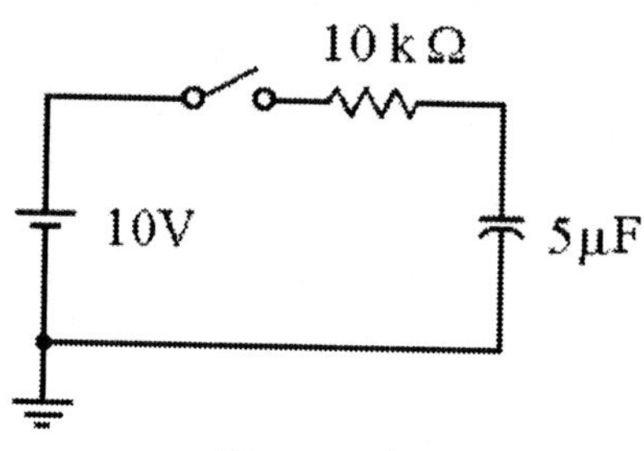

Figure 24.3

20) See Figure 24.3. Assume that the capacitor is initially charged to +3 V before the switch is closed. What is the peak current i_C that flows after the switch is closed?

A) infinity
B) 1.0 mA
C) 0.7 mA
D) 0.3 mA

21) See Figure 24.3. Assume that the capacitor is initially charged to +3 V before the switch is closed. What is the current that flows after an elapsed time of 20 ms?

A) 0.67 mA
B) 0.20 mA
C) 0.23 mA
D) 0.47 mA

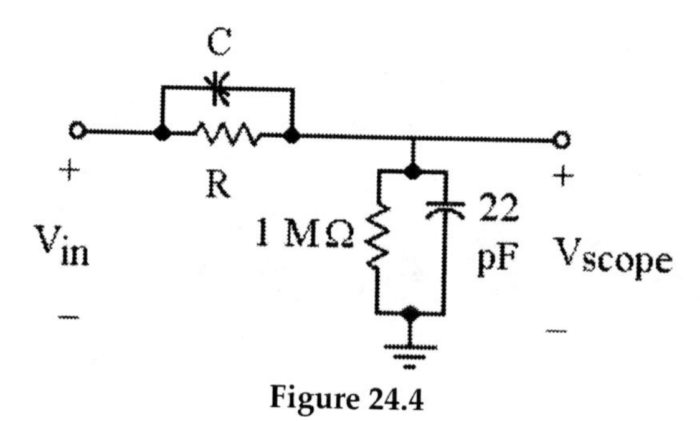

Figure 24.4

22) See Figure 24.4. This circuit is a frequency-compensated attenuator probe for an oscilloscope. If a 5x attenuation is desired, what is the value of resistor R?

A) 5 MΩ
B) 4 MΩ
C) 250 kΩ
D) 1 MΩ

23) See Figure 24.4. This circuit is a frequency-compensated attenuator probe for an oscilloscope. If a 5x attenuation is desired, what is the value of the capacitor C?

A) 88 pF B) 4.4 pF C) 5.5 pF D) 110 pF

24) See Figure 24.4. If the capacitor C is removed from the circuit, a square wave pulse train applied to the probe would appear to the oscilloscope to have

A) higher peak amplitude than before. B) rounded corners.

C) changed to a dc voltage level. D) overshoot and ringing.

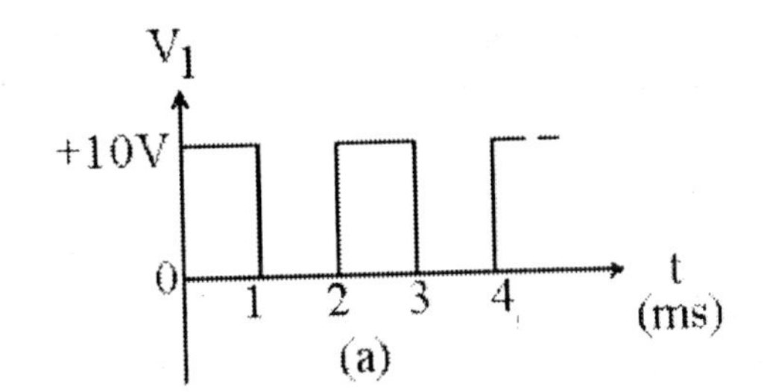

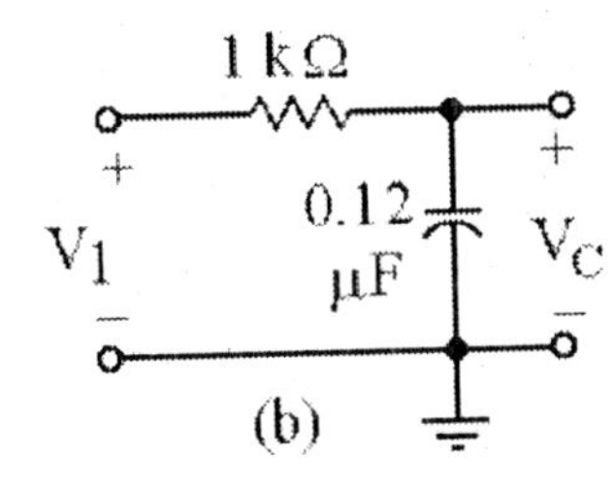

Figure 24.5

25) See Figure 24.5. The square wave shown in Figure (a) is applied to the circuit shown in Figure (b). How long is the pulse width T/2 compared with the time constant?

A) T/2 = 8.33x B) T/2 = 5x C) T/2 = 16.67x D) T/2 = x

26) See Figure 24.5. What is v_C at t = 1 ms? Assume that the capacitor is initially discharged.

A) $v_C \approx 10$ V B) $v_C \approx 8.33$ V C) $v_C \approx 5$ V D) $v_C \approx 0$ V

27) See Figure 24.5. What is the peak current that flows through the capacitor?

A) 0 mA B) 5 mA C) 1 mA D) 10 mA

28) See Figure 24.5. If the square wave pulse width is decreased to 1.0 µs, how will the v_C waveform change?

A) The average value will drop to zero.

B) The peak voltage reached will increase.

C) The peak voltage will decrease

D) The corners will be less rounded.

E) The waveform will become flattened.

29) A frequency-compensated attenuator probe

A) allows correct performance on any oscilloscope to which it is attached.

B) boosts midrange frequencies to enhance the signal displayed on the oscilloscope.

C) allows the user to balance the effects of oscilloscope input capacitance.

D) reduces high-frequency signals more than low-frequency signals.

30) Which PSpice (Windows) Probe command will find the maximum voltage of a pulse waveform?

A) Trace-Pulse-Max

B) Trace-Cursor-Max

C) Trace-Max

D) Trace-Peak-Pulse

31) A series of pulses is called a

A) tilt

B) pulse train

C) duty cycle

D) pulse width

E) rise time

32) A pulse level equal to 50% of the peak level is known as __________.

A) Pulse amplitude

B) Pulse waveform

C) Pulse width

D) Rise time

33) Which of the following describes the factor that reveals how much of a period is encompassed by the waveform?

A) Duty cycle

B) Rise time

C) Tilt

D) Fall time

34) Which of the following describes the drop in peak value across the pulse width waveform?

A) Rise time

B) Tilt

C) Fall time

D) Ideal pulse

35) Which of the following describes a periodic pulse waveform with a 50% duty cycle?

A) Ideal pulse

B) Pulse width

C) Saw-tooth wave

D) Square wave

Short Answer

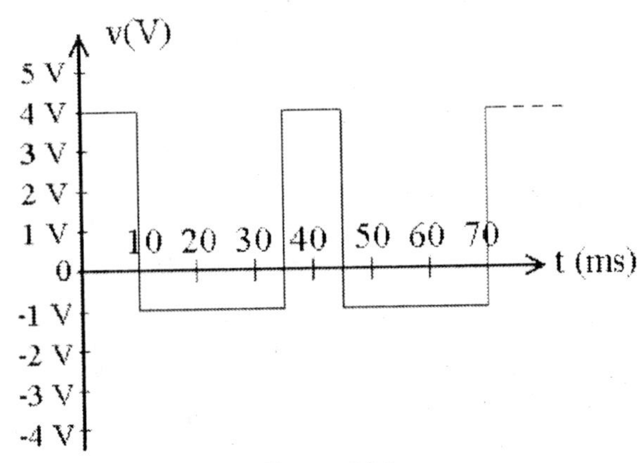

Figure 24.2

36) See Figure 24.2. What is the average value of this waveform?

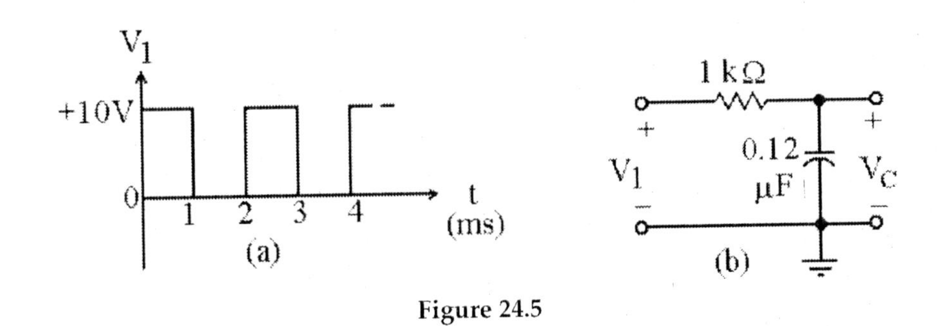

Figure 24.5

37) See Figure 24.5(a). What is the average value of this waveform?

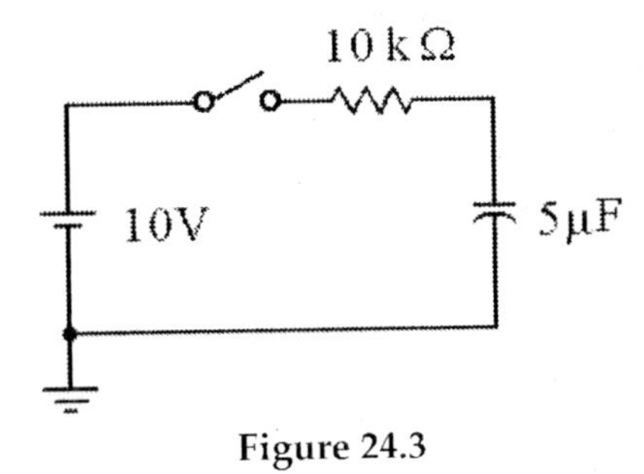

Figure 24.3

38) See Figure 24.3. Assume that the capacitor is initially charged to +2 V. How long after closing the switch will the capacitor voltage be +5 V?

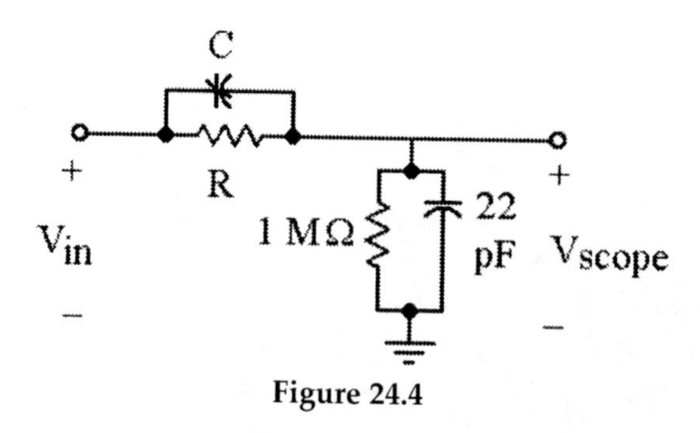

Figure 24.4

39) See Figure 24.4. Select R and C to produce a 10x frequency-compensated probe.

40) See Figure 24.4. An oscilloscope display shows that the perfect square wave being monitored includes an overshoot on each leading edge. How should the frequency-compensated probe on the oscilloscope be adjusted to correct this overshoot?

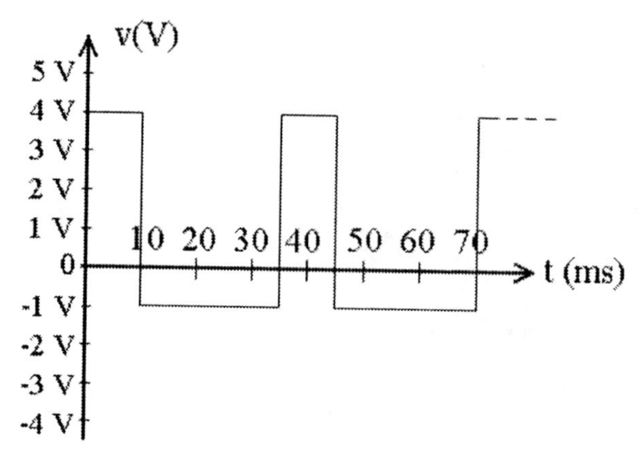

Figure 24.2

41) What is the average voltage of the waveform shown in Figure 24.2?

42) What pulse characteristics are defined in a PSpice (Windows) VPULSE part by the parameters PW, PER, V1, and V2?

43) The __________, is the pulse level equal to 50% of the peak value.

44) The less the percentage tilt or sag, the more __________ the pulse.

45) The ×10 attenuator probe employed with oscilloscopes is designed to reduce the magnitude of the input voltage by a factor of __________.

Answer Key
Testname: CHAPTER 24

1) TRUE
2) FALSE
3) TRUE
4) FALSE
5) TRUE
6) TRUE
7) FALSE
8) TRUE
9) FALSE
10) TRUE
11) TRUE
12) FALSE
13) FALSE
14) D
15) B
16) A
17) D
18) A
19) B
20) C
21) D
22) B
23) C
24) B
25) A
26) A
27) D
28) C
29) C
30) B
31) B
32) C
33) A
34) B
35) D
36) +0.43 V
37) +5 V
38) t = 23.5 ms
39) 9 MΩ, 2.44 pF
40) Decrease value of capacitor C.
41) 0.43 V
42) Pulse width, period, initial level, pulsed level.
43) pulse width (t_p)
44) ideal
45) 10

Chapter 25 Nonsinusoidal Circuits

True/False

1) An even harmonic is a frequency that is some even multiple of a fundamental frequency.

2) The fundamental component of a Fourier series expansion is the term with the maximum frequency.

3) Axis symmetry exists if the sinusoidal or nonsinusoidal function has symmetry about the vertical axis.

4) The Fourier series was developed in 1826 by Baron Jean Fourier.

5) A square wave can be produced by adding a fundamental frequency with its even harmonics.

6) Even functions are symmetric about the horizontal axis.

7) Odd functions are said to have axis symmetry and even functions are said to have point symmetry.

8) Waveforms with point symmetry can be modeled by just the dc and sine terms of the Fourier series.

9) Waveforms with axis symmetry can be modeled by just the dc and cosine terms of the Fourier series.

10) The first term of a sine and cosine series is known as the fundamental component and represents the minimum frequency term required to represent a particular waveform.

11) Waveform with point symmetry can be fully described by the average of the sine terms in a Fourier series.

12) The Fourier series representation of a nonsinusoidal waveform cannot be applied to a linear network because the Fourier series requires a sinewave.

13) Only a true RMS meter can read the RMS value of any waveform.

14) A diode is used to clip off the negative portion of the applied signal called half-wave rectification.

Multiple Choice

15) A sinusoidal or non-sinusoidal function that satisfies the relationship $f(\alpha) = -f(-\alpha)$ is said to have

A) half-wave symmetry.
B) point symmetry.
C) mirror symmetry.
D) absolute symmetry.

16) If the fundamental frequency is 10 Hz, what is the fourth harmonic?

A) 10 kHz
B) 2.5 Hz
C) 10 Hz
D) 40 Hz

17) The Fourier series representation of a non-sinusoidal input can be applied to a linear network using

A) reciprocity theorem.
B) Thevenin's theorem.
C) Millman's theorem.
D) superposition.

18) An even function

A) contains only odd harmonics.
B) contains only even harmonics.
C) is symmetric about the horizontal axis.
D) is symmetric about the vertical axis.

19) A sine wave is an example of

A) a waveform in which $f(\alpha) = f(-\alpha)$.

B) an even function.

C) an odd function.

D) a fundamental frequency and all odd harmonics.

20) The first part of a Fourier series is a term A_0 that

A) is the fundamental term of a series of sine terms.

B) is the fundamental term of a series of cosine terms.

C) is the average value of the waveform over one full cycle.

D) is the period of the fundamental frequency component.

21) An instrument used to measure harmonic frequencies and their corresponding amplitudes is the

A) phase-sequence indicator.
B) wave analyzer.
C) logic analyzer.
D) oscilloscope.

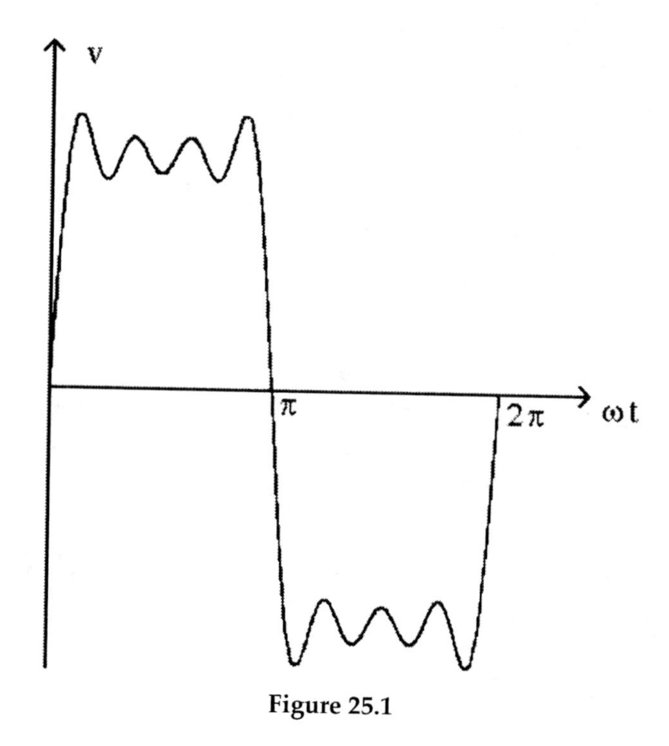

Figure 25.1

22) See Figure 25.1. The four peaks in the upper portion of this waveform indicate that

A) the amplitudes of each harmonic are identical.

B) four terms are added together to produce this waveform.

C) the function is an even function.

D) the fourth harmonic is the highest frequency term in the waveform.

23) See Figure 25.1. This waveform represents

A) a fundamental waveform plus some even harmonics.

B) a fundamental waveform plus both odd and even harmonics.

C) a fundamental waveform plus some odd harmonics.

D) a summation of a square wave and a sine wave.

24) When using the superposition theorem for non-sinusoidal circuits,

A) all cosine waves must be replaced with sine waves.

B) no dc sources will be allowed.

C) all voltage sources must be converted to current sources.

D) the frequency and reactance will be different for each term in the Fourier series.

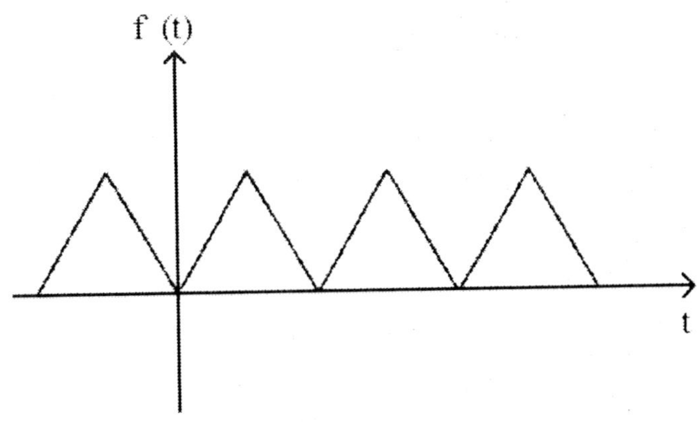

Figure 25.2

25) See Figure 25.2. This waveform is such that

A) $f(\alpha) = f(-\alpha)$

B) an even function is present.

C) the even harmonics of the series of sine and cosine terms are zero.

D) the odd harmonics of the series of sine and cosine terms are zero.

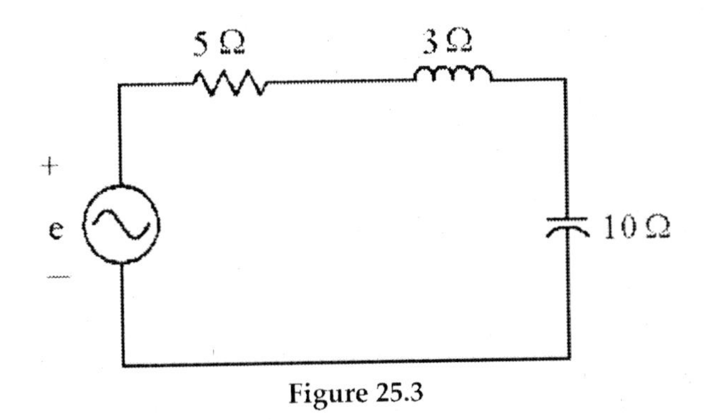

Figure 25.3

26) See Figure 25.3. If e = 20 + 5 sin 6t, what is the dc component of the input voltage?

A) 20 V B) 5 V C) 14.14 V D) 28.28 V

27) See Figure 25.3. If e = 20 + 5 sin 6t, what is the dc component of the current in this circuit?

A) 0 A B) 1 A C) 5 A D) 4 A

28) See Figure 25.3. If e = 20 + 5 sin 6t, what is the current I due to the ac supply?

A) 0.41 A ∠54.5° B) 0.16 A ∠54.5° C) 2.33 A ∠54.5° D) 0.58 A ∠54.5°

29) How many terms are needed to produce a good approximation of a square wave?

A) harmonics up to and including the twentieth

B) harmonics up to and including the ninth

C) two

D) one

30) The dc term of the Fourier series is

A) the duty cycle of the odd harmonic waveforms.

B) the offset above the 0–volt baseline.

C) the average value of the waveform over one full cycle.

D) the maximum voltage reached by the circuit.

31) The spectrum analyzer displays

A) signals in the frequency domain.

B) signals of all frequencies simultaneously.

C) phase angles of all frequency components.

D) true rms voltage readings of each harmonic component.

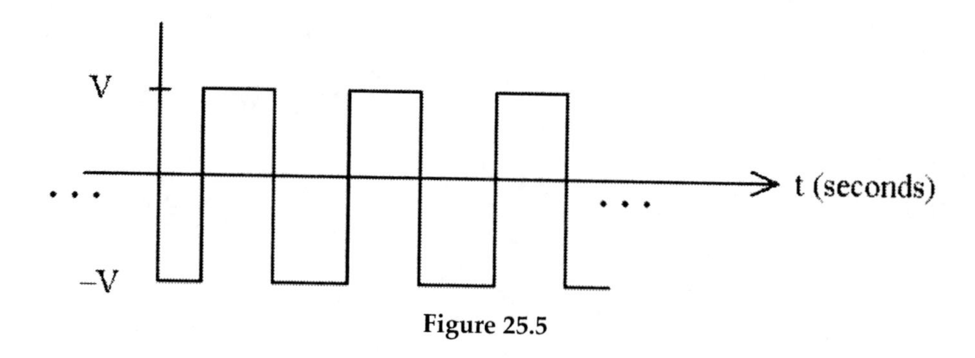

Figure 25.5

32) The waveform shown in Figure 25.5 can be easily evaluated by means of Fourier analysis because it has

A) odd function symmetry.

B) square symmetry.

C) rotational symmetry .

D) even function symmetry.

E) quarter–wave symmetry.

33) For a given function, it is found that f(t) = f(−t). What type of symmetry does f(t) have?

A) rotational symmetry

B) quarter–wave symmetry

C) even symmetry

D) odd symmetry

E) no symmetry

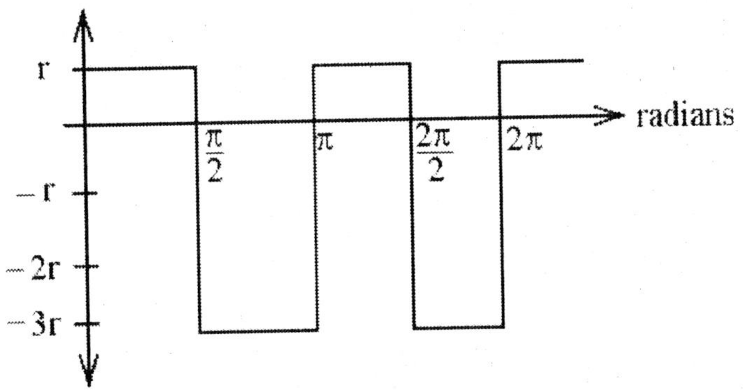

Figure 25.6

34) What is the minimum amplitude of the signal shown in Figure 25.6?

A) −3r B) −r C) r D) 0 E) −2r

35) If the even harmonics of a series of sine and cosine terms are zero, a waveform is known to have __________ symmetry.

A) Even B) Harmonic C) Axis D) Mirror

36) A true RMS voltmeter whose frequency of measurement can be changed manually is known as a __________.

A) Harmonic analyzer

B) RMS generator

C) Wave analyzer

D) Function analyzer

37) Which of the following describes the terms of the Fourier series expansion that have frequencies that are integer multiples of the fundamental component?

A) Even harmonics

B) Odd harmonics

C) Symmetrical terms

D) Harmonic terms

38) If a waveform is such that its value is the negative of that for −t, it is said to have __________ symmetry.

A) Positive B) Fourier C) Point D) Fullwave

39) If a waveform that is symmetric about the vertical axis, it is said to have which of the following?

A) An even function
B) Even slope
C) An extended horizontal axis
D) Equal voltage and current

Short Answer

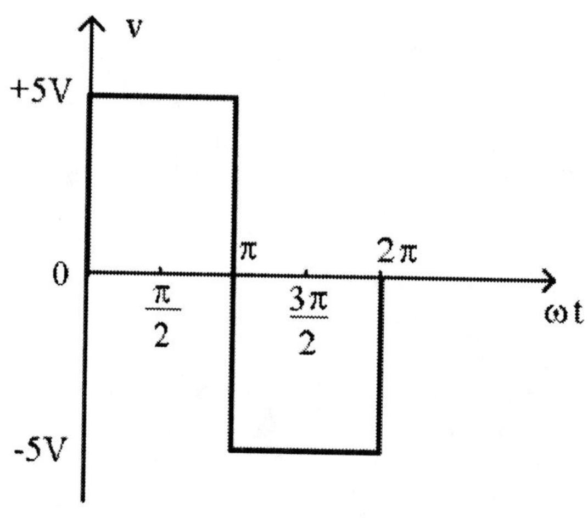

Figure 25.4

40) See Figure 25.4. Determine the amplitude at $\pi/2$ if the first four Fourier terms are added.

41) See Figure 25.4. Determine the amplitude at $\pi/2$ if the first ten Fourier terms are added.

42) What is the dc component in the waveform described by the equation $v = 10 + 2 \cos \alpha + 3 \sin \alpha$?

43) What is the ac component (expressed in the time domain) in the waveform described by the equation $v = 10 + 2 \cos \alpha + 3 \sin \alpha$?

44) Explain why a low-pass filter "rounds" the corners of a square wave.

45) What type of voltmeter can read and correctly display voltages associated with nonsinusoidal waveforms?

46) What type of function has a waveform that is symmetrical about the vertical axis?

47) What familiar circuit produces a waveform that is repetitive on the half cycle?

48) Using a spectrum analyzer requires choosing the __________ to be monitored.

49) The Fourier series is the __________ of an infinite number of sinusoidal terms.

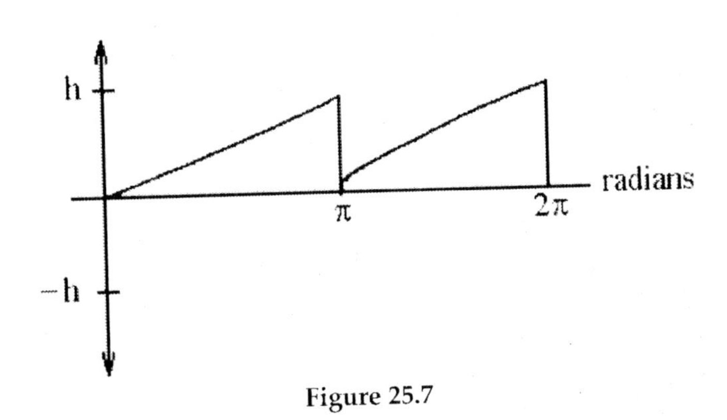

Figure 25.7

50) What is the value of the fundamental frequency a_0 of the graph shown in Figure 25.7?

51) The Fourier series representation of a nonsinusoidal input can be applied to a linear network using the principle of __________.

Answer Key
Testname: CHAPTER 25

1) TRUE
2) FALSE
3) TRUE
4) TRUE
5) FALSE
6) FALSE
7) FALSE
8) TRUE
9) TRUE
10) TRUE
11) TRUE
12) FALSE
13) TRUE
14) TRUE
15) B
16) D
17) D
18) D
19) C
20) C
21) B
22) B
23) C
24) D
25) D
26) A
27) A
28) A
29) B
30) C
31) A
32) D
33) C
34) E
35) D
36) C
37) D
38) C
39) A
40) 4.24 V
41) 5.315 V
42) 10 V
43) 3.6 V $\sin(\alpha + 33.7°)$
44) The low-pass filter reduces the high-frequency components, and those components make up the corner portions of the square wave.
45) true rms voltmeter
46) an even function
47) fullwave rectifier
48) frequency band
49) sum
50) 0.318 Hz
51) superposition

Workbook for Fundamentals of PSYCHOLOGY

Applications for Life & Work

Joseph Culkin, Ph.D.
Professor
Department of Social Sciences
Queensborough Community College
of the City University of New York

Richard S. Perrotto, Ph. D.
Professor
Department of Social Sciences
Queensborough Community College
of the City University of New York

South-Western Educational Publishing

I(T)P

International Thomson Publishing

South-Western Educational Publishing is a division of International Thomson Publishing Inc. The ITP trademark is used under license.

ISBN: 0-538-65049-4

9 MZ 03

Printed in the United States of America

Contents

To the Student

This student study guide has been prepared to help you grasp the material presented in the text and get the most out of this course. A beginning course in psychology, like any subject, will challenge you with many new themes, terms, and concepts that may seem overwhelming at first. Because this study guide is specially designed to correspond to the important material in the text, using it in conjunction with the text and lectures will assist you in developing a fundamental understanding of psychology.

Study Guide Features

Each study guide chapter consists of seven sections:
- Chapter Summary
- Chapter Objectives
- Chapter Outline
- Key Terms Worksheet
- Chapter Pretest
- Answer Key to Chapter Pretest
- Suggested Readings

Chapter Summary: Each chapter begins with a brief summary of the text chapter highlighting the major themes. This section refreshes your memory about the chapter's content.

Chapter Objectives: Taken from the chapter objectives presented at the beginning of each chapter, this section recounts the goals you should be able to accomplish by reading and studying the chapter. Each objective is followed by a brief paragraph that explains why the objective is important for you to achieve.

Chapter Outline: This is an activity which asks you to fill in details about important information from each section of the chapter. Reviewing each section of the chapter to complete this exercise helps to reinforce what you have read.

Key Terms Worksheet: This exercise asks you to write your definition for each boldfaced term found in the chapter. This helps you learn the chapter's most important terms.

Chapter Pretest: After reading the chapter and performing the previous exercises, this activity tests your knowledge of the chapter. Each chapter pretest consists of: 10 true/false questions; 10 mulitiple choice questions; and 10 short answer questions as well as a 20-item matching test and 10 fill in the blanks.

Answer Key to Pretest: This section provides the correct answers to your Pretest responses.

Suggested Readings: Readings about important or interesting topics are presented. Most of the selected readings are either classics in psychology or readable articles chosen from popular magazines. These articles elaborate on particular topics, and in some cases, present a point of view about a controversial issue in psychology.

Chapter 1

Introduction to Psychology

Chapter Summary

Psychology is the science of behavior and mental processes. Its goals are description, explanation, prediction, and control. Psychology has many areas of specialization and offers careers in mental health, education, research, business, and industry.

Psychology's schools and perspectives have different emphases, as in the schools of structuralism, functionalism, behaviorism, Gestalt psychology, psychoanalysis, humanistic psychology, and in the physiological and cognitive perspectives.

Naturalistic observation studies behavior in real-life settings. Case studies are in-depth studies of individuals or groups. Surveys use interviews or questionnaires to collect data. Correlational research estimates statistical associations—positive or negative correlations—between variables. In an experiment controlled manipulation of an independent variable is used to judge its effect on a dependent variable by comparing experimental and control groups.

Ethical principles in psychology protect the subjects' rights and dignity by requiring informed consent, limiting deception, and guiding the care of research animals.

1. **Define psychology and identify its goals.** This chapter gives an understanding of the scientific nature of psychology and its scope, and explains the scientific rationale behind psychology.

2. **Identify the main specializations and career areas in modern psychology.** This chapter reveals how diverse the field of psychology is, showing the many areas in which psychology is found today and the numerous career opportunities it presents.

3. **Summarize the ideas of the schools of psychology.** By learning about the history of psychology, one can understand the roots of the field as it exists today and the reasons behind many of the ongoing debates. This chapter also discusses some of the mistakes that have been made in the evolution of modern psychology.

4. **Distinguish among the research methods of naturalistic observation, case study, survey, and correlation.** After becoming familiar with the strategies used by psychological researchers, one can better comprehend and evaluate the results of the studies discussed throughout the text.

5. **Explain how a controlled experiment is conducted in psychology.** By gaining insight into the methods and limits of experimental research, one can better appreciate the complexity of this strategy in psychology and interpret the findings of experimental studies.

6. **Identify the major ethical principles in psychological research.** Learning about ethics helps one understand how psychology seeks to protect human welfare while pursuing its scientific goals.

Name Shanmin Zaman Class ______ Date 3/13/06.

Chapter Outline

Chapter 1 Introduction to Psychology

The Nature of Psychology

A. Psychology is defined as the science of observeable behavior and unobservable mental process.

B. Psychology has four goals:

(where, what, when) 1. description - answer question what, when & where
(why) 2. explanation - understand cause & consequence of events.
(will) 3. prediction - how people think.
(how) 4. control - attempts to influence the course of events.

Specializations

A. The major specializations in psychology are American Psychological Association (APA) has app. 48 divisions. modern psychology.

Careers in Psychology

A. Careers in mental health include clinical psychologist, psychiatrist, & social worker.

B. Careers in academic settings include school psychologist in elementary or high school. also educational psychologist - study teaching methods & develop programs to improve classroom instruction.

C. Careers in business and industry include consumer psychologists - work w/ business to innovate effective advertising & marketing strategies.

Schools of Psychology

Structuralism

Wundt the father of psychology

A. Structuralism emphasized the study of the conscious mind being structured. 1879 (Wilhelm Wundt) He conducted to open-up studies of vision, hearing, touch & memory.

B. Structuralism relied on the method of introspection-observe & analyze your subjective mental experiences, such as sensations & feelings.

William James (1842-1910)

Functionalism

A. Functionalism emphasized the study of the functions of the mind, not the structure (construction) your mind working & how is more important that what it contains.

John Dewey according to species evolve their ability to adapt to the environment.

B. Functionalism changed the course of psychology in the fields of education, learning and social behavior.

John B. Watson (1878-1958)

Behaviorism

A. Behaviorism stated that psychology must employ objective methods to study observable behaviors.

B. Behaviorism explored the areas of human & animal behavior, and its studies have revealed basic principles of learning and motivation that have led to applications in teaching, therapy, business, and everyday life.

Gestalt Psychology

Max Wertheimer (1880-1943) & Wolfgang Köhler (1887-1967)

A. The main interest of Gestalt psychology was conducting creative studies of visual perception. - school that studies organized patterns or wholes in mental activity.

B. Gestalt psychology promoted the study of mind and behavior as organized activities of the whole person.

Sigmund Freud (1856-1939) ↓ not a psychologist ↓ is a psychiatrist.

Psychoanalytic School

A. The psychoanalytic school emphasized psychological events as the results of unconscious mental forces.

B. The psychoanalytic school pioneered work in the areas of clinical methods, or strategies for treating mentally disturbed individuals.

Abraham Maslow (1916-1972) + Carl Rogers (1902-1987)

school that focuses on individual uniqueness and development.

Humanistic Psychology

A. Humanistic psychology assumes that free will is important in your behavior, & thus u have responsibility for your actions.

B. Humanistic psychology has influenced the psychology of rejecting both the behavioristic idea that you are controlled by your environment & the psychoanalytic concept of unconscious control.

Modern Trends

this view assumes that the primary causes of your thoughts, feelings, and actions lie in bodily activities, especially in your brain.

A. The physiological perspective is physiological mechanisms for explanations of behavior and mental processes.

B. The cognitive perspective is to stress the importance of mental activities such as thinking, decision making, & interpretation in shaping your behavior.

C. Eclecticism refers to approach that combines the ideas of different school or perspectives, rather than relying on a single point of view.

Research in Psychology

Scientific Method

A. The scientific method has three elements:

1. strategy of observation
2. theory formation
3. hypothesis testing.

B. A theory is a general and logical explanation that organizes concepts and facts.

C. A hypothesis is a testable prediction or assumption that you deduce from a theory.

D. A variable is any measurable characteristic or term.

Naturalistic Observation

A. Naturalistic observation research means the study of behavior in its natural setting or environment.

B. Two problems of naturalistic observation research are reactivity - after being observed subject will not behave as b4. observer bias - distort the observations bcoz of observer's prior expectations or attitudes.

Case study

A. A case study is an in-depth investigation of an individual or group.

B. Two problems of the case study method are abnormal development and functioning.

Survey Research

A. Surveys collect data by conducting interviews with or administering questionnaires to subjects.

B. A drawback to survey research is the questionable accuracy of the results. The validity of the results depends on the subjects giving complete and honest answers.

Correlational Research

A. Correlational research is a method that describes those relationships by analyzing statistical associations or correlations (between variables)

B. Positive correlation means variables change in the same direction, increase or decrease together.

C. Negative correlation means variables change in the opposite direction. As one increases, the other decreases.

D. The third-variable problem means may be at work; for ex, another variable, such as text-taking anxiety, may affect both failure and confidence.

Experimental Research

A. Experimental research is a method that examines cause & effect relationships through controlled manipulations and observations.

B. The three elements of an experiment are manipulation, observation, and control.

C. The three variables in an experiment are idependent variable, dependent variable & extraneous variable.

D. The experimental and control groups are subject groups of the independent variables.

E. The two procedures to select subjects are

1. random assignment.
2. matching method.

F. The placebo effect means a manipulation works because subjects believe it will work.

G. A double-blind design is ______

Ethics in Research

A. Milgram's obedience study was ethically controversial because ______

B. The ethical principles of psychology emphasize ______

______

______

Issues and Applications

Education and Employment in Psychology

A. With an associate's degree in psychology one can work as health service aide, alcoholism counselor, drug abuse counselor, mental health aide, ed. paraprofessional, laboratory assis

B. With a bachelor's degree in psychology one can work as human service caseworker, recreational therapist, high school teacher, special education teacher, research assist., public health assit.

C. With a master's degree in psychology one can work as ______

______

______

D. With a doctorate degree in psychology one can work as private practitioner college teacher, research director, health care adm. academic administrator.

On Being an Educated Consumer

A. One is likely to be a consumer of psychology in three main ways:

1. ______
2. ______
3. ______

Biography

Wilhelm Wundt

A. Wundt's education included training in ______

______

______

B. Wundt is best known for ______

______

______

Name ______________________ Class ______________ Date ____________

Key Terms Worksheet

Write a definition for each key term on the lines provided.

Term	Definition
psychology	Science of behavior and mental process.
structuralism	school that studies the structure of conscious mind through introspection.
functionalism	school that studies the functions of the mind.
behaviorism	school that uses objective methods to study observable behavior.
Gestalt psychology	school that studies organized patterns or wholes in mental activity.
psychoanalytic school	school that emphasizes unconscious forces in behavior and mind.
humanistic psychology	school that focuses on individual uniqueness and development.
scientific method	strategy of observation, theory formation, and hypothesis testing.
operational definition	objective measurement of a variable.
sample	a group of research subjects.
naturalistic observation	study of behavior in natural settings.
case study	in-depth investigation of individual or group.
survey	method of data collection by interview or questionnaire.

correlational research method to describe statistical ass. between variables

positive correlation values of associated variables change in same direction.

negative correlation values of associated variables change in opposite directions

experiment method that examines cause-&-effect relationships between variables.

independent variable the manipulated variable in an experiment, assumed to be a cause.

dependent variable the variable in an experiment observed for changes after a manipulation & assumed to be an affe[ct]

extraneous variables factors besides independent variable that affect dependent variable.

experimental group subjects in an experiment who are manipulated.

control group subjects in an expe. who are not manipulated for comparison purposes.

placebo effect a manipulation works because subjects believe it will work.

ethical principles guidelines that protect the rights and dignity of research subjects.

Name Shannin Zaman Class ____________ Date 03/13/03

Pretest

Chapter 1 Introduction to Psychology

I. True/False Circle the letter (T or F) that corresponds to the correct response.

(T) F **1.** Psychology is the science of behavior and mental processes.

(T) F **2.** Clinical psychologists typically work in mental health careers.

T (F) **3.** The first school of psychology was behaviorism.

T (F) **4.** The psychoanalytic school assumed that unconscious mental forces control human action.

T (F) **5.** Gestalt psychology emphasized the study of individual uniqueness and growth.

(T) F **6.** The scientific method involves observation, theory formation, and hypothesis testing.

T (F) **7.** Variables with a positive correlation have a strong cause-and-effect relationship.

T (F) **8.** In an experiment, the manipulated variable is called the dependent variable.

(T) F **9.** Naturalistic observation research involves the study of behavior in real-life settings.

(T) F **10.** Survey research collects data through interviews and questionnaires.

II. Multiple Choice Circle the letter that corresponds to the correct or best answer.

1. Which of these is NOT a goal of psychology?
- (**A.**) objectivity
- **B.** description
- **C.** prediction
- **D.** control

2. What is the interest of physiological psychology?
- **A.** cognition or thinking
- **B.** individual development across the life-span
- **C.** abnormal behavior and its treatment
- (**D.**) the biological basis of behavior and mental processes

3. What was the focus of structuralism?
- **A.** organized wholes or forms in behavior and mind
- **B.** adaptive functions of mind and behavior
- **C.** objective study of observable behavior
- (**D.**) structure of the conscious mind

4. What school of psychology did John Watson found?
   - **A.** Structuralism
   - **B.** Psychoanalysis
   - **C.** Behaviorism
   - **D.** Humanistic Psychology
5. Which idea is associated with humanistic psychology?
   - **A.** the scientific method
   - **B.** individual uniqueness
   - **C.** unconscious motives
   - **D.** elements of consciousness
6. Which term refers to a measurable characteristic?
   - **A.** variable
   - **B.** operational definition
   - **C.** sample
   - **D.** hypothesis
7. Dr. Jones interviews people about their drug use. What research method is Dr. Jones using?
   - **A.** case study
   - **B.** naturalistic observation
   - **C.** survey
   - **D.** correlation
8. Which of the following indicates a negative correlation between absences from class and grades?
   - **A.** Students with many absences have high grades.
   - **B.** Students with few absences have low grades.
   - **C.** Students with no absences have average grades.
   - **D.** Students with few absences have high grades.
9. What is the experimental group in an experiment?
   - **A.** the group that receives a manipulation
   - **B.** the group that directs the research
   - **C.** the group that is not manipulated
   - **D.** the group that is randomly assigned
10. What ethical principle states that research subjects must voluntarily agree to participate?
    - **A.** the no deception rule
    - **B.** the informed consent principle
    - **C.** the fair compensation rule
    - **D.** the confidentiality principle

III. Short Answer Write the answer in the space provided.

1. What are the goals of modern psychology?

2. What are the main ideas of Gestalt psychology?

3. What are the main ideas of functionalism?

4. What are the limitations of correlational research?

5. What variables are involved in an experiment?

IV. Matching Match the terms in column A with the correct choice in column B.

	A	B
______	**1.** introspection	**a.** an in-depth study of an individual or group
______	**2.** informed consent	**b.** a group of research subjects
______	**3.** Gestalt	**c.** a variable controlled in an experiment
______	**4.** negative correlation	**d.** a testable assumption or prediction
______	**5.** William James	**e.** one of the ethical principles
______	**6.** Sigmund Freud	**f.** when variables change in opposite directions
______	**7.** behaviorism	**g.** an organized whole
______	**8.** psychoanalytic school	**h.** the structuralist's method of study
______	**9.** cognitive perspective	**i.** the founder of the psychoanalytic school
______	**10.** hypothesis	**j.** a modern view that stresses thinking
______	**11.** operational definition	**k.** the manipulated variable in an experiment
______	**12.** sample	**l.** the school that studied objective behavior
______	**13.** extraneous variable	**m.** an objective measurement of a variable
______	**14.** case study	**n.** when variables change in the same direction
______	**15.** dependent variable	**o.** the estimated value of an association
______	**16.** correlation coefficient	**p.** the variable assumed to be an effect
______	**17.** positive correlation	**q.** the founder of functionalism
______	**18.** experiment	**r.** the study of behavior in a natural setting
______	**19.** naturalistic observation	**s.** the school that studied unconscious forces
______	**20.** independent variable	**t.** a method which tests cause-and-effect relationships

V. Fill In The Blanks Write the answers in the space provided.

1. The goal of ____________________ in psychology is the attempt to understand the causes of behavior which allows the psychologist to make ____________________ about future events in order to try to ____________________ the course of those events.

2. The first school of psychology was ____________________, which aimed to describe the structure of ____________________ with the method known as ____________________.

3. John Watson introduced the school of ____________________, which sought to employ ____________________ methods to study observable ____________________ and was dismayed by the ____________________ of structuralism and functionalism.

4. The ____________________ school, founded by ____________________, explained psychological events as the result of unconscious mental forces and relied on ____________________ methods to study the mind and behavior.

5. Psychologists Abraham Maslow and Carl Rogers developed the school of ____________________ psychology that focused on individual ____________________ and ____________________, and proposed that ____________________ is important in behavior.

6. The scientific method begins with ____________________ of events and the development of general explanations called ____________________ which lead to testable predictions, or ____________________.

7. Correlations tell us about the ____________________ between variables, but they reveal only general ____________________ rather than exceptions; they do not give definite conclusions about ____________________ relationships.

8. In an experiment, the researcher manipulates the ____________________ variable, observes any subsequent changes in the ____________________ variable, and tries to control the impact of ____________________ variables.

9. To control the effect of expectations on an experiment, researchers use a ____________________ design in which neither the subjects nor the experimenter know who is in the ____________________ or ____________________ group.

10. Milgram's ____________________ study violated the ethical principle of ____________________ because his manipulation involved ____________________ of his subjects.

Notes

Answer Key To Chapter 1 Pretest

I. True/False

1-T, **2**-T, **3**-F, **4**-T, **5**-F, **6**-T, **7**-F, **8**-F, **9**-T, **10**-T

II. Multiple Choice

1-A, **2**-D, **3**-D, **4**-C, **5**-B, **6**-A, **7**-C, **8**-D, **9**-A, **10**-B

III. Short Answer

1. The goals of modern psychology are to describe the features of behavior and mental processes, to explain their causes and consequences, to predict events that might occur, and to control the course of events.
2. Gestalt psychology emphasizes the study of organized wholes or forms (Gestalts) in mental activity and assumes that the whole is different than the sum of its parts. Gestalt psychology focuses on studies of visual perception, problem solving, art, and personality.
3. William James set the basis for functionalism, the school that emphasized the functions of the mind. Functionalism assumed that psychological processes have adaptive value which enable an individual to interact with the environment.
4. Correlational research informs us only of general trends or associations between variables, but does not tell about exceptions to the trends. Correlational research also does not explain the cause-and-effect relationships between variables.
5. Three kinds of variables are involved in an experiment. The independent variable is manipulated, the dependent variable is observed for changes following the manipulation, and the extraneous variables are controlled to reduce their impact on the dependent variable.

IV. Matching

1-h, **2**-e, **3**-g, **4**-f, **5**-q, **6**-i, **7**-l, **8**-s, **9**-j, **10**-d, **11**-m, **12**-b, **13**-c, **14**-a, **15**-p, **16**-o, **17**-n, **18**-t, **19**-r, **20**-k

V. Fill In The Blanks

1. explanation - predictions - control
2. structuralism - the conscious mind - introspection
3. behaviorism - objective - behavior - subjectivity
4. psychoanalytic - Sigmund Freud - clinical
5. humanistic - uniqueness - growth - free will
6. observation - theories - hypotheses
7. associations - trends - cause-and-effect
8. independent - dependent - extraneous
9. double-blind - experimental - control
10. obedience - informed consent - deception

Suggested Readings

American Psychological Association. 1986. *Careers in psychology*. Washington, D.C.: American Psychological Association.

An overview of job opportunities in psychology for individuals with different educational backgrounds and a practical look at the prospects for employment in psychology in the future.

American Psychological Association. 1992. *Ethical principles of psychologists and code of conduct.* Washington, DC: American Psychological Association.

A summary and explanation of the ethical principles that apply to psychologists, including general principles and principles specific to therapy, teaching, and research with human and animal subjects.

Dunham, Philip J. 1990. *Research methods in psychology.* New York: HarperCollins.

A solid introduction to the major strategies used in psychological research today with good examples of the methodology.

Kerlinger, Frederick N. 1986. *Foundations of behavioral research, 3rd ed.* New York: Harcourt Brace Jovanovich.

An in-depth discussion of the scientific method and techniques in modern psychology for those seeking a more thorough understanding of research.

Kimble, G. A., Wertheimer, M., and White, C. L. (eds.) 1991. *Portraits of pioneers in psychology.* Washington, D.C.: American Psychological Association.

A collection of profiles of 22 of the major figures in the history of psychology, including biographical information as well as contributions to the field.

Wertheimer, M. 1970. *A brief history of psychology.* New York: Holt, Rinehart, and Winston.

A concise account of the historical background and development of modern psychology, from its prescientific roots in Greek philosophy through its early years and the rise of the great schools.

Chapter 2

The Biological Roots of Behavior

Chapter Summary

The neuron is the fundamental basis of behavior. Neurons work by conducting neural impulses and discharging neurotransmitters, such as dopamine, serotonin, and GABA, into the synapse to communicate with other neurons. The peripheral nervous system is made up of the somatic division, which controls sensations and movement, and the autonomic division, which regulates physiology. The central nervous system consists of the brain and the spinal cord. Hindbrain structures are mainly responsible for sensory and vital functions. Midbrain regions are important in arousal while forebrain structures are involved in a variety of motivational, emotional, and sensory functions.

The cerebral hemispheres are divided into lobes. The occipital lobe is involved in vision; the temporal lobe is for hearing; the parietal lobe interprets sensations from the skin; and the frontal lobe controls higher mental functions and movement. Each hemisphere performs different functions, as shown in split-brain studies.

The left hemisphere is specialized for analytic functions such as language and calculation. The right hemisphere performs holistically and is specialized for visual-spatial and other nonverbal skills.

The endocrine system influences behavior through hormones secreted by endocrine glands such as the pituitary, adrenals, and gonads. Behavior is also determined, in part, by heredity. Behavior genetics research methods, such as family, twin, and adoption studies, are designed to determine heritability.

Chapter Objectives

1. **Describe the structure and function of a typical neuron.** It is important to be able to describe the parts of the neuron and understand the neuron's electrical and chemical properties because the neuron is the fundamental unit of behavior. The interaction of neurons is the basis for all mental activities and behavior.
2. **Summarize the chemical events that occur at the synapse.** Neurons communicate with each other by way of chemical events that occur at the synapse. Neural impulses are transformed into chemical messages at the synapse and are sent to other neurons. Neurotransmitter activity across many synapses determines the kind of mental activity or behavior experienced.
3. **Identify the major neurotransmitters and describe their functions in behavior.** Neurotransmitters are the chemical messengers in the nervous system. Different neurotransmitters have different functions in behavior. Understanding the functions of neurotransmitters has also increased knowledge of brain diseases, mental illness, and drug addiction, and has led to many treatments.
4. **Outline the major divisions of the nervous system.** Outlining the divisions of the nervous system allows a better understanding of how the nervous system is organized and works as a single unit to account for behavior.
5. **Explain the functions of the medulla, pons, cerebellum, reticular formation, hypothalamus, thalamus, and limbic system within the brain.** There are many mental activities and behaviors that the brain is able to perform. To a large degree, different brain structures are specialized to handle these functions. Understanding these specializations helps you to appreciate the complexity of the brain and behavior.
6. **Identify the activities of the four lobes of the cerebral cortex.** The cerebral cortex is the most sophisticated and complex part of the brain. Its four lobes put together information for many other brain regions, permitting an organized awareness of sensations and allowing higher mental functions and movements.
7. **Describe "split-brain" studies and the different functions of the left and right cerebral hemispheres.** Split-brain studies represent a unique opportunity for learning about brain functions and the nature of consciousness. Understanding the technique and findings of split-brain studies gives insight into the specializations of the cerebral hemispheres.
8. **List the major endocrine glands and explain how their hormones influence behavior.** Although all behavior is rooted in nervous system activity, the nervous system does not operate alone. Hormones secreted by the endocrine glands also influence behavior by their actions and through their effects on neurons.
9. **Distinguish among family, twin, and adoption studies used in behavior genetics research.** Genes help determine many aspects of behavior. Because it is not currently possible to isolate the genes responsible for specific behaviors, behavior geneticists use family, twin, and adoption studies to determine heritability.

Name ______________________ Class __________________ Date ______________

Chapter Outline

Chapter 2 The Biological Roots of Behavior

The Neuron

A. The neuron is ____

____

behavior and its function is to ____

____

B. The parts of the neuron are ____

____

____

C. The function of the dendrites is to ____

____

____

D. Fifty percent of the neurons ____

____

____

How Neurons Work and Communicate

A. At resting potential, there is an abundance of ____

____

and an abundance of ____

____

B. The three most important ions involved in the electrical activity of neurons are:

1. ____

2. ____

3. ____

C. When the resting potential changes to -55mv ____

____

____

D. The all-or-none law states that ____

____

____

E. During the electrical neural impulse, ______________________________

____

while ______________________________

____

Neurotransmitters, Mind, and Behavior

A. A neurotransmitter is ______________________________

____

____

B. Neurotransmitters can have an excitatory or inhibitory effect in the synapse depending on ______________________________

____

C. Three types of neurotransmitters are:

1. ______________________________
2. ______________________________
3. ______________________________

D. The function of acetylcholine is ______________________________

____

____

E. The function of GABA is ______________________________

____

____

F. Dopamine is responsible for ______________________________

____

____

G. Many drugs influence behavior by ______________________________

____

____

The Nervous System

A. The nervous system is divided into two main sections:

1. ______________________________
2. ______________________________

The Peripheral Nervous System

A. The two parts of the peripheral nervous system are:

1. ____________________

2. ____________________

B. Sensory nerves carry information from ____________________

____

Motor nerves relay commands from ____________________

____

C. The autonomic nervous system regulates ____________________

____

____

D. The function of the sympathetic division of the autonomic nervous system is

____

____

The Central Nervous System

A. A spinal reflex is ____________________

____

____

B. Four techniques to study the nervous system are:

1. ____________________

2. ____________________

3. ____________________

4. ____________________

C. The hindbrain consists of:

1. ____________________

2. ____________________

3. ____________________

D. The function of the cerebellum is ____________________

____

____

E. The main function of the reticular formation is ____________________

____

F. Three parts of the limbic system are:

1. ______________________________

2. ______________________________

3. ______________________________

G. The functions of the limbic system are ______________________________

____

H. The functions of the hypothalamus are ______________________________

____

____

I. The purpose of psychosurgery is ______________________________

____

The Cerebral Cortex

A. The cerebral cortex is ______________________________

____

and is divided into ______________________________

____

The Lobes of the Cerebral Cortex

A. The four lobes of the cerebral cortex are:

1. ______________________________

2. ______________________________

3. ______________________________

4. ______________________________

B. The frontal lobe is responsible for ______________________________

____

____

C. The temporal lobe is involved in ______________________________

____

____

D. One major function of the parietal lobe is ______________________________

____

____

E. An important function of the temporal lobe is ______________________

____

Hemispheric Specialization

A. Hemispheric specialization refers to ______________________

____

____

B. Four activities of the left cerebral hemisphere are:

1. ______________________
2. ______________________
3. ______________________
4. ______________________

C. The right cerebral hemisphere is specialized for:

1. ______________________
2. ______________________
3. ______________________
4. ______________________

D. Commissurotomy is ______________________

____

E. Regarding cognitive and perceptual abilities, women are more adept than men at

____

____

The Endocrine System

A. Hormones are ______________________

____

____

B. Five endocrine glands are:

1. ______________________
2. ______________________
3. ______________________
4. ______________________
5. ______________________

Hormones and Behavior

A. Corticosteroids are secreted by ______________________________

____

and help ______________________________

____

B. The gonads are ______________________________

____

____

C. Two hormones produced by the adrenal glands are:

1. ______________________________

2. ______________________________

Heredity and Behavior

A. Genetics is ______________________________

____

____

B. Chromosomes are ______________________________

____

____

Behavior Genetics

A. Behavior genetics is ______________________________

____

____

B. A behavior is said to exhibit heritability if ______________________________

____

____

C. Twin studies examine ______________________________

____

____

D. Adoption studies disentangle the effects of heredity and environment by ____

____

____

Issues and Applications

Neural Grafts as a Therapy for Brain Disease

A. To treat brain Parkinson's disease, doctors have been experimenting with the grafting ______________________________

____

____

B. Two reasons why fetal tissue research in the United States has been slow until recent years are:

1. ______________________________

2. ______________________________

Is It Possible to Educate Each Hemisphere of the Brain?

A. Two areas where the idea of cerebral hemispheres specialization has filtered into society are:

1. ______________________________

2. ______________________________

B. Two pieces of evidence that argue against the idea that each hemisphere of the brain can be independently educated are:

1. ______________________________

2. ______________________________

Biography

Roger Sperry

A. Roger Sperry's work with the cerebral hemispheres began while he ________

____

____

B. Roger Sperry's research on split-brain patients changed psychology's view of

____

____

Notes

Name ______________________________ Class ______________________ Date ________________

Key Terms Worksheet

Write your definition for each key term on the lines provided.

Term	Definition
neuron	______________________________
neural impulse	______________________________
neurotransmitters	______________________________
peripheral nervous system	______________________________
autonomic nervous system	______________________________
central nervous system	______________________________
brain	______________________________
medulla	______________________________
pons	______________________________
cerebellum	______________________________
reticular formation	______________________________
hypothalamus	______________________________
thalamus	______________________________

limbic system

cerebral cortex

corpus callosum

frontal lobe

temporal lobe

parietal lobe

occipital lobe

hemispheric specialization

endocrine system

hormones

genetics

behavior genetics

Name ______________________ Class ______________ Date __________

Pretest

Chapter 2 The Biological Roots of Behavior

I. True/False Circle the letter (T or F) that corresponds to the correct response.

T F **1.** The nucleus of the neuron is located in the axon.

T F **2.** Alzheimer's disease is caused by the destruction of dopamine neurons.

T F **3.** The central nervous system consists of the somatic and autonomic divisions.

T F **4.** Sex, aggression, and eating are functions of the hypothalamus.

T F **5.** The cerebellum controls vital functions like breathing and heart rate.

T F **6.** Research shows that it is possible to train each hemisphere of the brain independently.

T F **7.** Damage to the left cerebral hemisphere would result in problems with calculation, speech, and logic.

T F **8.** Insulin is a hormone secreted by the pancreas.

T F **9.** Humans have 48 chromosomes.

T F **10.** Adoption studies are the most effective behavior genetics method for separating heredity and environment.

II. Multiple Choice Circle the letter that corresponds to the correct or best answer.

1. The part of the neuron covered by myelin is the:

A. terminal button

B. axon

C. nucleus

D. cell body

2. Which of the following neurotransmitters is responsible for relaxation?

A. dopamine

B. GABA

C. acetylcholine

D. serotonin

3. If an individual were under extreme sympathetic nervous system arousal, which of the following would be LEAST likely to occur?

A. Heart rate would increase.

B. Digestion would slow down.

C. Digestion would improve.

D. The individual would perspire.

4. The ___________________ interprets all sensory information, except smell.

A. thalamus

B. corpus callosum

C. medulla

D. cerebellum

5. The _______________ lobe is responsible for the interpretation of visual stimuli.

A. occipital

B. temporal

C. frontal

D. parietal

6. Which is not a function of left cerebral hemisphere?

A. calculation

B. speech

C. shape recognition

D. logical analysis

7. Which endocrine gland secretes estrogen?

A. pancreas

B. thyroid

C. ovaries

D. pituitary

8. The hormone that is responsible for premenstrual syndrome (PMS) in women is:

A. testosterone

B. progesterone

C. insulin

D. dopamine

9. A heritable behavior is more likely to occur:

A. only in identical twins

B. in individuals who are genetically more similar to the person who expresses that behavior

C. in one identical twin but not the other

D. in fraternal twins more often than identical twins

10. ___________________ are twisted strands of genetic material composed of deoxyribonucleic acid.

A. Chromosomes

B. Genes

C. Nuclei

D. Endocrine glands

III. Short Answer Write the answer in the space provided.

1. What are the events that occur at the synapse?

2. Name the three types of neurotransmitters and give examples of each.

3. What are the main functions of the four lobes of the cerebral cortex?

4. How is the endocrine system involved in behavior?

5. Describe the basic design of twin studies.

IV. Matching Match the terms in column A with the correct choice in column B.

	A	B
_____	**1.** myelin sheath	**a.** type of automatic movement
_____	**2.** terminal button	**b.** consists of the amygdala and hippocampus
_____	**3.** serotonin	**c.** neuron structure that contains neurotransmitters
_____	**4.** norepinephrine	**d.** regulates brain arousal
_____	**5.** central nervous system	**e.** controls higher mental functions
_____	**6.** medulla	**f.** secretes hormones
_____	**7.** sympathetic division	**g.** studies heritability
_____	**8.** cerebellum	**h.** consists of the brain and spinal cord
_____	**9.** reticular formation	**i.** controls mood
_____	**10.** hypothalamus	**j.** controls mood and sleep
_____	**11.** thalamus	**k.** interprets all sensory information except smell
_____	**12.** limbic system	**l.** fatty substance that covers the axons
_____	**13.** cerebral cortex	**m.** controls vital functions
_____	**14.** frontal lobe	**n.** responsible for motor coordination
_____	**15.** temporal lobe	**o.** "fight or flight" reactions
_____	**16.** endocrine system	**p.** outer covering of the brain
_____	**17.** behavior genetics	**q.** separates heredity from environment
_____	**18.** adoption studies	**r.** area of cortex for hearing
_____	**19.** sodium	**s.** ion in neural impulse
_____	**20.** spinal reflex	**t.** responsible for sex, aggression, and eating

V. Fill in the Blanks Write the answers in the space provided.

1. The fundamental unit of behavior is the ____________________ ,which is responsible for ____________________ and ____________________ information.

2. The part of the neuron that contains the nucleus is the ____________________.

3. The electrical difference between the ____________________ and ____________________ of the neuron is called the ____________________.

4. ____________________ and ____________________ are types of____________________ neurotransmitters.

5. The part of the peripheral nervous system that carries information into and out of the central nervous system is the ____________________ division; the segment that controls "fight or flight" reactions is known as the ____________________ division.

6. The cerebral cortex is also known as the ____________________.

7. Intelligence, abstract thinking, and language abilities are functions of the ____________________ lobe.

8. The ____________________ of the cerebral cortex integrate information from the senses with motives, emotions, and memories.

9. An inability to recognize shapes would occur if the ____________________ cerebral hemisphere were damaged.

10. ____________________ and ____________________ are adrenal hormones whose levels increase during stressful situations.

Notes

Answer Key To Chapter 2 Pretest

I. True/False

1-F, **2**-F, **3**-F, **4**-T, **5**-F, **6**-F, **7**-T, **8**-T, **9**-T, **10**-F

II. Multiple Choice

1-B, **2**-B, **3**-C, **4**-A, **5**-A, **6**-C, **7**-C, **8**-B, **9**-B, **10**-A

III. Short Answer

1. Neural impulses trigger the release of neurotransmitters. These chemicals influence postsynaptic neurons, thereby communicating messages among neurons.
2. The three types of neurotransmitters are amines, amino acids, and neuropeptides. Acetylcholine, norepinephrine, dopamine and serotonin are amines. GABA, glutamate, and aspartate are amino acids, while substance-P and the endorphins belong to the neuropeptide class.
3. The frontal lobe governs higher mental functions and movement. The parietal lobe interprets sensory information from the skin. The temporal lobe allows one to hear and the occipital lobe interprets visual information.
4. The endocrine system consists of glands that secrete chemicals into the bloodstream. These chemicals, called hormones, affect the physiology of other glands and the brain.
5. Twin studies examine the prevalence of behaviors and traits among monozygotic and dizygotic twins. If a behavior is hereditary, its presence in both twins should be higher for monozygotic than dizygotic twins because the former are genetically identical.

IV. Matching

1-l, **2**-c, **3**-j, **4**-i, **5**-h, **6**-m, **7**-o, **8**-n, **9**-d, **10**-t, **11**-k, **12**-b, **13**-p, **14**-e, **15**-r, **16**-f, **17**-g, **18**-q, **19**-s, **20**-a

V. Fill In The Blanks

1. neuron - receiving - transmitting
2. cell body
3. inside - outside - resting potential
4. substance P - endorphins - neuropeptide
5. somatic - autonomic
6. neocortex
7. frontal
8. association areas
9. right
10. adrenalin - noradrenalin

Suggested Readings

Begley, Sharon. "Mapping the brain." *Newsweek*, 20 April 1992, 66-70.

This article describes how scientists are uncovering the biological foundations of mental activities using modern brain imaging techniques.

Fischbach, G. D. "Mind and brain." *Scientific American*, September 1992, 48-57.

This article presents an excellent discussion of brain-behavior relationships.

Gazzaniga, M. S. 1970. *The bisected brain.* New York: Appleton-Century-Crofts.

Psychologist Michael Gazzaniga describes the early research on split-brain studies and their implications for hemispheric specialization.

Hopson, J. L. "A pleasurable chemistry." *Psychology Today*, July/August 1988, 29-30, 30-32.

This article discusses the role of endorphins in behavior.

Kalat, J. W. 1992. *Biological psychology, (4th Ed.).* Belmont, CA: Wadsworth.

This is a comprehensive and readable introduction to physiological psychology.

Kimura, D. "Sex differences in the brain." *Scientific American*, September 1992, 119-125.

This is an excellent review of research on male-female differences in brain structure and hemispheric specialization.

Olds, J., and Milner, P. "Positive reinforcement produced by electrical stimulation of septal area and other regions of rat brain." *Journal of Comparative and Physiological Psychology* 47 (1954): 419-427.

This is a classic study about the physiological basis of reward and pleasure.

Plomin, R. "Environment and genes. Determinants of behavior." *American Psychologist* 44 (1989): 105-111.

Research about the influences of heredity and environment are reviewed and discussed.

Sachs, O. 1985. *The man who mistook his wife for a hat.* New York: Harper & Row.

This book provides fascinating insights into brain-behavior relationships by describing cases of individuals with brain disease.

Chapter 3

Sensation and Perception

Chapter Summary

Sensation depends on sensory receptors that detect and transduce stimuli. Perception is the interpretation of sensations involving higher-order mental activity.

Vision depends on sensory mechanisms in the retina. Color vision is explained by trichromatic theory, opponent mechanisms, and cortical detectors. Form perception is described by the Gestalt laws. Perceptual constancy is found for size, shape, and other visual features. Distance and depth perception relies on monocular and binocular cues.

The auditory system interprets soundwaves. Frequency (pitch), amplitude (loudness), and location of sounds affect hair cell responses which the auditory cortex analyzes.

Skin senses include touch (warmth, cold, pressure) and pain registered by receptors in the skin. The body senses are proprioception (movement) and the vestibular sense (balance).

Smell and taste are the chemical senses. Olfactory receptors in the nasal passages detect odors. Taste receptors produce sweet, sour, salty, and bitter taste qualities. Taste and smell interact to produce flavor.

1. **Define sensation and perception and describe their relationship.** This chapter explains how the mechanisms of sensation and perception are distinguished and how they interact to produce the sensory experiences of everyday life.

2. **Outline the visual system and discuss its functions.** Studying the pieces of the visual system reveals the connections between eye and brain and the sophistication of the visual sense.

3. **Identify the mechanisms of color vision.** Being able to recognize how color vision works gives insight into the variety of color experiences and the potential problems in color perception.

4. **Discuss the perception of forms.** This chapter focuses its attention on how one comes to see the many shapes of objects in the visual world through some inborn perceptual tendencies.

5. **Explain perceptual constancy.** How the brain combines and interprets information from the eyes in order to accurately see objects becomes clear through an understanding of constancy.

6. **Identify the cues for distance and depth perception.** This chapter shows how one comes to see the three-dimensional visual world by the mechanisms of distance and depth.

7. **Describe the auditory system and its functions.** By learning to identify the main structures that control hearing one can see the relationship between soundwave stimuli and sensory responses to them.

8. **Discuss the perception of pitch, loudness, and sound location.** Studying these fundamental aspects of auditory perception reveals the mechanisms that provide awareness of the world of sound.

9. **Identify the functions of the skin and body senses.** Touch, pain, balance, and the sense of motion are critical to interaction with the world as this chapter reveals by explaining the skin and body senses.

10. **Describe the mechanisms of taste and smell.** By learning about the senses of taste and smell one can understand sensitivity to the thousands of chemical stimuli responsible for odors and flavors.

Name ______________________ Class ______________________ Date ______________________

Chapter Outline

Chapter 3 Sensation and Perception

The Nature of Sensation and Perception

A. Sensation and perception refer to ______________________

____

____

Sensation

A. Sensation means ______________________

____

____

B. Sensory receptors are ______________________

____

____

C. The major senses are ______________________

____

____

D. Psychophysics is ______________________

____

____

E. Weber's law states ______________________

____

____

F. Signal detection theory refers to ______________________

____

____

Perception

A. Perception is influenced by ______________________

____

____

B. An illusion refers to ______________________

____

____

Vision The Visual System

A. The parts of the visual system are ______________________

____

____

B. The eye's major structures include ______________________

____

____

C. The retina contains ______________________

____

____

D. Foveal vision is ______________________

____

____

E. Peripheral vision is ______________________

____

____

F. Feature detectors are ______________________

____

____

Color Vision

A. The visible spectrum refers to ______________________

____

____

B. The dimensions of color are ______________________

____

____

C. Trichromatic theory states that ______________________

____

____

D. Color blindness means ______________________

____

____

Visual Organization

A. Visual organization is the result of ______________________________

____

____

B. The Gestalt laws are ______________________________

____

____

Perceptual Consistancy

A. Perceptual constancy refers to ______________________________

____

____

B. Size constancy depends on ______________________________

____

____

Distance and Depth Perception

A. A monocular cue is defined as ______________________________

____

____

B. A binocular cue is defined as ______________________________

____

____

C. There are six major monocular cues

1. ______________________________

2. ______________________________

3. ______________________________

4. ______________________________

5. ______________________________

6. ______________________________

D. There are two major binocular cues:

1. ______________________________

2. ______________________________

Hearing

The Auditory System

A. The main components of the auditory system are ______________________

____

____

B. The major structures of the ear are ______________________

____

____

C. Deafness refers to ______________________

____

____

Perceiving Sound

A. A soundwave stimulus is ______________________

____

____

B. Pitch and loudness refer to ______________________

____

____

C. Frequency theory states that ______________________

____

____

D. Place theory states that ______________________

____

____

E. Sound localization means ______________________

____

____

Skin and Body Senses

Skin Senses

A. The skin senses detect ______________________

____

____

B. The touch receptors are ______________________________

____

____

C. Pain perception depends on ______________________________

____

____

D. Gate-control theory states that ______________________________

____

____

E. A phantom pain means ______________________________

____

____

Body Senses

A. The body senses interpret ______________________________

____

____

B. Proprioception is ______________________________

____

____

C. The vestibular sense controls ______________________________

____

____

Chemical Senses

A. Taste and smell are considered chemical senses because ______________________________

____

____

Smell

A. The mechanisms by which odors are sensed are ______________________________

____

____

B. Smell is linked with emotion and memory because ______________________________

____

Taste

A. Taste mechanisms include ________________________________

____

____

B. The four taste qualities are:

1. ________________________________

2. ________________________________

3. ________________________________

4. ________________________________

C. The perception of flavor depends on ________________________________

____

____

Issues and Applications

Subliminal Persuasion

A. A subliminal message is ________________________________

____

____

B. Studies of subliminal persuasion find that________________________________

____

____

Issues and Applications

Being Led By Your Nose

A. Aroma therapists claim that________________________________

____

____

B. Studies of a smell-emotion connection find that ________________________________

____

____

Biography

David Hubel

A. Hubel's most important contributions are in the area of ________________________________

____

____

Notes

Notes

Name ______________________ Class ________________ Date ____________

Key Terms Worksheet

Write a definition for each key term on the lines provided.

Term	Definition
sensation	
sensory receptors	
psychophysics	
signal detection theory	
perception	
illusion	
retina	
rods	
cones	
fovea	
feature detectors	
trichromatic theory	
Gestalt laws	

perceptual constancy

monocular cues

binocular cues

cochlea

hair cells

frequency theory

place theory

skin senses

gate-control theory

body senses

proprioception

vestibular sense

chemical senses

Name ______________________ Class ______________ Date __________

Pretest

Chapter 3 Sensation and Perception

I. True/False Circle the letter (T or F) that corresponds to the correct response.

T F **1.** Sensory receptors are specialized neurons that detect physical stimuli.

T F **2.** The periphery is the region of the retina that contains all the cones.

T F **3.** The trichromatic theory is an explanation of form perception.

T F **4.** The closure law states that a person sees whole objects even when the eye's information is incomplete.

T F **5.** In size constancy an object's retinal image may change in size, but one sees its size as stable.

T F **6.** Motion parallax is a monocular cue for distance and depth perception.

T F **7.** Hair cells are the sensory receptors for hearing.

T F **8.** A sound's pitch is due to soundwave amplitude.

T F **9.** The skin senses depend on receptors for temperature, pressure, and pain.

T F **10.** Taste and smell are called proprioceptive senses.

II. Multiple Choice Circle the letter that corresponds to the correct or best answer.

1. What process detects and responds to stimuli?

A. adaptation
B. perception
C. conduction
D. sensation

2. What does the fovea do?

A. analyze details of visual stimuli
B. contain feature detectors
C. conduct signals from the eye to thalamus
D. regulate night vision

3. What color dimension does light wavelength determine?

A. frequency
B. purity
C. hue
D. brightness

4. Which statement describes the law of proximity?

A. One sees objects as having continuous, unbroken outlines or boundaries.
B. One sees objects as a group when they are close together.
C. One sees objects that are similar as belonging together in a group.
D. One sees objects as complete even when visual information is incomplete.

5. Which of the following statements best describes the cue of convergence?

A. Closer objects block portions of farther objects.

B. Closer objects are seen in greater detail than farther objects.

C. The retina of each eye sees a slightly different image of the world.

D. The eyes must be turned at a precise angle to focus on a visual object.

6. Which hearing theory emphasizes the sensitivity of different regions of the basilar membrane to different frequencies?

A. place theory

B. frequency theory

C. signal detection theory

D. stereochemical theory

7. Which of these qualities would explain the perception of a very loud noise, such as an explosion?

A. low frequency

B. high frequency

C. low amplitude

D. high amplitude

8. Which statement is consistent with the gate-control theory?

A. The sense of balance is based on mechanisms in the inner ear which detect the pull of gravity.

B. Temperature sensations are regulated by receptors in the skin which control the flow of warm and cold signals.

C. Pain sensations are channeled to the brain through mechanisms in the spinal cord.

D. Pairs of neurons in the thalamus are responsible for color vision.

9. What is the sense of muscle movement?

A. the vestibular sense

B. proprioception

C. gustation

D. olfaction

10. What are the four qualities of taste?

A. sweet, sour, bitter, acidic

B. sour, acidic, salty, bitter

C. sweet, sour, salty, bitter

D. acidic, sweet, bitter, salty

III. Short Answer Write the answer in the space provided.

1. Define sensation and perception.

2. Discuss the three dimensions of color.

3. What is size constancy?

4. What is the place theory of hearing?

5. What factors affect pain perception?

IV. Matching Match the terms in column A with the correct choice in column B.

A

_____ **1.** sensory receptor

_____ **2.** transduction

_____ **3.** absolute threshold

_____ **4.** Weber's law

_____ **5.** foveal vision

_____ **6.** peripheral vision

_____ **7.** hue

_____ **8.** opponent-pairs

_____ **9.** monochromat

_____ **10.** closure

_____ **11.** linear perspective

_____ **12.** retinal disparity

_____ **13.** basilar membrane

_____ **14.** pitch

_____ **15.** sound localization

_____ **16.** free nerve endings

_____ **17.** proprioceptors

_____ **18.** semicircular canals

_____ **19.** olfaction

_____ **20.** gustation

B

a. receding parallel lines appear to come closer together

b. sound-sensitive structure inside the cochlea

c. tendency to see complete objects

d. sound quality based on frequency

e. process of transforming stimuli into neural responses

f. difference thresholds for stimuli are relative to their values

g. the sense of smell

h. a color type on the visible spectrum

i. the minimum stimulus energy required to produce a sensation

j. touch receptors

k. ability to locate a sound in space

l. different images in the left and right eyes

m. neurons in the thalamus that respond to red-green, blue-yellow, and black-white combinations

n. organs of the vestibular sense

o. person with none of the usual cone pigments

p. sensory receptors that detect muscle movement

q. the sense of taste

r. neuron that detects and analyzes stimuli

s. the clear and detailed center of the visual field

t. vision of the sides of the visual field

V. Fill In The Blanks Write the answers in the space provided.

1. The field of ____________________ studies the relationships between physical stimuli and sensations. Traditionally, it has investigated the minimum stimulus energy required to produce sensations, or the ____________________, and the smallest detectable difference between stimuli,or the ____________________.

2. Light enters the eye through a membrane called the ____________________, passes through an opening called the ____________________, and is focused by the lens on the ____________________, which is a structure that contains the visual receptors known as ____________________.

3. The trichromatic theory explains color vision in terms of three types of ____________________ that respond selectively to light ____________________. Color is also processed by neurons in the thalamus known as ____________________.

4. Form perception is affected by the processes of visual organization described in the ____________________ laws, as well as by the characteristics of the ____________________ and the ____________________ in which one sees the object.

5. The main organ of the inner ear, the ____________________, contains the ____________________ membrane whose vibrations trigger responses in the auditory receptors known as ____________________.

6. The intensity, or ____________________, of a soundwave is measured in decibels and determines the perceived ____________________ of the sound. Pitch is mainly due to a soundwave's ____________________, which is measured in units called ____________________.

7. The experience of pain is affected by a neurotransmitter called ____________________ which conducts pain signals from the skin to the spinal cord where ____________________ mechanisms regulate the flow of pain information to the brain where ____________________ neurotransmitters modify the pain signals.

8. The vestibular sense controls bodily ____________________ by detecting how the head moves with the vestibular organs called ____________________ and ____________________.

9. Smell involves millions of odor receptors in the ____________________ whose signals are conducted to the ____________________ underneath the frontal lobes. Odors have strong connections to emotions because of the link between smell and the ____________________.

10. The sense of taste, or ____________________, depends on ____________________ in the tongue and roof of the mouth with receptors sensitive to ____________________ taste qualities.

Answer Key To Chapter 3 Pretest

I. True-False

1-T, **2**-F, **3**-F, **4**-T, **5**-T, **6**-T, **7**-T, **8**-F, **9**-T, **10**-F

II. Multiple Choice

1-D, **2**-A, **3**-C, **4**-B, **5**-D, **6**-A, **7**-D, **8**-C, **9**-B, **10**-C

III. Short Answer:

1. Sensation is the process by which the senses detect and respond to physical stimuli in vision, hearing, the body senses, and the chemical senses. Perception is an interpretation of the meaning of sensory information involving higher-order processes, such as memory and attention.
2. The dimensions of color are hue, brightness, and purity. Hue depends on the wavelength of light reflected by an object. Brightness depends on the intensity of reflected light. Purity is determined by the mixture of different reflected wavelengths.
3. Size constancy is the tendency to perceive objects as having a constant or stable size despite changes in the size of the retinal images of those objects. The brain adjusts its perception of an object's size in consideration of the retinal image size and distance to the object.
4. The place theory of hearing explains the perception of pitch in terms of the sensitivity of different parts of the basilar membrane to different soundwave frequencies.
5. Pain perception is influenced by several factors including the action of touch receptors in the skin, pathways using the neurotransmitter substance-P, gate-control mechanisms in the spinal cord, and brain endorphins, as well as emotional states and memory.

IV. Matching

1-r, **2**-e, **3**-i, **4**-f, **5**-s, **6**-t, **7**-h, **8**-m, **9**-o, **10**-c, **11**-a, **12**-l, **13**-b, **14**-d, **15**-k, **16**-j, **17**-p, **18**-n, **19**-g, **20**-q

V. Fill In The Blanks

1. psychophysics - absolute threshold - difference threshold
2. cornea - pupil - retina - rods and cones
3. cones - wavelength - opponent pairs
4. Gestalt - retinal image - context
5. cochlea - basilar - hair cells
6. amplitude - loudness - frequency - Hertz
7. substance-P - gate-control - endorphin
8. equilibrium - semicircular canals - otolith organs
9. nasal passages - olfactory bulbs - limbic system
10. gustation - taste buds - four

Suggested Readings

Hubel, D. H. 1988. *Eye, brain, and vision*. New York: Scientific American Library.

The author, a Nobel Prize winning neurobiologist, gives a grand tour of the visual system, examining the mechanisms by which the brain comes to understand what the eye senses. The material is rather technical, but excellent diagrams and photos help the reader along.

Key, B. W. 1973. *Subliminal seduction*. Englewood Cliffs, NJ: Prentice Hall.

This controversial book argues that marketing strategies exploit subliminal messages to induce consumers to favor products. Includes many photographic examples of alleged subliminal ads.

Rock, I. 1984. *Perception*. New York: Scientific American Library.

This slender volume offers a tour through the major principles and studies of perception by a leading visual perception researcher. The presentation is accompanied by numerous illustrations which help bring the material to life.

Sekuler, R. and Blake R. 1990. *Perception, 2nd ed*. New York: McGraw Hill.

An excellent introduction to the basic principles and mechanisms of perception, providing coverage of vision, hearing, touch, smell, and taste. The relationship of knowledge to perception and methods of studying perception are also discussed.

Whitfield, P. and D.M. Stoddart. 1984. *Hearing, taste and smell: Pathways of perception*. New York: Torstar.

This compact book is a colorfully illustrated introduction to the biological mechanisms and psychological factors in auditory perception and the chemical senses. Many superb figures and diagrams are employed. The authors also provide biographical profiles of people who have made important discoveries in these areas.

Chapter 4

States of Consciousness

Chapter Summary

Consciousness includes natural states like sleep and dreams and altered states such as hypnosis and drug states.

Sleep consists of REM and NREM stages that are defined by physical and behavioral changes. The functions of sleep include physical restoration and memory storage. Dream theories emphasize wish fulfillment, mental balancing, problem solving, and brain arousal. Sleep and dreaming disorders include insomnia, hypersomnia, nightmares, and NREM disturbances.

Hypnosis produces a state of suggestibility that can be influenced by trance dissociation and by the subject's beliefs and motivation. Hypnosis is used for pain control, memory improvement, and therapy for psychological problems.

Psychoactive drugs alter mental states. Depressants slow neural activity, relieve tension, impair judgment, and disrupt coordination. Stimulants produce neural arousal, energetic feelings, excitement, alertness, and excessive activity. Opiates are narcotic drugs that create euphoria, drowsiness, and reduced pain sensitivity. Hallucinogens cause hallucinations, mind-alterations, and emotional disruptions. Marijuana contains THC which causes a relaxed mood and mild sensory alterations.

1. **Outline the stages and functions of sleep.** This chapter describes the physiological and psychological changes that occur through the sleep cycle which leads to a better understanding of sleep behavior.
2. **Discuss dream theories and findings of dream research.** This chapter shows how biological and psychological sciences have tried to comprehend the meanings of dreams.
3. **Distinguish among the disorders of sleep and dreaming.** Learning about sleep and dream disorders shows how the physical and mental aspects of sleep and dreaming are intertwined and subject to interference by many factors.
4. **Summarize the characteristics of the hypnotic state.** The hypnotic state of consciousness has several unique features that make the practical applications of hypnosis possible.
5. **Discuss the uses of hypnosis.** This chapter details the flexibility and limits of hypnosis by showing how it is used in psychological applications today.
6. **Identify the major depressant drugs and their effects.** Depressants like alcohol are widely used drugs in society and by learning their effects one can understand their role in individual behavior.
7. **Describe how stimulants influence behavior and consciousness.** Learning about stimulants reveals the interaction between brain arousal and mental activity and illustratess why stimulant addiction is a pressing social problem.
8. **Discuss the opiates and their effects.** Dependence on heroin and other opiates is a major social issue; by studying the opiates one can see why they are so addictive.
9. **Name the major hallucinogens and describe how they alter consciousness.** In this chapter the impact of hallucinogens on consciousness and the dramatic results of their use are discussed.
10. **Summarize the psychological changes caused by marijuana.** The most widely used illegal drug, marijuana, has distinctive consequences that explain its popularity and potential dangers.

Name ______________________ Class ______________ Date ____________

Chapter Outline

Chapter 4 States of Consciousness

Sleep and Dreams

A. The sleep cycle is ______________________

The Stages of Sleep

A. NREM sleep is characterized by ______________________

B. REM sleep is characterized by ______________________

C. During a night's sleep, the sleep cycle changes include ______________________

D. The sleep cycle is influenced by ______________________

Functions of Sleep

A. Sleep deprivation research involves ______________________

B. Research on sleep deprivation shows that ______________________

C. Sleep rebound effects mean ______________________

D. Restoration theory proposes that ______________________

Dreaming

A. Freud's theory of dreams states that ______________________________

____

____

B. Carl Jung proposed that dreams ______________________________

____

____

C. The network model of dreaming states that ______________________________

____

____

D. The activation-synthesis theory states ______________________________

____

____

E. Research shows that dream contents are affected by ______________________________

____

____

Disorders of Sleep and Dreaming

A. Insomnia refers to ______________________________

____

____

B. Insomnia results from ______________________________

____

____

C. Narcolepsy is ______________________________

____

____

D. Nightmares are ______________________________

____

____

E. Sleep terrors and sleepwalking are ______________________________

____

____

Hypnosis

A. Hypnosis refers to ______________________________

____

____

The Hypnotic State

A. Neodissociation theory states that hypnosis ______________________________

____

____

B. Characteristics of hypnotic states include ______________________________

____

____

C. Suggestibility means that ______________________________

____

____

The Uses of Hypnosis

A. Hypnosis has many applications including ______________________________

____

____

Drugs and Consciousness

A. Psychoactive drugs refer to ______________________________

____

____

B. Drug dependence or addiction means ______________________________

____

____

Depressants

A. Depressants are drugs that ______________________________

____

____

B. The major types of depressants are ______________________________

____

____

C. The effects of alcohol include ______________________________

____

____

D. The effects of barbiturates and tranquilizers are ______________________________

____

____

Stimulants

A. Stimulants are drugs that ______________________________

____

____

B. Four stimulant drugs are ______________________________

____

____

C. The effects of cocaine and amphetamines are ______________________________

____

____

Opiates

A. Opiates are ______________________________

____

____

B. The opiates include ______________________________

____

____

C. The effects of opiates include ______________________________

____

____

Hallucinogens

A. Hallucinogens are drugs that ______________________________

____

____

B. Three kinds of hallucinogenic drugs are ______________________________

____

____

Marijuana

A. Marijuana is ____

____

____

B. The effects of marijuana include ____________________________

____

____

Issues and Applications

Meditation

A. Research shows that meditation can

1. Increase ____

2. Decrease ____

Drugs in the Workplace

A. Historically, people in many cultures have used drugs to ______________

____

____

B. The enormous cost of drug use in the workplace is due to ______________

____

____

Biography

Rosalind Cartwright

A. Cartwright's interest in sleep and dream research began when ____________

____

____

B. Cartwright's dream research focuses on ________________________

____

____

Notes

Name ______________________ Class ______________ Date ____________

Key Terms Worksheet

Write a definition for each key term on the lines provided.

Term	Definition
consciousness	________________________________
sleep cycle	________________________________
REM sleep	________________________________
NREM sleep	________________________________
restoration theory	________________________________
wish fulfillment hypothesis	________________________________
network model	________________________________
activation-synthesis theory	________________________________
lucid dream	________________________________
insomnia	________________________________
sleep apnea	________________________________
narcolepsy	________________________________
hypnosis	________________________________

neodissociation theory ______________________________

____

suggestibility ______________________________

____

psychoactive drug ______________________________

____

addiction ______________________________

____

depressant ______________________________

____

alcohol ______________________________

____

sedatives ______________________________

____

stimulants ______________________________

____

opiates ______________________________

____

hallucinogens ______________________________

____

marijuana ______________________________

____

Name ______________________ Class ______________________ Date ______________

Pretest

Chapter 4 States of Consciousness

I. True/False Circle the letter (T or F) that corresponds to the correct response.

T F **1.** NREM sleep involves slow brain wave patterns.

T F **2.** Restoration theory states that sleep enables the brain to store memories for future use.

T F **3.** Freud viewed dreams as wish fulfillments.

T F **4.** Someone who has trouble falling asleep or staying asleep has insomnia.

T F **5.** In hypnosis a person is less open to suggestions.

T F **6.** Hypnosis has been effective in the treatment of some emotional disorders.

T F **7.** Psychoactive drugs change thinking, emotions, and behavior.

T F **8.** Alcohol is classified as a depressant.

T F **9.** The opiates include heroin and morphine.

T F **10.** Marijuana is classified as a stimulant drug.

II. Multiple Choice Circle the letter that corresponds to the correct or best answer.

1. Which of the following is characteristic of REM sleep?

A. alpha waves
B. delta waves
C. sleepwalking
D. irregular fast waves

2. What causes the rebound effects in REM and NREM Stage 4 sleep?

A. insomnia
B. apnea
C. sleep deprivation
D. an impaired immune system

3. What does Hobson and McCarley's activation-synthesis theory state?

A. Dreams reflect unconscious problem-solving activity.
B. Dreams indicate the high brain arousal in REM sleep.
C. Dreams result from the emotional experiences of life.
D. Dreams represent memory storage activity.

4. Which of the following disorders is characterized by sudden "attacks" of REM sleep?

A. sleepwalking
B. insomnia
C. nightmares
D. narcolepsy

5. Which of the following statements describes the neodissociation theory?
   A. Hypnosis is a special kind of sleep state.
   B. Hypnosis is the result of role playing.
   C. Hypnotic suggestibility is a sign of mental illness.
   D. Hypnosis produces a state of divided consciousness.

6. Which statement about the uses of hypnosis is true?
   A. Hypnosis always improves memory for factual information.
   B. Hypnosis can relieve pain by distracting the subject's attention from pain signals.
   C. Hypnosis is a successful cure for most major mental illnesses.
   D. Hypnosis has no practical applications.

7. Which drugs increase neural arousal?
   A. opiates
   B. hallucinogens
   C. stimulants
   D. depressants

8. Drugs that have the features of tolerance and withdrawal are considered:
   A. addictive
   B. stimulants
   C. psychoactive
   D. therapeutic

9. Which of the following is not a common effect of hallucinogens?
   A. hallucinations
   B. suppressed neural arousal
   C. psychedelic mind-alterations
   D. emotional changes

10. Which statement about marijuana is true?
   A. It is highly addictive.
   B. It has sedative effects.
   C. It is classified as a stimulant.
   D. It has no effects on emotions.

III. Short Answer Write the answer in the space provided.

1. What are the features of NREM and REM sleep?

2. Discuss Freud's theory of dreaming.

3. What are the features of the hypnotic state?

4. What are the characteristics of drug addiction?

5. What are the psychological effects of alcohol?

IV. Matching Match the terms in column A with the correct choice in column B.

	A	B
______	**1.** electroencephalograph (EEG)	**a.** a type of stimulant
______	**2.** REM	**b.** irregular fast wave sleep
______	**3.** slow wave sleep	**c.** the plant source of marijuana
______	**4.** rebound effects	**d.** dream in which the dreamer is aware of dreaming
______	**5.** REM sleep	**e.** a state of physical dependence on alcohol
______	**6.** latent content	**f.** an NREM sleep disorder
______	**7.** network model	**g.** narcotic drugs obtained from the poppy plant
______	**8.** lucid dream	**h.** NREM sleep stages
______	**9.** hypersomnia	**i.** an early name for hypnosis
______	**10.** sleep terror	**j.** unconscious hidden meaning of dreams
______	**11.** mesmerism	**k.** a synthetic hallucinogen
______	**12.** trance state	**l.** a hypnotic condition of divided consciousness
______	**13.** hypnotherapy	**m.** treatment of mental problems with hypnosis
______	**14.** tolerance	**n.** consequences of sleep deprivation
______	**15.** blood alcohol level	**o.** adaptation of the body to a drug
______	**16.** alcoholism	**p.** the view that dreams solve emotional problems
______	**17.** amphetamines	**q.** a pattern of excessive sleep
______	**18.** opiates	**r.** the percent of blood that is alcohol
______	**19.** lysergic acid diethylamide (LSD)	**s.** a device to measure brain wave patterns
______	**20.** cannabis	**t.** rapid eye movement

V. Fill In The Blanks Write the answers in the space provided.

1. The ____________________ is defined by the regular mental and physiological changes during sleep. Irregular fast brain waves characterize the stage of ____________________, while ____________________ involves slow brain waves.

2. After subjects are prevented from sleeping in a ____________________ study they often exhibit temporary ____________________ in attention, perception, and memory, as well as increased time in ____________________ and ____________________ sleep the next night.

3. Freud viewed dreams as ____________________, which express a person's ____________________ needs and drives. The remembered dream is its ____________________ content and is considered a ____________________ expression of the dream's hidden or ____________________ content.

4. A delay in the start of sleep or a problem staying asleep is known as ____________________ and usually results from ____________________, but may also be due to drugs like ____________________ or a respiration problem called ____________________.

5. Neodissociation theory views hypnosis as a ____________________ state with divided ____________________, but critics argue that hypnosis is better explained by the subject's motivation to comply with ____________________.

6. Hypnosis can produce a state of reduced sensitivity to pain called ____________________; it sometimes improves ____________________ of eyewitnesses; and it has been used as ____________________ in the treatment of emotional problems.

7. A ____________________ drug usually changes feelings, thoughts, and behavior by interrupting the brain's ____________________. Addictive drugs promote a state of ____________________ as the body adapts to the drug.

8. The depressants are a classification of drugs that include ____________________ and ____________________. They ____________________ brain arousal and are generally addictive.

9. Two powerful stimulant drugs are ____________________ and ____________________. These stimulants excite or arouse the ____________________ and cause an ____________________ in heart rate, breathing rate, and blood pressure.

10. Opium, morphine, codeine, and heroin are ____________________, whose source is the ____________________ plant. They have medical uses for ____________________ and produce a state of pleasure, or ____________________.

Notes

Answer Key To Chapter 4 Pretest

I. True/False

1-T, **2**-F, **3**-T, **4**-T, **5**-F, **6**-T, **7**-T, **8**-T, **9**-T, **10**-F

II. Multiple Choice

1-D, **2**-C, **3**-B, **4**-D, **5**-D, **6**-B, **7**-C, **8**-A, **9**-B, **10**-B

III. Short Answer

1. NREM (non-rapid-eye-movement) sleep involves four stages of slow wave activity, muscle relaxation, and a reduction of heart, respiration and metabolic rates. REM sleep involves irregular fast waves, rapid eye movement, muscle inhibition, and dreaming.
2. Freud's wish fulfillment hypothesis states that dreams express unconscious wishes and needs. The remembered, or manifest, content is a symbolic expression of the hidden meaning, or latent content.
3. The hypnotic state is characterized by an openness to suggestions, focused attention or concentration, distorted sense of time and self, diminished self-consciousness, and nonrational thinking.
4. Addiction is drug dependence involving a physical need for the drug and is indicated by tolerance, or the body's adaptation to the drug, and withdrawal, the unpleasant reactions when drug use stops.
5. Alcohol disrupts most behavior and mental activity, depending on the blood alcohol level. Alcohol impairs reasoning, self-control, learning, memory, emotions, and consciousness.

IV. Matching

1-s, **2**-t, **3**-h, **4**-n, **5**-b, **6**-j, **7**-p, **8**-d, **9**-q, **10**-f, **11**-i, **12**-l, **13**-m, **14**-o, **15**-r, **16**-e, **17**-a, **18**-g, **19**-k, **20**-c

V. Fill In The Blanks

1. sleep cycle - REM sleep - NREM sleep
2. sleep deprivation - impairments - REM - NREM Stage 4
3. wish fulfillments - unconscious - manifest - latent
4. insomnia - stress - caffeine - apnea
5. trance - consciousness - suggestions
6. analgesia - memory - hypnotherapy
7. psychoactive - neurotransmitters - tolerance
8. alcohol - sedatives - suppress
9. cocaine - amphetamines - nervous system - increase
10. opiates - poppy - pain control - euphoria

Suggested Readings

Cartwright, R., and L. Lamberg. 1992. *Crisis dreaming: Using your dreams to solve your problems*. New York: HarperCollins.

This book is an accessible summary of the dream research and theory of Rosalind Cartwright. It takes a self-help approach to explaining the importance of dreams and gives numerous case examples to illustrate its ideas. Separate chapters deal with specific problems, including divorce, health problems, stress, and others.

Dowd, E. T., and J. M. Healy. 1986. *Case studies in hypnotherapy*. New York: Guilford.

Summarizing numerous case applications of hypnosis in the treatment of various emotional and behavioral problems, this book provides an excellent overview of modern hypnotherapy and gives the reader an appreciation of the subtle ways in which clinical hypnosis is used.

Frances, R. J., and S. I. Miller. (eds.) 1991. *Clinical textbook of addictive disorders*. New York: Guilford.

A collection of articles written by experts in the field of drug addiction. The articles have a technical edge and present superb summaries of the physical and psychological effects of the major addictive drugs.

Freud, S. 1900. *The interpretation of dreams*. London: Hogarth.

Freud's classic work on the meaning of dreams is still an all-time great nearly a century later. His case examples and interpretations are compelling and fascinating, and he articulates his dream theory with great care.

Hartmann, E. 1984. *The nightmare*. New York: Basic Books.

This compact book presents a summary of Hartmann's studies of people who suffer from chronic nightmares and offers a psychological theory of the nightmare which ties this phenomenon to personality characteristics.

Hobson, J. A. 1989. *Sleep*. New York: Scientific American Library.

An interesting introduction to research and theories on sleep. Written by a leading figure in the field, this book integrates animal and human studies and discusses both the biology and psychology of sleep, dreams, and sleep disorders.

Lynn, S. J., and J. W. Rhue. (eds.) 1991. *Theories of hypnosis: Current models and perspectives*. New York: Guilford.

In this award-winning book, leading figures in the field of hypnosis research and hypnotherapy present the major theoretical views of hypnosis. Although quite technical in sections, the motivated reader will find this a valuable guide to the contemporary state of thinking about hypnosis.

Ray, O., and C. Ksir. 1987. *Drugs, society, and human behavior*. St. Louis: Mosby.

This book is a clear and interesting introduction to psychoactive drugs, their history, and their impact on the individual. The authors look at drug use as a behavioral and social phenomenon.

Chapter 5

Learning

Chapter Summary

Learning is defined as a change in behavior as a result of experience. Classical conditioning is a type of learning in which a new stimulus comes to produce a reflexive response by its association with another stimulus that naturally triggers the reflex. The principles of classical conditioning have been applied to explain a variety of behaviors, including phobias, taste aversions, and drug abuse. These principles also form the basis of therapies designed to eliminate undesirable behaviors.

In operant conditioning, operants, responses that operate on the environment, are strengthened or weakened by their consequences. The principles of operant conditioning have been used to explain numerous aspects of learning, including infant memory, language and perceptual development, and personality, as well as child-rearing, workplace performance, and the treatment of abnormal behavior.

Cognitive learning is concerned with unobservable mental activity like paying attention, perceiving, thinking, and remembering. Examples of cognitive learning include insight learning and latent learning. Another type, observational learning, has been used to explain sex-role behaviors, family violence, and attitudes, as well as abnormal behavior and its treatment.

1. **Outline and describe the elements of classical conditioning.** Classical conditioning is a type of learning important in the history of psychology because it was the first kind of learning that was systematically studied. It has been used to explain many types of behavior and is the basis for certain treatments of abnormal behavior.
2. **Explain the principles of extinction, spontaneous recovery, generalization, discrimination, and higher-order conditioning in classical conditioning.** Because many psychologists believe that much of human behavior is the result of learning, they have sought to investigate the basic principles of different types of learning, such as classical conditioning. Many of the principles of classical conditioning are also fundamental to other types of learning.
3. **Provide two applications of classical conditioning to human behavior.** Psychologists are not only interested in understanding learning principles but are also concerned with how they can be applied to explain and modify behavior.
4. **Define the role of positive and negative reinforcers and punishment in operant conditioning.** Reinforcement and punishment are fundamental principles of operant conditioning because they act as consequences, responsible for strengthening or weakening behavior.
5. **Describe the different schedules of partial reinforcement.** The modification of behavior has always been a major goal of psychologists, like B. F. Skinner, who study operant conditioning. Accordingly, schedules of partial reinforcement represent different ways to accomplish behavior modification.
6. **Discuss the application of operant conditioning principles to human behavior.** More so than any other theory in psychology, operant theory and its principles have been applied to the understanding and modification of human behavior. For this reason, understanding the application of operant conditioning principles to human behavior not only provides insight into behavior but can also help form the basis of a more satisfying and successful life.
7. **Define cognitive learning and explain how it differs from classical and operant conditioning.** Unlike both classical and operant conditioning, cognitive learning emphasizes the role of unobservable mental activity in learning. Understanding cognitive learning not only acquaints one with a major theoretical force in psychology, but also provides a practical basis for altering cognitions and improving one's life.
8. **Discuss how Köhler's work on insight learning and Tolman's latent learning experiments provide evidence of cognitive learning.** Under the influence of classical and operant conditioning, human behavior was viewed as largely under the control of external forces. The work of Köhler and Tolman indicated that mental activities play a major role in behavior.
9. **Discuss Bandura's observational learning experiments and identify the principles of observational learning.** Bandura's observational learning experiments provided evidence of the influence of cognitive factors in human learning. The principles derived from his research have proven important in understanding many aspects of human behavior.
10. **Describe applications of observational learning in life and work.** Psychological principles, like those of observational learning, are important to learn because they can be used to explain everyday behavior. Observational learning has been applied to many aspects of behavior, such as personality development, the treatment of abnormal behavior, and management training.

Name ______________________ Class ______________ Date ____________

Chapter Outline

Chapter 5 Learning

Classical Conditioning

A. Classical conditioning is ______________________________

____

____

B. In classical conditioning, reflexive responses occur ______________________________

____

____

C. The fact that a person can be frightened by a horror movie shows that ______

____

____

Pavlov's Experiments

A. After presenting the meat many times, ______________________________

____

____

B. After repeated pairings of the tone and the meat, the dog ______________

____

____

Principles of Classical Conditioning

A. The unconditioned stimulus is defined as ______________________________

____

____

B. An unconditioned response is ______________________________

____

____

C. The conditioned stimulus comes to elicit a reflex by ______________

____

____

D. A conditioned response is ______________________________

____

____

E. In acquisition, the conditioned response becomes stronger through ________

____

____

F. Extinction refers to ________

____

____

G. In spontaneous recovery, the extinguished response ________

____

____

H. The principle of stimulus generalization states that ________

____

____

I. Stimulus discrimination occurs when ________

____

____

J. Higher-order conditioning is ________

____

____

Applications of Classical Conditioning

A. Watson evoked fear in Little Albert by ________

____

____

B. Little Albert demonstrated a conditioned emotional response by ________

____

____

C. One would exhibit a conditioned taste aversion if one learns to associate ____

____

____

D. The thought, sight, or smell of food can act as ________

____

____

E. Certain stimuli that drug abusers associate with using a drug can ______________

____

____

F. If one were being treated for a phobia one would probably be ______________

____

____

Current Views of Classical Conditioning

A. According to contingency theory, ______________

____

____

B. The blocking effect shows that ______________

____

____

Operant Conditioning

A. Operant conditioning is ______________

____

____

B. Instrumental conditioning is ______________

____

____

C. According to the law of effect, ______________

____

____

Skinner's Operant Theory

A. Three assumptions of operant theory are:

1. ____

2. ____

3. ____

B. The Skinner box is ______________

____

____

C. A reinforcer is ______________________________

____

____

D. Two types of reinforcers are:

1. ______________________________

2. ______________________________

E. A primary reinforcer is one that ______________________________

____

A secondary reinforcer is ______________________________

____

F. One problem with delayed reinforcement is that ______________________________

____

____

G. A punisher is ______________________________

____

____

H. Four rules for the appropriate use of punishment are:

1. ______________________________

2. ______________________________

3. ______________________________

4. ______________________________

Principles of Operant Conditioning

A. Shaping is ______________________________

____

____

B. Operant extinction is defined as ______________________________

____

____

C. A discriminative stimulus is ______________________________

____

____

D. A continuous reinforcement schedule is ______________________________

____

____

E. On a partial reinforcement schedule ______________________________

____

____

F. Four types of partial reinforcement schedules are:

1. ______________________________

2. ______________________________

3. ______________________________

4. ______________________________

Applications of Operant Conditioning

A. In behavior modification, ______________________________

____

____

B. With computer-assisted instruction, ______________________________

____

____

C. Skinner viewed Walden Two as ______________________________

____

____

D. The goal of the Juniper Gardens Children's Project is ______________________________

____

____

Cognitive Learning

A. Cognitive learning is concerned with ______________________________

____

____

Insight Learning

A. According to Köhler, Sultan solved the problem through ____________________

____

and he labeled this activity ____________________

____

Latent Learning

A. In Tolman's latent learning experiments, nonrewarded rats learned as much as rewarded rats, but ____________________

____

____

B. Two reasons why Tolman's latent learning experiments were important to psychology are:

1. ____________________

2. ____________________

C. Cognitive maps are ____________________

____

____

Social Learning Theory

A. Social learning theory emphasizes ____________________

____

____

B. For social learning theorists, much of what is learned comes ____________________

____

____

C. A model is ____________________

____

____

D. Observational learning requires ____________________

____

____

E. Four steps in observational learning are:

1. ______________________________
2. ______________________________
3. ______________________________
4. ______________________________

F. The results of Bandura's "Bobo studies" showed that ______________

____

____

G. Four variables that influence the relationship between observation and performance are:

1. ______________________________
2. ______________________________
3. ______________________________
4. ______________________________

H. The use of modeling techniques in business and industry help build ________

____

____

Issues and Applications

Operant Conditioning in the Workplace

A. Five factors associated with improved worker satisfaction and motivation, according to a study of 1500 American workers, are:

1. ______________________________
2. ______________________________
3. ______________________________
4. ______________________________
5. ______________________________

B. Reinforcement in the workplace should be delivered ______________

____

____

Issues and Applications **The Effects of the Media on Children's Behavior**

A. The relationship between media violence and behavior is not simple because ____

____

Biography **B. F. Skinner**

A. Though Skinner was accused of raising his daughter in a cage, like an animal, the baby tender was actually ____

____

____

Name ______________________ Class ________________ Date ____________

Key Terms Worksheet

Write a definition for each key term on the lines provided.

Term	Definition
learning	______________________________
classical conditioning	______________________________
unconditioned stimulus	______________________________
unconditioned response	______________________________
conditioned stimulus	______________________________
conditioned response	______________________________
acquisition	______________________________
extinction	______________________________
spontaneous recovery	______________________________
stimulus generalization	______________________________
stimulus discrimination	______________________________
higher-order conditioning	______________________________
operant conditioning	______________________________

instrumental conditioning ______

law of effect ______

operant theory ______

reinforcer ______

positive reinforcer ______

negative reinforcer ______

punisher ______

shaping ______

continuous reinforcement schedule ______

partial reinforcement schedule ______

cognitive learning ______

insight learning ______

latent learning ______

social learning theory ______

observational learning ______

Name ______________________ Class ____________________ Date ______________

Pretest

Chapter 5 Learning

I. True/False Circle the letter (T or F) that corresponds to the correct response.

T F **1.** In Pavlov's experiment the tone was the unconditioned stimulus.

T F **2.** A response to stimuli similar to the original shows higher-order conditioning.

T F **3.** Little Albert's fear of the white rat illustrates a conditioned emotional response.

T F **4.** The law of effect states that responses followed by satisfying consequences are strengthened and those followed by unsatisfying effects are weakened.

T F **5.** Both positive and negative reinforcement increase the chances that a response will occur.

T F **6.** Food is an example of a secondary reinforcer.

T F **7.** Köhler's research showed that chimpanzees solved problems by insight.

T F **8.** Latent learning studies reveal that performance does not always provide an accurate measure of learning.

T F **9.** Cognitive learning emphasizes the role of unobservable mental activity.

T F **10.** The research on media violence indicates that the observation of violence alone may not be sufficient to explain aggressive behavior.

II. Multiple Choice Circle the letter that corresponds to the correct or best answer.

1. In Pavlov's experiments the food was the:

A. unconditioned response

B. conditioned response

C. conditioned stimulus

D. unconditioned stimulus

2. The reappearance of a conditioned response after extinction is known as:

A. stimulus discrimination

B. spontaneous recovery

C. higher-order conditioning

D. acquisition

3. ____________________ theory says that the important element in classical conditioning is the information that the CS provides to subjects.

A. Operant

B. Social learning

C. Insight

D. Contingency

4. Billy gets candy each time he puts his toys away. After two weeks, his parents notice that he puts his toys away more regularly. In this example, the candy acts as an __________________.

   A. positive reinforcer

   B. negative reinforcer

   C. reward

   D. unconditioned stimulus

5. Encouraging a child to speak illustrates:

   A. shaping

   B. stimulus discrimination

   C. the law of instrumental conditioning

   D. observational learning

6. Barbara's job pays once a month. She is paid on a __________________ schedule.

   A. fixed interval

   B. variable ratio

   C. fixed ratio

   D. variable interval

7. The type of learning that emphasizes the role of unobservable mental activity is called:

   A. operant conditioning

   B. cognitive learning

   C. instrumental conditioning

   D. classical conditioning

8. Which of the following is NOT a conclusion drawn from Tolman's latent learning experiments?

   A. Learning depends on positive reinforcement.

   B. Learning is possible in the absence of reward.

   C. People use cognitive processes to solve problems.

   D. Performance may not accurately reflect learning.

9. Which of the following is a critical factor in observational learning?

   A. attention

   B. direct reinforcement

   C. insight

   D. higher-order conditioning

10. The major finding of Bandura's "Bobo" studies was:

   A. children learned aggression through observation

   B. only boys were likely to behave aggressively

   C. children learned aggression through insight

   D. only girls behaved aggressively

III. Short Answer Write the answer in the space provided.

1. Why is performance not a precise measure of learning?

2. How does classical conditioning explain phobias?

3. Distinguish between positive and negative reinforcement.

4. How did Köhler's experiments with chimpanzees demonstrate cognitive processes in learning?

5. What is the relationship between the observation of media violence and aggression?

IV. Matching Match the term in column A with the correct choice in column B.

A

_____ **1.** classical conditioning

_____ **2.** unconditioned stimulus

_____ **3.** conditioned stimulus

_____ **4.** conditioned response

_____ **5.** operant extinction

_____ **6.** stimulus generalization

_____ **7.** operant conditioning

_____ **8.** law of effect

_____ **9.** positive reinforcer

_____ **10.** negative reinforcer

_____ **11.** primary reinforcer

_____ **12.** punisher

_____ **13.** shaping

_____ **14.** continuous reinforcement schedule

_____ **15.** fixed interval schedule

_____ **16.** cognitive learning

_____ **17.** insight learning

_____ **18.** latent learning

_____ **19.** social learning theory

_____ **20.** observational learning

B

a. a stimulus that decreases the chance that a response will occur

b. a type of learning that involves reflexive responses

c. a stimulus that naturally elicits a reflexive response

d. rewarding successive approximations to the correct response

e. learning that involves perceptual interpretations

f. the gradual disappearance of an emitted behavior

g. learning through vicarious experience

h. emphasizes unobservable mental activity in learning

i. a previously neutral stimulus that is associated with the unconditioned stimulus

j. a reflexive response to a previously neutral stimulus

k. Thorndike's rule in instrumental conditioning

l. reinforcement after a specified time period has elapsed

m. Skinner's version of instrumental conditioning

n. responding to stimuli that are similar to the one used in training

o. a stimulus which when avoided, increases the probability that a response will occur

p. reinforcement for each correct response

q. a stimulus that satisfies a biological need

r. learning not evidenced until an incentive is provided

s. a stimulus, which when added, increases the probability of a response

t. emphasizes cognitive and environmental factors in learning

V. Fill In The Blanks Write the answers in the space provided.

1. In Pavlov's experiments, the food is the ____________________ stimulus and the tone is the ____________________ stimulus.

2. Stimuli that increase the probability of a response are known as ____________________; those that decrease the probability of a response are called ____________________.

3. ____________________ deliver reinforcement for the first correct response after a specified time period has elapsed, while ____________________ give reinforcement after a specified number of responses.

4. Giving tokens to reinforce desired behavior illustrates ____________________ in operant conditioning.

5. The reinforcement of successive approximations to the correct response is called ____________________.

6. According to Skinner, the main goals of psychology are the ____________________ and ____________________ of behavior.

7. A type of learning concerned with unobservable mental activity such as paying attention, perceiving, thinking, and remembering is known as ____________________.

8. Learning through perceptual interpretations is called ____________________.

9. According to Tolman, a ____________________ is a mental image or memory of the maze.

10. The approach to learning that emphasizes the interaction of cognitive and environmental factors is called ____________________.

Notes

Answer Key To Chapter 5 Pretest

I. True/False

1-F, **2**-F, **3**-T, **4**-T, **5**-T, **6**-F, **7**-T, **8**-T, **9**-T, **10**-T

II. Multiple Choice

1-D, **2**-B, **3**-D, **4**-A, **5**-A, **6**-A, **7**-B, **8**-A, **9**-A, **10**-A

III. Short Answer:

1. Performance is not always an accurate measure of learning because an individual may not show what was learned due to a lack of incentive, poor motivation, fatigue, or other factors.
2. According to classical conditioning, phobias are learned by associating a previously neutral stimulus with one that naturally evoke fear.
3. Positive reinforcement increases the probability that a response will occur by adding something. Negative reinforcement increases the probability by removing something.
4. Chimpanzees were unable to learn the solution to the problem by trial-and-error learning and reinforcement. Instead, the solution came from perceptual interpretations.
5. In general, the observation of media violence is related to increased violence on the part of the viewer. However, the age and sex of the observer and whether the model was punished are also important factors.

IV. Matching

1-b, **2**-c, **3**-i, **4**-j, **5**-f, **6**-n, **7**-m, **8**-k, **9**-s, **10**-o, **11**-q, **12**-a, **13**-d, **14**-p, **15**-l, **16**-h, **17**-e, **18**-r, **19**-t, **20**-g

V. Fill In The Blanks

1. unconditioned - conditioned
2. reinforcers - punishers
3. Interval schedules - ratio schedules
4. behavior modification
5. shaping
6. prediction - control
7. cognitive learning
8. insight learning
9. cognitive map
10. social learning theory

Suggested Readings

Bandura, A., and R. H. Walter. 1963. *Social learning and personal development.* New York: Holt, Rinehart and Winston.

The authors explain the early research in social learning theory and its applications to human behavior.

Bandura, A., S. A. Ross., and S. Ross. "Imitation of film-mediated aggressive models." *Journal of Abnormal and Social Psychology* 66 (1963): 3-11.

This is Bandura's classic study of children's imitation of aggressive models.

Fishman, S. 1993. "The town B. F. Skinner boxed." In K. G. Duffy (ed.) *Annual Editions: Psychology*. Guilford, CT: Dushkin.

This article provides a description of how Skinner's operant theory has been applied to a real-life society.

Rachlin, H. 1992. *Introduction to modern behaviorism, 3rd Ed.* New York: Freeman.

This book summarizes and describes the status of learning theory today.

Skinner, B. F. 1948. *Walden Two*. New York: Macmillan

An insight into Skinner's ideas and his utopian society.

Skinner, B. F. 1972. *Beyond freedom and dignity*. New York: Knopf.

Skinner, B. F. 1974. *About behaviorism.* New York: Knopf.

Provides an excellent look at Skinner's view of psychology.

Watson, J. B., and R. Raynor. "Conditioned emotional reactions." *Journal of Experimental Psychology* 3 (1920): 1-14.

Chapter 6

Memory

Chapter Summary

Memory depends on encoding, storage, and retrieval processes and is measured by tests of recall, recognition, and relearning. The information processing model describes three stages of memory—sensory, short-term, and long-term.

Sensory memory is a brief, preconscious memory. Short-term memory (STM) is an active, conscious stage involving attention with limited capacity and duration. Maintenance and elaborative rehearsal and mnemonics are STM storage processes. Long-term memory (LTM) is composed of declarative memory, including semantic and episodic memory, procedural memory, and implicit memory. LTM processes are affected by depth-of-processing, reconstruction, personal schemata, contextual cues, and the subject's state of mind.

Forgetting is explained by decay theory, proactive and retroactive interference, retrieval failures, physical factors, and motivated forgetting (repression).

Memory involves many brain structures, including the hippocampus, temporal and frontal lobes of the cortex, and the cerebellum. In consolidation hypothesis, neural circuits in the brain control memory. Also, neural connections, neurotransmitters, and hormones play a role in memory.

Chapter Objectives

1. **Describe the memory processes of encoding, storage, and retrieval.** These processes are the basis for all the features of memory.
2. **Summarize recall, recognition, and relearning tests of memory.** Learning how researchers test and measure memory illustrates the basic methods that are utilized in modern studies.
3. **Describe the information processing model of memory.** Since this model is the standard for most memory theory and research, it is the framework for the chapter.
4. **Discuss the characteristics of sensory memory.** Sensory memory is the first stage of memory and thus sets the foundation for later storage of information.
5. **Explain the features and processes of short-term memory.** Short-term, or working, memory is the conscious part of memory. Studying the principles of STM can help improve the use of memory ability.
6. **Outline the organization of long-term memory.** Studying LTM organization helps develop an understanding of the structure of knowledge and how to use it more effectively.
7. **Explain the processes of long-term memory.** Understanding the manner in which LTM works leads to knowledge about the many factors that influence retrieval and strategies for improving memory.
8. **Distinguish among decay, interference, retrieval errors, and motivated forgetting.** Forgetting is an ongoing feature of memory and by recognizing the several mechanisms of forgetting one can understand how to reduce this problem.
9. **Discuss the biological bases of memory.** Because brain activity is the bottom line to memory, knowing the biological basis of memory produces an appreciation of the subtleties of this amazing system.

Name ______________________ Class ______________ Date ____________

Chapter Outline

Chapter 6 Memory

An Overview of Memory

A. Psychologists use the term memory to mean ______________________

____

____

B. Memory is characterized by three processes:

1. ______________________
2. ______________________
3. ______________________

How Memory Is Measured

A. Ebbinghaus studied memory by ______________________

____

____

B. Memory researchers rely on three methods:

1. ______________________
2. ______________________
3. ______________________

The Information Processing Model of Memory

A. The information processing model assumes ______________________

____

____

Sensory Memory

A. Sensory memory is defined as ______________________

____

____

Iconic Memory

A. Iconic memory is ______________________

____

____

B. Sperling's partial report method was ______________________

____

The Sensory Registers

A. The sensory registers are ______________________________

____

____

B. Echoic memory refers to ______________________________

____

____

Short-Term Memory

A. Short-term memory refers to ______________________________

____

____

Attention

A. Selective attention means ______________________________

____

____

B. Two models of selective attention are:

1. ______________________________

2. ______________________________

The Features of Short Term Memory

A. The features of short-term memory are ______________________________

____

____

B. A distractor task is used to ______________________________

____

____

C. The Peterson and Peterson study found that ______________________________

____

____

D. The capacity of STM depends on ______________________________

____

____

Short-Term Memory Processes

A. Maintenance rehearsal means ______________________________

____

____

B. Elaborative rehearsal means ______________________________

____

____

C. A mnemonic is ______________________________

____

____

Long-Term Memory

A. Long-term memory refers to ______________________________

____

____

Organization of Long-Term Memory

A. There are four aspects of long-term memory:

1. ______________________________

2. ______________________________

3. ______________________________

4. ______________________________

B. Flashbulb memories refer to ______________________________

____

____

C. The priming effect shows ______________________________

____

____

Long-Term Memory Processes

A. According to the depth-of-processing model, long-term memory is ________

____

____

B. Bartlett's studies of reconstructive memory show that ________________

____

C. Two types of cue-dependent memory are:

1. ________________________________

2. ________________________________

Forgetting

A. The term forgetting means ________________________________

____

____

Decay

A. Decay theory explains forgetting as ________________________________

____

____

B. Eidetic imagery refers to ________________________________

____

____

Interference

A. Interference theory explains forgetting as the result of ________________________________

____

____

B. The two kinds of interference are:

1. ________________________________

2. ________________________________

C. Interference is affected by ________________________________

____

____

Retrieval Failure

A. Retrieval failure means that ________________________________

____

____

B. The tip-of-the-tongue phenomenon is ________________________________

____

____

C. Retrieval failure is influenced by ______________________________

____

Motivated Forgetting

A. Motivated forgetting refers to ______________________________

____

____

B. The defense mechanism of repression is ______________________________

____

____

The Biological Basis of Memory

A. Biogenic amnesia means ______________________________

____

____

How Memory Is Stored in the Brain

A. The engram is ______________________________

____

____

B. Four brain structures are especially important in memory:

1. ______________________________
2. ______________________________
3. ______________________________
4. ______________________________

Neural Mechanisms in Memory

A. The consolidation hypothesis is ______________________________

____

____

B. Brain changes in memory include ______________________________

____

____

C. The biochemistry of memory involves ______________________________

____

____

Issues and Applications

Improving Your Study Skills

A. The five steps of the SQ3R method are:

1. ____________________

2. ____________________

3. ____________________

4. ____________________

5. ____________________

B. Distributed practice means ____________________

____

____

C. Overlearning means ____________________

____

____

Eyewitness Memory

A. Studies find that the accuracy of an eyewitness memory depends on ________

____

____

Biography

Elizabeth Loftus

A. Elizabeth Loftus is best known for her studies of ____________________

____

____

Name ______________________ Class ______________ Date ____________

Key Terms Worksheet

Write a definition for each key term on the lines provided.

Term	Definition
memory	
information processing model	
sensory memory	
iconic memory	
short-term memory	
selective attention	
chunking	
maintenance rehearsal	
elaborative rehearsal	
mnemonic	
long-term memory	
semantic memory	
episodic memory	

procedural memory ______________________________

____

implicit memory ______________________________

____

depth-of-processing model ______________________________

____

reconstructive memory ______________________________

____

cue-dependent memory ______________________________

____

forgetting ______________________________

____

decay theory ______________________________

____

interference theory ______________________________

____

motivated forgetting ______________________________

____

engram ______________________________

____

consolidation hypothesis ______________________________

____

Name _______________ Class _______________ Date _______________

Pretest

Chapter 6 Memory

I. True/False Circle the letter (T or F) that corresponds to the correct response.

T F **1.** According to the information processing model, there are three stages of memory.

T F **2.** Iconic memory is sensory memory for hearing.

T F **3.** Short-term memory has a capacity of about seven items of information.

T F **4.** Elaborative rehearsal involves associating new information with familiar memories.

T F **5.** Personal, autobiographical facts are stored in procedural memory.

T F **6.** Implicit memory is the part of long-term memory in which information is consciously processed.

T F **7.** According to decay theory, forgetting is due to a weakening of unused memories over time.

T F **8.** Proactive interference occurs when new or recent memories inhibit older memories.

T F **9.** Freud explained motivated forgetting as the result of repression.

T F **10.** Several brain structures contribute to the storage and retrieval of memories.

II. Multiple Choice Circle the letter that corresponds to the correct or best answer.

1. Which of the following is an example of the recognition method of measuring memory?

A. essay exam
B. rehearsal test
C. multiple choice test
D. fill-in-the-blanks exam

2. Which method is best suited to studying sensory memory?

A. distractor task
B. decay test
C. recall test
D. partial report study

3. The role of meaning in selective attention is shown by:

A. the cocktail party phenomenon
B. the deja vu phenomenon
C. the tip-of-the-tongue phenomenon
D. the magic number seven phenomenon

4. What is the average duration of short-term memory?
   A. 1 to 5 seconds
   B. 10 to 15 seconds
   C. 20 to 30 seconds
   D. 50 to 60 seconds
5. Which information is contained in semantic memory?
   A. personal, autobiographical facts
   B. impersonal, verbal facts
   C. learned behaviors and conditioned responses
   D. unconsciously acquired skills and ideas
6. Which of these is an example of flashbulb memory?
   A. Kim vividly remembers the day she won the lottery.
   B. Lee can recall the name of every U.S. president.
   C. Dawn has memorized over 100 songs for her guitar.
   D. Roger exhibits a conditioned fear response to bugs.
7. Retrieval is influenced by the context in which it occurs and the state of the person. This statement describes the principle of:
   A. reconstructive memory
   B. implicit memory
   C. cue-dependent memory
   D. associative memory
8. What theory states that long-term memories depend on how well the information is initially encoded?
   A. repression theory
   B. interference theory
   C. depth-of-processing model
   D. filter model
9. Test-taking fear is likely to promote forgetting due to:
   A. proactive interference
   B. retrieval failure
   C. decay
   D. biogenic amnesia
10. Which hypothesis claims that the physical basis of memory is found in reverberating neural circuits?
    A. schemata hypothesis
    B. reconstruction hypothesis
    C. depth-of-processing hypothesis
    D. consolidation hypothesis

III. Short Answer Write the answer in the space provided.

1. What is sensory memory?

2. Discuss the duration and capacity of short-term memory.

3. What are the major aspects of long-term memory.

4. What is motivated forgetting?

5. Discuss the consolidation hypothesis.

IV. Matching Match the terms in column A with the correct choice in column B.

A

_____ **1.** encoding
_____ **2.** relearning test
_____ **3.** sensory registers
_____ **4.** working memory
_____ **5.** filter model
_____ **6.** distractor task
_____ **7.** maintenance rehearsal
_____ **8.** semantic memory
_____ **9.** episodic memory
_____ **10.** priming effect
_____ **11.** context-dependent memory
_____ **12.** flashbulb memory
_____ **13.** eidetic imagery
_____ **14.** proactive interference
_____ **15.** retroactive interference
_____ **16.** repression
_____ **17.** biogenic amnesia
_____ **18.** state-dependent memory
_____ **19.** engram
_____ **20.** mnemonic

B

a. evidence for implicit memory
b. memory measurement also known as the savings method
c. a strategy to reorganize information for better recall
d. independent, sense-specific mechanisms of sensory memory
e. short-term memory
f. memory influenced by associations to situational cues
g. method to stop rehearsal
h. vivid memory of an emotional experience
i. memory process for acquiring information
j. memory influenced by the subject's emotional state
k. older memories interfere with newer memories
l. personal, autobiographical memory
m. a defense mechanism behind motivated forgetting
n. memory loss due to biological factors
o. a theory of selective attention
p. newer memories interfere with older memories
q. photographic memory
r. memory for factual verbal information
s. memorization by repetition
t. the physical memory trace in the brain

V. Fill In The Blanks Write the answers in the space provided.

1. Memories are acquired by ____________________ processes that rely on ways of representing information called ____________________. Once established, memories are retained over time by ____________________ processes and access to them is gained by ____________________ processes.

2. George Sperling studied ____________________ memory by using a ____________________ method and found its duration to be about ____________________. In hearing the sensory register is called ____________________ memory.

3. Short-term memory is also known as ____________________ memory. The capacity of short-term memory is about ____________________ items, or chunks. Its duration is about ____________________ seconds, depending on whether or not ____________________ occurs.

4. When a new definition is memorized by repeating it over and over one is performing ____________________, but when one tries to associate the new definition with other concepts which are already familiar one is performing ____________________. Both of these activities are considered ____________________ processes.

5. Long-term memory stores impersonal verbal facts in ____________________ memory and personal, autobiographical facts in ____________________ memory. Skills and habits make up ____________________ memory, while memories learned with little conscious effort are found in ____________________ memory.

6. Bartlett's research on ____________________ memory showed that subjects often distort their recollections according to their personal beliefs, or ____________________. In remembering events, subjects also rely on familiar patterns of events stored as ____________________.

7. Forgetting results from the weakening of unused memories over time according to ____________________ theory. Such forgetting is apparent in both ____________________ memory and ____________________ memory, but the evidence of its effects on ____________________ memory is less certain.

8. When older memories interfere with newer memories, ____________________ interference is at work, but when newer memories interfere with older memories, ____________________ interference is to blame. Both types of interference are influenced by the ____________________ and ____________________ of the memories.

9. Emotionally disturbing experiences are at the root of _______________ forgetting. _______________ believed that the defense mechanism of _______________ blocked unpleasant memories from consciousness.

10. Hebb's _______________ hypothesis proposed that memories are grounded in reverberating _______________. Studies of the biological basis of memory have found evidence that learning experiences can cause _______________ changes in the brain and that several _______________ influence learning and memory.

Answer Key To Chapter 6 Pretest

I. True//False

1-T, **2**-F, **3**-T, **4**-T, **5**-F, **6**-F, **7**-T, **8**-F, **9**-T, **10**-T

II. Multiple Choice

1-C, **2**-D, **3**-A, **4**-C, **5**-B, **6**-A, **7**-C, **8**-C, **9**-B, **10**-D

III. Short Answer

1. Sensory memory is a very brief, high capacity memory for raw sensory information contained in independent sense-specific mechanisms called the sensory registers such as iconic memory in vision and echoic memory in hearing.
2. The duration of short-term memory is about 20 to 30 seconds unless rehearsal takes place. The capacity of short-term memory is approximately 7±2 items, or chunks, depending on the way the information is organized.
3. Semantic memory involves impersonal verbal facts; episodic memory contains personal, autobiographical facts; procedural memory is learned skills, habits, and conditioned responses; and implicit memory is learned and retrieved without conscious effort.
4. Motivated forgetting refers to forgetting due to emotionally disturbing experiences and is explained by the defense mechanism of repression which blocks memories out of conscious awareness to avoid distress.
5. According to the consolidation hypothesis, memories are established in the brain by reverberating neural circuits that are strengthened by the repetition of a stimulus or experience.

IV. Matching

1-i, **2**-b, **3**-d, **4**-e, **5**-o, **6**-g, **7**-s, **8**-r, **9**-l, **10**-a, **11**-f, **12**-h, **13**-q, **14**-k, **15**-p, **16**-m, **17**-n, **18**-j, **19**-t, **20**-c

V. Fill In The Blanks

1. encoding - memory codes - storage - retrieval
2. iconic - partial report - one-quarter second - echoic
3. working - 7±2 - 20 to 30 - rehearsal
4. maintenance rehearsal - elaborative rehearsal - short-term memory
5. semantic - episodic - procedural - implicit
6. reconstructive - schemata - memory scripts
7. decay - sensory - short-term - long-term
8. proactive - retroactive - similarity - timing
9. motivated - Freud - repression
10. consolidation - neural circuits - structural - neurotransmitters

Suggested Readings

Baddeley, A. 1982. *Your memory: A user's guide*. New York: Macmillan.

This book by a leading British memory researcher is a lively and reader-friendly introduction to human memory and forgetting. The illustrations and memory exercises are well done and the practical tips for improving memory are clear and helpful.

Higbee, K. L. 1977. *Your memory: How it works and how to improve it.* Englewood Cliffs, NJ: Prentice Hall.

Written by a research psychologist, this compact book presents a brief introduction to human memory followed by a discussion of the fundamental principles of memory improvement and effective learning. The chapters on mnemonics are a valuable resource for anyone serious about developing a better memory.

Johnson, G. 1991. *In the palaces of memory*. New York: Knopf.

Authored by a professional science writer and editor, this book tells the story of the dedicated researchers who are looking for the basis of memory in the brain. It highlights the insights of these investigators as well as the technical, theoretical, and philosophical problems that they face.

Loftus, E. F., and K. Ketcham. 1991. *Witness for the defense*. New York: St. Martin's Press.

This book provides fascinating accounts of several legal cases in which psychologist Elizabeth Loftus has served as expert witness to testify about the limits of eyewitness testimony. The presentation is lively and the material often dramatic The authors deliver a compelling case against the uncritical acceptance of eyewitness memories.

Solso, R. L. 1991. *Cognitive psychology, 3rd ed.* Boston: Allyn & Bacon.

This introductory textbook gives an excellent summary of research and theories on memory and forgetting, as well as other aspects of cognitive psychology. Although not an "easy read," the interested student will obtain a good overview of the field.

Chapter 7

Thinking, Language, and Intelligence

Chapter Summary

Thinking is a way of mentally representing information. We think in images and organize information in concepts. Thinking applied to problem solving is a four step process of preparation, production, incubation, and evaluation. Potential barriers to problem solving include mental set and functional fixedness.

As an expression of thinking, language is an important higher mental function. The structure of language consists of phonemes, morphemes, syntax, and semantics. The rules by which language elements are organized into meaningful expressions of thought is called grammar.

Definitions of intelligence emphasize the capacity to learn, solve problems, adapt, and act purposefully. Factor theories of intelligence emphasize inborn components of intelligence. The theory of multiple intelligences proposes seven distinct types of intelligence while triarchic theory stresses three interacting types of intelligence.

Useful intelligence tests like the Stanford-Binet and Wechsler scales are standardized and strive for reliability and validity. The criticisms of IQ tests are that they do not tap everyday problem solving abilities and are culturally and racially biased. The gifted and mentally retarded represent people at the extremes of intelligence. Many studies indicate that intelligence is influenced by both hereditary and environmental influences.

1. **Define thinking and show how it is related to the images and concepts.** As an important higher mental process, thinking is involved in memory, language comprehension, reasoning, problem solving, and intelligence. Thoughts are composed of images and thinking is organized into categories of information called concepts.
2. **Identify the four steps in problem solving.** A person faces many problems in everyday life. Research shows that the best way to solve a problem is to follow a sequence of steps that includes preparation, production, incubation, and evaluation.
3. **Describe the structure of language.** As an expression of thinking, language is one of the most important cognitive abilities. Language production and comprehension depend on the ability to understand the structure of language.
4. **Discuss the relationship between language and thought.** For many years psychologists have argued about whether language was a reflection of thought or whether thinking is influenced by language. Now psychologists agree that language is a reflection of thinking and provides a vehicle for psychologists to understand thinking content and processes.
5. **Define intelligence.** Historically, many definitions of intelligence have been offered and it has been extremely difficult to come to an agreement. The formal definition given in the text combines a number of the important aspects of intelligence offered by many psychologists as well as "ordinary" people.
6. **Explain the intelligence theories of Spearman, Thurstone, Guilford, Gardner, and Sternberg.** Many theories have been proposed to explain the nature of intelligence and how it is determined. Understanding these theories provides some of the more influential explanations for intelligence.
7. **Describe the mental abilities tested in the Stanford- Binet Intelligence Scale and the Wechsler Adult Intelligence Scale.** It is important to know about the mental abilities that these intelligence scales measure because the Stanford-Binet Intelligence Scale and the Wechsler Adult Intelligence Scale are two of the most popular and widely used intelligence tests today.
8. **Identify the characteristics of giftedness and mental retardation and their relationship to intelligence.** A complete understanding of intelligence requires an understanding not only measures of normal intelligence but also the extremes of intelligence. Individuals who score at the extremes of intelligence need special attention either to compensate for their low intellectual abilities or to enhance their special abilities.
9. **Discuss the role of heredity and environment in determining intelligence.** Intelligence is a critical factor in the ability to function at work as well as in everyday life. Understanding the roles of heredity and environment in determining intelligence is important not only for academic reasons but also in helping to improve intelligence where possible.

Name ______________________ Class ______________ Date ____________

Chapter Outline

Chapter 7 Thinking, Language, and Intelligence

Thinking

A. List six important higher mental functions that involve thinking include:

1. ______________________
2. ______________________
3. ______________________
4. ______________________
5. ______________________
6. ______________________

Thinking and Images

A. Shepard's mental rotation experiments showed that ______________________

____

____

Thinking and Concepts

A. Three types of categories that form the basis of a concept aare:

1. ______________________
2. ______________________
3. ______________________

B. Prototypes are ______________________

and are arranged from ______________________

____

____

Problem Solving

A. The four steps in problem solving are:

1. ______________________
2. ______________________
3. ______________________
4. ______________________

B. An algorithm is ______________________

____

____

C. A heuristic is ______________________________

____

____

Barriers to Problem Solving

A. Mental set refers to ______________________________

____

____

B. Functional fixedness involves ______________________________

____

____

Creative Problem Solving

A. Two types of thinking are:

1. ______________________________

2. ______________________________

B. In divergent thinking problems are solved by ______________________________

____

____

C. Brainstorming involves ______________________________

____

____

Language

A. Language is defined as ______________________________

____

____

The Structure of Language

A. Phonemes are ______________________________

____

____

B. Morphemes are ______________________________

____

____

C. Syntax refers to ______________________________

____

____

D. Semantics is ______________________________

____

____

E. Grammar is composed of ______________________________

____

____

F. In transformational grammar the deep structure is ______________

and the surface structure is ______________________________

____

G. Chomsky believes that the rules of transformational grammar are ______________

____

____

Language and Thought

A. The linguistic-relativity hypothesis states that ______________

____

____

B. Regarding the relationship between language and thought, psychologists today generally agree that ______________________________

____

____

Intelligence

A. Regarding intelligence, three major issues confronting psychologists today are:

1. ______________________________

2. ______________________________

3. ______________________________

What is Intelligence?

A. Most definitions of intelligence emphasize four things:

1. ______________________________

2. ______________________________

3. ______________________________

4. ______________________________

B. According to Sternberg, intelligence is ______________________________

____

____

Theories of Intelligence

A. Factor analysis is ______________________________

____

____

Spearman's Factor Theory

A. The two types of factors recognized by Spearman are:

1. ______________________________

2. ______________________________

Thurstone's Primary Mental Abilities

A. Four primary mental abilities proposed by Thurstone are:

1. ______________________________

2. ______________________________

3. ______________________________

4. ______________________________

Guilford's Structure-of-Intellect Model

A. In Guilford's model operations are ______________________________

contents refer to ______________________________

and products are ______________________________

Gardner's Theory of Multiple Intelligences

A. The theory of multiple intelligences proposes that ______________________________

____

____

B. Linguistic intelligence refers to ______________________________

____

____

C. Body-kinesthetic intelligence involves ______________________________

____

____

D. Intrapersonal intelligence is ______________________________

____

____

Sternberg's Triarchic Theory

A. The three types of intelligence in triarchic theory are:

1. ______________________________

2. ______________________________

3. ______________________________

B. Triarchic theory strives to understand the relationship between ____________

____

____

C. Componential intelligence consists of ______________________________

____

____

D. Experiential intelligence is ______________________________

____

____

E. Contextual intelligence refers to ______________________________

____

____

How Intelligence Is Measured

A. Alfred Binet and Theodore Simon devised the ______________________________

____

to identify ______________________________

____

B. The formula for the intelligence quotient is ______________________

____

____

C. Three assumptions upon which all major IQ tests are based today are:

1. ______________________

2. ______________________

3. ______________________

The Elements of Intelligence Tests

A. Standardization means ______________________

____

____

B. The normative group is ______________________

____

____

C. Reliability refers to ______________________

____

____

D. Validity is ______________________

____

____

E. Two important types of validity are:

1. ______________________

2. ______________________

F. An IQ test would have good predictive validity if ______________________

____

____

Types of Intelligence Tests

A. The Stanford-Binet Intelligence Scale is ______________________

____

____

B. The four types of mental abilities tested by the Stanford-Binet Intelligence Scale and a subtest which measures that ability are:

1. ______________________________

2. ______________________________

3. ______________________________

4. ______________________________

subset: ______________________________

C. The three Wechsler scales used to measure intelligence today are:

1. ______________________________

2. ______________________________

3. ______________________________

D. The digit span subtest of the WAIS-R measures ______________________________

____

____

E. The block design subtest of the WAIS-R measures ______________________________

____

____

F. The three types of IQ scores derived from the Wechsler scales are:

1. ______________________________

2. ______________________________

3. ______________________________

The Evaluation of Intelligence Tests

A. Three arguments which favor the use of intelligence tests are:

1. ______________________________

2. ______________________________

3. ______________________________

B. Three criticisms of the IQ test are:

1. ______________________________

2. ______________________________

3. ______________________________

C. Cattell's Culture-Fair Intelligence Tests downplay ______________________________

____

____

D. Culture-Fair intelligence tests are used infrequently because ______________

____

____

The Extremes of Intelligence

A. Giftedness is defined as ______________________________

____

____

B. The characteristics of gifted individuals are ______________________

____

____

C. Mental retardation is a condition characterized by ________________

____

____

D. The features of moderate mental retardation are __________________

____

____

What Determines Intelligence?

A. Adoption studies conducted in Texas and Colorado show that ____________

____

____

B. A study of monozygotic twins reared apart shows that________________

____

____

C. Family studies generally show that ___________________________

____

____

D. Four environmental factors that can negatively affect intelligence are:

1. ____
2. ____
3. ____
4. ____

E. Mainstreaming involves ______________________________
____
____

F. Segregation involves ______________________________
____
____

Biography

Robert Sternberg

A. Sternberg's interest in the topic of intelligence was stimulated when ________
____
____

B. Robert Sternberg is one of the most important figures in psychology because of
____
____

Issues and Applications

Thinking and Problem Solving by Business Executives

A. Three cognitive characteristics of opportunistic thinkers are:

1. ______________________________
2. ______________________________
3. ______________________________

B. Five activities that successful corporate general managers emphasize in their work are:

1. ______________________________
2. ______________________________
3. ______________________________
4. ______________________________
5. ______________________________

Improving Your Intelligence

A. Programs designed to improve intelligence teach strategies ______________
____
____

Notes

Name ______________ Class ______________ Date ______________

Key Terms Worksheet

Write a definition for each key term on the lines provided.

Term	Definition
thinking	______________
concept	______________
algorithm	______________
heuristic	______________
mental set	______________
functional fixedness	______________
creativity	______________
language	______________
transformational grammar	______________
linguistic-relativity hypothesis	______________
intelligence	______________
g-factor	______________
primary mental abilities	______________

structure of intellect model ______________________________

____

theory of multiple intelligences ______________________________

____

triarchic theory ______________________________

____

intelligence quotient ______________________________

____

standardization ______________________________

____

reliability ______________________________

____

validity ______________________________

____

Stanford-Binet Intelligence Scale ______________________________

____

Wechsler Adult Intelligence Scale-Revised ______________________________

____

giftedness ______________________________

____

mental retardation ______________________________

____

Name ______________________ Class ______________ Date __________

Pretest

Chapter 7 Thinking, Language, and Intelligence

I. True/False Circle the letter (T or F) that corresponds to the correct response.

T F **1.** Shepard's mental rotation experiment indicated that people think in mental images.

T F **2.** The correct order of the steps in problem solving are incubation-preparation-production-evaluation.

T F **3.** The solution to the nine-dot problem described in the text requires one to break set.

T F **4.** Morphemes are the basic speech sounds of a language.

T F **5.** The linguistic-relativity hypothesis proposes that language shapes thinking.

T F **6.** According to the survey described in the text, psychologists believe that the most important element of intelligence is mathematical ability.

T F **7.** Sternberg's theory of multiple intelligences maintains that intelligence is primarily composed of 150 factors.

T F **8.** The most widely used IQ test is Cattell's Culture Fair test.

T F **9.** Giftedness is defined as an IQ above 130; retardation is defined as an IQ below 90.

T F **10.** Behavior genetics studies indicate that heredity and the environment interact in determining intelligence.

II. Multiple Choice Circle the letter that corresponds to the best or correct answer.

1. The act of mentally representing information in images, words, symbols, or ideas is called:

A. problem solving
B. thinking
C. intelligence
D. giftedness

2. A heuristic is:

A. a "rule of thumb" used to simplify the solution to a problem
B. a formula for solving a difficult problem
C. an idea that represents a group of living things, objects, or events based on common features
D. a representative example of a category that shares most of the features, or attributes, with other members of that category

3. In the production stage of problem solving, one:

A. gathers information necessary to solve the problem
B. takes a rest from the problem if one cannot solve it after many attempts
C. looks at the outcome to determine if the problem has been solved
D. tries possible solutions to the problem using trial-and-error or hypotheses

4. Research shows that creative problem solving is usually associated with:
   - **A.** an IQ above 110
   - **B.** convergent thinking
   - **C.** divergent thinking
   - **D.** the use of transformational grammar
5. Syntax refers to:
   - **A.** the meaning of words and sentences
   - **B.** combinations of phonemes that make up a unit of meaning
   - **C.** the relations among words in a sentence
   - **D.** a set of rules that determines how sentences are transformed into one another
6. Most psychologists believe that the most important element of intelligence is:
   - **A.** general knowledge
   - **B.** mathematical reasoning
   - **C.** creativity
   - **D.** abstract thinking
7. Sternberg's triarchic theory proposes that intelligence is composed of:
   - **A.** 150 factors
   - **B.** seven primary mental abilities
   - **C.** three interacting types of intelligence
   - **D.** interpersonal intelligence
8. The first intelligence tests were developed by:
   - **A.** Alfred Binet and Theodore Simon
   - **B.** David Wechsler
   - **C.** Raymond Cattell
   - **D.** Robert Sternberg
9. Reliability refers to:
   - **A.** a test's accuracy
   - **B.** the consistency of test scores obtained
   - **C.** the degree of cultural and racial bias in an intelligence test
   - **D.** how well a test has been standardized
10. If Sam obtained an IQ score of 100, he would be more intelligent than ________ percent of the population.
    - **A.** 50
    - **B.** 68
    - **C.** 84
    - **D.** 95

III. Short Answers Write the answer in the space provided.

1. How does mental set act as a barrier to problem solving?

2. Discuss the importance of test standardization.

3. What are the three types of intelligence in triarchic theory?

4. Discuss the roles of heredity and environment in determining intelligence.

5. Discuss the issue of bias in intelligence testing.

IV. Matching Match the terms in column A with the correct choice in column B.

A

_____ **1.** prototype

_____ **2.** concept

_____ **3.** algorithm

_____ **4.** heuristic

_____ **5.** mental set

_____ **6.** functional fixedness

_____ **7.** incubation

_____ **8.** phonemes

_____ **9.** syntax

_____ **10.** linguistic-relativity hypothesis

_____ **11.** g-factor

_____ **12.** primary mental abilities

_____ **13.** structure-of-intellect model

_____ **14.** theory of multiple intelligences

_____ **15.** triarchic theory

_____ **16.** componential intelligence

_____ **17.** standardization

_____ **18.** validity

_____ **19.** Wechsler Adult Intelligence Scale-Revised

_____ **20.** giftedness

B

a. a formula for solving a problem

b. the tendency to approach problems in rigid ways

c. innate component of intelligence

d. Thurstone's intelligence factors

e. Guilford's model of intelligence

f. test accuracy

g. an IQ score of 130 or above

h. the step in problem solving that involves stepping back from the problem

i. the tendency to look at an object according to its typical use

j. model wherein language shapes perceptions of reality

k. mental processes used in planning and evaluating

l. Sternberg's model of intelligence based on interacting components

m. the most widely used IQ test

n. the specification of the conditions under which a test is taken, scored, and interpreted.

o. unique set of basic speech sounds

p. the relations among words in a sentence

q. model based on seven distinct types of intelligence

r. an idea that represents a group of living things, objects, or events

s. a representative example of a category

t. a "rule of thumb"

V. Fill In The Blanks Write the answers in the spaces provided.

1. A(n) ____________________ is an idea that represents a group of living things, objects, or events and is formed around a representative example of a category called a(n) ____________________.

2. A(n) ____________________ is a formula for solving a problem and a(n) ____________________ is a "rule of thumb" used to simplify the solution to a problem.

3. ____________________ thinking involves narrowing facts to find a problem's solution, while ____________________ thinking requires thinking of many possible solutions to a problem.

4. The relations among words in a sentence is called ____________________ while the study of the meaning of words and sentences is called ____________________.

5. In ____________________, the ____________________ is the real meaning of a sentence and the ____________________ is the actual wording.

6. In Spearman's factor theory, the ____________________ refers to general intelligence and ____________________ are types of specific traits.

7. In Guilford's structure-of-intellect model of intelligence, ____________________ are mental processes, ____________________ refer to whether the problem involves words, numbers, or pictures, and ____________________ are the types of responses required to correctly solve a problem.

8. ____________________ is the consistency of test scores while a test's accuracy is known as ____________________.

9. The WAIS-R consists of ____________________ and ____________________ subtests.

10. ____________________ places mentally retarded children in classes with nonretarded children and ____________________ involves placing them in classes with other retarded children.

Notes

Answer Key To Chapter 7 Pretest

I. True/False

1-T, **2**-F, **3**-T, **4**-F, **5**-F, **6**-F, **7**-F, **8**-F, **9**-F, **10**-T

II. Multiple Choice

1-B, 2-A, **3**-D, **4**-C, **5**-C, **6**-D, **7**-C, **8**-A, **9**-B, **10**-A

III. Short Answer

1. Mental set acts as a barrier to problem solving because the individual tends to approach problems in old and rigid ways. In the nine-dot problem one makes certain assumptions about the instructions. When one breaks set, one is able to solve the problem.

2. Test standardization is important because it sets the conditions under which the test will be taken and scored and it establishes norm groups. Because each person who takes the test will take it and have it scored in the same way, and because norms have been established for comparison, it is possible to meaningfully interpret individual test scores.

3. In triarchic theory, the three types of intelligence are componential, experiential, and contextual. Componential intelligence consists of mental processes; experiential intelligence refers to one's experience in coping with tasks; and contextual intelligence is the ability to adapt to and change the environment.

4. Heredity and environment interact in determining intelligence. Behavior genetics studies show that about 50 percent of differences in IQ scores are due to heredity. Environmental factors, such as prenatal experiences, childhood illnesses, malnutrition, and inadequate intellectual stimulation, can negatively affect intelligence. Intellectual stimulation, like special education programs, can improve intelligence.

5. Many critics complain that IQ tests are biased in favor of upper- and middle-class whites. The critics claim that many minorities are unfairly placed in special education programs and denied the enriching experiences of programs designed for whites.

IV. Matching

1-s, **2**-r, **3**-a, **4**-t, **5**-b, **6**-i, **7**-h, **8**-o, **9**-p, **10**-j, **11**-c, **12**-d, **13**-e, **14**-q, **15**-l, **16**-k, **17**-n, **18**-f, **19**-m, **20**-g

V. Fill In The Blanks

1. concept - prototype
2. algorithm - heuristic
3. convergent - divergent
4. syntax - semantics
5. transformational grammar - deep structure - surface structure
6. g-factor - specific factors
7. operations - contents - products
8. reliability - validity
9. verbal - performance
10. mainstreaming – segregation

Suggested Readings

Ellison, J. 1984. "The seven frames of mind: A conversation with Howard Gardner." In P. Chance and T. G. Harris, (eds.). *The best of psychology today.* New York: McGraw-Hill. 92-98.

Gardner discusses his belief that notions about intelligence are too narrow.

Finke, R. A. 1990. *Creative imagery: Discoveries and inventions in visualization.* Hillsdale, NJ: Erlbaum.

The author shows how creativity can be achieved through visualization techniques.

Gardner, H. 1983. *Frames of mind: The theory of multiple intelligences.* New York: Basic Books.

A presentation of Gardner's theory of multiple intelligences.

Gardner, H. 1985. *The mind's new science.* New York: Basic Books.

This work discusses the history of and current trends in cognitive psychology.

Granat, D. "Who is smart?" *NewDigest*, December (1992): 17-20, 22-23, 25.

The author discusses and compares Gardner's and Sternberg's theories of intelligence.

Jensen, A. R. 1994. "Compensatory education and the theory of intelligence." In B. L. Slife and J. Rubinstein, (eds.). *Taking sides, 7th ed.* Guilford, CT: Dushkin. 113–120.

Linden, E. "Can animals think?" *Time* March. 1993: 54-61.

A discussion of research on whether animals think.

Sternberg, R. J. 1994. "How can we teach intelligence?" In B. L. Slife and J. Rubinstein, (eds.) *Taking sides, 7th ed.* Guilford, CT: Dushkin. 102–112.

Sternberg argues that intelligence can be increased and provides examples of how it can be done.

Sternberg, R. J. 1988. *The triarchic mind.* New York: Viking.

This is an excellent presentation of Sternberg's triarchic theory of intelligence with many practical examples.

Chapter 8

Human Growth and Development

Chapter Summary

Prenatal development is strongly influenced by environmental factors, especially during the critical periods.

Early maturation sets the basis for motor and perceptual development, but the environment also contributes.

Piaget proposed four stages of cognitive development: sensory-motor, preoperational, concrete operations, and formal operations. Language develops by regular changes in the use and understanding of speech. Moral reasoning has three levels: preconventional, conventional, and postconventional. Erikson's theory describes eight stages of identity development. Early social development is influenced by temperament, attachment, parenting styles, gender identity formation, and socialization forces.

Adolescent physical development is marked by puberty and sexual maturation. Teen psychosocial development is dominated by identity formation and crisis, social behavior (especially with peers), and the initiation of sexual relationships. After young adulthood physical ability gradually declines and in senescence health problems accumulate. Adult personality is relatively stable. Family and work dominate adult psychosocial development. The five stages of coping with death are denial, anger, bargaining, depression, and acceptance.

1. **Outline the stages of prenatal development and discuss the effects of the prenatal environment on the developing individual.** Learning about the prenatal period demonstrates how development begins even before birth and how the events of that period set the stage for later changes.

2. **Describe physical maturation and perceptual and motor development during infancy and childhood.** Understanding the basis of physical, perceptual, and motor development reveals the complex interactions between innate maturational processes and the learning environment in the early years of life.

3. **Discuss cognitive, language, and moral development.** Studying the progress in a child's thinking, language use, and moral reasoning leads to understanding of how these kinds of cognition reflect and influence other aspects of psychological and social development

4. **Outline the major psychosocial changes during infancy and childhood.** Psychosocial development in infancy and childhood sets the foundation for personality, gender identity, and social relationships throughout the life span.

5. **Identify the main physical changes of adolescence.** Learning about the role of physical factors in adolescence gives an understanding of how bodily maturation sets the stage for behavioral changes in this period.

6. **Summarize psychosocial development in adolescence.** The transition from child to adult is a critical feature of adolescence and the events that unfold set the basis for later adult development.

7. **Discuss the physical changes during adulthood.** It is important to recognize the physical changes in adulthood to understand their impact on the lifestyles and psychological changes in that period.

8. **Describe psychosocial development in adulthood.** Development continues through adulthood and by learning how this proceeds one can better appreciate the changes in the adults with whom interacts.

Name ______________________ Class ________________ Date ____________

Chapter Outline

Chapter 8 Human Growth and Development

Prenatal Development

A. The prenatal stage of development is ______________________________

____

____

B. Prenatal development is controlled by ______________________________

____

____

Physical Development

A. Conception refers to ______________________________

____

____

B. The three stages of prenatal development are:

1. ______________________________

2. ______________________________

3. ______________________________

C. A critical period in development means ______________________________

____

____

The Prenatal Environment

A. Maternal nutrition is an important part of the prenatal environment because

____

____

B. Prenatal development is influenced by maternal diseases such as __________

____

____

C. Fetal alcohol syndrome refers to ______________________________

____

____

Infancy and Childhood

A. The terms infancy and childhood refer to ______________________________

____

____

Physical, Motor, and Perceptual Development

A. Maturation refers to ______________________________

____

____

Physical Development

A. Physical development in infancy and childhood is affected by ______________

____

____

B. Failure-to-thrive is ______________________________

____

____

C. Brain maturation in infancy and childhood is marked by ______________

____

____

Motor Development

A. The newborn infant's reflexes are ______________________________

____

____

B. The major motor milestones in infancy are ______________________________

____

____

Perceptual Development

A. Fantz's studies demonstrated that ______________________________

____

____

B. The visual cliff studies showed ______________________________

____

____

Cognitive, Language, and Moral Development

A. Cognitive changes in childhood are reflected in ______________________

____

____

Piaget's Theory of Cognitive Development

A. The four stages of cognitive development are:

1. ____

2. ____

3. ____

4. ____

B. Sensory-motor thinking is dominated by ______________________

____

____

C. Preoperational thinking is characterized by ______________________

____

____

D. The concrete operations stage involves ______________________

____

____

E. Formal operations thinking is marked by ______________________

____

____

Language Development

A. The development of language is important because ______________________

____

____

B. A holophrase is ______________________

____

____

C. Telegraphic speech means ______________________

____

____

Moral Development

A. Kohlberg's theory of moral reasoning looks at three levels:

1. ______________________________

2. ______________________________

3. ______________________________

B. Kohlberg's theory has been criticized because ______________________________

____

____

Psychosocial Development

A. Psychosocial development refers to the growth of ______________________________

____

____

Personality Development

A. Erik Erikson's theory of personality development emphasizes ______________________________

____

____

B. According to Erikson, healthy development involves ______________________________

____

____

C. Temperament means ______________________________

____

____

D. Attachment research has found that ______________________________

____

____

E. A child's self-esteem is influenced by ______________________________

____

____

F. Baumrind's three types of parenting styles are:

1. ______________________________

2. ______________________________

3. ______________________________

Gender Identity

A. Gender identity means ______________________________

____

____

B. Gender identity is affected by ______________________________

____

____

D. A gender schemata is ______________________________

____

____

Adolescence

A. Adolescence refers to ______________________________

____

____

Physical Development

A. Puberty is ______________________________

____

____

B. Menarche means that ______________________________

____

____

C. Research on the link between a teenager's behavior and hormones finds that

____

____

Psychosocial Development

A. The notion of an adolescent identity crisis means

____

____

Identity

A. According to James Marcia, teens undergo ______________________________

____

____

B. Ethnic identity refers to ____

____

____

Social Development

A. During adolescence, social life involves ______________________________

____

____

B. Peer relationships are important in adolescence because they ___________

____

____

C. Adolescent idealism and egocentrism refer to__________________________

____

____

Adulthood

A. Levinson's model of adulthood is based on ____________________________

____

____

B. Life structures are ____

____

____

Physical Development

A. The general course of physical development in adulthood is characterized by

____

____

B. Menopause refers to ____

____

____

Psychosocial Development

A. Psychosocial development in adulthood is generally marked by ___________

____

____

Personality

A. Research on personality development in adults finds that ______________

____

____

B. The concept of midlife crisis means ______________

____

____

Relationships

A. In young adulthood, the major developmental challenge in relationships is

____

____

B. The marital relationship is an important aspect of adult development because

____

____

Work

A. Work is a significant factor in adult development because ______________

____

____

B. In adulthood, job satisfaction is related to ______________

____

____

Aging and Dying

A. Senescence refers to ______________

____

____

B. The prominent stresses of old age include ______________

____

____

C. Kubler-Ross's five stage model is:

1. ______________________________
2. ______________________________
3. ______________________________
4. ______________________________
5. ______________________________

Issues and Applications

Building Self-Esteem

A. One's self-esteem reflects one's ______________________________

____

____

B. The principles for improving self-esteem are ______________________________

____

____

Teens at Work

A. The benefits of work for teenagers include ______________________________

____

____

B. The disadvantages of work for teenagers are ______________________________

____

____

Biography

Jean Piaget

A. Piaget is best known for his contributions to ______________________________

____

____

B. Piaget's education included training in ______________________________

____

____

Name ______________________ Class ____________________ Date ______________

Key Terms Worksheet

Write a definition for each key term on the lines provided.

Term	Definition
prenatal stage	
critical period	
fetal alcohol syndrome	
maturation	
failure-to-thrive	
sensory-motor stage	
preoperational stage	
concrete operations stage	
formal operations stage	
moral reasoning	
identity	
temperament	
self-esteem	

gender identity ____________________

____

puberty ____________________

____

menarche ____________________

____

identity crisis ____________________

____

ethnic identity ____________________

____

peer pressure ____________________

____

life structures ____________________

____

menopause ____________________

____

midlife crisis ____________________

____

senescence ____________________

____

Name ______________________ Class ________________ Date ____________

Pretest

Chapter 8 Human Growth and Development

I. True/False Circle the letter (T or F) that corresponds to the correct response.

T F **1.** The fetal stage of development lasts from conception to birth.

T F **2.** A critical period of development is one in which the organism is most sensitive to its environment.

T F **3.** Human infants have almost no perceptual abilities until the end of their first year of life.

T F **4.** Conservation is a characteristic of the concrete operations stage of cognitive development.

T F **5.** Temperament is the basis for later developments in personality and social behavior.

T F **6.** Postconventional moral reasoning is based on personal experiences of reward and punishment.

T F **7.** Puberty is the major feature of physical development in adolescence.

T F **8.** In adolescence, peer relationships have less importance in development than during childhood.

T F **9.** Physical capabilities reach their peak in young adulthood.

T F **10.** Levinson's theory of adult development is based on the concept of life structures.

II. Multiple Choice Circle the letter that corresponds to the correct or best answer.

1. What is the period of development from conception to birth called?

A. embryonic stage
B. neonatal stage
C. preoperational stage
D. prenatal stage

2. Which of the following is not an important influence on the prenatal environment?

A. the mother's drug use
B. maternal disease
C. the mother's nutrition
D. maternal intelligence

3. What does Fantz's research on infant perception show?

A. depth perception in infants
B. the development of fine motor skills in newborns
C. the link between sensation and cognition in infancy
D. form, color, and motion perception in infants

4. Which stage of cognitive development is marked by object permanence?
   - **A.** sensory-motor stage
   - **B.** preoperational stage
   - **C.** concrete operations stage
   - **D.** formal operations stage

5. Which level of moral development is characterized by reasoning in terms of the rules or laws of society?
   - **A.** preconventional
   - **B.** conventional
   - **C.** nonconventional
   - **D.** postconventional

6. What does self-esteem refer to?
   - **A.** the sense of conscience or morality
   - **B.** a stable sense of personal identity
   - **C.** self-evaluations and feelings about oneself
   - **D.** innate patterns of emotional responding

7. Which parenting style is most likely to produce a child who has problems in self control and social cooperation?
   - **A.** authoritarian
   - **B.** permissive
   - **C.** neglectful
   - **D.** authoritative

8. According to Erikson's theory of development, which of the following is typical of adolescence?
   - **A.** an identity crisis
   - **B.** postconventional moral reasoning
   - **C.** formal operational thinking
   - **D.** conflictual parent-child relationships

9. Which statement about adult personality is true?
   - **A.** Personality stabilizes during early adulthood.
   - **B.** Personality traits become exaggerated in old age.
   - **C.** Most adults have dramatic midlife crises.
   - **D.** Personality is more stable in men than women.

10. Kubler-Ross's last stage of coping with death is:
    - **A.** anger
    - **B.** bargaining
    - **C.** denial
    - **D.** acceptance

III. Short Answer Write the answer in the space provided.

1. What factors influence prenatal development?

2. Describe Piaget's theory of cognitive development.

3. Describe Erikson's theory of psychosocial development.

4. What factors influence adolescent social development?

5. What changes characterize physical development in adulthood?

IV. Matching Match the terms in column A with the correct choice in column B.

A

_____ **1.** fetal stage

_____ **2.** infancy

_____ **3.** gross motor skills

_____ **4.** visual cliff

_____ **5.** animism

_____ **6.** holophrases

_____ **7.** preconventional level

_____ **8.** self-schemata

_____ **9.** gender schemata

_____ **10.** identity crisis

_____ **11.** life structures

_____ **12.** midlife crisis

_____ **13.** senescence

_____ **14.** embryo

_____ **15.** full term infant

_____ **16.** maturation

_____ **17.** object permanence

_____ **18.** temperament

_____ **19.** menarche

_____ **20.** adolescent egocentrism

B

a. first two years of life

b. unfolding of innate biological programs for development

c. period of distress in middle adulthood

d. first stage of moral reasoning in Kohlberg's theory

e. beliefs about oneself

f. walking, running, and climbing

g. attitude of self-absorption and self-consciousness

h. method to study depth perception in infants

i. awareness that objects exist even when unseen

j. inborn style of emotional and behavioral responding

k. one-syllable expressions with complex meaning

l. organism from two to eight weeks after conception

m. second month after conception to birth

n. period of struggle to form a consistent self-concept

o. patterns of adult development based on relationships

p. the first instance of menstruation

q. old age

r. feature of preoperational stage thinking

s. infant born after 38 to 42 weeks of prenatal development

t. beliefs that motivate sex role behavior

V. Fill In The Blanks Write the answers in the space provided.

1. At the moment of conception ____________________ development begins with the ____________________ stage lasting for about two weeks, followed by a period from two to eight weeks called the ____________________ stage after which the ____________________ stage continues until birth.

2. At birth movement is dominated by simple ____________________ like sucking and grasping which are gradually replaced by more complex ____________________ movements. During infancy and early childhood increased coordination allows walking, running, and other ____________________ skills as well as more subtle finger coordination, or ____________________ skills.

3. Jean Piaget's theory of ____________________ development stresses the importance of children's concepts, or ____________________, which progress through ____________________ stages. Piaget's critics, however, argue that development is more ____________________ than his stage theory suggests.

4. Kohlberg describes three levels in the way in which children think about right and wrong in his theory of ____________________. The ____________________ level is based on personal experiences of reward and punishment. In the conventional level the child reasons according to social ____________________. In the ____________________ level personal principles and values dominate.

5. Personality development in childhood is a matter of ____________________ formation according to Erikson. However, other factors also influence personality, such as an inborn style of emotional and behavioral responding known as ____________________ and self-evaluations or ____________________.

6. Gender identity, the sense of being ____________________, is determined not only by ____________________ factors such as sex chromosomes but also by social forces such as ____________________ with male or female models and ____________________, or beliefs about sex role behavior.

7. The rapid development of secondary sex characteristics marks the onset of ____________________ which results mainly from increases in ____________________ in both boys and girls. Although the exact relation between hormones and behavior is uncertain, there appears to be a link between ____________________ and aggressiveness and between ____________________ and moodiness.

8. Erikson's theory views adolescence as a period in which the main challenge is to establish a stable ____________________ and in which many adolescents experience difficulties that result in a(n) ____________________. During the teenage years the awareness of and attitudes about one's racial and cultural group, or ____________________ identity, is also an important aspect of psychosocial development.

9. Daniel Levinson's theory of adult development emphasizes the concept of ____________________ that focus on family and work ____________________. Levinson discusses a period of distress in middle adulthood called the ____________________ during which uncharacteristic behaviors and attitudes occur.

10. The period of old age is called ____________________. In Erikson's theory, the main task during this period is developing a sense of ____________________ through evaluation of one's life achievements. In addition, late adulthood confronts the individual with death, and according to ____________________, coping with death involves ____________________ stages.

Answer Key To Chapter 8 Pretest

I. True/False

1-F, **2**-T, **3**-F, **4**-T, **5**-T, **6**-F, **7**-T, **8**-F, **9**-T, **10**-T

II. Multiple Choice

1-D, **2**-D, **3**-D, **4**-A, **5**-B, **6**-C, **7**-B, **8**-A, **9**-A, **10**-D

III. Short Answer

1. Prenatal development is controlled by both genes and the prenatal environment. Progress through the germinal, embryonic, and fetal stages depends on several environmental variables, including the quality of nutrition, the mother's health, and exposure to hazardous drugs such as alcohol.
2. Piaget's theory of cognitive development proposes that a child's thinking progresses through four stages at each of which distinctive schemata are found. The stages are known as sensory-motor, preoperational, concrete operations, and formal operations.
3. According to Erikson's theory, psychosocial development follows a sequence of eight stages in which the individual's formation of identity is affected by specific developmental challenges. Successfully coping with those challenges leads to a healthy personality.
4. In adolescence, social development involves a growing independence from family and greater influence of peers. Adjustment involves the acquisition of social skills and the formation of relationships including group membership and sexual relationships.
5. In young adulthood, physical capabilities reach their peak in terms of sensory ability and bodily strength. By middle adulthood a diminishment of physical ability begins and by late adulthood several characteristic signs of physical disability appear as well as age-related illnesses.

IV. Matching

1-m, **2**-a, **3**-f, **4**-h, **5**-r, **6**-k, **7**-d, **8**-e, **9**-t, **10**-n, **11**-o, **12**-c, **13**-q, **14**-l, **15**-s, **16**-b, **17**-i, **18**-j, **19**-p, **20**-g

V. Fill In The Blanks

1. prenatal - germinal - embryonic - fetal
2. reflexes - voluntary - gross motor - fine motor
3. cognitive - schemata - four - gradual
4. moral development - preconventional - rules and laws - postconventional
5. identity - temperament - self-esteem
6. male or female - biological - identification - gender - schemata
7. puberty - hormones - testosterone - estradiol
8. identity - identity crisis - ethnic
9. life structures - relationships - midlife crisis
10. senescence - integrity - Kubler-Ross - five

Suggested Readings

Dorris, M. 1989. *The broken cord.* New York: Harper & Row.

Written by the adoptive father of a Native American boy with fetal alcohol syndrome, this book gives insight into the everyday challenges of a family trying to cope with the behavioral and psychological problems that result from prenatal alcohol exposure.

Elkind, D. 1984. *All grown up and no place to go: Teenagers in crisis.* Reading, MA: Addison-Wesley.

The author, a leading figure in adolescent development, has written an excellent guide to the psychology of teenagers for both teens and their parents. He discusses the developmental problems of adolescence with attention to the role of family, peers, and society.

Erikson, E. H. 1963. *Childhood and society.* New York: Norton.

In this classic book by Erik Erikson the author explains his eight-stage theory of psychosocial development as well as his views on personality and psychological adjustment.

Gilligan, C. 1982. *In a different voice: Psychological theory and women's development.* Cambridge, MA: Harvard University Press.

By a leading female developmental psychologist, this book argues against the male biases in developmental theory and research, giving special attention to moral reasoning and a theory of female development.

Kubler-Ross, E. 1969. *On death and dying.* New York: Macmillan.

Through the excellent presentation of case examples psychiatrist Elisabeth Kubler-Ross illustrates her theory of the five stages of coping with death and dying. This book has become a classic in the field.

Levinson, D. J. 1978. *The seasons of a man's life.* New York: Knopf.
Levinson, D. J. 1987. *The Seasons of a woman's life.* New York: Knopf.

These two companion works by a leading researcher and theorist in adult development summarize the author's work on the life structures that define adulthood.

Phillips, J. L. 1969. *Origins of intellect: Piaget's theory.* San Francisco: Freeman.

An excellent summary of Piaget's theory of cognitive development presented in an accessible manner. Many examples of Piagetian studies are provided to illustrate the concepts relevant to each stage.

Santrock, J. W. 1992. *Life-span development, 4th edition.* Dubuque, IA: W. C. Brown.

This comprehensive textbook of developmental psychology provides discussion of physical, cognitive, perceptual, motor, and psychosocial changes from conception to death and offers excellent summaries of research on these aspects of development.

Chapter 9

Motivation and Emotion

Chapter Summary

Motivation is the process by which behavior is activated and directed toward a goal. Physiological motives stem from bodily needs necessary for survival. Stimulus motives are those in which the person seeks to increase stimulation. Social motives involve needs shaped by socialization. Biological theories, like instinct theory, sociobiology, and drive theory, assume that an individual is motivated by inborn patterns of behavior. Psychological theories, such as incentive, arousal, and expectancy theories, and Maslow's hierarchy of needs theory, focus on psychological determinants of motivation.

Emotion is a reaction composed of subjective feelings, cognitive evaluation, physiological changes, and observable behavior. Plutchik has proposed eight primary emotions. Lazarus has identified two main categories of emotions. Emotions are expressed and measured by self-reports, behavior–especially facial expressions–and physiological activity. The James-Lange theory holds that interpretations of bodily changes determines emotions. According to the Cannon-Bard theory, perception causes brain arousal which, in turn, causes bodily changes and emotional feelings. Cognitive labeling theory says that emotion is determined by how one interprets or labels the physiological changes that occur in certain situations.

1. **Distinguish among physiological, stimulus, and social motives and give examples of each.** It is important to be able to distinguish between physiological, stimulus, and social motives since categorizing motives is one way of scientifically studying them.

2. **Describe the determinants of hunger and sexual motivation.** Though hunger and sex are classified as physiological motives, it is necessary to realize that psychological factors play a crucial role in determining their expression.

3. **Define achievement motivation and identify the characteristics of individuals with a high need for achievement.** Achievement motivation is the most studied social motive. A high need for achievement has been associated with many aspects of behavior in everyday life and in business.

4. **Explain instinct theory, sociobiology, and the drive theory of motivation.** Studying these psychological theories which are rooted in biology helps one understand the bases of one's own motivation.

5. **Identify incentive, arousal, the expectancy-value, and need hierarchy theories of motivation.** An understanding of these psychologically based theories of motivation helps develop a more complete view of motivation.

6. **Describe the nature and range of emotion.** Before one can understand how emotion is expressed and measured, it is necessary to describe its nature and range.

7. **Identify three ways in which emotion is expressed and measured.** Since emotion cannot be observed directly, psychologists have looked for different ways in which emotion is expressed and can be measured.

8. **Summarize the James-Lange and Cannon-Bard theories of emotion.** These are important theories because, historically, they represent influential views of emotion. Modern research also provides some support for these theories as reasonable explanations for emotion.

9. **Explain cognitive theories of emotion.** Cognitive theories of emotion are important because they reflect current the thinking about the determinants of emotion.

Name ______________________________ Class ______________________ Date ________________

Chapter Outline

Chapter 9 Motivation And Emotion

Motivation

A. Motivation is ____

____

____

B. Extrinsic motivation is ____

____

____

C. Intrinsic motivation refers to ____

____

____

Physiological Motives

A. Physiological motives are those ____

____

____

B. Five physiological motives are:

1. ____

2. ____

3. ____

4. ____

5. ____

C. Hunger motivation is based in ____

____

____

D. Hunger is considered to be a physiological motive because ____________________

____

____

E. Schachter found that obese individuals were stimulus-bound and reactive, meaning that ____

____

____

F. The four stages of the sexual response cycle are:

1. ____________________

2. ____________________

3. ____________________

4. ____________________

G. Male and female changes during the excitement stage include ____________________

____

____

H. High testosterone levels in men are related to ____________________

____

____

Stimulus Motives

A. Three stimulus motives are:

1. ____________________

2. ____________________

3. ____________________

B. Contact comfort refers to ____________________

____

____

C. Harlow's monkeys showed a basic need for contact comfort by ____________________

____

____

Social Motives

A. Social motives are those which ____________________

____

____

B. Achievement motivation refers to ____________________

____

____

C. Describe three features of individuals with a high need for achievement:

1. ______________________________

2. ______________________________

3. ______________________________

D. The need for affiliation is describes as ______________________________

____

____

E. The power motive is ______________________________

____

____

Theories of Motivation

A. Two main types of theories of motivation are:

1. ______________________________

2. ______________________________

Biological Theories

A. Biological theories of motivation assume that ______________________________

____

____

Instinct Theory

A. Instinct theory holds that ______________________________

____

____

B. Instincts are ______________________________

____

____

Sociobiology

A. Sociobiology studies the ______________________________

____

____

B. Sociobiologists believe that ______________________________

____

____

Drive Theory

A. Drive theory argues that ______________________________

____

____

B. A drive is ______________________________

____

____

C. One shortcoming of drive theory is ______________________________

____

____

Psychological Theories

A. Psychological theories differ from biological theories in that ______________

____

____

B. Four psychological theories of motivation are:

1. ______________________________
2. ______________________________
3. ______________________________
4. ______________________________

Incentive Theory

A. Incentive theory says that ______________________________

____

____

B. An incentive is ______________________________

____

____

Arousal Theory

A. Arousal theory claims that ______________________________

____

____

B. The optimal level of arousal is ______________________________

____

____

C. According to the Yerkes-Dodson Law______________________________

____

____

D. Four dimensions of sensation-seeking are:

1. ______________________________

2. ______________________________

3. ______________________________

4. ______________________________

Cognitive Theories

A. Cognitive theories of motivation emphasize ______________________________

____

____

B. Expectancy-value theory says that ______________________________

____

____

C. Attributions are ______________________________

____

____

D. Two types of attributions are:

1. ______________________________

2. ______________________________

Maslow's Hierarchy of Needs

A. The need hierarchy is______________________________

____

____

B. Outline the need hierarchy from physiological to growth needs______________

____

____

Emotion

A. Emotion is tied to motivation because ______________________________

____

____

What is Emotion?

A. Emotion is defined as ______________________________

____

____

B. Four components of emotion are:

1. ______________________________
2. ______________________________
3. ______________________________
4. ______________________________

C. List Plutchik's eight primary emotions: ______________________________

____

____

D. Lazarus catalogs emotion into four groups:

1. ______________________________
2. ______________________________
3. ______________________________
4. ______________________________

The Expression and Measurement of Emotion

A. Three ways in which emotions are expressed and measured are:

1. ______________________________
2. ______________________________
3. ______________________________

B. Describe the self-report method of measuring emotions ______________________________

____

____

C. Facial expressions are universal, meaning that ______________________________

____

____

D. The expression of emotion is due to ______________________________

____

____

E. The Facial Action Coding System is ______________________________

____

____

F. The facial-feedback hypothesis states that ______________________________

____

____

G. Zajonc's version of the facial-feedback hypothesis states that ______________

____

____

H. The limbic system represents ______________________________

____

____

I. Emotional reactions are accompanied by ______________________________

____

____

J. Polygraph testing involves ______________________________

____

____

K. A major criticism of polygraph testing is ______________________________

____

____

Theories of Emotion

A. Three theories of emotion are:

1. ______________________________

2. ______________________________

3. ______________________________

The James-Lange and Cannon-Bard Theories

A. The James-Lange theory proposes that ______________________________

____

____

B. According to the Cannon-Bard theory ______________________________

____

____

Cognitive Theories

A. Cognitive theories focus on ______________________________

____

____

B. Cognitive labeling theory states that ______________________________

____

____

C. Three factors which determine emotions in Lazarus' theory are:

1. ____

2. ____

3. ____

Issues and Applications

Achievement Motivation and Success in Business

A. Individuals with a high need for achievement usually choose careers they find

____

____

B. Training in achievement motivation is related to ______________________________

____

____

Facial Expression and Lying

A. Catching a liar requires paying attention to ______________________________

____

____

Biography **Paul Ekman**

A. Paul Ekman is an expert on the topic of ______________________________

____

____

B. Ekman is internationally known for ______________________________

____

____

Notes

Name ______________________ Class ________________ Date ____________

Key Terms Worksheet

Write a definition for each key term on the lines provided.

Term	Definition
motivation	
physiological motives	
sexual response cycle	
stimulus motives	
social motives	
achievement motivation	
need for affiliation	
need for power	
instinct theory	
sociobiology	
drive theory	
drive	
incentive theory	

incentive

arousal theory

Yerkes-Dodson Law

expectancy-value theory

attributions

need hierarchy

self-actualization

emotion

facial feedback hypothesis

James-Lange Theory

Cannon-Bard Theory

cognitive labeling theory

Name ______________________________ Class ______________________ Date ______________

Pretest

Chapter 9 Motivation and Emotion

I. True/False Circle the letter (T or F) that corresponds to the correct response.

T F **1.** The three types of motives are physiological, psychological, and social.

T F **2.** An example of a physiological motive is hunger.

T F **3.** Social motives are characterized by a desire to increase stimulation.

T F **4.** Individuals with high achievement motivation are more likely to succeed in business than people with a high need for affiliation.

T F **5.** Incentive theory states that biological needs motivate behavior necessary to satisfy the need.

T F **6.** The most common way to measure emotion is by lie detector tests.

T F **7.** Paul Ekman's research shows that monitoring facial expression is the best indicator of lying.

T F **8.** The facial feedback hypothesis proposes that specific emotions are determined by the brain's interpretation of facial muscle contractions.

T F **9.** The research on polygraph testing shows that lying produces specific patterns of sympathetic nervous system activity.

T F **10.** The Cannon-Bard theory holds that emotions are determined by interpretations of bodily changes.

II. Multiple Choice Circle the letter that corresponds to the correct or best answer.

1. The motivation to obtain a reward in the external environment is known as ____________________ motivation.

A. intrinsic
B. arousal
C. reward
D. extrinsic

2. Which of the following is considered a social motive?

A. sex
B. achievement
C. contact
D. arousal

3. The motivation to seek out others best describes:

A. sexual motivation
B. achievement motivation
C. the need for contact
D. the need for affiliation

4. Which of the following is a cognitive model of motivation?
   - **A.** drive theory
   - **B.** expectancy-value theory
   - **C.** incentive theory
   - **D.** James-Lange theory

5. The idea that one behaves to preserve genes in offspring is central to the ____________________ theory of motivation.
   - **A.** Freudian
   - **B.** arousal
   - **C.** sociobiology
   - **D.** need hierarchy

6. Which of the following is NOT one of Plutchik's eight primary emotions?
   - **A.** envy
   - **B.** joy
   - **C.** fear
   - **D.** disgust

7. Which of the following statements is TRUE about the relationship between facial expression and emotion?
   - **A.** The meaning of facial expression can be understood only by members of the same race or culture.
   - **B.** People can accurately recognize only fear and anger.
   - **C.** Facial expression is universal.
   - **D.** Facial expressions can only be interpreted by individuals of the same sex.

8. George sees a bear in the woods and runs, making him afraid. Which theory explains emotion in this way?
   - **A.** cognitive-labeling theory
   - **B.** James-Lange theory
   - **C.** expectancy-value theory
   - **D.** Cannon-Bard theory

9. The ____________________ theory holds that emotion is determined by how one interprets physiological changes.
   - **A.** James-Lange
   - **B.** cognitive labeling
   - **C.** Cannon-Bard
   - **D.** expectancy-value

10. Which of the following is the correct sequence of events according to the facial feedback hypothesis?
    - **A.** event-emotion-facial expression
    - **B.** event-brain interpretation-muscle contractions-brain interpretation-emotion
    - **C.** event-facial expression-emotion
    - **D.** event-heart rate increase-facial expression-emotion

III. Short Answer Write the answer in the space provided.

1. How does the Yerkes-Dodson law explain the relationship between arousal and performance?

2. What are the differences between physiological motives and social motives?

3. What are the characteristics of individuals with high achievement motivation.

4. Describe three ways that emotions are measured and expressed.

5. Describe the facial-feedback hypothesis of emotion.

IV. Matching Match the terms in column A with the correct choice in column B

	A	B
______	**1.** physiological motives	**a.** tendency to reach full potential
______	**2.** stimulus motives	**b.** stimulus that has a positive or negative value in motivating behavior
______	**3.** social motives	**c.** view that biological needs motivate behavior
______	**4.** achievement motivation	**d.** interpretation of bodily changes determines emotions
______	**5.** need for affiliation	**e.** concern with doing things better and surpassing standards of excellence
______	**6.** instinct theory	**f.** motives that stem from bodily needs
______	**7.** sociobiology	**g.** explanations for outcomes of behavior
______	**8.** drive theory	**h.** stage of the sexual response cycle marked by a peaking of sexual excitement
______	**9.** incentive	**i.** emotion is determined by how we appraise physiological changes
______	**10.** plateau	**j.** perception causes brain arousal, bodily changes, and emotional feeling
______	**11.** growth need	**k.** view that traits which increase chances of survival are passed on to offspring
______	**12.** arousal theory	**l.** motives in which people try to increase stimulation
______	**13.** Yerkes-Dodson Law	**m.** view that behavior is motivated by a desire to maintain a preferred level of stimulation
______	**14.** Facial Action Coding System	**n.** method for measuring emotions
______	**15.** attributions	**o.** sequence of needs to be satisfied
______	**16.** need hierarchy	**p.** study of the genetic foundations of behavior
______	**17.** self-actualization	**q.** motives that are shaped by society
______	**18.** James-Lange Theory	**r.** motivation to seek out others
______	**19.** Cannon-Bard Theory	**s.** highest needs on Maslow's need hierarchy
______	**20.** cognitive labeling theory	**t.** rule that describes the relationship between arousal and performance

V. Fill In The Blanks Write the answers in the space provided.

1. Behavior controlled by ____________________ is that in which an individual tries to gain a reward from the environment while ____________________ describes behavior that is controlled by factors within you.

2. ____________________ are motives that stem from bodily needs necessary for survival; exploration and curiosity are examples of ____________________ motives.

3. Individuals with a high need for ____________________ typically pursue jobs that are challenging.

4. __________________ theory says that we are motivated by external stimuli called __________________.

5. According to ____________________ theory, individuals are motivated by biological needs and to maintain a state of ____________________.

6. Emotion is defined as a reaction composed of ____________________, ____________________, ____________________, and ____________________.

7. The ____________________ method of measuring emotions involves asking the individual about his or her subjective feelings.

8. Ekman's research shows that the most reliable indicators of lying come from ____________________ and ____________________ cues.

9. The idea that smiling can lift one's mood supports the ____________________ hypothesis of emotion.

10. The notion that "I'm afraid because I run" is consistent with the ____________________ theory of emotion.

Notes

Answer Key To Chapter 9 Pretest

I. True/False

1-F, **2**-T, **3**-F, **4**-T, **5**-F, **6**-F, **7**-T, **8**-T, **9**-F, **10**-T

II. Multiple Choice

1-D, **2**-B, **3**-D, **4**-B, **5**-C, **6**-A, **7**-C, **8**-B, **9**-B, **10**-B

III. Short Answer

1. The Yerkes-Dodson states that performance improves with increases in arousal up to a certain point; increases in arousal beyond the optimal level result in decreased performance.
2. Physiological motives are those which stem from bodily needs that are necessary for survival. Social motives come from the demands of society.
3. People with high achievement motivation prefer challenges that carry moderate risks, are motivated to avoid failure, and are motivated to determine their own behavior.
4. Emotions are expressed and measured in self-reports of subjective feelings, by observable behavior such as facial expression, and by physiological activity like heart rate and blood pressure.
5. The facial-feedback hypothesis states that specific emotions are determined by the brain's interpretation of muscle feedback from facial expression. The perception of a stimulus activates the brain to produce a general pleasant or unpleasant feeling which signals a facial expression. Feedback from the facial muscles is interpreted by the brain to produce a specific emotion.

IV. Matching

1-f, **2**-l, **3**-q, **4**-e, **5**-r, **6**-k, **7**-p, **8**-c, **9**-b, **10**-h, **11**-s, **12**-m, **13**-t, **14**-n, **15**-g, **16**-o, **17**-a, **18**-d, **19**-j, **20**-i

V. Fill In The Blanks

1. extrinsic motivation - intrinsic motivation
2. physiological motives - stimulus
3. achievement
4. incentive - incentives
5. drive - homeostasis
6. subjective feelings - cognitive evaluation - physiological changes - observable behavior
7. self-report
8. facial - vocal
9. facial-feedback
10. James-Lange

Suggested Readings

Davis, L. "A doubtful device." *Health*, November/December 1992: 28-29.

The author discusses the limitations of polygraph testing.

Ekman, P. 1985. *Telling lies: Clues to deceit in the marketplace, marriage, and politics*. New York: Norton.

Ekman explains how to use nonverbal cues, like facial expression, to determine lying.

Harlow, H. F. "Mice, monkey, men, and motives." *Psychology Reviews* 60 (1992): 23-32.

In this article, Harlow presents his classic research on the need for contact comfort.

Herman, P., and J. Polivy. "Fat is a psychological issue." In B. Slife (ed.) *Taking Sides, 8th ed.* Guilford, CT: Dushkin. 34–42.

The authors present their case that obesity stems primarily from psychological factors.

Hoffman, E. "The last interview of Abraham Maslow." *Psychology Today*, January/February 1992: 68-73, 89.

In this interview, Maslow discusses his famous theory of motivation and views of personality.

Marano, H. E. "Chemistry and craving." *Psychology Today*, January/February 1993: 30-36, 74.

This article discusses some recent research on the physiological basis of appetite.

Masters, W. H., and V. E. Johnson. 1966. *Human sexual response*. Boston: Little, Brown.

This is Masters' and Johnson's classic work on human sexual behavior.

Chapter 10

Personality

Chapter Summary

Freud's psychoanalytic theory proposed three parts of personality called id, ego, and superego, and five stages of psychosexual development. Later psychodynamic theorists emphasized other personality concepts: Jung, the collective unconscious; Adler, striving for superiority; Horney, neurotic strategies; Sullivan, self-system; and ego psychology, ego functions.

Humanistic theories stress self-actualization, as well as the hierarchy of needs (Maslow), and the self-concept (Rogers) in behavior and adjustment.

The trait view includes Allport's idiographic approach, as well as factor theories such as Cattell's 16 factors, Eysenck's type theory, and the five factor model.

Behaviorism defines personality as habits governed by the learning environment. In social learning theory, cognitive person variables like self-efficacy and locus-of-control interact with the environment.

Personality assessment involves self-report tests or questionnaires, projective tests, structured and unstructured interviews, and direct observation.

1. **Summarize Freud's theory of personality.** Understanding Freud's personality theory provides a basis for appreciating the modern origins of psychodynamic theory and its impact on psychology.

2. **Discuss four psychodynamic theories of personality that followed from Freud's theory.** Learning about later psychodynamic theories shows the limitations of Freudian psychoanalysis and the development of more modern personality theory.

3. **Outline Maslow's need theory.** Maslow's theory is an important contribution to humanistic psychology that has had impact on the study of motivation and personality.

4. **Identify the main concepts of Rogers' self theory.** A knowledge of Rogers' theory reveals how humanistic psychology considers the development of the self-concept.

5. **Discuss the trait view of personality and compare Allport's theory with the factor theories.** Trait theory is a major part of modern scientific psychology and has led to the development of many widely used personality tests.

6. **Outline the assumptions of behaviorism about personality.** Behaviorism offers an alternative to traditional personality psychology and its ideas about behavior provide a model that ties personality with learning theory.

7. **Describe the social learning view of personality.** By studying social learning theory one can understand how behavior, cognition, and learning are organized in personality and development.

8. **Distinguish among the methods of assessing personality.** Research and applications of personality psychology depend on the use of personality tests. A study of the different tests available reveals the advances and problems in this area.

Name ______________________ Class ________________ Date ____________

Chapter Outline

Chapter 10 Personality

The Psychodynamic View

A. The psychodynamic view describes personality as the result of ______________________
____
____

Freud's Psychoanalytic Theory

A. According to Freud, personality has three parts, called:

1. ______________________
2. ______________________
3. ______________________

B. The id is characterized by ______________________
____
____

C. Ego is the part of personality that involves ______________________
____
____

D. Superego is the part of personality that ______________________
____
____

E. The defense mechanisms are ______________________
____
____

F. Psychosexual development refers to ______________________
____
____

G. The Oedipus and Electra complexes are ______________________
____
____

Other Psychodynamic Theories

A. Jung's central concept was the collective unconscious, which means ______

____

____

Jung's Analytical Psychology

A. For Jung, an archetype meant ______

____

____

Adler's Individual Psychology

A. Adler's individual psychology stressed the importance of ______

____

____

B. The striving for superiority refers to ______

____

____

C. An inferiority complex is ______

____

____

Interpersonal Theory

A. Interpersonal theory proposes that personality is formed by ______

____

____

B. Horney described three neurotic strategies:

1. ______
2. ______
3. ______

C. Sullivan's personality theory is based on the concept of self-system, which refers to ______

____

____

Ego Psychology

A. Ego psychology assumes that ______________________________

____

____

B. Erik Erikson's theory emphasizes ______________________________

____

____

C. Object relations refer to ______________________________

____

____

The Humanistic View

A. Humanistic psychology assumes that ______________________________

____

____

B. Self-actualization means ______________________________

____

____

Maslow's Need Theory

A. Maslow's need theory depict personality as ______________________________

____

____

B. The need hierarchy refers to ______________________________

____

____

C. Self-actualizers are characterized by ______________________________

____

____

Rogers' Self Theory

A. In self theory, self-concept means ______________________________

____

____

B. Rogers proposed two aspects of self-concept:

1. ______

2. ______

C. Congruence means ______

D. Fully functioning personality refers to ______

E. In Rogers's theory, personality development is affected by ______

The Trait View

A. A personality trait is defined as ______

Allport's Theory

A. Allport's idiographic approached examined ______

B. Allport identified three types of traits:

1. ______

2. ______

3. ______

Factor Theories

A. A personality factor is ______

Cattell's Factor Theory

A. In Cattell's theory, a source trait is ______

Eysenck's Type Theory

A. Eysenck describes three personality dimensions:

1. ______________________________
2. ______________________________
3. ______________________________

B. Evidence for a biological basis of the personality dimensions includes ______

____

____

The Five Factor Model

A. The five factor model describes the "Big Five" dimensions of personality:

1. ______________________________
2. ______________________________
3. ______________________________
4. ______________________________
5. ______________________________

Learning View

A. In Skinner's theory, personality is ______________________________

____

Behaviorism

A. The principle of environmental determinism means ______________________________

____

____

Social Learning Theory

A. A cognitive person variable is ______________________________

____

____

B. Bandura's self-efficacy concept means ______________________________

____

____

C. Rotter's concept of locus-of-control means ______________________________

____

____

D. The two locus-of-control types are ______________________________

____

____

Assessing Personality

A. Three criteria for personality tests are:

1. ______________________________

2. ______________________________

3. ______________________________

Self-Report Tests

A. A self-report test of personality requires that the test taker______________________________

____

____

B. Some examples of self-report tests are ______________________________

____

____

C. The problems of self-report tests include ______________________________

____

____

Projective Tests

A. A projective test consists of______________________________

____

____

B. The assumption behind the use of projective tests is that ______________________________

____

____

C. Examples of projective tests are ______________________________

____

____

Other Assessment Methods

A. An interview assesses personality by ______________________________

____

____

B. There are two types of interviews:

1. ______________________________

2. ______________________________

C. The method of direct observation means ______________________________

____

____

Issues and Applications

Personality and Friendship

A. In terms of personality, the "birds of a feather" idea means that ______________

____

____

B. In terms of personality, the "opposites attract" idea means that ______________

____

____

C. Research on the "birds of a feather" and "opposites attract" ideas finds that

____

____

Vocations and Personality

A. Holland proposes six personality types that correspond to vocational interests:

1. ______________________________

2. ______________________________

3. ______________________________

4. ______________________________

5. ______________________________

6. ______________________________

B. The relationship between personality and vocation is important because

____

____

Biography

Sigmund Freud

A. Early in his career Freud conducted studies of ______________________________

____

____

B. Freud is best known for his contributions to ______________________________

____

____

Name ______________________ Class ______________ Date ____________

Key Terms Worksheet

Write a definition for each key term on the lines provided.

Term	Definition
personality	______________________
psychodynamic view	______________________
id	______________________
ego	______________________
superego	______________________
defense mechanisms	______________________
analytical psychology	______________________
individual psychology	______________________
interpersonal theory	______________________
ego psychology	______________________
need theory	______________________
self theory	______________________
fully functioning personality	______________________

traits ______________________________

____

idiographic approach ______________________________

____

Cattell's factor theory ______________________________

____

type theory ______________________________

____

five factor model ______________________________

____

environmental determinism ______________________________

____

self-efficacy ______________________________

____

locus-of-control ______________________________

____

self-report test ______________________________

____

projective test ______________________________

____

Name ______________________ Class ______________________ Date ______________

Pretest

Chapter 10 Personality

I. True/False Circle the letter (T or F) that corresponds to the correct response.

T F **1.** The psychodynamic view assumes that personality is controlled by unconscious forces.

T F **2.** Jung's analytical psychology emphasizes the role of inborn archetypes on personality.

T F **3.** Aggression is a growth need in Maslow's theory.

T F **4.** According to Rogers, a person who experiences many conditions of worth will be well-adjusted.

T F **5.** Factor theories rely on statistical analyses to define the structure of personality.

T F **6.** Eysenck identified introversion-extraversion, neuroticism, and psychoticism as the basic dimensions of personality.

T F **7.** Behaviorism assumes that personality consists of cognitive variables that interact with the environment.

T F **8.** Locus-of-control refers to beliefs about the variables that influence your behavior.

T F **9.** The MMPI is a projective test of personality.

T F **10.** In the Rorschach test and TAT, subjects are asked to interpret ambiguous stimuli.

II. Multiple Choice Circle the letter that corresponds to the correct or best answer.

1. In Freud's psychoanalytic theory, which part of personality is controlled by the reality principle?

A. id
B. ego
C. superego
D. real self

2. The main motive behind behavior is striving for superiority, according to:

A. Horney's interpersonal theory
B. Adler's individual psychology
C. Jung's analytical psychology
D. Erikson's ego psychology

3. Which of the following illustrates rationalization?

A. Blaming a family member for school failure.
B. Blocking unpleasant memories out of one's mind.
C. Inventing convenient excuses for one's misbehavior.
D. Refusing to accept the facts of reality.

4. Which point of view assumes the importance of self-actualization?
   A. ego psychology
   B. the trait view
   C. behaviorism
   D. humanistic psychology

5. In Rogers' theory, congruence is a sign of:
   A. a personality disorder
   B. an inborn archetype
   C. a healthy self-concept
   D. a neurotic personality

6. What traits characterize the introverted type?
   A. aggressive, self-centered, dominant
   B. quiet, reserved, thoughtful
   C. anxious, neurotic, unstable
   D. outgoing, active, assertive

7. In the five factor model, the "Big Five" factors of personality do not include:
   A. intelligence
   B. emotional stability
   C. openness
   D. conscientiousness

8. The principle of environmental determinism is associated with which view?
   A. behaviorism
   B. self theory
   C. analytical psychology
   D. social learning theory

9. Which example describes positive self-efficacy?
   A. Rich believes that he cannot control his future.
   B. Rich believes that luck is the major force in life.
   C. Rich believes that he will succeed in his math class.
   D. Rich believes that he will always be a failure.

10. The Rorschach test is an example of a:
    A. self-report test
    B. projective test
    C. multi-trait questionnaire
    D. structured interview

III. Short Answer Write the answer in the space provided.

1. Describe the parts of personality in Freud's theory.

2. What are the assumptions of the humanistic view?

3. What are the "Big Five" factors of personality?

4. What is the view of behaviorism on personality?

5. What is a self-report test of personality?

IV. Matching Match the terms in column A with the correct choice in column B.

	A	B
______	**1.** primary process thinking	**a.** love with "no strings attached"
______	**2.** ego-ideal	**b.** an image of the person one should become
______	**3.** Oedipus complex	**c.** the activity of the id
______	**4.** sublimation	**d.** the most pervasive motives or dispositions of personality
______	**5.** projection	**e.** a projective test
______	**6.** archetypes	**f.** a basic personality dimension according to Eysenck
______	**7.** inferiority complex	**g.** state of similarity between real and ideal selves
______	**8.** object relations	**h.** internalized images of others
______	**9.** growth needs	**i.** a developmental problem for boys
______	**10.** congruence	**j.** inborn structures of the collective unconscious
______	**11.** unconditional positive regard	**k.** feelings of self-doubt, anxiety, and insecurity
______	**12.** cardinal trait	**l.** directing feelings into socially acceptable behavior
______	**13.** personality factor	**m.** highest level of Maslow's need hierarchy
______	**14.** neuroticism	**n.** belief that one is responsible for events in one's life
______	**15.** conscientiousness	**o.** one of the "Big Five" personality factors
______	**16.** environmental determinism	**p.** placing unacceptable feelings onto other people
______	**17.** self-efficacy	**q.** a broad range self-report test
______	**18.** internal locus-of-control	**r.** a cognitive person variable from Bandura's theory
______	**19.** MMPI	**s.** a pattern of correlated personality traits
______	**20.** Thematic Apperception Test	**t.** belief that the learning environment controls behavior

V. Fill In The Blanks Write the answers in the space provided.

1. In Freud's theory, the most powerful part of personality, called the ____________________, is based on two unconscious drives, the ____________________ and ____________________ instincts, and works according to the ____________________ principle.

2. According to Freud, there are five stages of ____________________ development during which sexual energy, or ____________________ , is focused on specific activities. Problems in development may produce severe difficulties, such as the ____________________ complex in boys and ____________________ complex in girls.

3. Jung's analytical psychology stressed the importance of the ____________________ unconscious which includes inborn structures called ____________________, such as the masculine qualities of ____________________ and feminine qualities of ____________________.

4. In Maslow's theory, needs are organized into a need ____________________ that includes lower level ____________________ needs and higher level ____________________ needs. People who successfully satisfy these needs are psychologically well-adjusted individuals known as ____________________.

5. According to Rogers, personality is part of the subjective experience or ____________________ field in which the self-perceptions define ____________________ self and goals and aspirations comprise the ____________________ self. When the real and ideal selves are similar the individual is in a state of ____________________.

6. Allport examined individual trait organizations in his ____________________ approach to personality which assumed that every personality is ____________________. According to Allport, five to ten most basic characteristics are the ____________________ traits, and the one or two most pervasive motives or dispositions are the ____________________ traits.

7. Factor theories rely on a statistical procedure called ____________________ which describes patterns of ____________________ traits known as personality factors. Cattell's theory identified 16 factors or ____________________, while ____________________ found three basic dimensions.

8. The chief figure in modern behaviorism was ____________________ who argued that personality refers to an individual's ____________________ which is controlled by the ____________________ according to the principle of ____________________.

9. Social learning theory defines personality in terms of cognitive ___________________ that have ___________________ cause-and-effect relationships with behavior and the environment. Bandura's social learning theory stresses the concept of ___________________, while Rotter's stresses the concept of ___________________.

10. Personality assessment that requires you to answer a set of questions is a ___________________ test, such as the MMPI, which is an abbreviation for _____________________________________. Projective tests require one to interpret ___________________ stimuli, as in the famous ___________________ Inkblots test.

Answer Key To Chapter 10 Pretest

I. True/False

1-T, **2**-T, **3**-F, **4**-F, **5**-T, **6**-T, **7**-F, **8**-T, **9**-F, **10**-T

II. Multiple Choice

1-B, **2**-B, **3**-C, **4**-D, **5**-C, **6**-B, **7**-A, **8**-A, **9**-C, **10**-B

III. Short Answer

1. The id is the primitive irrational part of personality that is based on life and death instincts; the ego controls identity and adaptation to reality; the super-ego controls moral judgment.

2. Humanistic psychology assumes that people have freedom of choice, personal responsibility, an essential goodness, and a drive for self-fulfillment or self-actualization.

3. The five factor model states that the "Big Five" personality factors are extraversion, agreeableness, conscientiousness, emotional stability, and openness.

4. According to behaviorism, personality consists of learned behavior patterns that are controlled by the environment as described by the principle of environmental determinism.

5. A self-report test of personality is an assessment method that requires the test taker to respond to a set of questions regarding attitudes, beliefs, and behaviors.

IV. Matching

1-c, **2**-b, **3**-i, **4**-l, **5**-p, **6**-j, **7**-k, **8**-h, **9**-m, **10**-g, **11**-a, **12**-d, **13**-s, **14**-f, **15**-o, **16**-t, **17**-r, **18**-n, **19**-q, **20**-e

V. Fill In The Blanks

1. id - life - death - pleasure

2. psychosexual - libido - Oedipus - Electra

3. collective - archetypes - animus - anima

4. hierarchy - basic - growth - self-actualizers

5. phenomenal - real - ideal - congruence

6. idiographic - unique - central - cardinal

7. factor analysis - correlated - source traits - Eysenck

8. Skinner - behavior - learning environment - environmental determinism

9. person variables - reciprocal - self-efficacy - locus-of-control

10. self-report - Minnesota Multiphasic Personality Inventory - ambiguous - Rorschach

Suggested Readings

Bandura, A. 1977. *Social learning theory*. Englewood Cliffs, NJ: Prentice Hall.

In this compact book, Bandura develops the conceptual and research basis of modern social learning theory of personality and motivation.

Cattell, R. B. 1966. *The scientific analysis of personality*. Chicago: Aldine.

Cattell describes the assumptions and methods behind factor theories of personality. Although its presentation is generally non-technical, the material is fairly demanding of the reader. However, if one perseveres, one will learn about the foundations of modern personality research.

Freud, S. 1927. *The ego and the Id*. London: Hogarth.
1933. *New introductory lectures on psychoanalysis*. New York: Norton.

Although nearly any of Freud's works will provide information about the psychoanalytic theory of personality, these two slim books are a good foundation for the beginner. Both focus on the basic assumptions and concepts of Freudian personality theory.

Hall, C. S., and G. Lindzey. 1985 *Theories of personality, 4th ed.* New York: Wiley.

A classic on personality theory, this textbook provides excellent summaries and evaluations of the fundamental concepts of modern personality theories. For the student who is motivated to learn more about personality, this is an excellent source.

Rogers, C. R. 1961. *On becoming a person*. Boston: Houghton Mifflin.

This collection of essays by Carl Rogers, the main figure in the humanistic view, explores numerous aspects of the human condition, including personality, social relations, education, and other topics. A good entry point to humanistic philosophy and psychology.

Skinner, B. F. 1974. *About behaviorism*. New York: Knopf.

In this book, Skinner delivers his basic notions about psychology, learning, behavior, and personality. Clearly written and argued, this work is a summary of behaviorism.

Chapter 11

Psychology and Health

Chapter Summary

Stress is a reaction to a stimulus or event that a person appraises as threatening. Major sources of stress include change, hassles, pressure, frustration, conflict, and traumatic experiences. Stress can have many physical effects, such as alteration of the immune system and psychosomatic disorders. Stress can also result in psychological effects too, such as anger, depression, and anxiety, as well as learned helplessness, burnout, and posttraumatic stress disorder.

Strong coping abilities can help individuals resist the effects of stress and promote health. Ineffective attempts to cope can lead to physical and psychological illness. Social support can act as a buffer against stress. Personality factors, including the disease-prone personality, Type–A behavior pattern, and hostility complex, have been associated with illness. Type–B features and hardiness are related to health promotion. Stress effects are also related to one's attributional style.

Stress management techniques such as relaxation training, hypnosis, meditation, guided imagery, and biofeedback are designed to reduce bodily arousal and are useful in the treatment of headaches, hypertension, asthma, and gastrointestinal disorders. Illness prevention and health promotion involves the identification of illness risk factors and learning how to change risky behaviors and adopting behaviors that promote health.

1. **Describe the nature of stress.** Though stress is a word that is used often in everyday life, psychologists have had difficulty defining it. It is important to know that stress can be defined in terms of the stressor, the effects that the stressor has on a person, or as a relationship between the person and the environment.

2. **Identify the six main sources of stress.** Even using the cognitive definition presented in the text, there needs to be some stimulus or event to trigger appraisals. Identifying the various sources of stress acquaints one with the major stressors that psychologists study.

3. **Describe the physical effects of stress.** Besides its psychological effects, stress reactions can involve many negative physical changes, too. Because everyone is potentially susceptible to the physical effects of stress, it is important to become aware of what they are.

4. **Explain the psychological consequences of stress.** Stress reactions can involve many psychological and physical consequences. It is necessary to be aware of them because effects like anger and depression can seriously affect one's ability to function in school, relationships, and work.

5. **Define coping and discuss how it is related to health and illness.** It is important to realize that cognitive views of stress emphasize that coping abilities can moderate the effects of stress.

6. **Explain the relationships among personality, health, and illness.** Psychologists have identified several personality characteristics that are associated with health and illness. Knowing what these characteristics are gives insight into the role of personality variables in health and illness.

7. **Explain how health and illness depend on cognitive factors.** When people are stressed out they usually blame a stimulus or event. It should be realized, however, that how one appraises situations is a major determinant in whether one will be seriously affected by those stimuli.

8. **Describe stress management techniques.** It is important to know that psychologists have developed many easy-to-learn techniques that can be used to fight off the effects of stress.

9. **Discuss the factors in illness prevention and health promotion.** Because the best way to combat stress is to prevent it, one should be able to identify the important prevention factors.

Name ____________________ Class ____________________ Date ____________________

Chapter Outline

Chapter 11 Psychology and Health

The Nature of Stress

A. Today, psychologists believe that health and illness depend on the interaction of ____________________

____

B. Health psychology applies ____________________

____

What is Stress?

A. Three ways to define stress are:

1. ____________________
2. ____________________
3. ____________________

B. In general, events that you appraise as are likely to be most stressful ____________________

____

The Sources of Stress

A. The six major sources of stress are:

1. ____________________
2. ____________________
3. ____________________
4. ____________________
5. ____________________
6. ____________________

Change

A. The Social Readjustment Rating Scale measures stress in terms of ____________________

____

Hassles, Pressure, and Frustration

A. Hassles are ____

____

____

B. Pressure is ____

____

____

C. Frustration results when ____

____

____

Conflict

A. Conflict is defined as ____

____

____

B. Three types of conflict are:

1. ____

2. ____

3. ____

C. Approach-avoidance conflicts involve ____

____

____

D. Whether an individual ultimately approaches or avoids depends on ________

____

____

E. Avoidance-avoidance conflicts involve ____

____

____

F. In an approach-approach conflict one must ____

____

____

Traumatic Experiences

A. Traumatic experiences are ______________________________

____

____

B. Events which can lead to trauma include ______________________________

____

____

How Stress Affects You

A. Two main effects of stress are:

1. ______________________________

2. ______________________________

Physical Effects

A. The emergency theory states that ______________________________

____

____

B. The three stages of the general adaptation syndrome are:

1. ______________________________

2. ______________________________

3. ______________________________

C. During the alarm stage of the general adaptation syndrome ______________________________

____

____

D. Resistance involves ______________________________

____

____

E. In the exhaustion stage ______________________________

____

____

Stress and the Immune System

A. The immune system refers to ______________________________

____

____

B. Antibodies are ______________________________

____

____

C. Chronic stress is ______________________________

____

____

D. Two examples of acute stress are:

1. ______________________________

2. ______________________________

Psychosomatic Disorders

A. A psychosomatic disorder is ______________________________

____

____

B. Ulcers are ______________________________

____

____

C. Migraines are ______________________________

____

____

D. Asthma refers to a ______________________________

____

____

Psychological Effects

A. The frustration-aggression hypothesis states that ______________________________

____

____

B. Research shows that frustration is not the only cause of aggression and aggression

____

____

C. Learned helplessness is a state in which ______

______

______

D. Burnout is ______

______

______

E. Posttraumatic stress disorder is identified by ______

______

______

F. Three problems associated with posttraumatic stress disorder are:

1. ______

2. ______

3. ______

The Psychology of Health and Illness

A. Three psychological factors related to health and illness are:

1. ______

2. ______

3. ______

Coping

A. Coping is defined as ______

______

______

B. Generally, stronger coping abilities make a person ______

______

______

Coping Strategies

A. The three types of coping strategies are:

1. ______

2. ______

3. ______

B. Problem-focused coping is ______

______

C. An example of emotion-focused coping is ______________________________

____

____

D. Perception-focused coping means ______________________________

____

____

E. Problem-focused coping works best when ______________________________

____

____

F. Avoidance works best when ______________________________

____

____

Social Support

A. Social support is ______________________________

____

____

B. Two ways in which psychologists believe social support works are:

1. ______________________________

2. ______________________________

C. Three forms that social support can take are:

1. ______________________________

2. ______________________________

3. ______________________________

D. In general, women with marital problems experience______________________________

____

____

Personality

A. Franz Alexander proposed that ______________________________

____

____

B. The disease-prone personality consists of ______________________

____

____

C. A person with a repressed personality is ______________________

____

____

D. The Type–A behavior pattern is identified by ______________________

____

____

E. The hostility complex is expressed as ______________________

____

____

F. Three criticisms of the research linking Type–A behavior and the hostility complex to coronary heart disease are:

1. ____

2. ____

3. ____

G. Type–B individuals are ______________________

____

____

H. The features of hardiness are ______________________

____

____

Cognitive Factors

A. The belief that one lacks control of one's life leads to ______________________

____

____

B. An attributional style is ______________________

____

____

Stress Management and Promotion of Health

A. Three general ways to help people gain a sense of control are:

1. ______________________________

2. ______________________________

3. ______________________________

B. Behavioral medicine integrates ______________________________

____

____

Stress Management Techniques

A. Stress management refers to ______________________________

____

____

B. Muscle relaxation involves ______________________________

____

____

C. Guided imagery is ______________________________

____

____

D. In a standard biofeedback program, the individual learns to control:

1. ______________________________

2. ______________________________

3. ______________________________

Preventing Illness and Promoting Health

A. The prevention of illness requires ______________________________

____

____

B. Three risk factors associated with physical illness are:

1. ______________________________

2. ______________________________

3. ______________________________

C. Two important ways to prevent illness and promote health are:

1. ______________________________

2. ______________________________

Issues and Applications

Stress at Work

A. Three principal sources of work stress are:

1. ______________________________

2. ______________________________

3. ______________________________

B. Work stress is often worse for women because ______________________________

____

____

C. The cost of job stress is high because of ______________________________

____

____

Stress-Inoculation Training

A. The three steps of stress-inoculation training are:

1. ______________________________

2. ______________________________

3. ______________________________

B. Preparing oneself for stress involves ______________________________

____

____

Biography

Hans Selye

A. Selye's concept of the general adaptation syndrome has influenced our understanding of ______________________________

____

B. Selye owed much of his productivity as a researcher to ______________________________

____

____

Notes

Name ______________________ Class ________________ Date ____________

Key Terms Worksheet

Write a definition for each key term on the lines provided.

Terms	Definition
health psychology	
stressor	
stress	
approach-avoidance conflict	
avoidance-avoidance conflict	
approach-approach conflict	
emergency theory	
general adaptation syndrome	
immune system	
psychosomatic disorder	
frustration-aggression hypothesis	
learned helplessness	

posttraumatic stress disorder ______________________________

____

coping ______________________________

____

social support ______________________________

____

disease-prone personality ______________________________

____

Type–A behavior pattern ______________________________

____

hostility complex ______________________________

____

Type–B personality ______________________________

____

hardiness ______________________________

____

behavioral medicine ______________________________

____

stress management ______________________________

____

biofeedback ______________________________

____

Name ______________________ Class ________________ Date ____________

Pretest

Chapter 11 Psychology And Health

I. True/False Circle the letter (T or F) corresponding to the correct response.

T F **1.** Cognitive definitions of stress focus on people's appraisals of events.

T F **2.** Research indicates that nearly three quarters of all Americans find their jobs stressful.

T F **3.** A situation in which a person is both attracted to and repelled by a stimulus is called an approach-avoidance conflict.

T F **4.** The three stages of Cannon's emergency model are alarm, resistance, and exhaustion.

T F **5.** Psychosomatic disorders are imaginary conditions that people experience under stress.

T F **6.** The most common psychological effect of stress is posttraumatic stress disorder.

T F **7.** Emotion-focused coping means reappraising a situation so that it is viewed as less threatening.

T F **8.** Research shows that social support generally increases one's resistance to stress.

T F **9.** A negative emotional style marked by depression, anxiety, and hostility characterizes the disease-prone personality.

T F **10.** In biofeedback treatment a person is hooked up to a machine that monitors muscle tension.

II. Multiple Choice Circle the letter that corresponds to the correct or best answer.

1. The Social Readjustment Rating Scale views stress as:

A. conflict
B. life change
C. pressure
D. change

2. In an ________________ conflict an individual is faced with a stimulus that he or she appraises as both positive and negative.

A. avoidance-avoidance
B. approach-approach
C. unresolvable
D. approach-avoidance

3. The ________________ states that stress disrupts homeostasis and activates the sympathetic nervous system.

A. general adaptation syndrome
B. frustration-aggression hypothesis
C. learned helplessness model
D. emergency theory

4. The stage of the general adaptation syndrome marked by activation of the sympathetic division of the autonomic nervous system is the ____________________ stage.
   A. alarm
   B. resistance
   C. exhaustion
   D. helplessness
5. Stress can affect resistance to infection by impairing the functioning of the:
   A. immune system
   B. ability to cope with approach-avoidance conflicts
   C. biofeedback mechanisms
   D. ability to use emotion-focused coping mechanisms
6. Behavior characterized by striving for achievement, hostility, and time urgency is the ____________________ behavior pattern.
   A. Type–A
   B. Type–B
   C. Type–C
   D. disease-prone
7. A three-step method in which one uses cognitive preparation, skills acquisition, and application practice is called:
   A. guided imagery
   B. burnout prevention training
   C. stress-inoculation training
   D. biofeedback
8. Which of the following is NOT a stress management procedure?
   A. guided imagery
   B. hypnosis
   C. general adaptation training
   D. meditation
9. Psychosomatic disorders are those that:
   A. one imagines having
   B. are caused exclusively by stressors
   C. are caused, in part, by psychological factors
   D. are never serious because they are imaginary
10. One common psychological consequence of stress is:
    A. an immune system disorder
    B. Type-B personality
    C. learned helplessness
    D. an attributional illness

III. Short Answer Write the answer in the space provided.

1. Name and describe three ways of defining stress.

2. Describe the three types of conflicts.

3. Identify and describe the stages of the general adaptation syndrome.

4. What are the characteristics of the hostility complex?

5. What role do cognitive factors play in stress reactions?

IV. Matching Match the terms in column A with the correct choice in column B.

A

______ **1.** guided imagery
______ **2.** hypertension
______ **3.** stressor
______ **4.** approach-avoidance conflict
______ **5.** avoidance-avoidance conflict
______ **6.** emergency theory
______ **7.** general adaptation syndrome
______ **8.** immune system
______ **9.** psychosomatic disorder
______ **10.** frustration-aggression hypothesis
______ **11.** learned helplessness
______ **12.** posttraumatic stress disorder
______ **13.** social support
______ **14.** disease-prone personality
______ **15.** Type–A behavior pattern
______ **16.** hostility complex
______ **17.** Type–B personality
______ **18.** hardiness
______ **19.** stress-inoculation training
______ **20.** biofeedback

B

a. a physical disease caused by stress

b. an extreme emotional reaction to a catastrophic event

c. high blood pressure

d. a stress management technique that involves visualizing pleasant events

e. parts of the body which resist infection

f. a psychological consequence of stress related to depression

g. functions performed for distressed individuals by others

h. a negative emotional style involving depression, anxiety, and hostility

i. the idea that biological systems strive to maintain homeostasis

j. frequent anger and irritation at small things

k. traits of commitment, control, and challenge

l. the stimulus that causes stress

m. a stress management technique that involves the monitoring of body functions

n. a personality style in which the person is not competitive, easily angered, or time pressured

o. Selye's three stage model of stress

p. conflict that arises when a stimulus has both pleasant and unpleasant features

q. behavior marked by competitiveness, anger, and time pressure

r. a three step process to counter the effects of stress

s. the idea that being blocked from a goal has negative psychological and behavioral effects

t. a conflict involving two undesirable stimuli

V. Fill In The Blanks Write the answers in the space provided.

1. Stress is a relationship between a __________________ and the __________________ that is appraised as __________________ to one's well being.

2. In an __________________ conflict, the person is attracted to the pleasant features of a stimulus and motivated to __________________ the unpleasant features.

3. Headaches experienced on one side of the head are called __________________ while those which are felt as a dull ache are known as __________________ headaches.

4. Posttraumatic stress disorder is marked by __________________, __________________, depression, and reexperiences of the traumatic event called __________________.

5. Coping that involves direct efforts to change a stressful situation is known as __________________. Trying to relieve the unpleasant feeling associated with stress is called __________________ and __________________ means reappraising a situation so it appears less threatening.

6. A person with a __________________ personality would show symptoms of anxiety, depression, and hostility. Being passive, defensive, and emotionally unexpressive indicates a __________________ personality.

7. Competitive striving for achievement, hostility, aggressiveness, and time urgency mark the __________________ behavior pattern.

8. A consistent way of explaining responsibility for your condition is called a(n) __________________.

9. The integration of behavior therapy and techniques from medicine is called __________________.

10. A stress management technique that involves having a person imagine pleasurable sensory experiences is called __________________.

Notes

Answer Key To Chapter 11 Pretest

I. True/False

1-T, **2**-F, **3**-T, **4**-F, **5**-F, **6**-F, **7**-F, **8**-T, **9**-T, **10**-T

II. Multiple Choice

1-D, **2**-D, **3**-D, **4**-A, **5**-A, **6**-A, **7**-C, **8**-C, **9**-C, **10**-C

III. Short Answer

1. Stress can be defined in terms of the stressful stimulus, or stressor. Stress is often defined as the psychological and physical effects that stimuli have on a person. A third way is to define stress as a person-environment interaction based on how one appraises situations.
2. Approach-avoidance conflicts are characterized by approaching a stimulus because of its pleasant features, yet avoiding the stimulus because of its unpleasant features. In avoidance-avoidance conflicts, one is motivated to avoid unpleasant situations. With approach-approach conflicts, one is motivated to approach two pleasant situations.
3. The first stage is alarm, which is characterized by activation of the sympathetic nervous system. During the resistance stage there is activation of the hypothalamus and endocrine system. Coping fails in the exhaustion stage, marked by organ breakdown and disease.
4. The hostility complex is the active ingredient of the Type–A behavior pattern that is associated with coronary heart disease. It is marked by anger, hostility, and frequent irritation at small things.
5. Cognitive factors determine how one appraises situations. Stress generally results when one appraises a situation as threatening to well-being.

IV. Matching

1-d, **2**-c, **3**-l, **4**-p, **5**-t, **6**-i, **7**-o, **8**-e, **9**-a, **10**-s, **11**-f, **12**-b, **13**-g, **14**-h, **15**-q, **16**-j, **17**–n, **18**-k, **19**-r, **20**-m

V. Fill In The Blanks

1. person - environment - threatening
2. approach-avoidance - avoid
3. migraines - tension
4. anxiety - concentration problems - flashbacks
5. problem-focused coping - emotion-focused coping - perception-focused
6. disease-prone - repressed
7. Type–A
8. attribution
9. behavioral medicine
10. guided imagery

Suggested Readings

Folkman, S., and R. S. Lazarus. 1984. *Stress, appraisal, and coping*. New York: Springer.

The authors present their cognitive view of stress and the role of cognitions in coping.

Freudenberger, H. J. 1980. *Burnout: How to beat the high cost of success*. New York: Bantam.

This is the classic book about stress and burnout.

Friedman, M., and R. H. Rosenman. 1974. *Type A behavior and your heart*. New York: Knopf.

This work describes the pioneering research on the relationship between Type A behavior and coronary heart disease.

Grady, D. "Think right. Stay well?" *American Health* 1992: 50-54.

The author provides a critical evaluation that questions the relationship between stress and impaired immune system function.

Chapter 12

Abnormal Psychology and Therapy

Chapter Summary

Views of abnormal behavior have changed throughout history. Prescientific views were based on supernaturalism. The late 1800s were marked by scientific views of abnormal behavior from psychiatry and clinical psychology. Today, the four main definitions are that abnormal behavior is behavior that is statistically uncommon, a violation of the social norm, maladaptive, or that which causes personal distress. Abnormal behavior that causes pain, suffering, pain, death, or disability is called a mental disorder according to the DSM-IV.

Anxiety disorders are marked by anxiety and related thoughts, feelings, and behaviors that interfere with normal functioning. A physical symptom for which no medical basis can be found is the essential feature of the somatoform disorders. In dissociative disorders there is a sudden alteration of consciousness, memory, or identity. Substance-related disorders are those in which there is a maladaptive pattern of drug use, such as substance abuse or dependence. Mood disorders are marked by episodes of depression, mania, or an alternation of the two. Schizophrenia is marked by severe problems in judgment and reasoning, emotions, perceptions, and behavior. With personality disorders, maladaptive, inflexible, and distressing personality traits are seen. The causes of mental disorders are believed to involve the interaction of environmental factors, including early experiences, and biological variables, such as heredity and biochemical disturbances.

Treatments for mental disorders usually involve some form of psychotherapy, such as psychodynamic therapy, behavior therapy, and client-centered therapy. In some cases, antianxiety, antidepressant, or antipsychotic drugs, or electroconvulsive therapy may be used along with psychotherapy.

Chapter Objectives

1. **Summarize prescientific views of abnormal behavior.** History has been marked by different views of abnormal behavior. It is important to be aware of prescientific views of abnormal behavior because they are very different from those accepted today. By comparing prescientific and scientific views of abnormal behavior, one can appreciate that there are no absolute definitions for it.

2. **List four definitions of abnormal behavior.** Because there is no universally accepted definition of abnormal, it is important to understand the definitions most commonly used today.

3. **Identify the anxiety, somatoform, and dissociative disorders.** These disorders were formerly grouped together as neuroses. It is important to understand that modern research indicates that, in fact, these conditions represent distinct diagnostic categories.

4. **Distinguish between substance abuse and dependence.** Not all drug problems are the same. Research shows that substance abuse and dependence are different and may therefore require different treatments.

5. **Outline the mood disorders.** Mood disorders, especially those involving depression, are one of the most common types of disorders. As such, it is necessary to be able to distinguish them.

6. **Describe the main features of schizophrenia.** Schizophrenia is one of many different types of psychosis and is considered the gravest mental disorder. For these reasons, an understanding of the main features of schizophrenia is important to an overall appreciation of mental disorders.

7. **Summarize the personality disorders.** It is important to know about the personality disorders because they are common mental disorders and often underlie other types of mental disorders.

8. **Outline the psychotherapies for mental disorders.** Psychotherapy represents one of the most important contributions to the field of abnormal psychology. Understanding the major psychotherapies not only provides a basis for treating mental disorders, but also gives a view of some of the important names in the history of psychology.

9. **Describe biological therapies for mental disorders.** It is important to realize that psychotherapy is sometimes limited in its ability to resolve mental disorders. Knowing about biological therapies like drugs and ECT provides a more complete picture of the treatment options available for the treatment of mental disorders.

Name ______________________ Class ______________ Date ____________

Chapter Outline

Chapter 12 Abnormal Psychology and Therapy

What is Abnormal Behavior?

A. Abnormal psychology is defined as ______________________________

____

____

Historical Views

A. Supernaturalism is ______________________________

____

____

B. In supernaturalism, three procedures used to remove evil spirits were:

1. ______________________________

2. ______________________________

3. ______________________________

C. Psychiatry is ______________________________

____

____

D. Clinical psychology studies ______________________________

____

____

E. Five models of abnormal behavior are:

1. ______________________________

2. ______________________________

3. ______________________________

4. ______________________________

5. ______________________________

F. Four modern definitions of abnormal are:

1. ______________________________

2. ______________________________

3. ______________________________

4. ______________________________

G. Maladaptive behavior is ______________________________

____

____

H. According to the social norm definition, behavior is abnormal if__________

____

____

Abnormal Behavior and Mental Disorders

A. A mental disorder is defined as ______________________________

____

____

B. The DSM-IV is ______________________________

____

____

Anxiety, Somatoform, and Dissociative Disorders

A. The term neuroses formerly included ______________________________

____

____

B. For Freud, a neurosis indicated ______________________________

____

____

Anxiety Disorders

A. The anxiety disorders ______________________________

____

____

B. The five types of anxiety disorders are:

1. ______________________________
2. ______________________________
3. ______________________________
4. ______________________________
5. ______________________________

C. The features of generalized anxiety disorder include ______________________________

____

D. Panic disorders are marked by ______________________________

____

____

E. People with phobia disorder experience ______________________

____

____

F. Agoraphobia is ____

____

____

G. People suffering from social phobia have ____________________

____

____

H. The two main features of obsessive-compulsive disorder are:

1. ____

2. ____

I. Obsessions are ____

____

____

J. Compulsions involve ____

____

____

K. Evidence for an inherited tendency to develop anxiety disorders is ________

____

____

L. Three neurotransmitters involved in the anxiety disorders are:

1. ____

2. ____

3. ____

M. Psychodynamic psychologists view anxiety as __________________

____

____

Somatoform Disorders

A. The essential feature of a somatoform disorder is ______________________

____

____

B. Conversion disorder involves ______________________

____

____

C. The main feature of hypochondriasis is ______________________

____

____

Dissociative Disorders

A. Dissociation is ______________________

____

____

B. Dissociative disorders involve ______________________

____

____

C. Dissociative identity disorder is characterized by ______________________

____

____

Substance-Related Disorders

A. Substance-related disorders involve ______________________

____

____

B. The features of substance abuse are ______________________

____

____

C. The two outstanding features of substance dependence are:

____

____

D. Tolerance means ______________________________

____

____

E. Withdrawal refers to ______________________________

____

____

F. Evidence for a hereditary basis for alcoholism is that ______________________________

____

____

G. Psychological factors in alcoholism include ______________________________

____

____

Mood Disorders

A. Mood is ______________________________

____

____

B. A mood disorder is defined by ______________________________

____

____

C. Symptoms of major depression include ______________________________

____

____

D. Bipolar disorder involves ______________________________

____

____

E. Symptoms of a manic episode are ______________________________

____

____

F. The catecholamine hypothesis states that ______________________________

____

____

G. Beck's view of depression is that ________________________________

____

____

Schizophrenia

A. The main feature of a psychosis is ________________________________

____

____

B. Schizophrenia is marked by________________________________

____

____

C. Thought disorder means that ________________________________

____

____

D. A delusion is ________________________________

____

____

E. Hallucinations are ________________________________

____

____

F. Experts believe that auditory hallucinations are perceptions that ____________

____

____

G. Flat or blunted affect means ________________________________

____

____

H. Four types of schizophrenia and their descriptions are:

1. ____

2. ____

3. ____

4. ____

I. The Genains are ____

____

____

J. According to the dopamine hypothesis ______________________________

____

____

K. The diathesis-stress hypothesis holds that ___________________________

____

____

Personality Disorders

A. Personality disorders are marked by ______________________________

____

____

B. Problems encountered by people with personality disorders include ________

____

____

C. The three main types of personality disorders are:

1. ____

2. ____

3. ____

D. Paranoid personality disorder involves _______________________________

____

____

E. The features of borderline personality disorder include _______________

____

____

F. Dependent personality disorder is marked by ___________________________

____

____

G. Antisocial personality disorder is characterized by ______________________

____

____

H. A psychopath is ______________________________

____

____

Treatments For Mental Disorders

A. Two concerns of mental health professionals today include:

1. ______________________________

2. ______________________________

Psychological Therapies

A. Psychotherapy is ______________________________

____

____

B. Psychodynamic therapy is ______________________________

____

____

C. The "golden rule" of psychoanalysis refers to ______________________________

____

____

D. The "royal road to the unconscious" is ______________________________

____

____

E. Resistance refers to ______________________________

____

____

F. Transference means ______________________________

____

____

Behavior Therapy

A. Behavior therapy is ______________________________

____

____

B. Exposure therapy refers to ____________________

____

____

C. The technique of systematic desensitization involves ____________________

____

____

D. Flooding is ____________________

____

____

E. Aversion therapy is used for ____________________

____

____

F. Modeling involves ____________________

____

____

Cognitive Therapy

A. Cognitive therapy refers to ____________________

____

____

B. Two types of cognitive therapy are:

1. ____________________

2. ____________________

Client-Centered Therapy

A. The ingredients of client-centered therapy are ____________________

____

____

B. Empathy refers to ____________________

____

____

Group, Family, and Couples Therapy

A. Group, couples, and family therapy focus on ______________________________

____

____

B. Group therapy involves ______________________________

____

____

C. Family therapy insists that ______________________________

____

____

D. The goal of marital therapy is to ______________________________

____

____

An Evaluation of Psychotherapy

A. Psychotherapy provides ______________________________

____

____

B. Two questions that psychologists are trying to answer about psychotherapy are:

1. ______________________________

2. ______________________________

Biological Therapies

A. The most effective treatment for mental disorders often involves __________

____

____

Drug Therapy

A. Drugs work on mental disorders by ______________________________

____

____

B. Three types of drugs are:

1. ______________________________

2. ______________________________

3. ______________________________

C. Examples of antianxiety drugs are ______________________________

____

____

D. The effects of antidepressant drugs are ______________________________

____

____

E. Antipsychotic drugs work to ______________________________

____

____

Electroconvulsive Therapy

A. ECT involves ______________________________

____

____

B. ECT is usually used after ______________________________

____

____

An Evaluation of Biological Therapies

A. Research shows that drugs and ECT ______________________________

____

____

B. Side effects of antidepressants include ______________________________

____

____

C. One problem with the use of antianxiety drugs is ______________________________

____

____

D. The use of antipsychotic drugs can result in ______________________________

____

____

E. Problems with the use of ECT are ______________________________

____

____

Issues and Applications

Insanity and the Law

A. Legal insanity depends on ______________________________

____

B. According to the M'Naughten rule ______________________________

____

C. The Brawner rule states that ______________________________

____

D. The APA's position on the insanity defense is ______________________________

____

The Prevention and Treatment of Mental Disorders in the Workplace

A. Primary prevention is designed to ______________________________

____

B. Secondary prevention involves ______________________________

____

C. Tertiary prevention is ______________________________

____

____

Biography

Carl Rogers

A. Two areas in which Rogers made his greatest contributions are:

1. ______________________________

2. ______________________________

Name ______________________ Class ________________ Date ____________

Key Terms Worksheet

Write a definition for each key term on the lines provided.

Term	Definition
abnormal behavior	______________________
	______________________
mental disorder	______________________
	______________________
Diagnostic and Statistical Manual of Mental Disorders-4th. ed	______________________
	______________________
anxiety disorder	______________________
	______________________
generalized anxiety disorder	______________________
	______________________
panic disorders	______________________
	______________________
phobia disorder	______________________
	______________________
obsessive-compulsive disorder	______________________
	______________________
somatoform disorders	______________________
	______________________
conversion disorder	______________________
	______________________
hypochondriasis	______________________
	______________________
dissociative disorders	______________________
	______________________
dissociative identity disorder	______________________
	______________________

substance-related disorder ______________________________

____

mood disorder ______________________________

____

major depression ______________________________

____

bipolar disorder ______________________________

____

schizophrenia ______________________________

____

personality disorder ______________________________

____

paranoid personality disorder ______________________________

____

antisocial personality disorder ______________________________

____

borderline personality disorder ______________________________

____

dependent personality disorder ______________________________

____

psychotherapy ______________________________

____

psychodynamic therapy ______________________________

____

behavior therapy ______________________________

____

cognitive therapy ______________________________

client-centered therapy ______________________________

____

electroconvulsive therapy ______________________________

____

Name ______________________ Class ______________________ Date ______________

Pretest

Chapter 12 Abnormal Psychology and Therapy

I. True/False Circle the letter (T or F) that corresponds to the correct response.

T F **1.** The psychodynamic model of abnormal behavior focuses on internal mental conflicts.

T F **2.** The social norm definition sees abnormal behavior as that which causes personal distress.

T F **3.** The DSM-IV does not consider causes in classifying mental disorders.

T F **4.** The fear of being in situations from which escape might be difficult or embarrassing characterizes agoraphobia.

T F **5.** Hypochondriasis is characterized by an unrealistic, excessive fear of having a serious illness.

T F **6.** Schizophrenia is another term for dissociative identity disorder.

T F **7.** A type of schizophrenia marked by hallucinations and delusions of being harmed or controlled is called paranoid schizophrenia.

T F **8.** The "golden rule" of psychoanalysis is free association.

T F **9.** A type of exposure therapy is flooding.

T F **10.** Prozac, Tofranil, and Pamelor are types of antidepressant drugs.

II. Multiple Choice Circle the letter that corresponds to the correct or best answer.

1. The behavioral model of abnormal behavior focuses on:

A. maladaptive patterns of thinking

B. internal mental conflicts

C. faulty learning experiences

D. problems in individual choices

2. According to the M'Naughten rule an individual is judged to be insane if he or she:

A. has a mental disorder

B. exhibits behavior that violates the social norm

C. does not understand the nature of the crime

D. commits repeated violent crimes

3. When abnormal behavior is associated with suffering, pain, death, or disability it is known as:

A. deviant behavior

B. a mental disorder

C. supernatural behavior

D. craziness

4. Which of the following anxiety disorders is marked by recurrent, anxiety-provoking thoughts and ritualistic behaviors?
   A. generalized anxiety disorder
   B. panic disorder
   C. phobia disorder
   D. obsessive-compulsive disorder

5. Symptoms of tolerance and withdrawal are characteristic of:
   A. substance dependence
   B. substance abuse
   C. alcoholism
   D. recreational drug use

6. Which of the following factors is NOT associated with drug addiction?
   A. antisocial behavior
   B. childhood aggressiveness
   C. peer pressure
   D. addictive personality

7. Individuals with bipolar disorder have:
   A. alternating periods of mania and major depression
   B. two distinct personalities
   C. two depressive episodes per year
   D. a paranoid personality

8. The catecholamine hypothesis states that depression is caused by abnormal functioning of:
   A. dopamine
   B. serotonin
   C. GABA
   D. norepinephrine

9. Therapy in which the individual is exposed to increasingly more intense anxiety-provoking stimuli is:
   A. rational-emotive therapy
   B. systematic desensitization
   C. psychoanalysis
   D. client-centered therapy

10. Which of the following is classified as an antipsychotic drug?
   A. Tofranil
   B. Prozac
   C. Xanax
   D. Thorazine

III. Short Answer Write the answer in the space provided.

1. What are four definitions of abnormal?

2. How does the DSM-IV distinguish between paranoid and catatonic schizophrenia?

3. What are the symptoms of borderline personality disorder according to the DSM-IV?

4. What are the fundamental techniques used in psychoanalysis?

5. What are the main therapeutic effects of antianxiety, antidepressant, and antipsychotic drugs?

IV. Matching Match the terms in column A with the correct choice in column B.

A

_______ **1.** mental disorder

_______ **2.** generalized anxiety disorder

_______ **3.** phobia disorder

_______ **4.** obsessive-compulsive disorder

_______ **5.** somatoform disorders

_______ **6.** conversion disorder

_______ **7.** hypochondriasis

_______ **8.** dissociative identity disorder

_______ **9.** mood disorder

_______ **10.** major depression

_______ **11.** bipolar disorder

_______ **12.** schizophrenia

_______ **13.** paranoid personality disorder

_______ **14.** antisocial personality disorder

_______ **15.** borderline personality disorder

_______ **16.** psychodynamic therapy

_______ **17.** behavior therapy

_______ **18.** cognitive therapy

_______ **19.** client-centered therapy

_______ **20.** electroconvulsive therapy

B

a. biological therapy involving the use of small electrical currents applied to the patient's head

b. a type of treatment which focuses on the individual's internal conflicts and personality

c. procedures used to correct faulty beliefs and thought patterns

d. a disorder marked by unstable mood, self-image, and relationships, as well as impulsive, self-defeating behavior

e. an anxiety disorder involving excessive worry about several things

f. an approach to treatment based on the application of learning principles

g. an anxiety disorder involving excessive and unreasonable fears and avoidance

h. an anxiety disorder involving obsessions or compulsions

i. mental disorders in which a physical symptom suggests a physical disorder for which no medical basis can be found.

j. a somatoform disorder which involves symptoms affecting voluntary movement or sensory function

k. a somatoform disorder involving an excessive fear of having a serious illness

l. a mood disorder marked by serious depressive episodes

m. a disorder characterized by two or more distinct personalities

n. behavior that is maladaptive and causes pain and suffering

o. a mental disorder involving episodes of depression or mania, or an alternation of the two

p. a disorder characterized by antisocial behavior

q. a mood disorder in which mood alternates between periods of depression and mania

r. a psychosis involving problems in judgment and reasoning, emotions, perceptions, and behavior

s. a treatment in which the therapist uses honesty and empathy

t. a disorder with maladaptive traits of distrust, suspiciousness, fear, and jealousy

V. Fill In The Blanks Write the answers in the space provided.

1. ____________________ is a branch of medicine concerned with the diagnosis and treatment of mental disorders while ____________________ is a branch of psychology that studies the causes and treatments of abnormal behavior.

2. According to the ____________________ rule, a person is insane if at the time crime he or she suffered from a mental defect and could not understand the crime or tell right from wrong. The ____________________ rule states that a person is insane if he or she could not understand the wrongfulness of the crime and could not control his or her behavior.

3. Obsessive-compulsive disorder is marked by ____________________ or ____________________ while ____________________ is characterized by an intense fear of situations involving unfamiliar people or evaluation by others.

4. In dissociative disorders there is a sudden alteration of ____________________, ____________________, or ____________________.

5. The two outstanding signs of substance dependence are ____________________ and ____________________.

6. One popular biochemical explanation for depression is the ____________________ hypothesis while schizophrenia is explained in terms of the ____________________ hypothesis.

7. False perceptions without a basis in reality are known as ____________________. False beliefs maintained despite evidence for them are called ____________________.

8. The anxious personality disorders involve ____________________, ____________________, or ____________________ behavior.

9. Drugs used to treat anxiety are called ____________________ drugs. Drugs for depression are known as ____________________, and schizophrenia is treated with ____________________ drugs.

10. The "golden rule" of psychoanalysis is ____________________ and the "royal road to the unconscious" is called ____________________.

Notes

Answer Key To Chapter 12 Pretest

I. True/False

1-T, **2**-F, **3**-T, **4**-T, **5**-T, **6**-F, **7**-T, **8**-T, **9**-T, **10**-T

II. Multiple Choice

1-C, **2**-C, **3**-B, **4**-D, **5**-A, **6**-D, **7**-A, **8**-D, **9**-B, **10**-D

III. Short Answer

1. One definition of abnormal behavior is that which is rare or uncommon. Another is that abnormal behavior is that which violates the social norm. A third is that abnormal behavior is maladaptive behavior. Finally, abnormal behavior is behavior that causes personal distress.
2. Paranoid schizophrenia is marked by delusions and hallucinations of being harmed or controlled. Catatonic schizophrenia involves movement disturbances, like stupor, and negativism.
3. Borderline personality disorder involves unstable mood, self-image, and relationships, as well as impulsive, self-defeating behavior.
4. Psychoanalysis uses free association which involves the patient saying whatever comes to mind. It also utilizes dream interpretations to help discover unconscious conflicts.
5. Antianxiety drugs relieve anxiety and tension. Antidepressants improve mood and energize people. Antipsychotic drugs reduce the impact of hallucinations and delusions and produce emotional quieting.

IV. Matching

1-n, **2**-e, **3**-g, **4**-h, **5**-i, **6**-j, **7**-k, **8**-m, **9**-o, **10**-l, **11**-q, **12**-r, **13**-t, **14**-p, **15**-d, **16**-b, **17**-f, **18**-c, **19**-s, **20**-a

V. Fill In The Blanks

1. psychiatry - clinical psychology
2. M'Naughten - Brawner (ALI)
3. obsessions - compulsions - social anxiety disorder
4. consciousness - memory - identity
5. tolerance - withdrawal
6. catecholamine - dopamine
7. hallucinations - delusions
8. anxious - fearful - inhibited
9. antianxiety - antidepressant - antipsychotic
10. free association - dream interpretation

Suggested Readings

Fingarette, H. 1994. "We should reject the disease concept of alcoholism." In B. Slife (ed.) *Taking sides*. Guilford, CT: Dushkin.

Finagrette argues that viewing alcoholism as a disease is a political and moral notion without any scientific evidence.

Goleman, D. "Scientists trace voices in schizophrenia." *The New York Times*, 22 September 1993: C12.

Psychologist Daniel Goleman presents new evidence about the nature of hallucinations.

Goode, Erica E. "Does psychotherapy work?" *U. S. News and World Report*, May 24, 1993: 57-65.

This article presents the results of a survey that asked Americans whether they think psychotherapy could be helpful.

Keyes, D. 1982. *The minds of Billy Milligan.* New York: Bantam.

A fascinating account of a man with 24 distinct personalities who was arrested for the kidnap and rape of three women.

Rokeach, M. 1964. *The three Christs of Ypsilanti*. New York: Columbia University Press.

Social psychologist presents his insightful study of three hospitalized schizophrenic individuals who believed that they were Jesus Christ.

Schreiber, F. R. 1984. *The shoemaker: The anatomy of a psychotic*. New York: Signet.

This is chilling account of a serial psychotic killer gives one person's view of the development of schizophrenia.

Sheehy, S. 1983. *Is there no place on earth for me?* New York: Vintage.

This book tells the sad, but true and fascinating story of a schizophrenic woman.

Szasz, T. S. 1974. *The myth of mental illness: Foundations of a theory of personal conduct, (rev. ed.)* New York: Harper & Row.

In this controversial work, Psychiatrist Thomas Szasz argues that mental illness is not illness, but rather a problem in living.

Torrey, E. F. 1988. *Surviving schizophrenia: A family manual, (rev. ed.)* New York: Harper & Row.

Renowned psychiatrist E. Fuller Torrey provides help for families of schizophrenic individuals.

Vaillant, G. E. 1994. "We should retain the disease concept of alcoholism." In B. Slife (ed.) *Taking sides.* Guilford, CT: Dushkin.

Dr. Vaillant states his case regarding the controversy of whether alcoholism should be considered a disease.

Chapter 13

Psychology of Social Behavior

Chapter Summary

Person perception involves processes of social cognition such as impression formation and nonverbal communication.

Attribution theory explains judgments about the causes of behavior, as in Kelley's covariation model, as well as the biases that affect those judgments. Attitudes are affected by conditioning and observational learning, persuasive messages, cognitive dissonance, self-perception, intentions, social norms, stereotypes, and authoritarianism.

Conformity is affected by the situation and motives of the individual. Social norms and situational variables also support obedience to authority. Compliance strategies include the foot-in-the-door and door-in-the-face techniques. Social facilitation and social loafing show divergent effects of others' presence on performance.

Affiliation depends on attractiveness, social exchange, self-disclosure, reciprocity, and love. Helping is affected by characteristics of the helper and the environment, as in the bystander effect. Aggression is explained by several theories: instinct theory, the frustration-aggression hypothesis, social learning theory, and the deindividuation model. Group decision-making is marked by the risky shift effect and the groupthink phenomenon. Social identity theory views reference groups as frameworks for self-concept.

Chapter Objectives

1. **Describe the processes that affect how people perceive one another.** Because person perception is an integral facet of social behavior and interpersonal relations, understanding the processes behind this activity bestows a perspective on one's own social functioning.
2. **Discuss the principles that influence how people explain each other's behavior.** Attributions are central aspects of social cognition, and studying attributional processes helps to make sense of one's people behavior.
3. **Explain how attitudes form, change, and influence behavior.** Learning about attitudes creates a basis for thinking about one's own beliefs, their function in social behavior, and their role in relationships.
4. **Describe the nature and causes of prejudice and discrimination.** Examination of prejudice and discrimination shows how stereotypes can distort beliefs about others and influence perceptions of and responses to them.
5. **Define conformity and discuss the factors that influence it.** Everyone conforms to some degree, and learning about conformity can give an appreciation of how one's life has been shaped by conforming to social pressures.
6. **Identify the causes and consequences of obedience and compliance.** It is important to recognize the causes and consequences of obedience and compliance because they are widespread and common aspects of social behavior and can lead to undesirable results.
7. **Discuss the effects of social facilitation and social loafing.** How does the presence of others affect behavior? Studying social facilitation and loafing reveals the sometimes beneficial and sometimes harmful effects that an audience can have on actions.
8. **Explain the nature and development of social affiliation.** By studying the forces that promote and sustain affiliation with others, personal friendships and other relationships are better understood.
9. **Summarize the factors that influence helping.** Everyone gives and gets help at some time. Learning about the factors that influence helping behavior provides an awareness of the impact of social forces on prosocial behavior.
10. **Define aggression and explain its causes.** Understanding the nature and causes of aggression is important to appreciate one of the most problematic forms of social behavior and the conditions which promote it.
11. **Identify the processes that characterize group behavior.** Most people act differently in a group than when alone. Studying group behavior reveals the role of group membership on thoughts and actions.

Name ______________________________ Class ____________________ Date ______________

Chapter Outline

Chapter 13 Psychology of Social Behavior

Social Cognition

A. Social cognition refers to ____

____

____

Perceiving Other People

A. Studies of impression formation find that it is influenced by ______________

____

____

B. In impression formation, the primacy effect means ____________________

____

____

C. Asch's studies of impression formation showed that ____________________

____

____

D. Schema theory states that impressions are __________________________

____

____

E. Research on the effect of attractiveness on impression formation indicates that

____

____

G. Nonverbal communication is ______________________________________

____

____

Explaining People's Behavior

A. An attribution is ____

____

____

B. Attribution theory seeks to explain __________________________________

____

____

C. The three questions about behavior that attribution theory addresses are:

1. ______________________________

2. ______________________________

3. ______________________________

D. Kelley's covariation model points to three kinds of information in attributions:

1. ______________________________

2. ______________________________

3. ______________________________

E. Attribution bias means that ______________________________

____

____

Attitudes

A. An attitude is a pattern of ______________________________

____

____

B. Attitudes serve three main purposes:

1. ______________________________

2. ______________________________

3. ______________________________

C. The attitude-behavior link refers to ______________________________

____

____

D. Studies find that the attitude-behavior link is influenced by ______________________________

____

____

E. The planned action model states that ______________________________

____

____

Forming and Changing Attitudes

A. Attitude formation involves learning processes such as ________________

____

____

B. The influence of persuasive communications on attitudes depends on _______

____

____

C. Cognitive dissonance refers to ________________________________

____

____

D. According to self-perception theory, attitudes form and change as a result of

____

____

Prejudice and Discrimination

A. Prejudice means ____

____

____

B. Discrimination refers to ________________________________

____

____

C. According to Gordon Allport, the causes of prejudice include ____________

____

____

D. Stereotypes are ____

____

____

E. Authoritarianism is ____________________________________

____

____

Social Influence

Conformity

A. Conformity means ______________________________

____

____

B. Research on conformity finds that it is affected by ______________________________

____

____

Obedience and Compliance

A. Obedience refers to ______________________________

____

____

B. Milgram's studies of obedience to authority found that the average person is willing to ______________________________

____

____

C. Obedience is influenced by ______________________________

____

____

D. Compliance refers to ______________________________

____

____

E. The two main compliance techniques are:

1. ______________________________

2. ______________________________

Social Faciliation and Social Loafing

A. Social facilitation refers to ______________________________

____

____

B. Social facilitation is influenced by ______________________________

____

____

C. Social loafing refers to ____

____

____

D. Social loafing is most likely to occur when ____

____

____

Social Interaction

Affiliation

A. Affiliation is ____

____

____

B. Friendship formation depends on ____

____

____

C. The matching effect means that ____

____

____

D. According to social exchange theory, ____

____

____

E. The two types of love relationships are:

1. ____

2. ____

Helping Behavior

A. Altruism means ____

____

____

B. Helping behavior depends on ____

____

____

C. The bystander effect means ______________________________

____

____

D. Diffusion of responsibility refers to ______________________________

____

____

Aggression

A. Aggression is defined as ______________________________

____

____

B. According to instinct theory, aggression is ______________________________

____

____

C. The frustration-aggression hypothesis states that ______________________________

____

____

D. In social learning, theory aggression is ______________________________

____

____

E. In the deindividuation model aggression is ______________________________

____

____

Group Behavior

A. The risky shift effect means that ______________________________

____

____

B. Group polarization is ______________________________

____

____

C. Groupthink occurs when ______________________________

____

____

D. Social identity theory proposes that ______________________________

____

____

Issues and Applications

Employment Discrimination

A. Employment discrimination is affected by several prejudices including _____

____

____

B. Evidence of job discrimination includes ______________________________

____

____

The Power of Cults

A. Cults are distinguished by ______________________________

____

____

Biography

Stanley Milgram

A. Stanley Milgram is best known for his work on ______________________________

____

____

B. Milgram's 1963 obedience study was both important and controversial because

____

____

Notes

Name ______________________ Class ________________ Date ____________

Key Terms Worksheet

Write a definition for each key term on the lines provided.

Term	Definition
social psychology	
social cognition	
attribution theory	
attribution bias	
attitude	
cognitive dissonance	
self-perception theory	
prejudice	
discrimination	
stereotypes	
authoritarianism	
conformity	
obedience	

compliance ______________________________

____

social facilitation ______________________________

____

social loafing ______________________________

____

social exchange theory ______________________________

____

altruism ______________________________

____

bystander effect ______________________________

____

aggression ______________________________

____

deindividuation model ______________________________

____

group polarization ______________________________

____

social identity theory ______________________________

____

Name ______________________ Class ______________________ Date ______________

Pretest

Chapter 13 Psychology of Social Behavior

I. True/False Circle the letter (T or F) that corresponds to the correct response.

T F **1.** According to the primacy effect, the last information received about someone is most important in impression formation.

T F **2.** Kelley's covariation model is an example of attribution theory.

T F **3.** When one holds two inconsistent ideas or beliefs one is in a state of cognitive dissonance.

T F **4.** Stereotypes are generally favorable beliefs about the characteristics of some group.

T F **5.** Conformity is not affected by situational factors, but only by the individual's traits.

T F **6.** Milgram found that a majority of subjects obeyed an authority's commands to harm a stranger.

T F **7.** In social loafing, the presence of others leads to a decline in individual performance.

T F **8.** Social exchange theory states that mutual attractiveness is the most powerful force in maintaining a social relationship.

T F **9.** The bystander effect means that the likelihood of helping behavior decreases when more people are present.

T F **10.** According to the deindividuation model, the most important cause of aggression is frustration.

II. Multiple Choice Circle the letter that corresponds to the correct or best answer.

1. Which of the following models emphasizes the kinds of information used in social attribution?

A. the deindividuation model
B. the social learning model
C. the covariation model
D. the compliance model

2. According to cognitive dissonance theory, attitudes change because:

A. people have a need to conform to the attitudes of their peers
B. people are motivated to change their beliefs in order to reduce tension
C. people seek to eliminate their socially deviant beliefs
D. people change their ideas as a result of how they perceive their own actions

3. Which of the following is the root of prejudice in an individual?

A. altruism
B. groupthink
C. compliance
D. stereotypes

4. Which phrase describes the door-in-the-face technique?

   A. making a small request first and a large one later

   B. making a large request first and a small one later

   C. making a large and small request at the same time

   D. making two small requests at the same time

5. When the presence of others improves an individual's performance of some task, it illustrates:

   A. social facilitation

   B. conformity

   C. social loafing

   D. deindividuation

6. Which statement best describes reciprocity in a relationship?

   A. People attract others who complement their needs.

   B. People are friends with others who are similar to them in terms of physical qualities and attitudes.

   C. People like others who are different than themselves.

   D. People keep friends with whom they have equal exchanges of costs and benefits.

7. Which theory of aggression states that people in groups are more likely to lose their sense of personal responsibility?

   A. instinct theory

   B. deindividuation model

   C. cognitive dissonance theory

   D. frustration-aggression theory

8. The bystander effect is most relevant to:

   A. helping behavior

   B. aggression

   C. the risky shift

   D. affiliation

9. Group polarization is:

   A. the isolation of social groups with extreme attitudes

   B. conflict between groups with negative stereotypes of each other

   C. an increase in extreme opinions following a group discussion

   D. the organization of a social group into leader and follower subgroups

10. According to social identity theory:

    A. groups force their members to conform to group norms

    B. social reference groups provide a foundation for individual self-concept and social behavior

    C. individuals give up their separate identities in favor of a group identity and social role

    D. a strong identification with a group is a sign of social maladjustment

III. Short Answer Write the answer in the space provided.

1. According to Kelley's covariation model, what kinds of information are needed for attributions?

2. What factors are important in impression formation?

3. What did Milgram's obedience study demonstrate?

4. Discuss the variables that affect conformity.

5. What is the frustration-aggression hypothesis?

IV. Matching Match the terms in column A with the correct choice in column B.

A

_____ **1.** primacy effect
_____ **2.** halo effect
_____ **3.** fundamental attribution error
_____ **4.** planned action model
_____ **5.** cognitive dissonance
_____ **6.** stereotype
_____ **7.** covariation model
_____ **8.** authoritarianism
_____ **9.** scapegoating
_____ **10.** foot-in-the-door technique
_____ **11.** social facilitation
_____ **12.** affiliation
_____ **13.** matching effect
_____ **14.** reciprocity
_____ **15.** companionate love
_____ **16.** diffusion of responsibility
_____ **17.** instinct theory
_____ **18.** deindividuation
_____ **19.** risky shift effect
_____ **20.** groupthink

B

a. view that aggression is an inborn drive
b. displacement of hostility onto a stereotyped group
c. loss of individuality
d. Kelley's theory of attribution information
e. theory of the attitude-behavior link
f. state of tension from conflicting beliefs
g. general belief about typical characteristics of a group
h. assumption that attractive people have positive features
i. a mutual and equitable exchange of rewards and costs
j. influence of similarity on relationships
k. rigid conventional values and the need to obey authority
l. a type of group polarization
m. group decision-making problem due to consensus needs
n. the tendency to explain others' behavior by internal causes and one's own behavior by external causes
o. motive to seek relationships with others
p. a strategy for gaining compliance
q. mutual trust and tolerance in long-term relationships
r. improved performance in the presence of others
s. reduced individual responsibility in a group
t. the importance of first impressions in person perception

V. Fill In The Blanks Write the answers in the space provided.

1. According to the _______________ effect, impression formation is strongly affected by the first information one receives about someone, and according to _______________ theory, one's impressions reflect beliefs and assumptions. The assumption that attractive people also have other positive features is the _______________ effect.

2. _______________ theory explains how one judges the causes of others' behavior. Kelley's _______________ model emphasizes the importance of distinctiveness, consensus, and _______________ information. Attributions are often inaccurate because of _______________ .

3. Attitudes serve the purposes of value expression, need satisfaction, and _______________. The _______________ link is often inconsistent because intentions and social norms also mediate behavior according to the _______________ model.

4. A negative attitude toward members of a social group is _______________ , and this attitude may cause _______________ , or unfair treatment of group members. When prejudiced individuals displace their emotional distress onto a stereotyped group, they are _______________ .

5. Asch's _______________ studies showed that the size, unanimity, and _______________ of a group affect a subject's willingness to go along with an incorrect group judgment. Other studies find that a subject's need for _______________ also influences this behavior.

6. An improvement in individual performance in the presence of others is social _______________ , which Zajonc considers to depend on the effect of _______________ on simple tasks. By contrast, social _______________ shows that the presence of others may reduce individual performance.

7. Affiliation is influenced by the similarity of people, according to the _______________ effect and the exchange of costs and rewards, according to _______________ theory. In addition, a sharing of ideas and trust, or _______________, fosters intimate relationships.

8. Helping is a kind of _______________ behavior, while a type of helping performed without hope of reward is _______________. In the _______________ effect, a large number of potential helpers actually reduces the likelihood of help because of a diffusion of _______________.

9. Aggression is an inborn drive like sex and hunger according to _______________ theory, but it is a response to problems in seeking goals, according to _______________ hypothesis. Social learning theory assumes that _______________ learning is important in the development of aggression.

10. The _______________ effect shows that group decisions are often more daring than individual decisions, and this effect is an instance of group _______________ in which opinions are more extreme after group discussion. When groups struggle to maintain consensus, _______________ may result.

Answer Key To Chapter 13 Pretest

I. True-False

1-F, **2**-T, **3**-T, **4**-F, **5**-F, **6**-T, **7**-T, **8**-F, **9**-T, **10**-F

II. Multiple Choice

1-C, **2**-B, **3**-D, **4**-B, **5**-A, **6**-D, 7-B, **8**-A, **9**-C, **10**-B

III. Short Answer

1. Kelley's covariation model states that attributions are based on three types of information: the distinctiveness of the behavior, consensus with others' behavior, and consistency of behavior in different situations.
2. Impression formation is influenced by the first information received about someone (primacy effect), the perceiver's own beliefs or schemata, and interpretations of nonverbal communications from the person.
3. Milgram's study demonstrated that most people are willing to obey an authority's command to harm a stranger and that their obedience depended on the closeness of the victim, the status of the authority, the prestige of the setting, and their feeling of personal responsibility.
4. The likelihood of conformity depends on a group's unanimity, cohesiveness, and size, as well as on the person's self-esteem and motivation to be correct and liked.
5. According to the frustration-aggression hypothesis, aggression results from frustrated attempts at goal-striving. Berkowitz's version of this hypothesis also stresses the role of aversive events and aggression cues in prompting aggression.

IV. Matching

1-t, **2**-h, **3**-n, **4**-e, **5**-f, **6**-g, **7**-d, **8**-k, **9**-b, **10**-p, **11**-r, **12**-o, **13**-j, **14**-i, **15**-q, **16**-s, **17**-a, **18**-c, **19**-l, **20**-m

V. Fill In The Blanks

1. primacy - schema - halo
2. attribution - covariation - consistency - attribution bias
3. social adjustment - attitude-behavior - planned action
4. prejudice - discrimination - scapegoating
5. conformity - cohesiveness - approval
6. facilitation - arousal - loafing
7. matching - social exchange - self-disclosure
8. prosocial - altruism - bystander - responsibility
9. instinct - frustration-aggression - observational
10. risky shift - polarization - groupthink

Suggested Readings

Allport, G. W. 1954. *The nature of prejudice*. Garden City, NY: Doubleday.

Gordon Allport's classic study of prejudice is still current after forty years. His analysis of the social, historical, and individual roots of prejudice and discrimination remains pertinent today.

Cialdini, R. B. 1985. *Influence: Science and practice*. Glenview, IL: Scott Foresman.

Written by a prominent researcher and theorist in the area of social influence, this book discusses investigations of compliance and the real-world uses of their findings.

Festinger, L., H.W. Riecken, and Schachter S. 1956. *When prophecy fails*. Minneapolis: University of Minnesota.

A classic case study of cult behavior, this book looks at the structure of cult life in the Seekers, a doomsday group, and their response to the failure of their end-of-the-world prediction.

Fiske, S. T., and S.E. Taylor. 1991. *Social cognition, 2nd ed.* New York: McGraw Hill.

This textbook provides an overview of research and theory in person perception, impression formation, attribution, and other aspects of social cognition. A good sourcebook for the interested student.

Hall, E. T. 1966. *The hidden dimension*. New York: Doubleday.

Hall, an anthropologist, gives a tour through nonverbal communication with an eye toward the contributions of culture in sending and interpreting body language.

Milgram, S. 1974. *Obedience to authority: An experimental view*. New York: Harper & Row.

Milgram summarizes his famous obedience studies and offers a theoretical view of why we obey and the conditions that make obedience so easy. Milgram connects his research to everyday instances of obedience and the morality of social behavior.

Chapter 14

Applied Psychology

Chapter Summary

Applied psychology uses psychological methods and knowledge to solve practical problems. Industrial-organizational psychology studies human behavior in the workplace as in the selection and training of workers, worker motivation, and job satisfaction. Engineering psychology is concerned with the design of machines, systems, and environments to fit human perceptual and cognitive capacities. Environmental psychology studies the relationships between the physical environment and behavior. Factors like noise, violations of personal space, and overcrowding are important to environment psychologists.

Community psychology studies the effects of social and environmental factors on behavior to promote the well-being of individuals. With an emphasis on prevention, community psychologists are concerned with mental disorders, violence, the spread of AIDS, homelessness, and other problems. Other areas of applied psychology are consumer psychology, which studies consumer behavior, educational psychology, which applies psychology to teaching and learning, forensic psychology, which involves applications of psychology to legal matters, and sports psychology, which strives to improve athletic performance.

1. **Outline the important elements of personnel selection, placement, and training.** It is important to understand these elements because the selection, placement, and training of personnel is critical to the success of a business or organization. Furthermore, this is an area in which psychologists have played a major role.
2. **Identify the factors that increase work motivation.** There is a strong relationship between work motivation and job performance. This is another area in which psychologists have made major contributions.
3. **Describe the factors associated with job satisfaction.** This is important because job satisfaction is related to work motivation and job performance.
4. **Discuss how technology and social change influence human performance on the job.** This is important because of the many technological advances and changes in society. Any successful business or organization must consider these as important factors.
5. **Describe the effects of noise, violations of personal space, and overcrowding on human behavior.** This is important because psychologists recognize that factors found in the environment can have a negative impact on human behavior.
6. **Summarize the goals and methods of community psychology.** When one considers the drug problem, violence, AIDS, mental illness and other problems, community psychology as an applied area of psychology can affect the quality of life.
7. **Discuss the role of community psychology in the prevention of AIDS.** Learning about the role of community psychology in the prevention of AIDS is important because AIDS is a deadly disease which can only be stemmed by changing behavior.
8. **Identify the characteristics of homeless people and explain how they affect solutions to the problem of homelessness.** Homelessness is a major problem that affects us all. Any solution to the problem requires an understanding of the characteristics of homeless people.
9. **Define consumer, forensic, educational, and sports psychology.** It is important to become acquainted with the various areas of applied psychology not detailed in the chapter.

Name ______________________________ Class ______________________ Date _______________

Chapter Outline

Chapter 14 Applied Psychology

Industrial-Organizational Psychology

A. Industrial-organizational psychology is defined as ____________________

____

____

B. I-O psychology applies psychological principles to ____________________

____

____

Personnel Psychology

A. Personnel psychology is ____

____

____

Selection and Placement

A. Five methods used to select and place employees are:

1. ____

2. ____

3. ____

4. ____

5. ____

B. In an interview, the interviewer asks specific questions about _______________

____

____

C. The use of biodata is based on the assumption that____________________

____

____

D. The most commonly used psychological tests are ____________________

____

____

E. Two commonly used interest tests are:

1. ____

2. ____

F. Work samples are ______________________________

____

____

G. A job analysis is ______________________________

____

____

H. Three elements of a job analysis are:

1. ______________________________

2. ______________________________

3. ______________________________

Training

A. A needs analysis is ______________________________

____

____

B. Three factors that a needs analysis must address:

1. ______________________________

2. ______________________________

3. ______________________________

C. On-the-job training methods include ______________________________

____

____

Organizational Behavior

A. Organizational behavior is concerned with ______________________________

____

____

Job Motivation and Satisfaction

A. Seven theories of work motivation are:

1. ____________________

2. ____________________

3. ____________________

4. ____________________

5. ____________________

6. ____________________

7. ____________________

B. Motive-need theory states that ____________________

____

____

C. According to incentive-reward theory ____________________

____

____

D. Goal theory predicts that ____________________

____

____

E. Equity theory states that ____________________

____

____

F. According to expectancy-value theory, ____________________

____

____

G. Attitude theory predicts that ____________________

____

____

H. Attribution-self-efficacy theory holds that ____________________

____

____

Leadership

A. Quality circles are ______________________________

____

____

B. The best leadership approach is to ______________________________

____

____

C. The function of a self-managed work team is ______________________________

____

____

Engineering and Environmental Psychology

A. Two areas of applied psychology that are concerned with the effects of the environment are: ______________________________

____

Engineering Psychology

A. Engineering psychology involves ______________________________

____

B. Two other names for engineering psychology are: ______________________________

____

C. Engineering psychology seeks to provide ______________________________

____

D. Two forces that drive engineering psychology are: ______________________________

____

Environmental Psychology

A. Environmental psychology is concerned with factors like ______________________________

____

Noise

A. Research shows that noise can affect job performance when ______________________________

____

Personal Space and Overcrowding

A. Personal space refers to ______________________________

____

B. Personal space depends on ______________________________

____

____

C. The four types of interpersonal distance are:

1. ______________________________

2. ______________________________

3. ______________________________

4. ______________________________

D. People exposed to overcrowding are ______________________________

____

____

E. Compared to children in less densely populated schools, children in overcrowded schools ______________________________

____

Community Psychology

A. Deinstitutionalization involves ______________________________

____

____

B. Community psychology studies ______________________________

____

____

C. Four community psychology approaches to promote well-being are:

1. ______________________________

2. ______________________________

3. ______________________________

4. ______________________________

The Prevention of AIDS

A. AIDS is ______________________________

____

B. The most common behaviors associated with getting AIDS are ______________________________

____

C. Five AIDS prevention approaches recommended by community psychologists are:

1. ______________________________
2. ______________________________
3. ______________________________
4. ______________________________
5. ______________________________

Homelessness

A. Five characteristics that distinguish homeless individuals from ordinary Americans are:

1. ______________________________
2. ______________________________
3. ______________________________
4. ______________________________
5. ______________________________

B. Five proposed solutions to homelessness are:

1. ______________________________
2. ______________________________
3. ______________________________
4. ______________________________
5. ______________________________

Other Areas of Applied Psychology

A. Four prominent areas of applied psychology are:

1. ______________________________
2. ______________________________
3. ______________________________
4. ______________________________

Consumer Psychology

A. Consumer psychology applies ______________________________

____

____

B. Knowledge from consumer psychology is important because ______________

____

____

Forensic Psychology

A. Forensic psychology is concerned with ______________________________

____

____

B. Three matters that forensic psychologists are concerned with are:

1. ____

2. ____

3. ____

Educational Psychology

A. Educational psychology is ____

____

____

B. Three activities performed by educational psychologists are:

1. ____

2. ____

3. ____

Sports Psychology

A. Sports psychology is defined as ____________________________________

____

____

B. Sports psychologists are concerned with matters like ____________________

____

____

Issues and Applications

Sexual Harassment of Women in the Workplace

A. I-O psychologists are concerned with harassment because ________________

____

B. Sexual harassment is defined as ___________________________________

____

C. Examples of sexual harassment include ________________________________

____

____

D. The most common reasons cited for sexual harassment are ______________

____

____

E. Three measures suggested to stem sexual harassment are:

1. ____

2. ____

3. ____

Youth Violence

A. Surveys of youth violence show that one in five high school students _______

____

____

B. Homicide is the second leading cause of death among _________________

____

____

C. Factors that have been suggested as causes of youth violence include

____

____

D. The most sensible approach to the problem of youth violence is __________

____

____

Biography **Hortensia Amaro**

A. Hortensia Amaro is important because of her role in the development of

____

____

B. She was the founder of ______________________________________

____

____

Name ______________________ Class ________________ Date ____________

Key Terms Worksheet

Write a definition for each key term on the lines provided.

Term	Definition
applied psychology	
industrial-organizational psychology	
personnel psychology	
job analysis	
needs analysis	
organizational behavior	
quality circles	
self-managed work teams	
engineering psychology	
environmental psychology	
personal space	
deinstitutionalization	

community psychology

Acquired Immune Deficiency Syndrome

consumer psychology

forensic psychology

educational psychology

sports psychology

Name _______________ Class _______________ Date

Pretest

Chapter 14 Applied Psychology

I. True/False Circle the letter (T or F) that corresponds to the correct response.

T F **1.** Personnel psychology is concerned with the selection, placement, and training of employees.

T F **2.** The most commonly used psychological tests for the selection and placement of workers are personality tests.

T F **3.** The motive-need theory says that work is motivated by the need for fair treatment.

T F **4.** Another term for engineering psychology is human factors psychology.

T F **5.** Research in environmental psychology shows that noise affects occupational functioning but has little effect on social behavior.

T F **6.** The size of a person's personal space depends on personality as well as the situation.

T F **7.** Homicide is the second leading cause of death in children and adolescents in the United States.

T F **8.** Research on AIDS suggests that the only way to prevent AIDS is by behavior.

T F **9.** Mental disorders are more common among the homeless than in the general population.

T F **10.** Forensic psychology is concerned with the application of psychology to consumer behavior.

II. Multiple Choice Circle the letter that corresponds to the correct or best answer.

1. Which of the following is NOT a concern of industrial-organizational psychology?

A. personnel selection and placement
B. worker motivation
C. job satisfaction
D. the design of displays

2. The legal definition of sexual harassment requires:

A. that the sexual behavior is unwanted whether or not it interferes with job performance
B. physical touching
C. that the sexual advance be repeated at least three times
D. that the harasser be in a superior job position

3. Harry is motivated at work to perform behaviors that result in good pay and recognition. Harry's behavior is best explained by the ____________ theory.

A. goal
B. attitude
C. equity
D. incentive-reward

4. Research on the relationship between personality and job satisfaction reveals that, in general:
   A. no relationship exists
   B. people with a negative outlook are usually dissatisfied with any job
   C. personality is more important for men than women
   D. people with a Type-A personality are the most satisfied

5. The most widely used type of training is:
   A. audio-visual presentation
   B. on-the-job training
   C. programmed instruction
   D. computer-assisted instruction

6. The study of system failure due to human error is the concern of ____________ psychology.
   A. environmental
   B. organizational
   C. forensic
   D. engineering

7. Overcrowding has its greatest negative psychological effects only when:
   A. one cannot control it
   B. one lives in an apartment building
   C. one is in a prison
   D. it is accompanied by noise

8. The policy of moving mental patients from hospitals to the community is called:
   A. human factors psychology
   B. empowerment
   C. deinstitutionalization
   D. community reorganization

9. Which of the following is NOT considered a community psychology approach to the prevention of AIDS?
   A. development of a vaccine
   B. education about AIDS risk factors
   C. mass marketing of information about AIDS
   D. modification of social norms

10. Which of the following is NOT characteristic of homeless individuals?
    A. They are typical Americans who have had bad luck.
    B. They often have a history of mental disorders.
    C. More than 30 percent are women and children.
    D. They have had many childhood behavior problems.

III. Short Answer Write the answer in the space provided.

1. What is the focus of the job interview?

2. What are the elements of a job analysis?

3. Discuss the tools of empowerment and social support in community psychology.

4. What recommendations have community psychologist's made to stem the spread of AIDS?

5. What are the roles of forensic psychologists?

IV. Matching Match the terms in column A with the correct choice in column B.

A

_____ **1.** biodata
_____ **2.** ergonomics
_____ **3.** equity theory
_____ **4.** industrial-organizational psychology
_____ **5.** personnel psychology
_____ **6.** job analysis
_____ **7.** needs analysis
_____ **8.** organizational behavior
_____ **9.** quality circles
_____ **10.** self-managed work teams
_____ **11.** engineering psychology
_____ **12.** environmental psychology
_____ **13.** personal space
_____ **14.** deinstitutionalization
_____ **15.** community psychology
_____ **16.** Acquired Immune Deficiency Syndrome
_____ **17.** consumer psychology
_____ **18.** forensic psychology
_____ **19.** educational psychology
_____ **20.** sports psychology

B

a. a method to evaluate whether workers are doing their job as well as they are supposed to
b. applies psychological methods and principles to athletic performance
c. studies the effects of social and environmental factors on behavior and applies this knowledge to promote the well-being of individuals in the population
d. an area surrounding a person that he or she stakes as his or her own
e. a disease that kills its victims by making them more susceptible to life-threatening infections
f. the application of psychological methods and principles to the study of consumer behavior
g. a policy of moving mental patients out of overcrowded mental hospitals
h. application of scientific knowledge about people to the design of machines, systems, and environments..
i. an organizational method to determine the need for training
j. the application of psychological principles and methods to teaching and learning
k. studies the relationships between the physical environment and behavior
l. groups of employees who get together regularly to deal with work-related issues
m. the application of psychological research or assessment information to legal issues
n. groups of workers who are responsible for assigning jobs to members, solving production problems, and selecting and training new members
o. concerned with worker motivation, satisfaction, and leadership
p. information about job history, family background, and health
q. another term for engineering psychology
r. the need for fair treatment motivates job performance
s. concerned with human behavior in the workplace
t. concerned with the selection, placement, and training of employees

V. Fill In The Blanks Write the answers in the space provided.

1. Industrial-organizational psychology is concerned with the ____________________ and ____________________ of workers and worker motivation and ____________________.

2. Two commonly used interest tests are the ____________________ and the ____________________.

3. When an organization conducts an ____________________, it determines who requires training and what kind. An ____________________ is a method to evaluate job performance.

4. ____________________ theory says that one is motivated to seek and avoid certain stimuli on the job. According to ____________________ theory, motivation improves when one believes that job success is related to one's abilities and efforts.

5. The branch of applied psychology concerned with the application of scientific knowledge about people to the design of machines, systems, and environments is called ____________________.

6. Environmental psychologists study the effects of ____________________, ____________________, and ____________________ on behavior.

7. The policy of moving mental patients out of overcrowded mental hospitals so they can be treated in the community is called ____________________.

8. The branch of psychology that applies psychological research or assessment information to legal issues is called ____________________.

9. The community psychology approach in which individuals learn personal and social skills is ____________________.

10. Community psychologists believe that the most sensible approach to the prevention of youth violence is to teach ____________________, ____________________, and ____________________.

Notes

Answer Key To Chapter 14 Pretest

I. True/False

1-T, **2**-F, **3**-F, **4**-T, **5**-F, **6**-T, **7**-T, **8**-T, **9**-T, **10**-F

II. Multiple Choice

1-D, **2**-A, **3**-D, **4**-B, **5**-B, **6**-D, **7**-A, **8**-C, **9**-A, **10**-A

III. Short Answer

1. The job interview focuses on a person's technical abilities, work motivation, and interpersonal skills.
2. A job analysis has three parts. The job description specifies job duties and activities; the job specification indicates the required job skills and knowledge; and the job environment aspect is concerned with the physical and social environment and work conditions.
3. With empowerment, individuals get stronger and cope better when they develop a sense of control over their lives. Social support helps people fight stress through meaningful social interactions.
4. Community psychologists recommend education, helping individuals appraise their personal risk, training in the skills necessary to change faulty behavior the modification of social norms, and the mass marketing of AIDS information.
5. Forensic psychologists are involved in matters such as a person's competency to stand trial, insanity determinations, jury selection, and other legal proceedings in which knowledge about human behavior is important.

IV. Matching

1-p, **2**-q, **3**-r, **4**-s, **5**-t, **6**-a, **7**-i, **8**-o, **9**-l, **10**-n, **11**-h, **12**-k, **13**-d, **14**-g, **15**-c, **16**-e, **17**-f, **18**-m, **19**-j, **20**-b

V. Fill In The Blanks

1. selection - training - satisfaction
2. Strong-Campbell Interest Inventory - Kuder Occupational Interest Survey
3. needs analysis - job analysis
4. motive-need - attribution-self-efficacy
5. engineering psychology
6. noise - personal space - overcrowding
7. deinstitutionalization
8. forensic psychology
9. competence building
10. general communication - problem solving - social skills

Suggested Readings

Fiedler, F. E. 1990. "Style or circumstance: The leadership enigma." In P. Chance and T. G. Harris (eds.) *The best of Psychology Today*. New York: McGraw-Hill.

This article shows how leaders are made of a combination of the right personality and situation.

Janis, I. L. 1990. "Groupthink." In P. Chance and T. G. Harris (eds.) *The best of Psychology Today*. New York: McGraw-Hill.

The author discusses the role of groupthink in business and foreign policy decisions.

Morrison, A. M., R. P. White, and E.V. Velsor 1990. "Executive women on a tightrope." In P. Chance and T. G. Harris (eds.) *The best of Psychology Today*. New York: McGraw-Hill.

This article discusses how women must behave to succeed as business executives.